HOW DOES
THE WIND WALK?

HOW DOES

THE WIND WALK?

by Nancy White Carlstrom

illustrated by Deborah Kogan Ray

Macmillan Publishing Company New York
Maxwell Macmillan Canada Toronto
Maxwell Macmillan International New York Oxford Singapore Sydney

10 9 8 7 6 5 4 3 2 1

The text of this book is set in 18 pt. Palatino.
The illustrations are rendered in acrylic on canvas.

Library of Congress Cataloging-in-Publication Data
Carlstrom, Nancy White. How does the wind walk? / by Nancy White Carlstrom ;
illustrated by Deborah Kogan Ray. — 1st ed.   p.   cm. Summary: A little boy
watches the wind through the four seasons of the year. ISBN 0-02-717275-9
[1. Winds—Fiction.] I. Ray, Deborah Kogan, ill. II. Title. PZ7.C21684Ho 1993
[E]—dc20   90-25958

For Calvin Bradley Krogh
—N.W.C.

For Karen
—D.K.R.

How does the wind walk in autumn?

The wind walks in a rush,
brushing colored leaves
from the trees as she passes.

The wind walks in a whirl,
twirling the leaves
around and around,
before she waltzes them down streets
and scatters them in faraway places.

But the little boy sings a keeping song
for the leaves he gathers.
He piles them up and sits right in the middle.

How does the wind walk in winter?

The wind walks with a slip on the ice,
blowing through frosty lips
turning the trees to silver.

At night, the wind walks with a whistle
and a whip in her hand.
Windows shake and branches stand
trembling in the moonlight.

But the little boy sings a sleeping song
for the restless trees.
He wraps a blanket around his animals
so they won't shiver.

How does the wind walk in spring?

The wind walks with a trick up her sleeve,
blowing flower kisses one moment,
rough and gusting the next.

The wind walks with a bounce in her step,
playing games as she goes.
Taking a hat here, a kite there,
then tripping away without a backward glance.

But the little boy sings a mending song
for the torn kite.
He puts broken flowers in glasses of water.

How does the wind walk in summer?

The wind walks in a huff,
fluffing out clouds in the sky.
Snapping harbor flags,
flapping clothes in her stiff breeze.

And then,
on one hot, hot day in summer
the wind doesn't walk at all.

She rests by the bay
with the tumbling birds
and the sliding fish.
She makes everyone wait.

Everyone, except the little boy.

He sings his own sending song
and puffs his stick-boat
off into the world.

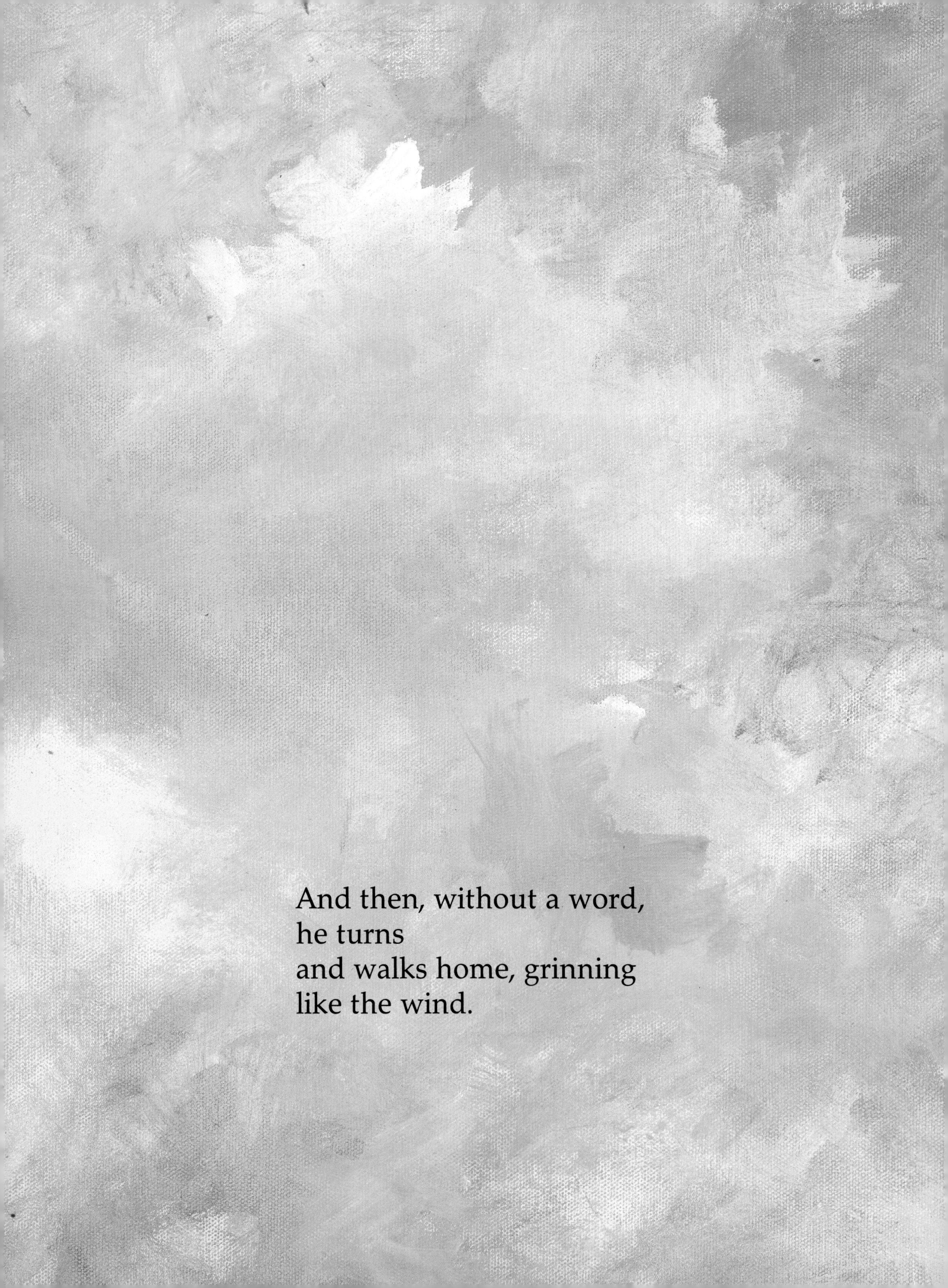

And then, without a word,
he turns
and walks home, grinning
like the wind.

HOLT McDOUGAL

GEORGIA

ANALYTIC GEOMETRY

Edward B. Burger

David J. Chard

Paul A. Kennedy

Steven J. Leinwand

Freddie L. Renfro

Tom W. Roby

Dale G. Seymour

Bert K. Waits

HOLT McDOUGAL

HOUGHTON MIFFLIN HARCOURT

Authors

Edward B. Burger, Ph.D., is Professor of Mathematics at Williams College and is the author of numerous articles, books, and videos. He has won several of the most prestigious writing and teaching awards offered by the Mathematical Association of America. Dr. Burger has made numerous television and radio appearances and has given countless mathematical presentations around the world.

Freddie L. Renfro, MA, has 35 years of experience in Texas education as a classroom teacher and director/coordinator of Mathematics PreK-12 for school districts in the Houston area. She has served as a reviewer and TXTEAM trainer for Texas Math Institutes and has presented at numerous math workshops.

David J. Chard, Ph.D., is the Leon Simmons Dean of the School of Education and Human Development at Southern Methodist University. He is a past president of the Divison of Research at the Council for Exceptional Children, a member of the International Academy for Research on Learning Disabilities, and has been the Principal Investigator on numerous research projects for the U.S. Department of Education.

Tom W. Roby, Ph.D., is Associate Professor of Mathematics and Director of the Quantitative Learning Center at the University of Connecticut. He founded and directed the Bay Area-based ACCLAIM professional development program. He also chaired the advisory board of the California Mathematics Project and reviewed content for the California Standards Tests.

Paul A. Kennedy, Ph.D., is a professor and Distinguished University Teaching Scholar in the Department of Mathematics at Colorado State University. Dr. Kennedy is a leader in mathematics education. His research focuses on developing algebraic thinking by using multiple representations and technology. He is the author of numerous publications.

Dale G. Seymour is a retired mathematics teacher, author, speaker and publisher. Dale founded Creative Publications in 1968, and went on to found two other mathematics publishing companies. Creating mathematical sculptures is one of his many hobbies.

Steven J. Leinwand is a Principal Research Analyst at the American Institutes for Research in Washington, D.C. He was previously, for 22 years, the Mathematics Supervisor with the Connecticut Department of Education.

Bert K. Waits, Ph.D., is a Professor Emeritus of Mathematics at The Ohio State University and cofounder of T^3 (Teachers Teaching with Technology), a national professional development program. Dr. Waits is also a former board member of the NCTM and an author of the original NCTM Standards.

Georgia Reviewers

Michelle Genovese
Sandy Creek High School
Tyrone, GA

Ashley McAfee
McIntosh High School
Peachtree City, GA

Kimberly Snell, Ed.S
Mathematics Teacher
Campbell High School
Smyrna, GA

C. Mark Henderson
Starr's Mill High School
Fayette County Board of
Education
Fayetteville, GA

Judy Riddell
Math Department Chair
Northgate High School
Newnan, GA

Melanie Tomlinson
East Coweta High School
Coweta County, GA

Steve Martin
Carrollton High School
Carrollton, GA

Susan S. Roach Ed.S.
Instructional Coach,
Mathematics
Newnan High School
Newnan, GA

Contributing Authors

Linda Antinone
Fort Worth, TX
Ms. Antinone teaches mathematics at R. L. Paschal
High School in Fort Worth, Texas. She has received
the Presidential Award for Excellence in Teaching
Mathematics and the National Radio Shack
Teacher award. She has coauthored several books
for Texas Instruments on the use of technology in
mathematics.

Carmen Whitman
Pflugerville, TX
Ms. Whitman travels nationally helping districts
improve mathematics education. She has been
a program coordinator on the mathematics team
at the Charles A. Dana Center, and has served
as a secondary math specialist for the Austin
Independent School District.

Contributing Writer

Karen Droga Campe
Instructor
Yale University
New Haven, CT

Field Test Participants

Jill Morris
Navasota High School
Navasota, TX

Carey Carter
Alvarado High School
Alvarado, TX

Ruth Stutzman
Jefferson Forest High School
Forest, VA

Reviewers

Robert Brouhle
Mathematics Department Chair, retired
Marina High School
Huntington Beach, CA

Carey Carter
Mathematics Teacher
Everman Joe C. Bean High School
Everman, TX

Greg Davis
Department Chair, retired
Lodi High School
Lodi, WI

Roger Fuller
Mathematics Department Chair
Grand Prairie High School
Grand Prairie, TX

Anthony Gugliotta
Supervisor of Math & Science
Rumson-Fair Haven Regional HS
Rumson, NJ

Marieta W. Harris
Mathematics Specialist
Memphis, TN

Debbie Hecky
Geometry Teacher
Scott High School
Covington, KY

Cynthia Hodges
Department Chair
Shoemaker High School
Killeen, TX

Kathleen Kelly
Mathematics Department Chair, retired
Lawrence High School
Fairfield, ME

Mike Kingery
Mathematics Teacher
Mayfield High School
Las Cruces, NM

Joy Lindsay
Mathematics Instructor
Bonita High School
LaVerne, CA

Kim Loggins
Geometry Teacher
Los Alamitos High School
Los Alamitos, CA

Elaine Pappas
Mathematics Department Chair
Cedar Shoals High School
Athens, GA

Terri Salas
Mathematics Consultant
Corpus Christi, TX

Jane Schneider
Mathematics Department Chair
Parkway West High School
Ballwin, MO

Jamae Sellari
Mathematics Instructor
Forest Hill High School
Jackson, MS

Caren Sorrells
Mathematics Coordinator
Birdville ISD
Haltom City, TX

E. Robin Staudenmeier
Middle/High School Math Coordinator
Olympia Community USD 16
Stanford, IL

Maureen "Marnie" Stockman
Geometry Specialist and Consultant
Cordova, MD

Anna Valdez
Geometry Teacher
Nikki Rowe High School
McAllen, TX

Lauralea Wright
Mathematics Teacher
Mauldin High School
Mauldin, SC

Denise Young
Mathematics Teacher
Blue Valley West High School
Overland Park, KS

UNIT 1

Similarity, Congruence, and Proofs

COMMON CORE GPS

COMMON CORE GPS

UNIT 1 CONTINUED

Right Triangle Trigonometry

UNIT 2

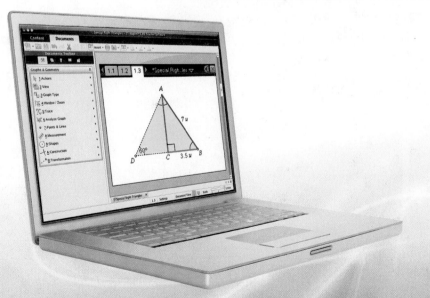

Extending the Number System

COMMON CORE GPS

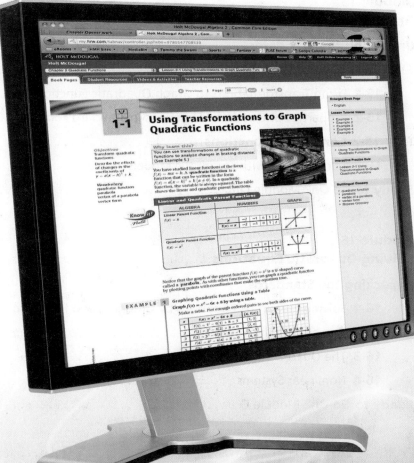

UNIT
5
Quadratic Functions

Modeling Geometry

UNIT 6

Applications of Probability

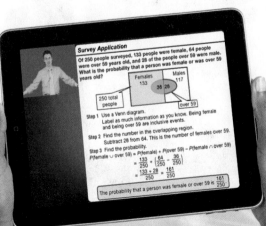

Common Core Georgia Performance Standards

Correlation for Holt McDougal Analytic Geometry

Standard	Descriptor	Page Citation
Number and Quantity: The Real Number System		
Extend the properties of exponents to rational exponents.		
MCC9-12.N.RN.1	Explain how the definition of the meaning of rational exponents follows from extending the properties of integer exponents to those values, allowing for a notation for radicals in terms of rational exponents. *For example, we define $5^{(1/3)}$ to be the cube root of 5 because we want $[5^{(1/3)}]^3 = 5^{(1/3) \times 3}$ to hold, so $[5^{(1/3)}]^3$ must equal 5.*	SE: 448–451
MCC9-12.N.RN.2	Rewrite expressions involving radicals and rational exponents using the properties of exponents.	SE: 448–451
Use properties of rational and irrational numbers.		
MCC9-12.N.RN.3	Explain why the sum or product of two rational numbers is rational; that the sum of a rational number and an irrational number is irrational; and that the product of a nonzero rational number and an irrational number is irrational.	SE: 452–453
Number and Quantity: The Complex Number System		
Perform arithmetic operations with complex numbers.		
MCC9-12.N.CN.1	Know there is a complex number i such that $i^2 = -1$, and every complex number has the form $a + bi$ with a and b real.	SE: 434–439
MCC9-12.N.CN.2	Use the relation $i^2 = -1$ and the commutative, associative, and distributive properties to add, subtract, and multiply complex numbers.	SE: 440–447
MCC9-12.N.CN.3(+)	Find the conjugate of a complex number; use conjugates to find moduli and quotients of complex numbers.	SE: 434–439, 440–447
Use complex numbers in polynomial identities and equations.		
MCC9-12.N.CN.7	Solve quadratic equations with real coefficients that have complex solutions.	SE: 434–439, 540–547

SE = Student Edition
+ = Advanced
* = Also a Modeling Standard

Common Core Georgia Performance Standards

Standard	Descriptor	Page Citation
Algebra: Seeing Structure in Expressions		
Interpret the structure of expressions		
MCC9-12.A.SSE.1	Interpret expressions that represent a quantity in terms of its context.*	SE: 501–508, 524–531, 532–539
MCC9-12.A.SSE.1a	a. Interpret parts of an expression, such as terms, factors, and coefficients.*	SE: 579–585
MCC9-12.A.SSE.1b	b. Interpret complicated expressions by viewing one or more of their parts as a single entity. For example, interpret $P(1 + r)^n$ as the product of P and a factor not depending on P.*	SE: 579–585
MCC9-12.A.SSE.2	Use the structure of an expression to identify ways to rewrite it. For example, see $x^4 - y^4$ as $(x^2)^2 - (y^2)^2$, thus recognizing it as a difference of squares that can be factored as $(x^2 - y^2)(x^2 + y^2)$.	SE: 462–463, 464–471, 472–478, 480–486, 501–508, 524–531, 532–539
Write expressions in equivalent forms to solve problems		
MCC9-12.A.SSE.3	Choose and produce an equivalent form of an expression to reveal and explain properties of the quantity represented by the expression.*	SE: 479, 524–531, 532–539
MCC9-12.A.SSE.3a	a. Factor a quadratic expression to reveal the zeros of the function it defines.*	SE: 479, 524–531
MCC9-12.A.SSE.3b	b. Complete the square in a quadratic expression to reveal the maximum or minimum value of the function it defines.*	SE: 532–539
Algebra: Arithmetic with Polynomials and Rational Expressions		
Perform arithmetic operations on polynomials		
MCC9-12.A.APR.1	Understand that polynomials form a system analogous to the integers, namely, they are closed under the operations of addition, subtraction, and multiplication; add, subtract, and multiply polynomials.	SE: 452–453

SE = Student Edition
+ = Advanced
* = Also a Modeling Standard

Standard	Descriptor	Page Citation
Algebra: Creating Equations*		
Create equations that describe numbers or relationships		
MCC9-12.A.CED.1	Create equations and inequalities in one variable and use them to solve problems. Include equations arising from linear and quadratic functions, and simple rational and exponential functions.*	SE: 7–13, 14–21, 117–124, 125–131, 138–145, 163–169, 209–215, 216–223, 224–231, 273–279, 354–359, 390–398, 400–407, 512–519, 540–547
MCC9-12.A.CED.2	Create equations in two or more variables to represent relationships between quantities; graph equations on coordinate axes with labels and scales.*	SE: 512–519, 524–531, 532–539
MCC9-12.A.CED.4	Rearrange formulas to highlight a quantity of interest, using the same reasoning as in solving equations. *For example, rearrange Ohm's law $V = IR$ to highlight resistance R.**	SE: 493–500
Algebra: Reasoning with Equations and Inequalities		
Solve equations and inequalities in one variable		
MCC9-12.A.REI.4	Solve quadratic equations in one variable.	SE: 524–531, 532–539
MCC9-12.A.REI.4a	a. Use the method of completing the square to transform any quadratic equation in x into an equation of the form $(x - p)^2 = q$ that has the same solutions. Derive the quadratic formula from this form.	SE: 532–539, 540–547
MCC9-12.A.REI.4b	b. Solve quadratic equations by inspection (e.g., for $x^2 = 49$), taking square roots, completing the square, the quadratic formula and factoring, as appropriate to the initial form of the equation. Recognize when the quadratic formula gives complex solutions and write them as $a \pm bi$ for real numbers a and b.	SE: 296–303, 532–539, 540–547
Solve systems of equations		
MCC9-12.A.REI.7	Solve a simple system consisting of a linear equation and a quadratic equation in two variables algebraically and graphically. *For example, find the points of intersection between the line $y = -3x$ and the circle $x^2 + y^2 = 3$.*	SE: 548–555

Common Core Georgia Performance Standards

Standard	Descriptor	Page Citation
Functions: Interpreting Functions		
Interpret functions that arise in applications in terms of the context		
MCC9-12.F.IF.4	For a function that models a relationship between two quantities, interpret key features of graphs and tables in terms of the quantities, and sketch graphs showing key features given a verbal description of the relationship. Key features include: intercepts; intervals where the function is increasing, decreasing, positive, or negative; relative maximums and minimums; symmetries; end behavior; and periodicity.*	SE: 501–508, 512–519
MCC9-12.F.IF.5	Relate the domain of a function to its graph and, where applicable, to the quantitative relationship it describes. *For example, if the function h(n) gives the number of person-hours it takes to assemble n engines in a factory, then the positive integers would be an appropriate domain for the function.* *	SE: 501–508, 512–519
MCC9-12.F.IF.6	Calculate and interpret the average rate of change of a function (presented symbolically or as a table) over a specified interval. Estimate the rate of change from a graph.*	SE: 501–508, 509–510, 512–519
Analyze functions using different representations		
MCC9-12.F.IF.7a	Graph functions expressed symbolically and show key features of the graph, by hand in simple cases and using technology for more complicated cases.* a. Graph linear and quadratic functions and show intercepts, maxima, and minima.*	SE: 493–500, 501–508, 524–531
MCC9-12.F.IF.8a	Write a function defined by an expression in different but equivalent forms to reveal and explain different properties of the function. a. Use the process of factoring and completing the square in a quadratic function to show zeros, extreme values, and symmetry of the graph, and interpret these in terms of a context.	SE: 501–508, 524–531
MCC9-12.F.IF.9	Compare properties of two functions each represented in a different way (algebraically, graphically, numerically in tables, or by verbal descriptions). *For example, given a graph of one quadratic function and an algebraic expression for another, say which has the larger maximum.*	SE: 509–510, 524–531
Functions: Building Functions		
Build a function that models a relationship between two quantities		
MCC9-12.F.BF.1	Write a function that describes a relationship between two quantities.*	SE: 493–500, 524–531, 532–539
MCC9-12.F.BF.1a	a. Determine an explicit expression, a recursive process, or steps for calculation from a context.*	SE: 532–539
MCC9-12.F.BF.1b	b. Combine standard function types using arithmetic operations. *For example, build a function that models the temperature of a cooling body by adding a constant function to a decaying exponential, and relate these functions to the model.*	SE: 493–500, 532–539

SE = Student Edition
+ = Advanced
* = Also a Modeling Standard

Standard	Descriptor	Page Citation
Build new functions from existing functions		
MCC9-12.F.BF.3	Identify the effect on the graph of replacing f(x) by f(x) + k, k f(x), f(kx), and f(x + k) for specific values of k (both positive and negative); find the value of k given the graphs. Experiment with cases and illustrate an explanation of the effects on the graph using technology. Include recognizing even and odd functions from their graphs and algebraic expressions for them.	SE: 492, 493–500
Functions: Linear, Quadratic, and Exponential*		
Construct and compare linear, quadratic, and exponential models and solve problems		
MCC9-12.F.LE.3	Observe using graphs and tables that a quantity increasing exponentially eventually exceeds a quantity increasing linearly, quadratically, or (more generally) as a polynomial function.	SE: 509–510, 524–531
Geometry: Congruence		
Understand congruence in terms of rigid motions		
MCC9-12.G.CO.6	Use geometric descriptions of rigid motions to transform figures and to predict the effect of a given rigid motion on a given figure; given two figures, use the definition of congruence in terms of rigid motions to decide if they are congruent.	SE: 108–115
MCC9-12.G.CO.7	Use the definition of congruence in terms of rigid motions to show that two triangles are congruent if and only if corresponding pairs of sides and corresponding pairs of angles are congruent.	SE: 125–131, 154–159
MCC9-12.G.CO.8	Explain how the criteria for triangle congruence (ASA, SAS, and SSS) follow from the definition of congruence in terms of rigid motions.	SE: 136–137
Prove geometric theorems		
MCC9-12.G.CO.9	Prove theorems about lines and angles. Theorems include: vertical angles are congruent; when a transversal crosses parallel lines, alternate interior angles are congruent and corresponding angles are congruent; points on a perpendicular bisector of a line segment are exactly those equidistant from the segment's endpoints.	SE: 46–51, 52–57, 58–64, 65, 66–73, 78, 79–85, 86–93, 96–102, 176–182, 183–189, 273–279
MCC9-12.G.CO.10	Prove theorems about triangles. Theorems include: measures of interior angles of a triangle sum to 180°; base angles of isosceles triangles are congruent; the segment joining midpoints of two sides of a triangle is parallel to the third side and half the length; the medians of a triangle meet at a point.	SE: 116, 117–124, 125–131, 154–159, 163–169, 190–196, 198–203
MCC9-12.G.CO.11	Prove theorems about parallelograms. Theorems include: opposite sides are congruent, opposite angles are congruent, the diagonals of a parallelogram bisect each other, and conversely, rectangles are parallelograms with congruent diagonals.	SE: 208, 209–215, 216–223, 224–231, 232–233, 234–241

Common Core Georgia Performance Standards

Standard	Descriptor	Page Citation
Geometry: Congruence		
Make geometric constructions		
MCC9-12.G.CO.12	Make formal geometric constructions with a variety of tools and methods (compass and straightedge, string, reflective devices, paper folding, dynamic geometric software, etc.). Copying a segment; copying an angle; bisecting a segment; bisecting an angle; constructing perpendicular lines, including the perpendicular bisector of a line segment; and constructing a line parallel to a given line through a point not on the line.	SE: 6, 7–13, 14–21, 94–95, 103, 197, 272, 311
MCC9-12.G.CO.13	Construct an equilateral triangle, a square, and a regular hexagon inscribed in a circle.	SE: 170–171
Geometry: Similarity, Right Triangles, and Trigonometry		
Understand similarity in terms of similarity transformations		
MCC9-12.G.SRT.1	Verify experimentally the properties of dilations given by a center and a scale factor:	SE: 252–259, 280–285
MCC9-12.G.SRT.1a	a. A dilation takes a line not passing through the center of the dilation to a parallel line, and leaves a line passing through the center unchanged.	SE: 252–259, 280–285
MCC9-12.G.SRT.1b	b. The dilation of a line segment is longer or shorter in the ratio given by the scale factor.	SE: 252–259, 280–285
MCC9-12.G.SRT.2	Given two figures, use the definition of similarity in terms of similarity transformations to decide if they are similar; explain using similarity transformations the meaning of similarity for triangles as the equality of all corresponding pairs of angles and the proportionality of all corresponding pairs of sides.	SE: 246–251, 280–285
MCC9-12.G.SRT.3	Use the properties of similarity transformations to establish the AA criterion for two triangles to be similar.	SE: 260–261, 262–269
Prove theorems involving similarity		
MCC9-12.G.SRT.4	Prove theorems about triangles. Theorems include: a line parallel to one side of a triangle divides the other two proportionally, and conversely; the Pythagorean Theorem proved using triangle similarity.	SE: 262–269, 270–271, 273–279
MCC9-12.G.SRT.5	Use congruence and similarity criteria for triangles to solve problems and to prove relationships in geometric figures.	SE: 138–145, 146–153, 154–159, 160–161, 262–269, 273–279, 280–285

SE = Student Edition
+ = Advanced
* = Also a Modeling Standard

Standard	Descriptor	Page Citation
Geometry: Similarity, Right Triangles, and Trigonometry		
Define trigonometric ratios and solve problems involving right triangles		
MCC9-12.G.SRT.6	Understand that by similarity, side ratios in right triangles are properties of the angles in the triangle, leading to definitions of trigonometric ratios for acute angles.	SE: 304–310, 316, 317–324
MCC9-12.G.SRT.7	Explain and use the relationship between the sine and cosine of complementary angles.	SE: 325–326
MCC9-12.G.SRT.8	Use trigonometric ratios and the Pythagorean Theorem to solve right triangles in applied problems.	SE: 270–271, 296–303, 304–310, 317–324, 328–335, 336–341, 354–359, 361–368, 390–398, 400–407, 408–413
Geometry: Circles		
Understand and apply theorems about circles		
MCC9-12.G.C.1	Prove that all circles are similar.	SE: 252–259
MCC9-12.G.C.2	Identify and describe relationships among inscribed angles, radii, and chords. Include the relationship between central, inscribed, and circumscribed angles; inscribed angles on a diameter are right angles; the radius of a circle is perpendicular to the tangent where the radius intersects the circle.	SE: 390–398, 400–407, 416–423
MCC9-12.G.C.3	Construct the inscribed and circumscribed circles of a triangle, and prove properties of angles for a quadrilateral inscribed in a circle.	SE: 183–189, 416–423
MCC9-12.G.C.4(+)	Construct a tangent line from a point outside a given circle to the circle.	SE: 416–423
Find arc lengths and areas of sectors of circles		
MCC9-12.G.C.5	Derive using similarity the fact that the length of the arc intercepted by an angle is proportional to the radius, and define the radian measure of the angle as the constant of proportionality; derive the formula for the area of a sector.	SE: 408–413, 414–415

Common Core Georgia Performance Standards

Standard	Descriptor	Page Citation
Geometry: Expressing Geometric Properties with Equations		
Translate between the geometric description and the equation for a conic section		
MCC9-12.G.GPE.1	Derive the equation of a circle of given center and radius using the Pythagorean Theorem; complete the square to find the center and radius of a circle given by an equation.	SE: 572–578
MCC9-12.G.GPE.2	Derive the equation of a parabola given a focus and directrix.	SE: 579–585
Use coordinates to prove simple geometric theorems algebraically		
MCC9-12.G.GPE.4	Use coordinates to prove simple geometric theorems algebraically. *For example, prove or disprove that a figure defined by four given points in the coordinate plane is a rectangle; prove or disprove that the point $\left(1, \sqrt{3}\right)$ lies on the circle centered at the origin and containing the point (0, 2).*	SE: 154–159, 190–196, 198–203, 209–215, 216–223, 224–231, 280–285, 566–571, 572–578
Geometry: Geometric Measurement and Dimension		
Explain volume formulas and use them to solve problems		
MCC9-12.G.GMD.1	Give an informal argument for the formulas for the circumference of a circle, area of a circle, volume of a cylinder, pyramid, and cone. Use dissection arguments, Cavalieri's principle, and informal limit arguments.	SE: 352–353, 354–359, 361–368, 369–376
MCC9-12.G.GMD.2(+)	Give an informal argument using Cavalieri's principle for the formulas for the volume of a sphere and other solid figures.	SE: 361–368, 378–385
MCC9-12.G.GMD.3	Use volume formulas for cylinders, pyramids, cones, and spheres to solve problems.*	SE: 361–368, 369–376, 378–385
Statistics and Probability: Interpreting Categorical and Quantitative Data		
Summarize, represent, and interpret data on two categorical and quantitative variables		
MCC9-12.S.ID.6a	Represent data on two quantitative variables on a scatter plot, and describe how the variables are related.* a. Fit a function to the data; use functions fitted to data to solve problems in the context of the data. Use given functions or choose a function suggested by the context. Emphasize linear and exponential models.*	SE: 512–519

SE = Student Edition
+ = Advanced
* = Also a Modeling Standard

Standard	Descriptor	Page Citation
Statistics and Probability: Conditional Probability and the Rules of Probability		
Understand independence and conditional probability and use them to interpret data		
MCC9-12.S.CP.1	Describe events as subsets of a sample space (the set of outcomes) using characteristics (or categories) of the outcomes, or as unions, intersections, or complements of other events ("or," "and," "not").	SE: 594–600, 610–617, 639–645
MCC9-12.S.CP.2	Understand that two events A and B are independent if the probability of A and B occurring together is the product of their probabilities, and use this characterization to determine if they are independent.*	SE: 623–630
MCC9-12.S.CP.3	Understand the conditional probability of A given B as P(A and B)/P(B), and interpret independence of A and B as saying that the conditional probability of A given B is the same as the probability of A, and the conditional probability of B given A is the same as the probability of B.*	SE: 623–630
MCC9-12.S.CP.4	Construct and interpret two-way frequency tables of data when two categories are associated with each object being classified. Use the two-way table as a sample space to decide if events are independent and to approximate conditional probabilities. *For example, collect data from a random sample of students in your school on their favorite subject among math, science, and English. Estimate the probability that a randomly selected student from your school will favor science given that the student is in tenth grade. Do the same for other subjects and compare the results.**	SE: 631–638
MCC9-12.S.CP.5	Recognize and explain the concepts of conditional probability and independence in everyday language and everyday situations. *For example, compare the chance of having lung cancer if you are a smoker with the chance of being a smoker if you have lung cancer.**	SE: 623–630, 639–645
Use the rules of probability to compute probabilities of compound events in a uniform probability model		
MCC9-12.S.CP.6	Find the conditional probability of A given B as the fraction of B's outcomes that also belong to A, and interpret the answer in terms of the model.*	SE: 623–630
MCC9-12.S.CP.7	Apply the Addition Rule, P(A or B) = P(A) + P(B) − P(A and B), and interpret the answer in terms of the model.*	SE: 639–645

Mastering *the* Standards

for Mathematical Practice

COMMON CORE GPS

The topics described in the Standards for Mathematical Content will vary from year to year. However, the way in which you learn, study, and think about mathematics will not. The Standards for Mathematical Practice describe skills that you will use in all of your math courses. These pages show some features of your book and the *Explorations in Core Math for Common Core GPS* workbook that will help you gain these skills and use them to master this year's topics.

1 | **Make sense of problems and persevere in solving them.**

Mathematically proficient students start by explaining to themselves the meaning of a problem… They analyze givens, constraints, relationships, and goals. They make conjectures about the form… of the solution and plan a solution pathway…

In your book

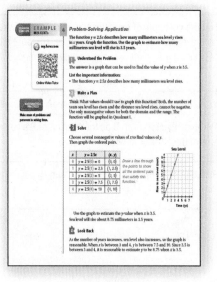

Problem Solving Applications in your book describe and illustrate a four-step plan for problem solving.

In *Explorations*

Problem Solving

Problem Solving in *Explorations* provides an opportunity to practice and refine your problem-solving skills.

2 Reason abstractly and quantitatively.

Mathematically proficient students... bring two complementary abilities to bear on problems...: the ability to decontextualize—to abstract a given situation and represent it symbolically...and the ability to contextualize, to pause... in order to probe into the referents for the symbols involved.

In your book

In *Explorations*

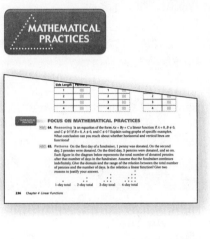

Focus on Mathematical Practices exercises in your book and **Performance Tasks** in *Explorations* require you to use logical reasoning, represent situations symbolically, use mathematical models to solve problems, and state your answers in terms of a problem context.

3 Construct viable arguments and critique the reasoning of others.

Mathematically proficient students... justify their conclusions, [and]... distinguish correct... reasoning from that which is flawed.

In your book

In *Explorations*

Think and Discuss in your book and **Reflect and Error Analysis** in *Explorations* ask you to evaluate statements, explain relationships, apply mathematical principles, make conjectures, construct arguments, and justify your reasoning.

4 Model with mathematics.

Mathematically proficient students can apply... mathematics... to problems... in everyday life, society, and the workplace...

In your book

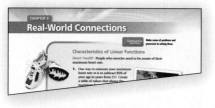

CHAPTER 4
Real-World Connections

Characteristics of Linear Functions

Heart Health People who exercise need to be aware of their maximum heart rate.

1. One way to estimate your maximum heart rate *m* is to subtract 85% of your age in years from 217. Create a table of values that shows...

In *Explorations*

Name _____ Class _____ Date _____ 5-6

Solving Systems of Linear Inequalities
Focus on Modeling

Essential question: *How can you use systems of linear equations or inequalities to model and solve contextual problems?*

You are purchasing jeans and T-shirts. Jeans cost $35 and T-shirts cost $15. You plan on spending $115 and purchasing a total of 5 items. How many pairs of jeans and how many T-shirts can you buy?

1 Write a system of linear equat...

Real-World Connections in your book and **Focus on Modeling** in *Explorations* apply mathematics to other disciplines and real-world contexts such as science and business.

5 Use appropriate tools strategically.

Mathematically proficient students consider the available tools when solving a problem... [and] are... able to use technological tools to explore and deepen their understanding...

In your book

Algebra TASK

Technology TASK

In *Explorations*

The **midpoint** of a line segment is the point that divides the segment into two segments that have the same length. The midpoint is said to **bisect** the segment. In the figure, the tick marks show that $PM = MQ$. Therefore, M is the midpoint of $\overline{PQ}$ and M bisects $\overline{PQ}$.

CC-9-12.G.CO.12
2 EXPLORE   Bisecting a Segment

A Use a straightedge to draw a segment on a piece of paper. Label the endpoints *A* and *B*.

B Fold the paper so that point *B* is on top of point *A*.

C Open the paper. Label the point where the crease intersects the segment as point *M*.

REFLECT

2a. How can you use a ruler to check the construction?
Measure the length of $\overline{AM}$ and $\overline{MB}$ to check that $AM = MB$.

2b. Explain how you could use paper folding to divide a linear segment into four segments of equal length.
Construct the midpoint of the segment. Then construct the midpoint of each of the new segments.

A **circle** is the set of all points in a plane that are...
distance from a point called...

Hands-On Tasks and **Technology Tasks** in your book and **Explore** in *Explorations* use concrete and technological tools, such as manipulatives or graphing calculators, to explore mathematical concepts.

6 Attend to precision.

Mathematically proficient students... communicate precisely... with others and in their own reasoning... [They] give carefully formulated explanations...

In your book

83. **Write About It** Explain why the FO... binomials at a time.

In *Explorations*

Key Vocabulary

Precision refers not only to the correctness of calculations but also to the proper use of mathematical language and symbols. **Write About It** in your book and **Key Vocabulary** in *Explorations* help you learn and use the language of math to communicate mathematics precisely.

7 **Look for and make use of structure.**

Mathematically proficient students… look closely to discern a pattern or structure… They can also step back for an overview and shift perspective.

In your book

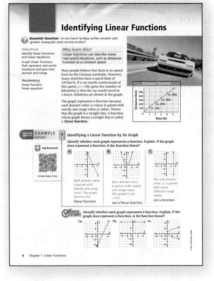

In *Explorations*

In both your book and Explorations, you will study regularity in mathematical structures, such as expressions, equations, operations, geometric figures, tables, graphs, and diagrams. Understanding the underlying structures of mathematics allows you to generalize beyond a specific case and to make connections between related problems..

8 **Look for and express regularity in repeated reasoning.**

Mathematically proficient students… look both for general methods and for shortcuts… [and] maintain oversight of the process, while attending to the details…

In your book

In *Explorations*

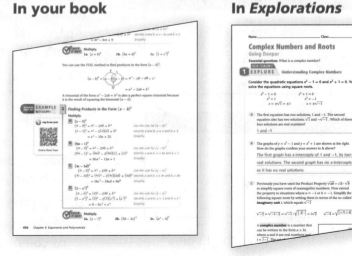

In both your book and *Explorations*, examples group similar types of problems together, and the solutions are carefully stepped out. This allows you to look for patterns or regularity and make generalizations while noticing variations in the details.

Review Test
Coordinate Algebra - Part 1

Selected Response

1. A movie theater charges $9.00 for a ticket. To help the local animal shelter, the theater agrees to reduce the price of each ticket by $0.50 for every can of pet food a customer donates. Write an equation for the ticket cost y for a customer who contributes x cans.

   Ⓐ $y = 9 - 0.50x$

   Ⓑ $y = 9x - 0.5$

   Ⓒ $y = -9x - 0.5$

   Ⓓ $y = 9x + 0.50x$

2. Which of the following tables represent(s) a function?

   I.

Input	Output
−2	2
−1	4
0	6
1	8

   II.

Input	Output
0	0
1	2
5	2
7	9

   III.

Input	Output
2	1
5	2
10	3
5	4

   Ⓕ All   Ⓗ I and III only

   Ⓖ I and II only   Ⓙ I only

3. Graph the system of inequalities.
   $$\begin{cases} y \geq 4x - 1 \\ y < -3x + 2 \end{cases}$$

   Ⓐ   Ⓒ

   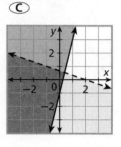

   Ⓑ   Ⓓ

   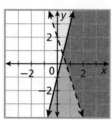

4. Maria buys lunch for $6.50 every day during her five-day work week. Her yearly budget allows $1500 for lunches. Write an equation to determine how much of Maria's lunch budget, in dollars, remains unspent at the end of a particular week of the year. Include definitions of the variables you used.

   Ⓕ $B = 1500 - 6.5n$, where B is her budget balance and n is the number of complete weeks of work

   Ⓖ $B = 32.5n - 1500$, where B is her budget balance and n is the number of complete weeks of work

   Ⓗ $B = 1500 - 32.5n$, where B is her budget balance and n is the number of complete weeks of work

   Ⓙ $B = 6.5n - 1500$, where B is her budget balance and n is the number of complete weeks of work

5. The population of a Midwestern suburb is growing exponentially. The chart shows its population for four consecutive years. Write a recursive rule for the population P_n after n years. Use $n = 1$ to represent Year 1.

Year	Year 1	Year 2	Year 3	Year 4
Population	5700	6441	7278	8225

(A) $P_1 = 5700, P_n = 1.13\, P_{n-1}$

(B) $P_1 = 6441, P_n = 2.23\, P_{n-1}$

(C) $P_1 = 6441, P_n = 1.13\, P_{n-1}$

(D) $P_1 = 5700, P_n = 2.23\, P_{n-1}$

6. A new play receives bad reviews on opening night and ticket sales start to decrease. Ticket sales for the first 5 nights form the sequence 500, 486, 472, 458, 444, ... Find an explicit rule for the number of tickets sold on the nth night.

(F) $a_n = 500 - 14n$

(G) $a_n = 500(.086)^n$

(H) $a_n = 500 - 14(n - 1)$

(J) $a_n = 500(.086)^{n-1}$

7. Which represents a price that increases at a constant rate per ounce for ordered pairs in the form (ounces, price)?

(A) (8, 0.60), (12, 0.90), (24, 1.80), (32, 2.40)

(B) (8, 0.40), (12, 0.80), (24, 1.60), (32, 3.20)

(C) (8, 0.80), (12, 1.20), (24, 1.60), (32, 2.00)

(D) (8, 0.50), (12, 1.00), (24, 1.50), (32, 2.00)

Mini-Tasks

8. How many terms are in the algebraic expression $2x - 8xy + 12y$?

9. Solve $p = \dfrac{11}{2}n + 22$ for n.

10. Solve $2.4 + 2.8x > -1.2 + 3.2x$.

11. Solve $\begin{cases} -8x - y = -15 \\ -9x - y = -2 \end{cases}$ by elimination. Express your answer as an ordered pair.

12. Write an exponential function to model a population of 470 animals that decreases at an annual rate of 16%. Then estimate the value of the function after 5 years (to the nearest whole number).

Performance Task

13. A doctor's office schedules 20-minute and half-hour appointments. The doctor also makes hospital rounds for two hours each weekday.

    Part A: If the doctor limits these activities to at most 30 hours per week, write an inequality to represent the number of each type of office visit that can be scheduled in one week. Use x to represent the number of 20-minute appointments and y to represent the number of half-hour appointments. Use minutes for all times. Graph the inequality.

    Part B: Is the point (48, 13) in the shaded area of the graph? What does that mean?

    Part C: If the doctor can have only 29 half-hour appointments next week, how many 20-minute appointments can be scheduled? Express the answer as an inequality and explain its meaning in words. Show the steps you use to find the inequality.

Review Test

Coordinate Algebra - Part 2

Selected Response

1. Aaron won $500 in an essay contest. He invests the money in an interest-earning account. The table shows how much money he has in the account. Find an appropriate model for the amount that Aaron will have in the account after t years. Then, use the model to predict approximately when Aaron will have $1000 in the account.

Aaron's Account	
Year	Value
1	$520.00
2	$540.80
3	$562.43
4	$584.93
5	$608.33

Ⓐ $V(t) = 500(1.04)^t$; about 18 years

Ⓑ $V(t) = 500(1.04t)$; about 20 years

Ⓒ $V(t) = 500(1.04t)$; about 10 years

Ⓓ $V(t) = 400(1.06)^t$; about 9 years

2. In a set of ordered pairs for which the x-coordinates increase by a constant amount, which identifies the set as representing linear growth?

Ⓕ The y-coordinates increase by a constant amount.

Ⓖ The y-coordinates increase by a constant factor greater than 1.

Ⓗ The y-coordinate is always a constant power (greater than 1) of the x-coordinate.

Ⓙ The y-coordinates are always positive and increasing.

3. Look for a pattern in the data set. Which kind of model best describes the data?

Population Growth of Bacteria	
Time (hours)	Number of Bacteria
0	1,800
1	4,400
2	11,000
3	28,500
4	71,250

Ⓐ linear

Ⓒ constant

Ⓑ polynomial

Ⓓ exponential

4. Point G is the midpoint of segment $\overline{AB}$, and point H is the midpoint of segment $\overline{DE}$. Which transformation(s) will create an image of the regular hexagon $ABCDEF$ that coincides with itself?

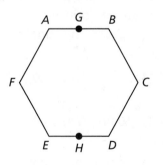

Ⓕ Reflection across the line $\overline{AE}$.

Ⓖ Rotation of 90 degrees about the center of the hexagon.

Ⓗ Rotation of 270 degrees about the center of the hexagon.

Ⓙ Reflection across the line $\overline{GH}$.

5. Lisa is a fitness instructor. For one month, she recorded the number of people who attended her aerobics class. She then used her data to make the box-and-whisker plot shown. Lisa's data set includes a single outlier and no duplicate data values.

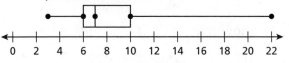

Which statement describes the effect on the range and interquartile range of Lisa's data set when the outlier is removed?

   Ⓐ The interquartile range increases but the range decreases.

   Ⓑ The range and interquartile range both decrease, but the interquartile range decreases more.

   Ⓒ The range decreases but the interquartile range increases.

   Ⓓ The range and interquartile range both decrease, but the range decreases more.

Mini-Tasks

6. Make a box-and-whisker plot of the data. Find the interquartile range.

   10, 6, 13, 4, 9, 4, 18, 7, 10, 7, 15, 9, 13, 9, 16, 7

7. Find the coordinates of the image of the point $(0, 2)$ when it is reflected across the line $y = 9$.

8. A small hotel with 10 rooms was destroyed in a fire. After the hotel was rebuilt, the owner took out a loan to buy new beds. The recursive rule $a_1 = \$12,000$, $a_n = a_{n-1} - \$1,000$ gives the amount left on the loan at the beginning of month n. Write an explicit rule for the sequence.

9. Identify a single transformation that is equivalent to reflecting the figure across line n and then reflecting the image across line m.

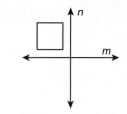

10. The table shows the number of people in thousands who had library cards in a certain city. During which time interval did the number of people with library cards increase at the greatest rate?

Year	1986	1990	1995	2000	2001
Number (millions)	32.37	33.59	36.43	31.05	32.91

Performance Task

11. Commission earnings for 50 salespeople are modeled by the functions in the table and the graph. Compare earnings as a function of rank for experienced and inexperienced salespeople.

Experienced Salespeople

Rank	Earnings (thousands of $)
1	4.95
10	3.53
20	2.87
30	2.41
40	1.88
50	1.61

Inexperienced Salespeople

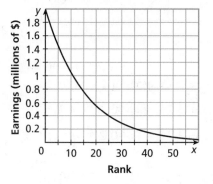

Benchmark Test

Analytic Geometry - Part 1

Selected Response

1. The revolving restaurant on top of a hotel in San Francisco, California takes 45 minutes to complete a full counterclockwise rotation. A table that is 30 ft from the center of the restaurant starts at position (30, 0). What are the coordinates of the table after 9 minutes? Round to the nearest tenth.

   (A) (9.3, 28.5)   (C) (23, 19.3)

   (B) (28.5, 9.3)   (D) (11.3, 17.3)

2. A camera is mounted at a point 4,400 ft from the base of a rocket launching pad. Assuming the rocket rises vertically, what is the height of the rocket from its base when the camera angle is 30°? Round your answer to the nearest foot.

   (F) 3,811 ft   (H) 7,621 ft

   (G) 2,540 ft   (J) 2,200 ft

3. Given that △ABC ~ △DEF solve for x and y.

   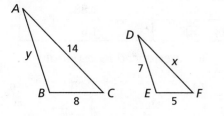

   (A) $x = 9.75$, $y = 11.2$

   (B) $x = 8.75$, $y = 11.2$

   (C) $x = 8.75$, $y = 10.2$

   (D) $x = 9.75$, $y = 10.2$

4. Show that *ABCD* is a parallelogram.

   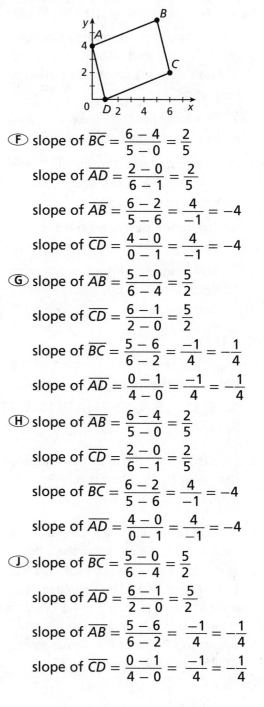

   (F) slope of $\overline{BC} = \dfrac{6-4}{5-0} = \dfrac{2}{5}$

   slope of $\overline{AD} = \dfrac{2-0}{6-1} = \dfrac{2}{5}$

   slope of $\overline{AB} = \dfrac{6-2}{5-6} = \dfrac{4}{-1} = -4$

   slope of $\overline{CD} = \dfrac{4-0}{0-1} = \dfrac{4}{-1} = -4$

   (G) slope of $\overline{AB} = \dfrac{5-0}{6-4} = \dfrac{5}{2}$

   slope of $\overline{CD} = \dfrac{6-1}{2-0} = \dfrac{5}{2}$

   slope of $\overline{BC} = \dfrac{5-6}{6-2} = \dfrac{-1}{4} = -\dfrac{1}{4}$

   slope of $\overline{AD} = \dfrac{0-1}{4-0} = \dfrac{-1}{4} = -\dfrac{1}{4}$

   (H) slope of $\overline{AB} = \dfrac{6-4}{5-0} = \dfrac{2}{5}$

   slope of $\overline{CD} = \dfrac{2-0}{6-1} = \dfrac{2}{5}$

   slope of $\overline{BC} = \dfrac{6-2}{5-6} = \dfrac{4}{-1} = -4$

   slope of $\overline{AD} = \dfrac{4-0}{0-1} = \dfrac{4}{-1} = -4$

   (J) slope of $\overline{BC} = \dfrac{5-0}{6-4} = \dfrac{5}{2}$

   slope of $\overline{AD} = \dfrac{6-1}{2-0} = \dfrac{5}{2}$

   slope of $\overline{AB} = \dfrac{5-6}{6-2} = \dfrac{-1}{4} = -\dfrac{1}{4}$

   slope of $\overline{CD} = \dfrac{0-1}{4-0} = \dfrac{-1}{4} = -\dfrac{1}{4}$

5. Find the area of the triangle with vertices $A(-3, 2)$, $B(1, -2)$, and $C(1, 3)$.

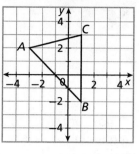

Ⓐ 10 units^2 Ⓒ 8 units^2

Ⓑ 20 units^2 Ⓓ 12 units^2

6. Which expression CANNOT be used to find BC?

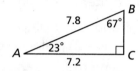

Ⓕ 7.8(sin 23°)

Ⓖ 7.8(cos 67°)

Ⓗ 7.8(tan 23°)

Ⓙ $\dfrac{7.2}{\tan 67°}$

Mini-Tasks

7. A cylindrical water tank with radius 2 feet and length 6 feet is filled with water to a depth of 3 feet when in a horizontal position. The chord formed by the level of the water intersecting the circular end of the tank has a length of $2\sqrt{3}$ feet. Find the volume of the water. Give your answer in terms of π.

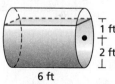

8. Prove that $A(1, 1)$, $B(3, 3)$, and $C(5, 1)$ are the vertices of a right triangle.

9. Tell whether a rigid motion can move the dashed figure onto the solid figure. If so, describe the transformation that you can use. If not, explain why the figures are not congruent.

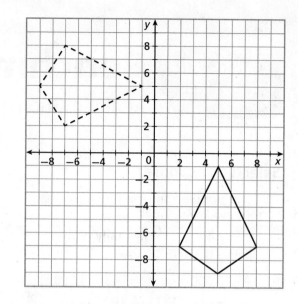

10. A group of students is digging out a rectangular garden bed that covers an area of 64 square feet to fill with planting soil. The students have a budget of $90 to purchase the soil. If 1 cubic foot of soil costs $2.75 and the depth of the soil is 6 inches, do the students have enough money? Explain your solution.

Performance Task

11. Quadrilateral *JKLM* is inscribed in circle *O*.

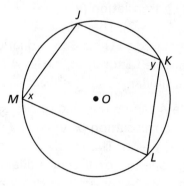

Write a formal proof that $\angle x$ and $\angle y$ are supplementary.

Benchmark Test

Analytic Geometry - Part 2

Selected Response

1. The population of a town is currently 1500 people and is expected to triple every 4 years. How many people will be living there in 20 years?

   Ⓐ 30,000   Ⓒ 364,500

   Ⓑ 121,500   Ⓓ 13,947,137,604

2. Which proof demonstrates that circle A with center $(-1, 1)$ and radius 1 is similar to circle B with center $(-3, 2)$ and radius 2?

   Ⓕ Circle A can be mapped to circle A' by a translation $(x, y) \rightarrow (x - 2, y + 1)$. Then circle A' can be mapped to circle B by a dilation with scale factor $\frac{1}{2}$. So, circles A and B are similar.

   Ⓖ Circle A can be mapped to circle A' by a translation $(x, y) \rightarrow (x + 1, y - 2)$. Then circle A' can be mapped to circle B by a dilation with scale factor 2. So, circles A and B are similar.

   Ⓗ Circle A can be mapped to circle A' by a translation $(x, y) \rightarrow (x + 1, y - 2)$. Then circle A' can be mapped to circle B by a dilation with scale factor $\frac{1}{2}$. So, circles A and B are similar.

   Ⓙ Circle A can be mapped to circle A' by a translation $(x, y) \rightarrow (x - 2, y + 1)$. Then circle A' can be mapped to circle B by a dilation with scale factor 2. So, circles A and B are similar.

3. Circle O has center $(5, 5)$ and radius 4. Circle P has center $(3, -1)$ and radius 5. Which describes how circle O can be transformed to show that circle P is similar to circle O?

   Ⓐ translation of circle O: $(x, y) \rightarrow (x - 2, y - 6)$; dilation of the image with center $(3, -1)$ and scale factor $\frac{4}{5}$

   Ⓑ translation of circle O: $(x, y) \rightarrow (x - 6, y - 2)$; dilation of the image with center $(3, -1)$ and scale factor $\frac{4}{5}$

   Ⓒ translation of circle O: $(x, y) \rightarrow (x - 2, y - 6)$; dilation of the image with center $(3, -1)$ and scale factor $\frac{5}{4}$

   Ⓓ translation of circle O: $(x, y) \rightarrow (x - 6, y - 2)$; dilation of the image with center $(3, -1)$ and scale factor $\frac{5}{4}$

4. Apply the dilation D to the polygon shown. What are the coordinates of the image points?

   D: $(x, y) \rightarrow (3x, 3y)$

   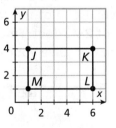

   Ⓕ J'(12, 3), K'(12, 18), L'(3, 18), M'(3, 3)

   Ⓖ J'(-3, -12), K'(-18, -12), L'(-18, -3), M'(-3, -3)

   Ⓗ J'(3, 12), K'(18, 12), L'(18, 3), M'(3, 3)

   Ⓙ J'(3, 12), K'(18, 12), L'(6, 1), M'(1, 1)

5. A bag contains orange, white, and purple marbles. The probability of randomly selecting an orange marble from this bag is 17%, and the probability of randomly selecting a white marble is 50%. What is the probability of selecting a purple marble?

Ⓐ 67%   Ⓒ 33%

Ⓑ $33\frac{1}{3}$%   Ⓓ 17%

6. What is the area of the I-shaped base of the I-beam shown below?

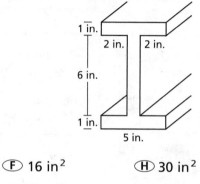

Ⓕ 16 in²   Ⓗ 30 in²

Ⓖ 28 in²   Ⓙ 40 in²

Mini-Tasks

7. The area of ⊙D is 113.1 square meters. The area of sector ADB is 34.6 square meters. Find the measure of $\overset{\frown}{ACB}$. Round to the nearest tenth of a degree.

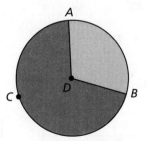

8. A drawer contains 10 red socks, 6 white socks, and 4 blue socks. Without looking, you draw out a sock, return it, and draw out a second sock. What is the probability that the first sock is red and the second sock is white? Round your answer to the nearest hundredth.

9. A right cylinder has a rectangular prism removed from it as shown in the figure. The cylinder has a height of 5 millimeters. The base area of the figure shown is 15.5π square millimeters. Find the volume of the figure.

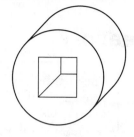

10. A saleswoman uses a coordinate plane to map her sales territory. She maps her office at $(0, 0)$. Her sales territory is represented by a circle whose center is at $(0, 0)$ and whose radius is equal to the distance between the office and the farthest client, who is located at $(-52, 3)$. Each grid unit represents one mile.

    Part A: Find the radius of the circle that represents the sales territory. Round to the nearest whole number.
    Part B: Use your answer to **Part A** to write the equation of the circle.

11. Luisa used the Law of Sines to solve for ∠A in triangle ABC. She found that sin A was equal to a negative number. Explain what, if anything, Luisa can conclude from this result.

Performance Task

12. Write a paragraph proof to show that m∠1 = m∠3 if m∠2 = m∠4. Include Given and Prove statements.

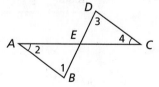

HOW TO STUDY ANALYTIC GEOMETRY

This book has many features designed to help you learn and study
effectively. Becoming familiar with these features will prepare you
for greater success on your exams.

Learn

The **vocabulary** is
listed at the beginning
of every lesson.

Look for the **Know-It-Note**
icons to identify important
information.

Study the **examples** to
apply new concepts and
skills. Examples include
stepped out solutions.

Test your understanding
of examples by trying the
Check It Out problems.
Check your work in the
Selected Answers.

Practice

Use a **graphic organizer**
to summarize each lesson.

Refer to the examples
from the lesson to
solve the **Guided
Practice** exercises.

If you get stuck, use the
internet for **Homework
Help Online**.

Complete **Test Prep**
exercises to prepare
for standardized
tests.

Go beyond the lesson
with **Challenge and
Extend** problems.

Develop your math
skills with **Focus
on Mathematical
Practice** exercises.

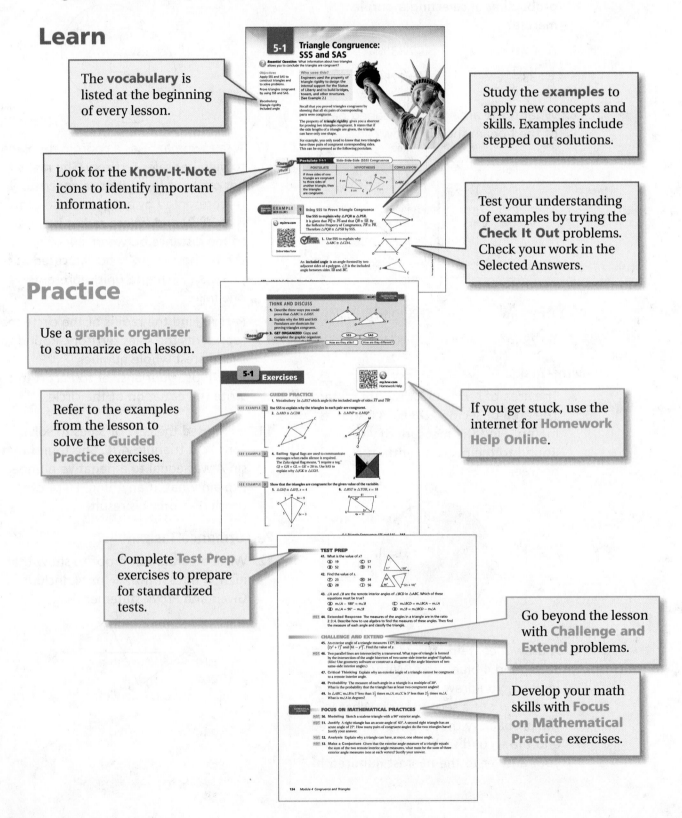

Focus on Problem Solving

PROBLEM SOLVING

The Problem Solving Plan

Mathematical problems are a part of daily life. You need to use a good problem-solving plan to be a good problem solver. The plan used in this textbook is outlined below.

UNDERSTAND the Problem

First make sure you understand the problem you are asked to solve.

■ **What are you asked to find?**	Restate the question in your own words.
■ **What information is given?**	Identify the key facts given in the problem.
■ **What information do you need?**	Determine what information you need to solve the problem.
■ **Do you have all the information needed?**	Determine if you need more information.
■ **Do you have too much information?**	Determine if there is unnecessary information and eliminate it from your list of important facts.

Make a PLAN

Plan how to use the information you are given.

■ **Have you solved similar problems?**	Think about similar problems you have solved successfully.
■ **What problem solving strategy or strategies could you use to solve this problem?**	Choose an appropriate problem solving strategy and decide how you will use it.

SOLVE

Use your plan to solve the problem. Show the steps in the solution, and write a final statement that gives the solution to the problem.

LOOK BACK

Check your answer against the original problem.

■ **Have you answered the question?**	Make sure you have answered the original question.
■ **Is the answer reasonable?**	The answer must make sense in relation to the question.
■ **Are your calculations correct?**	Check to make sure your calculations are accurate.
■ **Can you use another strategy or solve the problem in another way?**	Using another strategy is a good way to check your answer.
■ **Did you learn anyting that could help you solve similar problems in the future?**	Try to remember the types of problems you have solved and the strategies you applied.

Are You Ready?

my.hrw.com
Assessment and Intervention

✓ Vocabulary

Match each term on the left with a definition on the right.

1. coordinate
2. metric system of measurement
3. expression
4. order of operations

A. a mathematical phrase that contains operations, numbers, and/or variables

B. the measurement system often used in the United States

C. one of the numbers of an ordered pair that locates a point on a coordinate graph

D. a list of rules for evaluating expressions

E. a decimal system of weights and measures that is used universally in science and commonly throughout the world

✓ Measure with Customary and Metric Units

For each object tell which is the better measurement.

5. length of an unsharpened pencil
$7\frac{1}{2}$ in. or $9\frac{3}{4}$ in.

6. the diameter of a quarter
1 m or $2\frac{1}{2}$ cm

7. length of a soccer field
100 yd or 40 yd

8. height of a classroom
5 ft or 10 ft

9. height of a student's desk
30 in. or 4 ft

10. length of a dollar bill
15.6 cm or 35.5 cm

✓ Combine Like Terms

Simplify each expression.

11. $-y + 3y - 6y + 12y$

12. $63 + 2x - 7 - 4x$

13. $-5 - 9 - 7x + 6x$

14. $24 - 3y + y + 7$

✓ Evaluate Expressions

Evaluate each expression for the given value of the variable.

15. $x + 3x + 7x$ for $x = -5$

16. $5p + 10$ for $p = 78$

Career Readiness Lawyers

Lawyers represent clients in civil or criminal trials, and advise people and businesses on what they can and can't do under the law. In a trial, a lawyer must convince a judge or a jury by presenting chains of logical reasoning, much as you would prove a theorem. A lawyer must have a college degree plus three years of law school. Finally, a lawyer must pass a bar exam. Lawyers may work in government, in law offices or law schools, in for-profit or non-profit organizations, or be self-employed.

Similarity, Congruence, and Proofs

UNIT

1

Online Edition

my.hrw.com

Access the complete online textbook, interactive features, and additional resources.

Animated Math

Interactively explore key concepts with these online tutorials.

Multilingual Glossary

Enhance your math vocabulary with this illustrated online glossary in 13 languages.

Portable Devices

On the Spot

Watch video tutorials anywhere, anytime with this app for iPhone® and iPad®.

HMH Fuse

Make your learning experience completely portable and interactive with this app for iPad®.

Chapter Resources

Scan with your smart phone to jump directly to the online edition.

Homework Help provides video tutorials, step-by-step solutions, and additional practice for lesson exercises.

1 Tools of Geometry

COMMON CORE GPS

Contents

MATHEMATICAL PRACTICES   The Common Core Georgia Performance Standards for Mathematical Practice describe varieties of expertise that all students should seek to develop. Opportunities to develop these practices are integrated throughout this program.

1 Make sense of problems and persevere in solving them.

2 Reason abstractly and quantitatively.

3 Construct viable arguments and critique the reasoning of others.

4 Model with mathematics.

5 Use appropriate tools strategically.

6 Attend to precision.

7 Look for and make use of structure.

8 Look for and express regularity in repeated reasoning.

Unpacking the Standards

Understanding the standards and the vocabulary terms in the standards will help you know exactly what you are expected to learn in this chapter.

 MCC9-12.G.CO.12

Make formal geometric constructions with a variety of tools and methods (compass and straightedge, string, reflective devices, paper folding, dynamic geometric software, etc.).

Key Vocabulary

construction (construcción) A method of creating a figure that is considered to be mathematically precise. Figures may be constructed by using a compass and straightedge, geometry software, or paper folding.

What It Means For You

Construction methods give you precise ways to create or copy geometric figures without having to measure and/or estimate.

EXAMPLE

How can you divide $\overline{XY}$ in half without measuring?

Fold the paper in half so that the points X and Y line up exactly.

Unfold the paper and mark the point M where the fold meets the segment. You have found the midpoint of $\overline{XY}$!

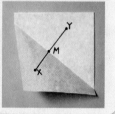

1-1

Technology TASK

Use with Measuring and Constructing Segments

Explore Properties Associated with Points

The two endpoints of a segment determine its length. Other points on the segment are *between* the endpoints. Only one of these points is the *midpoint* of the segment. In this task, you will use geometry software to measure lengths of segments and explore properties of points on segments.

MATHEMATICAL PRACTICES

Use appropriate tools strategically.

MCC9-12.G.CO.1 Know precise definitions ... based on the undefined notions of point, line, distance along a line ...

Activity

1 Construct a segment and label its endpoints *A* and *C*.

2 Create point *B* on $\overline{AC}$.

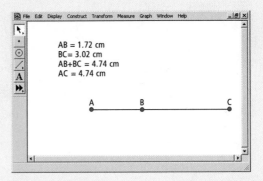

3 Measure the distances from *A* to *B* and from *B* to *C*. Use the Calculate tool to calculate the sum of *AB* and *BC*.

4 Measure the length of $\overline{AC}$. What do you notice about this length compared with the measurements found in Step 3?

5 Drag point *B* along $\overline{AC}$. Drag one of the endpoints of $\overline{AC}$. What relationships do you think are true about the three measurements?

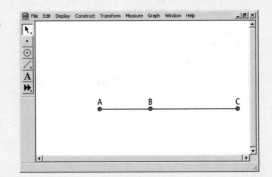

6 Construct the midpoint of $\overline{AC}$ and label it *M*.

7 Measure $\overline{AM}$ and $\overline{MC}$. What relationships do you think are true about the lengths of $\overline{AC}$, $\overline{AM}$, and $\overline{MC}$? Use the Calculate tool to confirm your findings.

8 How many midpoints of $\overline{AC}$ exist?

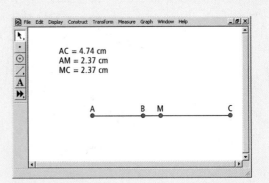

Try This

1. Repeat the activity with a new segment. Drag each of the points in your figure (the endpoints, the point on the segment, and the midpoint). Write down any relationships you observe about the measurements.

2. Create a point *D* not on $\overline{AC}$. Measure $\overline{AD}$, $\overline{DC}$, and $\overline{AC}$. Does *AD* + *DC* = *AC*? What do you think has to be true about *D* for the relationship to always be true?

1-1

Measuring and Constructing Segments

? **Essential Question:** How can you measure, construct, and describe segments?

Objectives
Use length and midpoint of a segment.

Construct midpoints and congruent segments.

Vocabulary
coordinate
distance
length
congruent segments
construction
between
midpoint
bisect
segment bisector

Why learn this?
You can measure a segment to calculate the distance between two locations. Maps of a race are used to show the distance between stations on the course. (See Example 4.)

A ruler can be used to measure the distance between two points. A point corresponds to one and only one number on the ruler. This number is called a **coordinate** . The following postulate summarizes this concept.

Postulate 1-1-1 | **Ruler Postulate**

The points on a line can be put into a one-to-one correspondence with the real numbers.

The **distance** between any two points is the absolute value of the difference of the coordinates. If the coordinates of points A and B are a and b, then the distance between A and B is $|a - b|$ or $|b - a|$. The distance between A and B is also called the **length** of $\overline{AB}$, or AB.

$$AB = |a - b| = |b - a|$$

COMMON CORE GPS MCC9-12.G.CO.1

EXAMPLE 1

Finding the Length of a Segment

Find each length.

A DC
$DC = |4.5 - 2|$
$= |2.5|$
$= 2.5$

B EF
$EF = |-4 - (-1)|$
$= |-4 + 1|$
$= |-3|$
$= 3$

my.hrw.com

Online Video Tutor

CHECK IT OUT! Find each length.
1a. XY
1b. XZ

Caution!
PQ represents a number, while $\overline{PQ}$ represents a geometric figure. Be sure to use equality for numbers ($PQ = RS$) and congruence for figures ($\overline{PQ} \cong \overline{RS}$).

Congruent segments are segments that have the same length. In the diagram, $PQ = RS$, so you can write $\overline{PQ} \cong \overline{RS}$. This is read as "segment PQ is congruent to segment RS." *Tick marks* are used in a figure to show congruent segments.

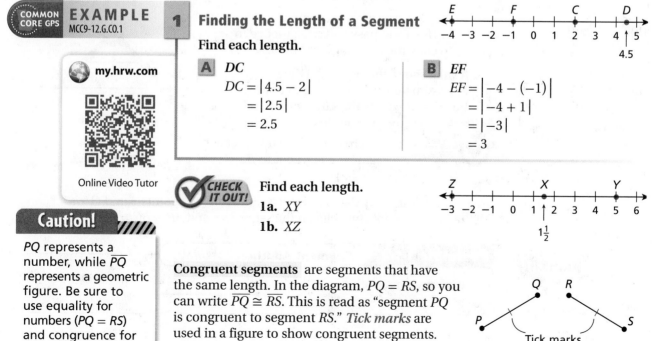

Tick marks

Tony Freeman/Photo Edit

You can make a sketch or measure and draw a segment. These may not be exact. A **construction** is a way of creating a figure that is more precise. One way to make a geometric construction is to use a compass and straightedge.

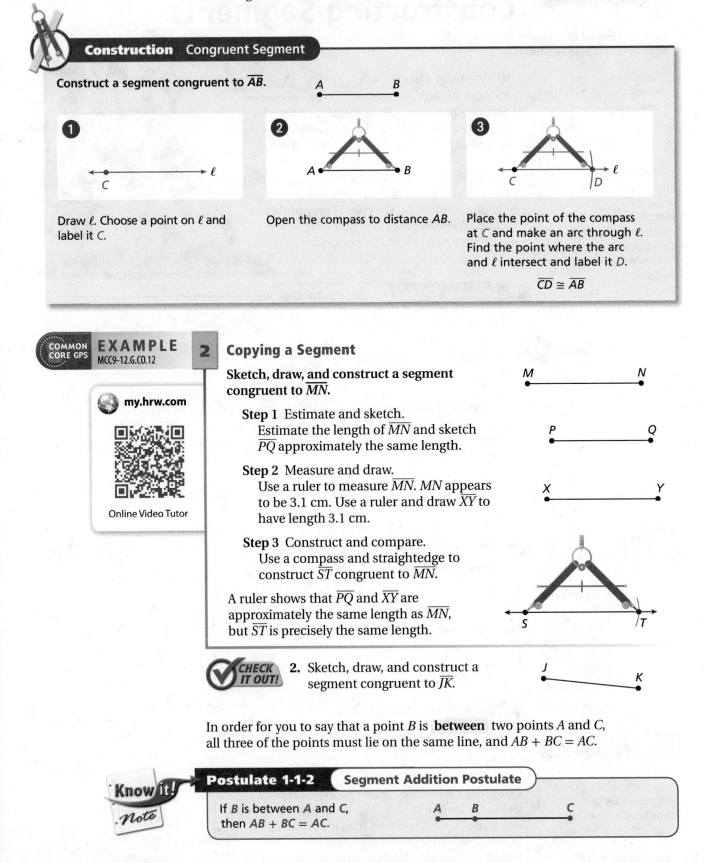

Construction Congruent Segment

Construct a segment congruent to $\overline{AB}$.

A •————————• B

1

Draw ℓ. Choose a point on ℓ and label it C.

2

Open the compass to distance AB.

3

Place the point of the compass at C and make an arc through ℓ. Find the point where the arc and ℓ intersect and label it D.

$\overline{CD} \cong \overline{AB}$

COMMON CORE GPS
EXAMPLE **2**
MCC9-12.G.CO.12

Copying a Segment

my.hrw.com

Online Video Tutor

Sketch, draw, **and construct a segment** congruent to $\overline{MN}$.

Step 1 Estimate and sketch.
Estimate the length of $\overline{MN}$ and sketch $\overline{PQ}$ approximately the same length.

Step 2 Measure and draw.
Use a ruler to measure $\overline{MN}$. MN appears to be 3.1 cm. Use a ruler and draw $\overline{XY}$ to have length 3.1 cm.

Step 3 Construct and compare.
Use a compass and straightedge to construct $\overline{ST}$ congruent to $\overline{MN}$.

A ruler shows that $\overline{PQ}$ and $\overline{XY}$ are approximately the same length as $\overline{MN}$, but $\overline{ST}$ is precisely the same length.

M ————————————— N

P ——————————— Q

X ——————————— Y

S ————————————— T

CHECK IT OUT! **2.** Sketch, draw, and construct a segment congruent to $\overline{JK}$.

J •————————• K

In order for you to say that a point B is **between** two points A and C, all three of the points must lie on the same line, and $AB + BC = AC$.

Know it!
Note

Postulate 1-1-2 **Segment Addition Postulate**

If B is between A and C, then $AB + BC = AC$.

A •———•————————• C
       B

EXAMPLE **3** **Using the Segment Addition Postulate**

my.hrw.com

Online Video Tutor

A *B* is between *A* and *C*, $AC = 14$, and $BC = 11.4$. Find *AB*.

$AC = AB + BC$	Seg. Add. Post.
$14 = AB + 11.4$	Substitute 14 for AC and 11.4 for BC.
$\underline{-11.4 \qquad -11.4}$	Subtract 11.4 from both sides.
$2.6 = AB$	Simplify.

B *S* is between *R* and *T*. Find *RT*.

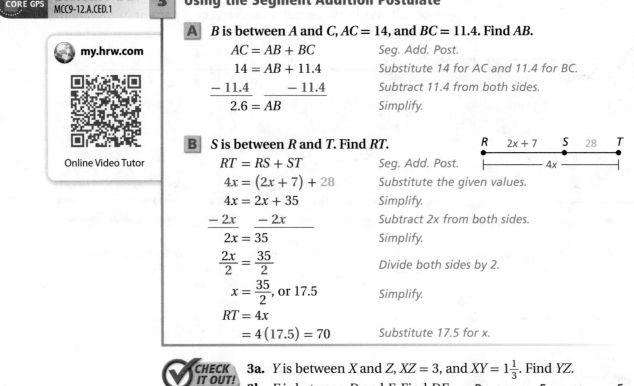

$RT = RS + ST$	Seg. Add. Post.
$4x = (2x + 7) + 28$	Substitute the given values.
$4x = 2x + 35$	Simplify.
$\underline{-2x \qquad -2x}$	Subtract 2x from both sides.
$2x = 35$	Simplify.
$\dfrac{2x}{2} = \dfrac{35}{2}$	Divide both sides by 2.
$x = \dfrac{35}{2}$, or 17.5	Simplify.
$RT = 4x$	
$\quad = 4(17.5) = 70$	Substitute 17.5 for x.

CHECK IT OUT!

3a. *Y* is between *X* and *Z*, $XZ = 3$, and $XY = 1\frac{1}{3}$. Find *YZ*.

3b. *E* is between *D* and *F*. Find *DF*.

The **midpoint** *M* of $\overline{AB}$ is the point that **bisects**, or divides, the segment into two congruent segments. If *M* is the midpoint of $\overline{AB}$, then $AM = MB$. So if $AB = 6$, then $AM = 3$ and $MB = 3$.

EXAMPLE **4** **Recreation Application**

my.hrw.com

Online Video Tutor

The map shows the route for a race. You are 365 m from drink station *R* and 2 km from drink station *S*. The first-aid station is located at the midpoint of the two drink stations. How far are you from the first-aid station?

Let your current location be *X* and the location of the first-aid station be *Y*.

$XR + RS = XS$	Seg. Add. Post.
$365 + RS = 2000$	Substitute 365 for XR and 2000 for XS.
$\underline{-365 \qquad -365}$	Subtract 365 from both sides.
$RS = 1635$	Simplify.
$RY = 817.5$	Y is the mdpt. of $\overline{RS}$, so $RY = \frac{1}{2}RS$.
$XY = XR + RY$	
$\quad = 365 + 817.5 = 1182.5$ m	Substitute 365 for XR and 817.5 for RY.

You are 1182.5 m from the first-aid station.

CHECK IT OUT!

4. What is the distance to a drink station located at the midpoint between your current location and the first-aid station?

A **segment bisector** is any ray, segment, or line that intersects a segment at its midpoint. It divides the segment into two equal parts at its midpoint.

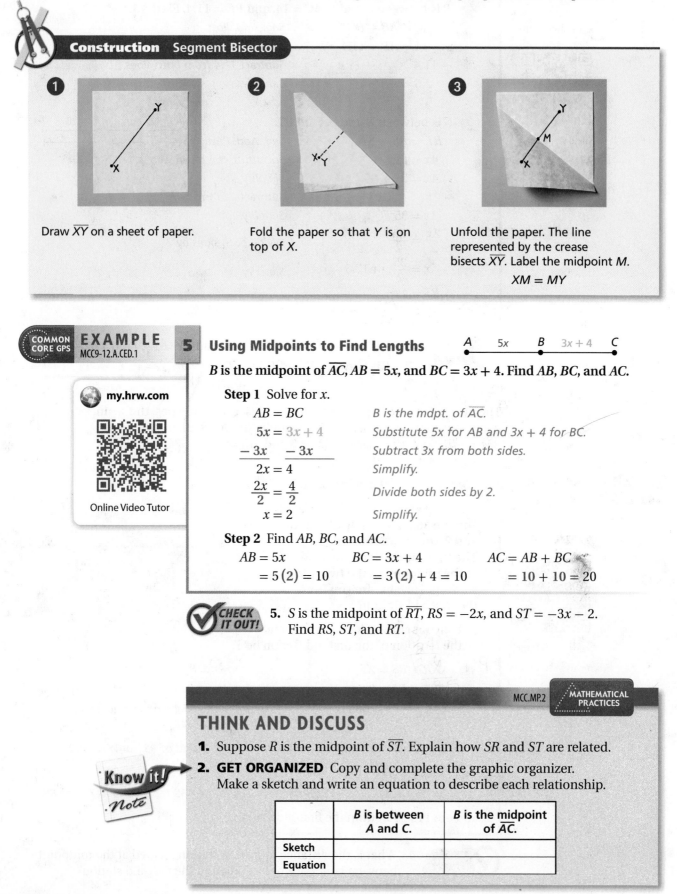

Construction   Segment Bisector

1 Draw $\overline{XY}$ on a sheet of paper.

2 Fold the paper so that Y is on top of X.

3 Unfold the paper. The line represented by the crease bisects $\overline{XY}$. Label the midpoint M.

$$XM = MY$$

COMMON CORE GPS

EXAMPLE 5

MCC9-12.A.CED.1

Using Midpoints to Find Lengths

A ——5x—— B ——3x + 4—— C

B is the midpoint of $\overline{AC}$, $AB = 5x$, and $BC = 3x + 4$. Find AB, BC, and AC.

Step 1 Solve for x.

$AB = BC$	B is the mdpt. of $\overline{AC}$.
$5x = 3x + 4$	Substitute $5x$ for AB and $3x + 4$ for BC.
$\underline{-3x \quad\quad -3x}$	Subtract $3x$ from both sides.
$2x = 4$	Simplify.
$\dfrac{2x}{2} = \dfrac{4}{2}$	Divide both sides by 2.
$x = 2$	Simplify.

Step 2 Find AB, BC, and AC.

$AB = 5x$	$BC = 3x + 4$	$AC = AB + BC$
$= 5(2) = 10$	$= 3(2) + 4 = 10$	$= 10 + 10 = 20$

my.hrw.com

Online Video Tutor

CHECK IT OUT!

5. S is the midpoint of $\overline{RT}$, $RS = -2x$, and $ST = -3x - 2$. Find RS, ST, and RT.

MCC.MP.2

MATHEMATICAL PRACTICES

THINK AND DISCUSS

1. Suppose R is the midpoint of $\overline{ST}$. Explain how SR and ST are related.

2. GET ORGANIZED Copy and complete the graphic organizer. Make a sketch and write an equation to describe each relationship.

Know it! Note

	B is between A and C.	B is the midpoint of $\overline{AC}$.
Sketch		
Equation		

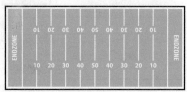

GUIDED PRACTICE

Vocabulary Apply the vocabulary from this lesson to answer each question.

1. Line ℓ bisects $\overline{XY}$ at M and divides $\overline{XY}$ into two equal parts. Name a pair of congruent segments.

2. ___?___ is the amount of space between two points on a line. It is always expressed as a nonnegative number. (*distance* or *midpoint*)

SEE EXAMPLE 1 — Find each length.
3. AB 4. BC

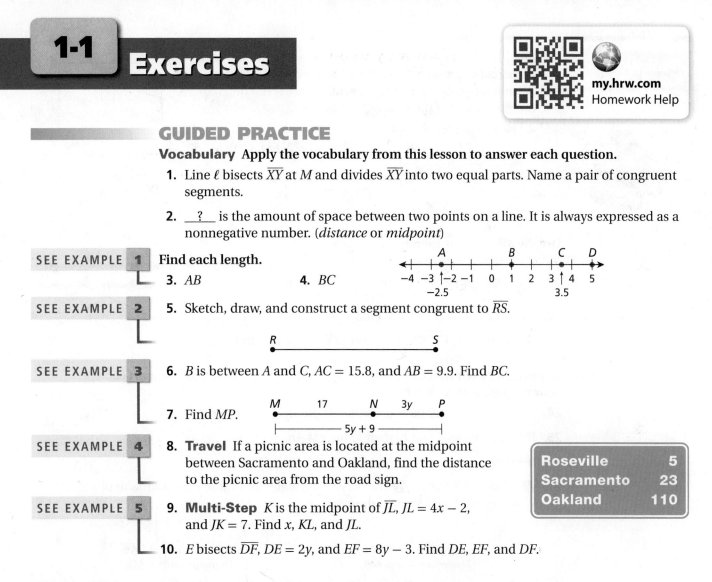

SEE EXAMPLE 2
5. Sketch, draw, and construct a segment congruent to $\overline{RS}$.

SEE EXAMPLE 3
6. B is between A and C, $AC = 15.8$, and $AB = 9.9$. Find BC.

7. Find MP.

SEE EXAMPLE 4
8. **Travel** If a picnic area is located at the midpoint between Sacramento and Oakland, find the distance to the picnic area from the road sign.

Roseville	5
Sacramento	23
Oakland	110

SEE EXAMPLE 5
9. **Multi-Step** K is the midpoint of $\overline{JL}$, $JL = 4x - 2$, and $JK = 7$. Find x, KL, and JL.

10. E bisects $\overline{DF}$, $DE = 2y$, and $EF = 8y - 3$. Find DE, EF, and DF.

PRACTICE AND PROBLEM SOLVING

| Independent Practice | |
For Exercises	See Example
11–12	1
13	2
14–15	3
16	4
17–18	5

my.hrw.com

Online Extra Practice

Find each length.
11. DB 12. CD

13. Sketch, draw, and construct a segment twice the length of $\overline{AB}$.

14. D is between C and E, $CE = 17.1$, and $DE = 8$. Find CD.

15. Find MN.

16. **Sports** During a football game, a quarterback standing at the 9-yard line passes the ball to a receiver at the 24-yard line. The receiver then runs with the ball halfway to the 50-yard line. How many total yards (passing plus running) did the team gain on the play?

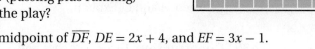

17. **Multi-Step** E is the midpoint of $\overline{DF}$, $DE = 2x + 4$, and $EF = 3x - 1$. Find DE, EF, and DF.

18. Q bisects $\overline{PR}$, $PQ = 3y$, and $PR = 42$. Find y and QR.

19. Prep. Archaeologists at Valley Forge were eager to find what remained of the winter camp that soldiers led by George Washington called home for several months. The diagram represents one of the restored log cabins.

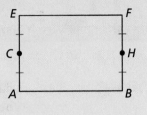

a. How is C related to $\overline{AE}$?

b. If $AC = 7$ ft, $EF = 2(AC) + 2$, and $AB = 2(EF) - 16$, what are AB and EF?

Use the diagram for Exercises 20–23.

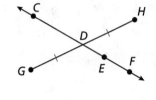

20. $GD = 4\frac{2}{3}$. Find GH.

21. $\overline{CD} \cong \overline{DF}$, E bisects $\overline{DF}$, and $CD = 14.2$. Find EF.

22. $GH = 4x - 1$, and $DH = 8$. Find x.

23. $\overline{GH}$ bisects $\overline{CF}$, $CF = 2y - 2$, and $CD = 3y - 11$. Find CD.

H.O.T. Tell whether each statement is sometimes, always, or never true. Support each of your answers with a sketch.

24. Two segments that have the same length must be congruent.

25. If M is between A and B, then M bisects $\overline{AB}$.

26. If Y is between X and Z, then X, Y, and Z are collinear.

27. ///ERROR ANALYSIS/// Below are two statements about the midpoint of $\overline{AB}$. Which is incorrect? Explain the error.

Ⓐ	Ⓑ
M is the mdpt. of $\overline{AB}$. Therefore $AM \cong MB$.	M is the mdpt. of $\overline{AB}$. Therefore $AM = MB$.

H.O.T. 28. Carpentry A carpenter has a wooden dowel that is 72 cm long. She wants to cut it into two pieces so that one piece is 5 times as long as the other. What are the lengths of the two pieces?

29. The coordinate of M is 2.5, and $MN = 4$. What are the possible coordinates for N?

30. Draw three collinear points where E is between D and F. Then write an equation using these points and the Segment Addition Postulate.

Suppose S is between R and T. Use the Segment Addition Postulate to solve for each variable.

31. $RS = 7y - 4$
$ST = y + 5$
$RT = 28$

32. $RS = 3x + 1$
$ST = \frac{1}{2}x + 3$
$RT = 18$

33. $RS = 2z + 6$
$ST = 4z - 3$
$RT = 5z + 12$

34. Write About It In the diagram, B is not between A and C. Explain.

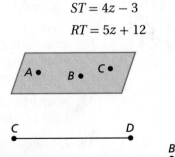

35. Construction Use a compass and straightedge to construct a segment whose length is $AB + CD$.

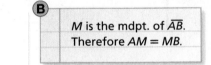
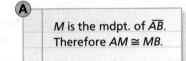

TEST PREP

36. Q is between P and R. S is between Q and R, and R is between Q and T. $PT = 34$, $QR = 8$, and $PQ = SQ = SR$. What is the length of $\overline{RT}$?

    Ⓐ 9   Ⓑ 10   Ⓒ 18   Ⓓ 22

37. C is the midpoint of $\overline{AD}$. B is the midpoint of $\overline{AC}$. $BC = 12$. What is the length of $\overline{AD}$?

    Ⓕ 12   Ⓖ 24   Ⓗ 36   Ⓙ 48

38. Which expression correctly states that $\overline{XY}$ is congruent to $\overline{VW}$?

    Ⓐ $XY \cong VW$ Ⓑ $\overline{XY} \cong \overline{VW}$ Ⓒ $\overline{XY} = \overline{VW}$ Ⓓ $XY = VW$

39. A, B, C, D, and E are collinear points. $AE = 34$, $BD = 16$, and $AB = BC = CD$. What is the length of $\overline{CE}$?

    Ⓕ 10   Ⓖ 16   Ⓗ 18   Ⓙ 24

CHALLENGE AND EXTEND

40. HJ is twice JK. J is between H and K. If $HJ = 4x$ and $HK = 78$, find JK.

41. A, D, N, and X are collinear points. D is between N and A. $NA + AX = NX$. Draw a diagram that represents this information.

Sports Use the following information for Exercises 42 and 43.

The table shows regulation distances between hurdles in women's and men's races. In both the women's and men's events, the race consists of a straight track with 10 equally spaced hurdles.

Event	Distance of Race	Distance from Start to First Hurdle	Distance Between Hurdles	Distance from Last Hurdle to Finish
Women's	100 m	13.00 m	8.50 m	▨
Men's	110 m	13.72 m	9.14 m	▨

42. Find the distance from the last hurdle to the finish line for the women's race.

43. Find the distance from the last hurdle to the finish line for the men's race.

H.O.T. 44. Critical Thinking Given that J, K, and L are collinear and that K is between J and L, is it possible that $JK = JL$? If so, draw an example. If not, explain.

Sports

Joanna Hayes, of the United States, clears a hurdle on her way to winning the gold medal in the women's 100 m hurdles during the 2004 Olympic Games.

FOCUS ON MATHEMATICAL PRACTICES

H.O.T. 45. Number Sense Kendra said that when you compare the lengths of two segments, there are three possible relationships. Is Kendra correct? If so, what are the three relationships?

H.O.T. 46. Analysis Can you use the method for constructing a segment bisector to construct a line bisector? Explain why or why not.

H.O.T. 47. Precision Zuzu said tick marks indicate congruent segments. Josh said tick marks indicate segments with equal measures. Who is correct? Explain.

1-2 Measuring and Constructing Angles

Essential Question: How can you measure, construct, and describe angles?

Objectives
Name and classify angles.

Measure and construct angles and angle bisectors.

Vocabulary
angle
vertex
interior of an angle
exterior of an angle
measure
degree
acute angle
right angle
obtuse angle
straight angle
congruent angles
angle bisector

Who uses this?

Surveyors use angles to help them measure and map the earth's surface. (See Exercise 27.)

A transit is a tool for measuring angles. It consists of a telescope that swivels horizontally and vertically. Using a transit, a surveyor can measure the *angle* formed by his or her location and two distant points.

An **angle** is a figure formed by two rays, or sides, with a common endpoint called the **vertex** (plural: *vertices*). You can name an angle several ways: by its vertex, by a point on each ray and the vertex, or by a number.

The set of all points between the sides of the angle is the **interior of an angle**. The **exterior of an angle** is the set of all points outside the angle.

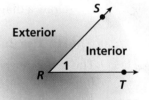

Angle Name

∠R, ∠SRT, ∠TRS, or ∠1

You cannot name an angle just by its vertex if the point is the vertex of more than one angle. In this case, you must use all three points to name the angle, and the middle point is always the vertex.

COMMON CORE GPS
MCC9-12.G.CO.1

EXAMPLE 1 Naming Angles

A surveyor recorded the angles formed by a transit (point *T*) and three distant points, *Q*, *R*, and *S*. Name three of the angles.

∠QTR, ∠QTS, and ∠RTS

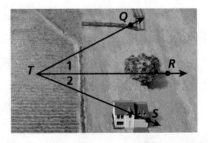

my.hrw.com

Online Video Tutor

CHECK IT OUT! 1. Write the different ways you can name the angles in the diagram.

The **measure** of an angle is usually given in degrees. Since there are 360° in a circle, one **degree** is $\frac{1}{360}$ of a circle. When you use a protractor to measure angles, you are applying the following postulate.

Know it!
Note

Postulate 1-2-1 **Protractor Postulate**

Given $\overrightarrow{AB}$ and a point *O* on $\overrightarrow{AB}$, all rays that can be drawn from *O* can be put into a one-to-one correspondence with the real numbers from 0 to 180.

Student to Student

José Muñoz
Lincoln High School

Using a Protractor

Most protractors have two sets of numbers around the edge. When I measure an angle and need to know which number to use, I first ask myself whether the angle is acute, right, or obtuse. For example, ∠RST looks like it is obtuse, so I know its measure must be 110°, not 70°.

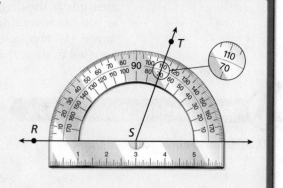

You can use the Protractor Postulate to help you classify angles by their measure. The measure of an angle is the absolute value of the difference of the real numbers that the rays correspond with on a protractor. If $\overrightarrow{OC}$ corresponds with c and $\overrightarrow{OD}$ corresponds with d, m∠DOC = $|d - c|$ or $|c - d|$.

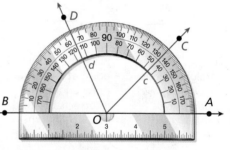

Know it! Note

Types of Angles

Acute Angle	Right Angle	Obtuse Angle	Straight Angle
Measures greater than 0° and less than 90°	Measures 90°	Measures greater than 90° and less than 180°	Formed by two opposite rays and meaures 180°

COMMON CORE GPS
EXAMPLE 2
MCC.MP.5

Measuring and Classifying Angles

Find the measure of each angle. Then classify each as acute, right, or obtuse.

A ∠AOD
m∠AOD = 165°
∠AOD is obtuse.

B ∠COD
m∠COD = $|165 - 75|$ = 90°
∠COD is a right angle.

my.hrw.com

Online Video Tutor

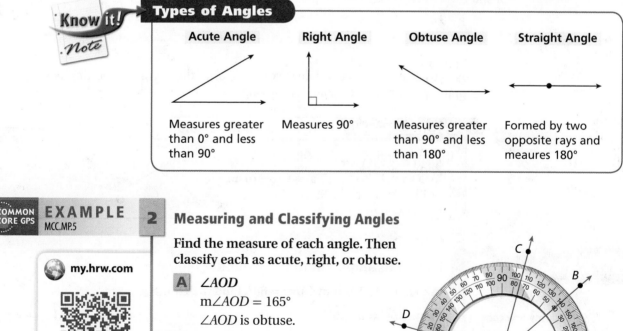

CHECK IT OUT! Use the diagram to find the measure of each angle. Then classify each as acute, right, or obtuse.

2a. ∠BOA   **2b.** ∠DOB   **2c.** ∠EOC

Congruent angles are angles that have the same measure. In the diagram, m∠ABC = m∠DEF, so you can write ∠ABC ≅ ∠DEF. This is read as "angle ABC is congruent to angle DEF." *Arc marks* are used to show that the two angles are congruent.

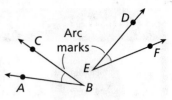

Construction   Congruent Angle

Construct an angle congruent to ∠A.

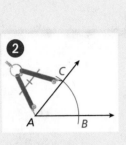
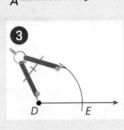
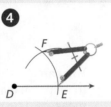

1

Use a straightedge to draw a ray with endpoint *D*.

2

Place the compass point at *A* and draw an arc that intersects both sides of ∠A. Label the intersection points *B* and *C*.

3

Using the same compass setting, place the compass point at *D* and draw an arc that intersects the ray. Label the intersection *E*.

4

Place the compass point at *B* and open it to the distance *BC*. Place the point of the compass at *E* and draw an arc. Label its intersection with the first arc *F*.

5

Use a straightedge to draw $\overrightarrow{DF}$.

∠D ≅ ∠A

The Angle Addition Postulate is very similar to the Segment Addition Postulate that you learned in the previous lesson.

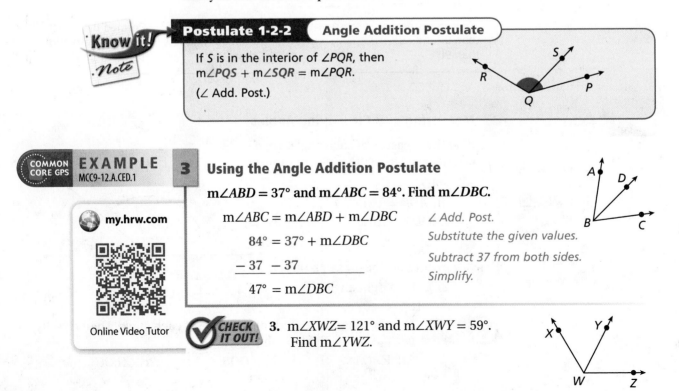

Postulate 1-2-2   **Angle Addition Postulate**

If *S* is in the interior of ∠PQR, then
m∠PQS + m∠SQR = m∠PQR.

(∠ Add. Post.)

COMMON CORE GPS   MCC9-12.A.CED.1

EXAMPLE 3   **Using the Angle Addition Postulate**

m∠ABD = 37° and m∠ABC = 84°. Find m∠DBC.

m∠ABC = m∠ABD + m∠DBC	∠ Add. Post.
84° = 37° + m∠DBC	Substitute the given values.
− 37 − 37	Subtract 37 from both sides.
47° = m∠DBC	Simplify.

my.hrw.com

Online Video Tutor

CHECK IT OUT!

3. m∠XWZ = 121° and m∠XWY = 59°. Find m∠YWZ.

An **angle bisector** is a ray that divides an angle into two congruent angles. $\overrightarrow{JK}$ bisects $\angle LJM$; thus $\angle LJK \cong \angle KJM$.

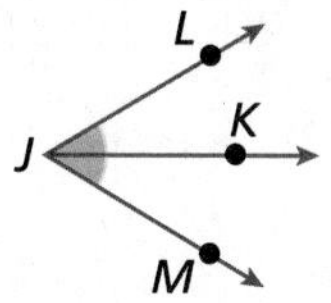

Construction Angle Bisector

Construct the bisector of $\angle A$.

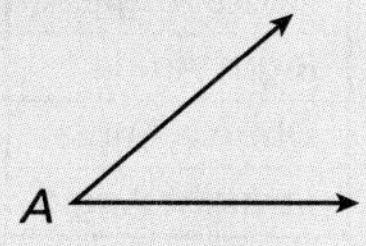

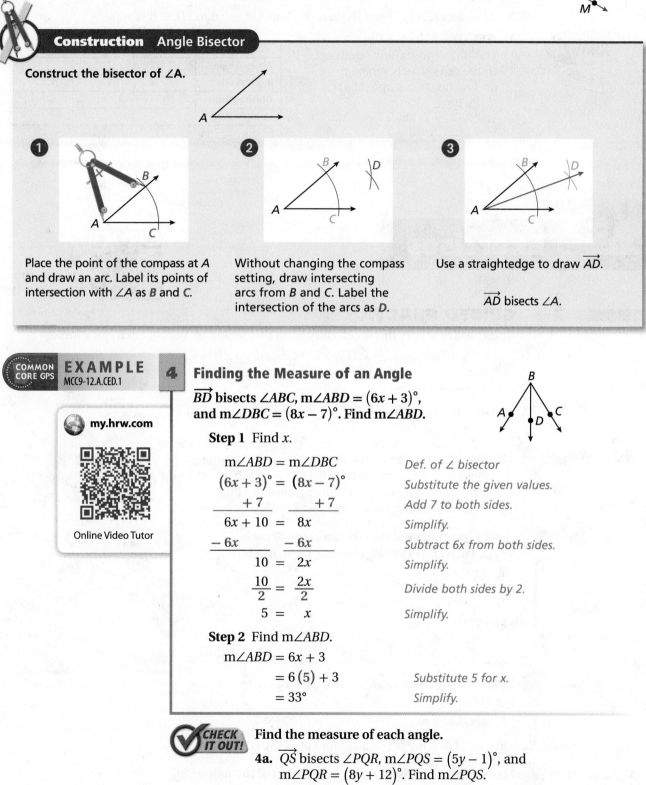

1

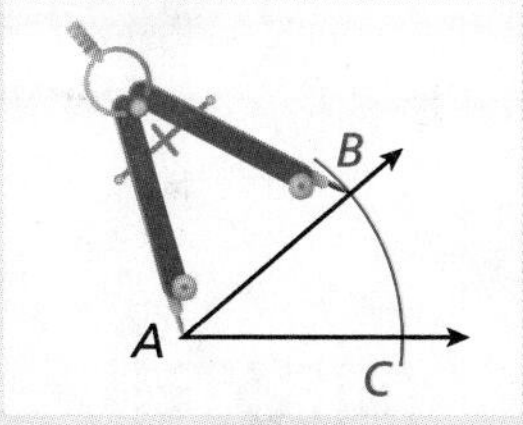

Place the point of the compass at A and draw an arc. Label its points of intersection with $\angle A$ as B and C.

2

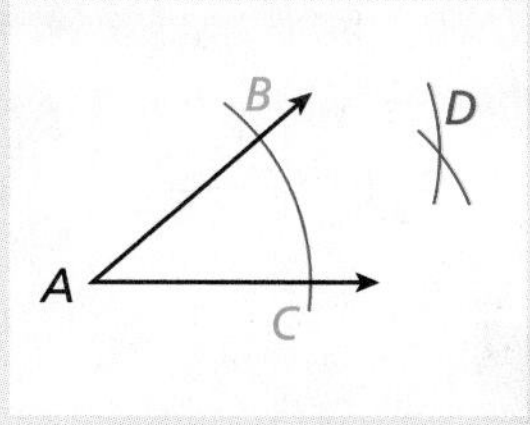

Without changing the compass setting, draw intersecting arcs from B and C. Label the intersection of the arcs as D.

3

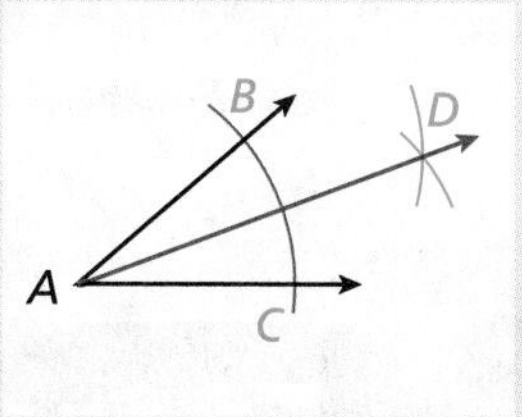

Use a straightedge to draw $\overrightarrow{AD}$.

$\overrightarrow{AD}$ bisects $\angle A$.

COMMON CORE GPS **EXAMPLE** 4
MCC9-12.A.CED.1

Finding the Measure of an Angle

my.hrw.com

Online Video Tutor

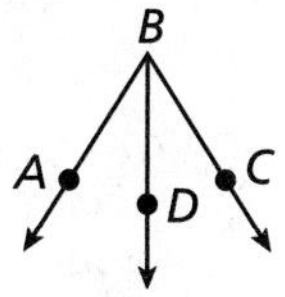

$\overrightarrow{BD}$ bisects $\angle ABC$, $m\angle ABD = (6x + 3)°$, and $m\angle DBC = (8x - 7)°$. Find $m\angle ABD$.

Step 1 Find x.

$m\angle ABD = m\angle DBC$	*Def. of ∠ bisector*
$(6x + 3)° = (8x - 7)°$	*Substitute the given values.*
$+7 \qquad +7$	*Add 7 to both sides.*
$6x + 10 = 8x$	*Simplify.*
$-6x \qquad -6x$	*Subtract 6x from both sides.*
$10 = 2x$	*Simplify.*
$\frac{10}{2} = \frac{2x}{2}$	*Divide both sides by 2.*
$5 = x$	*Simplify.*

Step 2 Find $m\angle ABD$.

$m\angle ABD = 6x + 3$	
$= 6(5) + 3$	*Substitute 5 for x.*
$= 33°$	*Simplify.*

CHECK IT OUT!

Find the measure of each angle.

4a. $\overrightarrow{QS}$ bisects $\angle PQR$, $m\angle PQS = (5y - 1)°$, and $m\angle PQR = (8y + 12)°$. Find $m\angle PQS$.

4b. $\overrightarrow{JK}$ bisects $\angle LJM$, $m\angle LJK = (-10x + 3)°$, and $m\angle KJM = (-x + 21)°$. Find $m\angle LJM$.

THINK AND DISCUSS

1. Explain why any two right angles are congruent.

2. $\overrightarrow{BD}$ bisects $\angle ABC$. How are m$\angle ABC$, m$\angle ABD$, and m$\angle DBC$ related?

3. **GET ORGANIZED** Copy and complete the graphic organizer. In the cells sketch, measure, and name an example of each angle type.

	Diagram	Measure	Name
Acute Angle			
Right Angle			
Obtuse Angle			
Straight Angle			

1-2 Exercises

my.hrw.com
Homework Help

GUIDED PRACTICE

Vocabulary Apply the vocabulary from this lesson to answer each question.

1. $\angle A$ is an acute angle. $\angle O$ is an obtuse angle. $\angle R$ is a right angle. Put $\angle A$, $\angle O$, and $\angle R$ in order from least to greatest by measure.

2. Which point is the vertex of $\angle BCD$? Which rays form the sides of $\angle BCD$?

SEE EXAMPLE 1

3. **Music** Musicians use a metronome to keep time as they play. The metronome's needle swings back and forth in a fixed amount of time. Name all of the angles in the diagram.

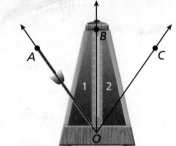

SEE EXAMPLE 2

Use the protractor to find the measure of each angle. Then classify each as acute, right, or obtuse.

4. $\angle VXW$

5. $\angle TXW$

6. $\angle RXU$

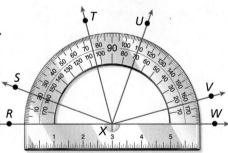

SEE EXAMPLE 3

L is in the interior of $\angle JKM$. Find each of the following.

7. m$\angle JKM$ if m$\angle JKL = 42°$ and m$\angle LKM = 28°$

8. m$\angle LKM$ if m$\angle JKL = 56.4°$ and m$\angle JKM = 82.5°$

SEE EXAMPLE 4

Multi-Step $\overrightarrow{BD}$ bisects $\angle ABC$. Find each of the following.

9. m$\angle ABD$ if m$\angle ABD = (6x + 4)°$ and m$\angle DBC = (8x - 4)°$

10. m$\angle ABC$ if m$\angle ABD = (5y - 3)°$ and m$\angle DBC = (3y + 15)°$

PRACTICE AND PROBLEM SOLVING

Independent Practice

For Exercises	See Example
11	1
12–14	2
15–16	3
17–18	4

my.hrw.com

Online Extra Practice

11. Physics Pendulum clocks have been used since 1656 to keep time. The pendulum swings back and forth once or twice per second. Name all of the angles in the diagram.

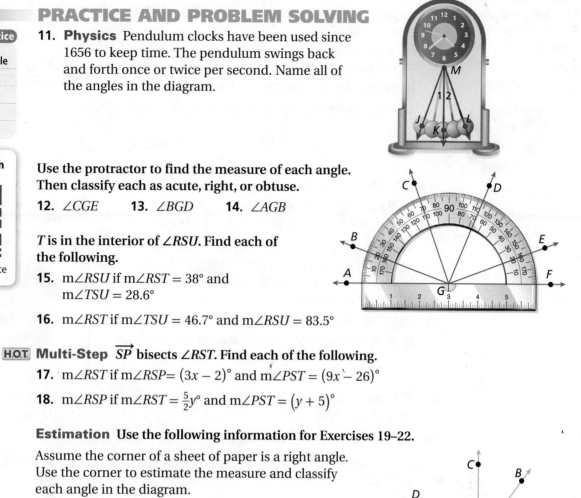

Use the protractor to find the measure of each angle. Then classify each as acute, right, or obtuse.

12. ∠*CGE*   **13.** ∠*BGD*   **14.** ∠*AGB*

T is in the interior of ∠*RSU*. Find each of the following.

15. m∠*RSU* if m∠*RST* = 38° and m∠*TSU* = 28.6°

16. m∠*RST* if m∠*TSU* = 46.7° and m∠*RSU* = 83.5°

H.O.T. Multi-Step $\overrightarrow{SP}$ bisects ∠*RST*. Find each of the following.

17. m∠*RST* if m∠*RSP* = $(3x - 2)°$ and m∠*PST* = $(9x - 26)°$

18. m∠*RSP* if m∠*RST* = $\frac{5}{2}y°$ and m∠*PST* = $(y + 5)°$

Estimation Use the following information for Exercises 19–22.

Assume the corner of a sheet of paper is a right angle. Use the corner to estimate the measure and classify each angle in the diagram.

19. ∠*BOA*   **20.** ∠*COA*

21. ∠*EOD*   **22.** ∠*EOB*

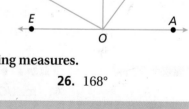

Use a protractor to draw an angle with each of the following measures.

23. 33°   **24.** 142°   **25.** 90°   **26.** 168°

27. Surveying A surveyor at point *S* discovers that the angle between peaks *A* and *B* is 3 times as large as the angle between peaks *B* and *C*. The surveyor knows that ∠*ASC* is a right angle. Find m∠*ASB* and m∠*BSC*.

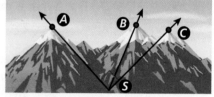

28. Math History As far back as the 5th century B.C., mathematicians have been fascinated by the problem of trisecting an angle. It is possible to construct an angle with $\frac{1}{4}$ the measure of a given angle. Explain how to do this.

Find the value of *x*.

29. m∠*AOC* = 7*x* − 2, m∠*DOC* = 2*x* + 8, m∠*EOD* = 27

30. m∠*AOB* = 4*x* − 2, m∠*BOC* = 5*x* + 10, m∠*COD* = 3*x* − 8

31. m∠*AOB* = 6*x* + 5, m∠*BOC* = 4*x* − 2, m∠*AOC* = 8*x* + 21

H.O.T. 32. Multi-Step *Q* is in the interior of right ∠*PRS*. If m∠*PRQ* is 4 times as large as m∠*QRS*, what is m∠*PRQ*?

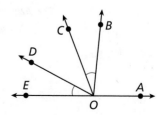

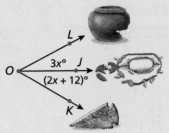

33. An archaeologist standing at *O* looks for clues on where to dig for artifacts.

    a. What value of *x* will make the angle between the pottery and the arrowhead measure 57°?

    b. What value of *x* makes ∠*LOJ* ≅ ∠*JOK*?

    c. What values of *x* make ∠*LOK* an acute angle?

Data Analysis Use the circle graph for Exercises 34–36.

34. Find m∠*AOB*, m∠*BOC*, m∠*COD*, and m∠*DOA*. Classify each angle as acute, right, or obtuse.

35. **What if...?** Next year, the music store will use some of the shelves currently holding jazz music to double the space for rap. What will m∠*COD* and m∠*BOC* be next year?

36. Suppose a fifth type of music, salsa, is added. If the space is divided equally among the five types, what will be the angle measure for each type of music in the circle graph?

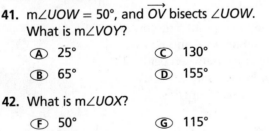

37. **Critical Thinking** Can an obtuse angle be congruent to an acute angle? Why or why not?

38. The measure of an obtuse angle is $(5x + 45)°$. What is the largest value for *x*?

39. **Write About It** $\overrightarrow{FH}$ bisects ∠*EFG*. Use the Angle Addition Postulate to explain why m∠*EFH* = $\frac{1}{2}$m∠*EFG*.

40. **Multi-Step** Use a protractor to draw a 70° angle. Then use a compass and straightedge to bisect the angle. What do you think will be the measure of each angle formed? Use a protractor to support your answer.

TEST PREP

41. m∠*UOW* = 50°, and $\overrightarrow{OV}$ bisects ∠*UOW*. What is m∠*VOY*?

    Ⓐ 25°   Ⓒ 130°

    Ⓑ 65°   Ⓓ 155°

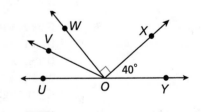

42. What is m∠*UOX*?

    Ⓕ 50°   Ⓖ 115°   Ⓗ 140°   Ⓙ 165°

43. $\overrightarrow{BD}$ bisects ∠*ABC*, m∠*ABC* = $(4x + 5)°$, and m∠*ABD* = $(3x - 1)°$. What is the value of *x*?

    Ⓐ 2.2   Ⓑ 3   Ⓒ 3.5   Ⓓ 7

44. If an angle is bisected and then 30° is added to the measure of the bisected angle, the result is the measure of a right angle. What is the measure of the original angle?

    Ⓕ 30°   Ⓖ 60°   Ⓗ 75°   Ⓙ 120°

H.O.T. 45. **Short Response** If an obtuse angle is bisected, are the resulting angles acute or obtuse? Explain.

CHALLENGE AND EXTEND

H.O.T. **46.** Find the measure of the angle formed by the hands of a clock when it is 7:00.

H.O.T. **47.** $\overrightarrow{QS}$ bisects $\angle PQR$, $m\angle PQR = (x^2)°$, and $m\angle PQS = (2x + 6)°$. Find all the possible measures for $\angle PQR$.

48. For more precise measurements, a degree can be divided into 60 minutes, and each minute can be divided into 60 seconds. An angle measure of 42 degrees, 30 minutes, and 10 seconds is written as 42°30′10″. Subtract this angle measure from the measure 81°24′15″.

49. If 1 degree equals 60 minutes and 1 minute equals 60 seconds, how many seconds are in 2.25 degrees?

50. $\angle ABC \cong \angle DBC$. $m\angle ABC = \left(\frac{3x}{2} + 4\right)°$ and $m\angle DBC = \left(2x - 27\frac{1}{4}\right)°$. Is $\angle ABD$ a straight angle? Explain.

MATHEMATICAL PRACTICES

FOCUS ON MATHEMATICAL PRACTICES

H.O.T. **51.** **Estimation** Flo says she can use the corner of a piece of paper to accurately estimate the measures of common angles such as 30°, 45°, 60°, and 90°. Explain how Flo can make these estimates.

H.O.T. **52.** **Analysis** Some textbooks state the Angle Addition Postulate separately for straight angles. What makes straight angles a special case of the Angle Addition Postulate?

H.O.T. **53.** **Constructions** Explain how to construct an angle that is exactly twice the measure of another angle.

Using Technology Segment and Angle Bisectors

1. Construct the bisector of $\overline{MN}$.

2. Construct the bisector of $\angle BAC$.

a. Draw $\overline{MN}$ and construct the midpoint B.

b. Construct a point A not on the segment.

c. Construct bisector $\overrightarrow{AB}$ and measure $\overline{MB}$ and $\overline{NB}$.

d. Drag M and N and observe MB and NB.

a. Draw $\angle BAC$.

b. Construct the angle bisector $\overrightarrow{AD}$ and measure $\angle DAC$ and $\angle DAB$.

c. Drag the angle and observe $m\angle DAB$ and $m\angle DAC$.

1-3 Using Inductive Reasoning to Make Conjectures

? **Essential Question:** How can you make and disprove conjectures?

Objectives
Use inductive reasoning to identify patterns and make conjectures.

Find counterexamples to disprove conjectures.

Vocabulary
inductive reasoning
conjecture
counterexample

Who uses this?
Biologists use inductive reasoning to develop theories about migration patterns.

Biologists studying the migration patterns of California gray whales developed two theories about the whales' route across Monterey Bay. The whales either swam directly across the bay or followed the shoreline.

COMMON CORE GPS
MCC.MP.3

EXAMPLE 1 **Identifying a Pattern**

my.hrw.com

Online Video Tutor

Find the next item in each pattern.

A **Monday, Wednesday, Friday, …**
Alternating days of the week make up the pattern.
The next day is Sunday.

B **3, 6, 9, 12, 15, …**
Multiples of 3 make up the pattern. The next multiple is 18.

C **←, ↖, ↑, …**
In this pattern, the figure rotates 45° clockwise each time.
The next figure is ↗.

 1. Find the next item in the pattern 0.4, 0.04, 0.004, …

When several examples form a pattern and you assume the pattern will continue, you are applying *inductive reasoning*. **Inductive reasoning** is the process of reasoning that a rule or statement is true because specific cases are true. You may use inductive reasoning to draw a conclusion from a pattern. A statement you believe to be true based on inductive reasoning is called a **conjecture**.

COMMON CORE GPS
MCC.MP.3

EXAMPLE 2 **Making a Conjecture**

Complete each conjecture.

A **The product of an even number and an odd number is ___?___ .**
List some examples and look for a pattern.
$(2)(3) = 6$ $(2)(5) = 10$ $(4)(3) = 12$ $(4)(5) = 20$
The product of an even number and an odd number is even.

Complete each conjecture.

B The number of segments formed by n collinear points is __?__ .

Draw a segment. Mark points on the segment, and count the number of individual segments formed. Be sure to include overlapping segments.

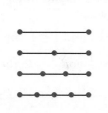

Points	Segments
2	1
3	2 + 1 = 3
4	3 + 2 + 1 = 6
5	4 + 3 + 2 + 1 = 10

The number of segments formed by n collinear points is the sum of the whole numbers less than n.

 **2.** Complete the conjecture: The product of two odd numbers is __?__ .

Biology Application

To learn about the migration behavior of California gray whales, biologists observed whales along two routes. For seven days they counted the numbers of whales seen along each route. Make a conjecture based on the data.

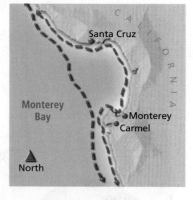

Santa Cruz

Monterey Bay

Monterey
Carmel

North

Numbers of Whales Each Day							
Direct Route	1	3	0	2	1	1	0
Shore Route	7	9	5	8	8	6	7

More whales were seen along the shore route each day. The data supports the conjecture that most California gray whales migrate along the shoreline.

 **3.** Make a conjecture about the lengths of male and female whales based on the data.

Average Whale Lengths						
Length of Female (ft)	49	51	50	48	51	47
Length of Male (ft)	47	45	44	46	48	48

To show that a conjecture is always true, you must prove it. To show that a conjecture is false, you have to find only one example in which the conjecture is not true. This case is called a **counterexample** . A counterexample can be a drawing, a statement, or a number.

Inductive Reasoning
1. Look for a pattern
2. Make a conjecture.
3. Prove the conjecture or find a counterexample.

EXAMPLE 4 Finding a Counterexample

Show that each conjecture is false by finding a counterexample.

A For all positive numbers n, $\frac{1}{n} \leq n$.

Pick positive values for n and substitute them into the equation to see if the conjecture holds.

Let $n = 1$. Since $\frac{1}{n} = 1$ and $1 \leq 1$, the conjecture holds.

Let $n = 2$. Since $\frac{1}{n} = \frac{1}{2}$ and $\frac{1}{2} \leq 2$, the conjecture holds.

Let $n = \frac{1}{2}$. Since $\frac{1}{n} = \frac{1}{\frac{1}{2}} = 2$ and $2 \not\leq \frac{1}{2}$, the conjecture is false.

$n = \frac{1}{2}$ is a counterexample.

B For any three points in a plane, there are three different lines that contain two of the points.

 Draw three collinear points.

If the three points are collinear, the conjecture is false.

C The temperature in Abilene, Texas, never exceeds 100°F during the spring months (March, April, and May).

Monthly High Temperatures (°F) in Abilene, Texas											
Jan	Feb	Mar	Apr	May	Jun	Jul	Aug	Sep	Oct	Nov	Dec
88	89	97	99	107	109	110	107	106	103	92	89

The temperature in May was 107°F, so the conjecture is false.

CHECK IT OUT!

Show that each conjecture is false by finding a counterexample.

4a. For any real number x, $x^2 \geq x$.

4b. Supplementary angles are adjacent.

4c. The radius of every planet in the solar system is less than 50,000 km.

Planets' Diameters (km)							
Mercury	Venus	Earth	Mars	Jupiter	Saturn	Uranus	Neptune
4880	12,100	12,800	6790	143,000	121,000	51,100	49,500

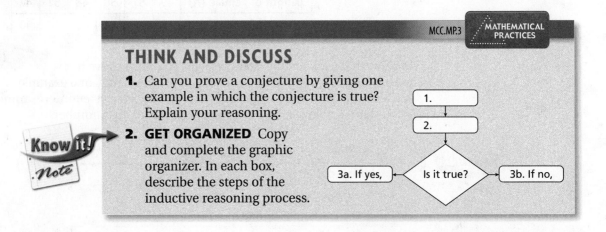

MCC.MP.3 MATHEMATICAL PRACTICES

THINK AND DISCUSS

1. Can you prove a conjecture by giving one example in which the conjecture is true? Explain your reasoning.

2. GET ORGANIZED Copy and complete the graphic organizer. In each box, describe the steps of the inductive reasoning process.

1.
2.
Is it true?
3a. If yes,
3b. If no,

NASA Images

GUIDED PRACTICE

1. **Vocabulary** Explain why a *conjecture* may be true or false.

SEE EXAMPLE 1 **Find the next item in each pattern.**

2. March, May, July, ...

3. $\frac{1}{3}, \frac{2}{4}, \frac{3}{5}, ...$

4. $|\circ|, \overline{\underset{\circ}{\circ}}, |\circ|\circ|, ...$

SEE EXAMPLE 2 **Complete each conjecture.**

5. The product of two even numbers is   ? .

6. A rule in terms of n for the sum of the first n odd positive integers is   ? .

SEE EXAMPLE 3

7. **Biology** A laboratory culture contains 150 bacteria. After twenty minutes, the culture contains 300 bacteria. After one hour, the culture contains 1200 bacteria. Make a conjecture about the rate at which the bacteria increases.

SEE EXAMPLE 4 **Show that each conjecture is false by finding a counterexample.**

8. Kennedy is the youngest U.S. president to be inaugurated.

9. Three points on a plane always form a triangle.

10. For any real number x, if $x^2 \geq 1$, then $x \geq 1$.

President	Age at Inauguration
Washington	57
T. Roosevelt	42
Truman	60
Kennedy	43
Clinton	46

PRACTICE AND PROBLEM SOLVING

Independent Practice	
For Exercises	See Example
11–13	1
14–15	2
16	3
17–19	4

my.hrw.com

Online Extra Practice

Find the next item in each pattern.

11. 8 A.M., 11 A.M., 2 P.M., ...

12. 75, 64, 53, ...

13. $\triangle, \square, \pentagon, ...$

Complete each conjecture.

14. A rule in terms of n for the sum of the first n even positive integers is   ? .

15. The number of nonoverlapping segments formed by n collinear points is   ? .

16. **Industrial Arts** About 5% of the students at Lincoln High School usually participate in the robotics competition. There are 526 students in the school this year. Make a conjecture about the number of students who will participate in the robotics competition this year.

Show that each conjecture is false by finding a counterexample.

17. If $1 - y > 0$, then $0 < y < 1$.

18. For any real number x, $x^3 \geq x^2$.

19. Every pair of supplementary angles includes one obtuse angle.

Make a conjecture about each pattern. Write the next two items.

20. 2, 4, 16, ...

21. $\frac{1}{2}, \frac{1}{4}, \frac{1}{8}, ...$

22. –3, 6, –9, 12, ...

23. Draw a square of dots. Make a conjecture about the number of dots needed to increase the size of the square from $n \times n$ to $(n + 1) \times (n + 1)$.

Determine if each conjecture is true. If not, write or draw a counterexample.

24. Points X, Y, and Z are coplanar.

25. If n is an integer, then $-n$ is positive.

26. In a triangle with one right angle, two of the sides are congruent.

27. If $\overrightarrow{BD}$ bisects $\angle ABC$, then $m\angle ABD = m\angle CBD$.

28. Estimation The Westside High School band is selling coupon books to raise money for a trip. The table shows the amount of money raised for the first four days of the sale. If the pattern continues, estimate the amount of money raised during the sixth day.

Day	Money Raised ($)
1	146.25
2	195.75
3	246.25
4	295.50

29. Write each fraction in the pattern $\dfrac{1}{11}, \dfrac{2}{11}, \dfrac{3}{11}, \dots$ as a repeating decimal. Then write a description of the fraction pattern and the resulting decimal pattern.

30. Math History Remember that a prime number is a whole number greater than 1 that has exactly two factors, itself and 1. Goldbach's conjecture states that every even number greater than 2 can be written as the sum of two primes. For example, $4 = 2 + 2$. Write the next five even numbers as the sum of two primes.

31. The pattern 1, 1, 2, 3, 5, 8, 13, 21, … is known as the *Fibonacci sequence*. Find the next three terms in the sequence and write a conjecture for the pattern.

32. Look at a monthly calendar and pick any three squares in a row—across, down, or diagonal. Make a conjecture about the number in the middle.

12	13	14
19	20	21
26	27	28

33. Make a conjecture about the value of $2n - 1$ when n is an integer.

H.O.T. 34. Critical Thinking The turnaround date for migrating gray whales occurs when the number of northbound whales exceeds the number of southbound whales. Make a conjecture about the turnaround date, based on the table below. What factors might affect the validity of your conjecture in the future?

Migration Direction of Gray Whales							
	Feb. 16	Feb. 17	Feb. 18	Feb. 19	Feb. 20	Feb. 21	Feb. 22
Southbound	0	2	3	0	1	1	0
Northbound	0	0	2	5	3	2	1

H.O.T. 35. Write About It Explain why a true conjecture about even numbers does not necessarily hold for all numbers. Give an example to support your answer.

36. a. For how many hours did the Mock Turtle do lessons on the third day?

b. On what day did the Mock Turtle do 1 hour of lessons?

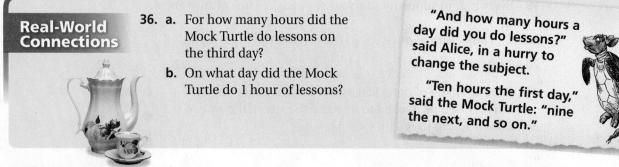

"And how many hours a day did you do lessons?" said Alice, in a hurry to change the subject.

"Ten hours the first day," said the Mock Turtle: "nine the next, and so on."

(cl) North Wind Picture Archive/Alamy; (bl) Victoria Smith/HMH; (br) The Granger Collection

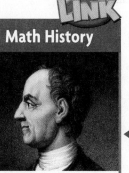

Math History

Goldbach first stated his conjecture in a letter to Leonhard Euler in 1742. Euler, a Swiss mathematician who published over 800 papers, replied, "I consider [the conjecture] a theorem which is quite true, although I cannot demonstrate it."

37. Which of the following conjectures is false?

    (A) If x is odd, then $x + 1$ is even.

    (B) The sum of two odd numbers is even.

    (C) The difference of two even numbers is positive.

    (D) If x is positive, then $-x$ is negative.

38. A student conjectures that if x is a prime number, then $x + 1$ is not prime. Which of the following is a counterexample?

    (F) $x = 11$ (G) $x = 6$ (H) $x = 3$ (J) $x = 2$

39. The class of 2004 holds a reunion each year. In 2005, 87.5% of the 120 graduates attended. In 2006, 90 students went, and in 2007, 75 students went. About how many students do you predict will go to the reunion in 2010?

    (A) 12   (B) 15   (C) 24   (D) 30

CHALLENGE AND EXTEND

H.O.T. 40. **Multi-Step** Make a table of values for the rule $x^2 + x + 11$ when x is an integer from 1 to 8. Make a conjecture about the type of number generated by the rule. Continue your table. What value of x generates a counterexample?

41. **Political Science** Presidential elections are held every four years. U.S. senators are elected to 6-year terms, but only $\frac{1}{3}$ of the Senate is up for election every two years. If $\frac{1}{3}$ of the Senate is elected during a presidential election year, how many years must pass before these same senate seats are up for election during another presidential election year?

H.O.T. 42. **Physical Fitness** Rob is training for the President's Challenge physical fitness program. During his first week of training, Rob does 15 sit-ups each day. He will add 20 sit-ups to his daily routine each week. His goal is to reach 150 sit-ups per day.

    a. Make a table of the number of sit-ups Rob does each week from week 1 through week 10.

    b. During which week will Rob reach his goal?

    c. Write a conjecture for the number of sit-ups Rob does during week n.

43. **Construction** Draw $\overline{AB}$. Then construct point C so that it is not on $\overline{AB}$ and is the same distance from A and B. Construct $\overline{AC}$ and $\overline{BC}$. Compare m$\angle CAB$ and m$\angle CBA$ and compare AC and CB. Make a conjecture.

FOCUS ON MATHEMATICAL PRACTICES

H.O.T. 44. **Modeling** Every cut of a round pizza divides it along a diameter. There are two pieces of pizza after one cut, four pieces after two cuts, and so on. How many pieces do n cuts create?

H.O.T. 45. **Counterexamples** Teri says that the sum of the measures of any two vertical angles is less than or equal to 180°. Describe all possible counterexamples to the statement "The sum of the measures of any two vertical angles is less than or equal to 180°."

H.O.T. 46. **Analysis** Consider the statement "If the sun is not visible, then it is raining." Describe three scenarios besides raining where the sun is not visible.

Venn Diagrams

Connecting Geometry to Number Theory

Recall that in a Venn diagram, ovals are used to represent each set. The ovals can overlap if the sets share common elements.

The real number system contains an infinite number of subsets. The following chart shows some of them. Other examples of subsets are even numbers, multiples of 3, and numbers less than 6.

Set	Description	Examples
Natural numbers	The counting numbers	1, 2, 3, 4, 5, ...
Whole numbers	The set of natural numbers and 0	0, 1, 2, 3, 4, ...
Integers	The set of whole numbers and their opposites	..., −2, −1, 0, 1, 2, ...
Rational numbers	The set of numbers that can be written as a ratio of integers	$-\frac{3}{4}, 5, -2, 0.5, 0$
Irrational numbers	The set of numbers that cannot be written as a ratio of integers	$\pi, \sqrt{10}, 8 + \sqrt{2}$

Example

Draw a Venn diagram to show the relationship between the set of even numbers and the set of natural numbers.

The set of even numbers includes all numbers that are divisible by 2. This includes natural numbers such as 2, 4, and 6. But even numbers such as −4 and −10 are not natural numbers.

So the set of even numbers includes some, but not all, elements in the set of natural numbers. Similarly, the set of natural numbers includes some, but not all, even numbers.

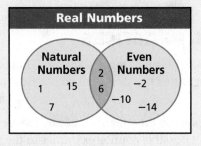

Draw a rectangle to represent all real numbers.

Draw overlapping ovals to represent the sets of even and natural numbers. You may write individual elements in each region.

Try This

Draw a Venn diagram to show the relationship between the given sets.

1. natural numbers, whole numbers

2. odd numbers, whole numbers

3. irrational numbers, integers

Conditional Statements

? **Essential Question:** How can you express and symbolize if-then statements?

Objectives
Identify, write, and analyze the truth value of conditional statements.

Write the inverse, converse, and contrapositive of a conditional statement.

Vocabulary
conditional statement
hypothesis
conclusion
truth value
negation
converse
inverse
contrapositive
logically equivalent
    statements

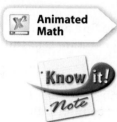
Animated Math

Know it! Note

Why learn this?
To identify a species of butterfly, you must know what characteristics one butterfly species has that another does not.

It is thought that the viceroy butterfly mimics the bad-tasting monarch butterfly to avoid being eaten by birds. By comparing the appearance of the two butterfly species, you can make the following conjecture:

If a butterfly has a curved black line on its hind wing, then it is a viceroy.

Conditional Statements

DEFINITION	SYMBOLS	VENN DIAGRAM
A **conditional statement** is a statement that can be written in the form "if *p*, then *q*."		
The **hypothesis** is the part *p* of a conditional statement following the word *if*.	$p \rightarrow q$	
The **conclusion** is the part *q* of a conditional statement following the word *then*.		

By phrasing a conjecture as an if-then statement, you can quickly identify its hypothesis and conclusion.

COMMON CORE GPS MCC.MP.3

EXAMPLE 1 Identifying the Parts of a Conditional Statement

my.hrw.com

Online Video Tutor

Identify the hypothesis and conclusion of each conditional.

A If a butterfly has a curved black line on its hind wing, then it is a viceroy.
Hypothesis: A butterfly has a curved black line on its hind wing.
Conclusion: The butterfly is a Viceroy.

B A number is an integer if it is a natural number.
Hypothesis: A number is a natural number.
Conclusion: The number is an integer.

Writing Math
"If *p*, then *q*" can also be written as "if *p*, *q*," "*q*, if *p*," "*p* implies *q*," and "*p* only if *q*."

CHECK IT OUT! 1. Identify the hypothesis and conclusion of the statement "A number is divisible by 3 if it is divisible by 6."

Many sentences without the words *if* and *then* can be written as conditionals. To do so, identify the sentence's hypothesis and conclusion by figuring out which part of the statement depends on the other.

(t)©Nancy Nehring/Getty Images; (b)©Ian Shaw/Alamy; (bg)©PhotoDisc/Getty Images

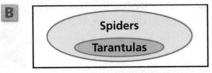

EXAMPLE 2 · Writing a Conditional Statement

COMMON CORE GPS MCC.MP.3

Write a conditional statement from each of the following.

A The midpoint *M* of a segment bisects the segment.

The midpoint *M* of a segment bisects the segment. *Identify the hypothesis and conclusion.*

Conditional: If *M* is the midpoint of a segment, then *M* bisects the segment.

B

Spiders
Tarantulas

The **inner** oval represents the **hypothesis,** and the **outer** oval represents the **conclusion.**

Conditional: If an animal is a tarantula, then it is a spider.

> **CHECK IT OUT!** **2.** Write a conditional statement from the sentence "Two angles that are complementary are acute."

A conditional statement has a **truth value** of either true (T) or false (F). It is false only when the hypothesis is true and the conclusion is false. Consider the conditional "If I get paid, I will take you to the movie." If I don't get paid, I haven't broken my promise. So the statement is still true.

To show that a conditional statement is false, you need to find only one counterexample where the hypothesis is true and the conclusion is false.

EXAMPLE 3 · Analyzing the Truth Value of a Conditional Statement

COMMON CORE GPS MCC.MP.3

Determine if each conditional is true. If false, give a counterexample.

A If today is Sunday, then tomorrow is Monday.

When the hypothesis is true, the conclusion is also true because Monday follows Sunday. So the conditional is true.

B If an angle is obtuse, then it has a measure of 100°.

You can draw an obtuse angle whose measure is not 100°. In this case, the hypothesis is true, but the conclusion is false. Since you can find a counterexample, the conditional is false.

C If an odd number is divisible by 2, then 8 is a perfect square.

An odd number is never divisible by 2, so the hypothesis is false. The number 8 is not a perfect square, so the conclusion is false. However, the conditional is true because the hypothesis is false.

Remember!

If the hypothesis is false, the conditional statement is true, regardless of the truth value of the conclusion.

> **CHECK IT OUT!** **3.** Determine if the conditional "If a number is odd, then it is divisible by 3" is true. If false, give a counterexample.

The **negation** of statement *p* is "not *p*," written as ~*p*. The negation of the statement "*M* is the midpoint of $\overline{AB}$" is "*M* is *not* the midpoint of $\overline{AB}$." The negation of a true statement is false, and the negation of a false statement is true. Negations are used to write related conditional statements.

Related Conditionals

	DEFINITION	SYMBOLS
	A conditional is a statement that can be written in the form "If p, then q."	$p \rightarrow q$
	The **converse** is the statement formed by exchanging the hypothesis and conclusion.	$q \rightarrow p$
	The **inverse** is the statement formed by negating the hypothesis and the conclusion.	$\sim p \rightarrow \sim q$
	The **contrapositive** is the statement formed by both exchanging and negating the hypothesis and conclusion.	$\sim q \rightarrow \sim p$

COMMON CORE GPS

EXAMPLE 4
MCC.MP.3

Biology Application

Write the converse, inverse, and contrapositive of the conditional statement. Use the photos to find the truth value of each.

If an insect is a butterfly, then it has four wings.

If an insect is a butterfly, then it has four wings.

Converse: If an insect has four wings, then it is a butterfly.

A moth also is an insect with four wings. So the converse is false.

Inverse: If an insect is not a butterfly, then it does not have four wings.

A moth is not a butterfly, but it has four wings. So the inverse is false.

Contrapositive: If an insect does not have four wings, then it is not a butterfly.

Butterflies must have four wings. So the contrapositive is true.

Butterfly

my.hrw.com

Online Video Tutor

Moth

CHECK IT OUT!

4. Write the converse, inverse, and contrapositive of the conditional statement "If an animal is a cat, then it has four paws." Find the truth value of each.

Helpful Hint

The logical equivalence of a conditional and its contrapositive is known as the Law of Contrapositive.

In the example above, the conditional statement and its contrapositive are both true, and the converse and inverse are both false. Related conditional statements that have the same truth value are called **logically equivalent statements**. A conditional and its contrapositive are logically equivalent, and so are the converse and inverse.

Statement	Example	Truth Value
Conditional	If m∠A = 95°, then ∠A is obtuse.	T
Converse	If ∠A is obtuse, then m∠A = 95°.	F
Inverse	If m∠A ≠ 95°, then ∠A is not obtuse.	F
Contrapositive	If ∠A is not obtuse, then m∠A ≠ 95°.	T

However, the converse of a true conditional is not necessarily false. All four related conditionals can be true, or all four can be false, depending on the statement.

(cl) Digital Vision/Getty Images; (cr) Arville/Getty Images

THINK AND DISCUSS

1. If a conditional statement is false, what are the truth values of its hypothesis and conclusion?

2. What is the truth value of a conditional whose hypothesis is false?

3. Can a conditional statement and its converse be logically equivalent? Support your answer with an example.

Know it! *Note*

4. **GET ORGANIZED** Copy and complete the graphic organizer. In each box, write the definition and give an example.

Conditional statement

Converse | Inverse | Contrapositive

1-4 Exercises

GUIDED PRACTICE

Vocabulary Apply the vocabulary from this lesson to answer each question.

1. The ___?___ of a *conditional statement* is formed by exchanging the hypothesis and conclusion. (*converse, inverse,* or *contrapositive*)

2. A *conditional* and its *contrapositive* are ___?___ because they have the same truth value. (*logically equivalent* or *converses*)

SEE EXAMPLE 1 **Identify the hypothesis and conclusion of each conditional.**

3. If a person is at least 16 years old, then the person can drive a car.

4. A figure is a parallelogram if it is a rectangle.

5. The statement $a - b < a$ implies that b is a positive number.

SEE EXAMPLE 2 **Write a conditional statement from each of the following.**

6. Eighteen-year-olds are eligible to vote.

7. $\left(\dfrac{a}{b}\right)^2 < \dfrac{a}{b}$ when $0 < a < b$.

8.
Transformations
Rotations

SEE EXAMPLE 3 **Determine if each conditional is true. If false, give a counterexample.**

9. If three points form the vertices of a triangle, then they lie in the same plane.

10. If $x > y$, then $|x| > |y|$.

11. If the season is spring, then the month is March.

SEE EXAMPLE 4 12. **Travel** Write the converse, inverse, and contrapositive of the following conditional statement. Find the truth value of each.

If Brielle drives at exactly 30 mi/h, then she travels 10 mi in 20 min.

PRACTICE AND PROBLEM SOLVING

Independent Practice

For Exercises	See Example
13–15	1
16–18	2
19–21	3
22–23	4

my.hrw.com

Online Extra Practice

Identify the hypothesis and conclusion of each conditional.

13. If an animal is a tabby, then it is a cat.

14. Four angles are formed if two lines intersect.

15. If 8 ounces of cereal cost $2.99, then 16 ounces of cereal cost $5.98.

Write a conditional statement from each sentence.

16. You should monitor the heart rate of a patient who is ill.

17. After three strikes, the batter is out.

18. Congruent segments have equal measures.

Determine if each conditional is true. If false, give a counterexample.

19. If you subtract -2 from -6, then the result is -4.

20. If two planes intersect, then they intersect in exactly one point.

21. If a cat is a bird, then today is Friday.

H.O.T. **Write the converse, inverse, and contrapositive of each conditional statement. Find the truth value of each.**

22. Probability If the probability of an event is 0.1, then the event is unlikely to occur.

23. Meteorology If freezing rain is falling, then the air temperature is 32°F or less. (*Hint:* The freezing point of water is 32°F.)

Find the truth value of each statement.

24. E lies in plane $\mathcal{R}$.

25. $\overleftrightarrow{CD}$ lies in plane $\mathcal{F}$.

26. C, E, and D are coplanar.

27. Plane $\mathcal{F}$ contains $\overrightarrow{ED}$.

28. B and E are collinear.

29. $\overleftrightarrow{BC}$ contains $\mathcal{F}$ and $\mathcal{R}$.

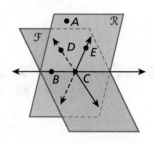

Draw a Venn diagram.

30. All integers are rational numbers.

31. All natural numbers are real.

32. All rectangles are quadrilaterals.

33. Plane is an undefined term.

Write a conditional statement from each Venn diagram.

34.

> Mammals
> Dolphins

35.

> Americans
> Texans

36.

> $x < -1$
> $x < -4$

37. a. Identify the hypothesis and conclusion in the Duchess's statement.

b. Rewrite the Duchess's claim as a conditional statement.

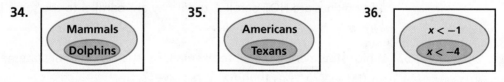

"Tut, tut, child!" said the Duchess. "Everything's got a moral, if only you can find it." And she squeezed herself up closer to Alice's side as she spoke.

Find a counterexample to show that the converse of each conditional is false.

38. If $x = -5$, then $x^2 = 25$.

39. If two angles are vertical angles, then they are congruent.

40. If two angles are adjacent, then they share a vertex.

41. If you use sunscreen, then you will not get sunburned.

Geology

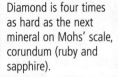

Diamond is four times as hard as the next mineral on Mohs' scale, corundum (ruby and sapphire).

Geology Mohs' scale is used to identify minerals. A mineral with a higher number is harder than a mineral with a lower number.

Use the table and the statements below for Exercises 42–47. Write each conditional and find its truth value.

Mohs' Scale	
Hardness	**Mineral**
1	Talc
2	Gypsum
3	Calcite
4	Fluorite
5	Apatite
6	Orthoclase
7	Quartz
8	Topaz
9	Corundum
10	Diamond

p: calcite   *q*: not apatite

r: a hardness of 3   *s*: a hardness less than 5

42. $p \to r$ **43.** $s \to q$ **44.** $q \to s$

45. $q \to p$ **46.** $r \to q$ **47.** $p \to s$

H.O.T. 48. Critical Thinking Consider the conditional "If two angles are congruent, then they have the same measure." Write the converse, inverse, and contrapositive and find the truth value of each. Use the related conditionals to draw a Venn diagram that represents the relationship between congruent angles and their measures.

H.O.T. 49. Write About It When is a conditional statement false? Explain why a true conditional statement can have a hypothesis that is false.

TEST PREP

50. What is the inverse of "If it is Saturday, then it is the weekend"?

Ⓐ If it is the weekend, then it is Saturday.

Ⓑ If it is not Saturday, then it is the weekend.

Ⓒ If it is not Saturday, then it is not the weekend.

Ⓓ If it is not the weekend, then it is not Saturday.

51. Let *a* represent "Two lines are parallel to the same line," and let *b* represent "The two lines are parallel." Which symbolic statement represents the conditional "If two lines are NOT parallel, then they are parallel to the same line"?

Ⓕ $a \to b$ Ⓖ $b \to a$ Ⓗ $\sim b \to a$ Ⓙ $b \to \sim a$

52. Which statement is a counterexample for the conditional statement "If $f(x) = \sqrt{25 - x^2}$, then $f(x)$ is positive"?

Ⓐ $x = 0$ Ⓑ $x = 3$ Ⓒ $x = 4$ Ⓓ $x = 5$

53. Which statement has the same truth value as its converse?

Ⓕ If a triangle has a right angle, its side lengths are 3 centimeters, 4 centimeters, and 5 centimeters.

Ⓖ If an angle measures 104°, then the angle is obtuse.

Ⓗ If a number is an integer, then it is a natural number.

Ⓙ If an angle measures 90°, then it is an acute angle.

CHALLENGE AND EXTEND

For each Venn diagram, write two statements beginning with *Some, All,* or *No.*

54.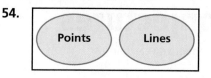

55.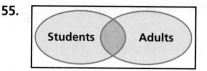

56. Given: If a figure is a square, then it is a rectangle. Figure *A* is not a rectangle.
Conclusion: Figure *A* is not a square.

   a. Draw a Venn diagram to represent the given conditional statement.
   Use the Venn diagram to explain why the conclusion is valid.

   b. Write the contrapositive of the given conditional. How can you use the
   contrapositive to justify the conclusion?

57. **Multi-Step** How many true conditionals can you write using the statements below?

   p: n is an integer.   *q: n* is a whole number.   *r: n* is a natural number.

FOCUS ON MATHEMATICAL PRACTICES

H.O.T. 58. **Analysis** Write a conditional statement about money for which the converse,
inverse, and contrapositive statements are all false. Write each statement.

H.O.T. 59. **Justify** Explain why the statement "If the contrapositive of a conditional statement
is false, then the conditional statement is false" is true.

H.O.T. 60. **Reasoning** Vivian says that if a conditional and its inverse are both true, then the
contrapositive and converse are false. Is she correct? Explain.

Career Path

Stephanie Poulin
Desktop Publisher
Daily Reporter

Q: What high school math classes did you take?
A: I took three years of math: Pre-Algebra, Algebra, and Geometry.

Q: What training do you need to be a desktop publisher?
A: Most of my training was done on the job. The computer science and
typing classes I took in high school have been helpful.

Q: How do you use math?
A: Part of my job is to make sure all the text, charts, and photographs
are formatted to fit the layout of each page. I have to manipulate
things by comparing ratios, calculating areas, and using estimation.

Q: What future plans do you have?
A: My goal is to start my own business as a freelance graphic artist.

1-5 Using Deductive Reasoning to Verify Conjectures

? Essential Question: What are some valid forms of deductive reasoning?

Objective
Apply the Law of Detachment and the Law of Syllogism in logical reasoning.

Vocabulary
deductive reasoning

Why learn this?
You can use inductive and deductive reasoning to decide whether a common myth is accurate.

You have learned that one counterexample is enough to disprove a conjecture. But to prove that a conjecture is true, you must use *deductive reasoning*. **Deductive reasoning** is the process of using logic to draw conclusions from given facts, definitions, and properties.

COMMON CORE GPS **EXAMPLE** MCC.MP.3 **1**

my.hrw.com

Online Video Tutor

Media Application

Urban legends and modern myths spread quickly through the media. Many Web sites and television shows are dedicated to confirming or disproving such myths. Is each conclusion a result of inductive or deductive reasoning?

A There is a myth that toilets and sinks drain in opposite directions in the Southern and Northern Hemispheres. However, if you were to observe sinks draining in the two hemispheres, you would see that this myth is false.

Since the conclusion is based on a pattern of observation, it is a result of inductive reasoning.

B There is a myth that you should not touch a baby bird that has fallen from its nest because the mother bird will disown the baby if she detects human scent. However, biologists have shown that birds cannot detect human scent. Therefore, the myth cannot be true.

The conclusion is based on logical reasoning from scientific research. It is a result of deductive reasoning.

1. There is a myth that an eelskin wallet will demagnetize credit cards because the skin of the electric eels used to make the wallet holds an electric charge. However, eelskin products are not made from electric eels. Therefore, the myth cannot be true. Is this conclusion a result of inductive or deductive reasoning?

In deductive reasoning, if the given facts are true and you apply the correct logic, then the conclusion must be true. The Law of Detachment is one valid form of deductive reasoning.

(cr) Alamy Images; (br) Taxi/Getty Images

Law of Detachment

If $p \rightarrow q$ is a true statement and p is true, then q is true.

COMMON CORE GPS MCC.MP.3

EXAMPLE 2 Verifying Conjectures by Using the Law of Detachment

Determine if each conjecture is valid by the Law of Detachment.

my.hrw.com

Online Video Tutor

A Given: If two segments are congruent, then they have the same length. $\overline{AB} \cong \overline{XY}$.

Conjecture: $AB = XY$

Identify the hypothesis and conclusion in the given conditional.

If two segments are congruent, then they have the same length.

The given statement $\overline{AB} \cong \overline{XY}$ matches the hypothesis of a true conditional. By the Law of Detachment $AB = XY$. The conjecture is valid.

B Given: If you are tardy 3 times, you must go to detention. Shea is in detention.

Conjecture: Shea was tardy at least 3 times.

Identify the hypothesis and conclusion in the given conditional.

If you are tardy 3 times, you must go to detention.

The given statement "Shea is in detention" matches the conclusion of a true conditional. But this does not mean the hypothesis is true. Shea could be in detention for another reason. The conjecture is not valid.

2. Determine if the conjecture is valid by the Law of Detachment.
Given: If a student passes his classes, the student is eligible to play sports. Ramon passed his classes.
Conjecture: Ramon is eligible to play sports.

Another valid form of deductive reasoning is the Law of Syllogism. It allows you to draw conclusions from two conditional statements when the conclusion of one is the hypothesis of the other.

Law of Syllogism

If $p \rightarrow q$ and $q \rightarrow r$ are true statements, then $p \rightarrow r$ is a true statement.

COMMON CORE GPS MCC.MP.3

EXAMPLE 3 Verifying Conjectures by Using the Law of Syllogism

Determine if each conjecture is valid by the Law of Syllogism.

my.hrw.com

Online Video Tutor

A Given: If m∠A < 90°, then ∠A is acute. If ∠A is acute, then it is not a right angle.

Conjecture: If m∠A < 90°, then it is not a right angle.

Let p, q, and r represent the following.

p: The measure of an angle is less than 90°.

q: The angle is acute.

r: The angle is not a right angle.

You are given that $p \rightarrow q$ and $q \rightarrow r$. Since q is the conclusion of the first conditional and the hypothesis of the second conditional, you can conclude that $p \rightarrow r$. The conjecture is valid by the Law of Syllogism.

Determine if each conjecture is valid by the Law of Syllogism.

B **Given:** If a number is divisible by 4, then it is divisible by 2.
      If a number is even, then it is divisible by 2.

Conjecture: If a number is divisible by 4, then it is even.

Let x, y, and z represent the following.

    x: A number is divisible by 4.

    y: A number is divisible by 2.

    z: A number is even.

You are given that $x \rightarrow y$ and $z \rightarrow y$. The Law of Syllogism cannot be used to draw a conclusion since y is the conclusion of both conditionals. Even though the conjecture $x \rightarrow z$ is true, the logic used to draw the conclusion is not valid.

> **Caution!**
>
> It is possible to arrive at a true conclusion by applying invalid logical reasoning, as in Example 3B.

CHECK IT OUT!
3. Determine if the conjecture is valid by the Law of Syllogism.
    Given: If an animal is a mammal, then it has hair.
           If an animal is a dog, then it is a mammal.
    Conjecture: If an animal is a dog, then it has hair.

COMMON CORE GPS
MCC.MP.3
EXAMPLE 4

Applying the Laws of Deductive Reasoning

Draw a conclusion from the given information.

A **Given:** If a team wins 10 games, then they play in the finals. If a team plays in the finals, then they travel to Boston. The Ravens won 10 games.

Conclusion: The Ravens will travel to Boston.

B **Given:** If two angles form a linear pair, then they are adjacent. If two angles are adjacent, then they share a side. $\angle 1$ and $\angle 2$ form a linear pair.

Conclusion: $\angle 1$ and $\angle 2$ share a side.

my.hrw.com

Online Video Tutor

CHECK IT OUT!
4. Draw a conclusion from the given information.
    Given: If a polygon is a triangle, then it has three sides.
           If a polygon has three sides, then it is not a quadrilateral. Polygon P is a triangle.

MCC.MP.2 | MATHEMATICAL PRACTICES

THINK AND DISCUSS

1. Could "A square has exactly two sides" be the conclusion of a valid argument? If so, what do you know about the truth value of the given information?

2. Explain why writing conditional statements as symbols might help you evaluate the validity of an argument.

3. **GET ORGANIZED** Copy and complete the graphic organizer. Write each law in your own words and give an example of each.

Know it! Note

```
          Deductive Reasoning
                  |
        ┌─────────┴─────────┐
  Law of Detachment    Law of Syllogism
```

GUIDED PRACTICE

1. **Vocabulary** Explain how *deductive reasoning* differs from inductive reasoning.

SEE EXAMPLE 1   **Does each conclusion use inductive or deductive reasoning?**

2. At Bell High School, students must take Biology before they take Chemistry. Sam is in Chemistry, so Marcia concludes that he has taken Biology.

3. A detective learns that his main suspect was out of town the day of the crime. He concludes that the suspect is innocent.

SEE EXAMPLE 2   **Determine if each conjecture is valid by the Law of Detachment.**

4. Given: If you want to go on a field trip, you must have a signed permission slip.
Zola has a signed permission slip.
Conjecture: Zola wants to go on a field trip.

5. Given: If the side lengths of a rectangle are 3 ft and 4 ft, then its area is 12 ft².
A rectangle has side lengths of 3 ft and 4 ft.
Conjecture: The area of the rectangle is 12 ft².

SEE EXAMPLE 3   **Determine if each conjecture is valid by the Law of Syllogism.**

6. Given: If you fly from Texas to California, you travel from the central to the Pacific time zone. If you travel from the central to the Pacific time zone, then you gain two hours.
Conjecture: If you fly from Texas to California, you gain two hours.

7. Given: If a figure is a **square**, then the figure is a **rectangle**. If a figure is a **square**, then it is a **parallelogram**.
Conjecture: If a figure is a **parallelogram**, then it is a **rectangle**.

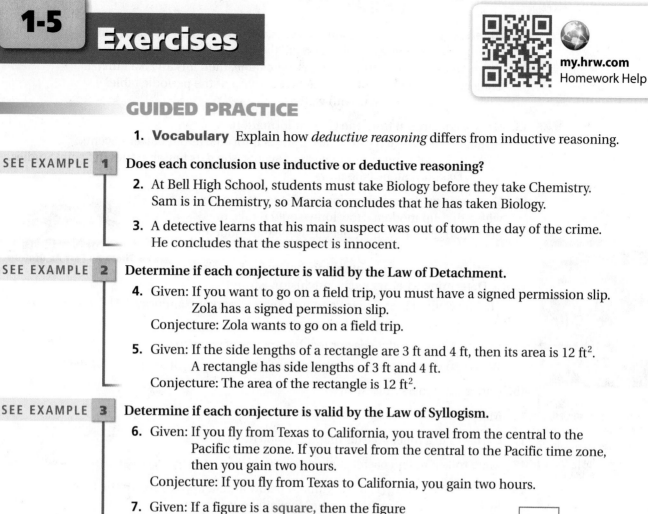

SEE EXAMPLE 4   8. Draw a conclusion from the given information.
Given: If you leave your car lights on overnight, then your car battery will drain. If your battery is drained, your car might not start. Alex left his car lights on last night.

PRACTICE AND PROBLEM SOLVING

Independent Practice	
For Exercises	See Example
9–10	1
11	2
12	3
13	4

my.hrw.com

Online Extra Practice

Does each conclusion use inductive or deductive reasoning?

9. The sum of the angle measures of a triangle is 180°. Two angles of a triangle measure 40° and 60°, so Kandy concludes that the third angle measures 80°.

10. All of the students in Henry's Geometry class are juniors. Alexander takes Geometry, but has another teacher. Henry concludes that Alexander is also a junior.

11. Determine if the conjecture is valid by the Law of Detachment.
Given: If one integer is odd and another integer is even, their product is even.
The product of two integers is 24.
Conjecture: One of the two integers is odd.

12. **Science** Determine if the conjecture is valid by the Law of Syllogism.
Given: If an element is an alkali metal, then it reacts with water. If an element is in the first column of the periodic table, then it is an alkali metal.
Conjecture: If an element is in the first column of the periodic table, then it reacts with water.

H.O.T. 13. Draw a conclusion from the given information.
Given: If Dakota watches the news, she is informed about current events.
If Dakota knows about current events, she gets better grades in Social Studies.
Dakota watches the news.

14. **Technology** Joseph downloads a file in 18 minutes with a dial-up modem. How long would it take to download the file with a Cheetah-Net cable modem?

CHEETAH-NET CABLE
75 Times As Fast As Dial-Up

Recreation Use the true statements below for Exercises 15–18. Determine whether each conclusion is valid.

I. The Gemini is at Cedar Point amusement park in Sandusky, OH.

II. Carter and Mary go to Cedar Point.

III. The Gemini roller coaster reaches speeds of 60 mi/h.

IV. When Carter goes to an amusement park, he rides all the roller coasters.

15. Carter went to Sandusky, OH.

16. Mary rode the Gemini.

17. Carter rode a roller coaster that travels 60 mi/h.

18. Mary rode a roller coaster that travels 60 mi/h.

19. **Critical Thinking** Is the argument below a valid application of the Law of Syllogism? Is the conclusion true? Explain your answers.

If $3 - x < 5$, then $x < -2$. If $x < -2$, then $-5x > 10$. Thus, if $3 - x < 5$, then $-5x > 10$.

H.O.T. 20. **/// ERROR ANALYSIS ///** Below are two conclusions. Which is incorrect? Explain the error.

If two angles are complementary, their measures add to 90°. If an angle measures 90°, then it is a right angle. $\angle A$ and $\angle B$ are complementary.

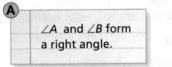

Ⓐ $\angle A$ and $\angle B$ form a right angle.

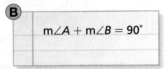

Ⓑ $m\angle A + m\angle B = 90°$

H.O.T. 21. **Write About It** Write one example of a real-life logical argument that uses the Law of Detachment and one that uses the Law of Syllogism. Explain why the conclusions are valid.

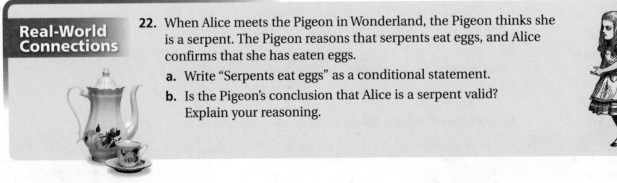

Real-World Connections

22. When Alice meets the Pigeon in Wonderland, the Pigeon thinks she is a serpent. The Pigeon reasons that serpents eat eggs, and Alice confirms that she has eaten eggs.

a. Write "Serpents eat eggs" as a conditional statement.

b. Is the Pigeon's conclusion that Alice is a serpent valid? Explain your reasoning.

23. The Supershots scored over 75 points in each of ten straight games. The newspaper predicts that they will score more than 75 points tonight. Which form of reasoning is this conclusion based on?

Ⓐ Deductive reasoning, because the conclusion is based on logic

Ⓑ Deductive reasoning, because the conclusion is based on a pattern

Ⓒ Inductive reasoning, because the conclusion is based on logic

Ⓓ Inductive reasoning, because the conclusion is based on a pattern

24. $\overrightarrow{HF}$ bisects $\angle EHG$. Which conclusion is NOT valid?

Ⓕ E, F, and G are coplanar.

Ⓖ $\angle EHF \cong \angle FHG$

Ⓗ $\overline{EF} \cong \overline{FG}$

Ⓘ $m\angle EHF = m\angle FHG$

25. **Gridded Response** If Whitney plays a low G on her piano, the frequency of the note is 24.50 hertz. The frequency of a note doubles with each octave. What is the frequency in hertz of a G note that is 3 octaves above low G?

CHALLENGE AND EXTEND

H.O.T. 26. **Political Science** To be eligible to hold the office of the president of the United States, a person must be at least 35 years old, be a natural-born U.S. citizen, and have been a U.S. resident for at least 14 years. Given this information, what conclusion, if any, can be drawn from the statements below? Explain your reasoning.

Andre is not eligible to be the president of the United States.
Andre has lived in the United States for 16 years.

H.O.T. 27. **Multi-Step** Consider the two conditional statements below.
If you live in San Diego, then you live in California.
If you live in California, then you live in the United States.

a. Draw a conclusion from the given conditional statements.

b. Write the contrapositive of each conditional statement.

c. Draw a conclusion from the two contrapositives.

d. How does the conclusion in part **a** relate to the conclusion in part **c**?

28. If Cassie goes to the skate park, Hanna and Amy will go. If Hanna or Amy goes to the skate park, then Marc will go. If Marc goes to the skate park, then Dallas will go. If only two of the five people went to the skate park, who were they?

FOCUS ON MATHEMATICAL PRACTICES

H.O.T. 29. **Analysis** Find the missing statement so that the following conjecture is true:
If the mountains are to my left, then I'm driving to visit a friend.

Given: If I am going to Ingleton, then I'm driving to visit a friend.
If the mountains are to my left, then I am driving north.

H.O.T. 30. **Reasoning** Rewrite each statement in symbolic form. Explain the validity of the following conjecture: If Gavin likes geometry, then Alice and Gavin will study math together.

I. If Gavin likes geometry, then he likes math.

II. If Alice likes Gavin, then they will study math together.

III. If Alice doesn't like Gavin, then Gavin doesn't like math.

Ready to Go On?

my.hrw.com
Assessment and Intervention

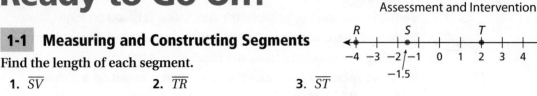

1-1 Measuring and Constructing Segments

Find the length of each segment.

1. $\overline{SV}$ **2.** $\overline{TR}$ **3.** $\overline{ST}$

4. The diagram represents a straight highway with three towns, Henri, Joaquin, and Kenard. Find the distance from Henri H to Joaquin J.

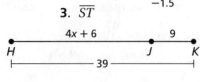

5. Sketch, draw, and construct a segment congruent to $\overline{CD}$.

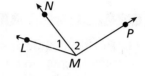

6. Q is the midpoint of $\overline{PR}$, $PQ = 2z$, and $PR = 8z - 12$. Find z, PQ, and PR.

1-2 Measuring and Constructing Angles

7. Name all the angles in the diagram.

Classify each angle by its measure.

8. $m\angle PVQ = 21°$ **9.** $m\angle RVT = 96°$ **10.** $m\angle PVS = 143°$

11. $\overrightarrow{RS}$ bisects $\angle QRT$, $m\angle QRS = (3x + 8)°$, and $m\angle SRT = (9x - 4)°$. Find $m\angle SRT$.

12. Use a protractor and straightedge to draw a 130° angle. Then bisect the angle.

1-3 Using Inductive Reasoning to Make Conjectures

Find the next item in each pattern.

13. 1, 10, 18, 25, … **14.** July, May, March, … **15.** $\frac{1}{8}, -\frac{1}{4}, \frac{1}{2}, …$ **16.** |, +, ‡, …

17. A biologist recorded the following data about the weight of male lions in a wildlife park in Africa. Use the table to make a conjecture about the average weight of a male lion.

18. Complete the conjecture "The sum of two negative numbers is ___?___."

19. Show that the conjecture "If an even number is divided by 2, then the result is an even number" is false by finding a counterexample.

ID Number	Weight (lb)
A1902SM	387.2
A1904SM	420.5
A1920SM	440.6
A1956SM	398.7
A1974SM	415.0

1-4 Conditional Statements

20. Identify the hypothesis and conclusion of the conditional statement "An angle is obtuse if its measure is 107°."

Write a conditional statement from each of the following.

21. A whole number is an integer.

22.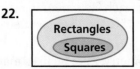

23. The diagonals of a square are congruent.

Determine if each conditional is true. If false, give a counterexample.

24. If an angle is acute, then it has a measure of 30°.

25. If $9x - 11 = 2x + 3$, then $x = 2$.

26. Write the converse, inverse, and contrapositive of the statement "If a number is even, then it is divisible by 4." Find the truth value of each.

 1-5 Using Deductive Reasoning to Verify Conjectures

27. Determine if the following conjecture is valid by the Law of Detachment.
    Given: If Sue finishes her science project, she can go to the movie. Sue goes to the movie.
    Conjecture: Sue finished her science project.

28. Use the Law of Syllogism to draw a conclusion from the given information.
    Given: If one angle of a triangle is 90°, then the triangle is a right triangle. If a triangle is a right triangle, then its acute angle measures are complementary.

PARCC Assessment Readiness

COMMON CORE GPS

Selected Response

1. Identify the hypothesis and conclusion of the conditional statement.

   If it is raining then it is cloudy.

   (A) Hypothesis: It is raining.
       Conclusion: It is cloudy.

   (B) Hypothesis: It is cloudy.
       Conclusion: It is raining.

   (C) Hypothesis: Clouds make rain.
       Conclusion: Rain does not make clouds.

   (D) Hypothesis: Rain and clouds happen together.
       Conclusion: Rain and clouds do not happen together.

2. Complete the conjecture.

   The sum of two odd numbers is _____.

   (F) even
   (G) odd
   (H) sometimes odd, sometimes even
   (J) even most of the time

3. Find the length of $\overline{BC}$.

   (A) $BC = -7$
   (B) $BC = -9$
   (C) $BC = 7$
   (D) $BC = 8$

4. Determine if the conjecture is valid by the Law of Detachment.

   Given: If Tommy makes cookies tonight, then Tommy must have an oven. Tommy has an oven.

   Conjecture: Tommy made cookies tonight.

   (F) The conjecture is valid, because if Tommy didn't have an oven then he didn't make cookies tonight.

   (G) The conjecture is not valid, because if Tommy didn't have an oven then he didn't make cookies tonight.

   (H) The conjecture is valid, because Tommy could have an oven but he could make something besides cookies tonight.

   (J) The conjecture is not valid, because Tommy could have an oven but he could make something besides cookies tonight.

Mini-Tasks

5. $\overrightarrow{BD}$ bisects $\angle ABC$, $m\angle ABD = (7x - 1)°$, and $m\angle DBC = (4x + 8)°$. Find $m\angle ABD$.

6. Point C is the midpoint of $\overline{AB}$ and point D is the midpoint of $\overline{CB}$. If $AB = 20$, what is AD?

2 Algebraic and Geometric Proofs

Contents

MATHEMATICAL PRACTICES The Common Core Georgia Performance Standards for Mathematical Practice describe varieties of expertise that all students should seek to develop. Opportunities to develop these practices are integrated throughout this program.

1 Make sense of problems and persevere in solving them.

2 Reason abstractly and quantitatively.

3 Construct viable arguments and critique the reasoning of others.

4 Model with mathematics.

5 Use appropriate tools strategically.

6 Attend to precision.

7 Look for and make use of structure.

8 Look for and express regularity in repeated reasoning.

Unpacking the Standards

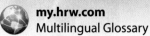

Understanding the standards and the vocabulary terms in the standards will help you know exactly what you are expected to learn in this chapter.

 MCC9-12.G.CO.9

Prove theorems about lines and angles.

Key Vocabulary

proof (demostración)
An argument that uses logic to show that a conclusion is true.

theorem (teorema)
A statement that has been proven.

line (línea)
An undefined term in geometry, a line is a straight path that has no thickness and extends forever.

angle (ángulo)
A figure formed by two rays with a common endpoint.

What It Means For You

With just a few definitions, properties, and postulates, you can begin to prove simple theorems about line segments, linear pairs, right angles, vertical angles, and complementary or supplementary angles.

EXAMPLE

Given: ∠1 and ∠3 are vertical angles.
Prove: ∠1 ≅ ∠3

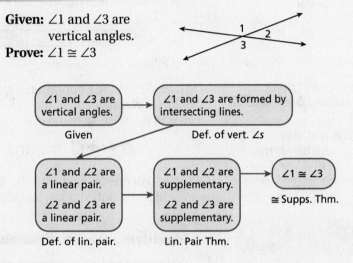

Biconditional Statements and Definitions

? Essential Question: How can definitions be written as biconditional statements?

Objective
Write and analyze biconditional statements.

Vocabulary
biconditional statement
definition
polygon
triangle
quadrilateral

Who uses this?
A gardener can plan the color of the hydrangeas she plants by checking the pH of the soil.

The pH of a solution is a measure of the concentration of hydronium ions in the solution. If a solution has a pH less than 7, it is an acid. Also, if a solution is an acid, it has a pH less than 7.

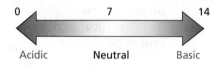

0   7   14

Acidic   Neutral   Basic

Writing Math

The biconditional "*p* if and only if *q*" can also be written as "*p* iff *q*" or $p \leftrightarrow q$.

When you combine a conditional statement and its converse, you create a *biconditional statement*. A **biconditional statement** is a statement that can be written in the form "*p* if and only if *q*." This means "if *p*, then *q*" and "if *q*, then *p*."

$$p \longleftrightarrow q \text{ means } p \longrightarrow q \text{ and } q \longrightarrow p$$

So you can define an acid with the following biconditional statement: A solution is an acid if and only if it has a pH less than 7.

COMMON CORE GPS Prep for MCC9-12.G.CO.9

EXAMPLE 1 Identifying the Conditionals within a Biconditional Statement

my.hrw.com

Online Video Tutor

Write the conditional statement and converse within each biconditional.

A Two angles are congruent if and only if their measures are equal.

Let *p* and *q* represent the following.

   p: Two angles are congruent.
   q: Two angle measures are equal.

The two parts of the biconditional $p \leftrightarrow q$ are $p \rightarrow q$ and $q \rightarrow p$.

Conditional: If two angles are congruent, then their measures are equal.

Converse: If two angle measures are equal, then the angles are congruent.

B A solution is a base $\leftrightarrow$ it has a pH greater than 7.

Let *x* and *y* represent the following.

   x: A solution is a base.
   y: A solution has a pH greater than 7.

The two parts of the biconditional $x \leftrightarrow y$ are $x \rightarrow y$ and $y \rightarrow x$.

Conditional: If a solution is a base, then it has a pH greater than 7.

Converse: If a solution has a pH greater than 7, then it is a base.

 CHECK IT OUT!

Write the conditional statement and converse within each biconditional.

1a. An angle is acute iff its measure is greater than 0° and less than 90°.

1b. Cho is a member if and only if he has paid the $5 dues.

EXAMPLE 2 Writing a Biconditional Statement

For each conditional, write the converse and a biconditional statement.

A If $2x + 5 = 11$, then $x = 3$.

Converse: If $x = 3$, then $2x + 5 = 11$.
Biconditional: $2x + 5 = 11$ if and only if $x = 3$.

B If a point is a midpoint, then it divides the segment into two congruent segments.

Converse: If a point divides a segment into two congruent segments, then the point is a midpoint.

Biconditional: A point is a midpoint if and only if it divides the segment into two congruent segments.

CHECK IT OUT! For each conditional, write the converse and a biconditional statement.

2a. If the date is July 4th, then it is Independence Day.

2b. If points lie on the same line, then they are collinear.

For a biconditional statement to be true, both the conditional statement and its converse must be true. If either the conditional or the converse is false, then the biconditional statement is false.

EXAMPLE 3 Analyzing the Truth Value of a Biconditional Statement

Determine if each biconditional is true. If false, give a counterexample.

A A square has a side length of 5 if and only if it has an area of 25.

Conditional: If a square has a side length of 5, then it has an area of 25. *The conditional is true.*

Converse: If a square has an area of 25, then it has a side length of 5. *The converse is true.*

Since the conditional and its converse are true, the biconditional is true.

B The number n is a positive integer $\leftrightarrow 2n$ is a natural number.

Conditional: If n is a positive integer, then $2n$ is a natural number. *The conditional is true.*

Converse: If $2n$ is a natural number, then n is a positive integer. *The converse is false.*

If $2n = 1$, then $n = \frac{1}{2}$, which is not an integer. Because the converse is false, the biconditional is false.

CHECK IT OUT! Determine if each biconditional is true. If false, give a counterexample.

3a. An angle is a right angle iff its measure is 90°.

3b. $y = -5 \leftrightarrow y^2 = 25$

In geometry, biconditional statements are used to write *definitions*. A **definition** is a statement that describes a mathematical object and can be written as a true biconditional. Most definitions in the glossary are not written as biconditional statements, but they can be. The "if and only if" is implied.

In the glossary, a **polygon** is defined as a closed plane figure formed by three or more line segments. Each segment intersects exactly two other segments only at their endpoints, and no two segments with a common endpoint are collinear.

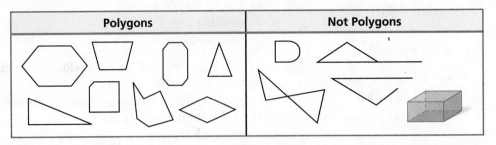

Polygons	Not Polygons

A **triangle** is defined as a three-sided polygon, and a **quadrilateral** is a four-sided polygon.

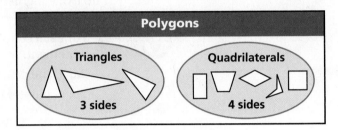

Polygons

Triangles — 3 sides

Quadrilaterals — 4 sides

Helpful Hint

Think of definitions as being reversible. Postulates, however, are not necessarily true when reversed.

A good, precise definition can be used forward and backward. For example, if a figure is a quadrilateral, then it is a four-sided polygon. If a figure is a four-sided polygon, then it is a quadrilateral. To make sure a definition is precise, it helps to write it as a biconditional statement.

COMMON CORE GPS MCC.MP.6

EXAMPLE 4 Writing Definitions as Biconditional Statements

Write each definition as a biconditional.

A A triangle is a three-sided polygon.

A figure is a triangle if and only if it is a three-sided polygon.

B A segment bisector is a ray, segment, or line that divides a segment into two congruent segments.

A ray, segment, or line is a segment bisector if and only if it divides a segment into two congruent segments.

my.hrw.com

Online Video Tutor

CHECK IT OUT! Write each definition as a biconditional.

4a. A quadrilateral is a four-sided polygon.

4b. The measure of a straight angle is 180°.

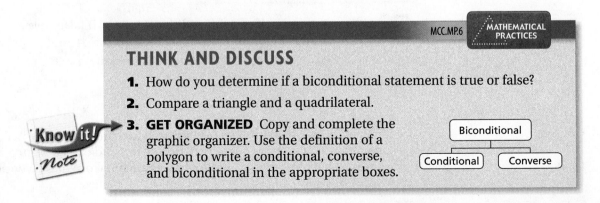

MCC.MP.6 MATHEMATICAL PRACTICES

THINK AND DISCUSS

1. How do you determine if a biconditional statement is true or false?

2. Compare a triangle and a quadrilateral.

3. GET ORGANIZED Copy and complete the graphic organizer. Use the definition of a polygon to write a conditional, converse, and biconditional in the appropriate boxes.

Biconditional

Conditional   Converse

GUIDED PRACTICE

1. **Vocabulary** How is a *biconditional statement* different from a conditional statement?

SEE EXAMPLE 1 **Write the conditional statement and converse within each biconditional.**

2. Perry can paint the entire living room if and only if he has enough paint.

3. Your medicine will be ready by 5 P.M. if and only if you drop your prescription off by 8 A.M.

SEE EXAMPLE 2 **For each conditional, write the converse and a biconditional statement.**

4. If a student is a sophomore, then the student is in the tenth grade.

5. If two segments have the same length, then they are congruent.

SEE EXAMPLE 3 **Multi-Step** Determine if each biconditional is true. If false, give a counterexample.

6. $xy = 0 \leftrightarrow x = 0$ or $y = 0$.

7. A figure is a quadrilateral if and only if it is a polygon.

SEE EXAMPLE 4 **Write each definition as a biconditional.**

8. Parallel lines are two coplanar lines that never intersect.

9. A hummingbird is a tiny, brightly colored bird with narrow wings, a slender bill, and a long tongue.

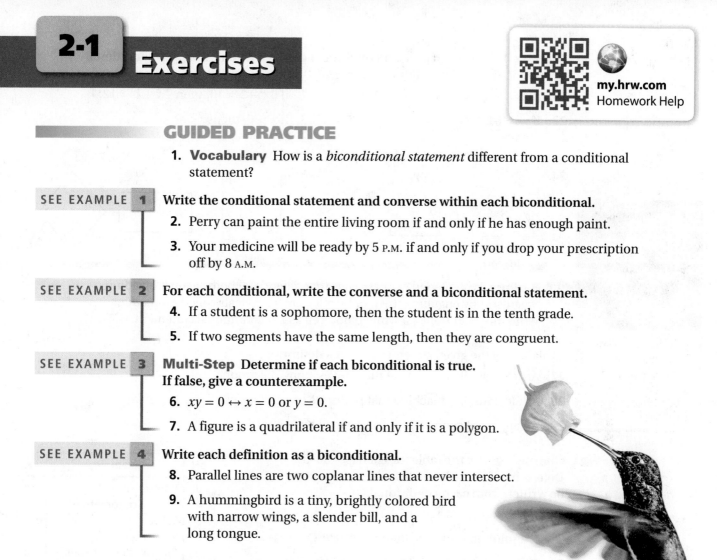

PRACTICE AND PROBLEM SOLVING

Independent Practice	
For Exercises	See Example
10–12	1
13–15	2
16–17	3
18–19	4

Write the conditional statement and converse within each biconditional.

10. Three points are coplanar if and only if they lie in the same plane.

11. A parallelogram is a rectangle if and only if it has four right angles.

12. A lunar eclipse occurs if and only if Earth is between the Sun and the Moon.

For each conditional, write the converse and a biconditional statement.

13. If today is Saturday or Sunday, then it is the weekend.

14. If Greg has the fastest time, then he wins the race.

15. If a triangle contains a right angle, then it is a right triangle.

Multi-Step Determine if each biconditional is true. If false, give a counterexample.

16. Felipe is a swimmer if and only if he is an athlete.

17. The number $2n$ is even if and only if n is an integer.

Write each definition as a biconditional.

18. A circle is the set of all points in a plane that are a fixed distance from a given point.

19. A catcher is a baseball player who is positioned behind home plate and who catches throws from the pitcher.

Algebra Determine if a true biconditional can be written from each conditional statement. If not, give a counterexample.

20. If $a = b$, then $|a| = |b|$.

21. If $3x - 2 = 13$, then $\frac{4}{5}x + 8 = 12$.

22. If $y^2 = 64$, then $3y = 24$.

23. If $x > 0$, then $x^2 > 0$.

Use the diagrams to write a definition for each figure.

24.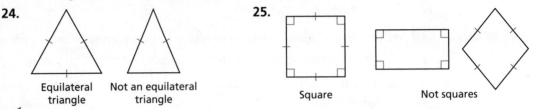

Equilateral triangle   Not an equilateral triangle

25.

Square   Not squares

26. **Biology** White blood cells are cells that defend the body against invading organisms by engulfing them or by releasing chemicals called *antibodies*. Write the definition of a white blood cell as a biconditional statement.

Explain why the given statement is not a definition.

27. An automobile is a vehicle that moves along the ground.

28. A calculator is a machine that performs computations with numbers.

29. An angle is a geometric object formed by two rays.

H.O.T. **Chemistry** Use the table for Exercises 30–32. Determine if a true biconditional statement can be written from each conditional.

30. If a solution has a pH of 4, then it is tomato juice.

31. If a solution is bleach, then its pH is 13.

32. If a solution has a pH greater than 7, then it is not battery acid.

pH	Examples
0	Battery Acid
4	Acid rain, tomato juice
6	Saliva
8	Sea water
13	Bleach, oven cleaner
14	Drain cleaner

Complete each statement to form a true biconditional.

33. The circumference of a circle is 10π if and only if its radius is __?__ .

34. Four points in a plane form a __?__ if and only if no three of them are collinear.

H.O.T. **35.** **Critical Thinking** Write the definition of a biconditional statement as a biconditional statement. Use the conditional and converse within the statement to explain why your biconditional is true.

36. **Write About It** Use the definition of an angle bisector to explain what is meant by the statement "A good definition is reversible."

Real-World Connections

37. **a.** Write "I say what I mean" and "I mean what I say" as conditionals.

b. Explain why the biconditional statement implied by Alice is false.

"Then you should say what you mean," the March Hare went on.

"I do," Alice hastily replied; "at least—at least I mean what I say—that's the same thing, you know."

38. Which is a counterexample for the biconditional "An angle measures 80° if and only if the angle is acute"?

    Ⓐ m∠S = 60°   Ⓑ m∠S = 115°   Ⓒ m∠S = 90°   Ⓓ m∠S = 360°

39. Which biconditional is equivalent to the spelling phrase "*I* before *E* except after *C*"?

    Ⓕ The letter *I* comes before *E* if and only if *I* follows *C*.

    Ⓖ The letter *E* comes before *I* if and only if *E* follows *C*.

    Ⓗ The letter *E* comes before *I* if and only if *E* comes before *C*.

    Ⓙ The letter *I* comes before *E* if and only if *I* comes before *C*.

40. Which conditional statement can be used to write a true biconditional?

    Ⓐ If a number is divisible by 4, then it is even.

    Ⓑ If a ratio compares two quantities measured in different units, the ratio is a rate.

    Ⓒ If two angles are supplementary, then they are adjacent.

    Ⓓ If an angle is right, then it is not acute.

H.O.T. **41. Short Response** Write the two conditional statements that make up the biconditional "You will get a traffic ticket if and only if you are speeding." Is the biconditional true or false? Explain your answer.

CHALLENGE AND EXTEND

H.O.T. **42. Critical Thinking** Describe what the Venn diagram of a true biconditional statement looks like. How does this support the idea that a definition can be written as a true biconditional?

43. Consider the conditional "If an angle measures 105°, then the angle is obtuse."

    a. Write the inverse of the conditional statement.

    b. Write the converse of the inverse.

    c. How is the converse of the inverse related to the original conditional?

    d. What is the truth value of the biconditional statement formed by the inverse of the original conditional and the converse of the inverse? Explain.

44. Suppose *A*, *B*, *C*, and *D* are coplanar, and *A*, *B*, and *C* are not collinear. What is the truth value of the biconditional formed from the true conditional "If m∠*ABD* + m∠*DBC* = m∠*ABC*, then *D* is in the interior of ∠*ABC*"? Explain.

45. Find a counterexample for "*n* is divisible by 4 if and only if n^2 is even."

FOCUS ON MATHEMATICAL PRACTICES

H.O.T. **46. Error Analysis** Blake wrote, "An angle is obtuse if and only if it is not an acute angle." What did Blake overlook? Complete this statement: "An angle is obtuse if and only if __?__ ."

H.O.T. **47. Precision** Is the following a good, precise definition? Explain.
If a polygon has exactly three acute angles, then it is a triangle.

H.O.T. **48. Justify** A conditional statement is true, and so is its inverse. Explain why the conditional statement is a valid biconditional statement.

2-2 Algebraic Proof

Essential Question: What kinds of justifications can you use in writing algebraic and geometric proofs?

Objectives
Review properties of equality and use them to write algebraic proofs.

Identify properties of equality and congruence.

Vocabulary
proof

Who uses this?
Game designers and animators solve equations to simulate motion. (See Example 2.)

A **proof** is an argument that uses logic, definitions, properties, and previously proven statements to show that a conclusion is true.

If you've ever solved an equation in Algebra, then you've already done a proof! An algebraic proof uses algebraic properties such as the properties of equality and the Distributive Property.

Remember!

The Distributive Property states that $a(b + c) = ab + ac$.

Properties of Equality

Addition Property of Equality	If $a = b$, then $a + c = b + c$.
Subtraction Property of Equality	If $a = b$, then $a - c = b - c$.
Multiplication Property of Equality	If $a = b$, then $ac = bc$.
Division Property of Equality	If $a = b$ and $c \neq 0$, then $\frac{a}{c} = \frac{b}{c}$.
Reflexive Property of Equality	$a = a$
Symmetric Property of Equality	If $a = b$, then $b = a$.
Transitive Property of Equality	If $a = b$ and $b = c$, then $a = c$.
Substitution Property of Equality	If $a = b$, then b can be substituted for a in any expression.

As you have learned, if you start with a true statement and each logical step is valid, then your conclusion is valid.

An important part of writing a proof is giving justifications to show that every step is valid. For each justification, you can use a definition, postulate, property, or a piece of information that is given.

COMMON CORE GPS
MCC9-12.A.REI.1

EXAMPLE 1 Solving an Equation in Algebra

Solve the equation $-5 = 3n + 1$. Write a justification for each step.

my.hrw.com

Online Video Tutor

$-5 = 3n + 1$	Given equation
$\underline{-1 \qquad -1}$	Subtraction Property of Equality
$-6 = 3n$	Simplify.
$\dfrac{-6}{3} = \dfrac{3n}{3}$	Division Property of Equality
$-2 = n$	Simplify.
$n = -2$	Symmetric Property of Equality

CHECK IT OUT! **1.** Solve the equation $\frac{1}{2}t = -7$. Write a justification for each step.

© Getty Images

my.hrw.com

Online Video Tutor

MATHEMATICAL
PRACTICES

Make sense of problems and persevere in solving them.

Problem-Solving Application

To simulate the motion of an object in a computer game, the designer uses the formula $sr = 3.6p$ to find the number of pixels the object must travel during each second of animation. In the formula, s is the desired speed of the object in kilometers per hour, r is the scale of pixels per meter, and p is the number of pixels traveled per second.

The graphics in a game are based on a scale of 6 pixels per meter. The designer wants to simulate a vehicle moving at 75 km/h. How many pixels must the vehicle travel each second? Solve the equation for p and justify each step.

1 Understand the Problem

The **answer** will be the number of pixels traveled per second.

List the important information:

- $sr = 3.6p$
- p: pixels traveled per second
- $s = 75$ km/h
- $r = 6$ pixels per meter

2 Make a Plan

Substitute the given information into the formula and solve.

3 Solve

$sr = 3.6p$	Given equation
$(75)(6) = 3.6p$	Substitution Property of Equality
$450 = 3.6p$	Simplify.
$\dfrac{450}{3.6} = \dfrac{3.6p}{3.6}$	Division Property of Equality
$125 = p$	Simplify.
$p = 125$ pixels	Symmetric Property of Equality

4 Look Back

Check your answer by substituting it back into the original formula.

$$sr = 3.6p$$
$$(75)(6) = 3.6(125)$$
$$450 = 450 \checkmark$$

Helpful Hint

$A \qquad B$

AB represents the length of $\overline{AB}$, so you can think of AB as a variable representing a number.

CHECK IT OUT!

2. What is the temperature in degrees Celsius C when it is 86°F? Solve the equation $C = \dfrac{5}{9}(F - 32)$ for C and justify each step.

Like algebra, geometry also uses numbers, variables, and operations. For example, segment lengths and angle measures are numbers. So you can use these same properties of equality to write algebraic proofs in geometry.

EXAMPLE 3 Solving an Equation in Geometry

Write a justification for each step.

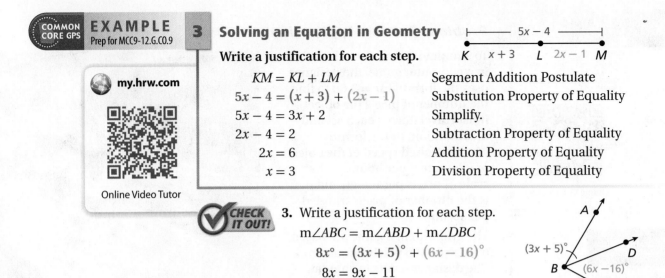

$$KM = KL + LM$$ — Segment Addition Postulate
$$5x - 4 = (x + 3) + (2x - 1)$$ — Substitution Property of Equality
$$5x - 4 = 3x + 2$$ — Simplify.
$$2x - 4 = 2$$ — Subtraction Property of Equality
$$2x = 6$$ — Addition Property of Equality
$$x = 3$$ — Division Property of Equality

my.hrw.com

Online Video Tutor

CHECK IT OUT!

3. Write a justification for each step.

$$m\angle ABC = m\angle ABD + m\angle DBC$$
$$8x° = (3x + 5)° + (6x - 16)°$$
$$8x = 9x - 11$$
$$-x = -11$$
$$x = 11$$

$(3x + 5)°$
$(6x - 16)°$
$m\angle ABC = 8x°$

You have learned that segments with equal lengths are congruent and angles with equal measures are congruent. So the Reflexive, Symmetric, and Transitive Properties of Equality have corresponding properties of congruence.

Know it! Note

Properties of Congruence

SYMBOLS	EXAMPLE
Reflexive Property of Congruence figure $A \cong$ figure A (Reflex. Prop. of $\cong$)	$\overline{EF} \cong \overline{EF}$
Symmetric Property of Congruence If figure $A \cong$ figure B, then figure $B \cong$ figure A. (Sym. Prop. of $\cong$)	If $\angle 1 \cong \angle 2$, then $\angle 2 \cong \angle 1$.
Transitive Property of Congruence If figure $A \cong$ figure B and figure $B \cong$ figure C, then figure $A \cong$ figure C. (Trans. Prop. of $\cong$)	If $\overline{PQ} \cong \overline{RS}$ and $\overline{RS} \cong \overline{TU}$, then $\overline{PQ} \cong \overline{TU}$.

Remember!

Numbers are equal (=) and figures are congruent ($\cong$).

EXAMPLE 4 Identifying Properties of Equality and Congruence

Identify the property that justifies each statement.

A $m\angle 1 = m\angle 1$ — Reflex. Prop. of =

B $\overline{XY} \cong \overline{VW}$, so $\overline{VW} \cong \overline{XY}$. — Sym. Prop. of $\cong$

C $\angle ABC \cong \angle ABC$ — Reflex. Prop. of $\cong$

D $\angle 1 \cong \angle 2$, and $\angle 2 \cong \angle 3$. So $\angle 1 \cong \angle 3$. — Trans. Prop. of $\cong$

my.hrw.com

Online Video Tutor

CHECK IT OUT! Identify the property that justifies each statement.

4a. $DE = GH$, so $GH = DE$. **4b.** $94° = 94°$

4c. $0 = a$, and $a = x$. So $0 = x$. **4d.** $\angle A \cong \angle Y$, so $\angle Y \cong \angle A$.

THINK AND DISCUSS

1. Tell what property you would use to solve the equation $\frac{k}{6} = 3.5$.

2. Explain when to use a congruence symbol instead of an equal sign.

3. **GET ORGANIZED** Copy and complete the graphic organizer. In each box, write an example of the property, using the correct symbol.

Property	Equality	Congruence
Reflexive		
Symmetric		
Transitive		

2-2 Exercises

my.hrw.com
Homework Help

GUIDED PRACTICE

1. Vocabulary Write the definition of *proof* in your own words.

SEE EXAMPLE 1 **Multi-Step** Solve each equation. Write a justification for each step.

2. $y + 1 = 5$

3. $t - 3.2 = -8.3$

4. $2p - 30 = -4p + 6$

5. $\frac{x + 3}{-2} = 8$

6. $\frac{1}{2}n = \frac{3}{4}$

7. $0 = 2(r - 3) + 4$

SEE EXAMPLE 2

8. Nutrition Amy's favorite breakfast cereal has 102 Calories per serving. The equation $C = 9f + 90$ relates the grams of fat f in one serving to the Calories C in one serving. How many grams of fat are in one serving of the cereal? Solve the equation for f and justify each step.

9. Movie Rentals The equation $C = \$5.75 + \$0.89m$ relates the number of movie rentals m to the monthly cost C of a movie club membership. How many movies did Elias rent this month if his membership cost $11.98? Solve the equation for m and justify each step.

SEE EXAMPLE 3 Write a justification for each step.

10.

5y + 6   2y + 21

A   B   C

$AB = BC$
$5y + 6 = 2y + 21$
$3y + 6 = 21$
$3y = 15$
$y = 5$

11.

|—— 9n − 5 ——|
P 3n Q   25   R

$PQ + QR = PR$
$3n + 25 = 9n - 5$
$25 = 6n - 5$
$30 = 6n$
$5 = n$

SEE EXAMPLE 4 Identify the property that justifies each statement.

12. $\overline{AB} \cong \overline{AB}$

13. $m\angle 1 = m\angle 2$, and $m\angle 2 = m\angle 4$. So $m\angle 1 = m\angle 4$.

14. $x = y$, so $y = x$.

15. $\overline{ST} \cong \overline{YZ}$, and $\overline{YZ} \cong \overline{PR}$. So $\overline{ST} \cong \overline{PR}$.

PRACTICE AND PROBLEM SOLVING

Independent Practice

For Exercises	See Example
16–21	1
22	2
23–24	3
25–28	4

my.hrw.com

Online Extra Practice

Multi-Step Solve each equation. Write a justification for each step.

16. $5x - 3 = 4(x + 2)$

17. $1.6 = 3.2n$

18. $\dfrac{z}{3} - 2 = -10$

19. $-(h + 3) = 72$

20. $9y + 17 = -19$

21. $\dfrac{1}{2}(p - 16) = 13$

22. Ecology The equation $T = 0.03c + 0.05b$ relates the numbers of cans c and bottles b collected in a recycling rally to the total dollars T raised. How many cans were collected if \$147 was raised and 150 bottles were collected? Solve the equation for c and justify each step.

Write a justification for each step.

23.
$$\begin{aligned}
m\angle XYZ &= m\angle 2 + m\angle 3 \\
4n - 6 &= 58 + (2n - 12) \\
4n - 6 &= 2n + 46 \\
2n - 6 &= 46 \\
2n &= 52 \\
n &= 26
\end{aligned}$$

24.
$$\begin{aligned}
m\angle WYV &= m\angle 1 + m\angle 2 \\
5n &= 3(n - 2) + 58 \\
5n &= 3n - 6 + 58 \\
5n &= 3n + 52 \\
2n &= 52 \\
n &= 26
\end{aligned}$$

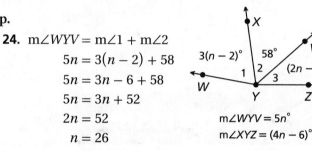

$m\angle WYV = 5n^\circ$
$m\angle XYZ = (4n - 6)^\circ$

Identify the property that justifies each statement.

25. $\overline{KL} \cong \overline{PR}$, so $\overline{PR} \cong \overline{KL}$.

26. $412 = 412$

27. If $a = b$ and $b = 0$, then $a = 0$.

28. figure $A \cong$ figure A

29. Estimation Round the numbers in the equation $2(3.1x - 0.87) = 94.36$ to the nearest whole number and estimate the solution. Then solve the equation, justifying each step. Compare your estimate to the exact solution.

Use the indicated property to complete each statement.

30. Reflexive Property of Equality: $3x - 1 = \underline{\quad ? \quad}$

31. Transitive Property of Congruence: If $\angle A \cong \angle X$ and $\angle X \cong \angle T$, then $\underline{\quad ? \quad}$.

32. Symmetric Property of Congruence: If $\overline{BC} \cong \overline{NP}$, then $\underline{\quad ? \quad}$.

33. Recreation The north campground is midway between the Northpoint Overlook and the waterfall. Use the midpoint formula to find the values of x and y, and justify each step.

H.O.T. 34. Business A computer repair technician charges \$35 for each job plus \$21 per hour of labor and 110% of the cost of parts. The total charge for a 3-hour job was \$169.50. What was the cost of parts for this job? Write and solve an equation and justify each step in the solution.

H.O.T. 35. Finance Morgan spent a total of \$1,733.65 on her car last year. She spent \$92.50 on registration, \$79.96 on maintenance, and \$983 on insurance. She spent the remaining money on gas. She drove a total of 10,820 miles.

   a. How much on average did the gas cost per mile? Write and solve an equation and justify each step in the solution.

   b. What if...? Suppose Morgan's car averages 32 miles per gallon of gas. How much on average did Morgan pay for a gallon of gas?

H.O.T. 36. Critical Thinking Use the definition of segment congruence and the properties of equality to show that all three properties of congruence are true for segments.

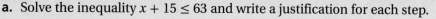

37. Recall from Algebra 1 that the Multiplication and Division Properties of Inequality tell you to reverse the inequality sign when multiplying or dividing by a negative number.

   a. Solve the inequality $x + 15 \leq 63$ and write a justification for each step.

   b. Solve the inequality $-2x > 36$ and write a justification for each step.

38. Write About It Compare the conclusion of a deductive proof and a conjecture based on inductive reasoning.

TEST PREP

39. Which could NOT be used to justify the statement $\overline{AB} \cong \overline{CD}$?

   (A) Definition of congruence   (C) Symmetric Property of Congruence

   (B) Reflexive Property of Congruence   (D) Transitive Property of Congruence

40. A club membership costs $35 plus $3 each time t the member uses the pool. Which equation represents the total cost C of the membership?

   (F) $35 = C + 3t$ (G) $C + 35 = 3t$ (H) $C = 35 + 3t$ (J) $C = 35t + 3$

41. Which statement is true by the Reflexive Property of Equality?

   (A) $x = 35$ (B) $\overline{CD} = \overline{CD}$ (C) $\overline{RT} \cong \overline{TR}$ (D) $CD = CD$

42. Gridded Response In the triangle, $m\angle 1 + m\angle 2 + m\angle 3 = 180°$. If $m\angle 3 = 2m\angle 1$ and $m\angle 1 = m\angle 2$, find $m\angle 3$ in degrees.

CHALLENGE AND EXTEND

43. In the gate, $PA = QB$, $QB = RA$, and $PA = 18$ in. Find PR, and justify each step.

44. Critical Thinking Explain why there is no Addition Property of Congruence.

H.O.T. 45. Algebra Justify each step in the solution of the inequality $7 - 3x > 19$.

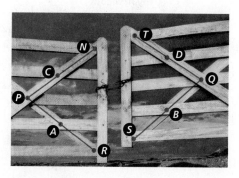

FOCUS ON MATHEMATICAL PRACTICES

H.O.T. 46. Reasoning Petra is writing an algebraic proof. She states that $2x = 9$ is true because of the Symmetric Property of Equality. What was her statement just prior to that? Explain.

H.O.T. 47. Draw Conclusions Students are asked to prove that $n = 1.5$ is a solution of $12n - 3 = 15$. Kevyn used the Addition Property of Equality followed by the Division Property of Equality. Carla used the Substitution Property of Equality and simplified the expression. Are both proofs valid? Explain.

Geometric Proof

 Essential Question: How can you organize the deductive reasoning of a geometric proof?

Objectives
Write two-column proofs.

Prove geometric theorems by using deductive reasoning.

Vocabulary
theorem
two-column proof

Who uses this?
To persuade your parents to increase your allowance, your argument must be presented logically and precisely.

When writing a geometric proof, you use deductive reasoning to create a chain of logical steps that move from the hypothesis to the conclusion of the conjecture you are proving. By proving that the conclusion is true, you have proven that the original conjecture is true.

When writing a proof, it is important to justify each logical step with a reason. You can use symbols and abbreviations, but they must be clear enough so that anyone who reads your proof will understand them.

COMMON CORE GPS MCC9-12.G.CO.9

EXAMPLE 1 Writing Justifications

my.hrw.com

Online Video Tutor

Write a justification for each step, given that $\angle A$ and $\angle B$ are complementary and $\angle A \cong \angle C$.

1. $\angle A$ and $\angle B$ are complementary.   Given information
2. $m\angle A + m\angle B = 90°$ Def. of comp. $\angle$
3. $\angle A \cong \angle C$ Given information
4. $m\angle A = m\angle C$ Def. of $\cong$ $\angle$
5. $m\angle C + m\angle B = 90°$ Subst. Prop. of =   *Steps 2, 4*
6. $\angle C$ and $\angle B$ are complementary.   Def. of comp. $\angle$

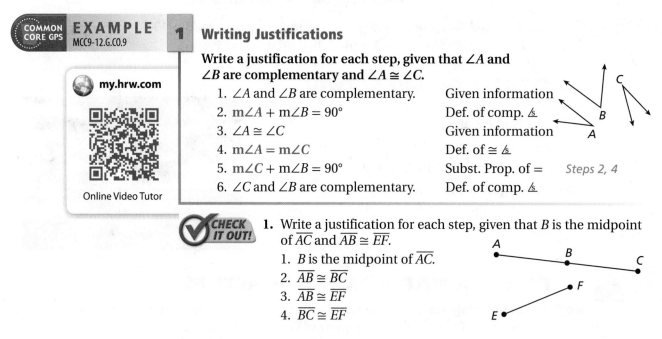

CHECK IT OUT!

1. Write a justification for each step, given that B is the midpoint of $\overline{AC}$ and $\overline{AB} \cong \overline{EF}$.
   1. B is the midpoint of $\overline{AC}$.
   2. $\overline{AB} \cong \overline{BC}$
   3. $\overline{AB} \cong \overline{EF}$
   4. $\overline{BC} \cong \overline{EF}$

A **theorem** is any statement that you can prove. Once you have proven a theorem, you can use it as a reason in later proofs.

Know it! Note

Theorem

	THEOREM	HYPOTHESIS	CONCLUSION
2-3-1	**Linear Pair Theorem** If two angles form a linear pair, then they are supplementary.	$\angle A$ and $\angle B$ form a linear pair.	$\angle A$ and $\angle B$ are supplementary.

Theorem

THEOREM	HYPOTHESIS	CONCLUSION
2-3-2 Congruent Supplements Theorem If two angles are supplementary to the same angle (or to two congruent angles), then the two angles are congruent.	$\angle 1$ and $\angle 2$ are supplementary. $\angle 2$ and $\angle 3$ are supplementary.	$\angle 1 \cong \angle 3$

A geometric proof begins with *Given* and *Prove* statements, which restate the hypothesis and conclusion of the conjecture. In a **two-column proof**, you list the steps of the proof in the left column. You write the matching reason for each step in the right column.

COMMON CORE GPS
MCC9-12.G.CO.9

EXAMPLE 2 Completing a Two-Column Proof

my.hrw.com

Online Video Tutor

Fill in the blanks to complete a two-column proof of the Linear Pair Theorem.
Given: $\angle 1$ and $\angle 2$ form a linear pair.
Prove: $\angle 1$ and $\angle 2$ are supplementary.
Proof:

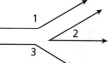

Statements	Reasons
1. $\angle 1$ and $\angle 2$ form a linear pair.	1. Given
2. $\overrightarrow{BA}$ and $\overrightarrow{BC}$ form a line.	2. Def. of lin. pair
3. $m\angle ABC = 180°$	3. Def. of straight $\angle$
4. **a.** ____?____	4. $\angle$ Add. Post.
5. **b.** ____?____	5. Subst. *Steps 3, 4*
6. $\angle 1$ and $\angle 2$ are supplementary.	6. **c.** ____?____

Use the existing statements and reasons in the proof to fill in the blanks.

a. $m\angle 1 + m\angle 2 = m\angle ABC$ *The $\angle$ Add. Post. is given as the reason.*
b. $m\angle 1 + m\angle 2 = 180°$ *Substitute 180° for $m\angle ABC$.*
c. Def. of supp. $\angle\!\!\!\triangle$ *The measures of supp. $\angle\!\!\!\triangle$ add to 180° by def.*

Remember!

A *linear pair* of angles is a pair of angles in the same plane that have a common vertex and a common side, no common interior points, and noncommon sides that are opposite rays.

CHECK IT OUT!

2. Fill in the blanks to complete a two-column proof of one case of the Congruent Supplements Theorem.

Given: $\angle 1$ and $\angle 2$ are supplementary, and $\angle 2$ and $\angle 3$ are supplementary.

Prove: $\angle 1 \cong \angle 3$
Proof:

Statements	Reasons
1. **a.** ____?____	1. Given
2. $m\angle 1 + m\angle 2 = 180°$ $m\angle 2 + m\angle 3 = 180°$	2. Def. of supp. $\angle\!\!\!\triangle$
3. **b.** ____?____	3. Subst.
4. $m\angle 2 = m\angle 2$	4. Reflex. Prop. of $=$
5. $m\angle 1 = m\angle 3$	5. **c.** ____?____
6. **d.** ____?____	6. Def. of $\cong$ $\angle\!\!\!\triangle$

Before you start writing a proof, you should plan out your logic. Sometimes you will be given a plan for a more challenging proof. This plan will detail the major steps of the proof for you.

Know it! Note — Theorems

	THEOREM	HYPOTHESIS	CONCLUSION
2-3-3	**Right Angle Congruence Theorem** All right angles are congruent.	$\angle A$ and $\angle B$ are right angles.	$\angle A \cong \angle B$
2-3-4	**Congruent Complements Theorem** If two angles are complementary to the same angle (or to two congruent angles), then the two angles are congruent.	$\angle 1$ and $\angle 2$ are complementary. $\angle 2$ and $\angle 3$ are complementary.	$\angle 1 \cong \angle 3$

COMMON CORE GPS
EXAMPLE 3
MCC9-12.G.CO.9

Writing a Two-Column Proof from a Plan

my.hrw.com

Online Video Tutor

Use the given plan to write a two-column proof of the Right Angle Congruence Theorem.
Given: $\angle 1$ and $\angle 2$ are right angles.
Prove: $\angle 1 \cong \angle 2$

Plan: Use the definition of a right angle to write the measure of each angle. Then use the Transitive Property and the definition of congruent angles.
Proof:

Statements	Reasons
1. $\angle 1$ and $\angle 2$ are right angles.	**1.** Given
2. $m\angle 1 = 90°$, $m\angle 2 = 90°$	**2.** Def. of rt. $\angle$
3. $m\angle 1 = m\angle 2$	**3.** Trans. Prop. of =
4. $\angle 1 \cong \angle 2$	**4.** Def. of $\cong$ $\angle$s

CHECK IT OUT!

3. Use the given plan to write a two-column proof of one case of the Congruent Complements Theorem.

Given: $\angle 1$ and $\angle 2$ are complementary, and $\angle 2$ and $\angle 3$ are complementary.

Prove: $\angle 1 \cong \angle 3$

Plan: The measures of complementary angles add to 90° by definition. Use substitution to show that the sums of both pairs are equal. Use the Subtraction Property and the definition of congruent angles to conclude that $\angle 1 \cong \angle 3$.

Know it! Note

The Proof Process
1. Write the conjecture to be proven.
2. Draw a diagram to represent the hypothesis of the conjecture.
3. State the given information and mark it on the diagram.
4. State the conclusion of the conjecture in terms of the diagram.
5. Plan your argument and prove the conjecture.

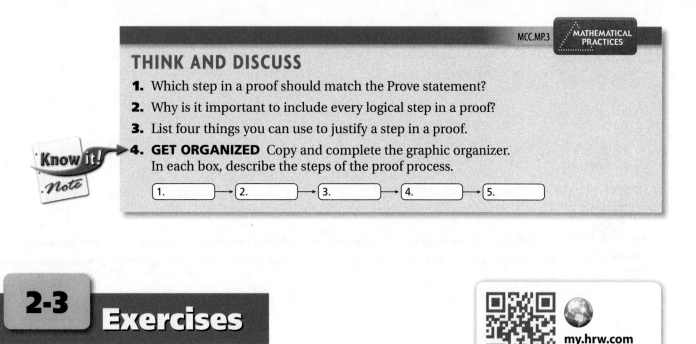

MCC.MP.3

THINK AND DISCUSS

1. Which step in a proof should match the Prove statement?

2. Why is it important to include every logical step in a proof?

3. List four things you can use to justify a step in a proof.

4. **GET ORGANIZED** Copy and complete the graphic organizer. In each box, describe the steps of the proof process.

1. → 2. → 3. → 4. → 5.

2-3 Exercises

my.hrw.com
Homework Help

GUIDED PRACTICE

Vocabulary Apply the vocabulary from this lesson to answer each question.

1. In a *two-column proof*, you list the __?__ in the left column and the __?__ in the right column. (*statements* or *reasons*)

2. A __?__ is a statement you can prove. (*postulate* or *theorem*)

SEE EXAMPLE 1

3. Write a justification for each step, given that m∠A = 60° and m∠B = 2m∠A.

   1. m∠A = 60°, m∠B = 2m∠A
   2. m∠B = 2(60°)
   3. m∠B = 120°
   4. m∠A + m∠B = 60° + 120°
   5. m∠A + m∠B = 180°
   6. ∠A and ∠B are supplementary.

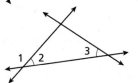

SEE EXAMPLE 2

4. Fill in the blanks to complete the two-column proof.

   Given: ∠2 ≅ ∠3
   Prove: ∠1 and ∠3 are supplementary.
   Proof:

Statements	Reasons
1. ∠2 ≅ ∠3	1. Given
2. m∠2 = m∠3	2. a. __?__
3. b. __?__	3. Lin. Pair Thm.
4. m∠1 + m∠2 = 180°	4. Def. of supp. ∠
5. m∠1 + m∠3 = 180°	5. c. __?__ *Steps 2, 4*
6. d. __?__	6. Def. of supp. ∠

SEE EXAMPLE 3

5. Use the given plan to write a two-column proof.

   Given: *X* is the midpoint of $\overline{AY}$, and *Y* is the midpoint of $\overline{XB}$.
   Prove: $\overline{AX} \cong \overline{YB}$

   Plan: By the definition of midpoint, $\overline{AX} \cong \overline{XY}$, and $\overline{XY} \cong \overline{YB}$. Use the Transitive Property to conclude that $\overline{AX} \cong \overline{YB}$.

2-3 Geometric Proof **61**

PRACTICE AND PROBLEM SOLVING

Independent Practice

For Exercises	See Example
6	1
7–8	2
9–10	3

my.hrw.com

Online Extra Practice

6. Write a justification for each step, given that $\overrightarrow{BX}$ bisects $\angle ABC$ and m$\angle XBC = 45°$.

1. $\overrightarrow{BX}$ bisects $\angle ABC$.
2. $\angle ABX \cong \angle XBC$
3. m$\angle ABX =$ m$\angle XBC$
4. m$\angle XBC = 45°$
5. m$\angle ABX = 45°$
6. m$\angle ABX +$ m$\angle XBC =$ m$\angle ABC$
7. $45° + 45° =$ m$\angle ABC$
8. $90° =$ m$\angle ABC$
9. $\angle ABC$ is a right angle.

Fill in the blanks to complete each two-column proof.

7. Given: $\angle 1$ and $\angle 2$ are supplementary, and
$\angle 3$ and $\angle 4$ are supplementary.
$\angle 2 \cong \angle 3$
Prove: $\angle 1 \cong \angle 4$

Proof:

Statements	Reasons
1. $\angle 1$ and $\angle 2$ are supplementary. $\angle 3$ and $\angle 4$ are supplementary.	1. Given
2. a. ___?___	2. Def. of supp. $\angle$s
3. m$\angle 1 +$ m$\angle 2 =$ m$\angle 3 +$ m$\angle 4$	3. b. ___?___
4. $\angle 2 \cong \angle 3$	4. Given
5. m$\angle 2 =$ m$\angle 3$	5. Def. of $\cong$ $\angle$s
6. c. ___?___	6. Subtr. Prop. of = *Steps 3, 5*
7. $\angle 1 \cong \angle 4$	7. d. ___?___

8. Given: $\angle BAC$ is a right angle. $\angle 2 \cong \angle 3$
Prove: $\angle 1$ and $\angle 3$ are complementary.

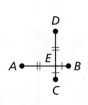

Proof:

Statements	Reasons
1. $\angle BAC$ is a right angle.	1. Given
2. m$\angle BAC = 90°$	2. a. ___?___
3. b. ___?___	3. $\angle$ Add. Post.
4. m$\angle 1 +$ m$\angle 2 = 90°$	4. Subst. *Steps 2, 3*
5. $\angle 2 \cong \angle 3$	5. Given
6. c. ___?___	6. Def. of $\cong$ $\angle$s
7. m$\angle 1 +$ m$\angle 3 = 90°$	7. d. ___?___ *Steps 4, 6*
8. e. ___?___	8. Def. of comp. $\angle$s

Use the given plan to write a two-column proof.

9. Given: $\overline{BE} \cong \overline{CE}$, $\overline{DE} \cong \overline{AE}$
Prove: $\overline{AB} \cong \overline{CD}$

Plan: Use the definition of congruent segments to write
the given information in terms of lengths. Then use
the Segment Addition Postulate to show that $AB = CD$
and thus $\overline{AB} \cong \overline{CD}$.

Use the given plan to write a two-column proof.

10. **Given:** ∠1 and ∠3 are complementary, and ∠2 and ∠4 are complementary. ∠3 ≅ ∠4

    Prove: ∠1 ≅ ∠2

    Plan: Since ∠1 and ∠3 are complementary and ∠2 and ∠4 are complementary, both pairs of angle measures add to 90°. Use substitution to show that the sums of both pairs are equal. Since ∠3 ≅ ∠4, their measures are equal. Use the Subtraction Property of Equality and the definition of congruent angles to conclude that ∠1 ≅ ∠2.

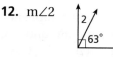

Find each angle measure.

11. m∠1

12. m∠2

13. m∠3

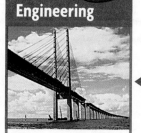
14. **Engineering** The Oresund Bridge, which connects the countries of Denmark and Sweden, was completed in 1999. If ∠1 ≅ ∠2, which theorem can you use to conclude that ∠3 ≅ ∠4?

15. **Critical Thinking** Explain why there are two cases to consider when proving the Congruent Supplements Theorem and the Congruent Complements Theorem.

Tell whether each statement is sometimes, always, or never true.

16. An angle and its complement are congruent.

17. A pair of right angles forms a linear pair.

18. An angle and its complement form a right angle.

19. A linear pair of angles is complementary.

Algebra Find the value of each variable.

20.

$(4n + 5)°$ $(8n - 5)°$

21.

$(9x - 6)°$

$(8.5x + 2)°$

22.

$4z°$

$(3z + 6)°$

H.O.T. 23. **Write About It** How are a theorem and a postulate alike? How are they different?

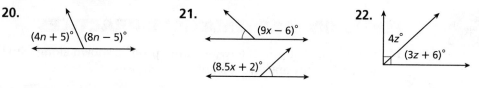

Real-World Connections

24. Sometimes you may be asked to write a proof without a specific statement of the Given and Prove information being provided for you. For each of the following situations, use the triangle to write a Given and Prove statement.

   a. The segment connecting the midpoints of two sides of a triangle is half as long as the third side.

   b. The acute angles of a right triangle are complementary.

   c. In a right triangle, the sum of the squares of the legs is equal to the square of the hypotenuse.

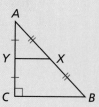

25. Which theorem justifies the conclusion that $\angle 1 \cong \angle 4$?

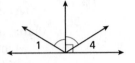

Ⓐ Linear Pair Theorem

Ⓑ Congruent Supplements Theorem

Ⓒ Congruent Complements Theorem

Ⓓ Right Angle Congruence Theorem

26. What can be concluded from the statement $m\angle 1 + m\angle 2 = 180°$?

Ⓕ $\angle 1$ and $\angle 2$ are congruent.

Ⓖ $\angle 1$ and $\angle 2$ are supplementary.

Ⓗ $\angle 1$ and $\angle 2$ are complementary.

Ⓙ $\angle 1$ and $\angle 2$ form a linear pair.

27. Given: Two angles are complementary. The measure of one angle is 10° less than the measure of the other angle. Conclusion: The measures of the angles are 85° and 95°. Which statement is true?

Ⓐ The conclusion is correct because 85° is 10° less than 95°.

Ⓑ The conclusion is verified by the first statement given.

Ⓒ The conclusion is invalid because the angles are not congruent.

Ⓓ The conclusion is contradicted by the first statement given.

CHALLENGE AND EXTEND

28. Write a two-column proof.

Given: $m\angle LAN = 30°$, $m\angle 1 = 15°$

Prove: $\overrightarrow{AM}$ bisects $\angle LAN$.

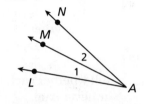

H.O.T. Multi-Step Find the value of the variable and the measure of each angle.

29.

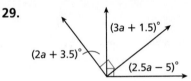

30.

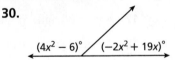

FOCUS ON MATHEMATICAL PRACTICES

H.O.T. 31. Proof The left side of a two-column proof is shown along with the supporting figure. Identify any given. Justify your choices.

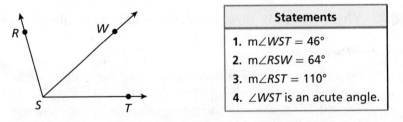

Statements
1. $m\angle WST = 46°$
2. $m\angle RSW = 64°$
3. $m\angle RST = 110°$
4. $\angle WST$ is an acute angle.

H.O.T. 32. Communication Lynne wants to prove that if two angles form a linear pair, then they are supplementary. Can she use the Linear Pair Theorem as a reason to justify the statement? Why or why not?

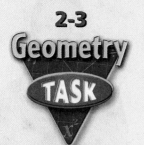

2-3 Geometry TASK

Use with Geometric Proof

Design Plans for Proofs

Sometimes the most challenging part of writing a proof is planning the logical steps that will take you from the Given statement to the Prove statement. Like working a jigsaw puzzle, you can start with any piece. Write down everything you know from the Given statement. If you don't see the connection right away, start with the Prove statement and work backward. Then connect the pieces into a logical order.

MATHEMATICAL PRACTICES Construct viable arguments and critique the reasoning of others.

MCC9-12.G.CO.9 Prove theorems about lines and angles.

Activity

Prove the Common Angles Theorem.
Given: $\angle AXB \cong \angle CXD$
Prove: $\angle AXC \cong \angle BXD$

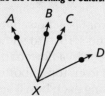

1 Start by considering the difference in the Given and Prove statements. How does $\angle AXB$ compare to $\angle AXC$? How does $\angle CXD$ compare to $\angle BXD$?

In both cases, $\angle BXC$ is combined with the first angle to get the second angle.

2 The situation involves combining adjacent angle measures, so list any definitions, properties, postulates, and theorems that might be helpful.

Definition of congruent angles, Angle Addition Postulate, properties of equality, and Reflexive, Symmetric, and Transitive Properties of Congruence

3 Start with what you are given and what you are trying to prove and then work toward the middle.

$\angle AXB \cong \angle CXD$	*The first reason will be "Given."*
$m\angle AXB = m\angle CXD$	*Def. of $\cong \angle$*
???	???
$m\angle AXC = m\angle BXD$	???
$\angle AXC \cong \angle BXD$	*The last statement will be the Prove statement.*

4 Based on Step 1, $\angle BXC$ is the missing piece in the middle of the logical flow. So write down what you know about $\angle BXC$.

$\angle BXC \cong \angle BXC$	*Reflex. Prop. of $\cong$*
$m\angle BXC = m\angle BXC$	*Reflex. Prop. of $=$*

5 Now you can see that the Angle Addition Postulate needs to be used to complete the proof.

$m\angle AXB + m\angle BXC = m\angle AXC$	*$\angle$ Add. Post.*
$m\angle BXC + m\angle CXD = m\angle BXD$	*$\angle$ Add. Post.*

6 Use the pieces to write a complete two-column proof of the Common Angles Theorem.

Try This

1. Describe how a plan for a proof differs from the actual proof.

2. Write a plan and a two-column proof.
Given: $\overrightarrow{BD}$ bisects $\angle ABC$.
Prove: $2m\angle 1 = m\angle ABC$

3. Write a plan and a two-column proof.
Given: $\angle LXN$ is a right angle.
Prove: $\angle 1$ and $\angle 2$ are complementary.

2-4 Flowchart and Paragraph Proofs

Essential Question: What are some formats you can use to organize geometric proofs?

Objectives
Write flowchart and paragraph proofs.

Prove geometric theorems by using deductive reasoning.

Vocabulary
flowchart proof
paragraph proof

Why learn this?
Flowcharts make it easy to see how the steps of a process are linked together.

A second style of proof is a **flowchart proof**, which uses boxes and arrows to show the structure of the proof. The steps in a flowchart proof move from left to right or from top to bottom, shown by the arrows connecting each box. The justification for each step is written below the box.

Know it! Note

| Theorem 2-4-1 | Common Segments Theorem |

THEOREM	HYPOTHESIS	CONCLUSION
Given collinear points *A*, *B*, *C*, and *D* arranged as shown, if $\overline{AB} \cong \overline{CD}$, then $\overline{AC} \cong \overline{BD}$. A B C D	$\overline{AB} \cong \overline{CD}$	$\overline{AC} \cong \overline{BD}$

COMMON CORE GPS MCC9-12.G.CO.9

EXAMPLE 1 Reading a Flowchart Proof

my.hrw.com

Online Video Tutor

X² Animated Math

Use the given flowchart proof to write a two-column proof of the Common Segments Theorem.

Given: $\overline{AB} \cong \overline{CD}$
Prove: $\overline{AC} \cong \overline{BD}$

A B   C D

Flowchart proof:

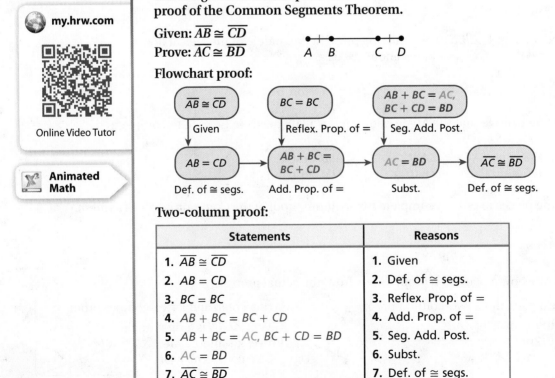

Two-column proof:

Statements	Reasons
1. $\overline{AB} \cong \overline{CD}$	1. Given
2. $AB = CD$	2. Def. of ≅ segs.
3. $BC = BC$	3. Reflex. Prop. of =
4. $AB + BC = BC + CD$	4. Add. Prop. of =
5. $AB + BC = AC$, $BC + CD = BD$	5. Seg. Add. Post.
6. $AC = BD$	6. Subst.
7. $\overline{AC} \cong \overline{BD}$	7. Def. of ≅ segs.

CHECK IT OUT!

1. Use the given flowchart proof to write a two-column proof.

Given: $RS = UV$, $ST = TU$

Prove: $\overline{RT} \cong \overline{TV}$

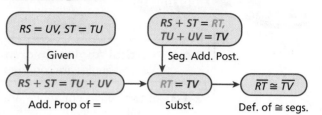

Flowchart proof:

```
┌─────────────────┐                    ┌─────────────────┐
│ RS = UV, ST = TU│                    │ RS + ST = RT,   │
└────────┬────────┘                    │ TU + UV = TV    │
      Given                            └────────┬────────┘
         │                              Seg. Add. Post.
         ▼                                      ▼
┌─────────────────┐      ┌─────────┐      ┌──────────┐
│ RS + ST = TU + UV│────▶│ RT = TV │────▶│ RT ≅ TV   │
└─────────────────┘      └─────────┘      └──────────┘
   Add. Prop of =          Subst.        Def. of ≅ segs.
```

COMMON CORE GPS **EXAMPLE** **2**
MCC9-12.G.CO.9

Writing a Flowchart Proof

my.hrw.com

Online Video Tutor

Use the given two-column proof to write a flowchart proof of the Converse of the Common Segments Theorem.

Given: $\overline{AC} \cong \overline{BD}$

Prove: $\overline{AB} \cong \overline{CD}$

A   B   C   D

Two-column proof:

Statements	Reasons
1. $\overline{AC} \cong \overline{BD}$	1. Given
2. $AC = BD$	2. Def. of $\cong$ segs.
3. $AB + BC = AC$, $BC + CD = BD$	3. Seg. Add. Post.
4. $AB + BC = BC + CD$	4. Subst. *Steps 2, 3*
5. $BC = BC$	5. Reflex. Prop. of $=$
6. $AB = CD$	6. Subtr. Prop. of $=$
7. $\overline{AB} \cong \overline{CD}$	7. Def. of $\cong$ segs.

Helpful Hint

Like the converse of a conditional statement, the converse of a theorem is found by switching the hypothesis and conclusion.

Flowchart proof:

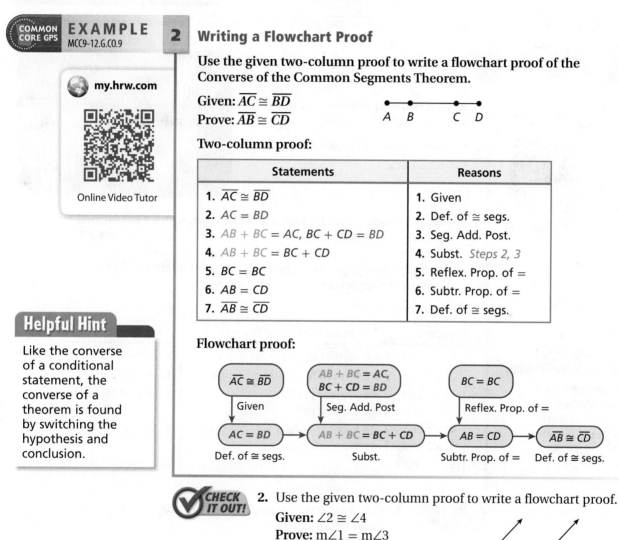

```
┌─────────┐      ┌──────────────┐      ┌─────────┐
│ AC ≅ BD │      │ AB + BC = AC,│      │ BC = BC │
└────┬────┘      │ BC + CD = BD │      └────┬────┘
   Given         └──────┬───────┘      Reflex. Prop. of =
     │           Seg. Add. Post                │
     ▼                  ▼                       ▼
┌─────────┐   ┌───────────────────┐   ┌─────────┐   ┌──────────┐
│ AC = BD │──▶│ AB + BC = BC + CD │──▶│ AB = CD │──▶│ AB ≅ CD  │
└─────────┘   └───────────────────┘   └─────────┘   └──────────┘
Def. of ≅ segs.       Subst.         Subtr. Prop. of =  Def. of ≅ segs.
```

CHECK IT OUT!

2. Use the given two-column proof to write a flowchart proof.

Given: $\angle 2 \cong \angle 4$

Prove: $m\angle 1 = m\angle 3$

Two-column proof:

Statements	Reasons
1. $\angle 2 \cong \angle 4$	1. Given
2. $\angle 1$ and $\angle 2$ are supplementary. $\angle 3$ and $\angle 4$ are supplementary.	2. Lin. Pair Thm.
3. $\angle 1 \cong \angle 3$	3. $\cong$ Supps. Thm.
4. $m\angle 1 = m\angle 3$	4. Def. of $\cong$ $\angle$

A **paragraph proof** is a style of proof that presents the steps of the proof and their matching reasons as sentences in a paragraph. Although this style of proof is less formal than a two-column proof, you still must include every step.

Know it! Note

Theorems

THEOREM	HYPOTHESIS	CONCLUSION
2-4-2 Vertical Angles Theorem Vertical angles are congruent.	$\angle A$ and $\angle B$ are vertical angles.	$\angle A \cong \angle B$
2-4-3 If two congruent angles are supplementary, then each angle is a right angle. ($\cong \angle$s supp. → rt. $\angle$s)	$\angle 1 \cong \angle 2$ $\angle 1$ and $\angle 2$ are supplementary.	$\angle 1$ and $\angle 2$ are right angles.

COMMON CORE GPS
MCC9-12.G.CO.9

EXAMPLE 3

my.hrw.com

Online Video Tutor

Reading a Paragraph Proof

Use the given paragraph proof to write a two-column proof of the Vertical Angles Theorem.

Given: $\angle 1$ and $\angle 3$ are vertical angles.
Prove: $\angle 1 \cong \angle 3$

Paragraph proof: $\angle 1$ and $\angle 3$ are vertical angles, so they are formed by intersecting lines. Therefore $\angle 1$ and $\angle 2$ are a linear pair, and $\angle 2$ and $\angle 3$ are a linear pair. By the Linear Pair Theorem, $\angle 1$ and $\angle 2$ are supplementary, and $\angle 2$ and $\angle 3$ are supplementary. So by the Congruent Supplements Theorem, $\angle 1 \cong \angle 3$.

Two-column proof:

Statements	Reasons
1. $\angle 1$ and $\angle 3$ are vertical angles.	1. Given
2. $\angle 1$ and $\angle 3$ are formed by intersecting lines.	2. Def. of vert. $\angle$s
3. $\angle 1$ and $\angle 2$ are a linear pair. $\angle 2$ and $\angle 3$ are a linear pair.	3. Def. of lin. pair
4. $\angle 1$ and $\angle 2$ are supplementary. $\angle 2$ and $\angle 3$ are supplementary.	4. Lin. Pair Thm.
5. $\angle 1 \cong \angle 3$	5. $\cong$ Supps. Thm.

Remember!

Vertical angles are angles formed by intersecting lines that share a vertex but do not have common sides.

CHECK IT OUT!

3. Use the given paragraph proof to write a two-column proof.

Given: $\angle WXY$ is a right angle. $\angle 1 \cong \angle 3$
Prove: $\angle 1$ and $\angle 2$ are complementary.

Paragraph proof: Since $\angle WXY$ is a right angle, m$\angle WXY = 90°$ by the definition of a right angle. By the Angle Addition Postulate, m$\angle WXY = $ m$\angle 2 + $ m$\angle 3$. By substitution, m$\angle 2 + $ m$\angle 3 = 90°$. Since $\angle 1 \cong \angle 3$, m$\angle 1 = $ m$\angle 3$ by the definition of congruent angles. Using substitution, m$\angle 2 + $ m$\angle 1 = 90°$. Thus by the definition of complementary angles, $\angle 1$ and $\angle 2$ are complementary.

© Alamy Images

Student to Student

Writing a Proof

When I have to write a proof and I don't see how to start, I look at what I'm supposed to be proving and see if it makes sense. If it does, I ask myself why. Sometimes this helps me to see what the reasons in the proof might be. If all else fails, I just start writing down everything I know based on the diagram and the given statement. By brainstorming like this, I can usually figure out the steps of the proof. You can even write each thing on a separate piece of paper and arrange the pieces of paper like a flowchart.

Claire Jeffords
Riverbend High School

COMMON CORE GPS

EXAMPLE 4
MCC9-12.G.CO.9

my.hrw.com

Online Video Tutor

Writing a Paragraph Proof

Use the given two-column proof to write a paragraph proof of Theorem 2-4-3.

Given: ∠1 and ∠2 are supplementary. ∠1 ≅ ∠2
Prove: ∠1 and ∠2 are right angles.

Two-column proof:

Statements	Reasons
1. ∠1 and ∠2 are supplementary. ∠1 ≅ ∠2	1. Given
2. $m\angle 1 + m\angle 2 = 180°$	2. Def. of supp. ∡
3. $m\angle 1 = m\angle 2$	3. Def. of ≅ ∡ *Step 1*
4. $m\angle 1 + m\angle 1 = 180°$	4. Subst. *Steps 2, 3*
5. $2m\angle 1 = 180°$	5. Simplification
6. $m\angle 1 = 90°$	6. Div. Prop. of =
7. $m\angle 2 = 90°$	7. Trans. Prop. of = *Steps 3, 6*
8. ∠1 and ∠2 are right angles.	8. Def. of rt. ∠

Paragraph proof: ∠1 and ∠2 are supplementary, so $m\angle 1 + m\angle 2 = 180°$ by the definition of supplementary angles. They are also congruent, so their measures are equal by the definition of congruent angles. By substitution, $m\angle 1 + m\angle 1 = 180°$, so $m\angle 1 = 90°$ by the Division Property of Equality. Because $m\angle 1 = m\angle 2$, $m\angle 2 = 90°$ by the Transitive Property of Equality. So both are right angles by the definition of a right angle.

CHECK IT OUT!

4. Use the given two-column proof to write a paragraph proof.

Given: ∠1 ≅ ∠4
Prove: ∠2 ≅ ∠3

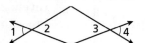

Two-column proof:

Statements	Reasons
1. ∠1 ≅ ∠4	1. Given
2. ∠1 ≅ ∠2, ∠3 ≅ ∠4	2. Vert. ∡ Thm.
3. ∠2 ≅ ∠4	3. Trans. Prop. of ≅ *Steps 1, 2*
4. ∠2 ≅ ∠3	4. Trans. Prop. of ≅ *Steps 2, 3*

THINK AND DISCUSS

1. Explain why there might be more than one correct way to write a proof.

2. Describe the steps you take when writing a proof.

3. GET ORGANIZED
Copy and complete the graphic organizer. In each box, describe the proof style in your own words.

Proof Styles
- Two-column
- Flowchart
- Paragraph

Know it! Note

2-4 Exercises

my.hrw.com
Homework Help

GUIDED PRACTICE

Vocabulary Apply the vocabulary from this lesson to answer each question.

1. In a ___?___ proof, the logical order is represented by arrows that connect each step. (*flowchart* or *paragraph*)

2. The steps and reasons of a ___?___ proof are written out in sentences. (*flowchart* or *paragraph*)

SEE EXAMPLE 1

3. Use the given flowchart proof to write a two-column proof.

Given: ∠1 ≅ ∠2
Prove: ∠1 and ∠2 are right angles.

Flowchart proof:

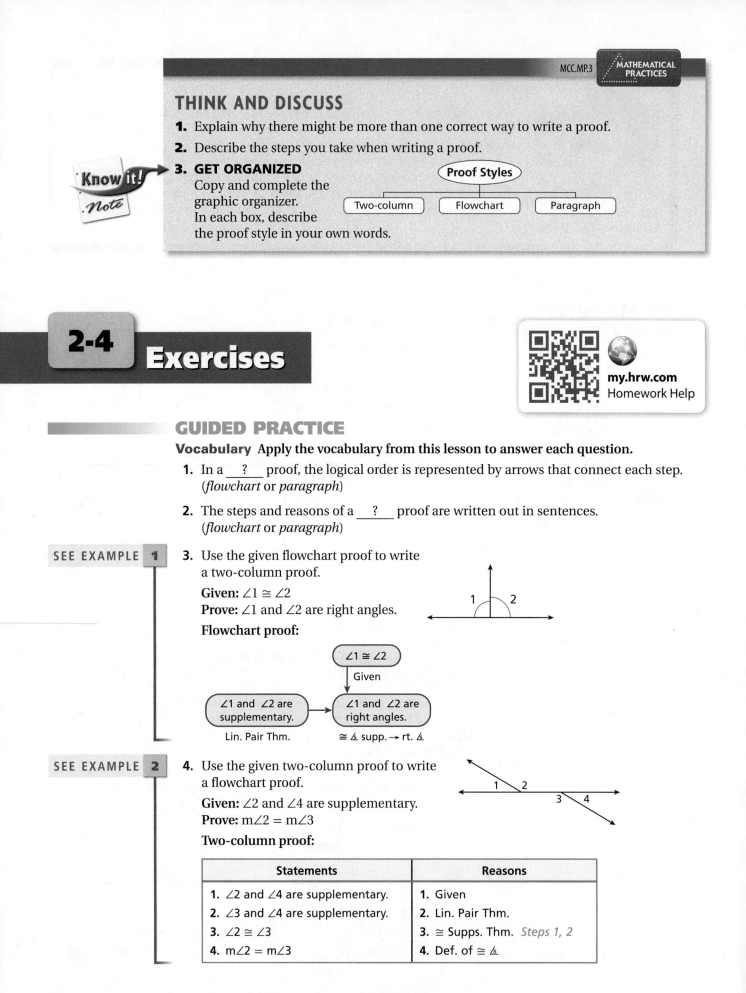

∠1 ≅ ∠2
Given

∠1 and ∠2 are supplementary. → ∠1 and ∠2 are right angles.

Lin. Pair Thm.   ≅ ∡ supp. → rt. ∡

SEE EXAMPLE 2

4. Use the given two-column proof to write a flowchart proof.

Given: ∠2 and ∠4 are supplementary.
Prove: m∠2 = m∠3

Two-column proof:

Statements	Reasons
1. ∠2 and ∠4 are supplementary.	1. Given
2. ∠3 and ∠4 are supplementary.	2. Lin. Pair Thm.
3. ∠2 ≅ ∠3	3. ≅ Supps. Thm. *Steps 1, 2*
4. m∠2 = m∠3	4. Def. of ≅ ∡

SEE EXAMPLE **3**

5. Use the given paragraph proof to write a two-column proof.

Given: ∠2 ≅ ∠4
Prove: ∠1 ≅ ∠3

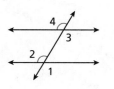

Paragraph proof:

By the Vertical Angles Theorem, ∠1 ≅ ∠2, and ∠3 ≅ ∠4. It is given that ∠2 ≅ ∠4. By the Transitive Property of Congruence, ∠1 ≅ ∠4, and thus ∠1 ≅ ∠3.

SEE EXAMPLE **4**

6. Use the given two-column proof to write a paragraph proof.

Given: $\overrightarrow{BD}$ bisects ∠ABC.
Prove: $\overrightarrow{BG}$ bisects ∠FBH.

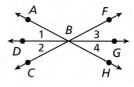

Two-column proof:

Statements	Reasons
1. $\overrightarrow{BD}$ bisects ∠ABC.	1. Given
2. ∠1 ≅ ∠2	2. Def. of ∠ bisector
3. ∠1 ≅ ∠4, ∠2 ≅ ∠3	3. Vert. ∡ Thm.
4. ∠4 ≅ ∠2	4. Trans. Prop. of ≅ *Steps 2, 3*
5. ∠4 ≅ ∠3	5. Trans. Prop. of ≅ *Steps 3, 4*
6. $\overrightarrow{BG}$ bisects ∠FBH.	6. Def. of ∠ bisector

PRACTICE AND PROBLEM SOLVING

Independent Practice

For Exercises	See Example
7	1
8	2
9	3
10	4

my.hrw.com

Online Extra Practice

7. Use the given flowchart proof to write a two-column proof.

Given: *B* is the midpoint of $\overline{AC}$.
       AD = EC
Prove: DB = BE

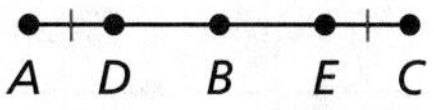

Flowchart proof:

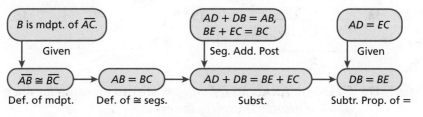

8. Use the given two-column proof to write a flowchart proof.

Given: ∠3 is a right angle.
Prove: ∠4 is a right angle.

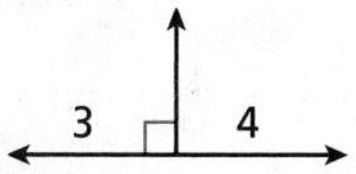

Two-column proof:

Statements	Reasons
1. ∠3 is a right angle.	1. Given
2. m∠3 = 90°	2. Def. of rt. ∠
3. ∠3 and ∠4 are supplementary.	3. Lin. Pair Thm.
4. m∠3 + m∠4 = 180°	4. Def. of supp. ∡
5. 90° + m∠4 = 180°	5. Subst. *Steps 2, 4*
6. m∠4 = 90°	6. Subtr. Prop. of =
7. ∠4 is a right angle.	7. Def. of rt. ∠

9. Use the given paragraph proof to write a two-column proof.

Given: $\angle 1 \cong \angle 4$

Prove: $\angle 2$ and $\angle 3$ are supplementary.

Paragraph proof:

$\angle 4$ and $\angle 3$ form a linear pair, so they are supplementary by the Linear Pair Theorem. Therefore, $m\angle 4 + m\angle 3 = 180°$. Also, $\angle 1$ and $\angle 2$ are vertical angles, so $\angle 1 \cong \angle 2$ by the Vertical Angles Theorem. It is given that $\angle 1 \cong \angle 4$. So by the Transitive Property of Congruence, $\angle 4 \cong \angle 2$, and by the definition of congruent angles, $m\angle 4 = m\angle 2$. By substitution, $m\angle 2 + m\angle 3 = 180°$, so $\angle 2$ and $\angle 3$ are supplementary by the definition of supplementary angles.

10. Use the given two-column proof to write a paragraph proof.

Given: $\angle 1$ and $\angle 2$ are complementary.

Prove: $\angle 2$ and $\angle 3$ are complementary.

Two-column proof:

Statements	Reasons
1. $\angle 1$ and $\angle 2$ are complementary.	1. Given
2. $m\angle 1 + m\angle 2 = 90°$	2. Def. of comp. ∡
3. $\angle 1 \cong \angle 3$	3. Vert. ∡ Thm.
4. $m\angle 1 = m\angle 3$	4. Def. of ≅ ∡
5. $m\angle 3 + m\angle 2 = 90°$	5. Subst. *Steps 2, 4*
6. $\angle 2$ and $\angle 3$ are complementary.	6. Def. of comp. ∡

H.O.T. Find each measure and name the theorem that justifies your answer.

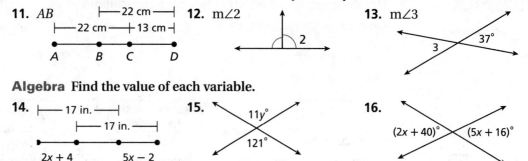

11. AB |—22 cm—| |—22 cm—|—13 cm—| A B C D

12. $m\angle 2$

13. $m\angle 3$ 37°

Algebra Find the value of each variable.

14. |— 17 in. —| |— 17 in. —| $2x + 4$ $5x - 2$

15. $11y°$ 121°

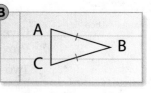

16. $(2x + 40)°$ $(5x + 16)°$

H.O.T. 17. /// ERROR ANALYSIS /// Below are two drawings for the given proof. Which is incorrect? Explain the error.

Given: $\overline{AB} \cong \overline{BC}$

Prove: $\angle A \cong \angle C$

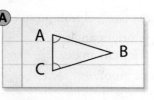

Ⓐ A B C

Ⓑ A B C

Real-World Connections

18. Rearrange the pieces to create a flowchart proof.

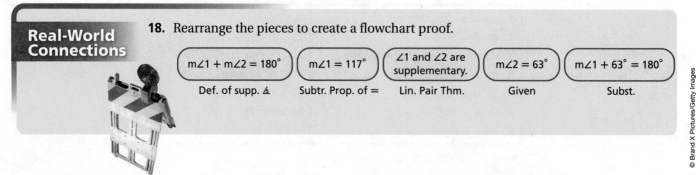

$m\angle 1 + m\angle 2 = 180°$ Def. of supp. ∡

$m\angle 1 = 117°$ Subtr. Prop. of =

$\angle 1$ and $\angle 2$ are supplementary. Lin. Pair Thm.

$m\angle 2 = 63°$ Given

$m\angle 1 + 63° = 180°$ Subst.

19. Critical Thinking Two lines intersect, and one of the angles formed is a right angle. Explain why all four angles are congruent.

20. Write About It Which style of proof do you find easiest to write? to read?

TEST PREP

21. Which pair of angles in the diagram must be congruent?

Ⓐ ∠1 and ∠5   Ⓒ ∠5 and ∠8

Ⓑ ∠3 and ∠4   Ⓓ None of the above

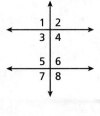

22. What is the measure of ∠2?

Ⓕ 38°   Ⓗ 128°

Ⓖ 52°   Ⓙ 142°

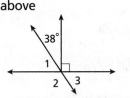

23. Which statement is NOT true if ∠2 and ∠6 are supplementary?

Ⓐ m∠2 + m∠6 = 180°

Ⓑ ∠2 and ∠3 are supplementary.

Ⓒ ∠1 and ∠6 are supplementary.

Ⓓ m∠1 + m∠4 = 180°

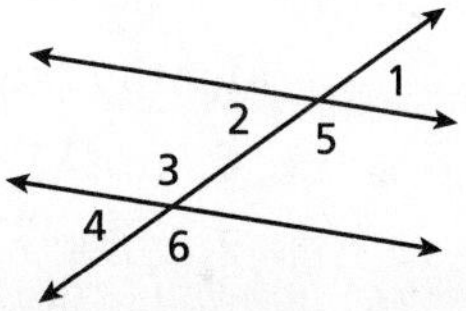

CHALLENGE AND EXTEND

24. Textiles Use the woven pattern to write a flowchart proof.

Given: ∠1 ≅ ∠3
Prove: m∠4 + m∠5 = m∠6

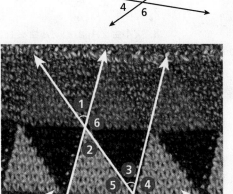

25. Write a two-column proof.

Given: ∠AOC ≅ ∠BOD
Prove: ∠AOB ≅ ∠COD

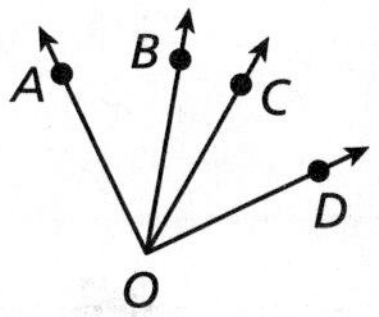

26. Write a paragraph proof.

Given: ∠2 and ∠5 are right angles.
     m∠1 + m∠2 + m∠3 = m∠4 + m∠5 + m∠6
Prove: ∠1 ≅ ∠4

H.O.T. 27. Multi-Step Find the value of each variable and the measures of all four angles.

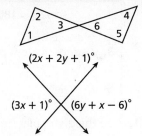

$(2x + 2y + 1)°$

$(3x + 1)°$ $(6y + x - 6)°$

FOCUS ON MATHEMATICAL PRACTICES

H.O.T. 28. Reasoning One of the statements within a proof with the diagram shown at the right is ∠PRS ≅ ∠SRT, and the Transitive Property of Congruence is given as the reason. What other statement or statements may also be in the proof? Why?

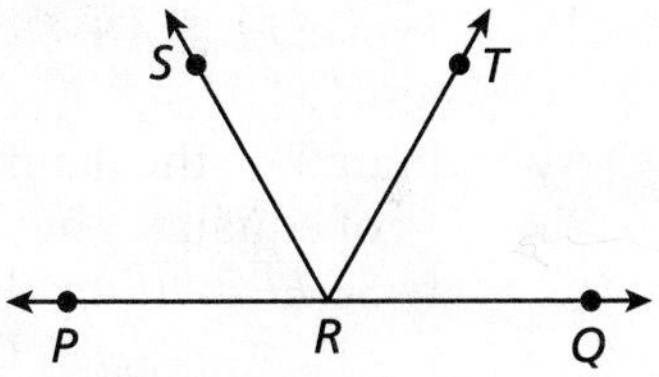

H.O.T. 29. Communication Compare a flowchart proof to a two-column proof. In what ways are they similar? In what ways are they different?

Ready to Go On?

my.hrw.com
Assessment and Intervention

 2-1   Biconditional Statements and Definitions

1. For the conditional "If two angles are supplementary, the sum of their measures is 180°," write the converse and a biconditional statement.

2. Determine if the biconditional "$\sqrt{x} = 4$ if and only if $x = 16$" is true. If false, give a counterexample.

 2-2   Algebraic Proof

Solve each equation. Write a justification for each step.

3. $m - 8 = 13$ 4. $4y - 1 = 27$ 5. $-\dfrac{x}{3} = 2$

Identify the property that justifies each statement.

6. $m\angle XYZ = m\angle PQR$, so $m\angle PQR = m\angle XYZ$.

7. $\overline{AB} \cong \overline{AB}$

8. $\angle 4 \cong \angle A$, and $\angle A \cong \angle 1$. So $\angle 4 \cong \angle 1$.

9. $k = 7$, and $m = 7$. So $k = m$.

 2-3   Geometric Proof

10. Fill in the blanks to complete the two-column proof.

    Given: $m\angle 1 + m\angle 3 = 180°$
    Prove: $\angle 1 \cong \angle 4$

    Proof:

Statements	Reasons
1. $m\angle 1 + m\angle 3 = 180°$	**1. a.** ___?___
2. b. ___?___	**2.** Def. of supp. △
3. $\angle 3$ and $\angle 4$ are supplementary.	**3.** Lin. Pair Thm.
4. $\angle 3 \cong \angle 3$	**4. c.** ___?___
5. d. ___?___	**5.** ≅ Supps. Thm.

11. Use the given plan to write a two-column proof of the Symmetric Property of Congruence.

    Given: $\overline{AB} \cong \overline{EF}$
    Prove: $\overline{EF} \cong \overline{AB}$

    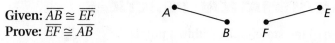

    Plan: Use the definition of congruent segments to write $\overline{AB} \cong \overline{EF}$ as a statement of equality. Then use the Symmetric Property of Equality to show that $EF = AB$. So $\overline{EF} \cong \overline{AB}$ by the definition of congruent segments.

2-4 **Flowchart and Paragraph Proofs**

Use the given two-column proof to write the following.

Given: $\angle 1 \cong \angle 3$
Prove: $\angle 2 \cong \angle 4$

Proof:

Statements	Reasons
1. $\angle 1 \cong \angle 3$	**1.** Given
2. $\angle 1 \cong \angle 2$, $\angle 3 \cong \angle 4$	**2.** Vert. $\angle$ Thm.
3. $\angle 2 \cong \angle 3$	**3.** Trans. Prop. of $\cong$
4. $\angle 2 \cong \angle 4$	**4.** Trans. Prop. of $\cong$

12. a flowchart proof

13. a paragraph proof

PARCC Assessment Readiness

COMMON CORE GPS

Selected Response

1. Write the conditional statement and converse within the biconditional.

A rectangle is a square if and only if all four sides of the rectangle have equal lengths.

Ⓐ Conditional: If all four sides of the rectangle have equal lengths, then it is a square.
Converse: If a rectangle is a square, then its four sides have equal lengths.

Ⓑ Conditional: If a rectangle is a square, then it is also a rhombus.
Converse: If a rectangle is a rhombus, then it is also a square.

Ⓒ Conditional: If all four sides have equal lengths, then all four angles are 90°.
Converse: If all four angles are 90°, then all four sides have equal lengths.

Ⓓ Conditional: If a rectangle is not a square, then its sides are of different lengths.
Converse: If the sides are of different lengths, then the rectangle is not a square.

2. Give the missing justifications in the solution of $4x - 6 = 34$ shown below.

$4x - 6 = 34$		Given equation
$\underline{+6 \quad +6}$		[1]
$4x = 40$		Simplify.
$\dfrac{4x}{4} = \dfrac{40}{4}$		[2]
$x = 10$		Simplify.

Ⓕ [1] Substitution Property of Equality;
[2] Division Property of Equality

Ⓖ [1] Addition Property of Equality;
[2] Division Property of Equality

Ⓗ [1] Division Property of Equality;
[2] Subtraction Property of Equality

Ⓙ [1] Addition Property of Equality;
[2] Reflexive Property of Equality

Mini-Task

3. Two angles with measures $(5x + 35)°$ and $(7x + 85)°$ are supplementary. Find the value of x and the measure of each angle.

3 Proving Theorems about Lines and Angles

Contents

MATHEMATICAL PRACTICES The Common Core Georgia Performance Standards for Mathematical Practice describe varieties of expertise that all students should seek to develop. Opportunities to develop these practices are integrated throughout this program.

1 Make sense of problems and persevere in solving them.

2 Reason abstractly and quantitatively.

3 Construct viable arguments and critique the reasoning of others.

4 Model with mathematics.

5 Use appropriate tools strategically.

6 Attend to precision.

7 Look for and make use of structure.

8 Look for and express regularity in repeated reasoning.

Unpacking the Standards

my.hrw.com
Multilingual Glossary

Understanding the standards and the vocabulary terms in the standards will help you know exactly what you are expected to learn in this chapter.

 MCC9-12.G.CO.9

Prove theorems about lines and angles.

Key Vocabulary

proof (demostración)
An argument that uses logic to show that a conclusion is true.

theorem (teorema)
A statement that has been proven.

line (línea)
An undefined term in geometry, a line is a straight path that has no thickness and extends forever.

angle (ángulo)
A figure formed by two rays with a common endpoint.

What It Means For You

A line crossing a pair of parallel lines forms pairs of angles that are either congruent or supplementary. You can use simple proofs to show these relationships.

EXAMPLE

In the diagram, line p is parallel to line q.

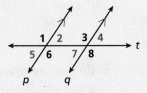

You can show that:

(1) Any pair of black numbered angles is a pair of congruent angles.

(2) Any pair of blue numbered angles is a pair of congruent angles.

(3) Any pair of one black and one blue numbered angle is a pair of supplementary angles.

3-1

Technology TASK

Explore Parallel Lines and Transversals

Geometry software can help you explore angles that are formed when a transversal intersects a pair of parallel lines.

Use with Angles Formed by Parallel Lines and Transversals

Use appropriate tools strategically.

MCC9-12.G.CO.9 Prove theorems about lines and angles.

Activity

1. Construct a line and label two points on the line *A* and *B*.

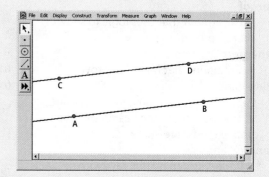

2. Create point *C* not on $\overleftrightarrow{AB}$. Construct a line parallel to $\overleftrightarrow{AB}$ through point *C*. Create another point on this line and label it *D*.

3. Create two points outside the two parallel lines and label them *E* and *F*. Construct transversal $\overleftrightarrow{EF}$. Label the points of intersection *G* and *H*.

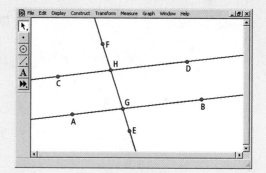

4. Measure the angles formed by the parallel lines and the transversal. Write the angle measures in a chart like the one below. Drag point *E* or *F* and chart with the new angle measures. What relationships do you notice about the angle measures? What conjectures can you make?

Angle	∠AGE	∠BGE	∠AGH	∠BGH	∠CHG	∠DHG	∠CHF	∠DHF
Measure								
Measure								

Try This

1. Identify the pairs of corresponding angles in the diagram. What conjecture can you make about their angle measures? Drag a point in the figure to confirm your conjecture.

2. Repeat steps in the previous problem for alternate interior angles, alternate exterior angles, and same-side interior angles.

3. Try dragging point *C* to change the distance between the parallel lines. What happens to the angle measures in the figure? Why do you think this happens?

Angles Formed by Parallel Lines and Transversals

? Essential Question: How can you prove and use theorems about angles formed by transversals that intersect parallel lines?

Objective
Prove and use theorems about the angles formed by parallel lines and a transversal.

Who uses this?
Piano makers use parallel strings for the higher notes. The longer strings used to produce the lower notes can be viewed as transversals. (See Example 3.)

When parallel lines are cut by a transversal, the angle pairs formed are either congruent or supplementary.

Know it!
·note

Postulate 3-1-1 **Corresponding Angles Postulate**

POSTULATE	HYPOTHESIS	CONCLUSION
If two parallel lines are cut by a transversal, then the pairs of corresponding angles are congruent.		$\angle 1 \cong \angle 3$ $\angle 2 \cong \angle 4$ $\angle 5 \cong \angle 7$ $\angle 6 \cong \angle 8$

x^2 **Animated Math**

COMMON CORE GPS **EXAMPLE** MCC9-12.G.CO.9 **1**

Using the Corresponding Angles Postulate

Find each angle measure.

my.hrw.com

Online Video Tutor

A $m\angle ABC$
$$x = 80 \qquad \text{Corr. } \angle \text{ Post.}$$
$$m\angle ABC = 80°$$

B $m\angle DEF$
$$(2x - 45)° = (x + 30)° \qquad \text{Corr. } \angle \text{ Post.}$$
$$x - 45 = 30 \qquad \text{Subtract } x \text{ from both sides.}$$
$$x = 75 \qquad \text{Add 45 to both sides.}$$
$$m\angle DEF = x + 30$$
$$= 75 + 30 \qquad \text{Substitute 75 for } x.$$
$$= 105°$$

CHECK IT OUT! **1.** Find $m\angle QRS$.

Remember that postulates are statements that are accepted without proof. Since the Corresponding Angles Postulate is given as a postulate, it can be used to prove the next three theorems.

Alamy Photos

Theorems | Parallel Lines and Angle Pairs

THEOREM	HYPOTHESIS	CONCLUSION
3-1-2 Alternate Interior Angles Theorem If two parallel lines are cut by a transversal, then the pairs of alternate interior angles are congruent.	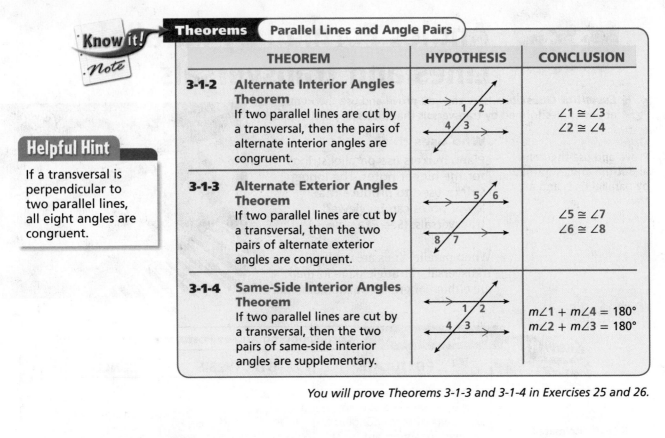	∠1 ≅ ∠3 ∠2 ≅ ∠4
3-1-3 Alternate Exterior Angles Theorem If two parallel lines are cut by a transversal, then the two pairs of alternate exterior angles are congruent.		∠5 ≅ ∠7 ∠6 ≅ ∠8
3-1-4 Same-Side Interior Angles Theorem If two parallel lines are cut by a transversal, then the two pairs of same-side interior angles are supplementary.		m∠1 + m∠4 = 180° m∠2 + m∠3 = 180°

You will prove Theorems 3-1-3 and 3-1-4 in Exercises 25 and 26.

PROOF ■ **Alternate Interior Angles Theorem**

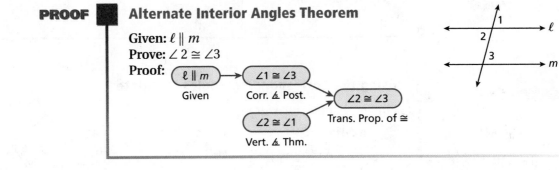

Given: $\ell \parallel m$
Prove: $\angle 2 \cong \angle 3$
Proof:

$\boxed{\ell \parallel m}$ → $\boxed{\angle 1 \cong \angle 3}$ → $\boxed{\angle 2 \cong \angle 3}$
Given   Corr. ∠ Post.   Trans. Prop. of ≅

$\boxed{\angle 2 \cong \angle 1}$
Vert. ∠ Thm.

COMMON CORE GPS MCC9-12.G.CO.9 **EXAMPLE** **2** **Finding Angle Measures**

my.hrw.com

Online Video Tutor

Find each angle measure.

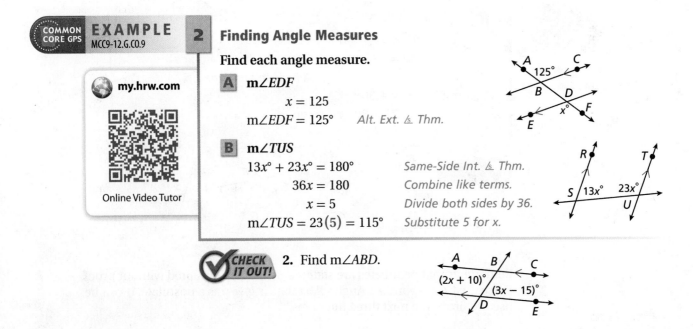

A **m∠EDF**
$x = 125$
$m\angle EDF = 125°$ *Alt. Ext. ∠ Thm.*

B **m∠TUS**
$13x° + 23x° = 180°$ *Same-Side Int. ∠ Thm.*
$36x = 180$ *Combine like terms.*
$x = 5$ *Divide both sides by 36.*
$m\angle TUS = 23(5) = 115°$ *Substitute 5 for x.*

CHECK IT OUT! **2.** Find m∠ABD.

Student to Student

Parallel Lines and Transversals

Nancy Martin
East Branch
High School

When I solve problems with parallel lines and transversals, I remind myself that every pair of angles is either congruent or supplementary.

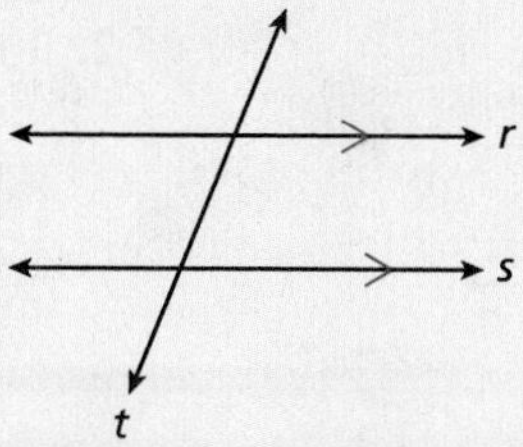

If r ∥ s, all the acute angles are congruent and all the obtuse angles are congruent. The acute angles are supplementary to the obtuse angles.

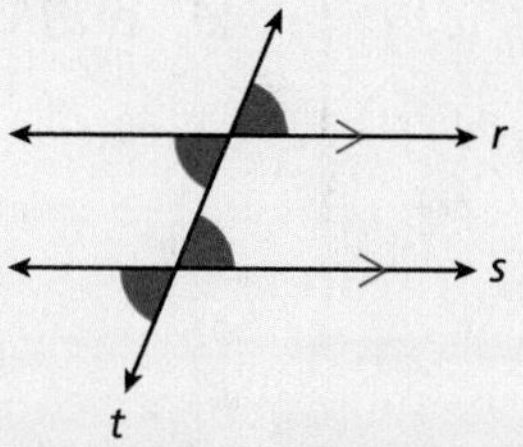

COMMON
CORE GPS
EXAMPLE 3
MCC9-12.G.CO.9

my.hrw.com

Online Video Tutor

Music Application

The treble strings of a grand piano are parallel. Viewed from above, the bass strings form transversals to the treble strings. Find x and y in the diagram.

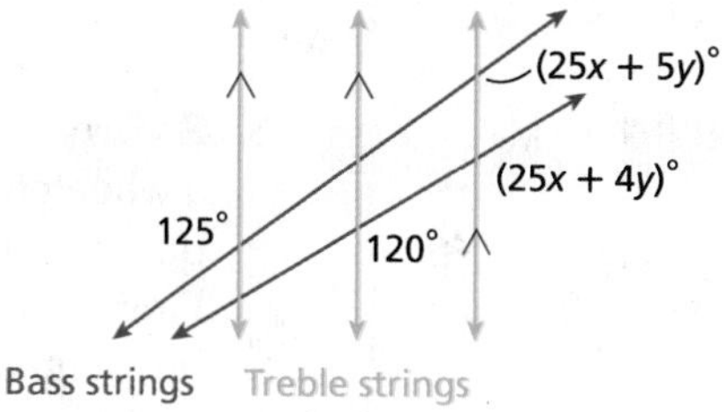

Bass strings   Treble strings

By the Alternate Exterior Angles Theorem, $(25x + 5y)° = 125°$.

By the Corresponding Angles Postulate, $(25x + 4y)° = 120°$.

$$25x + 5y = 125$$
$$-\left(25x + 4y = 120\right)$$
Subtract the second equation from the first equation.
$$y = 5$$

$$25x + 5(5) = 125$$
Substitute 5 for y in 25x + 5y = 125. Simplify and solve for x.
$$x = 4, \, y = 5$$

CHECK IT OUT! **3.** Find the measures of the acute angles in the diagram.

MCC.MP.1   **MATHEMATICAL PRACTICES**

THINK AND DISCUSS

1. Explain why a transversal that is perpendicular to two parallel lines forms eight congruent angles.

2. GET ORGANIZED Copy the diagram and graphic organizer. Complete the graphic organizer by explaining why each of the three theorems is true.

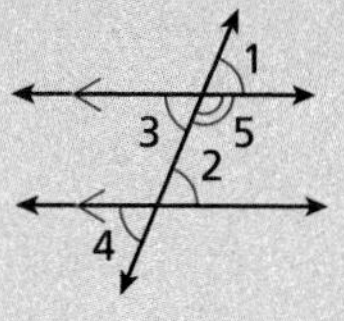

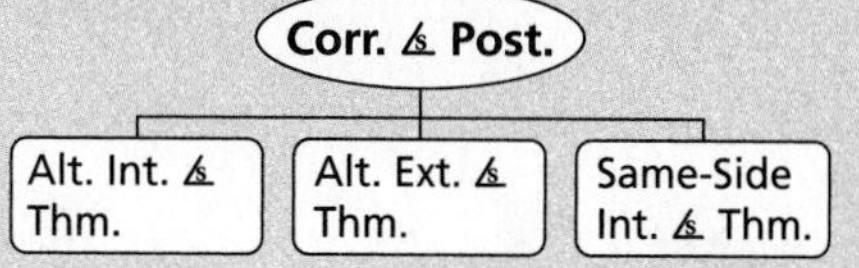

Corr. ∡ Post.

| Alt. Int. ∡ Thm. | Alt. Ext. ∡ Thm. | Same-Side Int. ∡ Thm. |

GUIDED PRACTICE

SEE EXAMPLE 1   Find each angle measure.

1. m∠JKL

127°

$x°$

J   K   L

2. m∠BEF

$(7x - 14)°$ G   B   A

C

$(4x + 19)°$ E

F   H   D

SEE EXAMPLE 2

3. m∠1

1

4. m∠CBY

X   A   D

E   Y   B

$6x°$ $(3x + 9)°$ C

Z

SEE EXAMPLE 3

5. **Safety** The railing of a wheelchair ramp is parallel to the ramp. Find x and y in the diagram.

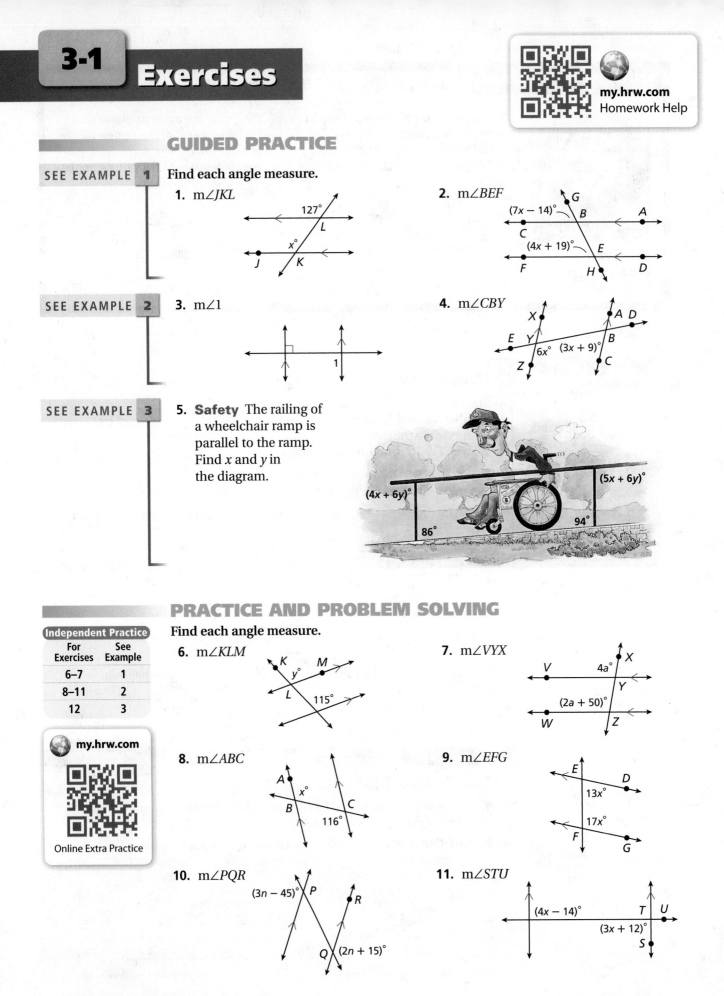

$(4x + 6y)°$ $(5x + 6y)°$

86°   94°

PRACTICE AND PROBLEM SOLVING

Find each angle measure.

Independent Practice	
For Exercises	See Example
6–7	1
8–11	2
12	3

my.hrw.com

Online Extra Practice

6. m∠KLM

K   M

$y°$

L   115°

7. m∠VYX

V $4a°$ X

Y

$(2a + 50)°$

W   Z

8. m∠ABC

A

$x°$

B   C

116°

9. m∠EFG

E   D

$13x°$

$17x°$

F   G

10. m∠PQR

$(3n - 45)°$ P   R

Q $(2n + 15)°$

11. m∠STU

$(4x - 14)°$ T   U

$(3x + 12)°$

S

12. Parking In the parking lot shown, the lines that mark the width of each space are parallel.

$m\angle 1 = (2x - 3y)°$

$m\angle 2 = (x + 3y)°$

Find x and y.

Find each angle measure. Justify each answer with a postulate or theorem.

13. $m\angle 1$ **14.** $m\angle 2$ **15.** $m\angle 3$

16. $m\angle 4$ **17.** $m\angle 5$ **18.** $m\angle 6$

19. $m\angle 7$

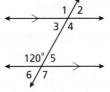

Algebra State the theorem or postulate that is related to the measures of the angles in each pair. Then find the angle measures.

20. $m\angle 1 = (7x + 15)°$, $m\angle 2 = (10x - 9)°$

21. $m\angle 3 = (23x + 11)°$, $m\angle 4 = (14x + 21)°$

22. $m\angle 4 = (37x - 15)°$, $m\angle 5 = (44x - 29)°$

23. $m\angle 1 = (6x + 24)°$, $m\angle 4 = (17x - 9)°$

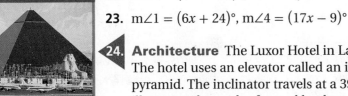

24. Architecture The Luxor Hotel in Las Vegas, Nevada, is a 30-story pyramid. The hotel uses an elevator called an inclinator to take people up the side of the pyramid. The inclinator travels at a 39° angle. Which theorem or postulate best illustrates the angles formed by the path of the inclinator and each parallel floor? (*Hint:* Draw a picture.)

25. Complete the two-column proof of the Alternate Exterior Angles Theorem.

Given: $\ell \parallel m$

Prove: $\angle 1 \cong \angle 2$

Proof:

Statements	Reasons
1. $\ell \parallel m$	**1.** Given
2. a. _____?_____	**2.** Vert. ∡ Thm.
3. $\angle 3 \cong \angle 2$	**3. b.** _____?_____
4. c. _____?_____	**4. d.** _____?_____

H.O.T. 26. Write a paragraph proof of the Same-Side Interior Angles Theorem.

Given: $r \parallel s$

Prove: $m\angle 1 + m\angle 2 = 180°$

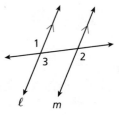

H.O.T. Draw the given situation or tell why it is impossible.

27. Two parallel lines are intersected by a transversal so that the corresponding angles are supplementary.

28. Two parallel lines are intersected by a transversal so that the same-side interior angles are complementary.

B.S.P.I./Corbis Images

29. In the diagram, which represents the side view of a mystery spot, m∠SRT = 25°. $\overleftrightarrow{RT}$ is a transversal to $\overleftrightarrow{PS}$ and $\overleftrightarrow{QR}$.

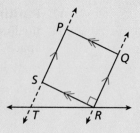

   a. What type of angle pair is ∠QRT and ∠STR?

   b. Find m∠STR. Use a theorem or postulate to justify your answer.

H.O.T. **30.** **Land Development** A piece of property lies between two parallel streets as shown. m∠1 = $(2x + 6)°$, and m∠2 = $(3x + 9)°$. What is the relationship between the angles? What are their measures?

H.O.T. **31.** ///**ERROR ANALYSIS**/// In the figure, m∠ABC = $(15x + 5)°$, and m∠BCD = $(10x + 25)°$. Which value of $m∠BCD$ is incorrect? Explain.

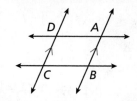

A

15x + 5 =	10x + 25
− 10x	− 10x
5x + 5 =	25
− 5	− 5
5x =	20
x = 4	

m∠BCD = 10(4) + 25 = 65°

B

(15x + 5) + (10x + 25) =	180
25x + 30 =	180
− 30 − 30	
25x =	150
x = 6	

m∠BCD = 10(6) + 25 = 85°

32. **Critical Thinking** In the diagram, ℓ ∥ m. Explain why $\frac{x}{y} = 1$.

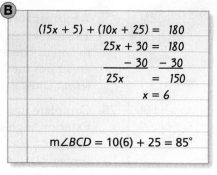

H.O.T. **33.** **Write About It** Suppose that lines ℓ and m are intersected by transversal p. One of the angles formed by ℓ and p is congruent to every angle formed by m and p. Draw a diagram showing lines ℓ, m, and p, mark any congruent angles that are formed, and explain what you know is true.

TEST PREP

34. m∠RST = $(x + 50)°$, and m∠STU = $(3x + 20)°$. Find m∠RVT.

   Ⓐ 15°   Ⓒ 65°

   Ⓑ 27.5°   Ⓓ 77.5°

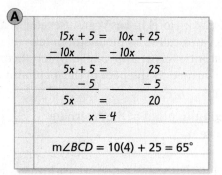

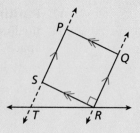

35. For two parallel lines and a transversal, m∠1 = 83°. For which pair of angle measures is the sum the least?

　　(F) ∠1 and a corresponding angle

　　(G) ∠1 and a same-side interior angle

　　(H) ∠1 and its supplement

　　(J) ∠1 and its complement

36. Short Response Given a ∥ b with transversal t, explain why ∠1 and ∠3 are supplementary.

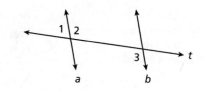

CHALLENGE AND EXTEND

Multi-Step Find m∠1 in each diagram. (*Hint:* Draw a line parallel to the given parallel lines.)

37.

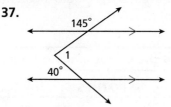

38.

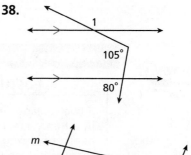

39. Find x and y in the diagram. Justify your answer.

H.O.T. 40. Two lines are parallel. The measures of two corresponding angles are $a°$ and $2b°$, and the measures of two same-side interior angles are $a°$ and $b°$. Find the value of a.

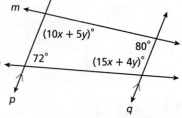

FOCUS ON MATHEMATICAL PRACTICES

H.O.T. 41. Error Analysis Sarah found that m∠D = 70° and m∠B = 70°. Explain her error.

H.O.T. 42. Reasonableness Write a convincing argument that ∠1 is congruent to ∠15 in the figure.

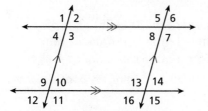

H.O.T. 43. Problem Solving 18th Street and 20th Street both cross the canal as shown in the figure. Find x and y. Show your work.

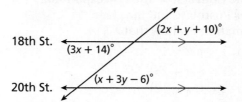

3-1 Angles Formed by Parallel Lines and Transversals **85**

3-2 Proving Lines Parallel

Essential Question: How can you prove lines are parallel?

Objective
Use the angles formed by a transversal to prove two lines are parallel.

Who uses this?
Rowers have to keep the oars on each side parallel in order to travel in a straight line. (See Example 4.)

Recall that the converse of a theorem is found by exchanging the hypothesis and conclusion. The converse of a theorem is not automatically true. If it is true, it must be stated as a postulate or proved as a separate theorem.

Know it! Note

Postulate 3-2-1	Converse of the Corresponding Angles Postulate	
POSTULATE	**HYPOTHESIS**	**CONCLUSION**
If two coplanar lines are cut by a transversal so that a pair of corresponding angles are congruent, then the two lines are parallel.	$\angle 1 \cong \angle 2$	$m \parallel n$

COMMON CORE GPS **EXAMPLE 1** MCC9-12.G.CO.9

Using the Converse of the Corresponding Angles Postulate

Use the Converse of the Corresponding Angles Postulate and the given information to show that $\ell \parallel m$.

my.hrw.com
Online Video Tutor

A $\angle 1 \cong \angle 5$

$\angle 1 \cong \angle 5$ *$\angle 1$ and $\angle 5$ are corresponding angles.*
$\ell \parallel m$ *Conv. of Corr. $\angle$s Post.*

B $m\angle 4 = (2x + 10)°, m\angle 8 = (3x - 55)°, x = 65$

$m\angle 4 = 2(65) + 10 = 140$ *Substitute 65 for x.*
$m\angle 8 = 3(65) - 55 = 140$ *Substitute 65 for x.*
$m\angle 4 = m\angle 8$ *Trans. Prop. of Equality*
$\angle 4 \cong \angle 8$ *Def. of $\cong$ $\angle$*
$\ell \parallel m$ *Conv. of Corr. $\angle$ Post.*

CHECK IT OUT! Use the Converse of the Corresponding Angles Postulate and the given information to show that $\ell \parallel m$.

1a. $m\angle 1 = m\angle 3$

1b. $m\angle 7 = (4x + 25)°,$
$m\angle 5 = (5x + 12)°, x = 13$

Ken Hawkins/Mira.com

Postulate 3-2-2 **Parallel Postulate**

Through a point P not on line ℓ, there is exactly one line parallel to ℓ.

The Converse of the Corresponding Angles Postulate is used to construct parallel lines. The Parallel Postulate guarantees that for any line ℓ, you can always construct a parallel line through a point that is not on ℓ.

Construction Parallel Lines

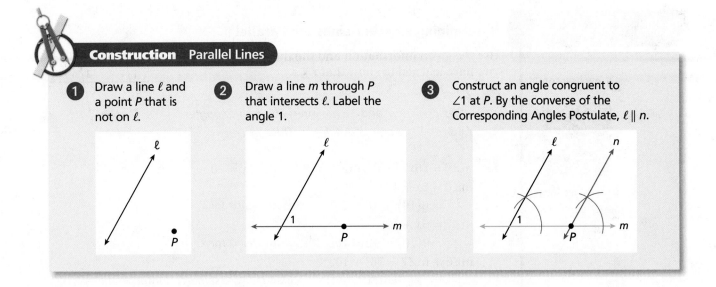

① Draw a line ℓ and a point P that is not on ℓ.

② Draw a line m through P that intersects ℓ. Label the angle 1.

③ Construct an angle congruent to ∠1 at P. By the converse of the Corresponding Angles Postulate, $\ell \parallel n$.

Theorems **Proving Lines Parallel**

	THEOREM	HYPOTHESIS	CONCLUSION
3-2-3	**Converse of the Alternate Interior Angles Theorem** If two coplanar lines are cut by a transversal so that a pair of alternate interior angles are congruent, then the two lines are parallel.	∠1 ≅ ∠2	$m \parallel n$
3-2-4	**Converse of the Alternate Exterior Angles Theorem** If two coplanar lines are cut by a transversal so that a pair of alternate exterior angles are congruent, then the two lines are parallel.	∠3 ≅ ∠4	$m \parallel n$
3-2-5	**Converse of the Same-Side Interior Angles Theorem** If two coplanar lines are cut by a transversal so that a pair of same-side interior angles are supplementary, then the two lines are parallel.	m∠5 + m∠6 = 180°	$m \parallel n$

You will prove Theorems 3-2-3 and 3-2-5 in Exercises 38 and 39.

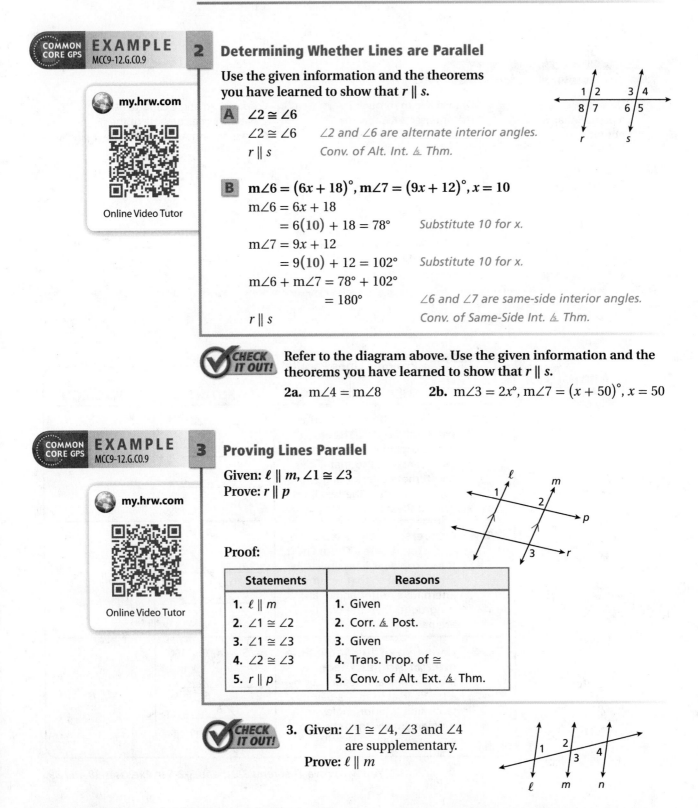

PROOF 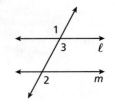 **Converse of the Alternate Exterior Angles Theorem**

Given: ∠1 ≅ ∠2
Prove: ℓ ∥ m
Proof: It is given that ∠1 ≅ ∠2. Vertical angles are congruent, so ∠1 ≅ ∠3. By the Transitive Property of Congruence, ∠2 ≅ ∠3. So ℓ ∥ m by the Converse of the Corresponding Angles Postulate.

COMMON CORE GPS
MCC9-12.G.CO.9

my.hrw.com

Online Video Tutor

EXAMPLE 2 Determining Whether Lines are Parallel

Use the given information and the theorems you have learned to show that $r \parallel s$.

A ∠2 ≅ ∠6

  ∠2 ≅ ∠6 *∠2 and ∠6 are alternate interior angles.*

  $r \parallel s$ *Conv. of Alt. Int. ∠ Thm.*

B $m∠6 = (6x + 18)°, m∠7 = (9x + 12)°, x = 10$

  $m∠6 = 6x + 18$

  $= 6(10) + 18 = 78°$ *Substitute 10 for x.*

  $m∠7 = 9x + 12$

  $= 9(10) + 12 = 102°$ *Substitute 10 for x.*

  $m∠6 + m∠7 = 78° + 102°$

  $= 180°$ *∠6 and ∠7 are same-side interior angles.*

  $r \parallel s$ *Conv. of Same-Side Int. ∠ Thm.*

CHECK IT OUT! Refer to the diagram above. Use the given information and the theorems you have learned to show that $r \parallel s$.

  2a. $m∠4 = m∠8$ **2b.** $m∠3 = 2x°, m∠7 = (x + 50)°, x = 50$

COMMON CORE GPS
MCC9-12.G.CO.9

my.hrw.com

Online Video Tutor

EXAMPLE 3 Proving Lines Parallel

Given: $ℓ \parallel m, ∠1 ≅ ∠3$
Prove: $r \parallel p$

Proof:

Statements	Reasons
1. ℓ ∥ m	1. Given
2. ∠1 ≅ ∠2	2. Corr. ∠ Post.
3. ∠1 ≅ ∠3	3. Given
4. ∠2 ≅ ∠3	4. Trans. Prop. of ≅
5. r ∥ p	5. Conv. of Alt. Ext. ∠ Thm.

CHECK IT OUT! **3. Given:** ∠1 ≅ ∠4, ∠3 and ∠4 are supplementary.
    Prove: ℓ ∥ m

Sports Application

During a race, all members of a rowing team should keep the oars parallel on each side. If $m\angle 1 = (3x + 13)°$, $m\angle 2 = (5x - 5)°$, and $x = 9$, show that the oars are parallel.

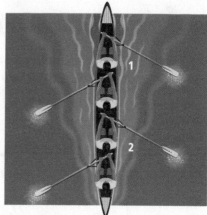

A line through the center of the boat forms a transversal to the two oars on each side of the boat.

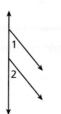

$\angle 1$ and $\angle 2$ are corresponding angles. If $\angle 1 \cong \angle 2$, then the oars are parallel.

Substitute 9 for x in each expression:

$m\angle 1 = 3x + 13$
$\quad\quad = 3(9) + 13 = 40°$ *Substitute 9 for x in each expression.*

$m\angle 2 = 5x - 5$
$\quad\quad = 5(9) - 5 = 40°$ *$m\angle 1 = m\angle 2$, so $\angle 1 \cong \angle 2$.*

The corresponding angles are congruent, so the oars are parallel by the Converse of the Corresponding Angles Postulate.

 CHECK IT OUT!

4. What if...? Suppose the corresponding angles on the opposite side of the boat measure $(4y - 2)°$ and $(3y + 6)°$, where $y = 8$. Show that the oars are parallel.

MCC.MP.3   MATHEMATICAL PRACTICES

THINK AND DISCUSS

1. Explain three ways of proving that two lines are parallel.

2. If you know $m\angle 1$, how could you use the measures of $\angle 5$, $\angle 6$, $\angle 7$, or $\angle 8$ to prove $m \parallel n$?

3. GET ORGANIZED Copy and complete the graphic organizer. Use it to compare the Corresponding Angles Postulate with the Converse of the Corresponding Angles Postulate.

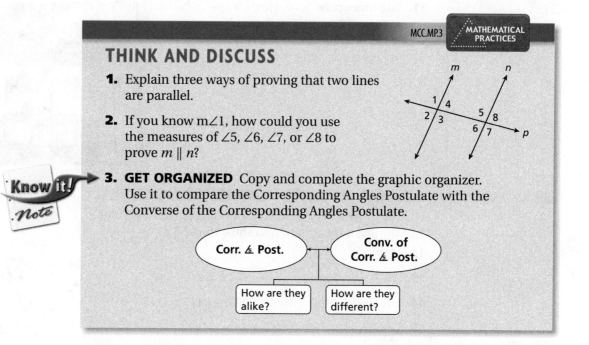

Know it! Note

GUIDED PRACTICE

SEE EXAMPLE **1**

Use the Converse of the Corresponding Angles Postulate and the given information to show that $p \parallel q$.

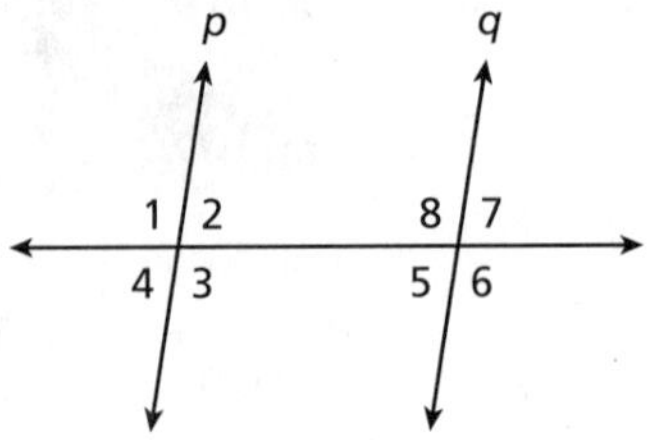

1. $\angle 4 \cong \angle 5$

2. $m\angle 1 = (4x + 16)^\circ$, $m\angle 8 = (5x - 12)^\circ$, $x = 28$

3. $m\angle 4 = (6x - 19)^\circ$, $m\angle 5 = (3x + 14)^\circ$, $x = 11$

SEE EXAMPLE **2**

Use the theorems and given information to show that $r \parallel s$.

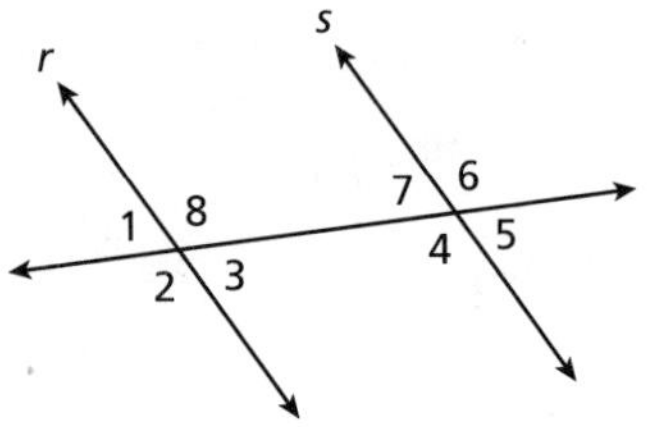

4. $\angle 1 \cong \angle 5$

5. $m\angle 3 + m\angle 4 = 180^\circ$

6. $\angle 3 \cong \angle 7$

7. $m\angle 4 = (13x - 4)^\circ$, $m\angle 8 = (9x + 16)^\circ$, $x = 5$

8. $m\angle 8 = (17x + 37)^\circ$, $m\angle 7 = (9x - 13)^\circ$, $x = 6$

9. $m\angle 2 = (25x + 7)^\circ$, $m\angle 6 = (24x + 12)^\circ$, $x = 5$

SEE EXAMPLE **3**

10. Complete the following two-column proof.

Given: $\angle 1 \cong \angle 2$, $\angle 3 \cong \angle 1$
Prove: $\overline{XY} \parallel \overline{WV}$

Proof:

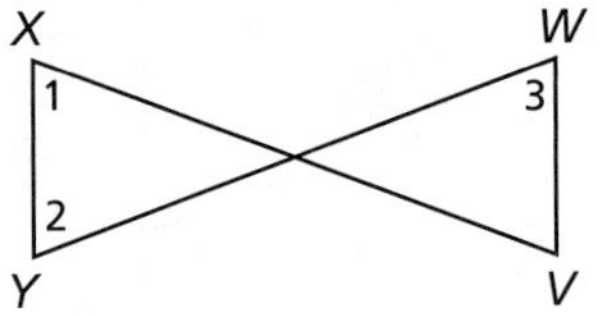

Statements	Reasons
1. $\angle 1 \cong \angle 2$, $\angle 3 \cong \angle 1$	**1.** Given
2. $\angle 2 \cong \angle 3$	**2. a.** ___?___
3. b. ___?___	**3. c.** ___?___

SEE EXAMPLE **4**

11. **Architecture** In the fire escape, $m\angle 1 = (17x + 9)^\circ$, $m\angle 2 = (14x + 18)^\circ$, and $x = 3$. Show that the two landings are parallel.

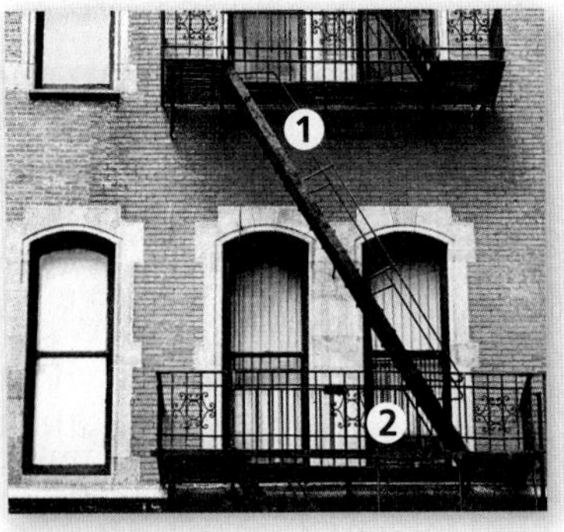

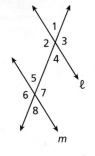

PRACTICE AND PROBLEM SOLVING

Use the Converse of the Corresponding Angles Postulate and the given information to show that $\ell \parallel m$.

12. $\angle 3 \cong 7$

13. $m\angle 4 = 54^\circ$, $m\angle 8 = (7x + 5)^\circ$, $x = 7$

14. $m\angle 2 = (8x + 4)^\circ$, $m\angle 6 = (11x - 41)^\circ$, $x = 15$

15. $m\angle 1 = (3x + 19)^\circ$, $m\angle 5 = (4x + 7)^\circ$, $x = 12$

Use the theorems and given information to show that $n \parallel p$.

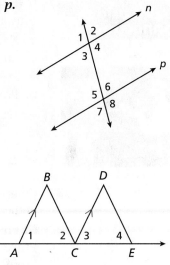

16. $\angle 3 \cong \angle 6$

17. $\angle 2 \cong \angle 7$

18. $m\angle 4 + m\angle 6 = 180°$

19. $m\angle 1 = (8x - 7)°$, $m\angle 8 = (6x + 21)°$, $x = 14$

20. $m\angle 4 = (4x + 3)°$, $m\angle 5 = (5x - 22)°$, $x = 25$

21. $m\angle 3 = (2x + 15)°$, $m\angle 5 = (3x + 15)°$, $x = 30$

22. Complete the following two-column proof.

Given: $\overline{AB} \parallel \overline{CD}$, $\angle 1 \cong \angle 2$, $\angle 3 \cong \angle 4$
Prove: $\overline{BC} \parallel \overline{DE}$

Proof:

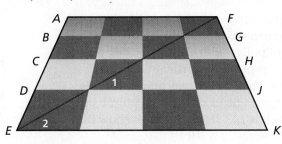

Statements	Reasons
1. $\overline{AB} \parallel \overline{CD}$	1. Given
2. $\angle 1 \cong \angle 3$	2. a. _____
3. $\angle 1 \cong \angle 2$, $\angle 3 \cong \angle 4$	3. b. _____
4. $\angle 2 \cong \angle 4$	4. c. _____
5. d. _____	5. e. _____

H.O.T. **23.** **Art** Edmund Dulac used perspective when drawing the floor titles in an illustration for *The Wind's Tale* by Hans Christian Andersen. Show that $\overline{DJ} \parallel \overline{EK}$ if $m\angle 1 = (3x + 2)°$, $m\angle 2 = (5x - 10)°$, and $x = 6$.

Name the postulate or theorem that proves that $\ell \parallel m$.

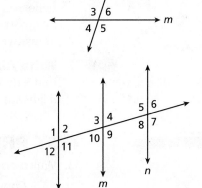

24. $\angle 8 \cong \angle 6$ **25.** $\angle 8 \cong \angle 4$

26. $\angle 2 \cong \angle 6$ **27.** $\angle 7 \cong \angle 5$

28. $\angle 3 \cong \angle 7$ **29.** $m\angle 2 + m\angle 3 = 180°$

For the given information, tell which pair of lines must be parallel. Name the postulate or theorem that supports your answer.

30. $m\angle 2 = m\angle 10$ **31.** $m\angle 8 + m\angle 9 = 180°$

32. $\angle 1 \cong \angle 7$ **33.** $m\angle 10 = m\angle 6$

34. $\angle 11 \cong \angle 5$ **35.** $m\angle 2 + m\angle 5 = 180°$

36. **Multi-Step** Two lines are intersected by a transversal so that $\angle 1$ and $\angle 2$ are corresponding angles, $\angle 1$ and $\angle 3$ are alternate exterior angles, and $\angle 3$ and $\angle 4$ are corresponding angles. If $\angle 2 \cong \angle 4$, what theorem or postulate can be used to prove the lines parallel?

37. In the diagram, which represents the side view of a mystery spot, m∠SRT = 25°, and m∠SUR = 65°.

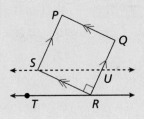

   a. Name a same-side interior angle of ∠SUR for lines $\overleftrightarrow{SU}$ and $\overleftrightarrow{RT}$ with transversal $\overleftrightarrow{RU}$. What is its measure? Explain your reasoning.

   b. Prove that $\overleftrightarrow{SU}$ and $\overleftrightarrow{RT}$ are parallel.

38. Complete the flowchart proof of the Converse of the Alternate Interior Angles Theorem.

   Given: ∠2 ≅ ∠3
   Prove: ℓ ∥ m
   Proof:

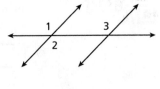

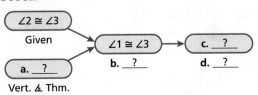

39. Use the diagram to write a paragraph proof of the Converse of the Same-Side Interior Angles Theorem.

   Given: ∠1 and ∠2 are supplementary.
   Prove: ℓ ∥ m

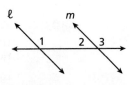

H.O.T. 40. **Carpentry** A *plumb bob* is a weight hung at the end of a string, called a *plumb line*. The weight pulls the string down so that the plumb line is perfectly vertical. Suppose that the angle formed by the wall and the roof is 123° and the angle formed by the plumb line and the roof is 123°. How does this show that the wall is perfectly vertical?

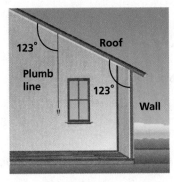

H.O.T. 41. **Critical Thinking** Are the Reflexive, Symmetric, and Transitive Properties true for parallel lines? Explain why or why not.

   Reflexive: ℓ ∥ ℓ
   Symmetric: If ℓ ∥ m, then m ∥ ℓ.
   Transitive: If ℓ ∥ m and m ∥ n, then ℓ ∥ n.

H.O.T. 42. **Write About It** Does the information given in the diagram allow you to conclude that *a* ∥ *b*? Explain.

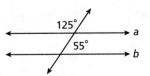

TEST PREP

43. Which postulate or theorem can be used to prove ℓ ∥ m?

   Ⓐ Converse of the Corresponding Angles Postulate

   Ⓑ Converse of the Alternate Interior Angles Theorem

   Ⓒ Converse of the Alternate Exterior Angles Theorem

   Ⓓ Converse of the Same-Side Interior Angles Theorem

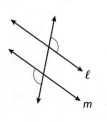

44. Two coplanar lines are cut by a transversal. Which condition does NOT guarantee that the two lines are parallel?

    Ⓐ A pair of alternate interior angles are congruent.

    Ⓑ A pair of same-side interior angles are supplementary.

    Ⓒ A pair of corresponding angles are congruent.

    Ⓓ A pair of alternate exterior angles are complementary.

45. Gridded Response Find the value of x so that $\ell \parallel m$.

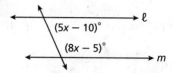

CHALLENGE AND EXTEND

Determine which lines, if any, can be proven parallel using the given information. Justify your answers.

46. $\angle 1 \cong \angle 15$ **47.** $\angle 8 \cong \angle 14$

48. $\angle 3 \cong \angle 7$ **49.** $\angle 8 \cong \angle 10$

50. $\angle 6 \cong \angle 8$ **51.** $\angle 13 \cong \angle 11$

52. $m\angle 12 + m\angle 15 = 180°$ **53.** $m\angle 5 + m\angle 8 = 180°$

54. Write a paragraph proof that $\overline{AE} \parallel \overline{BD}$.

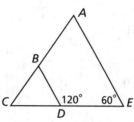

Use the diagram for Exercises 55 and 56.

55. Given: $m\angle 2 + m\angle 3 = 180°$
    Prove: $\ell \parallel m$

56. Given: $m\angle 2 + m\angle 5 = 180°$
    Prove: $\ell \parallel n$

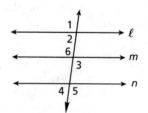

FOCUS ON MATHEMATICAL PRACTICES

57. Communication Explain when the Alternate Interior Angles Theorem can be applied, and when the Converse of the Alternate Interior Angles Theorem can be applied.

58. Reasoning In the figure, line a is parallel to line b. Is line c parallel to line d? Justify your answer.

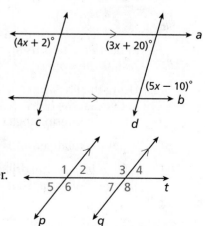

59. Justify June named $\angle 5$ and $\angle 8$ same-side exterior angles. How are their measures related if the lines p and q are parallel? Support your answer.

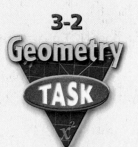

3-2

Geometry TASK

Use with Proving Lines Parallel

Construct Parallel Lines

You have learned one method of constructing parallel lines using a compass and straightedge. Another method, called the rhombus method, uses a property of a figure called a *rhombus*. The rhombus method is shown below.

MATHEMATICAL PRACTICES   **Use appropriate tools strategically.**   **MCC9-12.G.CO.12** Make formal geometric constructions with a variety of tools and methods …

Activity 1

1 Draw a line ℓ and a point P not on the line.

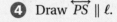

2 Choose a point Q on the line. Place your compass point at Q and draw an arc through P that intersects ℓ. Label the intersection R.

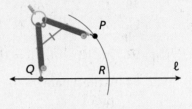

3 Using the same compass setting as the first arc, draw two more arcs: one from P, the other from R. Label the intersection of the two arcs S.

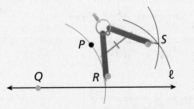

4 Draw $\overleftrightarrow{PS} \parallel \ell$.

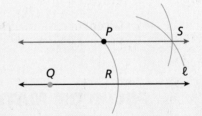

Try This

1. Repeat Activity 1 using a different point not on the line. Are your results the same?

2. Using the lines you constructed in Problem 1, draw transversal $\overleftrightarrow{PQ}$. Verify that the lines are parallel by using a protractor to measure alternate interior angles.

3. What postulate ensures that this construction is always possible?

4. A *rhombus* is a quadrilateral with four congruent sides. Explain why this method is called the rhombus method.

Activity 2

1 Draw a line ℓ and point P on a piece of patty paper.

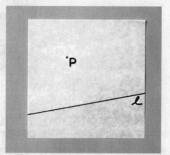

2 Fold the paper through P so that both sides of line ℓ match up

3 Crease the paper to form line m. P should be on line m.

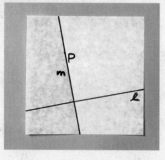

4 Fold the paper again through P so that both sides of line m match up.

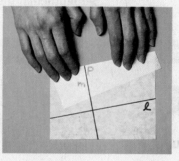

5 Crease the paper to form line n. Line n is parallel to line ℓ through P.

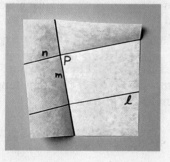

Try This

5. Repeat Activity 2 using a point in a different place not on the line. Are your results the same?

6. Use a protractor to measure corresponding angles. How can you tell that the lines are parallel?

7. Draw a triangle and construct a line parallel to one side through the vertex that is not on that side.

8. Line m is perpendicular to both ℓ and n. Use this statement to complete the following conjecture: If two lines in a plane are perpendicular to the same line, then _____?_____ .

3-3 Perpendicular Lines

 Essential Question: How can you prove and use theorems about perpendicular lines?

Objective
Prove and apply theorems about perpendicular lines.

Vocabulary
perpendicular bisector
distance from a point to a line

Why learn this?
Rip currents are strong currents that flow away from the shoreline and are perpendicular to it. A swimmer who gets caught in a rip current can get swept far out to sea. (See Example 3.)

The **perpendicular bisector** of a segment is a line perpendicular to a segment at the segment's midpoint. A construction of a perpendicular bisector is shown below.

Construction Perpendicular Bisector of a Segment

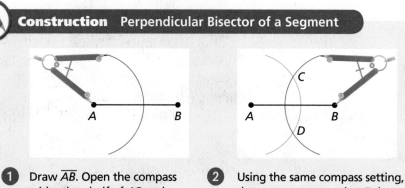

1 Draw $\overline{AB}$. Open the compass wider than half of AB and draw an arc centered at A.

2 Using the same compass setting, draw an arc centered at B that intersects the first arc at C and D.

3 Draw $\overleftrightarrow{CD}$. $\overleftrightarrow{CD}$ is the perpendicular bisector of $\overline{AB}$.

The shortest segment from a point to a line is perpendicular to the line. This fact is used to define the **distance from a point to a line** as the length of the perpendicular segment from the point to the line.

COMMON CORE GPS
MCC9-12.A.REI.3

EXAMPLE **1** **Distance From a Point to a Line**

A **Name the shortest segment from P to $\overleftrightarrow{AC}$.**
The shortest distance from a point to a line is the length of the perpendicular segment, so $\overline{PB}$ is the shortest segment from P to $\overleftrightarrow{AC}$.

my.hrw.com

Online Video Tutor

B **Write and solve an inequality for x.**

$PA > PB$	$\overline{PB}$ is the shortest segment.
$x + 3 > \quad 5$	Substitute $x + 3$ for PA and 5 for PB.
$\underline{-3 \quad -3}$	Subtract 3 from both sides of the inequality.
$x > \quad 2$	

CHECK IT OUT! **1a.** Name the shortest segment from A to $\overleftrightarrow{BC}$.
1b. Write and solve an inequality for x.

	THEOREM	HYPOTHESIS	CONCLUSION
3-3-1	If two intersecting lines form a linear pair of congruent angles, then the lines are perpendicular. (2 intersecting lines form lin. pair of ≅ ∢ → lines ⊥.)		$\ell \perp m$
3-3-2	**Perpendicular Transversal Theorem** In a plane, if a transversal is perpendicular to one of two parallel lines, then it is perpendicular to the other line.		$q \perp p$
3-3-3	If two coplanar lines are perpendicular to the same line, then the two lines are parallel to each other. (2 lines ⊥ to same line → 2 lines ∥.)		$r \parallel s$

You will prove Theorems 3-3-1 and 3-3-3 in Exercises 37 and 38.

PROOF ▪ **Perpendicular Transversal Theorem**

Given: $\overleftrightarrow{BC} \parallel \overleftrightarrow{DE}$, $\overleftrightarrow{AB} \perp \overleftrightarrow{BC}$

Prove: $\overleftrightarrow{AB} \perp \overleftrightarrow{DE}$

Proof:

It is given that $\overleftrightarrow{BC} \parallel \overleftrightarrow{DE}$, so $\angle ABC \cong \angle BDE$ by the Corresponding Angles Postulate. It is also given that $\overleftrightarrow{AB} \perp \overleftrightarrow{BC}$, so m$\angle ABC = 90°$. By the definition of congruent angles, m$\angle ABC = $ m$\angle BDE$, so m$\angle BDE = 90°$ by the Transitive Property of Equality. By the definition of perpendicular lines, $\overleftrightarrow{AB} \perp \overleftrightarrow{DE}$.

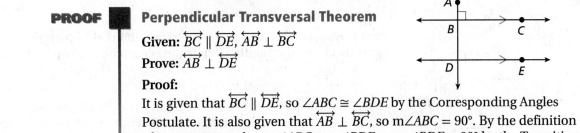

COMMON CORE GPS MCC9-12.G.CO.9 **EXAMPLE** **2**

Proving Properties of Lines

my.hrw.com

Online Video Tutor

Write a two-column proof.

Given: $\overleftrightarrow{AD} \parallel \overleftrightarrow{BC}$, $\overleftrightarrow{AD} \perp \overleftrightarrow{AB}$, $\overleftrightarrow{BC} \perp \overleftrightarrow{DC}$

Prove: $\overleftrightarrow{AB} \parallel \overleftrightarrow{DC}$

Proof:

Statements	Reasons
1. $\overleftrightarrow{AD} \parallel \overleftrightarrow{BC}$, $\overleftrightarrow{BC} \perp \overleftrightarrow{DC}$	1. Given
2. $\overleftrightarrow{AD} \perp \overleftrightarrow{DC}$	2. ⊥ Transv. Thm.
3. $\overleftrightarrow{AD} \perp \overleftrightarrow{AB}$	3. Given
4. $\overleftrightarrow{AB} \parallel \overleftrightarrow{DC}$	4. 2 lines ⊥ to same line → 2 lines ∥.

CHECK IT OUT! **2.** Write a two-column proof.

Given: $\angle EHF \cong \angle HFG$, $\overleftrightarrow{FG} \perp \overleftrightarrow{GH}$

Prove: $\overleftrightarrow{EH} \perp \overleftrightarrow{GH}$

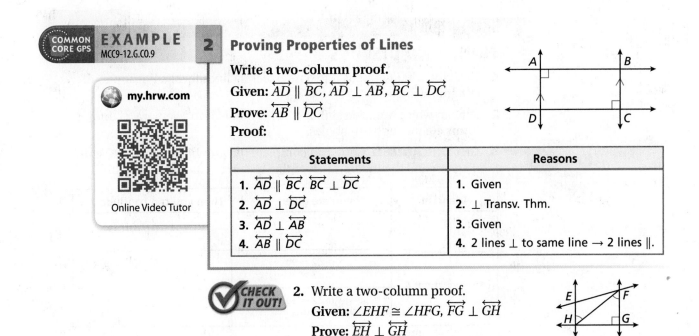

EXAMPLE 3

Oceanography Application

my.hrw.com

Online Video Tutor

Rip currents may be caused by a sandbar parallel to the shoreline. Waves cause a buildup of water between the sandbar and the shoreline. When this water breaks through the sandbar, it flows out in a direction perpendicular to the sandbar. Why must the rip current be perpendicular to the shoreline?

The rip current forms a transversal to the shoreline and the sandbar.

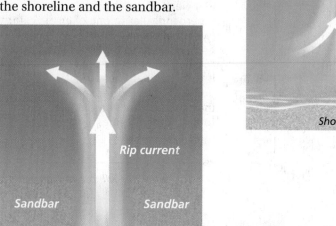

The shoreline and the sandbar are parallel, and the rip current is perpendicular to the sandbar. So by the Perpendicular Transversal Theorem, the rip current is perpendicular to the shoreline.

CHECK IT OUT!

3. A swimmer who gets caught in a rip current should swim in a direction perpendicular to the current. Why should the path of the swimmer be parallel to the shoreline?

MCC.MP.3 · MATHEMATICAL PRACTICES

THINK AND DISCUSS

1. Describe what happens if two intersecting lines form a linear pair of congruent angles.

2. Explain why a transversal that is perpendicular to two parallel lines forms eight congruent angles.

3. GET ORGANIZED Copy and complete the graphic organizer. Use the diagram and the theorems from this lesson to complete the table.

Diagram	If you are given . . .	Then you can conclude . . .
	$m\angle 1 = m\angle 2$	
(diagram with lines m, n, p and angles 1, 2, 3)	$m\angle 2 = 90°$ $m\angle 3 = 90°$	
	$m\angle 2 = 90°$ $m \parallel n$	

GUIDED PRACTICE

1. **Vocabulary** $\overleftrightarrow{CD}$ is the *perpendicular bisector* of $\overline{AB}$. $\overleftrightarrow{CD}$ intersects $\overline{AB}$ at C. What can you say about $\overline{AB}$ and $\overleftrightarrow{CD}$? What can you say about $\overline{AC}$ and $\overline{BC}$?

SEE EXAMPLE **1**

2. Name the shortest segment from point E to $\overleftrightarrow{AD}$.

3. Write and solve an inequality for x.

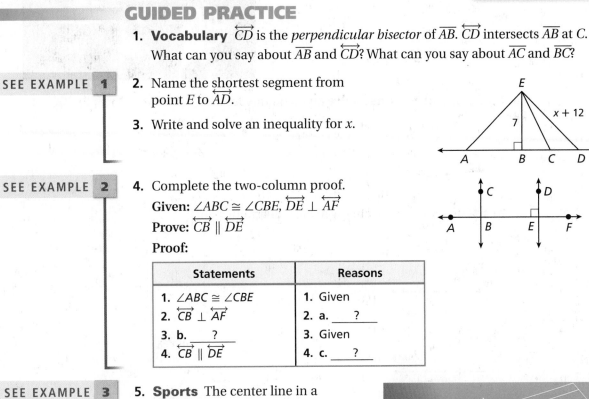

SEE EXAMPLE **2**

4. Complete the two-column proof.

Given: $\angle ABC \cong \angle CBE$, $\overleftrightarrow{DE} \perp \overleftrightarrow{AF}$

Prove: $\overleftrightarrow{CB} \parallel \overleftrightarrow{DE}$

Proof:

Statements	Reasons
1. $\angle ABC \cong \angle CBE$	1. Given
2. $\overleftrightarrow{CB} \perp \overleftrightarrow{AF}$	2. a. ___?___
3. b. ___?___	3. Given
4. $\overleftrightarrow{CB} \parallel \overleftrightarrow{DE}$	4. c. ___?___

SEE EXAMPLE **3**

5. **Sports** The center line in a tennis court is perpendicular to both service lines. Explain why the service lines must be parallel to each other.

PRACTICE AND PROBLEM SOLVING

Independent Practice	
For Exercises	See Example
6–7	1
8	2
9	3

my.hrw.com

Online Extra Practice

6. Name the shortest segment from point W to $\overleftrightarrow{XZ}$.

7. Write and solve an inequality for x.

8. Complete the two-column proof below.

Given: $\overleftrightarrow{AB} \perp \overleftrightarrow{BC}$, $m\angle 1 + m\angle 2 = 180°$

Prove: $\overleftrightarrow{BC} \perp \overleftrightarrow{CD}$

Proof:

Statements	Reasons
1. $\overleftrightarrow{AB} \perp \overleftrightarrow{BC}$	1. Given
2. $m\angle 1 + m\angle 2 = 180°$	2. a. ___?___
3. $\angle 1$ and $\angle 2$ are supplementary.	3. Def. of supplementary
4. b. ___?___	4. Converse of the Same-Side Interior Angles Theorem
5. $\overleftrightarrow{BC} \perp \overleftrightarrow{CD}$	5. c. ___?___

9. **Music** The *frets* on a guitar are all perpendicular to one of the strings. Explain why the frets must be parallel to each other.

String
Fret

For each diagram, write and solve an inequality for *x*.

10.

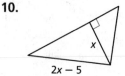

x

2*x* − 5

11.

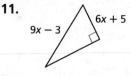

9*x* − 3

6*x* + 5

Multi-Step Solve to find *x* and *y* in each diagram.

12.

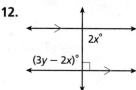

2*x*°

(3*y* − 2*x*)°

13.

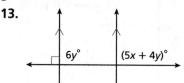

6*y*°

(5*x* + 4*y*)°

14.

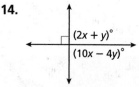

(2*x* + *y*)°

(10*x* − 4*y*)°

15.

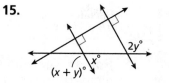

2*y*°

x°

(*x* + *y*)°

Determine if there is enough information given in the diagram to prove each statement.

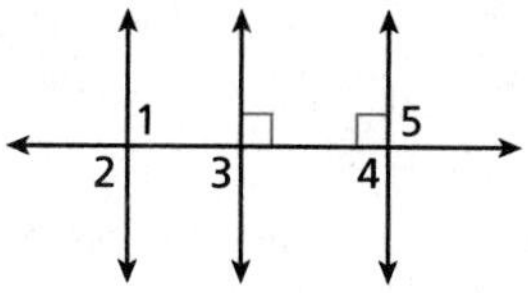

16. ∠1 ≅ ∠2

17. ∠1 ≅ ∠3

18. ∠2 ≅ ∠3

19. ∠2 ≅ ∠4

20. ∠3 ≅ ∠4

21. ∠3 ≅ ∠5

1
2 3 4
5

H.O.T. 22. **Critical Thinking** Are the Reflexive, Symmetric, and Transitive Properties true for perpendicular lines? Explain why or why not.
Reflexive: ℓ ⊥ ℓ
Symmetric: If ℓ ⊥ *m*, then *m* ⊥ ℓ.
Transitive: If ℓ ⊥ *m* and *m* ⊥ *n*, then ℓ ⊥ *n*.

Real-World Connections

23. In the diagram, which represents the side view of a mystery spot, $\overline{QR} \perp \overline{PQ}$, $\overline{PQ} \parallel \overline{RS}$, and $\overline{PS} \parallel \overline{QR}$.
   a. Prove $\overline{QR} \perp \overline{RS}$ and $\overline{PS} \perp \overline{RS}$.
   b. Prove $\overline{PQ} \perp \overline{PS}$.

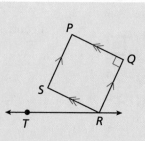

P
Q
S
T
R

24. **Geography** Felton Avenue, Arlee Avenue, and Viehl Avenue are all parallel. Broadway Street is perpendicular to Felton Avenue. Use the satellite photo and the given information to determine the values of x and y.

25. **Estimation** Copy the diagram onto a grid with 1 cm by 1 cm squares. Estimate the distance from point P to line ℓ.

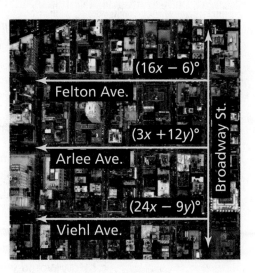

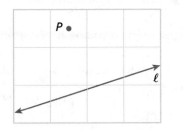

H.O.T. 26. **Critical Thinking** Draw a figure to show that Theorem 3-3-3 is not true if the lines are not in the same plane.

27. Draw a figure in which $\overline{AB}$ is a perpendicular bisector of $\overline{XY}$ but $\overline{XY}$ is not a perpendicular bisector of $\overline{AB}$.

H.O.T. 28. **Write About It** A ladder is formed by rungs that are perpendicular to the sides of the ladder. Explain why the rungs of the ladder are parallel.

Construction Construct a segment congruent to each given segment and then construct its perpendicular bisector.

29.

30.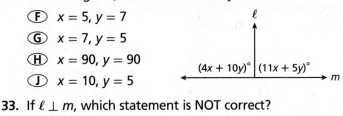

TEST PREP

31. Which inequality is correct for the given diagram?

    (A) $2x + 5 < 3x$ (C) $2x + 5 > 3x$

    (B) $x > 1$ (D) $x > 5$

    $2x + 5$ / $3x$

32. In the diagram, $\ell \perp m$. Find x and y.

    (F) $x = 5, y = 7$
    (G) $x = 7, y = 5$
    (H) $x = 90, y = 90$
    (J) $x = 10, y = 5$

    ℓ
    $(4x + 10y)° \mid (11x + 5y)°$ m

33. If $\ell \perp m$, which statement is NOT correct?

    (A) $m\angle 2 = 90°$
    (B) $m\angle 1 + m\angle 2 = 180°$
    (C) $\angle 1 \cong \angle 2$
    (D) $\angle 1 \perp \angle 2$

    ℓ
    $1 \mid 2$ m

34. In a plane, both lines m and n are perpendicular to both lines p and q. Which conclusion CANNOT be made?

    (A) $p \parallel q$

    (B) $m \parallel n$

    (C) $p \perp q$

    (D) All angles formed by lines m, n, p, and q are congruent.

H.O.T. 35. Extended Response Lines m and n are parallel. Line p intersects line m at A and line n at B, and is perpendicular to line m.

    a. What is the relationship between line n and line p? Draw a diagram to support your answer.

    b. What is the distance from point A to line n? What is the distance from point B to line m? Explain.

    c. How would you define the distance between two parallel lines in a plane?

CHALLENGE AND EXTEND

H.O.T. 36. Multi-Step Find m∠1 in the diagram. (*Hint:* Draw a line parallel to the given parallel lines.)

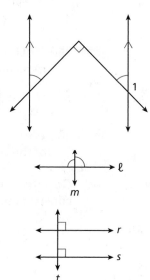

37. Prove Theorem 3-3-1: If two intersecting lines form a linear pair of congruent angles, then the two lines are perpendicular.

38. Prove Theorem 3-3-3: If two coplanar lines are perpendicular to the same line, then the two lines are parallel to each other.

FOCUS ON MATHEMATICAL PRACTICES

H.O.T. 39. Modeling Korey said that two lines parallel to the same line are perpendicular. Draw a figure to prove or disprove his statement.

H.O.T. 40. Reasoning $\overline{CD}$ is the perpendicular bisector of $\overline{AB}$ and intersects it at point E. $AE = 2x + 6$, $BE = 5x - 12$, $CE = 4x + 9$, and $DE = 6x - 3$. Is $\overline{AB}$ the perpendicular bisector of $\overline{CD}$? Justify your answer.

H.O.T. 41. Communication Explain how you know that the distance from the origin to the line shown is less than 3.

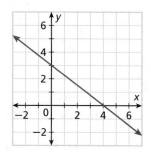

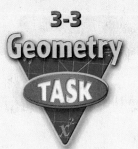

3-3

Geometry TASK

Use with Perpendicular Lines

Construct Perpendicular Lines

You have learned to construct the perpendicular bisector of a segment. This is the basis of the construction of a line perpendicular to a given line through a given point. The steps in the construction are the same whether the point is on or off the line.

 **Use appropriate tools strategically.**

 MCC9-12.G.CO.12 Make formal geometric constructions with a variety of tools and methods …

Activity

Copy the given line ℓ and point P.

• P

⟵——————————→ ℓ

① Place the compass point on P and draw an arc that intersects ℓ at two points. Label the points A and B.

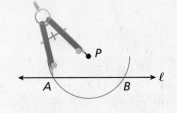

② Construct the perpendicular bisector of $\overline{AB}$.

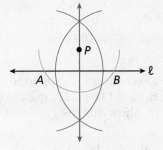

Try This

Copy each diagram and construct a line perpendicular to line ℓ through point P.
Use a protractor to verify that the lines are perpendicular.

1. $P \bullet$ ... ℓ

2. ℓ ... P

3. Follow the steps below to construct two parallel lines. Explain why $\ell \parallel n$.

Step 1 Given a line ℓ, draw a point P not on ℓ.

Step 2 Construct line m perpendicular to ℓ through P.

Step 3 Construct line n perpendicular to m through P.

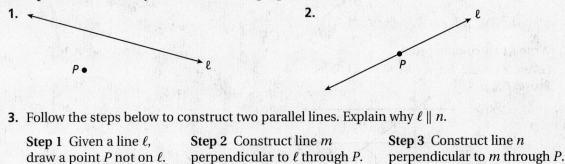

Ready to Go On?

my.hrw.com
Assessment and Intervention

✓ 3-1 Angles Formed by Parallel Lines and Transversals

Find each angle measure.

1.

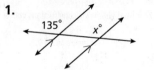

135°   x°

2.

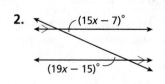

$(15x - 7)°$

$(19x - 15)°$

3.

$(54x + 14)°$

$(43x + 36)°$

✓ 3-2 Proving Lines Parallel

Use the given information and the theorems and postulates you have learned to show that $a \parallel b$.

4. $m\angle 8 = (13x + 20)°$, $m\angle 6 = (7x + 38)°$, $x = 3$

5. $\angle 1 \cong \angle 5$

6. $m\angle 8 + m\angle 7 = 180°$

7. $m\angle 8 = m\angle 4$

8. The tower shown is supported by guy wires such that $m\angle 1 = (3x + 12)°$, $m\angle 2 = (4x - 2)°$, and $x = 14$. Show that the guy wires are parallel.

1 8   7 6
2 3   4 5
a   b

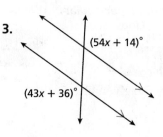

✓ 3-3 Perpendicular Lines

9. Name the shortest segment from point K to $\overline{LN}$.

10. Write and solve an inequality for x.

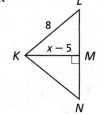

L
8
K   x − 5   M
N

11. Write a two-column proof.

Given: $\angle 1 \cong \angle 2$, $\ell \perp n$

Prove: $\ell \perp p$

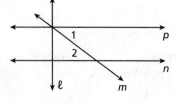

1
2
p
n
ℓ   m

PARCC Assessment Readiness

Selected Response

1. Find m∠RST.

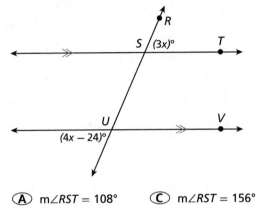

- **(A)** m∠RST = 108°
- **(C)** m∠RST = 156°
- **(B)** m∠RST = 24°
- **(D)** m∠RST = 72°

2. From the ocean, salmon swim perpendicularly toward the shore to lay their eggs in rivers. Waves in the ocean are parallel to the shore. Why must the salmon swim perpendicularly to the waves?

- **(F)** Swimming salmon form a transversal to the shore and the waves. The shore and the waves are parallel, and the swimming salmon are perpendicular to the shore. So by the Perpendicular Transversal Theorem, the salmon are perpendicular to the waves.

- **(G)** Swimming salmon form a transversal to the shore and the waves. The shore and the waves are perpendicular, and the swimming salmon are parallel to the shore. So by the Perpendicular Transversal Theorem, the salmon are perpendicular to the waves.

- **(H)** Swimming salmon form a transversal to the shore and the waves. The shore and the waves are parallel, and the swimming salmon are parallel to the shore. So by the Perpendicular Transversal Theorem, the salmon are perpendicular to the waves.

- **(J)** Swimming salmon form a transversal to the shore and the waves. The shore and the waves are parallel, and the swimming salmon are perpendicular to the shore. So by the Parallel Transversal Theorem, the salmon are perpendicular to the waves.

Mini-Tasks

3. In a swimming pool, two lanes are represented by lines l and m. If a string of flags strung across the lanes is represented by transversal t, and $x = 10$, show that the lanes are parallel.

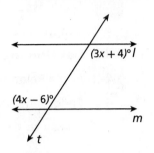

4. **Given:** $\overline{AD} \parallel \overline{BC}$, $\overline{AD} \perp \overline{AB}$, $\overline{DC} \perp \overline{BC}$
Prove: $\overline{AB} \parallel \overline{CD}$

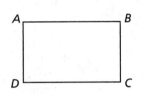

5. **Given:** $m \perp p$, $\angle 1$ and $\angle 2$ are complementary.
Prove: $p \parallel q$

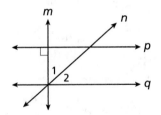

Congruence and Triangles

MATHEMATICAL PRACTICES   The Common Core Georgia Performance Standards for Mathematical Practice describe varieties of expertise that all students should seek to develop. Opportunities to develop these practices are integrated throughout this program.

1 Make sense of problems and persevere in solving them.

2 Reason abstractly and quantitatively.

3 Construct viable arguments and critique the reasoning of others.

4 Model with mathematics.

5 Use appropriate tools strategically.

6 Attend to precision.

7 Look for and make use of structure.

8 Look for and express regularity in repeated reasoning.

Unpacking the Standards

my.hrw.com
Multilingual Glossary

Understanding the standards and the vocabulary terms in the standards will help you know exactly what you are expected to learn in this chapter.

 MCC9-12.G.CO.10

Prove theorems about triangles.

Key Vocabulary

proof (demostración)
 An argument that uses logic to show that a conclusion is true.

theorem (teorema)
 A statement that has been proven.

What It Means For You

There are theorems about angle measures involved with triangles, about sides and angles in special types of triangles, and about side and angle relationships that identify when triangles are congruent. Proving these theorems makes them available for solving new problems.

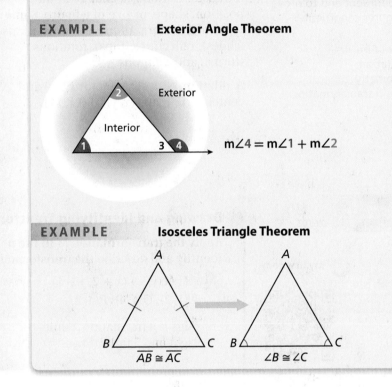

EXAMPLE   **Exterior Angle Theorem**

Exterior

Interior

$m\angle 4 = m\angle 1 + m\angle 2$

EXAMPLE   **Isosceles Triangle Theorem**

$\overline{AB} \cong \overline{AC}$ $\angle B \cong \angle C$

Congruence and Transformations

Essential Question: How can you use properties of transformations to determine whether figures are congruent?

Objectives

Draw, identify, and describe transformations in the coordinate plane.

Use properties of rigid motions to determine whether figures are congruent and to prove figures congruent.

Vocabulary

dilation
isometry
rigid transformation

Why learn this?

Transformations can be used to create frieze patterns in art and architecture, such as in this cast iron gate.

A transformation is a change in the position, shape, or size of a figure. Some types of transformations are translations (slides), reflections (flips), rotations (turns), and *dilations*.

A **dilation** with scale factor $k > 0$ and center $(0, 0)$ maps (x, y) to (kx, ky).

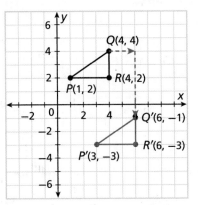

COMMON CORE GPS
MCC9-12.G.CO.5

EXAMPLE 1

Drawing and Identifying Transformations

Apply the transformation M to the polygon with the given vertices. Identify and describe the transformation.

my.hrw.com

Online Video Tutor

A $M : (x, y) \rightarrow (x + 2, y - 5)$
$P(1, 2), Q(4, 4), R(4, 2)$

This is a translation 2 units right and 5 units down.

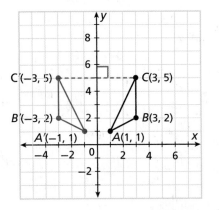

Remember!

In a transformation, the original figure is the preimage. The resulting figure is the image.

B $M : (x, y) \rightarrow (-x, y)$
$A(1, 1), B(3, 2), C(3, 5)$

This is a reflection across the *y*-axis.

© Allan Baxter/Getty Images

C $M : (x, y) \rightarrow (-y, x)$
$R(1, 2), E(1, 4), C(5, 4), T(5, 2)$

This is a 90° rotation counterclockwise with center of rotation (0, 0).

D $M : (x, y) \rightarrow (2x, 2y)$
$K(-1, 2), L(2, 2), N(1, 3)$

This is a dilation with scale factor 2 and center (0, 0).

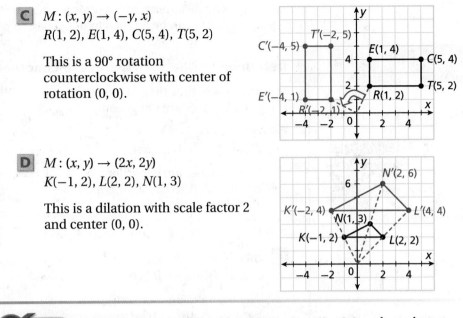

CHECK IT OUT!

1. Apply the transformation $M : (x, y) \rightarrow (3x, 3y)$ to the polygon with vertices $D(1, 3)$, $E(1, -2)$, and $F(3, 0)$. Name the coordinates of the image points. Identify and describe the transformation.

Representing Transformations in the Coordinate Plane

TRANSFORMATION	COORDINATE MAPPING AND DESCRIPTION
Translation	$(x, y) \rightarrow (x + a, y + b)$ Translation *a* units horizontally and *b* units vertically
Reflection	$(x, y) \rightarrow (-x, y)$ Reflection across *y*-axis
	$(x, y) \rightarrow (x, -y)$ Reflection across *x*-axis
Rotation	$(x, y) \rightarrow (y, -x)$ Rotation about (0, 0), 90° clockwise
	$(x, y) \rightarrow (-y, x)$ Rotation about (0, 0), 90° counterclockwise
	$(x, y) \rightarrow (-x, -y)$ Rotation about (0, 0), 180°
Dilation	$(x, y) \rightarrow (kx, ky), k > 0$ Dilation with scale factor *k* and center (0, 0)

An **isometry** is a transformation that preserves length, angle measure, and area. Because of these properties, an isometry produces an image that is congruent to the preimage. A **rigid transformation** is another name for an isometry.

Helpful Hint

Translations, reflections, and rotations can be called congruence transformations.

Transformations and Congruence

Translations, reflections, and rotations produce images that are congruent to their preimages.

Dilations with scale factor $k \neq 1$ produce images that are not congruent to their preimages.

You can determine whether some figures are congruent by determining what type of transformation(s) can be applied to one figure to produce the other figure.

COMMON CORE GPS
MCC9-12.G.CO.6

EXAMPLE 2 Determining Whether Figures are Congruent

Determine whether the polygons with the given vertices are congruent.

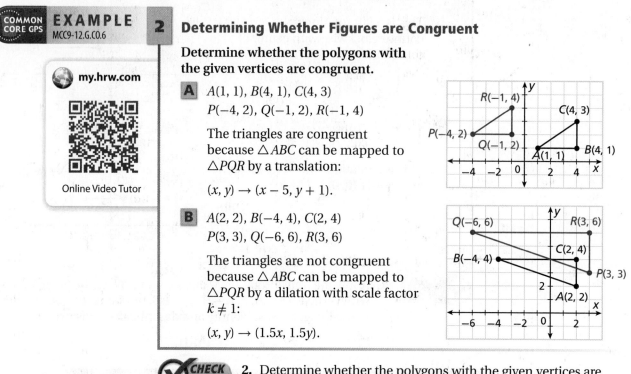

A $A(1, 1)$, $B(4, 1)$, $C(4, 3)$
$P(-4, 2)$, $Q(-1, 2)$, $R(-1, 4)$

The triangles are congruent because $\triangle ABC$ can be mapped to $\triangle PQR$ by a translation:

$(x, y) \rightarrow (x - 5, y + 1)$.

B $A(2, 2)$, $B(-4, 4)$, $C(2, 4)$
$P(3, 3)$, $Q(-6, 6)$, $R(3, 6)$

The triangles are not congruent because $\triangle ABC$ can be mapped to $\triangle PQR$ by a dilation with scale factor $k \neq 1$:

$(x, y) \rightarrow (1.5x, 1.5y)$.

CHECK IT OUT!

2. Determine whether the polygons with the given vertices are congruent. Support your answer by describing a transformation: $A(2, -1)$, $B(3, 0)$, $C(2, 3)$ and $P(1, 2)$, $Q(0, 3)$, $R(-3, 2)$.

You can prove two figures are congruent by showing there are one or more translations, reflections, or rotations that map one figure to the other.

COMMON CORE GPS
MCC9-12.G.CO.5

EXAMPLE 3 Applying Transformations

Prove that the polygons with the given vertices are congruent.

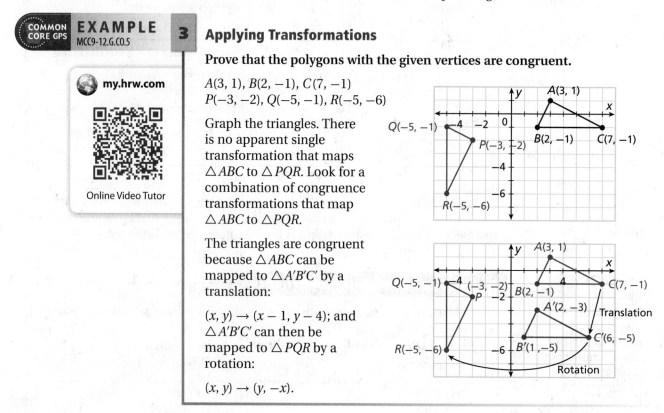

$A(3, 1)$, $B(2, -1)$, $C(7, -1)$
$P(-3, -2)$, $Q(-5, -1)$, $R(-5, -6)$

Graph the triangles. There is no apparent single transformation that maps $\triangle ABC$ to $\triangle PQR$. Look for a combination of congruence transformations that map $\triangle ABC$ to $\triangle PQR$.

The triangles are congruent because $\triangle ABC$ can be mapped to $\triangle A'B'C'$ by a translation:

$(x, y) \rightarrow (x - 1, y - 4)$; and $\triangle A'B'C'$ can then be mapped to $\triangle PQR$ by a rotation:

$(x, y) \rightarrow (y, -x)$.

CHECK IT OUT! 3. Prove that the polygons with the given vertices are congruent: $A(-4, -2)$, $B(-2, 1)$, $C(-2, -2)$ and $P(1, 0)$, $Q(3, -3)$, $R(3, 0)$.

COMMON CORE GPS **EXAMPLE 4** MCC9-12.G.CO.6

my.hrw.com

Online Video Tutor

Architecture Application

What transformation is used to create the frieze pattern in this cast iron gate? Are sections of the gate congruent? Explain your answer.

Repeated horizontal translations create the frieze pattern. A translation of any section either to the left or to the right by a distance equal to the width of the section produces an image that is congruent to the preimage.

CHECK IT OUT! 4. Sketch a frieze pattern that can be produced by using reflections.

MCC.MP.2   **MATHEMATICAL PRACTICES**

THINK AND DISCUSS

1. Think of the transformation mapping $(x, y) \rightarrow (x + 5, y - 2)$ as a function with input (x, y). What is the output of the function? If the transformation is applied to a polygon, describe the size, shape, and position of the image compared to the preimage.

2. What type of transformation preserves angle but does not preserve distance?

3. Describe a dilation with center $(0, 0)$ that would produce an image such that every image point is closer to $(0, 0)$ than its corresponding preimage point.

4. GET ORGANIZED Copy and complete the graphic organizer, including coordinate transformation rules.

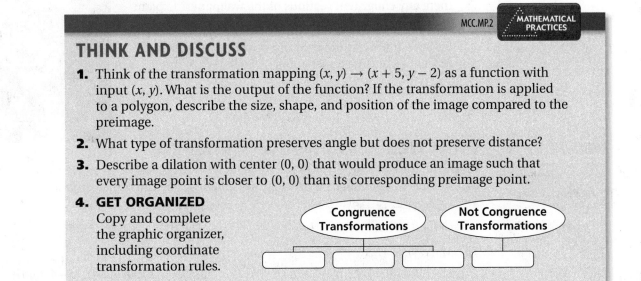

4-1

Exercises

my.hrw.com
Homework Help

GUIDED PRACTICE

Vocabulary Apply the vocabulary from this lesson to answer each question.

1. Dilations with scale factor $k \neq 1$ produce images that ____?____ (*are, are not*) congruent to their preimages.

2. An ____?____ (*isometry, image*) is a transformation that preserves length, angle, and area; it is also called a ____?____ (*translation, rigid transformation*).

Apply the transformation *M* to the polygon with the given vertices. Name the coordinates of the image points. Identify and describe the transformation.

3. $M: (x, y) \rightarrow (x, -y)$
$A(2, 1), B(5, 4), C(5, 1)$

4. $M: (x, y) \rightarrow (3x, 3y)$
$P(-2, 1), Q(-1, 2), R(0, 1)$

5. $M: (x, y) \rightarrow (y, -x)$
$L(3, 1), M(3, 4), N(5, 4), O(5, 1)$

6. $M: (x, y) \rightarrow (x - 3, y + 2)$
$D(4, -1), E(7, 3), F(7, -1)$

Determine whether the polygons with the given vertices are congruent. Support your answer by describing a transformation.

7. $A(-4, 4), B(-4, 6), C(2, 6), D(2, 4)$ and $W(-2, 2), X(-2, 3), Y(1, 3), Z(1, 2)$

8. $A(-2, -2), B(-4, -1), C(-1, -1)$ and $T(2, 2), U(4, 1), V(1, 1)$

Prove that the polygons with the given vertices are congruent.

9. $J(-5, 2), K(-2, 5), L(-2, 2)$ and $M(5, 0), N(2, 3), O(2, 0)$

10. $D(-1, -5), E(-4, -4), F(-1, -2)$ and $X(3, 4), Y(6, 3), Z(3, 1)$

11. Victorian Crafts What transformation is used to create the frieze pattern in the wallpaper shown? Are there any congruent sections of the wallpaper? Explain your answer.

12. Sketch a frieze pattern that can be produced by using reflections and/or translations.

PRACTICE AND PROBLEM SOLVING

Apply the transformation *M* to the polygon with the given vertices. Name the coordinates of the image points. Identify and describe the transformation.

13. $M: (x, y) \rightarrow (x + 5, y - 4)$
$G(4, -1), H(7, 3), I(7, -1)$

14. $M: (x, y) \rightarrow (-x, y)$
$P(3, 2), Q(6, 2), R(3, 5)$

15. $M: (x, y) \rightarrow (1.5x, 1.5y)$
$L(-1, 4), M(-4, 4), N(-4, 3)$

16. $M: (x, y) \rightarrow (-y, x)$
$A(-7, 6), B(-7, 4), C(-4, 6), D(-4, 4)$

17. $M: (x, y) \rightarrow (x - 1, y + 1)$
$N(1, -2), O(0, 4), P(2, 4)$

18. $M: (x, y) \rightarrow (-x, -y)$
$W(5, 2), X(2, 2), Y(5, 5)$

Determine whether the polygons with the given vertices are congruent. Support your answer by describing a transformation.

19. $J(-4, 4), K(-4, 6), L(2, 6), M(2, 4)$ and $A(4, 4), B(6, 4), C(6, -2), D(4, -2)$

20. $P(-2, -2), Q(-4, -1), R(-1, -1)$ and $X(2, 2), Y(4, 1), Z(1, 1)$

21. $E(-1, -1), F(2, 2), G(-3, 3)$ and $U(-1, 2), V(2, 5), W(-3, 6)$

Prove that the polygons with the given vertices are congruent.

22. $D(-5, -1), E(-2, 1), F(2, -1)$ and $X(-1, 1), Y(2, -1), Z(6, 1)$

23. $A(2, -1), B(4, -2), C(6, 0)$ and $D(-3, -2), E(-4, -4), F(-2, -6)$

24. $P(-7, 3), Q(-8, 7), R(-4, 7)$ and $G(4, -3), H(5, -7), I(1, -7)$

my.hrw.com

Online Extra Practice

H.O.T. 25. **Quilting** Jennifer is designing a quilt. She made this diagram to follow when making her quilt.

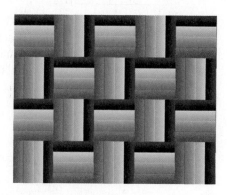

a. What transformation or combination of transformations is used to create the pattern in this quilt design?

b. Are sections of the quilt congruent? Explain your answer.

c. **What if ... ?** How might the design look different if she had used 180° rotations instead?

Apply the transformation M to the polygon with the given vertices. Name the coordinates of the image points. Identify and describe the transformation.

26. $M: (x, y) \rightarrow (x - 3, y + 2)$

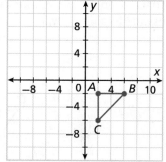

27. $M: (x, y) \rightarrow (y, -x)$

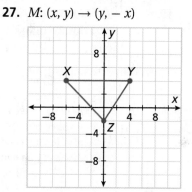

28. **Logo Design** Eli made this logo design for a company letterhead. What transformation(s) did he use to make the design? Are there any congruent shapes in the design?

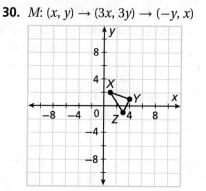

Apply the transformations M to the polygon with the given vertices. Name the coordinates of the image points. Identify and describe the transformations.

29. $M: (x, y) \rightarrow (x, -y) \rightarrow (x + 3, y)$

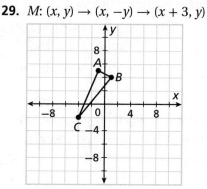

30. $M: (x, y) \rightarrow (3x, 3y) \rightarrow (-y, x)$

31. **Tessellations** Frank developed a tessellating shape to use in a repeating design. Describe the series of transformations he used to create this square design of his tessellated shape.

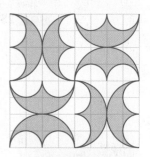

32. **Signal Flags** Seth is going to recreate this signal flag out of fabric. He has light blue and dark blue fabric. What transformations will he perform on the light blue triangles to position them correctly, if he starts in the upper left corner?

H.O.T. 33. **///ERROR ANALYSIS///** Erin and Dave are looking at the triangles on the coordinate plane shown. They are each trying to prove that the triangles are congruent. Who has the correct answer? Explain why.

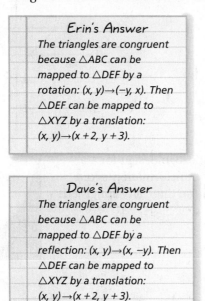

Erin's Answer

The triangles are congruent because △ABC can be mapped to △DEF by a rotation: $(x, y) \rightarrow (-y, x)$. Then △DEF can be mapped to △XYZ by a translation: $(x, y) \rightarrow (x + 2, y + 3)$.

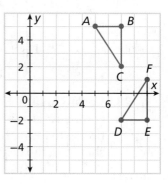

Dave's Answer

The triangles are congruent because △ABC can be mapped to △DEF by a reflection: $(x, y) \rightarrow (x, -y)$. Then △DEF can be mapped to △XYZ by a translation: $(x, y) \rightarrow (x + 2, y + 3)$.

34. **Write About It** Describe the differences in reflecting a polygon and rotating a polygon in terms of the coordinate mapping directions.

H.O.T. 35. **Critical Thinking** How does a dilation of a figure with scale factor 0.5 compare to a dilation of the figure with scale factor 2? Explain.

TEST PREP

36. Alex is trying two transformations that will map the preimage to the image.

$D(-5, -2)$, $E(-2, -2)$, $F(-4, -5)$ and $X(10, -4)$, $Y(4, -4)$, $Z(8, -10)$

Which two transformations should he choose?

(A) translation and reflection

(B) dilation and reflection

(C) reflection and rotatoin

(D) rotation and dilation

37. Bill applied the transformation M to the polygon. What are the coordinates of the image points for the polygon?

$M: (x, y) \rightarrow (x, -y)$

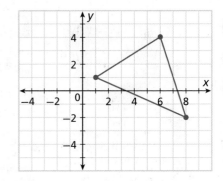

Ⓐ $A'(1, 1)$, $B'(6, 4)$, $C'(8, -2)$

Ⓑ $A'(-1, 1)$, $B'(-6, 4)$, $C'(-8, -2)$

Ⓒ $A'(-1, -1)$, $B'(-6, -4)$, $C'(-8, 2)$

Ⓓ $A'(1, -1)$, $B'(6, -4)$, $C'(8, 2)$

CHALLENGE AND EXTEND

38. Architecture Steve was visiting the ruins at Mitla, an archeological site in Mexico. He saw this frieze design.

a. Does the frieze have congruent shapes? What transformation or combination of tranformations are used to create the pattern in this frieze design?

b. What if … ? How might the design have looked if the designers had rotated the S-shapes 90 degrees clockwise and then translated an entire row to make the next row? Sketch your answer.

FOCUS ON MATHEMATICAL PRACTICES

MATHEMATICAL PRACTICES

H.O.T. **39. Communication** Given the coordinates of the vertices of a polygon and the corresponding coordinates of a second polygon, explain how to determine whether one polygon is a dilation of the other with center $(0, 0)$.

H.O.T. **40. Patterns** An arrow in Quadrant I is pointing to the right. It is reflected repeatedly across the x-axis and y-axis until there is an image in every quadrant. What direction does the arrow point in each of the other three quadrants? How would you answer this question if the arrow in Quadrant I is pointing down?

H.O.T. **41. Analysis** The vertices of a triangle are $K(-4, 9)$, $L(2, 0)$, and $M(8, -1)$. After a transformation, two of the image vertices are $L'(-2, 0)$ and $M'(-8, 1)$. What are the coordinates of K'? Describe the transformation.

H.O.T. **42. Proof** Given that $(x, y) \rightarrow (-y, x)$ represents a 90° counterclockwise rotation about $(0, 0)$, prove that $(x, y) \rightarrow (-x, -y)$ represents a 180° rotation about $(0, 0)$.

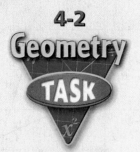

Develop the Triangle Sum Theorem

In this task, you will use patty paper to discover a relationship between the measures of the interior angles of a triangle.

Use with *Angle Relationships in Triangles*

MATHEMATICAL PRACTICES

Look for and express regularity in repeated reasoning.

MCC9-12.G.CO.10 Prove theorems about triangles.

Activity

1 Draw and label △*ABC* on a sheet of notebook paper.

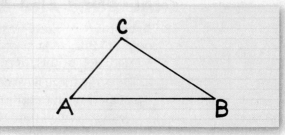

2 On patty paper draw a line *ℓ* and label a point *P* on the line.

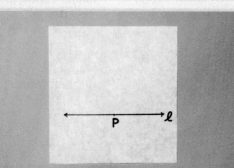

3 Place the patty paper on top of the triangle you drew. Align the papers so that $\overline{AB}$ is on line *ℓ* and *P* and *B* coincide. Trace ∠*B*. Rotate the triangle and trace ∠*C* adjacent to ∠*B*. Rotate the triangle again and trace ∠*A* adjacent to ∠*C*. The diagram shows your final step.

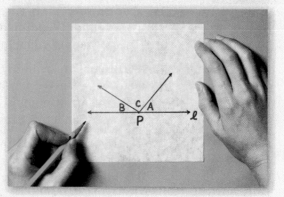

Try This

1. What do you notice about the three angles of the triangle that you traced?

2. Repeat the activity two more times using two different triangles. Do you get the same results each time?

3. Write an equation describing the relationship among the measures of the angles of △*ABC*.

4. Use inductive reasoning to write a conjecture about the sum of the measures of the angles of a triangle.

Angle Relationships in Triangles

Essential Question: What are some theorems about the measures of angles in triangles?

Objectives
Find the measures of interior and exterior angles of triangles.

Apply theorems about the interior and exterior angles of triangles.

Vocabulary
auxiliary line
corollary
interior
exterior
interior angle
exterior angle
remote interior angle

Who uses this?
Surveyors use triangles to make measurements and create boundaries. (See Example 1.)

Triangulation is a method used in surveying. Land is divided into adjacent triangles. By measuring the sides and angles of one triangle and applying properties of triangles, surveyors can gather information about adjacent triangles.

This engraving shows the county surveyor and commissioners laying out the town of Baltimore in 1730.

Know it!
Note

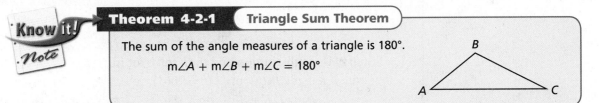

Theorem 4-2-1 | **Triangle Sum Theorem**

The sum of the angle measures of a triangle is 180°.

$$m\angle A + m\angle B + m\angle C = 180°$$

The proof of the Triangle Sum Theorem uses an *auxiliary line*. An **auxiliary line** is a line that is added to a figure to aid in a proof.

PROOF | **Triangle Sum Theorem**

Given: △ABC
Prove: m∠1 + m∠2 + m∠3 = 180°

Proof:

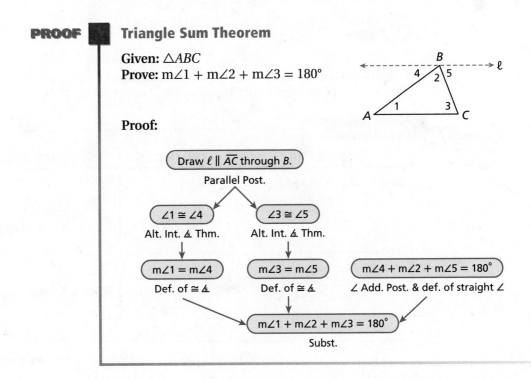

Draw ℓ ∥ $\overline{AC}$ through *B*.
Parallel Post.

∠1 ≅ ∠4
Alt. Int. ∠ Thm.

∠3 ≅ ∠5
Alt. Int. ∠ Thm.

m∠1 = m∠4
Def. of ≅ ∠

m∠3 = m∠5
Def. of ≅ ∠

m∠4 + m∠2 + m∠5 = 180°
∠ Add. Post. & def. of straight ∠

m∠1 + m∠2 + m∠3 = 180°
Subst.

Surveying Application

The map of France commonly used in the 1600s was significantly revised as a result of a triangulation land survey. The diagram shows part of the survey map. Use the diagram to find the indicated angle measures.

my.hrw.com

Online Video Tutor

A m∠NKM

$$m\angle KMN + m\angle MNK + m\angle NKM = 180°$$ △ Sum Thm.

$$88 + 48 + m\angle NKM = 180$$ Substitute 88 for m∠KMN and 48 for m∠MNK.

$$136 + m\angle NKM = 180$$ Simplify.

$$m\angle NKM = 44°$$ Subtract 136 from both sides.

B m∠JLK

Step 1 Find m∠JKL.

$$m\angle NKM + m\angle MKJ + m\angle JKL = 180°$$ Lin. Pair Thm. & ∠ Add. Post.

$$44 + 104 + m\angle JKL = 180$$ Substitute 44 for m∠NKM and 104 for m∠MKJ.

$$148 + m\angle JKL = 180$$ Simplify.

$$m\angle JKL = 32°$$ Subtract 148 from both sides.

Step 2 Use substitution and then solve for m∠JLK.

$$m\angle JLK + m\angle JKL + m\angle KJL = 180°$$ △ Sum Thm.

$$m\angle JLK + 32 + 70 = 180$$ Substitute 32 for m∠JKL and 70 for m∠KJL.

$$m\angle JLK + 102 = 180$$ Simplify.

$$m\angle JLK = 78°$$ Subtract 102 from both sides.

 CHECK IT OUT!   **1.** Use the diagram to find m∠MJK.

A **corollary** is a theorem whose proof follows directly from another theorem. Here are two corollaries to the Triangle Sum Theorem.

Know it! Note   **Corollaries**

	COROLLARY	HYPOTHESIS	CONCLUSION
4-2-2	The acute angles of a right triangle are complementary.		∠D and ∠E are complementary. m∠D + m∠E = 90°
4-2-3	The measure of each angle of an equiangular triangle is 60°.		m∠A = m∠B = m∠C = 60°

You will prove Corollaries 4-2-2 and 4-2-3 in Exercises 24 and 25.

EXAMPLE 2
MCC9-12.A.CED.1

Finding Angle Measures in Right Triangles

One of the acute angles in a right triangle measures 22.9°. What is the measure of the other acute angle?

Let the acute angles be ∠M and ∠N, with m∠M = 22.9°.

m∠M + m∠N = 90	*Acute ⦞ of rt. △ are comp.*
22.9 + m∠N = 90	*Substitute 22.9 for m∠M.*
m∠N = 67.1°	*Subtract 22.9 from both sides.*

my.hrw.com

Online Video Tutor

CHECK IT OUT! The measure of one of the acute angles in a right triangle is given. What is the measure of the other acute angle?

2a. 63.7°   **2b.** $x°$ **2c.** $48\frac{2}{5}°$

The **interior** is the set of all points inside the figure. The **exterior** is the set of all points outside the figure. An **interior angle** is formed by two sides of a triangle. An **exterior angle** is formed by one side of the triangle and the extension of an adjacent side. Each exterior angle has two *remote interior angles*. A **remote interior angle** is an interior angle that is not adjacent to the exterior angle.

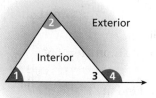

∠4 is an exterior angle. Its remote interior angles are ∠1 and ∠2.

Know it!
Note

Theorem 4-2-4   Exterior Angle Theorem

The measure of an exterior angle of a triangle is equal to the sum of the measures of its remote interior angles.

$$m∠4 = m∠1 + m∠2$$

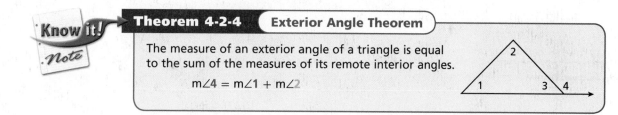

You will prove Theorem 4-2-4 in Exercise 28.

EXAMPLE 3
MCC9-12.A.CED.1

Applying the Exterior Angle Theorem

Find m∠J.

m∠J + m∠H = m∠FGH	*Ext. ∠ Thm.*
5x + 17 + 6x − 1 = 126	*Substitute 5x + 17 for m∠J, 6x − 1 for m∠H, and 126 for m∠FGH.*
11x + 16 = 126	*Simplify.*
11x = 110	*Subtract 16 from both sides.*
x = 10	*Divide both sides by 11.*

m∠J = 5x + 17 = 5(10) + 17 = 67°

my.hrw.com

Online Video Tutor

CHECK IT OUT! **3.** Find m∠ACD.

Theorem 4-2-5 (**Third Angles Theorem**)

THEOREM	HYPOTHESIS	CONCLUSION
If two angles of one triangle are congruent to two angles of another triangle, then the third pair of angles are congruent.	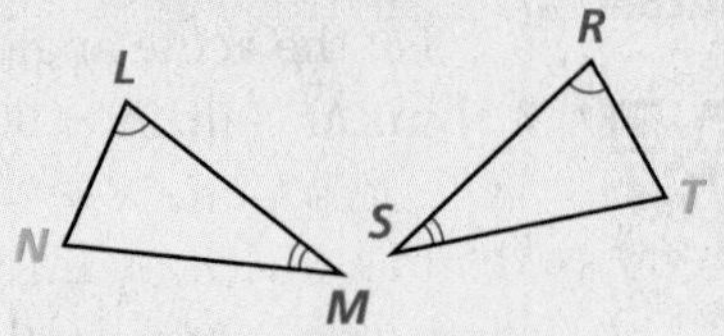	$\angle N \cong \angle T$

You will prove Theorem 4-2-5 in Exercise 27.

COMMON CORE GPS
MCC9-12.A.CED.1

EXAMPLE **4**

Applying the Third Angles Theorem

Find m∠C and m∠F.

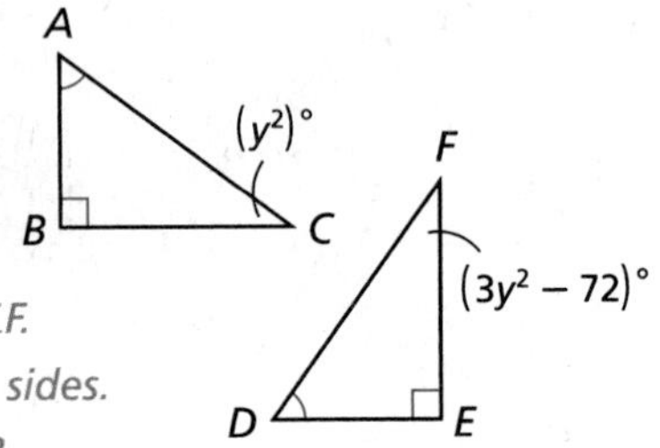

my.hrw.com

Online Video Tutor

$\angle C \cong \angle F$	Third ∠ Thm.
m∠C = m∠F	Def. of ≅ ∠.
$y^2 = 3y^2 - 72$	Substitute y^2 for m∠C and $3y^2 - 72$ for m∠F.
$-2y^2 = -72$	Subtract $3y^2$ from both sides.
$y^2 = 36$	Divide both sides by −2.

So m∠C = 36°.

Since m∠F = m∠C, m∠F = 36°.

CHECK IT OUT!

4. Find m∠P and m∠T.

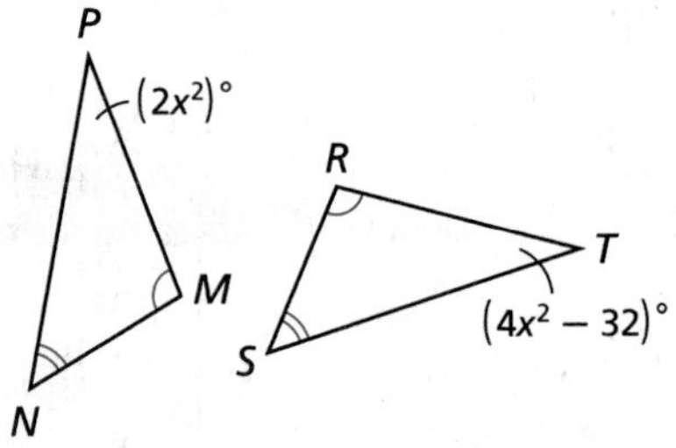

MCC.MP.3

MATHEMATICAL PRACTICES

THINK AND DISCUSS

1. Use the Triangle Sum Theorem to explain why the supplement of one of the angles of a triangle equals in measure the sum of the other two angles of the triangle. Support your answer with a sketch.

2. Sketch a triangle and draw all of its exterior angles. How many exterior angles are there at each vertex of the triangle? How many total exterior angles does the triangle have?

3. **GET ORGANIZED** Copy and complete the graphic organizer. In each box, write each theorem in words and then draw a diagram to represent it.

Theorem	Words	Diagram
Triangle Sum Theorem		
Exterior Angle Theorem		
Third Angles Theorem		

GUIDED PRACTICE

Vocabulary Apply the vocabulary from this lesson to answer each question.

1. To remember the meaning of *remote interior angle*, think of a television remote control. What is another way to remember the term *remote*?

2. An *exterior angle* is drawn at vertex *E* of △*DEF*. What are its *remote interior angles*?

3. What do you call segments, rays, or lines that are added to a given diagram?

SEE EXAMPLE 1

Astronomy Use the following information for Exercises 4 and 5.

An *asterism* is a group of stars that is easier to recognize than a constellation. One popular asterism is the Summer Triangle, which is composed of the stars Deneb, Altair, and Vega.

4. What is the value of *y*?

5. What is the measure of each angle in the Summer Triangle?

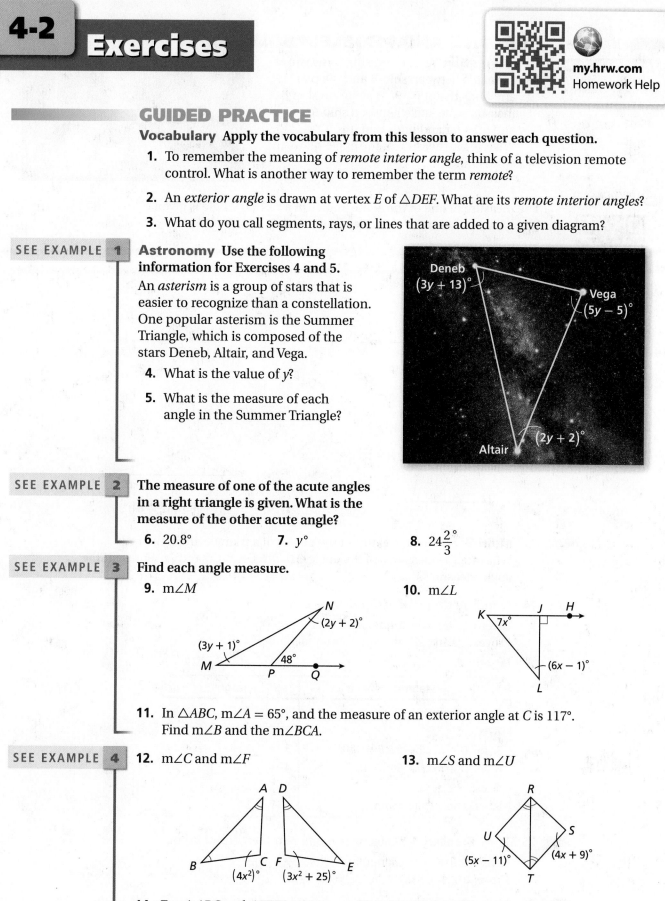

Deneb $(3y + 13)°$
Vega $(5y - 5)°$
Altair $(2y + 2)°$

SEE EXAMPLE 2

The measure of one of the acute angles in a right triangle is given. What is the measure of the other acute angle?

6. $20.8°$　　　7. $y°$　　　8. $24\frac{2}{3}°$

SEE EXAMPLE 3

Find each angle measure.

9. m∠*M*

N $(2y + 2)°$
$(3y + 1)°$
M　$48°$　*P*　*Q*

10. m∠*L*

K 　*J*　*H*
$7x°$
$(6x - 1)°$
L

11. In △*ABC*, m∠*A* = 65°, and the measure of an exterior angle at *C* is 117°. Find m∠*B* and the m∠*BCA*.

SEE EXAMPLE 4

12. m∠*C* and m∠*F*

A *D*
B *C* *F* *E*
$(4x^2)°$　$(3x^2 + 25)°$

13. m∠*S* and m∠*U*

R
U　　*S*
$(5x - 11)°$　$(4x + 9)°$
T

14. For △*ABC* and △*XYZ*, m∠*A* = m∠*X* and m∠*B* = m∠*Y*. Find the measures of ∠*C* and ∠*Z* if m∠*C* = 4x + 7 and m∠*Z* = 3(x + 5).

PRACTICE AND PROBLEM SOLVING

Independent Practice

For Exercises	See Example
15	1
16–18	2
19–20	3
21–22	4

my.hrw.com

Online Extra Practice

15. Navigation A sailor on ship A measures the angle between ship B and the pier and finds that it is 39°. A sailor on ship B measures the angle between ship A and the pier and finds that it is 57°. What is the measure of the angle between ships A and B?

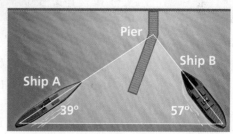

The measure of one of the acute angles in a right triangle is given. What is the measure of the other acute angle?

16. $76\frac{1}{4}°$ **17.** $2x°$ **18.** $56.8°$

Find each angle measure.

19. $m\angle XYZ$

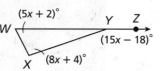

20. $m\angle C$

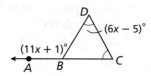

21. $m\angle N$ and $m\angle P$

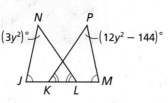

22. $m\angle Q$ and $m\angle S$

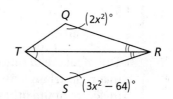

H.O.T. 23. Multi-Step The measures of the angles of a triangle are in the ratio $1:4:7$. What are the measures of the angles? (*Hint:* Let x, $4x$, and $7x$ represent the angle measures.)

24. Complete the proof of Corollary 4-2-2.

Given: $\triangle DEF$ with right $\angle F$
Prove: $\angle D$ and $\angle E$ are complementary.

Proof:

Statements	Reasons
1. $\triangle DEF$ with rt. $\angle F$	1. a. ___?___
2. b. ___?___	2. Def. of rt. $\angle$
3. $m\angle D + m\angle E + m\angle F = 180°$	3. c. ___?___
4. $m\angle D + m\angle E + 90° = 180°$	4. d. ___?___
5. e. ___?___	5. Subtr. Prop.
6. $\angle D$ and $\angle E$ are comp.	6. f. ___?___

H.O.T. 25. Prove Corollary 4-2-3 using two different methods of proof.

Given: $\triangle ABC$ is equiangular.
Prove: $m\angle A = m\angle B = m\angle C = 60°$

H.O.T. 26. Multi-Step The measure of one acute angle in a right triangle is $1\frac{1}{4}$ times the measure of the other acute angle. What is the measure of the larger acute angle?

27. Write a two-column proof of the Third Angles Theorem.

28. Prove the Exterior Angle Theorem.

Given: $\triangle ABC$ with exterior angle $\angle ACD$
Prove: $m\angle ACD = m\angle A + m\angle B$
(*Hint:* $\angle BCA$ and $\angle DCA$ form a linear pair.)

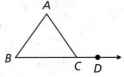

Find each angle measure.

29. $\angle UXW$ **30.** $\angle UWY$

31. $\angle WZX$ **32.** $\angle XYZ$

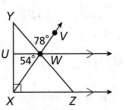

33. Critical Thinking What is the measure of any exterior angle of an equiangular triangle? What is the sum of the exterior angle measures?

34. Find $m\angle SRQ$, given that $\angle P \cong \angle U$, $\angle Q \cong \angle T$, and $m\angle RST = 37.5°$.

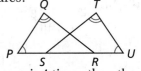

35. Multi-Step In a right triangle, one acute angle measure is 4 times the other acute angle measure. What is the measure of the smaller angle?

36. Aviation To study the forces of lift and drag, the Wright brothers built a glider, attached two ropes to it, and flew it like a kite. They modeled the two wind forces as the legs of a right triangle.

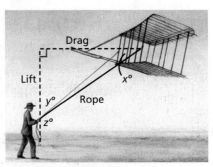

    a. What part of a right triangle is formed by each rope?

    b. Use the Triangle Sum Theorem to write an equation relating the angle measures in the right triangle.

    c. Simplify the equation from part **b**. What is the relationship between x and y?

    d. Use the Exterior Angle Theorem to write an expression for z in terms of x.

    e. If $x = 37°$, use your results from parts **c** and **d** to find y and z.

37. Estimation Draw a triangle and two exterior angles at each vertex. Estimate the measure of each angle. How are the exterior angles at each vertex related? Explain.

38. Given: $\overline{AB} \perp \overline{BD}$, $\overline{BD} \perp \overline{DC}$, $\angle A \cong \angle C$
     Prove: $\overline{AD} \parallel \overline{CB}$

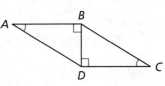

H.O.T. 39. Write About It A triangle has angle measures of 115°, 40°, and 25°. Explain how to find the measures of the triangle's exterior angles. Support your answer with a sketch.

40. One of the steps in making an origami crane involves folding a square sheet of paper into the shape shown.

    a. $\angle DCE$ is a right angle. $\overline{FC}$ bisects $\angle DCE$, and $\overline{BC}$ bisects $\angle FCE$. Find $m\angle FCB$.

    b. Use the Triangle Sum Theorem to find $m\angle CBE$.

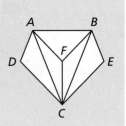

41. What is the value of x?

    (A) 19   (C) 57

    (B) 52   (D) 71

42. Find the value of s.

    (F) 23   (H) 34

    (G) 28   (J) 56

43. $\angle A$ and $\angle B$ are the remote interior angles of $\angle BCD$ in $\triangle ABC$. Which of these equations must be true?

    (A) $m\angle A - 180° = m\angle B$ (C) $m\angle BCD = m\angle BCA - m\angle A$

    (B) $m\angle A = 90° - m\angle B$ (D) $m\angle B = m\angle BCD - m\angle A$

H.O.T. **44. Extended Response** The measures of the angles in a triangle are in the ratio 2:3:4. Describe how to use algebra to find the measures of these angles. Then find the measure of each angle and classify the triangle.

CHALLENGE AND EXTEND

45. An exterior angle of a triangle measures 117°. Its remote interior angles measure $\left(2y^2 + 7\right)°$ and $\left(61 - y^2\right)°$. Find the value of y.

H.O.T. **46.** Two parallel lines are intersected by a transversal. What type of triangle is formed by the intersection of the angle bisectors of two same-side interior angles? Explain. (*Hint:* Use geometry software or construct a diagram of the angle bisectors of two same-side interior angles.)

47. Critical Thinking Explain why an exterior angle of a triangle cannot be congruent to a remote interior angle.

48. Probability The measure of each angle in a triangle is a multiple of 30°. What is the probability that the triangle has at least two congruent angles?

49. In $\triangle ABC$, $m\angle B$ is 5° less than $1\frac{1}{2}$ times $m\angle A$. $m\angle C$ is 5° less than $2\frac{1}{2}$ times $m\angle A$. What is $m\angle A$ in degrees?

FOCUS ON MATHEMATICAL PRACTICES

MATHEMATICAL PRACTICES

H.O.T. **50. Modeling** Sketch a scalene triangle with a 90° exterior angle.

H.O.T. **51. Justify** A right triangle has an acute angle of 63°. A second right triangle has an acute angle of 27°. How many pairs of congruent angles do the two triangles have? Justify your answer.

H.O.T. **52. Analysis** Explain why a triangle can have, at most, one obtuse angle.

H.O.T. **53. Make a Conjecture** Given that the exterior angle measure of a triangle equals the sum of the two remote interior angle measures, what must be the sum of three exterior angle measures (one at each vertex)? Justify your answer.

Congruent Triangles

 Essential Question: How can you use corresponding sides and corresponding angles to show that triangles are congruent?

Objectives
Use properties of congruent triangles.

Prove triangles congruent by using the definition of congruence.

Vocabulary
corresponding angles
corresponding sides
congruent polygons

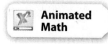
Animated Math

Who uses this?
Machinists used triangles to construct a model of the International Space Station's support structure.

Geometric figures are congruent if they are the same size and shape. **Corresponding angles** and **corresponding sides** are in the same position in polygons with an equal number of sides. Two polygons are **congruent polygons** if and only if their corresponding angles and sides are congruent. Thus triangles that are the same size and shape are congruent.

Know it! Note

Properties of Congruent Polygons

DIAGRAM	CORRESPONDING ANGLES	CORRESPONDING SIDES
$\triangle ABC \cong \triangle DEF$	$\angle A \cong \angle D$ $\angle B \cong \angle E$ $\angle C \cong \angle F$	$\overline{AB} \cong \overline{DE}$ $\overline{BC} \cong \overline{EF}$ $\overline{AC} \cong \overline{DF}$
polygon $PQRS \cong$ polygon $WXYZ$	$\angle P \cong \angle W$ $\angle Q \cong \angle X$ $\angle R \cong \angle Y$ $\angle S \cong \angle Z$	$\overline{PQ} \cong \overline{WX}$ $\overline{QR} \cong \overline{XY}$ $\overline{RS} \cong \overline{YZ}$ $\overline{PS} \cong \overline{WZ}$

Helpful Hint

Two vertices that are the endpoints of a side are called consecutive vertices. For example, P and Q are consecutive vertices.

To name a polygon, write the vertices in consecutive order. For example, you can name polygon $PQRS$ as $QRSP$ or $SRQP$, but **not** as $PRQS$. In a congruence statement, the order of the vertices indicates the corresponding parts.

COMMON CORE GPS MCC9-12.G.CO.7

EXAMPLE 1

my.hrw.com

Online Video Tutor

Naming Congruent Corresponding Parts

$\triangle RST$ and $\triangle XYZ$ represent the triangles of the space station's support structure. If $\triangle RST \cong \triangle XYZ$, identify all pairs of congruent corresponding parts.

Angles: $\angle R \cong \angle X$, $\angle S \cong \angle Y$, $\angle T \cong \angle Z$
Sides: $\overline{RS} \cong \overline{XY}$, $\overline{ST} \cong \overline{YZ}$, $\overline{RT} \cong \overline{XZ}$

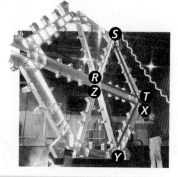

CHECK IT OUT!
1. If polygon $LMNP \cong$ polygon $EFGH$, identify all pairs of corresponding congruent parts.

NASA

EXAMPLE **2**
MCC9-12.A.CED.1

Using Corresponding Parts of Congruent Triangles

Given: $\triangle EFH \cong \triangle GFH$

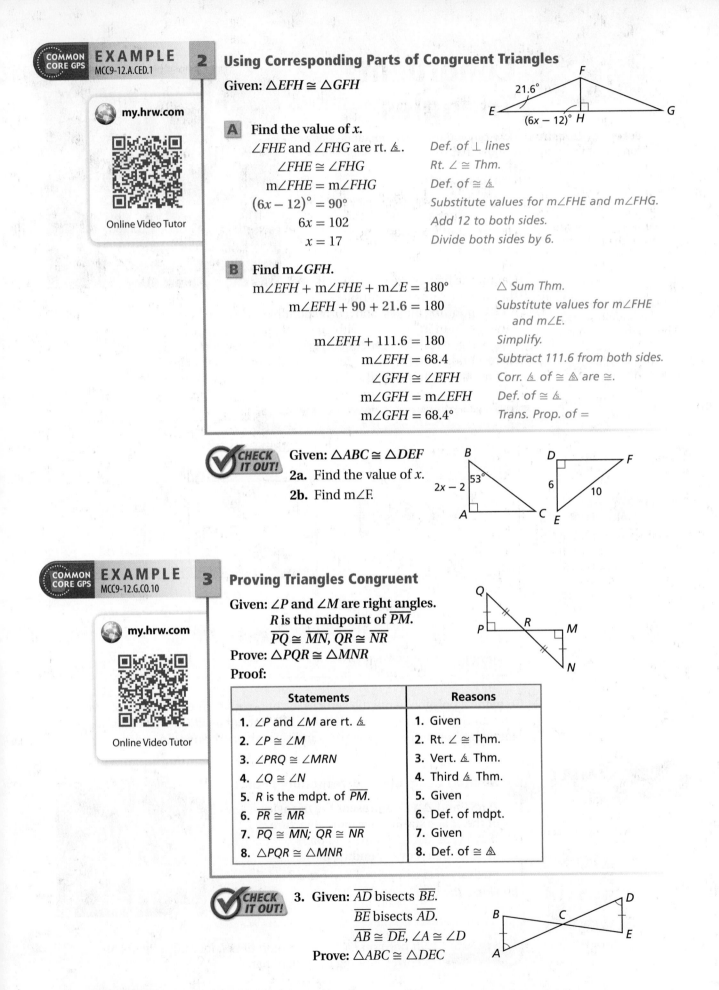

A Find the value of x.

$\angle FHE$ and $\angle FHG$ are rt. $\angle$.	Def. of $\perp$ lines
$\angle FHE \cong \angle FHG$	Rt. $\angle \cong$ Thm.
$m\angle FHE = m\angle FHG$	Def. of $\cong \angle$
$(6x - 12)^\circ = 90^\circ$	Substitute values for $m\angle FHE$ and $m\angle FHG$.
$6x = 102$	Add 12 to both sides.
$x = 17$	Divide both sides by 6.

B Find $m\angle GFH$.

$m\angle EFH + m\angle FHE + m\angle E = 180^\circ$	$\triangle$ Sum Thm.
$m\angle EFH + 90 + 21.6 = 180$	Substitute values for $m\angle FHE$ and $m\angle E$.
$m\angle EFH + 111.6 = 180$	Simplify.
$m\angle EFH = 68.4$	Subtract 111.6 from both sides.
$\angle GFH \cong \angle EFH$	Corr. $\angle$ of $\cong \triangle$ are $\cong$.
$m\angle GFH = m\angle EFH$	Def. of $\cong \angle$
$m\angle GFH = 68.4^\circ$	Trans. Prop. of =

CHECK IT OUT!

Given: $\triangle ABC \cong \triangle DEF$

2a. Find the value of x.

2b. Find $m\angle F$.

EXAMPLE **3**
MCC9-12.G.CO.10

Proving Triangles Congruent

Given: $\angle P$ and $\angle M$ are right angles.
R is the midpoint of $\overline{PM}$.
$\overline{PQ} \cong \overline{MN}$, $\overline{QR} \cong \overline{NR}$
Prove: $\triangle PQR \cong \triangle MNR$

Proof:

Statements	Reasons
1. $\angle P$ and $\angle M$ are rt. $\angle$	1. Given
2. $\angle P \cong \angle M$	2. Rt. $\angle \cong$ Thm.
3. $\angle PRQ \cong \angle MRN$	3. Vert. $\angle$ Thm.
4. $\angle Q \cong \angle N$	4. Third $\angle$ Thm.
5. R is the mdpt. of $\overline{PM}$.	5. Given
6. $\overline{PR} \cong \overline{MR}$	6. Def. of mdpt.
7. $\overline{PQ} \cong \overline{MN}$; $\overline{QR} \cong \overline{NR}$	7. Given
8. $\triangle PQR \cong \triangle MNR$	8. Def. of $\cong \triangle$

CHECK IT OUT!

3. Given: $\overline{AD}$ bisects $\overline{BE}$.
$\overline{BE}$ bisects $\overline{AD}$.
$\overline{AB} \cong \overline{DE}$, $\angle A \cong \angle D$
Prove: $\triangle ABC \cong \triangle DEC$

Student to Student

Cecelia Medina
Lamar High School

Overlapping Triangles

"With overlapping triangles, it helps me to redraw the triangles separately. That way I can mark what I know about one triangle without getting confused by the other one."

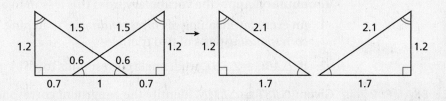

COMMON CORE GPS

EXAMPLE 4
MCC9-12.G.CO.10

my.hrw.com

Online Video Tutor

Engineering Application

The bars that give structural support to a roller coaster form triangles. Since the angle measures and the lengths of the corresponding sides are the same, the triangles are congruent.

Given: $\overline{JK} \perp \overline{KL}$, $\overline{ML} \perp \overline{KL}$, $\angle KLJ \cong \angle LKM$, $\overline{JK} \cong \overline{ML}$, $\overline{JL} \cong \overline{MK}$

Prove: $\triangle JKL \cong \triangle MLK$

Proof:

Statements	Reasons
1. $\overline{JK} \perp \overline{KL}$, $\overline{ML} \perp \overline{KL}$	1. Given
2. $\angle JKL$ and $\angle MLK$ are rt. ∡.	2. Def. of ⊥ lines
3. $\angle JKL \cong \angle MLK$	3. Rt. ∠ ≅ Thm.
4. $\angle KLJ \cong \angle LKM$	4. Given
5. $\angle KJL \cong \angle LMK$	5. Third ∡ Thm.
6. $\overline{JK} \cong \overline{ML}$, $\overline{JL} \cong \overline{MK}$	6. Given
7. $\overline{KL} \cong \overline{LK}$	7. Reflex. Prop. of ≅
8. $\triangle JKL \cong \triangle MLK$	8. Def. of ≅ ▲

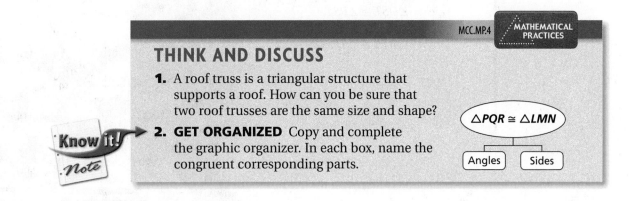

Helpful Hint

When you write a statement such as $\triangle JKL \cong \triangle MLK$, you are also stating which parts are congruent.

CHECK IT OUT!
4. Use the diagram to prove the following.
Given: $\overline{MK}$ bisects $\overline{JL}$. $\overline{JL}$ bisects $\overline{MK}$. $\overline{JK} \cong \overline{ML}$, $\overline{JK} \parallel \overline{ML}$
Prove: $\triangle JKN \cong \triangle LMN$

MCC.MP.4   **MATHEMATICAL PRACTICES**

THINK AND DISCUSS

1. A roof truss is a triangular structure that supports a roof. How can you be sure that two roof trusses are the same size and shape?

2. GET ORGANIZED Copy and complete the graphic organizer. In each box, name the congruent corresponding parts.

Know it! Note

$\triangle PQR \cong \triangle LMN$
— Angles
— Sides

GUIDED PRACTICE

Vocabulary Apply the vocabulary from this lesson to answer each question.

1. An everyday meaning of *corresponding* is "matching." How can this help you find the *corresponding* parts of two triangles?

2. If △*ABC* ≅ △*RST*, what angle corresponds to ∠*S*?

SEE EXAMPLE 1 Given: △*RST* ≅ △*LMN*. Identify the congruent corresponding parts.

3. $\overline{RS} \cong$ ___?___   4. $\overline{LN} \cong$ ___?___   5. ∠*S* ≅ ___?___

6. $\overline{TS} \cong$ ___?___   7. ∠*L* ≅ ___?___   8. ∠*N* ≅ ___?___

SEE EXAMPLE 2 Given: △*FGH* ≅ △*JKL*. Find each value.

9. *KL*   10. *x*

(Figure: Triangle FGH with side 12 near F, angle $(4x - 20)°$ at G, and triangle JKL with $3y - 15$ near J, angle $108°$ at K, and y near L.)

SEE EXAMPLE 3 11. **Given:** *E* is the midpoint of $\overline{AC}$ and $\overline{BD}$.
$\overline{AB} \cong \overline{CD}$, $\overline{AB} \parallel \overline{CD}$

Prove: △*ABE* ≅ △*CDE*

Proof:

(Figure: Rectangle ABCD with diagonals intersecting at E.)

Statements	Reasons
1. $\overline{AB} \parallel \overline{CD}$	1. a. ___?___
2. ∠*ABE* ≅ ∠*CDE*, ∠*BAE* ≅ ∠*DCE*	2. b. ___?___
3. $\overline{AB} \cong \overline{CD}$	3. c. ___?___
4. *E* is the mdpt. of $\overline{AC}$ and $\overline{BD}$.	4. d. ___?___
5. e. ___?___	5. Def. of mdpt.
6. ∠*AEB* ≅ ∠*CED*	6. f. ___?___
7. △*ABE* ≅ △*CDE*	7. g. ___?___

SEE EXAMPLE 4 12. **Engineering** The geodesic dome shown is a 14-story building that models Earth. Use the given information to prove that the triangles that make up the sphere are congruent.

Given: $\overline{SU} \cong \overline{ST} \cong \overline{SR}$, $\overline{TU} \cong \overline{TR}$,
∠*UST* ≅ ∠*RST*,
and ∠*U* ≅ ∠*R*

Prove: △*RTS* ≅ △*UTS*

(Figure: Quadrilateral with vertices U, S, T, R with tick marks.)

Gunter Marx Photographer/Corbis

PRACTICE AND PROBLEM SOLVING

Independent Practice

For Exercises	See Example
13–16	1
17–18	2
19	3
20	4

my.hrw.com

Online Extra Practice

Given: Polygon $CDEF \cong$ polygon $KLMN$. Identify the congruent corresponding parts.

13. $\overline{DE} \cong$ ___?___

14. $\overline{KN} \cong$ ___?___

15. $\angle F \cong$ ___?___

16. $\angle L \cong$ ___?___

Given: $\triangle ABD \cong \triangle CBD$. Find each value.

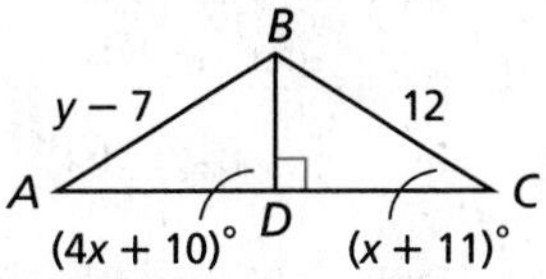

17. $m\angle C$

18. y

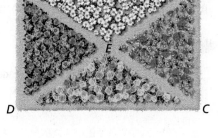

19. **Given:** $\overline{MP}$ bisects $\angle NMR$. P is the midpoint of $\overline{NR}$. $\overline{MN} \cong \overline{MR}$, $\angle N \cong \angle R$

Prove: $\triangle MNP \cong \triangle MRP$

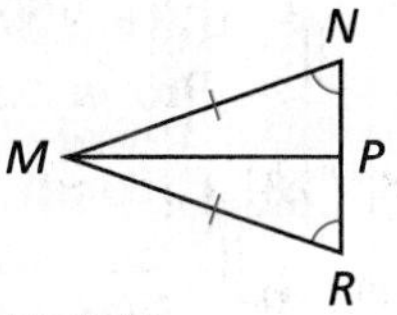

Proof:

Statements	Reasons
1. $\angle N \cong \angle R$	1. a. ___?___
2. $\overline{MP}$ bisects $\angle NMR$.	2. b. ___?___
3. c. ___?___	3. Def. of ∠ bisector
4. d. ___?___	4. Third ⨺ Thm.
5. P is the mdpt. of $\overline{NR}$.	5. e. ___?___
6. f. ___?___	6. Def. of mdpt.
7. $\overline{MN} \cong \overline{MR}$	7. g. ___?___
8. $\overline{MP} \cong \overline{MP}$	8. h. ___?___
9. $\triangle MNP \cong \triangle MRP$	9. Def. of ≅ ⨺

H.O.T. **20. Hobbies** In a garden, triangular flower beds are separated by straight rows of grass as shown.

Given: $\angle ADC$ and $\angle BCD$ are right angles. $\overline{AC} \cong \overline{BD}$, $\overline{AD} \cong \overline{BC}$ $\angle DAC \cong \angle CBD$

Prove: $\triangle ADC \cong \triangle BCD$

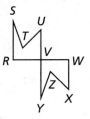

21. For two triangles, the following corresponding parts are given: $\overline{GS} \cong \overline{KP}$, $\overline{GR} \cong \overline{KH}$, $\overline{SR} \cong \overline{PH}$, $\angle S \cong \angle P$, $\angle G \cong \angle K$, and $\angle R \cong \angle H$. Write three different congruence statements.

22. The two polygons in the diagram are congruent. Complete the following congruence statement for the polygons.
polygon R___?___ $\cong$ polygon V___?___

Write and solve an equation for each of the following.

23. $\triangle ABC \cong \triangle DEF$. $AB = 2x - 10$, and $DE = x + 20$. Find the value of x and AB.

24. $\triangle JKL \cong \triangle MNP$. $m\angle L = (x^2 + 10)^\circ$, and $m\angle P = (2x^2 + 1)^\circ$. What is $m\angle L$?

25. Polygon $ABCD \cong$ polygon $PQRS$. $BC = 6x + 5$, and $QR = 5x + 7$. Find the value of x and BC.

26. Many origami models begin with a square piece of paper, *JKLM*, that is folded along both diagonals to make the creases shown. $\overline{JL}$ and $\overline{MK}$ are perpendicular bisectors of each other, and $\angle NML \cong \angle NKL$.

    a. Explain how you know that $\overline{KL}$ and $\overline{ML}$ are congruent.

    b. Prove $\triangle NML \cong \triangle NKL$.

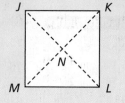

H.O.T. 27. Draw a diagram and then write a proof.
    Given: $\overline{BD} \perp \overline{AC}$. *D* is the midpoint of $\overline{AC}$. $\overline{AB} \cong \overline{CB}$, and $\overline{BD}$ bisects $\angle ABC$.
    Prove: $\triangle ABD \cong \triangle CBD$

28. **Critical Thinking** Draw two triangles that are not congruent but have an area of 4 cm^2 each.

29. ///**ERROR ANALYSIS**/// Given $\triangle MPQ \cong \triangle EDF$. Two solutions for finding m$\angle E$ are shown. Which is incorrect? Explain the error.

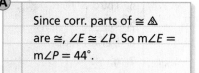

A
> Since corr. parts of ≅ △ are ≅, $\angle E \cong \angle P$. So m$\angle E$ = m$\angle P$ = 44°.

B
> Since the acute ∠ of a rt. △ are comp., m$\angle M$ = 46°. $\angle E \cong \angle M$, so m$\angle E$ = 46°.

H.O.T. 30. **Write About It** Given the diagram of the triangles, is there enough information to prove that $\triangle HKL$ is congruent to $\triangle YWX$? Explain.

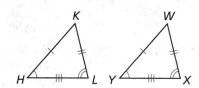

TEST PREP

31. Which congruence statement correctly indicates that the two given triangles are congruent?
    Ⓐ $\triangle ABC \cong \triangle EFD$ Ⓒ $\triangle ABC \cong \triangle DEF$
    Ⓑ $\triangle ABC \cong \triangle FDE$ Ⓓ $\triangle ABC \cong \triangle FED$

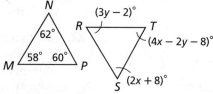

32. $\triangle MNP \cong \triangle RST$. What are the values of *x* and *y*?
    Ⓕ $x = 26$, $y = 21\frac{1}{3}$ Ⓗ $x = 25$, $y = 20\frac{2}{3}$
    Ⓖ $x = 27$, $y = 20$ Ⓙ $x = 30\frac{1}{3}$, $y = 16\frac{2}{3}$

33. $\triangle ABC \cong \triangle XYZ$. m$\angle A$ = 47.1°, and m$\angle C$ = 13.8°. Find m$\angle Y$.
    Ⓐ 13.8   Ⓒ 76.2
    Ⓑ 42.9   Ⓓ 119.1

34. $\triangle MNR \cong \triangle SPQ$, $NL = 18$, $SP = 33$, $SR = 10$, $RQ = 24$, and $QP = 30$. What is the perimeter of $\triangle MNR$?
    Ⓕ 79   Ⓗ 87
    Ⓖ 85   Ⓙ 97

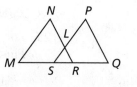

H.O.T. 35. Multi-Step Given that the perimeter of *TUVW* is 149 units, find the value of *x*. Is $\triangle TUV \cong \triangle TWV$? Explain.

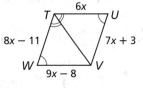

H.O.T. 36. Multi-Step Polygon $ABCD \cong$ polygon *EFGH*. $\angle A$ is a right angle. $m\angle E = (y^2 - 10)°$, and $m\angle H = (2y^2 - 132)°$. Find $m\angle D$.

37. Given: $\overline{RS} \cong \overline{RT}$, $\angle S \cong \angle T$
Prove: $\triangle RST \cong \triangle RTS$

FOCUS ON MATHEMATICAL PRACTICES

H.O.T. 38. Analysis Two triangles are congruent. Are their perimeters necessarily equal? Explain why or why not.

H.O.T. 39. Justify $\triangle ABC$ is an isosceles right triangle with $AB = 3$ and $BC = 3$. $\triangle PQR$ is also an isosceles right triangle with $PR = 3$. Is $\triangle ABC \cong \triangle PQR$? Justify your answer.

H.O.T. 40. Problem Solving $\triangle SFT \cong \triangle MKD$, $m\angle M = 54°$, and $m\angle T = 58°$. Find $m\angle S + m\angle F$. Explain.

Career Path

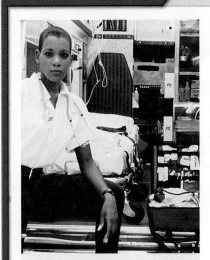

Jordan Carter
Emergency Medical
Services Program

Q: What math classes did you take in high school?
A: Algebra 1 and 2, Geometry, Precalculus

Q: What kind of degree or certification will you receive?
A: I will receive an associate's degree in applied science. Then I will take an exam to be certified as an EMT or paramedic.

Q: How do you use math in your hands-on training?
A: I calculate dosages based on body weight and age. I also calculate drug doses in milligrams per kilogram per hour or set up an IV drip to deliver medications at the correct rate.

Q: What are your future career plans?
A: When I am certified, I can work for a private ambulance service or with a fire department. I could also work in a hospital, transporting critically ill patients by ambulance or helicopter.

Ready to Go On?

my.hrw.com
Assessment and Intervention

 4-1 **Congruence and Transformations**

Apply the transformation M to the polygon with vertices $A(5, 2)$, $B(-3, 4)$, and $C(-1, -6)$. Identify and describe the transformation.

1. $M : (x, y) \rightarrow (x - 2, y + 3)$

2. $M : (x, y) \rightarrow (x, -y)$

3. $M : (x, y) \rightarrow (-y, x)$

4. $M : (x, y) \rightarrow (3x, 3y)$

 4-2 **Angle Relationships in Triangles**

Find each angle measure.

5. $m\angle M$

6. $m\angle ABC$

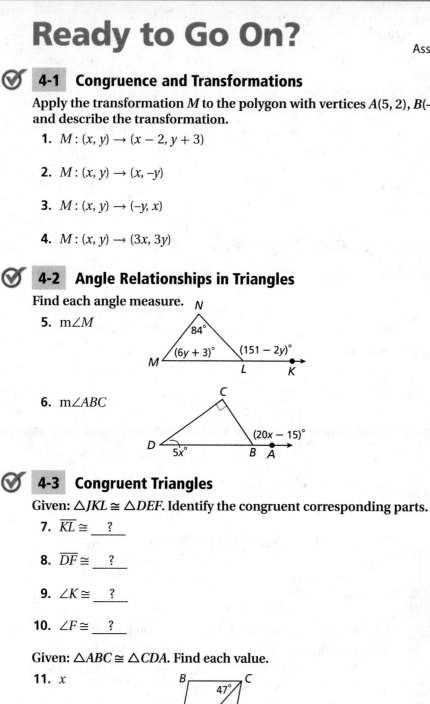

 4-3 **Congruent Triangles**

Given: $\triangle JKL \cong \triangle DEF$. Identify the congruent corresponding parts.

7. $\overline{KL} \cong$ ___?___

8. $\overline{DF} \cong$ ___?___

9. $\angle K \cong$ ___?___

10. $\angle F \cong$ ___?___

Given: $\triangle ABC \cong \triangle CDA$. Find each value.

11. x

12. CD

13. Given: $\overleftrightarrow{AB} \parallel \overleftrightarrow{CD}$, $\overline{AB} \cong \overline{CD}$, $\overline{AC} \cong \overline{BD}$,
$\overline{AC} \perp \overline{CD}$, $\overline{DB} \perp \overline{AB}$

Prove: $\triangle ACD \cong \triangle DBA$

Proof:

Statements	Reasons
1. $\overleftrightarrow{AB} \parallel \overleftrightarrow{CD}$	1. a. ____?____
2. $\angle BAD \cong \angle CDA$	2. b. ____?____
3. $\overline{AC} \perp \overline{CD}, \overline{DB} \perp \overline{AB}$	3. c. ____?____
4. $\angle ACD$ and $\angle DBA$ are rt. $\angle$	4. d. ____?____
5. e. ____?____	5. Rt. $\angle \cong$ Thm.
6. f. ____?____	6. Third $\angle$ Thm.
7. $\overline{AB} \cong \overline{CD}, \overline{AC} \cong \overline{BD}$	7. g. ____?____
8. h. ____?____	8. Reflex Prop. of $\cong$
9. $\triangle ACD \cong \triangle DBA$	9. i. ____?____

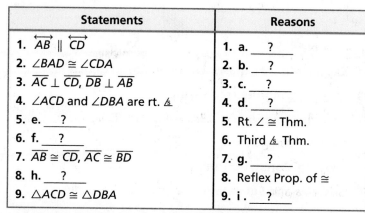

PARCC Assessment Readiness

Selected Response

1. Prove that the triangles with the given vertices are congruent.

$A(3, 1)$, $B(4, 5)$, $C(2, 3)$
$D(-1, -3)$, $E(-5, -4)$, $F(-3, -2)$

(A) The triangles are congruent because $\triangle ABC$ can be mapped onto $\triangle DEF$ by a rotation: $(x, y) \rightarrow (y, -x)$, followed by a reflection: $(x, y) \rightarrow (x, -y)$.

(B) The triangles are congruent because $\triangle ABC$ can be mapped onto $\triangle DEF$ by a reflection: $(x, y) \rightarrow (-x, y)$, followed by a rotation: $(x, y) \rightarrow (y, -x)$.

(C) The triangles are congruent because $\triangle ABC$ can be mapped onto $\triangle DEF$ by a translation: $(x, y) \rightarrow (x - 4, y)$, followed by another translation: $(x, y) \rightarrow (x, y - 6)$.

(D) The triangles are congruent because $\triangle ABC$ can be mapped onto $\triangle DEF$ by a rotation: $(x, y) \rightarrow (-y, x)$, followed by a reflection: $(x, y) \rightarrow (x, -y)$.

2. Find $m\angle K$.

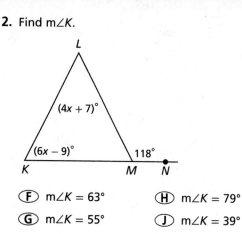

(F) $m\angle K = 63°$ (H) $m\angle K = 79°$

(G) $m\angle K = 55°$ (J) $m\angle K = 39°$

Mini-Task

3. Given: $\triangle ABC \cong \triangle MNO$

Identify all pairs of congruent corresponding parts.

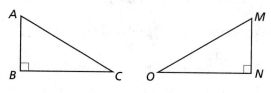

5 Proving Triangles Congruent

COMMON
CORE GPS

Contents

MATHEMATICAL PRACTICES The Common Core Georgia Performance Standards for Mathematical Practice describe varieties of expertise that all students should seek to develop. Opportunities to develop these practices are integrated throughout this program.

1 Make sense of problems and persevere in solving them.

2 Reason abstractly and quantitatively.

3 Construct viable arguments and critique the reasoning of others.

4 Model with mathematics.

5 Use appropriate tools strategically.

6 Attend to precision.

7 Look for and make use of structure.

8 Look for and express regularity in repeated reasoning.

Unpacking the Standards

my.hrw.com
Multilingual Glossary

Understanding the standards and the vocabulary terms in the standards will help you know exactly what you are expected to learn in this chapter.

COMMON CORE GPS **MCC9-12.G.SRT.5**

Use congruence ... criteria for triangles to solve problems and to prove relationships in geometric figures.

Key Vocabulary

congruent (congruente)
  Having the same size and shape, denoted by $\cong$.
triangle (triángulo)
  A three-sided polygon.

What It Means For You

When two triangles are *congruent,* it means that matching sides have the same measure and matching angles have the same measure. You can use this fact to help you solve problems.

EXAMPLE

You can use congruent triangles to find the distance across a canyon by measuring distances on only one side of the canyon.

Walk from D perpendicular to $\overline{BD}$ until you are in line with C and A. Call this point E. The distance DE is the same as the distance AB across the canyon.

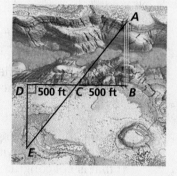

© Corbis

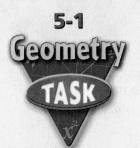
Explore SSS and SAS Triangle Congruence

You have used the definition of congruent triangles to prove triangles congruent. To use the definition, you need to prove that all three pairs of corresponding sides and all three pairs of corresponding angles are congruent.

In this task, you will discover some shortcuts for proving triangles congruent.

Use with *Triangle Congruence: SSS and SAS*

 **Use appropriate tools strategically.**

MCC9-12.G.CO.8 Explain how the criteria for triangle congruence … follow from … rigid motions.

 **Activity 1**

① Measure and cut six pieces from the straws: two that are 2 inches long, two that are 4 inches long, and two that are 5 inches long.

② Cut two pieces of string that are each about 20 inches long.

③ Thread one piece of each size of straw onto a piece of string. Tie the ends of the string together so that the pieces of straw form a triangle.

④ Using the remaining pieces, try to make another triangle with the same side lengths that is *not* congruent to the first triangle.

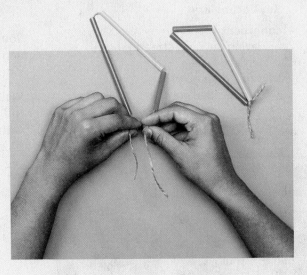

Try This

1. Repeat Activity 1 using side lengths of your choice. Are your results the same?

2. Do you think it is possible to make two triangles that have the same side lengths but that are not congruent? Why or why not?

3. How does your answer to Problem 2 provide a shortcut for proving triangles congruent?

4. Complete the following conjecture based on your results. Two triangles are congruent if _____?_____.

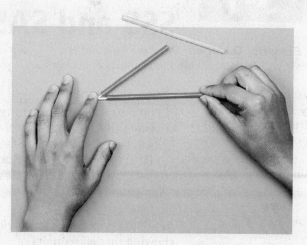

Activity 2

1 Measure and cut two pieces from the straws: one that is 4 inches long and one that is 5 inches long.

2 Use a protractor to help you bend a paper clip to form a 30° angle.

3 Place the pieces of straw on the sides of the 30° angle. The straws will form two sides of your triangle.

4 Without changing the angle formed by the paper clip, use a piece of straw to make a third side for your triangle, cutting it to fit as necessary. Use additional paper clips or string to hold the straws together in a triangle.

Try This

5. Repeat Activity 2 using side lengths and an angle measure of your choice. Are your results the same?

6. Suppose you know two side lengths of a triangle and the measure of the angle between these sides. Can the length of the third side be any measure? Explain.

7. How does your answer to Problem 6 provide a shortcut for proving triangles congruent?

8. Use the two given sides and the given angle from Activity 2 to form a triangle that is not congruent to the triangle you formed. (*Hint:* One of the given sides does not have to be adjacent to the given angle.)

9. Complete the following conjecture based on your results. Two triangles are congruent if _____?_____ .

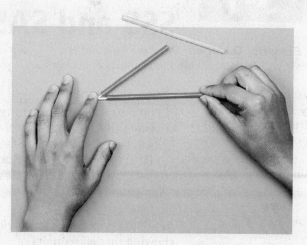

5-1 Triangle Congruence: SSS and SAS

? **Essential Question:** What information about two triangles allows you to conclude the triangles are congruent?

Objectives
Apply SSS and SAS to construct triangles and to solve problems.

Prove triangles congruent by using SSS and SAS.

Vocabulary
triangle rigidity
included angle

Who uses this?
Engineers used the property of triangle rigidity to design the internal support for the Statue of Liberty and to build bridges, towers, and other structures. (See Example 2.)

Recall that you proved triangles congruent by showing that all six pairs of corresponding parts were congruent.

The property of **triangle rigidity** gives you a shortcut for proving two triangles congruent. It states that if the side lengths of a triangle are given, the triangle can have only one shape.

For example, you only need to know that two triangles have three pairs of congruent corresponding sides. This can be expressed as the following postulate.

Know it!
Note

Postulate 5-1-1 — Side-Side-Side (SSS) Congruence

POSTULATE	HYPOTHESIS	CONCLUSION
If three sides of one triangle are congruent to three sides of another triangle, then the triangles are congruent.	4 cm, 7 cm, 6 cm (△ABC); 4 cm, 6 cm, 7 cm (△FDE)	△ABC ≅ △FDE

COMMON CORE GPS MCC9-12.G.SRT.5

EXAMPLE 1 **Using SSS to Prove Triangle Congruence**

Use SSS to explain why △PQR ≅ △PSR.
It is given that $\overline{PQ} \cong \overline{PS}$ and that $\overline{QR} \cong \overline{SR}$. By the Reflexive Property of Congruence, $\overline{PR} \cong \overline{PR}$. Therefore △PQR ≅ △PSR by SSS.

🌐 **my.hrw.com**

Online Video Tutor

✓ **CHECK IT OUT!**
1. Use SSS to explain why △ABC ≅ △CDA.

An **included angle** is an angle formed by two adjacent sides of a polygon. ∠B is the included angle between sides $\overline{AB}$ and $\overline{BC}$.

The image Bank/Getty Images

It can also be shown that only two pairs of congruent corresponding sides are needed to prove the congruence of two triangles if the included angles are also congruent.

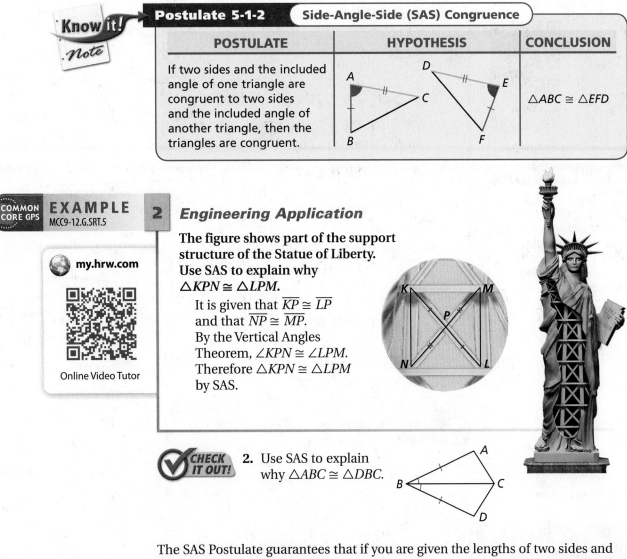

Postulate 5-1-2 **Side-Angle-Side (SAS) Congruence**

POSTULATE	HYPOTHESIS	CONCLUSION
If two sides and the included angle of one triangle are congruent to two sides and the included angle of another triangle, then the triangles are congruent.		$\triangle ABC \cong \triangle EFD$

Know it! Note

COMMON CORE GPS MCC9-12.G.SRT.5 **EXAMPLE 2**

Engineering Application

The figure shows part of the support structure of the Statue of Liberty. Use SAS to explain why $\triangle KPN \cong \triangle LPM$.

It is given that $\overline{KP} \cong \overline{LP}$ and that $\overline{NP} \cong \overline{MP}$. By the Vertical Angles Theorem, $\angle KPN \cong \angle LPM$. Therefore $\triangle KPN \cong \triangle LPM$ by SAS.

my.hrw.com

Online Video Tutor

CHECK IT OUT!

2. Use SAS to explain why $\triangle ABC \cong \triangle DBC$.

The SAS Postulate guarantees that if you are given the lengths of two sides and the measure of the included angle, you can construct one and only one triangle.

Construction **Congruent Triangles Using SAS**

Use a straightedge to draw two segments and one angle, or copy the given segments and angle.

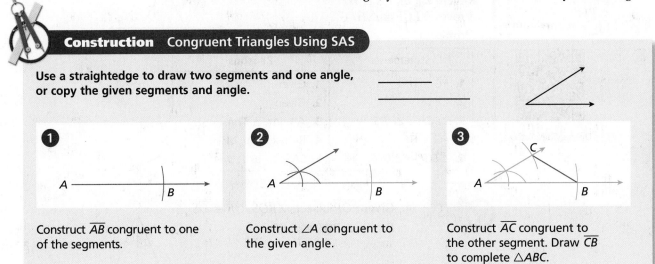

1 Construct $\overline{AB}$ congruent to one of the segments.

2 Construct $\angle A$ congruent to the given angle.

3 Construct $\overline{AC}$ congruent to the other segment. Draw $\overline{CB}$ to complete $\triangle ABC$.

EXAMPLE 3
MCC9-12.A.CED.1

Verifying Triangle Congruence

Show that the triangles are congruent for the given value of the variable.

my.hrw.com

Online Video Tutor

A $\triangle UVW \cong \triangle YXZ, x = 3$

$ZY = x - 1$
$\quad = 3 - 1 = 2$
$XZ = x = 3$
$XY = 3x - 5$
$\quad = 3(3) - 5 = 4$

$\overline{UV} \cong \overline{YX}$. $\overline{VW} \cong \overline{XZ}$, and $\overline{UW} \cong \overline{YZ}$.
So $\triangle UVW \cong \triangle YXZ$ by SSS.

Caution!

The letters SAS are written in that order because the congruent angles must be between pairs of congruent corresponding sides.

B $\triangle DEF \cong \triangle JGH, y = 7$

$JG = 2y + 1$
$\quad = 2(7) + 1$
$\quad = 15$
$GH = y^2 - 4y + 3$
$\quad = (7)^2 - 4(7) + 3$
$\quad = 24$
$m\angle G = 12y + 42$
$\quad = 12(7) + 42$
$\quad = 126°$

$\overline{DE} \cong \overline{JG}$. $\overline{EF} \cong \overline{GH}$, and $\angle E \cong \angle G$.
So $\triangle DEF \cong \triangle JGH$ by SAS.

CHECK IT OUT!

3. Show that $\triangle ADB \cong \triangle CDB$ when $t = 4$.

EXAMPLE 4
MCC9-12.G.SRT.5

Proving Triangles Congruent

Given: $\ell \parallel m, \overline{EG} \cong \overline{HF}$
Prove: $\triangle EGF \cong \triangle HFG$
Proof:

my.hrw.com

Online Video Tutor

Statements	Reasons
1. $\overline{EG} \cong \overline{HF}$	1. Given
2. $\ell \parallel m$	2. Given
3. $\angle EGF \cong \angle HFG$	3. Alt. Int. ∡ Thm.
4. $\overline{FG} \cong \overline{GF}$	4. Reflex Prop. of $\cong$
5. $\triangle EGF \cong \triangle HFG$	5. SAS *Steps 1, 3, 4*

CHECK IT OUT!

4. Given: $\overrightarrow{QP}$ bisects $\angle RQS$. $\overline{QR} \cong \overline{QS}$
Prove: $\triangle RQP \cong \triangle SQP$

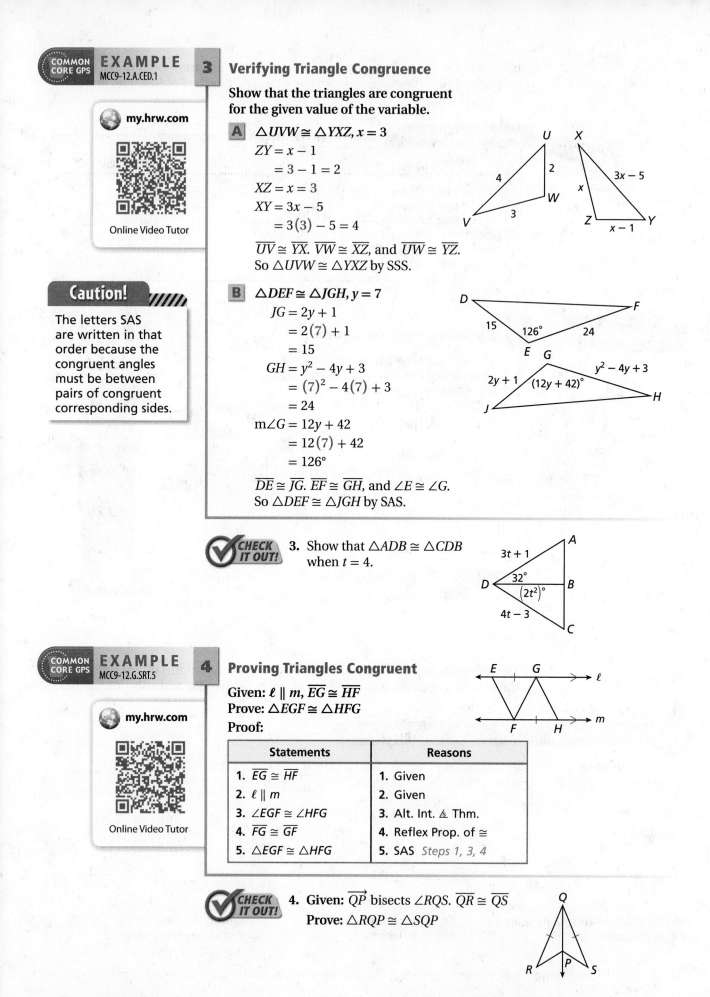

THINK AND DISCUSS

1. Describe three ways you could prove that $\triangle ABC \cong \triangle DEF$.

2. Explain why the SSS and SAS Postulates are shortcuts for proving triangles congruent.

3. **GET ORGANIZED** Copy and complete the graphic organizer. Use it to compare the SSS and SAS postulates.

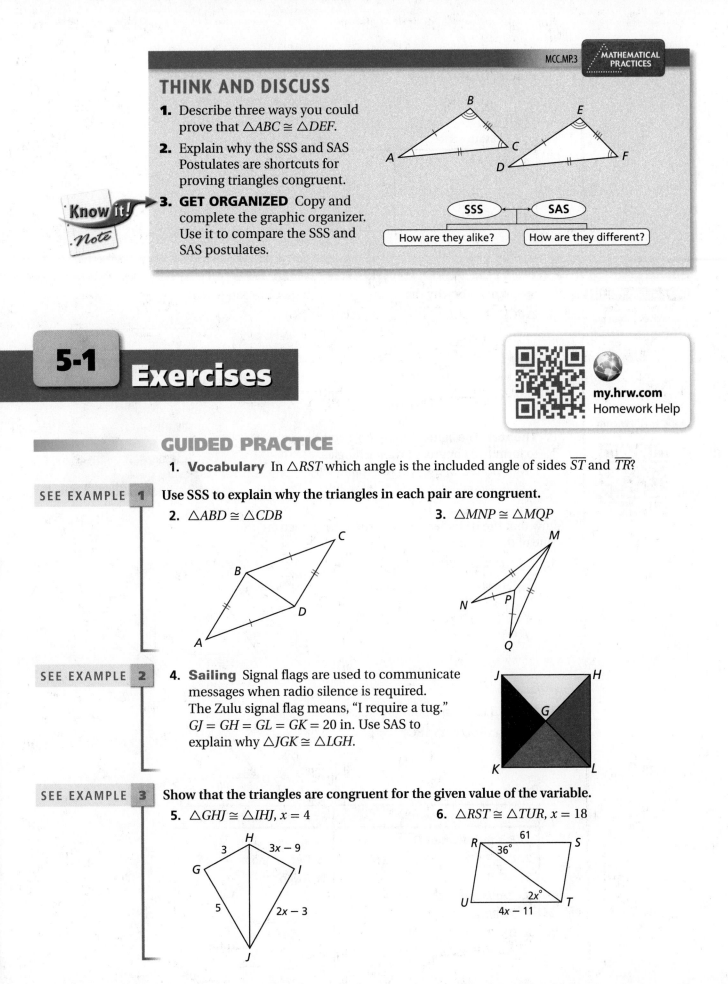

Know it! Note

SSS ←→ SAS

| How are they alike? | How are they different? |

5-1 Exercises

my.hrw.com
Homework Help

GUIDED PRACTICE

1. **Vocabulary** In $\triangle RST$ which angle is the included angle of sides $\overline{ST}$ and $\overline{TR}$?

SEE EXAMPLE **1** **Use SSS to explain why the triangles in each pair are congruent.**

2. $\triangle ABD \cong \triangle CDB$

3. $\triangle MNP \cong \triangle MQP$

SEE EXAMPLE **2** 4. **Sailing** Signal flags are used to communicate messages when radio silence is required. The Zulu signal flag means, "I require a tug." $GJ = GH = GL = GK = 20$ in. Use SAS to explain why $\triangle JGK \cong \triangle LGH$.

SEE EXAMPLE **3** **Show that the triangles are congruent for the given value of the variable.**

5. $\triangle GHJ \cong \triangle IHJ$, $x = 4$

6. $\triangle RST \cong \triangle TUR$, $x = 18$

SEE EXAMPLE 4

7. Given: $\overline{JK} \cong \overline{ML}$, $\angle JKL \cong \angle MLK$

Prove: $\triangle JKL \cong \triangle MLK$

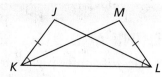

Proof:

Statements	Reasons
1. $\overline{JK} \cong \overline{ML}$	1. a. ___?___
2. b. ___?___	2. Given
3. $\overline{KL} \cong \overline{LK}$	3. c. ___?___
4. $\triangle JKL \cong \triangle MLK$	4. d. ___?___

PRACTICE AND PROBLEM SOLVING

Independent Practice

For Exercises	See Example
8–9	1
10	2
11–12	3
13	4

my.hrw.com

Online Extra Practice

Use SSS to explain why the triangles in each pair are congruent.

8. $\triangle BCD \cong \triangle EDC$

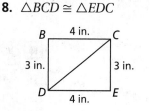

9. $\triangle GJK \cong \triangle GJL$

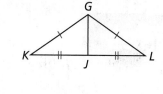

10. Theater The lights shining on a stage appear to form two congruent right triangles. Given $\overline{EC} \cong \overline{DB}$, use SAS to explain why $\triangle ECB \cong \triangle DBC$.

Show that the triangles are congruent for the given value of the variable.

11. $\triangle MNP \cong \triangle QNP$, $y = 3$

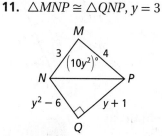

12. $\triangle XYZ \cong \triangle STU$, $t = 5$

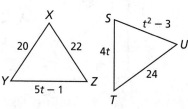

13. Given: B is the midpoint of $\overline{DC}$. $\overline{AB} \perp \overline{DC}$

Prove: $\triangle ABD \cong \triangle ABC$

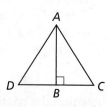

Proof:

Statements	Reasons
1. B is the mdpt. of $\overline{DC}$.	1. a. ___?___
2. b. ___?___	2. Def. of mdpt.
3. c. ___?___	3. Given
4. $\angle ABD$ and $\angle ABC$ are rt. $\angle$s.	4. d. ___?___
5. $\angle ABD \cong \angle ABC$	5. e. ___?___
6. f. ___?___	6. Reflex. Prop. of $\cong$
7. $\triangle ABD \cong \triangle ABC$	7. g. ___?___

Which postulate, if any, can be used to prove the triangles congruent?

14. **15.**

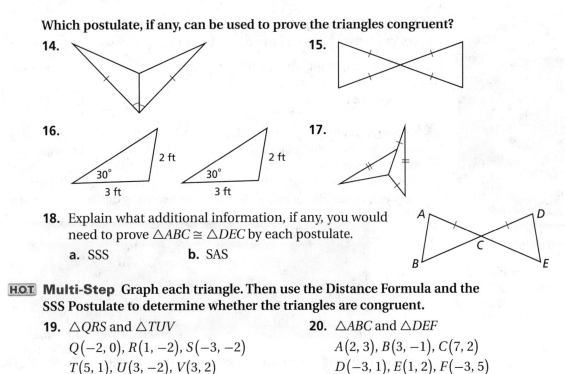

16. **17.**

18. Explain what additional information, if any, you would need to prove $\triangle ABC \cong \triangle DEC$ by each postulate.

    a. SSS   **b.** SAS

H.O.T. **Multi-Step** Graph each triangle. Then use the Distance Formula and the SSS Postulate to determine whether the triangles are congruent.

19. $\triangle QRS$ and $\triangle TUV$
    $Q(-2, 0), R(1, -2), S(-3, -2)$
    $T(5, 1), U(3, -2), V(3, 2)$

20. $\triangle ABC$ and $\triangle DEF$
    $A(2, 3), B(3, -1), C(7, 2)$
    $D(-3, 1), E(1, 2), F(-3, 5)$

21. **Given:** $\angle ZVY \cong \angle WYV$,
           $\angle ZVW \cong \angle WYZ$,
           $\overline{VW} \cong \overline{YZ}$
    Prove: $\triangle ZVY \cong \triangle WYV$

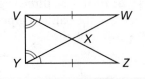

    Proof:

Statements	Reasons
1. $\angle ZVY \cong \angle WYV$, $\angle ZVW \cong WYZ$	**1. a.** ?
2. $m\angle ZVY = m\angle WYV$, $m\angle ZVW = m\angle WYZ$	**2. b.** ?
3. $m\angle ZVY + m\angle ZVW = m\angle WYV + m\angle WYZ$	**3.** Add. Prop. of =
4. c. ?	**4.** $\angle$ Add. Post.
5. $\angle WVY \cong \angle ZYV$	**5. d.** ?
6. $\overline{VW} \cong \overline{YZ}$	**6. e.** ?
7. f. ?	**7.** Reflex. Prop. of $\cong$
8. $\triangle ZVY \cong \triangle WYV$	**8. g.** ?

Real-World Connections

22. The diagram shows two triangular trusses that were built for the roof of a doghouse.

    a. You can use a protractor to check that $\angle A$ and $\angle D$ are right angles. Explain how you could make just two additional measurements on each truss to ensure that the trusses are congruent.

    b. You verify that the trusses are congruent and find that $AB = AC = 2.5$ ft. Find the length of $\overline{EF}$ to the nearest tenth. Explain.

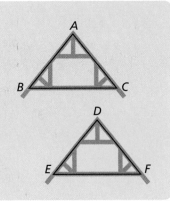

23. Critical Thinking Draw two isosceles triangles that are not congruent but that have a perimeter of 15 cm each.

24. $\triangle ABC \cong \triangle ADC$ for what value of x? Explain why the SSS Postulate can be used to prove the two triangles congruent.

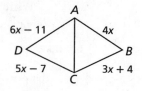

25. Ecology A *wing deflector* is a triangular structure made of logs that is filled with large rocks and placed in a stream to guide the current or prevent erosion. Wing deflectors are often used in pairs. Suppose an engineer wants to build two wing deflectors. The logs that form the sides of each wing deflector are perpendicular. How can the engineer make sure that the two wing deflectors are congruent?

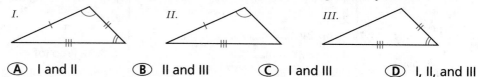

Wing deflectors

26. Write About It If you use the same two sides and included angle to repeat the construction of a triangle, are your two constructed triangles congruent? Explain.

H.O.T. 27. Construction Use three segments (SSS) to construct a scalene triangle. Suppose you then use the same segments in a different order to construct a second triangle. Will the result be the same? Explain.

TEST PREP

28. Which of the three triangles below can be proven congruent by SSS or SAS?

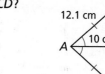

I.   II.   III.

Ⓐ I and II   Ⓑ II and III   Ⓒ I and III   Ⓓ I, II, and III

29. What is the perimeter of polygon $ABCD$?

Ⓕ 29.9 cm   Ⓗ 49.8 cm

Ⓖ 39.8 cm   Ⓙ 59.8 cm

12.1 cm
10 cm
7.8 cm

30. Jacob wants to prove that $\triangle FGH \cong \triangle JKL$ using SAS. He knows that $\overline{FG} \cong \overline{JK}$ and $\overline{FH} \cong \overline{JL}$. What additional piece of information does he need?

Ⓐ $\angle F \cong \angle J$ Ⓒ $\angle H \cong \angle L$

Ⓑ $\angle G \cong \angle K$ Ⓓ $\angle F \cong \angle G$

31. What must the value of x be in order to prove that $\triangle EFG \cong \triangle EHG$ by SSS?

Ⓕ 1.5   Ⓗ 4.67

Ⓖ 4.25   Ⓙ 5.5

$6x - 4$ $4x + 7$
24   24

Jack Fields/Photo Researchers, Inc.

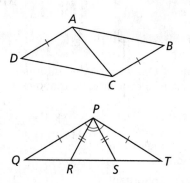

CHALLENGE AND EXTEND

H.O.T. 32. **Given:**. $\angle ADC$ and $\angle BCD$ are supplementary. $\overline{AD} \cong \overline{CB}$
Prove: $\triangle ADB \cong \triangle CBD$
(*Hint:* Draw an auxiliary line.)

H.O.T. 33. **Given:** $\angle QPS \cong \angle TPR$, $\overline{PQ} \cong \overline{PT}$, $\overline{PR} \cong \overline{PS}$
Prove: $\triangle PQR \cong \triangle PTS$

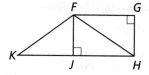

Algebra **Use the following information for Exercises 34 and 35.** Find the value of x. Then use SSS or SAS to write a paragraph proof showing that two of the triangles are congruent.

34. $m\angle FKJ = 2x°$
$m\angle KFJ = (3x + 10)°$
$KJ = 4x + 8$
$HJ = 6(x - 4)$

35. $\overline{FJ}$ bisects $\angle KFH$.
$m\angle KFJ = (2x + 6)°$
$m\angle HFJ = (3x - 21)°$
$FK = 8x - 45$
$FH = 6x + 9$

MATHEMATICAL PRACTICES

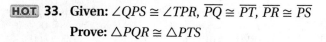

FOCUS ON MATHEMATICAL PRACTICES

H.O.T. 36. **Modeling** The vertices of $\triangle ABC$ are $A(-1, 5)$, $B(-1, -1)$, and $C(3, -1)$. Consider points $M(2, 1)$ and $N(2, -5)$. At which location, or locations, for P is $\triangle MNP \cong \triangle ABC$ by SSS?

H.O.T. 37. **Proof** **Given:** $\triangle XYZ$ is an equilateral triangle.
$\overrightarrow{XM}$ bisects $\angle X$ and intersects $\overline{YZ}$ at M.
Prove: $\triangle XMY \cong \triangle XMZ$

Using Technology

Use geometry software to complete the following.

1. Draw a triangle and label the vertices A, B, and C. Draw a point and label it D. Mark a vector from A to B and translate D by the marked vector. Label the image E. Draw $\overleftrightarrow{DE}$. Mark $\angle BAC$ and rotate $\overleftrightarrow{DE}$ about D by the marked angle. Mark $\angle ABC$ and rotate $\overleftrightarrow{DE}$ about E by the marked angle. Label the intersection F.
2. Drag A, B, and C to different locations. What do you notice about the two triangles?
3. Write a conjecture about $\triangle ABC$ and $\triangle DEF$.
4. Test your conjecture by measuring the sides and angles of $\triangle ABC$ and $\triangle DEF$.

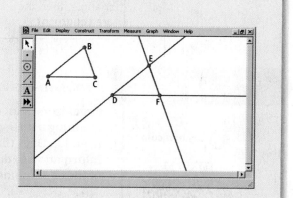

5-2 Triangle Congruence: ASA, AAS, and HL

Essential Question: What information about two triangles allows you to conclude the triangles are congruent?

Objectives

Apply ASA, AAS, and HL to construct triangles and to solve problems.

Prove triangles congruent by using ASA, AAS, and HL.

Vocabulary

included side

Why use this?

Bearings are used to convey direction, helping people find their way to specific locations.

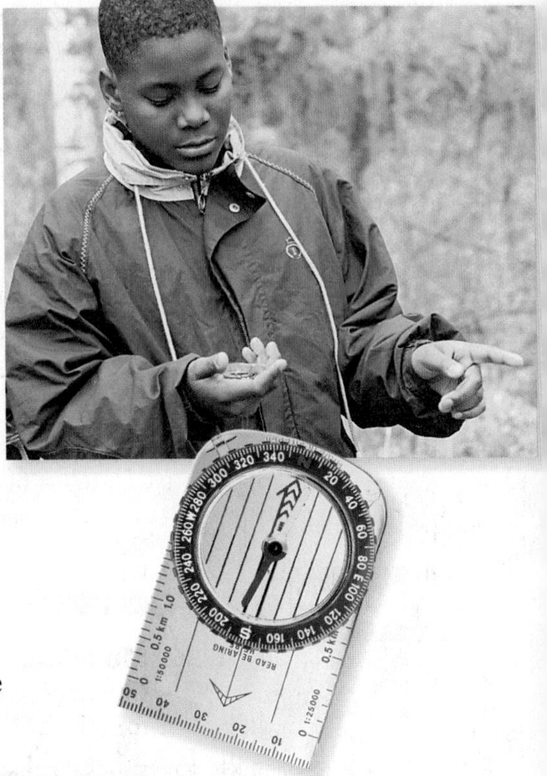

Participants in an *orienteering* race use a map and a compass to find their way to checkpoints along an unfamiliar course. Directions are given by *bearings*, which are based on compass headings. For example, to travel along the bearing S 43° E, you face south and then turn 43° to the east.

An **included side** is the common side of two consecutive angles in a polygon. The following postulate uses the idea of an *included side*.

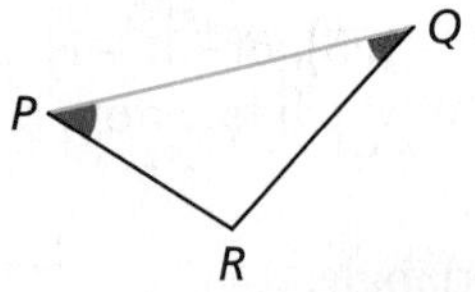

$\overline{PQ}$ is the included side of $\angle P$ and $\angle Q$.

Know it! Note

Postulate 5-2-1 Angle-Side-Angle (ASA) Congruence

POSTULATE	HYPOTHESIS	CONCLUSION
If two angles and the included side of one triangle are congruent to two angles and the included side of another triangle, then the triangles are congruent.	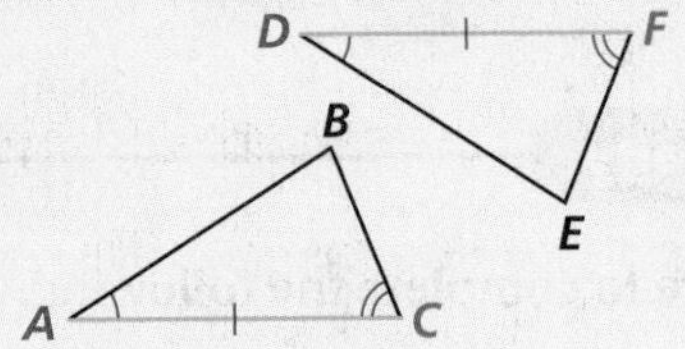	$\triangle ABC \cong \triangle DEF$

COMMON CORE GPS **EXAMPLE 1** MCC9-12.G.MG.1

my.hrw.com

Online Video Tutor

Problem-Solving Application

Organizers of an orienteering race are planning a course with checkpoints *A*, *B*, and *C*. Does the table give enough information to determine the location of the checkpoints?

	Bearing	Distance
A to *B*	N 55° E	7.6 km
B to *C*	N 26° W	
C to *A*	S 20° W	

1 Understand the Problem

The **answer** is whether the information in the table can be used to find the position of checkpoints *A*, *B*, and *C*. List the **important information:** The bearing from *A* to *B* is N 55° E. From *B* to *C* is N 26° W, and from *C* to *A* is S 20° W. The distance from *A* to *B* is 7.6 km.

(tr), ©Steve Skjold/Alamy Photos; (cr), Stockbyte Royalty-Free Images/HMH Library

Make sense of problems and persevere in solving them.

2 Make a Plan

Draw the course using vertical lines to show north-south directions. Then use these parallel lines and the alternate interior angles to help find angle measures of $\triangle ABC$.

3 Solve

$m\angle CAB = 55° - 20° = 35°$

$m\angle CBA = 180° - (26° + 55°) = 99°$

You know the measures of $\angle CAB$ and $\angle CBA$ and the length of the included side $\overline{AB}$. Therefore by ASA, a unique triangle ABC is determined.

4 Look Back

One and only one triangle can be made using the information in the table, so the table does give enough information to determine the location of all the checkpoints.

CHECK IT OUT!

1. What if...? If 7.6 km is the distance from B to C, is there enough information to determine the location of all the checkpoints? Explain.

EXAMPLE 2
MCC9-12.G.SRT.5

Applying ASA Congruence

my.hrw.com

Online Video Tutor

Determine if you can use ASA to prove $\triangle UVX \cong \triangle WVX$. Explain.

$\angle UXV \cong \angle WXV$ as given. Since $\angle WVX$ is a right angle that forms a linear pair with $\angle UVX$, $\angle WVX \cong \angle UVX$. Also $\overline{VX} \cong \overline{VX}$ by the Reflexive Property. Therefore $\triangle UVX \cong \triangle WVX$ by ASA.

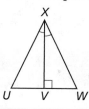

CHECK IT OUT!

2. Determine if you can use ASA to prove $\triangle NKL \cong \triangle LMN$. Explain.

Construction Congruent Triangles Using ASA

Use a straightedge to draw a segment and two angles, or copy the given segment and angles.

❶	❷	❸	❹

Construct $\overline{CD}$ congruent to the given segment.

Construct $\angle C$ congruent to one of the angles.

Construct $\angle D$ congruent to the other angle.

$\triangle CDE$

Label the intersection of the rays as E.

You can use the Third Angles Theorem to prove another congruence relationship based on ASA. This theorem is Angle-Angle-Side (AAS).

Know it! Note

Theorem 5-2-2   **Angle-Angle-Side (AAS) Congruence**

THEOREM	HYPOTHESIS	CONCLUSION
If two angles and a nonincluded side of one triangle are congruent to the corresponding angles and nonincluded side of another triangle, then the triangles are congruent.	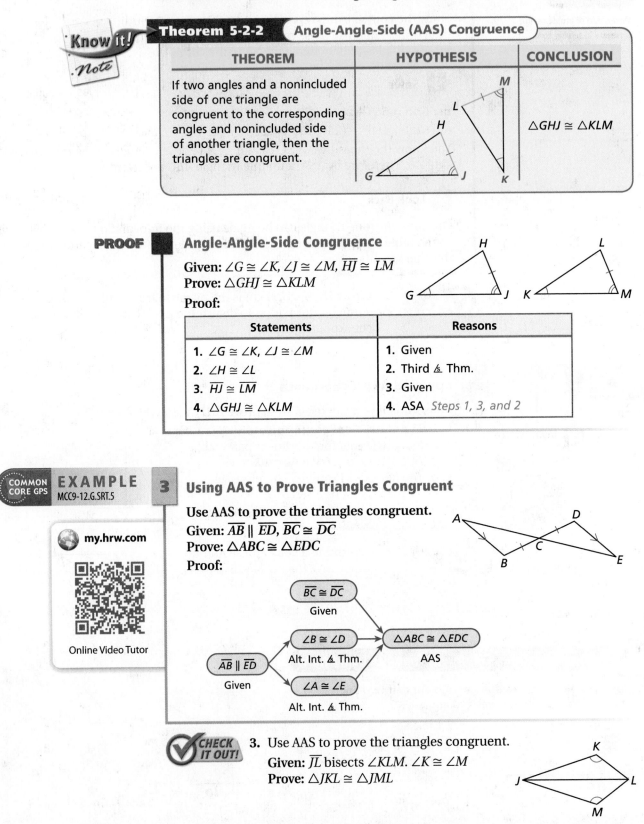	$\triangle GHJ \cong \triangle KLM$

PROOF   **Angle-Angle-Side Congruence**

Given: $\angle G \cong \angle K$, $\angle J \cong \angle M$, $\overline{HJ} \cong \overline{LM}$
Prove: $\triangle GHJ \cong \triangle KLM$
Proof:

Statements	Reasons
1. $\angle G \cong \angle K$, $\angle J \cong \angle M$	1. Given
2. $\angle H \cong \angle L$	2. Third $\angle$ Thm.
3. $\overline{HJ} \cong \overline{LM}$	3. Given
4. $\triangle GHJ \cong \triangle KLM$	4. ASA *Steps 1, 3, and 2*

COMMON CORE GPS   **EXAMPLE 3**   MCC9-12.G.SRT.5

Using AAS to Prove Triangles Congruent

Use AAS to prove the triangles congruent.
Given: $\overline{AB} \parallel \overline{ED}$, $\overline{BC} \cong \overline{DC}$
Prove: $\triangle ABC \cong \triangle EDC$
Proof:

my.hrw.com

Online Video Tutor

$\overline{BC} \cong \overline{DC}$ — Given
$\angle B \cong \angle D$ — Alt. Int. $\angle$ Thm.
$\overline{AB} \parallel \overline{ED}$ — Given
$\angle A \cong \angle E$ — Alt. Int. $\angle$ Thm.
$\triangle ABC \cong \triangle EDC$ — AAS

CHECK IT OUT!

3. Use AAS to prove the triangles congruent.
Given: $\overline{JL}$ bisects $\angle KLM$. $\angle K \cong \angle M$
Prove: $\triangle JKL \cong \triangle JML$

There are four theorems for right triangles that are not used for acute or obtuse triangles. They are Leg-Leg (LL), Hypotenuse-Angle (HA), Leg-Angle (LA), and Hypotenuse-Leg (HL). You will prove LL, HA, and LA in Exercises 21, 23, and 33.

Theorem 5-2-3 (**Hypotenuse-Leg (HL) Congruence**)

THEOREM	HYPOTHESIS	CONCLUSION
If the hypotenuse and a leg of a right triangle are congruent to the hypotenuse and a leg of another right triangle, then the triangles are congruent.		$\triangle ABC \cong \triangle DEF$

You will prove the Hypotenuse-Leg Theorem in Lesson 5-4, Exercise 41.

COMMON CORE GPS MCC.MP.3

EXAMPLE 4

my.hrw.com

Online Video Tutor

Applying HL Congruence

Determine if you can use the HL Congruence Theorem to prove the triangles congruent. If not, tell what else you need to know.

A $\triangle VWX$ and $\triangle YXW$

According to the diagram, $\triangle VWX$ and $\triangle YXW$ are right triangles that share hypotenuse $\overline{WX}$. $\overline{WX} \cong \overline{XW}$ by the Reflexive Property. It is given that $\overline{WV} \cong \overline{XY}$, therefore $\triangle VWX \cong \triangle YXW$ by HL.

B $\triangle VWZ$ and $\triangle YXZ$

This conclusion cannot be proved by HL. According to the diagram, $\triangle VWZ$ and $\triangle YXZ$ are right triangles, and $\overline{WV} \cong \overline{XY}$. You do not know that hypotenuse $\overline{WZ}$ is congruent to hypotenuse $\overline{XZ}$.

CHECK IT OUT!

4. Determine if you can use the HL Congruence Theorem to prove $\triangle ABC \cong \triangle DCB$. If not, tell what else you need to know.

MCC.MP.7   **MATHEMATICAL PRACTICES**

THINK AND DISCUSS

1. Could you use AAS to prove that these two triangles are congruent? Explain.

2. The arrangement of the letters in ASA matches the arrangement of what parts of congruent triangles? Include a sketch to support your answer.

Know it! *Note*

3. GET ORGANIZED Copy and complete the graphic organizer. In each column, write a description of the method and then sketch two triangles, marking the appropriate congruent parts.

Proving Triangles Congruent						
	Def. of △ ≅	SSS	SAS	ASA	AAS	HL
Words						
Pictures						

GUIDED PRACTICE

1. **Vocabulary** A triangle contains ∠ABC and ∠ACB with $\overline{BC}$ "closed in" between them. How would this help you remember the definition of *included side*?

SEE EXAMPLE 1

Surveying Use the table for Exercises 2 and 3.
A landscape designer surveyed the boundaries of a triangular park. She made the following table for the dimensions of the land.

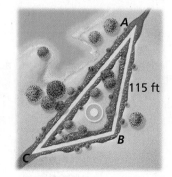

115 ft

	A to B	B to C	C to A
Bearing	E	S 25° E	N 62° W
Distance	115 ft	?	?

2. Draw the plot of land described by the table. Label the measures of the angles in the triangle.

3. Does the table have enough information to determine the locations of points *A*, *B*, and *C*? Explain.

SEE EXAMPLE 2

Determine if you can use ASA to prove the triangles congruent. Explain.

4. △VRS and △VTS, given that $\overline{VS}$ bisects ∠RST and ∠RVT

5. △DEH and △FGH

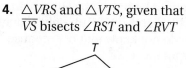

SEE EXAMPLE 3

6. Use AAS to prove the triangles congruent.

Given: ∠R and ∠P are right angles.
$\overline{QR} \parallel \overline{SP}$
Prove: △QPS ≅ △SRQ
Proof:

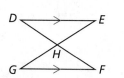

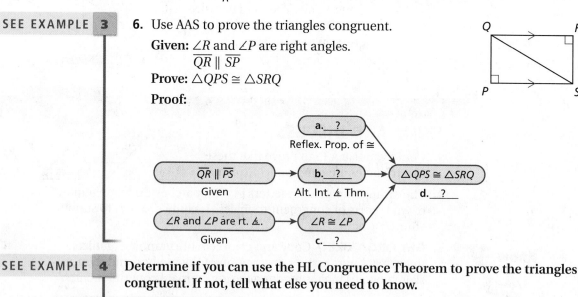

SEE EXAMPLE 4

Determine if you can use the HL Congruence Theorem to prove the triangles congruent. If not, tell what else you need to know.

7. △ABC and △CDA

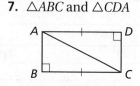

8. △XYV and △ZYV

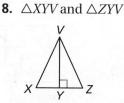

PRACTICE AND PROBLEM SOLVING

Independent Practice

For Exercises	See Example
9–10	1
11–12	2
13	3
14–15	4

my.hrw.com

Online Extra Practice

Surveying Use the table for Exercises 9 and 10.

From two different observation towers a fire is sighted. The locations of the towers are given in the following table.

	X to Y	X to F	Y to F
Bearing	E	N 53° E	N 16° W
Distance	6 km	?	?

9. Draw the diagram formed by observation tower X, observation tower Y, and the fire F. Label the measures of the angles.

10. Is there enough information given in the table to pinpoint the location of the fire? Explain.

Determine if you can use ASA to prove the triangles congruent. Explain.

11. △MKJ and △MKL

12. △RST and △TUR

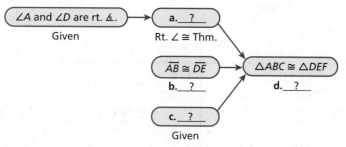

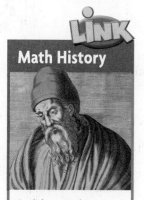

Math History

Euclid wrote the mathematical text *The Elements* around 2300 years ago. It may be the second most reprinted book in history.

13. Given: $\overline{AB} \cong \overline{DE}$, ∠C ≅ ∠F
    Prove: △ABC ≅ △DEF

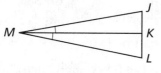

Proof:

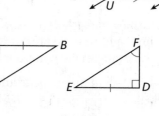

Determine if you can use the HL Congruence Theorem to prove the triangles congruent. If not, tell what else you need to know.

14. △GHJ and △JKG

15. △ABE and △DCE, given that E is the midpoint of $\overline{AD}$ and $\overline{BC}$

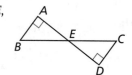

H.O.T. **Multi-Step** For each pair of triangles write a triangle congruence statement. Identify the transformation that moves one triangle to the position of the other triangle.

16.

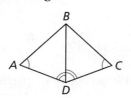

17.

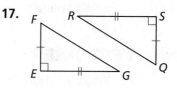

H.O.T. **18. Critical Thinking** Side-Side-Angle (SSA) cannot be used to prove two triangles congruent. Draw a diagram that shows why this is true.

19. A carpenter built a truss to support the roof of a doghouse.

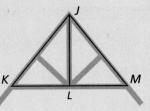

   a. The carpenter knows that $\overline{KJ} \cong \overline{MJ}$. Can the carpenter conclude that $\triangle KJL \cong \triangle MJL$? Why or why not?

   b. Suppose the carpenter also knows that $\angle JLK$ is a right angle. Which theorem can be used to show that $\triangle KJL \cong \triangle MJL$?

20. ///ERROR ANALYSIS/// Two proofs that $\triangle EFH \cong \triangle GHF$ are given. Which is incorrect? Explain the error.

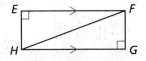

A
It is given that $\overline{EF} \parallel \overline{GH}$. By the Alt. Int. ∡ Thm., $\angle EFH \cong \angle GHF$. $\angle E \cong \angle G$ by the Rt. $\angle \cong$ Thm. By the Reflex. Prop. of $\cong$, $\overline{HF} \cong \overline{HF}$. So by AAS, $\triangle EFH \cong \triangle GHF$.

B
$\overline{HF}$ is the hyp. of both rt. ▵. $\overline{HF} \cong \overline{HF}$ by the Reflex. Prop. of $\cong$. Since the opp. sides of a rect. are $\cong$, $\overline{EF} \cong \overline{GH}$. So by HL, $\triangle EFH \cong \triangle FHG$.

21. Write a paragraph proof of the Leg-Leg (LL) Congruence Theorem. If the legs of one right triangle are congruent to the corresponding legs of another right triangle, the triangles are congruent.

22. Use AAS to prove the triangles congruent.
   Given: $\overline{AD} \parallel \overline{BC}$, $\overline{AD} \cong \overline{CB}$
   Prove: $\triangle AED \cong \triangle CEB$

   Proof:

Statements	Reasons
1. $\overline{AD} \parallel \overline{BC}$	1. a. ?
2. $\angle DAE \cong \angle BCE$	2. b. ?
3. c. ?	3. Vert. ∡ Thm.
4. d. ?	3. Given
5. e. ?	4. f. ?

23. Prove the Hypotenuse-Angle (HA) Theorem.
   Given: $\overline{KM} \perp \overline{JL}$, $\overline{JM} \cong \overline{LM}$, $\angle JMK \cong \angle LMK$
   Prove: $\triangle JKM \cong \triangle LKM$

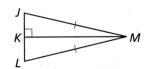

24. **Write About It** The legs of both right $\triangle DEF$ and right $\triangle RST$ are 3 cm and 4 cm. They each have a hypotenuse 5 cm in length. Describe two different ways you could prove that $\triangle DEF \cong \triangle RST$.

25. **Construction** Use the method for constructing perpendicular lines to construct a right triangle.

TEST PREP

26. What additional congruence statement is necessary to prove $\triangle XWY \cong \triangle XVZ$ by ASA?

   (A) $\angle XVZ \cong \angle XWY$

   (B) $\angle VUY \cong \angle WUZ$

   (C) $\overline{VZ} \cong \overline{WY}$

   (D) $\overline{XZ} \cong \overline{XY}$

27. Which postulate or theorem justifies the congruence statement △STU ≅ △VUT?

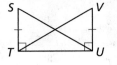

    (F) ASA   **(H)** HL

    (G) SSS   **(J)** SAS

28. Which of the following congruence statements is true?

    (A) ∠A ≅ ∠B   **(C)** △AED ≅ △CEB

    (B) $\overline{CE} \cong \overline{DE}$ **(D)** △AED ≅ △BEC

29. In △RST, RT = 6y − 2. In △UVW, UW = 2y + 7. ∠R ≅ ∠U, and ∠S ≅ ∠V. What must be the value of y in order to prove that △RST ≅ △UVW?

    (F) 1.25   **(G)** 2.25   **(H)** 9.0   **(J)** 11.5

30. Extended Response Draw a triangle. Construct a second triangle that has the same angle measures but is not congruent. Compare the lengths of each pair of corresponding sides. Consider the relationship between the lengths of the sides and the measures of the angles. Explain why Angle-Angle-Angle (AAA) is not a congruence principle.

CHALLENGE AND EXTEND

H.O.T. 31. Sports This bicycle frame includes △VSU and △VTU, which lie in intersecting planes. From the given angle measures, can you conclude that △VSU ≅ △VTU? Explain.

$$m\angle VUS = (7y - 2)° \qquad m\angle VUT = \left(5\tfrac{1}{2}x - \tfrac{1}{2}\right)°$$

$$m\angle USV = 5\tfrac{2}{3}y° \qquad\qquad m\angle UTV = (4x + 8)°$$

$$m\angle SVU = (3y - 6)° \qquad m\angle TVU = 2x°$$

32. Given: △ABC is equilateral. C is the midpoint of $\overline{DE}$. ∠DAC and ∠EBC are congruent and supplementary.

    Prove: △DAC ≅ △EBC

H.O.T. 33. Write a two-column proof of the Leg-Angle (LA) Congruence Theorem. If a leg and an acute angle of one right triangle are congruent to the corresponding parts of another right triangle, the triangles are congruent. (*Hint:* There are two cases to consider.)

34. If two triangles are congruent by ASA, what theorem could you use to prove that the triangles are also congruent by AAS? Explain.

FOCUS ON MATHEMATICAL PRACTICES

MATHEMATICAL PRACTICES

H.O.T. 35. Analysis In the figure, ∠VWL ≅ ∠VRL, $\overline{WG}$ bisects ∠VWL, $\overline{RG}$ bisects ∠VRL, $\overline{VW} \cong \overline{VR}$, and $\overline{VL} \perp \overline{WR}$ at L. Clarita says △GWL ≅ △GRL by AAS. Is she correct? Explain.

H.O.T. 36. Reasoning Two right triangles share a side. A leg of one triangle, which is not the shared side, is congruent to a leg of the second triangle, which is also not the shared side. Are the two triangles necessarily congruent? Explain.

Victoria Smith/HMH

5-3 Triangle Congruence: CPCTC

Essential Question: If you know two figures are congruent, what can you conclude about corresponding sides and corresponding angles?

Objective
Use CPCTC to prove parts of triangles are congruent.

Vocabulary
CPCTC

Why learn this?
You can use congruent triangles to estimate distances.

CPCTC is an abbreviation for the phrase "Corresponding Parts of Congruent Triangles are Congruent." It can be used as a justification in a proof after you have proven two triangles congruent.

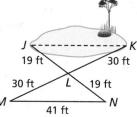

COMMON CORE GPS MCC9-12.G.CO.7

EXAMPLE 1 Engineering Application

my.hrw.com

Online Video Tutor

To design a bridge across a canyon, you need to find the distance from *A* to *B*. Locate points *C*, *D*, and *E* as shown in the figure. If *DE* = 600 ft, what is *AB*?

∠*D* ≅ ∠*B*, because they are both right angles.
$\overline{DC} \cong \overline{CB}$, because *DC* = *CB* = 500 ft.

∠*DCE* ≅ ∠*BCA*, because vertical angles are congruent. Therefore △*DCE* ≅ △*BCA* by ASA or LA. By CPCTC, $\overline{ED} \cong \overline{AB}$, so *AB* = *ED* = 600 ft.

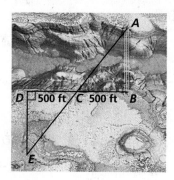

CHECK IT OUT!

1. A landscape architect sets up the triangles shown in the figure to find the distance *JK* across a pond. What is *JK*?

COMMON CORE GPS MCC9-12.G.SRT.5

EXAMPLE 2 Proving Corresponding Parts Congruent

my.hrw.com

Online Video Tutor

Given: $\overline{AB} \cong \overline{DC}$, ∠*ABC* ≅ ∠*DCB*
Prove: ∠*A* ≅ ∠*D*
Proof:

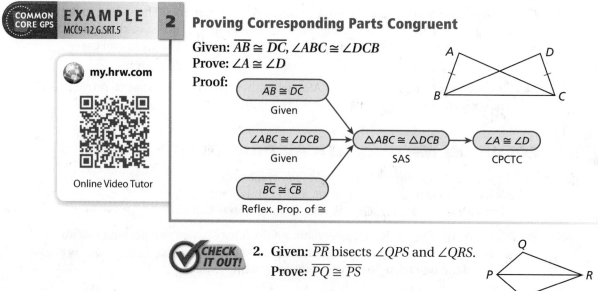

CHECK IT OUT!

2. **Given:** $\overline{PR}$ bisects ∠*QPS* and ∠*QRS*.
   Prove: $\overline{PQ} \cong \overline{PS}$

Chris Lisle/CORBIS

3 Using CPCTC in a Proof

Given: $\overline{EG} \parallel \overline{DF}$, $\overline{EG} \cong \overline{DF}$
Prove: $\overline{ED} \parallel \overline{GF}$
Proof:

Statements	Reasons
1. $\overline{EG} \cong \overline{DF}$	1. Given
2. $\overline{EG} \parallel \overline{DF}$	2. Given
3. $\angle EGD \cong \angle FDG$	3. Alt. Int. ∡ Thm.
4. $\overline{GD} \cong \overline{DG}$	4. Reflex. Prop. of $\cong$
5. $\triangle EGD \cong \triangle FDG$	5. SAS *Steps 1, 3, and 4*
6. $\angle EDG \cong \angle FGD$	6. CPCTC
7. $\overline{ED} \parallel \overline{GF}$	7. Converse of Alt. Int. ∡ Thm.

Helpful Hint

Work backward when planning a proof. To show that $\overline{KL} \parallel \overline{MN}$, look for a pair of angles that are congruent. Then look for triangles that contain these angles.

CHECK IT OUT!
3. **Given:** J is the midpoint of $\overline{KM}$ and $\overline{NL}$.
Prove: $\overline{KL} \parallel \overline{MN}$

You can also use CPCTC when triangles are on a coordinate plane.
You use the Distance Formula to find the lengths of the sides of each triangle.
Then, after showing that the triangles are congruent, you can make conclusions about their corresponding parts.

4 Using CPCTC in the Coordinate Plane

Given: $A(2, 3)$, $B(5, -1)$, $C(1, 0)$,
$D(-4, -1)$, $E(0, 2)$, $F(-1, -2)$
Prove: $\angle ABC \cong \angle DEF$

Step 1 Plot the points on a coordinate plane.

Step 2 Use the Distance Formula to find the lengths of the sides of each triangle.

$$D = \sqrt{(x_2 - x_1)^2 + (y_2 - y_1)^2}$$

$$AB = \sqrt{(5-2)^2 + (-1-3)^2} \qquad DE = \sqrt{(0-(-4))^2 + (2-(-1))^2}$$
$$= \sqrt{9 + 16} = \sqrt{25} = 5 \qquad = \sqrt{16 + 9} = \sqrt{25} = 5$$

$$BC = \sqrt{(1-5)^2 + (0-(-1))^2} \qquad EF = \sqrt{(-1-0)^2 + (-2-2)^2}$$
$$= \sqrt{16 + 1} = \sqrt{17} \qquad = \sqrt{1 + 16} = \sqrt{17}$$

$$AC = \sqrt{(1-2)^2 + (0-3)^2} \qquad DF = \sqrt{(-1-(-4))^2 + (-2-(-1))^2}$$
$$= \sqrt{1 + 9} = \sqrt{10} \qquad = \sqrt{9 + 1} = \sqrt{10}$$

So $\overline{AB} \cong \overline{DE}$, $\overline{BC} \cong \overline{EF}$, and $\overline{AC} \cong \overline{DF}$. Therefore $\triangle ABC \cong \triangle DEF$ by SSS, and $\angle ABC \cong \angle DEF$ by CPCTC.

Remember!

SSS, SAS, ASA, AAS, and HL use corresponding parts to prove triangles congruent. CPCTC uses congruent triangles to prove corresponding parts congruent.

CHECK IT OUT!
4. **Given:** $J(-1, -2)$, $K(2, -1)$, $L(-2, 0)$, $R(2, 3)$, $S(5, 2)$, $T(1, 1)$
Prove: $\angle JKL \cong \angle RST$

THINK AND DISCUSS

1. In the figure, $\overline{UV} \cong \overline{XY}$, $\overline{VW} \cong \overline{YZ}$, and $\angle V \cong \angle Y$. Explain why $\triangle UVW \cong \triangle XYZ$. By CPCTC, which additional parts are congruent?

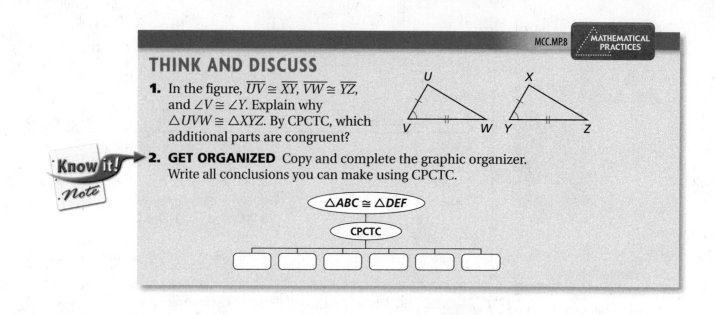

Know it! Note

2. GET ORGANIZED Copy and complete the graphic organizer. Write all conclusions you can make using CPCTC.

$\triangle ABC \cong \triangle DEF$

CPCTC

5-3 Exercises

my.hrw.com
Homework Help

GUIDED PRACTICE

1. Vocabulary You use CPCTC after proving triangles are congruent. Which parts of congruent triangles are referred to as corresponding parts?

SEE EXAMPLE **1**

2. Archaeology An archaeologist wants to find the height *AB* of a rock formation. She places a marker at *C* and steps off the distance from *C* to *B*. Then she walks the same distance from *C* and places a marker at *D*. If *DE* = 6.3 m, what is *AB*?

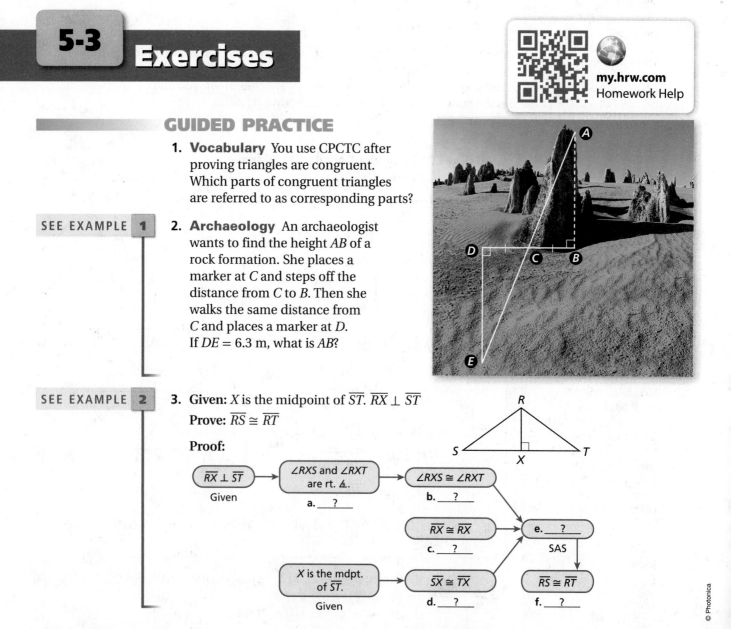

SEE EXAMPLE **2**

3. Given: *X* is the midpoint of $\overline{ST}$. $\overline{RX} \perp \overline{ST}$

Prove: $\overline{RS} \cong \overline{RT}$

Proof:

$\overline{RX} \perp \overline{ST}$
Given
→ $\angle RXS$ and $\angle RXT$ are rt. $\angle$s. → $\angle RXS \cong \angle RXT$
a. ? **b.** ?

$\overline{RX} \cong \overline{RX}$
c. ?

X is the mdpt. of $\overline{ST}$.
Given → $\overline{SX} \cong \overline{TX}$
d. ?

e. ?
SAS → $\overline{RS} \cong \overline{RT}$
f. ?

© Photonica

SEE EXAMPLE 3

4. Given: $\overline{AC} \cong \overline{AD}$, $\overline{CB} \cong \overline{DB}$
   Prove: $\overline{AB}$ bisects $\angle CAD$.

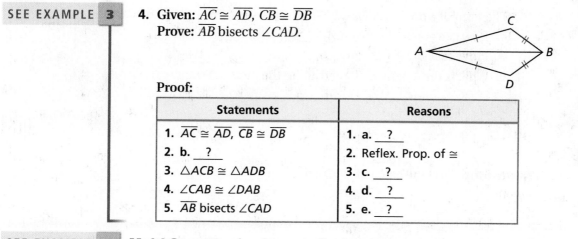

Proof:

Statements	Reasons
1. $\overline{AC} \cong \overline{AD}$, $\overline{CB} \cong \overline{DB}$	1. a. ___?___
2. b. ___?___	2. Reflex. Prop. of $\cong$
3. $\triangle ACB \cong \triangle ADB$	3. c. ___?___
4. $\angle CAB \cong \angle DAB$	4. d. ___?___
5. $\overline{AB}$ bisects $\angle CAD$	5. e. ___?___

SEE EXAMPLE 4

Multi-Step Use the given set of points to prove each congruence statement.

5. $E(-3, 3), F(-1, 3), G(-2, 0), J(0, -1), K(2, -1), L(1, 2)$; $\angle EFG \cong \angle JKL$

6. $A(2, 3), B(4, 1), C(1, -1), R(-1, 0), S(-3, -2), T(0, -4)$; $\angle ACB \cong \angle RTS$

PRACTICE AND PROBLEM SOLVING

Independent Practice

For Exercises	See Example
7	1
8–9	2
10–11	3
12–13	4

my.hrw.com

Online Extra Practice

7. Surveying To find the distance AB across a river, a surveyor first locates point C. He measures the distance from C to B. Then he locates point D the same distance east of C. If $DE = 420$ ft, what is AB?

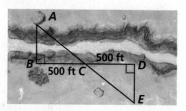

8. Given: M is the midpoint of $\overline{PQ}$ and $\overline{RS}$.
   Prove: $\overline{QR} \cong \overline{PS}$

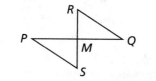

9. Given: $\overline{WX} \cong \overline{XY} \cong \overline{YZ} \cong \overline{ZW}$
   Prove: $\angle W \cong \angle Y$

10. Given: G is the midpoint of $\overline{FH}$.
   $\overline{EF} \cong \overline{EH}$
   Prove: $\angle 1 \cong \angle 2$

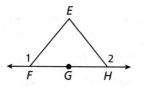

11. Given: $\overline{LM}$ bisects $\angle JLK$. $\overline{JL} \cong \overline{KL}$
   Prove: M is the midpoint of $\overline{JK}$.

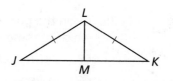

H.O.T. **Multi-Step** Use the given set of points to prove each congruence statement.

12. $R(0, 0), S(2, 4), T(-1, 3), U(-1, 0), V(-3, -4), W(-4, -1)$; $\angle RST \cong \angle UVW$

13. $A(-1, 1), B(2, 3), C(2, -2), D(2, -3), E(-1, -5), F(-1, 0)$; $\angle BAC \cong \angle EDF$

14. Given: $\triangle QRS$ is adjacent to $\triangle QTS$. $\overline{QS}$ bisects $\angle RQT$. $\angle R \cong \angle T$
   Prove: $\overline{QS}$ bisects $\overline{RT}$.

15. Given: $\triangle ABE$ and $\triangle CDE$ with E the midpoint of $\overline{AC}$ and $\overline{BD}$
   Prove: $\overline{AB} \parallel \overline{CD}$

Real-World Connections

16. The front of a doghouse has the dimensions shown.
  a. How can you prove that $\triangle ADB \cong \triangle ADC$?
  b. Prove that $\overline{BD} \cong \overline{CD}$.
  c. What is the length of $\overline{BD}$ and $\overline{BC}$ to the nearest tenth?

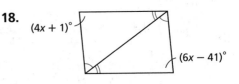

Multi-Step Find the value of *x*.

H.O.T. **17.**

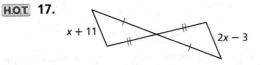

18.

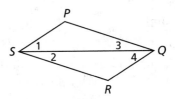

Use the diagram for Exercises 19–21.

19. **Given:** $PS = RQ$, m$\angle 1 =$ m$\angle 4$
  Prove: m$\angle 3 =$ m$\angle 2$

20. **Given:** m$\angle 1 =$ m$\angle 2$, m$\angle 3 =$ m$\angle 4$
  Prove: $PS = RS$

21. **Given:** $PS = RQ$, $PQ = RS$
  Prove: $\overline{PQ} \parallel \overline{RS}$

22. **Critical Thinking** Does the diagram contain enough information to allow you to conclude that $\overline{JK} \parallel \overline{ML}$? Explain.

H.O.T. **23.** **Write About It** Draw a diagram and explain how a surveyor can set up triangles to find the distance across a lake. Label each part of your diagram. List which sides or angles must be congruent.

TEST PREP

24. Which of these will NOT be used as a reason in a proof of $\overline{AC} \cong \overline{AD}$?
  (A) SAS
  (B) CPCTC
  (C) ASA
  (D) Reflexive Property

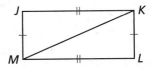

25. Given the points $K(1, 2)$, $L(0, -4)$, $M(-2, -3)$, and $N(-1, 3)$, which of these is true?
  (F) $\angle KNL \cong \angle MNL$
  (G) $\angle LNK \cong \angle NLM$
  (H) $\angle MLN \cong \angle KLN$
  (J) $\angle MNK \cong \angle NKL$

26. What is the value of *y*?
  (A) 10
  (B) 20
  (C) 35
  (D) 85

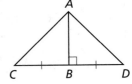

27. Which of these are NOT used to prove angles congruent?
  (F) congruent triangles
  (G) noncorresponding parts
  (H) parallel lines
  (J) perpendicular lines

28. Which set of coordinates represents the vertices of a triangle congruent to △RST? (*Hint:* Find the lengths of the sides of △RST.)

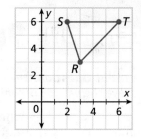

(A) (3, 4), (3, 0), (0, 0)   (C) (3, 1), (3, 3), (4, 6)

(B) (3, 3), (0, 4), (0, 0)   (D) (3, 0), (4, 4), (0, 6)

CHALLENGE AND EXTEND

H.O.T. 29. All of the edges of a cube are congruent. All of the angles on each face of a cube are right angles. Use CPCTC to explain why any two diagonals on the faces of a cube (for example, $\overline{AC}$ and $\overline{AF}$) must be congruent.

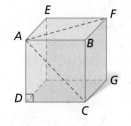

30. Given: $\overline{JK} \cong \overline{ML}$, $\overline{JM} \cong \overline{KL}$
Prove: $\angle J \cong \angle L$
(*Hint:* Draw an auxiliary line.)

31. Given: R is the midpoint of $\overline{AB}$.
S is the midpoint of $\overline{DC}$.
$\overline{RS} \perp \overline{AB}$, $\angle ASD \cong \angle BSC$
Prove: $\triangle ASD \cong \triangle BSC$

H.O.T. 32. △ABC is in plane M. △CDE is in plane P. Both planes have C in common and $\angle A \cong \angle E$. What is the height AB to the nearest foot?

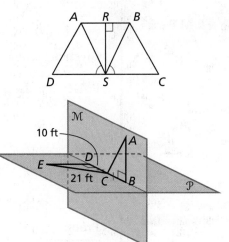

FOCUS ON MATHEMATICAL PRACTICES

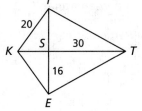

H.O.T. 33. Problem Solving In the figure, $\overrightarrow{KT}$ bisects $\angle IKE$, $\overline{KI} \cong \overline{KE}$, $ST = 30$, $KI = 20$, and $ES = 16$. Use this information to find the perimeter of △KIT. Explain your steps.

H.O.T. 34. Make a Conjecture Two congruent right triangles share a hypotenuse. An auxiliary segment has endpoints on the vertex of each right angle. Under what conditions is the auxiliary segment perpendicular to the shared hypotenuse?

H.O.T. 35. Proof In the figure, △PTQ ≅ △RTS. Prove that $\overline{PS} \parallel \overline{QR}$.

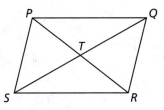

EXTENSION Proving Constructions Valid

Essential Question: How can triangle congruence criteria be used to prove the validity of some geometric constructions?

Objective

Use congruent triangles to prove constructions valid.

When performing a compass and straight edge construction, the compass setting remains the same width until you change it. This fact allows you to construct a segment congruent to a given segment. You can assume that two distances constructed with the same compass setting are congruent.

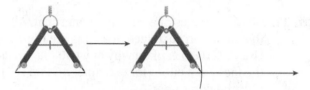

The steps in the construction of a figure can be justified by combining the assumptions of compass and straightedge constructions and the postulates and theorems that are used for proving triangles congruent.

You have learned that there exists exactly one midpoint on any line segment. The proof below justifies the construction of a midpoint.

| COMMON CORE GPS | EXAMPLE | 1 |
| MCC9-12.G.SRT.5 |

Proving the Construction of a Midpoint

Given: diagram showing the steps in the construction
Prove: M is the midpoint of $\overline{AB}$.

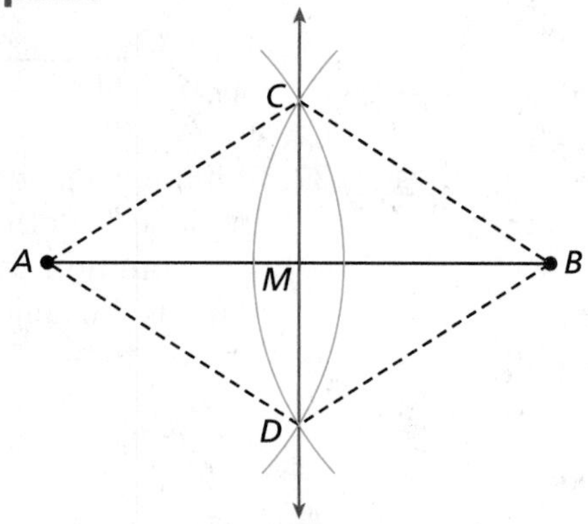

Remember!

To construct a midpoint, see the construction of a perpendicular bisector in *Perpendicular Lines*.

Proof:

Statements	Reasons
1. Draw $\overline{AC}$, $\overline{BC}$, $\overline{AD}$, and $\overline{BD}$.	1. Through any two pts. there is exactly one line.
2. $\overline{AC} \cong \overline{BC} \cong \overline{AD} \cong \overline{BD}$	2. Same compass setting used
3. $\overline{CD} \cong \overline{CD}$	3. Reflex. Prop. of $\cong$
4. $\triangle ACD \cong \triangle BCD$	4. SSS *Steps 2, 3*
5. $\angle ACD \cong \angle BCD$	5. CPCTC
6. $\overline{CM} \cong \overline{CM}$	6. Reflex. Prop. of $\cong$
7. $\triangle ACM \cong \triangle BCM$	7. SAS *Steps 2, 5, 6*
8. $\overline{AM} \cong \overline{BM}$	8. CPCTC
9. M is the midpt. of $\overline{AB}$.	9. Def. of mdpt.

CHECK IT OUT! 1. **Given:** above diagram
Prove: $\overleftrightarrow{CD}$ is the perpendicular bisector of $\overline{AB}$.

EXAMPLE **2**
MCC9-12.G.SRT.5

Proving the Construction of an Angle

Given: diagram showing the steps in the construction

Prove: $\angle A \cong \angle D$

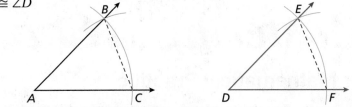

Proof: Since there is a straight line through any two points, you can draw $\overline{BC}$ and $\overline{EF}$. The same compass setting was used to construct $\overline{AC}$, $\overline{AB}$, $\overline{DF}$, and $\overline{DE}$, so $\overline{AC} \cong \overline{AB} \cong \overline{DF} \cong \overline{DE}$. The same compass setting was used to construct $\overline{BC}$ and $\overline{EF}$, so $\overline{BC} \cong \overline{EF}$. Therefore $\triangle BAC \cong \triangle EDF$ by SSS, and $\angle A \cong \angle D$ by CPCTC.

CHECK IT OUT!

2. Prove the construction for bisecting an angle.

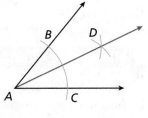

EXTENSION

Exercises

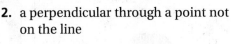
my.hrw.com
Homework Help

Use each diagram to prove the construction valid.

1. parallel lines

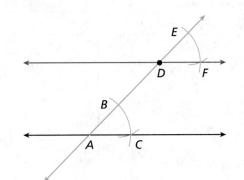

2. a perpendicular through a point not on the line

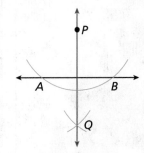

3. constructing a triangle using SAS

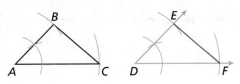

4. constructing a triangle using ASA

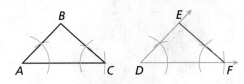

COMMON CORE GPS

Mastering the Standards

for Mathematical Practice

The topics described in the Standards for Mathematical Content will vary from year to year. However, the *way* in which you learn, study, and think about mathematics will not. The Standards for Mathematical Practice describe skills that you will use in all of your math courses.

Mathematical Practices

1. *Make sense of problems and persevere in solving them.*
2. *Reason abstractly and quantitatively.*
3. *Construct viable arguments and critique the reasoning of others.*
4. *Model with mathematics.*
5. *Use appropriate tools strategically.*
6. *Attend to precision.*
7. *Look for and make use of structure.*
8. *Look for and express regularity in repeated reasoning.*

① Make sense of problems and persevere in solving them.

Mathematically proficient students start by explaining to themselves the meaning of a problem... They analyze givens, constraints, relationships, and goals. They make conjectures about the form... of the solution and plan a solution pathway...

In your book

Focus on Problem Solving describes a four-step plan for problem solving. The plan is introduced at the beginning of your book, and practice with the plan appears throughout the book.

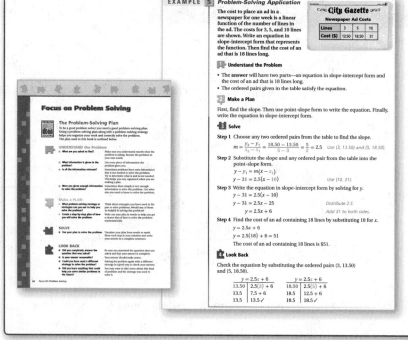

Comstock/Getty Images

5-4 Isosceles and Equilateral Triangles

Essential Question: What special relationships exist among the sides and angles of isosceles and equilateral triangles?

Objectives
Prove theorems about isosceles and equilateral triangles.

Apply properties of isosceles and equilateral triangles.

Vocabulary
legs of an isosceles triangle
vertex angle
base
base angles

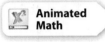

Who uses this?
Astronomers use geometric methods. (See Example 1.)

Recall that an isosceles triangle has at least two congruent sides. The congruent sides are called the **legs**. The **vertex angle** is the angle formed by the legs. The side opposite the vertex angle is called the **base**, and the **base angles** are the two angles that have the base as a side.

∠3 is the vertex angle.
∠1 and ∠2 are the base angles.

Know it!
·Note

Theorems   Isosceles Triangle

	THEOREM	HYPOTHESIS	CONCLUSION
5-4-1	**Isosceles Triangle Theorem** If two sides of a triangle are congruent, then the angles opposite the sides are congruent.	*A* / *B* *C*	$\angle B \cong \angle C$
5-4-2	**Converse of Isosceles Triangle Theorem** If two angles of a triangle are congruent, then the sides opposite those angles are congruent.	*D* / *E* *F*	$\overline{DE} \cong \overline{DF}$

Theorem 5-4-1 is proven below. You will prove Theorem 5-4-2 in Exercise 35.

PROOF

Isosceles Triangle Theorem

Given: $\overline{AB} \cong \overline{AC}$
Prove: $\angle B \cong \angle C$
Proof:

Reading Math
The Isosceles Triangle Theorem is sometimes stated as "Base angles of an isosceles triangle are congruent."

Statements	Reasons
1. Draw *X*, the mdpt. of $\overline{BC}$.	1. Every seg. has a unique mdpt.
2. Draw the auxiliary line $\overline{AX}$.	2. Through two pts. there is exactly one line.
3. $\overline{BX} \cong \overline{CX}$	3. Def. of mdpt.
4. $\overline{AB} \cong \overline{AC}$	4. Given
5. $\overline{AX} \cong \overline{AX}$	5. Reflex. Prop. of ≅
6. $\triangle ABX \cong \triangle ACX$	6. SSS *Steps 3, 4, 5*
7. $\angle B \cong \angle C$	7. CPCTC

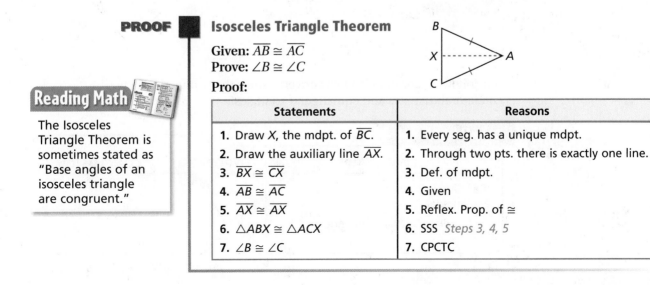

EXAMPLE 1 MCC9-12.G.MG.1

🌐 my.hrw.com

Online Video Tutor

Astronomy Application

The distance from Earth to nearby stars can be measured using the parallax method, which requires observing the positions of a star 6 months apart. If the distance LM to a star in July is 4.0×10^{13} km, explain why the distance LK to the star in January is the same. (Assume the distance from Earth to the Sun does not change.)

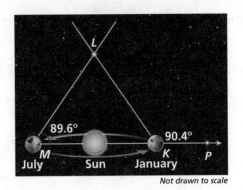

Not drawn to scale

m∠LKM = 180 − 90.4, so m∠LKM = 89.6°. Since ∠LKM ≅ ∠M, △LMK is isosceles by the Converse of the Isosceles Triangle Theorem. Thus $LK = LM = 4.0 \times 10^{13}$ km.

✓ **CHECK IT OUT!**

1. If the distance from Earth to a star in September is 4.2×10^{13} km, what is the distance from Earth to the star in March? Explain.

EXAMPLE 2 MCC9-12.A.CED.1

🌐 my.hrw.com

Online Video Tutor

Finding the Measure of an Angle

Find each angle measure.

A m∠C

m∠C = m∠B = $x°$	*Isosc. △ Thm.*
m∠C + m∠B + m∠A = 180	*△ Sum Thm.*
$x + x + 38 = 180$	*Substitute the given values.*
$2x = 142$	*Simplify and subtract 38 from both sides.*
$x = 71$	*Divide both sides by 2.*

Thus m∠C = 71°.

B m∠S

m∠S = m∠R	*Isosc. △ Thm.*
$2x° = (x + 30)°$	*Substitute the given values.*
$x = 30$	*Subtract x from both sides.*

Thus m∠S = $2x°$ = 2(30) = 60°.

✓ **CHECK IT OUT!**

Find each angle measure.

2a. m∠H **2b.** m∠N

The following corollary and its converse show the connection between equilateral triangles and equiangular triangles.

Know it! Note

Corollary 5-4-3   **Equilateral Triangle**

COROLLARY	HYPOTHESIS	CONCLUSION
If a triangle is equilateral, then it is equiangular. (equilateral △ → equiangular △)		∠A ≅ ∠B ≅ ∠C

You will prove Corollary 5-4-3 in Exercise 36.

Corollary 5-4-4 — **Equiangular Triangle**

COROLLARY	HYPOTHESIS	CONCLUSION
If a triangle is equiangular, then it is equilateral. (equiangular $\triangle \rightarrow$ equilateral $\triangle$)	D, E, F triangle	$\overline{DE} \cong \overline{DF} \cong \overline{EF}$

You will prove Corollary 5-4-4 in Exercise 37.

COMMON CORE GPS MCC9-12.A.CED.1

EXAMPLE 3 **Using Properties of Equilateral Triangles**

my.hrw.com

Online Video Tutor

Find each value.

A *x*

$\triangle ABC$ is equiangular.

$(3x + 15)^\circ = 60^\circ$ *Equilateral $\triangle \rightarrow$ equiangular $\triangle$*

                  The measure of each $\angle$ of an equiangular $\triangle$ is 60°.

$3x = 45$ *Subtract 15 from both sides.*

$x = 15$ *Divide both sides by 3.*

B *t*

$\triangle JKL$ is equilateral.

$4t - 8 = 2t + 1$ *Equiangular $\triangle \rightarrow$ equilateral $\triangle$*

                     Def. of equilateral $\triangle$

$2t = 9$ *Subtract 2t and add 8 to both sides.*

$t = 4.5$ *Divide both sides by 2.*

CHECK IT OUT! **3.** Use the diagram to find *JL*.

COMMON CORE GPS MCC9-12.G.GPE.4

EXAMPLE 4 **Using Coordinate Proof**

my.hrw.com

Online Video Tutor

Prove that the triangle whose vertices are the midpoints of the sides of an isosceles triangle is also isosceles.

Given: $\triangle ABC$ is isosceles. *X* is the mdpt. of $\overline{AB}$. *Y* is the mdpt. of $\overline{AC}$. *Z* is the mdpt. of $\overline{BC}$.

Prove: $\triangle XYZ$ is isosceles.

Proof:

Draw a diagram and place the coordinates of $\triangle ABC$ and $\triangle XYZ$ as shown. By the Midpoint Formula, the coordinates of *X* are $\left(\frac{2a + 0}{2}, \frac{2b + 0}{2}\right) = (a, b)$, the coordinates of *Y* are $\left(\frac{2a + 4a}{2}, \frac{2b + 0}{2}\right) = (3a, b)$, and the coordinates of *Z* are $\left(\frac{4a + 0}{2}, \frac{0 + 0}{2}\right) = (2a, 0)$.

By the Distance Formula, $XZ = \sqrt{(2a - a)^2 + (0 - b)^2} = \sqrt{a^2 + b^2}$, and $YZ = \sqrt{(2a - 3a)^2 + (0 - b)^2} = \sqrt{a^2 + b^2}$.

Since $XZ = YZ$, $\overline{XZ} \cong \overline{YZ}$ by definition. So $\triangle XYZ$ is isosceles.

CHECK IT OUT! **4. What if...?** The coordinates of $\triangle ABC$ are $A(0, 2b)$, $B(-2a, 0)$, and $C(2a, 0)$. Prove $\triangle XYZ$ is isosceles.

THINK AND DISCUSS

Know it!
Note

1. Explain why each of the angles in an equilateral triangle measures 60°.

2. GET ORGANIZED Copy and complete the graphic organizer. In each box, draw and mark a diagram for each type of triangle.

Triangle
— Equilateral
— Equiangular

5-4 Exercises

my.hrw.com
Homework Help

GUIDED PRACTICE

1. **Vocabulary** Draw isosceles △*JKL* with ∠*K* as the vertex angle. Name the legs, base, and base angles of the triangle.

SEE EXAMPLE 1

2. **Surveying** To find the distance *QR* across a river, a surveyor locates three points *Q*, *R*, and *S*. *QS* = 41 m, and m∠*S* = 35°. The measure of exterior ∠*PQS* = 70°. Draw a diagram and explain how you can find *QR*.

SEE EXAMPLE 2

Find each angle measure.

3. m∠*ECD*

4. m∠*K*

5. m∠*X*

6. m∠*A*

SEE EXAMPLE 3

Find each value.

7. *y*

8. *x*

9. *BC*

10. *JK*

SEE EXAMPLE 4

11. **Given:** △*ABC* is right isosceles. *X* is the midpoint of $\overline{AC}$. $\overline{AB} \cong \overline{BC}$

   Prove: △*AXB* is isosceles.

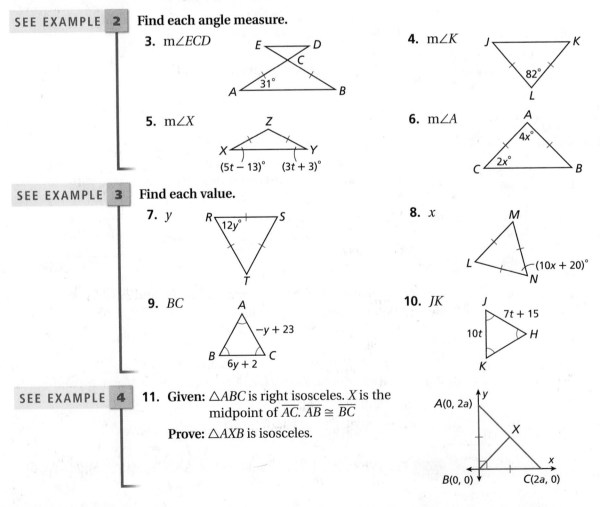

PRACTICE AND PROBLEM SOLVING

my.hrw.com

Online Extra Practice

12. Aviation A plane is flying parallel to the ground along $\overrightarrow{AC}$. When the plane is at A, an air-traffic controller in tower T measures the angle to the plane as 40°. After the plane has traveled 2.4 mi to B, the angle to the plane is 80°. How can you find BT?

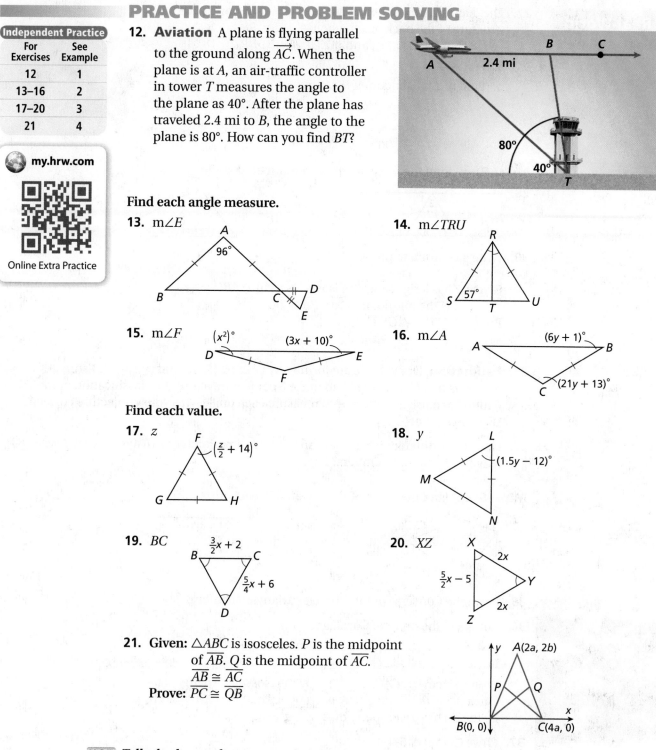

Find each angle measure.

13. m∠E

14. m∠TRU

15. m∠F

16. m∠A

Find each value.

17. z

18. y

19. BC

20. XZ

21. **Given:** △ABC is isosceles. P is the midpoint of $\overline{AB}$. Q is the midpoint of $\overline{AC}$.
$\overline{AB} \cong \overline{AC}$
Prove: $\overline{PC} \cong \overline{QB}$

H.O.T. Tell whether each statement is sometimes, always, or never true. Support your answer with a sketch.

22. An equilateral triangle is an isosceles triangle.

23. The vertex angle of an isosceles triangle is congruent to the base angles.

24. An isosceles triangle is a right triangle.

25. An equilateral triangle and an obtuse triangle are congruent.

H.O.T. 26. Critical Thinking Can a base angle of an isosceles triangle be an obtuse angle? Why or why not?

Real-World Connections

27. The diagram shows the inside view of the support structure of the back of a doghouse. $\overline{PQ} \cong \overline{PR}$, $\overline{PS} \cong \overline{PT}$, m$\angle PST = 71°$, and m$\angle QPS = $ m$\angle RPT = 18°$.

    a. Find m$\angle SPT$.

    b. Find m$\angle PQR$ and m$\angle PRQ$.

Multi-Step Find the measure of each numbered angle.

28.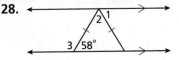

29.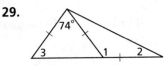

30. Write a coordinate proof.

    Given: $\angle B$ is a right angle in isosceles right $\triangle ABC$. X is the midpoint of $\overline{AC}$. $\overline{BA} \cong \overline{BC}$

    Prove: $\triangle AXB \cong \triangle CXB$

31. **Estimation** Draw the figure formed by $(-2, 1)$, $(5, 5)$, and $(-1, -7)$. Estimate the measure of each angle and make a conjecture about the classification of the figure. Then use a protractor to measure each angle. Was your conjecture correct? Why or why not?

32. **H.O.T.** How many different isosceles triangles have a perimeter of 18 and sides whose lengths are natural numbers? Explain.

Multi-Step Find the value of the variable in each diagram.

33.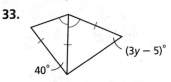

34.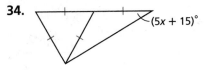

35. Prove the Converse of the Isosceles Triangle Theorem.

36. Complete the proof of Corollary 5-4-3.

    Given: $\overline{AB} \cong \overline{AC} \cong \overline{BC}$

    Prove: $\angle A \cong \angle B \cong \angle C$

    Proof: Since $\overline{AB} \cong \overline{AC}$, **a.** __?__ by the Isosceles Triangle Theorem. Since $\overline{AC} \cong \overline{BC}$, $\angle A \cong \angle B$ by **b.** __?__ . Therefore $\angle A \cong \angle C$ by **c.** __?__ . By the Transitive Property of $\cong$, $\angle A \cong \angle B \cong \angle C$.

37. Prove Corollary 5-4-4.

Navigation

The taffrail log is dragged from the stern of a vessel to measure the speed or distance traveled during a voyage. The log consists of a rotator, recording device, and governor.

38. **Navigation** The captain of a ship traveling along $\overrightarrow{AB}$ sights an island C at an angle of 45°. The captain measures the distance the ship covers until it reaches B, where the angle to the island is 90°. Explain how to find the distance BC to the island.

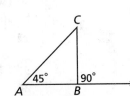

39. **Given:** $\triangle ABC \cong \triangle CBA$

    Prove: $\triangle ABC$ is isosceles.

40. **Write About It** Write the Isosceles Triangle Theorem and its converse as a biconditional.

41. Rewrite the paragraph proof of the Hypotenuse-Leg (HL) Congruence Theorem as a two-column proof.

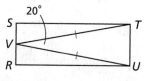

Given: $\triangle ABC$ and $\triangle DEF$ are right triangles. $\angle C$ and $\angle F$ are right angles. $\overline{AC} \cong \overline{DF}$, and $\overline{AB} \cong \overline{DE}$.

Prove: $\triangle ABC \cong \triangle DEF$

Proof: On $\triangle DEF$ draw $\overrightarrow{EF}$. Mark G so that $FG = CB$. Thus $\overline{FG} \cong \overline{CB}$. From the diagram, $\overline{AC} \cong \overline{DF}$ and $\angle C$ and $\angle F$ are right angles. $\overline{DF} \perp \overline{EG}$ by definition of perpendicular lines. Thus $\angle DFG$ is a right angle, and $\angle DFG \cong \angle C$. $\triangle ABC \cong \triangle DGF$ by SAS. $\overline{DG} \cong \overline{AB}$ by CPCTC. $\overline{AB} \cong \overline{DE}$ as given. $\overline{DG} \cong \overline{DE}$ by the Transitive Property. By the Isosceles Triangle Theorem $\angle G \cong \angle E$. $\angle DFG \cong \angle DFE$ since right angles are congruent. So $\triangle DGF \cong \triangle DEF$ by AAS. Therefore $\triangle ABC \cong \triangle DEF$ by the Transitive Property.

TEST PREP

42. Lorena is designing a window so that $\angle R$, $\angle S$, $\angle T$, and $\angle U$ are right angles, $\overline{VU} \cong \overline{VT}$, and $m\angle UVT = 20°$. What is $m\angle RUV$?

Ⓐ 10° 　　Ⓒ 20°

Ⓑ 70° 　　Ⓓ 80°

43. Which of these values of y makes $\triangle ABC$ isosceles?

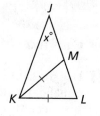

Ⓕ $1\frac{1}{4}$ 　　Ⓗ $7\frac{1}{2}$

Ⓖ $2\frac{1}{2}$ 　　Ⓙ $15\frac{1}{2}$

44. Gridded Response The vertex angle of an isosceles triangle measures $(6t - 9)°$, and one of the base angles measures $(4t)°$. Find t.

CHALLENGE AND EXTEND

H.O.T. 45. In the figure, $\overline{JK} \cong \overline{JL}$, and $\overline{KM} \cong \overline{KL}$. Let $m\angle J = x°$. Prove $m\angle MKL$ must also be $x°$.

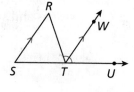

H.O.T. 46. An equilateral $\triangle ABC$ is placed on a coordinate plane. Each side length measures $2a$. B is at the origin, and C is at $(2a, 0)$. Find the coordinates of A.

47. An isosceles triangle has coordinates $A(0, 0)$ and $B(a, b)$. What are all possible coordinates of the third vertex?

FOCUS ON MATHEMATICAL PRACTICES

H.O.T. 48. Draw Conclusions In the figure, $\overrightarrow{RS} \parallel \overrightarrow{TW}$, and $\overrightarrow{TW}$ bisects $\angle RTU$. Classify $\triangle RST$. Justify your answer.

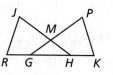

H.O.T. 49. Analysis In the figure, $\angle R \cong \angle K$, $\angle PGK \cong \angle JHR$, and $\overline{JM} \cong \overline{PM}$. Is this enough to prove $\triangle JRH \cong \triangle PKG$? Explain.

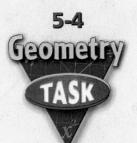

5-4
Geometry TASK

Use with Properties and Attributes of Polygons

Construct Regular Polygons

An equilateral triangle is a triangle with three congruent sides. You also learned that an equilateral triangle is equiangular, meaning that all its angles are congruent.

In this task, you will construct polygons that are both equilateral and equiangular by inscribing them in circles.

  Use appropriate tools strategically.

MCC9-12.G.CO.13 Construct an equilateral triangle, a square, and a regular hexagon inscribed in a circle.

Activity 1

1. Construct circle *P*. Draw a diameter $\overline{AC}$.

2. Construct the perpendicular bisector of $\overline{AC}$. Label the intersections of the bisector and the circle as *B* and *D*.

3. Draw $\overline{AB}$, $\overline{BC}$, $\overline{CD}$, and $\overline{DA}$. The polygon *ABCD* is a *regular quadrilateral*. This means it is a four-sided polygon that has four congruent sides and four congruent angles.

Try This

1. Describe a different method for constructing a regular quadrilateral.

2. The regular quadrilateral in Activity 1 is inscribed in the circle. What is the relationship between the circle and the regular quadrilateral?

3. A *regular octagon* is an eight-sided polygon that has eight congruent sides and eight congruent angles. Use angle bisectors to construct a regular octagon from a regular quadrilateral.

Activity 2

1. Construct circle *P*. Draw a point *A* on the circle.

2. Use the same compass setting. Starting at *A*, draw arcs to mark off equal parts along the circle. Label the other points where the arcs intersect the circle as *B*, *C*, *D*, *E*, and *F*.

3. Draw $\overline{AB}$, $\overline{BC}$, $\overline{CD}$, $\overline{DE}$, $\overline{EF}$, and $\overline{FA}$. The polygon *ABCDEF* is a *regular hexagon*. This means it is a six-sided polygon that has six congruent sides and six congruent angles.

Try This

4. Justify the conclusion that *ABCDEF* is a regular hexagon. (*Hint:* Draw diameters $\overline{AD}$, $\overline{BE}$, and $\overline{CF}$. What types of triangles are formed?)

5. A *regular dodecagon* is a 12-sided polygon that has 12 congruent sides and 12 congruent angles. Use the construction of a regular hexagon to construct a regular dodecagon. Explain your method.

Activity 3

1 Construct circle *P*. Draw a diameter $\overline{AB}$.

2 Construct the perpendicular bisector of $\overline{AB}$. Label one point where the bisector intersects the circle as point *E*.

3 Construct the midpoint of radius $\overline{PB}$. Label it as point *C*.

4 Set your compass to the length *CE*. Place the compass point at *C* and draw an arc that intersects $\overline{AB}$. Label the point of intersection *D*.

5 Set the compass to the length *ED*. Starting at *E*, draw arcs to mark off equal parts along the circle. Label the other points where the arcs intersect the circle as *F*, *G*, *H*, and *J*.

6 Draw $\overline{EF}$, $\overline{FG}$, $\overline{GH}$, $\overline{HJ}$, and $\overline{JE}$. The polygon *EFGHJ* is a *regular pentagon*. This means it is a five-sided polygon that has five congruent sides and five congruent angles.

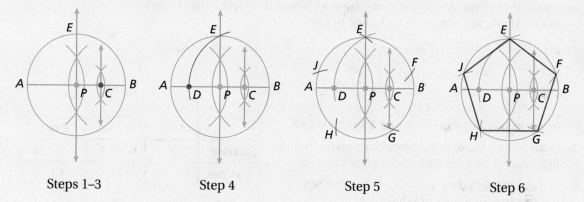

Steps 1–3   Step 4   Step 5   Step 6

Try This

6. A *regular decagon* is a ten-sided polygon that has ten congruent sides and ten congruent angles. Use the construction of a regular pentagon to construct a regular decagon. Explain your method.

7. Measure each angle of the regular polygons in Activities 1–3 and complete the following table.

REGULAR POLYGONS				
Number of Sides	3	4	5	6
Measure of Each Angle	60°			
Sum of Angle Measures	180°			

8. Make a Conjecture What is a general rule for finding the sum of the angle measures in a regular polygon with *n* sides?

9. Make a Conjecture What is a general rule for finding the measure of each angle in a regular polygon with *n* sides?

Ready to Go On?

my.hrw.com
Assessment and Intervention

✓ 5-1 Triangle Congruence: SSS and SAS

1. The figure shows one tower and the cables of a suspension bridge. Given that $\overline{AC} \cong \overline{BC}$, use SAS to explain why $\triangle ACD \cong \triangle BCD$.

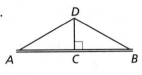

2. **Given:** $\overline{JK}$ bisects $\angle MJN$. $\overline{MJ} \cong \overline{NJ}$
   Prove: $\triangle MJK \cong \triangle NJK$

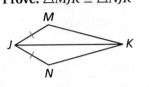

✓ 5-2 Triangle Congruence: ASA, AAS, and HL

Determine if you can use the HL Congruence Theorem to prove the triangles congruent. If not, tell what else you need to know.

3. $\triangle RSU$ and $\triangle TUS$

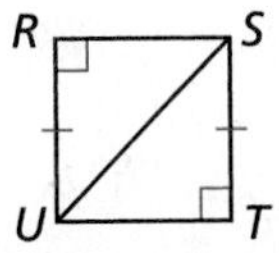

4. $\triangle ABC$ and $\triangle DCB$

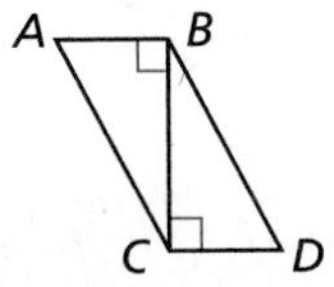

Observers in two lighthouses K and L spot a ship S.

5. Draw a diagram of the triangle formed by the lighthouses and the ship. Label each measure.

6. Is there enough data in the table to pinpoint the location of the ship? Why?

	K to L	K to S	L to S
Bearing	E	N 58° E	N 77° W
Distance	12 km	?	?

✓ 5-3 Triangle Congruence: CPCTC

7. **Given:** $\overline{CD} \parallel \overline{BE}$, $\overline{DE} \parallel \overline{CB}$
   Prove: $\angle D \cong \angle B$

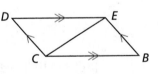

8. **Given:** $\overline{PQ} \cong \overline{RQ}$,
   $\overline{PS} \cong \overline{RS}$
   Prove: $\overline{QS}$ bisects $\angle PQR$.

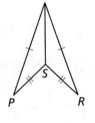

Find each value.

9. m∠C

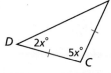

10. ST

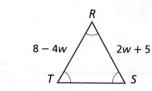

11. **Given:** Isosceles △JKL has coordinates J(0, 0), K(2a, 2b), and L(4a, 0).
M is the midpoint of $\overline{JK}$, and N is the midpoint of $\overline{KL}$.
Prove: △KMN is isosceles.

PARCC Assessment Readiness

COMMON
CORE GPS

Selected Response

1. A pilot uses triangles to find the angle of elevation ∠A from the ground to her plane. How can she find m∠A?

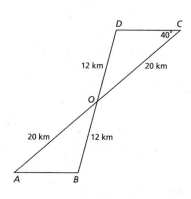

Ⓐ △ABO ≅ △CDO by SAS and ∠A ≅ ∠C by CPCTC, so m∠A = 40° by substitution.

Ⓑ △ABO ≅ △CDO by CPCTC and ∠A ≅ ∠C by SAS, so m∠A = 40° by substitution.

Ⓒ △ABO ≅ △CDO by ASA and ∠A ≅ ∠C by CPCTC, so m∠A = 40° by substitution.

Ⓓ △ABO ≅ △CDO by CPCTC and ∠A ≅ ∠C by ASA, so m∠A = 40° by substitution.

2. Given the lengths marked on the figure and that $\overline{AD}$ bisects $\overline{BE}$, use SSS to explain why △ABC ≅ △DEC.

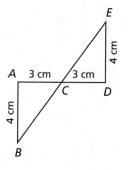

Ⓕ $\overline{AC} \cong \overline{CD}, \overline{AB} \cong \overline{ED}, \overline{BC} \cong \overline{CE}$

Ⓖ $\overline{AC} \cong \overline{CD}, \overline{AB} \cong \overline{ED}, \overline{BC} \cong \overline{BC}$

Ⓗ $\overline{AC} \cong \overline{CB}, \overline{AB} \cong \overline{ED}, \overline{CD} \cong \overline{CE}$

Ⓙ The triangles are not congruent.

Mini-Task

3. Determine if you can use ASA to prove △CBA ≅ △CED. Explain.

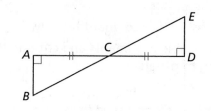

6 Special Points and Segments in Triangles

COMMON CORE GPS

MATHEMATICAL PRACTICES The Common Core Georgia Performance Standards for Mathematical Practice describe varieties of expertise that all students should seek to develop. Opportunities to develop these practices are integrated throughout this program.

1 Make sense of problems and persevere in solving them.

2 Reason abstractly and quantitatively.

3 Construct viable arguments and critique the reasoning of others.

4 Model with mathematics.

5 Use appropriate tools strategically.

6 Attend to precision.

7 Look for and make use of structure.

8 Look for and express regularity in repeated reasoning.

Unpacking the Standards

my.hrw.com
Multilingual Glossary

Understanding the standards and the vocabulary terms in the standards will help you know exactly what you are expected to learn in this chapter.

 MCC9-12.G.CO.9

Prove theorems about lines and angles.

Key Vocabulary

proof (demostración)
An argument that uses logic to show that a conclusion is true.

theorem (teorema)
A statement that has been proven.

line (línea)
An undefined term in geometry, a line is a straight path that has no thickness and extends forever.

angle (ángulo)
A figure formed by two rays with a common endpoint.

What It Means For You

Many segments associated with triangles, such as those that bisect angles or sides, are perpendiculars, connect midpoints, and so on, have special properties that you can prove.

EXAMPLE

Medians $\overline{AY}$, $\overline{CX}$, and $\overline{BZ}$ meet in a single point P.

Midsegment $\overline{DE}$ is parallel to side $\overline{AC}$.

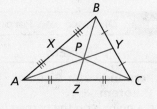

 MCC9-12.G.CO.10

Prove theorems about triangles.

Key Vocabulary

proof (demostración)
An argument that uses logic to show that a conclusion is true.

theorem (teorema)
A statement that has been proven.

triangle (triángulo)
A three-sided polygon.

What It Means For You

You can prove theorems about the relationships among side lengths and angle measures within a single triangle and between two or more triangles.

EXAMPLE   Relationships within a triangle

Because m∠PSQ = 51° by the Triangle Sum Theorem, it is the smallest angle in △PSQ. So, the opposite side, $\overline{PQ}$, is the shortest side of △PSQ.

EXAMPLE   Relationships between triangles

By the Hinge Theorem, if $m\angle B > m\angle E$ in the two triangles shown with congruent sides as marked, then $AC > DF$.

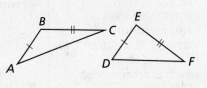

6-1 Perpendicular and Angle Bisectors

 Essential Question: How can you describe the set of points equidistant from the endpoints of a segment or from the sides of an angle?

Objectives
Prove and apply theorems about perpendicular bisectors.

Prove and apply theorems about angle bisectors.

Vocabulary
equidistant
locus

Who uses this?
The suspension and steering lines of a parachute keep the sky diver centered under the parachute. (See Example 3.)

When a point is the same distance from two or more objects, the point is said to be **equidistant** from the objects. Triangle congruence theorems can be used to prove theorems about equidistant points.

Know it! Note

Animated Math

Theorems	Distance and Perpendicular Bisectors		
	THEOREM	**HYPOTHESIS**	**CONCLUSION**
6-1-1	**Perpendicular Bisector Theorem** If a point is on the perpendicular bisector of a segment, then it is equidistant from the endpoints of the segment.	$\overline{XY} \perp \overline{AB}$ $\overline{YA} \cong \overline{YB}$	$XA = XB$
6-1-2	**Converse of the Perpendicular Bisector Theorem** If a point is equidistant from the endpoints of a segment, then it is on the perpendicular bisector of the segment.	$XA = XB$	$\overline{XY} \perp \overline{AB}$ $\overline{YA} \cong \overline{YB}$

You will prove Theorem 6-1-2 in Exercise 30.

PROOF **Perpendicular Bisector Theorem**

Reading Math

The word *locus* comes from the Latin word for location. The plural of *locus* is *loci*, which is pronounced LOW-sigh.

Given: ℓ is the perpendicular bisector of $\overline{AB}$.
Prove: $XA = XB$

Proof:
Since ℓ is the perpendicular bisector of $\overline{AB}$, $\ell \perp \overline{AB}$ and Y is the midpoint of $\overline{AB}$. By the definition of perpendicular, $\angle AYX$ and $\angle BYX$ are right angles and $\angle AYX \cong \angle BYX$. By the definition of midpoint, $\overline{AY} \cong \overline{BY}$. By the Reflexive Property of Congruence, $\overline{XY} \cong \overline{XY}$. So $\triangle AYX \cong \triangle BYX$ by SAS, and $\overline{XA} \cong \overline{XB}$ by CPCTC. Therefore $XA = XB$ by the definition of congruent segments.

A **locus** is a set of points that satisfies a given condition. The perpendicular bisector of a segment can be defined as the locus of points in a plane that are equidistant from the endpoints of the segment.

EXAMPLE **1** **Applying the Perpendicular Bisector Theorem and Its Converse**

Find each measure.

my.hrw.com

Online Video Tutor

A *YW*

$YW = XW$	⊥ Bisector Thm.
$YW = 7.3$	Substitute 7.3 for XW.

B *BC*

Since $AB = AC$ and $\ell \perp \overline{BC}$, ℓ is the perpendicular bisector of $\overline{BC}$ by the Converse of the Perpendicular Bisector Theorem.

$BC = 2CD$	Def. of seg. bisector
$BC = 2(16) = 32$	Substitute 16 for CD.

C *PR*

$PR = RQ$	⊥ Bisector Thm.
$2n + 9 = 7n - 18$	Substitute the given values.
$9 = 5n - 18$	Subtract 2n from both sides.
$27 = 5n$	Add 18 to both sides.
$5.4 = n$	Divide both sides by 5.

So $PR = 2(5.4) + 9 = 19.8$.

CHECK IT OUT! Find each measure.

1a. Given that line ℓ is the perpendicular bisector of $\overline{DE}$ and $EG = 14.6$, find DG.

1b. Given that $DE = 20.8$, $DG = 36.4$, and $EG = 36.4$, find EF.

Remember that the distance between a point and a line is the length of the perpendicular segment from the point to the line.

Know it! Note

Theorems — Distance and Angle Bisectors

THEOREM	HYPOTHESIS	CONCLUSION
6-1-3 **Angle Bisector Theorem** If a point is on the bisector of an angle, then it is equidistant from the sides of the angle.	∠APC ≅ ∠BPC	$AC = BC$
6-1-4 **Converse of the Angle Bisector Theorem** If a point in the interior of an angle is equidistant from the sides of the angle, then it is on the bisector of the angle.	AC = BC	∠APC ≅ ∠BPC

You will prove these theorems in Exercises 31 and 40.

Based on these theorems, an angle bisector can be defined as the locus of all points in the interior of the angle that are equidistant from the sides of the angle.

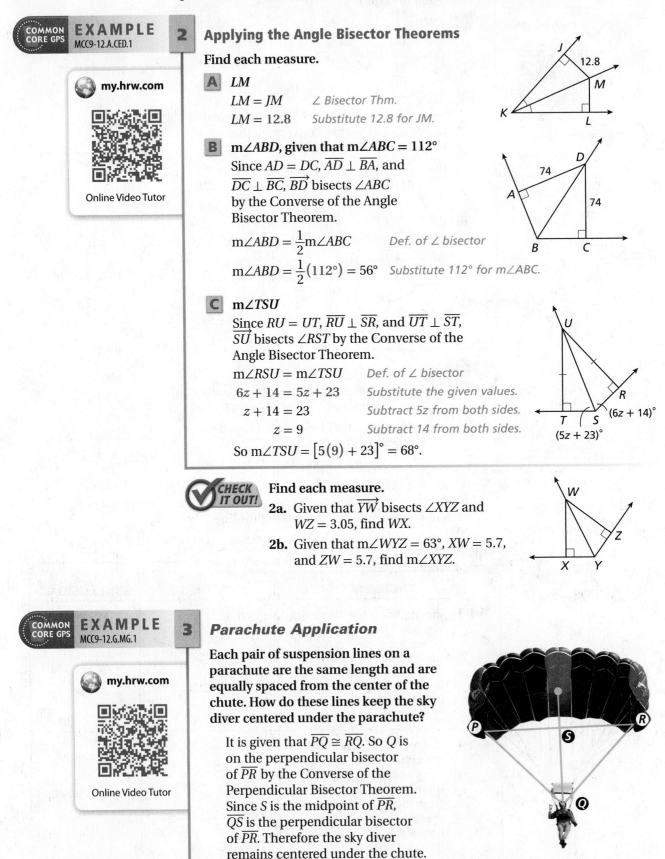

EXAMPLE 2 MCC9-12.A.CED.1

Applying the Angle Bisector Theorems

Find each measure.

A *LM*

$LM = JM$ ∠ Bisector Thm.

$LM = 12.8$ Substitute 12.8 for JM.

B m∠*ABD*, given that m∠*ABC* = 112°

Since $AD = DC$, $\overline{AD} \perp \overline{BA}$, and $\overline{DC} \perp \overline{BC}$, $\overrightarrow{BD}$ bisects ∠*ABC* by the Converse of the Angle Bisector Theorem.

$m\angle ABD = \frac{1}{2}m\angle ABC$ Def. of ∠ bisector

$m\angle ABD = \frac{1}{2}(112°) = 56°$ Substitute 112° for m∠ABC.

C m∠*TSU*

Since $RU = UT$, $\overline{RU} \perp \overline{SR}$, and $\overline{UT} \perp \overline{ST}$, $\overrightarrow{SU}$ bisects ∠*RST* by the Converse of the Angle Bisector Theorem.

$m\angle RSU = m\angle TSU$ Def. of ∠ bisector

$6z + 14 = 5z + 23$ Substitute the given values.

$z + 14 = 23$ Subtract 5z from both sides.

$z = 9$ Subtract 14 from both sides.

So $m\angle TSU = [5(9) + 23]° = 68°$.

CHECK IT OUT!

Find each measure.

2a. Given that $\overrightarrow{YW}$ bisects ∠*XYZ* and $WZ = 3.05$, find *WX*.

2b. Given that m∠*WYZ* = 63°, $XW = 5.7$, and $ZW = 5.7$, find m∠*XYZ*.

EXAMPLE 3 MCC9-12.G.MG.1

Parachute Application

Each pair of suspension lines on a parachute are the same length and are equally spaced from the center of the chute. How do these lines keep the sky diver centered under the parachute?

It is given that $\overline{PQ} \cong \overline{RQ}$. So *Q* is on the perpendicular bisector of $\overline{PR}$ by the Converse of the Perpendicular Bisector Theorem. Since *S* is the midpoint of $\overline{PR}$, $\overline{QS}$ is the perpendicular bisector of $\overline{PR}$. Therefore the sky diver remains centered under the chute.

CHECK IT OUT! **3.** *S* is equidistant from each pair of suspension lines. What can you conclude about $\overrightarrow{QS}$?

COMMON CORE GPS **EXAMPLE 4**
MCC9-12.G.GPE.5

Writing Equations of Bisectors in the Coordinate Plane

Write an equation in point-slope form for the perpendicular bisector of the segment with endpoints $A(-1, 6)$ and $B(3, 4)$.

Step 1 Graph $\overline{AB}$.

The perpendicular bisector of $\overline{AB}$ is perpendicular to $\overline{AB}$ at its midpoint.

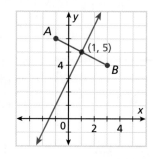

Step 2 Find the midpoint of $\overline{AB}$.

$$\left(\frac{x_1 + x_2}{2}, \frac{y_1 + y_2}{2}\right) \quad \textit{Midpoint formula}$$

mdpt. of $\overline{AB} = \left(\dfrac{-1 + 3}{2}, \dfrac{6 + 4}{2}\right) = (1, 5)$

Step 3 Find the slope of the perpendicular bisector.

$$\text{slope} = \frac{y_2 - y_1}{x_2 - x_1} \quad \textit{Slope formula}$$

slope of $\overline{AB} = \dfrac{4 - 6}{3 - (-1)} = \dfrac{-2}{4} = -\dfrac{1}{2}$

Since the slopes of perpendicular lines are opposite reciprocals, the slope of the perpendicular bisector is 2.

Step 4 Use point-slope form to write an equation.

The perpendicular bisector of $\overline{AB}$ has slope 2 and passes through $(1, 5)$.

$y - y_1 = m(x - x_1)$ *Point-slope form*
$y - 5 = 2(x - 1)$ *Substitute 5 for y_1, 2 for m, and 1 for x_1.*

 CHECK IT OUT! **4.** Write an equation in point-slope form for the perpendicular bisector of the segment with endpoints $P(5, 2)$ and $Q(1, -4)$.

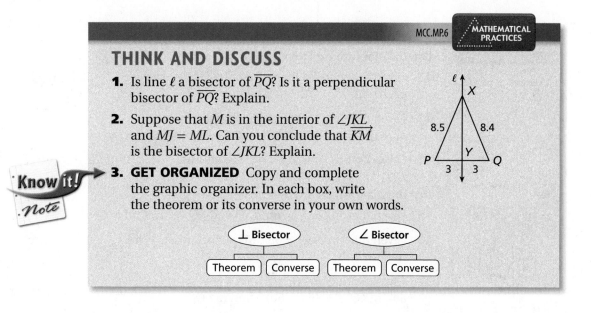

MCC.MP.6   **MATHEMATICAL PRACTICES**

THINK AND DISCUSS

1. Is line ℓ a bisector of $\overline{PQ}$? Is it a perpendicular bisector of $\overline{PQ}$? Explain.

2. Suppose that *M* is in the interior of $\angle JKL$ and $MJ = ML$. Can you conclude that $\overrightarrow{KM}$ is the bisector of $\angle JKL$? Explain.

3. GET ORGANIZED Copy and complete the graphic organizer. In each box, write the theorem or its converse in your own words.

$\perp$ **Bisector** $\angle$ **Bisector**

| Theorem | Converse | Theorem | Converse |

GUIDED PRACTICE

1. **Vocabulary** A ___?___ is the *locus* of all points in a plane that are *equidistant* from the endpoints of a segment. (*perpendicular bisector* or *angle bisector*)

SEE EXAMPLE 1 | **Use the diagram for Exercises 2–4.**

2. Given that $PS = 53.4$, $QT = 47.7$, and $QS = 53.4$, find PQ.

3. Given that m is the perpendicular bisector of $\overline{PQ}$ and $SQ = 25.9$, find SP.

4. Given that m is the perpendicular bisector of $\overline{PQ}$, $PS = 4a$, and $QS = 2a + 26$, find QS.

SEE EXAMPLE 2 | **Use the diagram for Exercises 5–7.**

5. Given that $\overrightarrow{BD}$ bisects $\angle ABC$ and $CD = 21.9$, find AD.

6. Given that $AD = 61$, $CD = 61$, and $m\angle ABC = 48°$, find $m\angle CBD$.

7. Given that $DA = DC$, $m\angle DBC = (10y + 3)°$, and $m\angle DBA = (8y + 10)°$, find $m\angle DBC$.

SEE EXAMPLE 3 | 8. **Carpentry** For a king post truss to be constructed correctly, P must lie on the bisector of $\angle JLN$. How can braces $\overline{PK}$ and $\overline{PM}$ be used to ensure that P is in the proper location?

SEE EXAMPLE 4 | **Write an equation in point-slope form for the perpendicular bisector of the segment with the given endpoints.**

9. $M(-5, 4)$, $N(1, -2)$
10. $U(2, -6)$, $V(4, 0)$
11. $J(-7, 5)$, $K(1, -1)$

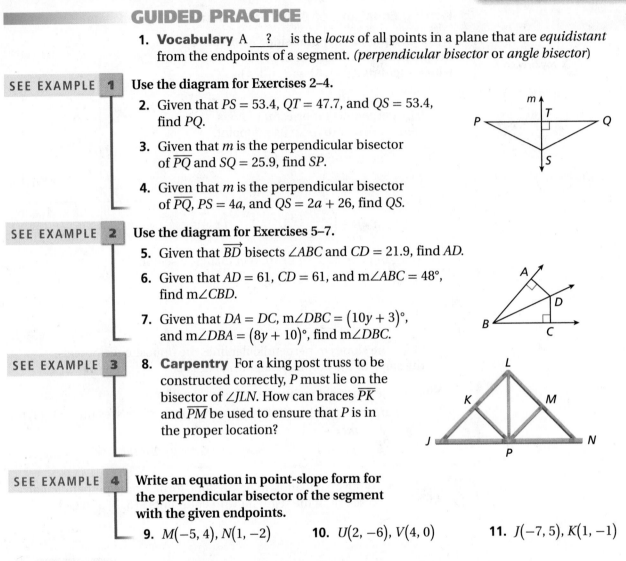

PRACTICE AND PROBLEM SOLVING

Independent Practice	
For Exercises	See Example
12–14	1
15–17	2
18	3
19–21	4

my.hrw.com

Online Extra Practice

Use the diagram for Exercises 12–14.

12. Given that line t is the perpendicular bisector of $\overline{JK}$ and $GK = 8.25$, find GJ.

13. Given that line t is the perpendicular bisector of $\overline{JK}$, $JG = x + 12$, and $KG = 3x - 17$, find KG.

14. Given that $GJ = 70.2$, $JH = 26.5$, and $GK = 70.2$, find JK.

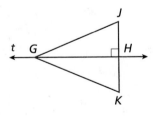

Use the diagram for Exercises 15–17.

15. Given that $m\angle RSQ = m\angle TSQ$ and $TQ = 1.3$, find RQ.

16. Given that $m\angle RSQ = 58°$, $RQ = 49$, and $TQ = 49$, find $m\angle RST$.

17. Given that $RQ = TQ$, $m\angle QSR = (9a + 48)°$, and $m\angle QST = (6a + 50)°$, find $m\angle QST$.

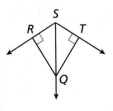

18. City Planning The planners for a new section of the city want every location on Main Street to be equidistant from Elm Street and Grove Street. How can the planners ensure that this is the case?

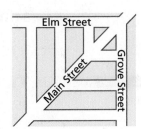

Write an equation in point-slope form for the perpendicular bisector of the segment with the given endpoints.

19. $E(-4, -7)$, $F(0, 1)$ **20.** $X(-7, 5)$, $Y(-1, -1)$ **21.** $M(-3, -1)$, $N(7, -5)$

22. $\overleftrightarrow{PQ}$ is the perpendicular bisector of $\overline{ST}$. Find the values of m and n.

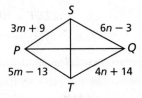

Shuffleboard Use the diagram of a shuffleboard and the following information to find each length in Exercises 23–28.

$\overleftrightarrow{KZ}$ is the perpendicular bisector of $\overline{GN}$, $\overline{HM}$, and $\overline{JL}$.

23. JK **24.** GN **25.** ML

26. HY **27.** JL **28.** NM

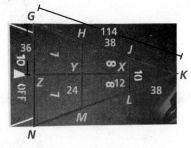

29. Multi-Step The endpoints of $\overline{AB}$ are $A(-2, 1)$ and $B(4, -3)$. Find the coordinates of a point C other than the midpoint of $\overline{AB}$ that is on the perpendicular bisector of $\overline{AB}$. How do you know it is on the perpendicular bisector?

30. Write a paragraph proof of the Converse of the Perpendicular Bisector Theorem.

Given: $AX = BX$
Prove: X is on the perpendicular bisector of $\overline{AB}$.

Plan: Draw ℓ perpendicular to $\overline{AB}$ through X. Show that $\triangle AYX \cong \triangle BYX$ and thus $\overline{AY} \cong \overline{BY}$. By definition, ℓ is the perpendicular bisector of $\overline{AB}$.

31. Write a two-column proof of the Angle Bisector Theorem.

Given: $\overrightarrow{PS}$ bisects $\angle QPR$. $\overline{SQ} \perp \overrightarrow{PQ}$, $\overline{SR} \perp \overrightarrow{PR}$
Prove: $SQ = SR$

Plan: Use the definitions of angle bisector and perpendicular to identify two pairs of congruent angles. Show that $\triangle PQS \cong \triangle PRS$ and thus $\overline{SQ} \cong \overline{SR}$.

32. Critical Thinking In the Converse of the Angle Bisector Theorem, why is it important to say that the point must be in the interior of the angle?

Real-World Connections

33. A music company has stores in Abby $(-3, -2)$ and Cardenas $(3, 6)$. Each unit in the coordinate plane represents 1 mile.

    a. The company president wants to build a warehouse that is equidistant from the two stores. Write an equation that describes the possible locations.

    b. A straight road connects Abby and Cardenas. The warehouse will be located exactly 4 miles from the road. How many locations are possible?

    c. To the nearest tenth of a mile, how far will the warehouse be from each store?

H.O.T. **34. Write About It** How is the construction of the perpendicular bisector of a segment related to the Converse of the Perpendicular Bisector Theorem?

TEST PREP

35. If $\overleftrightarrow{JK}$ is perpendicular to $\overline{XY}$ at its midpoint M, which statement is true?

　Ⓐ $JX = KY$ 　　Ⓑ $JX = KX$ 　　Ⓒ $JM = KM$ 　　Ⓓ $JX = JY$

36. What information is needed to conclude that $\overrightarrow{EF}$ is the bisector of $\angle DEG$?

　Ⓕ $m\angle DEF = m\angle DEG$ 　　　Ⓗ $m\angle GED = m\angle GEF$

　Ⓖ $m\angle FEG = m\angle DEF$ 　　　Ⓙ $m\angle DEF = m\angle EFG$

37. Short Response The city wants to build a visitor center in the park so that it is equidistant from Park Street and Washington Avenue. They also want the visitor center to be equidistant from the museum and the library. Find the point V where the visitor center should be built. Explain your answer.

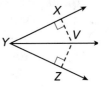

CHALLENGE AND EXTEND

H.O.T. **38.** Consider the points $P(2, 0)$, $A(-4, 2)$, $B(0, -6)$, and $C(6, -3)$.

　a. Show that P is on the bisector of $\angle ABC$.

　b. Write an equation of the line that contains the bisector of $\angle ABC$.

39. Find the locus of points that are equidistant from the x-axis and y-axis.

H.O.T. **40.** Write a two-column proof of the Converse of the Angle Bisector Theorem.

　Given: $\overline{VX} \perp \overrightarrow{YX}$, $\overline{VZ} \perp \overrightarrow{YZ}$, $VX = VZ$
　Prove: $\overrightarrow{YV}$ bisects $\angle XYZ$.

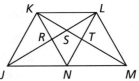

H.O.T. **41.** Write a paragraph proof.

　Given: $\overline{KN}$ is the perpendicular bisector of $\overline{JL}$.
　　　　$\overline{LN}$ is the perpendicular bisector of $\overline{KM}$.
　　　　$\overline{JR} \cong \overline{MT}$
　Prove: $\angle JKM \cong \angle MLJ$

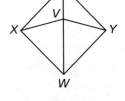

FOCUS ON MATHEMATICAL PRACTICES

H.O.T. **42. Communication** In the figure, $TX = TY$ and $XV = YV$. Explain how you can prove that $WX = WY$ without proving pairs of triangles congruent.

H.O.T. **43. Problem Solving** $\overline{AB}$ has endpoints $A(1, -4)$ and $B(x, y)$. The line $y = -\frac{1}{2}x + 4$ is the perpendicular bisector of $\overline{AB}$.

　a. Write an equation for the line that contains $\overline{AB}$.

　b. Find the intersection of the two lines.

　c. Find the change in x-values from point A to the intersection of the two lines. Do the same for the change in y-values.

　d. Use the changes in x and y to locate point B.

6-2 Bisectors of Triangles

Essential Question: How can you construct the circumcircle and incircle of any triangle?

Objectives
Prove and apply properties of perpendicular bisectors of a triangle.

Prove and apply properties of angle bisectors of a triangle.

Vocabulary
concurrent
point of concurrency
circumcenter of a triangle
circumscribed
incenter of a triangle
inscribed

Who uses this?
An event planner can use perpendicular bisectors of triangles to find the best location for a fireworks display. (See Example 4.)

Since a triangle has three sides, it has three perpendicular bisectors. When you construct the perpendicular bisectors, you find that they have an interesting property.

Helpful Hint
The perpendicular bisector of a side of a triangle does not always pass through the opposite vertex.

Construction   Circumcenter of a Triangle

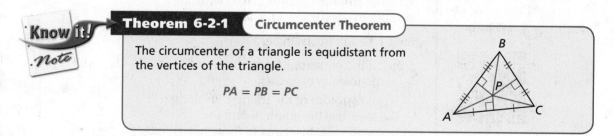

① Draw a large scalene acute triangle *ABC* on a piece of patty paper.

② Fold the perpendicular bisector of each side.

③ Label the point where the three perpendicular bisectors intersect as *P*.

When three or more lines intersect at one point, the lines are said to be **concurrent**. The **point of concurrency** is the point where they intersect. In the construction, you saw that the three perpendicular bisectors of a triangle are concurrent. This point of concurrency is the **circumcenter of the triangle**.

Know it!
Note

Theorem 6-2-1   Circumcenter Theorem

The circumcenter of a triangle is equidistant from the vertices of the triangle.

$$PA = PB = PC$$

The circumcenter can be inside the triangle, outside the triangle, or on the triangle.

Acute triangle

Obtuse triangle

Right triangle

(tr), Firefly Productions/CORBIS; (cl)(c)(cr), Sam Dudgeon/HMH Photo;

The circumcenter of $\triangle ABC$ is the center of its *circumscribed* circle. A circle that contains all the vertices of a polygon is **circumscribed** about the polygon.

PROOF ■ **Circumcenter Theorem**

Given: Lines ℓ, m, and n are the perpendicular bisectors of $\overline{AB}$, $\overline{BC}$, and $\overline{AC}$, respectively.

Prove: $PA = PB = PC$

Proof:

P is the circumcenter of $\triangle ABC$. Since P lies on the perpendicular bisector of $\overline{AB}$, $PA = PB$ by the Perpendicular Bisector Theorem. Similarly, P also lies on the perpendicular bisector of $\overline{BC}$, so $PB = PC$. Therefore $PA = PB = PC$ by the Transitive Property of Equality.

COMMON CORE GPS **EXAMPLE** 1 MCC9-12.G.C.3

Using Properties of Perpendicular Bisectors

$\overline{KZ}$, $\overline{LZ}$, and $\overline{MZ}$ are the perpendicular bisectors of $\triangle GHJ$. Find HZ.

my.hrw.com

Online Video Tutor

Z is the circumcenter of $\triangle GHJ$. By the Circumcenter Theorem, Z is equidistant from the vertices of $\triangle GHJ$.

$HZ = GZ$ *Circumcenter Thm.*

$HZ = 19.9$ *Substitute 19.9 for GZ.*

CHECK IT OUT! Use the diagram above. Find each length.

1a. GM **1b.** GK **1c.** JZ

COMMON CORE GPS **EXAMPLE** 2 MCC9-12.G.C.3

Finding the Circumcenter of a Triangle

my.hrw.com

Online Video Tutor

Find the circumcenter of $\triangle RSO$ with vertices $R(-6, 0)$, $S(0, 4)$, and $O(0, 0)$.

Step 1 Graph the triangle.

Step 2 Find equations for two perpendicular bisectors.

Since two sides of the triangle lie along the axes, use the graph to find the perpendicular bisectors of these two sides. The perpendicular bisector of $\overline{RO}$ is $x = -3$, and the perpendicular bisector of $\overline{OS}$ is $y = 2$.

Step 3 Find the intersection of the two equations.

The lines $x = -3$ and $y = 2$ intersect at $(-3, 2)$, the circumcenter of $\triangle RSO$.

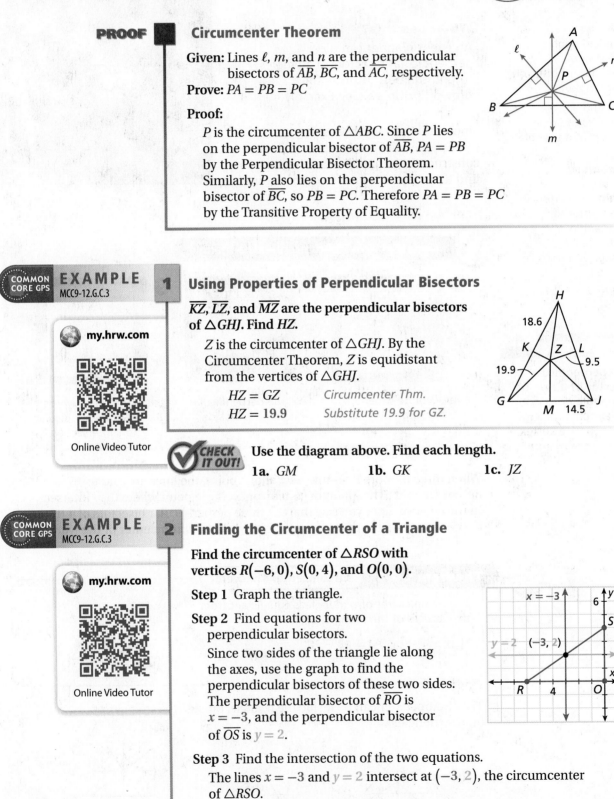

CHECK IT OUT! **2.** Find the circumcenter of △GOH with vertices G(0, −9), O(0, 0), and H(8, 0).

A triangle has three angles, so it has three angle bisectors. The angle bisectors of a triangle are also concurrent. This point of concurrency is the **incenter of the triangle**.

> **Know it!**
> *Note*

Theorem 6-2-2   (Incenter Theorem)

The incenter of a triangle is equidistant from the sides of the triangle.

$$PX = PY = PZ$$

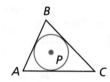

You will prove Theorem 6-2-2 in Exercise 35.

> **Remember!**
>
> The distance between a point and a line is the length of the perpendicular segment from the point to the line.

Unlike the circumcenter, the incenter is always inside the triangle.

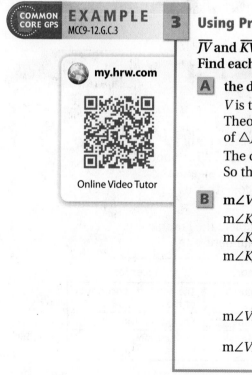

| Acute triangle | Obtuse triangle | Right triangle |

The incenter is the center of the triangle's *inscribed circle*. A circle **inscribed** in a polygon intersects each line that contains a side of the polygon at exactly one point.

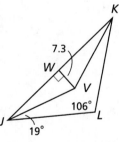

> **COMMON CORE GPS**
> MCC9-12.G.C.3

EXAMPLE **3**

> **my.hrw.com**
>
> **Online Video Tutor**

Using Properties of Angle Bisectors

$\overline{JV}$ and $\overline{KV}$ are angle bisectors of △JKL. Find each measure.

A the distance from V to $\overline{KL}$

V is the incenter of △JKL. By the Incenter Theorem, V is equidistant from the sides of △JKL.

The distance from V to $\overline{JK}$ is 7.3.
So the distance from V to $\overline{KL}$ is also 7.3.

B m∠VKL

m∠KJL = 2m∠VJL	$\overline{JV}$ is the bisector of ∠KJL.
m∠KJL = 2(19°) = 38°	Substitute 19° for m∠VJL.
m∠KJL + m∠JLK + m∠JKL = 180°	△ Sum Thm.
38 + 106 + m∠JKL = 180	Substitute the given values.
m∠JKL = 36°	Subtract 144° from both sides.
m∠VKL = $\frac{1}{2}$m∠JKL	$\overline{KV}$ is the bisector of ∠JKL.
m∠VKL = $\frac{1}{2}$(36°) = 18°	Substitute 36° for m∠JKL.

CHECK IT OUT! $\overline{QX}$ and $\overline{RX}$ are angle bisectors of △PQR. Find each measure.

3a. the distance from X to $\overline{PQ}$

3b. m∠PQX

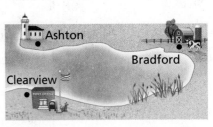

EXAMPLE **4**
MCC9-12.G.MG.3

my.hrw.com

Online Video Tutor

Community Application

For the next Fourth of July, the towns of Ashton, Bradford, and Clearview will launch a fireworks display from a boat in the lake. Draw a sketch to show where the boat should be positioned so that it is the same distance from all three towns. Justify your sketch.

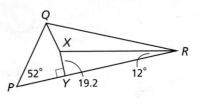

Let the three towns be vertices of a triangle. By the Circumcenter Theorem, the circumcenter of the triangle is equidistant from the vertices.

Trace the outline of the lake. Draw the triangle formed by the towns. To find the circumcenter, find the perpendicular bisectors of each side. The position of the boat is the circumcenter, F.

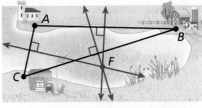

CHECK IT OUT! **4.** A city plans to build a firefighters' monument in the park between three streets. Draw a sketch to show where the city should place the monument so that it is the same distance from all three streets. Justify your sketch.

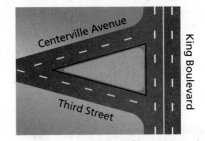

MCC.MP.7 **MATHEMATICAL PRACTICES**

THINK AND DISCUSS

1. Sketch three lines that are concurrent.

2. P and Q are the circumcenter and incenter of △RST, but not necessarily in that order. Which point is the circumcenter? Which point is the incenter? Explain how you can tell without constructing any of the bisectors.

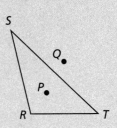

 Know it! Note

3. GET ORGANIZED Copy and complete the graphic organizer. Fill in the blanks to make each statement true.

	Circumcenter	Incenter
Definition	The point of concurrency of the ?	The point of concurrency of the ?
Distance	Equidistant from the ?	Equidistant from the ?
Location (Inside, Outside, or On)	Can be ? the triangle	? the triangle

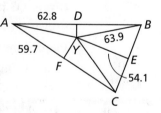
GUIDED PRACTICE

Vocabulary Apply the vocabulary from this lesson to answer each question.

1. Explain why lines ℓ, m, and n are NOT *concurrent*.

2. A circle that contains all the vertices of a polygon is
   ___?___ the polygon. (*circumscribed about* or *inscribed in*)

SEE EXAMPLE 1 $\overline{SN}$, $\overline{TN}$, and $\overline{VN}$ are the perpendicular bisectors
of $\triangle PQR$. Find each length.

3. NR　　　　4. RV

5. TR　　　　6. QN

SEE EXAMPLE 2 **Multi-Step** Find the circumcenter of a triangle with the given vertices.

7. $O(0, 0)$, $K(0, 12)$, $L(4, 0)$

8. $A(-7, 0)$, $O(0, 0)$, $B(0, -10)$

SEE EXAMPLE 3 $\overline{CF}$ and $\overline{EF}$ are angle bisectors of $\triangle CDE$.
Find each measure.

9. the distance from F to $\overline{CD}$

10. $m\angle FED$

SEE EXAMPLE 4 11. **Design** The designer of the
Newtown High School pennant
wants the circle around the bear
emblem to be as large as possible.
Draw a sketch to show where the
center of the circle should be located.
Justify your sketch.

PRACTICE AND PROBLEM SOLVING

Independent Practice	
For Exercises	See Example
12–15	1
16–17	2
18–19	3
20	4

my.hrw.com

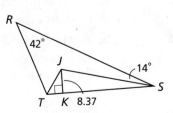

Online Extra Practice

$\overline{DY}$, $\overline{EY}$, and $\overline{FY}$ are the perpendicular bisectors
of $\triangle ABC$. Find each length.

12. CF　　　　13. YC

14. DB　　　　15. AY

Multi-Step Find the circumcenter of a triangle with the given vertices.

16. $M(-5, 0)$, $N(0, 14)$, $O(0, 0)$　　　17. $O(0, 0)$, $V(0, 19)$, $W(-3, 0)$

$\overline{TJ}$ and $\overline{SJ}$ are angle bisectors of $\triangle RST$.
Find each measure.

18. the distance from J to $\overline{RS}$

19. $m\angle RTJ$

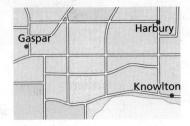

H.O.T. 20. Business A company repairs photocopiers in Harbury, Gaspar, and Knowlton. Draw a sketch to show where the company should locate its office so that it is the same distance from each city. Justify your sketch.

21. Critical Thinking If *M* is the incenter of △*JKL*, explain why ∠*JML* cannot be a right angle.

Tell whether each segment lies on a perpendicular bisector, an angle bisector, or neither. Justify your answer.

22. $\overline{AE}$ **23.** $\overline{DG}$ **24.** $\overline{BG}$

25. $\overline{CR}$ **26.** $\overline{FR}$ **27.** $\overline{DR}$

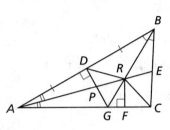

Tell whether each statement is sometimes, always, or never true. Support your answer with a sketch.

28. The angle bisectors of a triangle intersect at a point outside the triangle.

29. An angle bisector of a triangle bisects the opposite side.

30. A perpendicular bisector of a triangle passes through the opposite vertex.

31. The incenter of a right triangle is on the triangle.

32. The circumcenter of a scalene triangle is inside the triangle.

H.O.T. Algebra Find the circumcenter of the triangle with the given vertices.

33. $O(0, 0)$, $A(4, 8)$, $B(8, 0)$ **34.** $O(0, 0)$, $Y(0, 12)$, $Z(6, 6)$

H.O.T. 35. Complete this proof of the Incenter Theorem by filling in the blanks.

Given: $\overrightarrow{AP}$, $\overrightarrow{BP}$, and $\overrightarrow{CP}$ bisect ∠*A*, ∠*B*, and ∠*C*, respectively. $\overline{PX} \perp \overline{AC}$, $\overline{PY} \perp \overline{AB}$, $\overline{PZ} \perp \overline{BC}$

Prove: $PX = PY = PZ$

Proof: Let *P* be the incenter of △*ABC*. Since *P* lies on the bisector of ∠*A*, $PX = PY$ by **a.** ___?___ . Similarly, *P* also lies on **b.** ___?___ , so $PY = PZ$. Therefore **c.** ___?___ by the Transitive Property of Equality.

H.O.T. 36. Prove that the bisector of the vertex angle of an isosceles triangle is the perpendicular bisector of the base.

Given: $\overleftrightarrow{QS}$ bisects ∠*PQR*. $\overline{PQ} \cong \overline{RQ}$

Prove: $\overleftrightarrow{QS}$ is the perpendicular bisector of $\overline{PR}$.

Plan: Show that △*PQS* ≅ △*RQS*. Then use CPCTC to show that *S* is the midpoint of $\overline{PR}$ and that $\overleftrightarrow{QS} \perp \overline{PR}$.

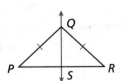

Real-World Connections

37. A music company has stores at $A(0, 0)$, $B(8, 0)$, and $C(4, 3)$, where each unit of the coordinate plane represents one mile.

a. A new store will be built so that it is equidistant from the three existing stores. Find the coordinates of the new store's location.

b. Where will the new store be located in relation to △*ABC*?

c. To the nearest tenth of a mile, how far will the new store be from each of the existing stores?

38. Write About It How are the inscribed circle and the circumscribed circle of a triangle alike? How are they different?

39. Construction Draw a large scalene acute triangle.

  a. Construct the angle bisectors to find the incenter. Inscribe a circle in the triangle.

  b. Construct the perpendicular bisectors to find the circumcenter. Circumscribe a circle around the triangle.

TEST PREP

40. P is the incenter of $\triangle ABC$. Which must be true?

  (A) $PA = PB$ (C) $YA = YB$

  (B) $PX = PY$ (D) $AX = BZ$

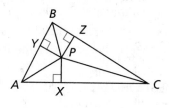

41. Lines r, s, and t are concurrent. The equation of line r is $x = 5$, and the equation of line s is $y = -2$. Which could be the equation of line t?

  (F) $y = x - 7$ (H) $y = x + 3$

  (G) $y = x - 3$ (J) $y = x + 7$

42. Gridded Response Lines a, b, and c are the perpendicular bisectors of $\triangle KLM$. Find LN.

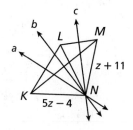

CHALLENGE AND EXTEND

43. Use the right triangle with the given coordinates.

  a. Prove that the midpoint of the hypotenuse of a right triangle is equidistant from all three vertices.

  b. Make a conjecture about the circumcenter of a right triangle.

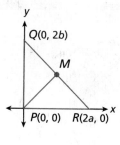

44. Design A *trefoil* is created by constructing three overlapping circles. In the figure, an equilateral triangle is inscribed inside a trefoil, and $\overline{AB}$ is a perpendicular bisector of the triangle. If the distance from one vertex to the circumcenter is 28 cm, what is the distance AB across the trefoil?

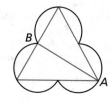

Design LINK

The trefoil shape, as seen in this stained glass window, has been used in design for centuries.

FOCUS ON MATHEMATICAL PRACTICES

H.O.T. 45. Reasoning For every triangle, a line exists such that every point on the line is equidistant from each vertex of the triangle. Describe this line.

H.O.T. 46. Problem Solving Point I is the incenter of $\triangle RST$. $IL = LS = 10$. $\angle S$ is a right angle, and $RS = 30$.

  a. Why is $LS = NS = IL = IN = 10$?

  b. Find RL. Explain why $RL = RM$ and $MT = NT$.

  c. Let $x = MT = NT$. Use the Pythagorean Theorem to find the value of x.

  d. Find ST and RT.

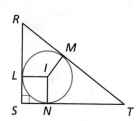

Corbis Images

Medians and Altitudes of Triangles

Essential Question: How can you find the balancing point in the interior of any triangle?

Objectives

Apply properties of medians of a triangle.

Apply properties of altitudes of a triangle.

Vocabulary

median of a triangle
centroid of a triangle
altitude of a triangle
orthocenter of a triangle

Who uses this?

Sculptors who create mobiles of moving objects can use centers of gravity to balance the objects. (See Example 2.)

A **median of a triangle** is a segment whose endpoints are a vertex of the triangle and the midpoint of the opposite side.

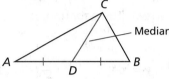

Every triangle has three medians, and the medians are concurrent, as shown in the construction below.

Construction Centroid of a Triangle

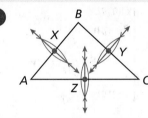

❶ Draw △ABC. Construct the midpoints of $\overline{AB}$, $\overline{BC}$, and $\overline{AC}$. Label the midpoints of the sides X, Y, and Z, respectively.

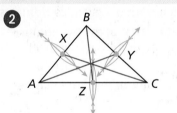

❷ Draw $\overline{AY}$, $\overline{BZ}$, and $\overline{CX}$. These are the three medians of △ABC.

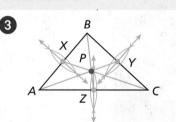

❸ Label the point where $\overline{AY}$, $\overline{BZ}$, and $\overline{CX}$ intersect as P.

The point of concurrency of the medians of a triangle is the **centroid of the triangle**. The centroid is always inside the triangle. The centroid is also called the *center of gravity* because it is the point where a triangular region will balance.

Know it!
Note

Theorem 6-3-1 **Centroid Theorem**

The centroid of a triangle is located $\frac{2}{3}$ of the distance from each vertex to the midpoint of the opposite side.

$$AP = \frac{2}{3}AY \qquad BP = \frac{2}{3}BZ \qquad CP = \frac{2}{3}CX$$

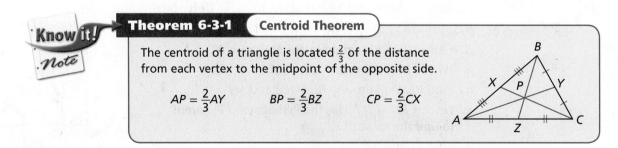

Using the Centroid to Find Segment Lengths

In $\triangle ABC$, $AF = 9$, and $GE = 2.4$. Find each length.

A AG

$AG = \frac{2}{3}AF$	*Centroid Thm.*
$AG = \frac{2}{3}(9)$	*Substitute 9 for AF.*
$AG = 6$	*Simplify.*

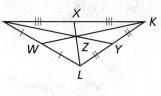

B CE

$CG = \frac{2}{3}CE$	*Centroid Thm.*
$CG + GE = CE$	*Seg. Add. Post.*
$\frac{2}{3}CE + GE = CE$	*Substitute $\frac{2}{3}$CE for CG.*
$GE = \frac{1}{3}CE$	*Subtract $\frac{2}{3}$CE from both sides.*
$2.4 = \frac{1}{3}CE$	*Substitute 2.4 for GE.*
$7.2 = CE$	*Multiply both sides by 3.*

CHECK IT OUT!

In $\triangle JKL$, $ZW = 7$, and $LX = 8.1$.
Find each length.

1a. KW

1b. LZ

Problem-Solving Application

The diagram shows the plan for a triangular
piece of a mobile. Where should the
sculptor attach the support so that the
triangle is balanced?

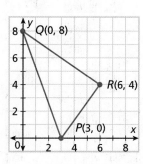

1 Understand the Problem

The **answer** will be the coordinates of
the centroid of $\triangle PQR$. The **important
information** is the location of the vertices,
$P(3, 0)$, $Q(0, 8)$, and $R(6, 4)$.

2 Make a Plan

The centroid of the triangle is the point of intersection of
the three medians. So write the equations for two medians
and find their point of intersection.

3 Solve

Let M be the midpoint of $\overline{QR}$ and N be the midpoint of $\overline{QP}$.

$$M = \left(\frac{0 + 6}{2}, \frac{8 + 4}{2}\right) = (3, 6) \qquad N = \left(\frac{0 + 3}{2}, \frac{8 + 0}{2}\right) = (1.5, 4)$$

$\overline{PM}$ is vertical. Its equation is $x = 3$. $\overline{RN}$ is horizontal.
Its equation is $y = 4$. The coordinates of the centroid are $S(3, 4)$.

4 Look Back

Let L be the midpoint of $\overline{PR}$. The equation for $\overleftrightarrow{QL}$ is $y = -\frac{4}{3}x + 8$, which intersects $x = 3$ at $S(3, 4)$.

 **CHECK IT OUT!** **2.** Find the average of the x-coordinates and the average of the y-coordinates of the vertices of $\triangle PQR$. Make a conjecture about the centroid of a triangle.

Helpful Hint

The height of a triangle is the length of an altitude.

An **altitude of a triangle** is a perpendicular segment from a vertex to the line containing the opposite side. Every triangle has three altitudes. An altitude can be inside, outside, or on the triangle.

In $\triangle QRS$, altitude $\overline{QY}$ is inside the triangle, but $\overline{RX}$ and $\overline{SZ}$ are not. Notice that the lines containing the altitudes are concurrent at P. This point of concurrency is the **orthocenter of the triangle**.

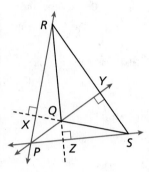

COMMON CORE GPS
EXAMPLE **3**
MCC9-12.G.GPE.5

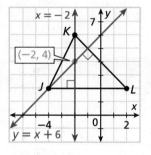 my.hrw.com

Online Video Tutor

Finding the Orthocenter

Find the orthocenter of $\triangle JKL$ with vertices $J(-4, 2)$, $K(-2, 6)$, and $L(2, 2)$.

Step 1 Graph the triangle.

Step 2 Find an equation of the line containing the altitude from K to $\overline{JL}$.

Since $\overleftrightarrow{JL}$ is horizontal, the altitude is vertical. The line containing it must pass through $K(-2, 6)$, so the equation of the line is $x = -2$.

Step 3 Find an equation of the line containing the altitude from J to $\overline{KL}$.

$$\text{slope of } \overleftrightarrow{KL} = \frac{2 - 6}{2 - (-2)} = -1$$

The slope of a line perpendicular to $\overleftrightarrow{KL}$ is 1. This line must pass through $J(-4, 2)$.

$\quad y - y_1 = m(x - x_1)$ *Point-slope form*

$\quad y - 2 = 1\big[x - (-4)\big]$ *Substitute 2 for y_1, 1 for m, and -4 for x_1.*

$\quad y - 2 = x + 4$ *Distribute 1.*

$\quad\quad y = x + 6$ *Add 2 to both sides.*

Step 4 Solve the system to find the coordinates of the orthocenter.

$$\begin{cases} x = -2 \\ y = x + 6 \end{cases}$$

$\quad y = -2 + 6 = 4$ *Substitute -2 for x.*

The coordinates of the orthocenter are $(-2, 4)$.

 **CHECK IT OUT!** **3.** Show that the altitude to $\overline{JK}$ passes through the orthocenter of $\triangle JKL$.

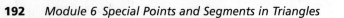

THINK AND DISCUSS

1. Draw a triangle in which a median and an altitude are the same segment. What type of triangle is it?

2. Draw a triangle in which an altitude is also a side of the triangle. What type of triangle is it?

3. The centroid of a triangle divides each median into two segments. What is the ratio of the two lengths of each median?

4. **GET ORGANIZED** Copy and complete the graphic organizer. Fill in the blanks to make each statement true.

	Centroid	Orthocenter
Definition	The point of concurrency of the __?__	The point of concurrency of the __?__
Location (Inside, Outside, or On)	__?__ the triangle	Can be __?__ the triangle

Know it! Note

6-3 Exercises

my.hrw.com Homework Help

GUIDED PRACTICE

Vocabulary Apply the vocabulary from this lesson to answer each question.

1. The __?__ of a triangle is located $\frac{2}{3}$ of the distance from each vertex to the midpoint of the opposite side. (*centroid* or *orthocenter*)

2. The __?__ of a triangle is perpendicular to the line containing a side. (*altitude* or *median*)

SEE EXAMPLE 1

$VX = 204$, and $RW = 104$. Find each length.

3. VW 4. WX

5. RY 6. WY

SEE EXAMPLE 2

7. **Design** The diagram shows a plan for a piece of a mobile. A chain will hang from the centroid of the triangle. At what coordinates should the artist attach the chain?

SEE EXAMPLE 3

Multi-Step Find the orthocenter of a triangle with the given vertices.

8. $K(2, -2)$, $L(4, 6)$, $M(8, -2)$

9. $U(-4, -9)$, $V(-4, 6)$, $W(5, -3)$

10. $P(-5, 8)$, $Q(4, 5)$, $R(-2, 5)$

11. $C(-1, -3)$, $D(-1, 2)$, $E(9, 2)$

PRACTICE AND PROBLEM SOLVING

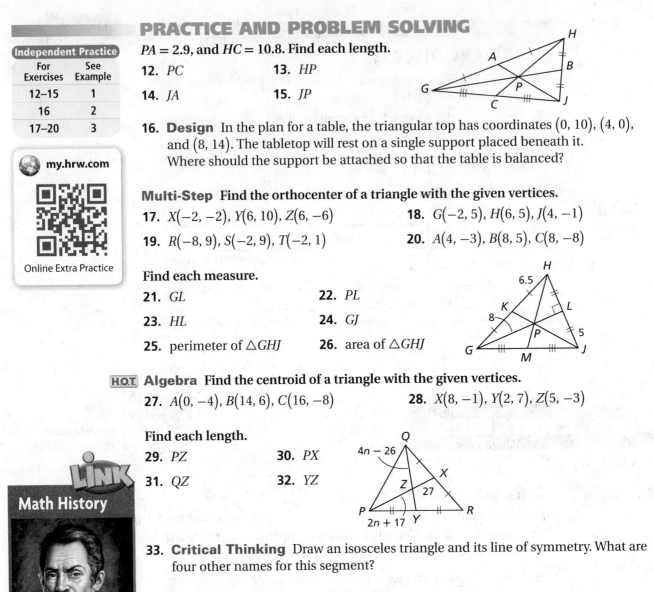

Independent Practice

For Exercises	See Example
12–15	1
16	2
17–20	3

my.hrw.com

Online Extra Practice

$PA = 2.9$, and $HC = 10.8$. Find each length.

12. PC **13.** HP

14. JA **15.** JP

16. Design In the plan for a table, the triangular top has coordinates $(0, 10)$, $(4, 0)$, and $(8, 14)$. The tabletop will rest on a single support placed beneath it. Where should the support be attached so that the table is balanced?

Multi-Step Find the orthocenter of a triangle with the given vertices.

17. $X(-2, -2)$, $Y(6, 10)$, $Z(6, -6)$ **18.** $G(-2, 5)$, $H(6, 5)$, $J(4, -1)$

19. $R(-8, 9)$, $S(-2, 9)$, $T(-2, 1)$ **20.** $A(4, -3)$, $B(8, 5)$, $C(8, -8)$

Find each measure.

21. GL **22.** PL

23. HL **24.** GJ

25. perimeter of $\triangle GHJ$ **26.** area of $\triangle GHJ$

H.O.T. Algebra Find the centroid of a triangle with the given vertices.

27. $A(0, -4)$, $B(14, 6)$, $C(16, -8)$ **28.** $X(8, -1)$, $Y(2, 7)$, $Z(5, -3)$

Find each length.

29. PZ **30.** PX

31. QZ **32.** YZ

Math History

In 1678, Giovanni Ceva published his famous theorem that states the conditions necessary for three *Cevians* (segments from a vertex of a triangle to the opposite side) to be concurrent. The medians and altitudes of a triangle meet these conditions.

33. Critical Thinking Draw an isosceles triangle and its line of symmetry. What are four other names for this segment?

Tell whether each statement is sometimes, always, or never true. Support your answer with a sketch.

34. A median of a triangle bisects one of the angles.

35. If one altitude of a triangle is in the triangle's exterior, then a second altitude is also in the triangle's exterior.

36. The centroid of a triangle lies in its exterior.

37. In an isosceles triangle, the altitude and median from the vertex angle are the same line as the bisector of the vertex angle.

38. Write a two-column proof.

Given: $\overline{PS}$ and $\overline{RT}$ are medians of $\triangle PQR$. $\overline{PS} \cong \overline{RT}$
Prove: $\triangle PQR$ is an isosceles triangle.

Plan: Show that $\triangle PTR \cong \triangle RSP$ and use CPCTC to conclude that $\angle QPR \cong \angle QRP$.

39. Write About It Draw a large triangle on a sheet of paper and cut it out. Find the centroid by paper folding. Try to balance the shape on the tip of your pencil at a point other than the centroid. Now try to balance the shape at its centroid. Explain why the centroid is also called the center of gravity.

Corbis Images

Real-World Connections

40. The towns of Davis, El Monte, and Fairview have the coordinates shown in the table, where each unit of the coordinate plane represents one mile. A music company has stores in each city and a distribution warehouse at the centroid of $\triangle DEF$.

City	Location
Davis	$D(0, 0)$
El Monte	$E(0, 8)$
Fairview	$F(8, 0)$

   a. What are the coordinates of the warehouse?

   b. Find the distance from the warehouse to the Davis store. Round your answer to the nearest tenth of a mile.

   c. A straight road connects El Monte and Fairview. What is the distance from the warehouse to the road?

TEST PREP

41. $\overline{QT}$, $\overline{RV}$, and $\overline{SW}$ are medians of $\triangle QRS$. Which statement is NOT necessarily true?

   Ⓐ $QP = \frac{2}{3}QT$ Ⓒ $RT = ST$

   Ⓑ $RP = 2PV$ Ⓓ $QT = SW$

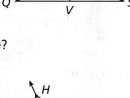

42. Suppose that the orthocenter of a triangle lies outside the triangle. Which points of concurrency are inside the triangle?

   I. incenter   **II.** circumcenter   **III.** centroid

   Ⓕ I and II only   Ⓗ II and III only

   Ⓖ I and III only   Ⓙ I, II, and III

43. In the diagram, which of the following correctly describes $\overline{LN}$?

   Ⓐ Altitude   Ⓒ Median

   Ⓑ Angle bisector   Ⓓ Perpendicular bisector

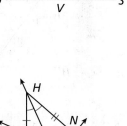

CHALLENGE AND EXTEND

H.O.T. **44.** Draw an equilateral triangle.

   a. Explain why the perpendicular bisector of any side contains the vertex opposite that side.

   b. Explain why the perpendicular bisector through any vertex also contains the median, the altitude, and the angle bisector through that vertex.

   c. Explain why the incenter, circumcenter, centroid, and orthocenter are the same point.

H.O.T. **45.** Use coordinates to show that the lines containing the altitudes of a triangle are concurrent.

   a. Find the slopes of $\overline{RS}$, $\overline{ST}$, and $\overline{RT}$.

   b. Find the slopes of lines ℓ, m, and n.

   c. Write equations for lines ℓ, m, and n.

   d. Solve a system of equations to find the point P where lines ℓ and m intersect.

   e. Show that line n contains P.

   f. What conclusion can you draw?

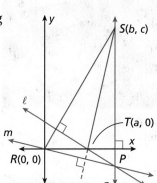

FOCUS ON MATHEMATICAL PRACTICES

H.O.T. 46. Reasoning Classify the triangle for which the circumcenter, incenter, centroid, and orthocenter all lie inside the triangle.

H.O.T. 47. Communication The orthocenter of a triangle is outside the triangle. Is its circumcenter also outside the triangle? Explain.

H.O.T. 48. Draw Conclusions △*ABC* is an equilateral triangle. A circle is inscribed in △*ABC* and another circle is circumscribed about △*ABC*.

    a. The radius of the inscribed circle is *r*. What is the radius of the circumscribed circle?

    b. For an equilateral triangle, what is the ratio of the radius of the inscribed circle to the radius of the circumscribed circle?

Construction   Orthocenter of a Triangle

①	②	③
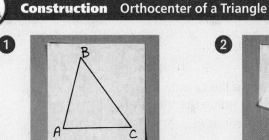	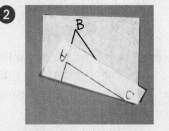	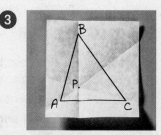
Draw a large scalene acute triangle *ABC* on a piece of patty paper.	Find the altitude of each side by folding the side so that it overlaps itself and so that the fold intersects the opposite vertex.	Mark the point where the three lines containing the altitudes intersect and label it *P*. *P* is the orthocenter of △*ABC*.

1. Repeat the construction for a scalene obtuse triangle and a scalene right triangle.

2. Make a conjecture about the location of the orthocenter in an acute, an obtuse, and a right triangle.

Career Path

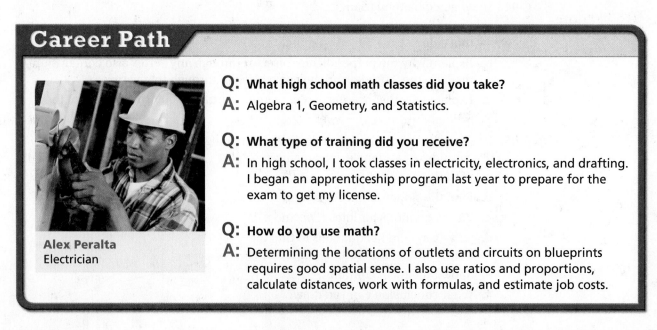

Alex Peralta
Electrician

Q: What high school math classes did you take?
A: Algebra 1, Geometry, and Statistics.

Q: What type of training did you receive?
A: In high school, I took classes in electricity, electronics, and drafting. I began an apprenticeship program last year to prepare for the exam to get my license.

Q: How do you use math?
A: Determining the locations of outlets and circuits on blueprints requires good spatial sense. I also use ratios and proportions, calculate distances, work with formulas, and estimate job costs.

6-3
Technology TASK

Special Points in Triangles

In this task, you will use geometry software to explore properties of the four points of concurrency you have studied.

Use with Medians and Altitudes of Triangles

MATHEMATICAL PRACTICES

Use appropriate tools strategically.

MCC9-12.G.CO.10 Prove theorems about triangles.

Activity

1 Construct a triangle.

2 Construct the perpendicular bisector of each side of the triangle. Construct the point of intersection of these three lines. This is the circumcenter of the triangle. Label it *U* and hide the perpendicular bisectors.

3 In the same triangle, construct the bisector of each angle. Construct the point of intersection of these three lines. This is the incenter of the triangle. Label it *I* and hide the angle bisectors.

4 In the same triangle, construct the midpoint of each side. Then construct the three medians. Construct the point of intersection of these three lines. Label the centroid *C* and hide the medians.

5 In the same triangle, construct the altitude to each side. Construct the point of intersection of these three lines. Label the orthocenter *O* and hide the altitudes.

6 Move a vertex of the triangle and observe the positions of the four points of concurrency. In 1765, Swiss mathematician Leonhard Euler showed that three of these points are always collinear. The line containing them is called the *Euler line*.

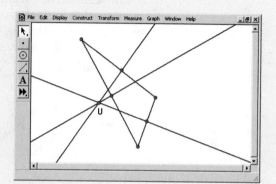

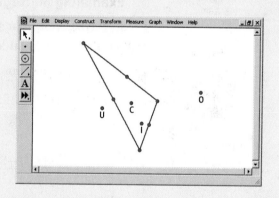

Try This

1. Which three points of concurrency lie on the Euler line?

2. **Make a Conjecture** Which point on the Euler line is always between the other two? Measure the distances between the points. Make a conjecture about the relationship of the distances between these three points.

3. **Make a Conjecture** Move a vertex of the triangle until all four points of concurrency are collinear. In what type of triangle are all four points of concurrency on the Euler line?

4. **Make a Conjecture** Find a triangle in which all four points of concurrency coincide. What type of triangle has this special property?

The Triangle Midsegment Theorem

Essential Question: What are properties of the triangle whose vertices are the midpoints of the three sides of a triangle?

Objective
Prove and use properties of triangle midsegments.

Vocabulary
midsegment of a triangle

Why learn this?
You can use triangle midsegments to make indirect measurements of distances, such as the distance across a volcano. (See Example 3.)

A **midsegment of a triangle** is a segment that joins the midpoints of two sides of the triangle. Every triangle has three midsegments, which form the *midsegment triangle.*

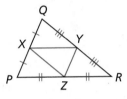

Midsegments: $\overline{XY}$, $\overline{YZ}$, $\overline{ZX}$
Midsegment triangle: $\triangle XYZ$

EXAMPLE 1

Examining Midsegments in the Coordinate Plane

In $\triangle GHJ$, show that midsegment $\overline{KL}$ is parallel to $\overline{GJ}$ and that $KL = \frac{1}{2}GJ$.

Step 1 Find the coordinates of K and L.

$$\text{mdpt. of } \overline{GH} = \left(\frac{-7 + (-5)}{2}, \frac{-2 + 6}{2}\right)$$
$$= (-6, 2)$$

$$\text{mdpt. of } \overline{HJ} = \left(\frac{-5 + 1}{2}, \frac{6 + 2}{2}\right) = (-2, 4)$$

Step 2 Compare the slopes of $\overline{KL}$ and $\overline{GJ}$.

$$\text{slope of } \overline{KL} = \frac{4 - 2}{-2 - (-6)} = \frac{1}{2} \qquad \text{slope of } \overline{GJ} = \frac{2 - (-2)}{1 - (-7)} = \frac{1}{2}$$

Since the slopes are the same, $\overline{KL} \parallel \overline{GJ}$.

Step 3 Compare the lengths of $\overline{KL}$ and $\overline{GJ}$.

$$KL = \sqrt{[-2 - (-6)]^2 + (4 - 2)^2} = 2\sqrt{5}$$
$$GJ = \sqrt{[1 - (-7)]^2 + [2 - (-2)]^2} = 4\sqrt{5}$$

Since $2\sqrt{5} = \frac{1}{2}(4\sqrt{5})$, $KL = \frac{1}{2}GJ$.

my.hrw.com

Online Video Tutor

CHECK IT OUT!

1. The vertices of $\triangle RST$ are $R(-7, 0)$, $S(-3, 6)$, and $T(9, 2)$. M is the midpoint of $\overline{RT}$, and N is the midpoint of $\overline{ST}$. Show that $\overline{MN} \parallel \overline{RS}$ and $MN = \frac{1}{2}RS$.

The relationship shown in Example 1 is true for the three midsegments of every triangle.

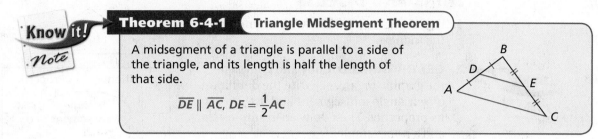

Theorem 6-4-1 | **Triangle Midsegment Theorem**

A midsegment of a triangle is parallel to a side of the triangle, and its length is half the length of that side.

$$\overline{DE} \parallel \overline{AC}, DE = \frac{1}{2}AC$$

You will prove Theorem 6-4-1 in Exercise 38.

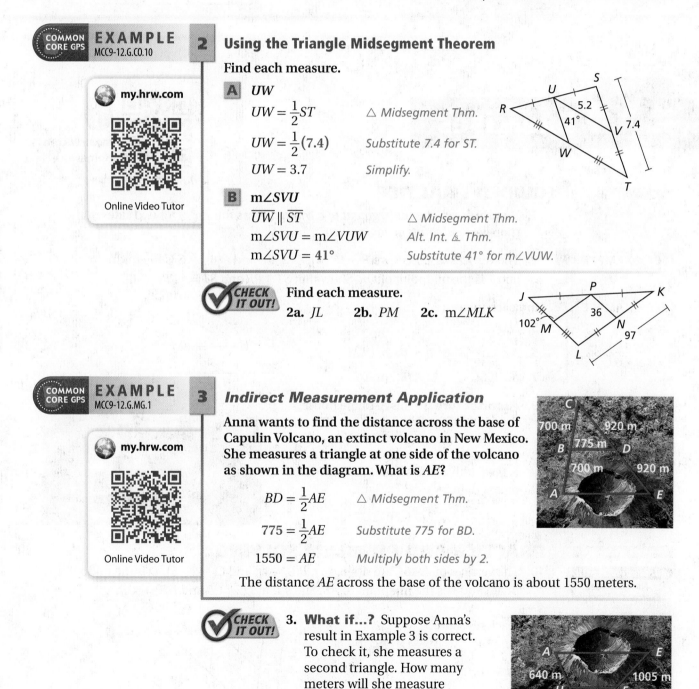

COMMON CORE GPS
MCC9-12.G.CO.10

EXAMPLE 2 Using the Triangle Midsegment Theorem

Find each measure.

A *UW*

$$UW = \frac{1}{2}ST \qquad \triangle \text{ Midsegment Thm.}$$

$$UW = \frac{1}{2}(7.4) \qquad \text{Substitute 7.4 for ST.}$$

$$UW = 3.7 \qquad \text{Simplify.}$$

B m∠*SVU*

$$\overline{UW} \parallel \overline{ST} \qquad \triangle \text{ Midsegment Thm.}$$

$$m\angle SVU = m\angle VUW \qquad \text{Alt. Int. } \angle\text{s Thm.}$$

$$m\angle SVU = 41° \qquad \text{Substitute 41° for m∠VUW.}$$

my.hrw.com

Online Video Tutor

CHECK IT OUT! Find each measure.

2a. *JL*   **2b.** *PM*   **2c.** m∠*MLK*

COMMON CORE GPS
MCC9-12.G.MG.1

EXAMPLE 3 *Indirect Measurement Application*

Anna wants to find the distance across the base of Capulin Volcano, an extinct volcano in New Mexico. She measures a triangle at one side of the volcano as shown in the diagram. What is *AE*?

$$BD = \frac{1}{2}AE \qquad \triangle \text{ Midsegment Thm.}$$

$$775 = \frac{1}{2}AE \qquad \text{Substitute 775 for BD.}$$

$$1550 = AE \qquad \text{Multiply both sides by 2.}$$

The distance *AE* across the base of the volcano is about 1550 meters.

my.hrw.com

Online Video Tutor

CHECK IT OUT!

3. What if...? Suppose Anna's result in Example 3 is correct. To check it, she measures a second triangle. How many meters will she measure between *H* and *F*?

MATHEMATICAL
PRACTICES

THINK AND DISCUSS

1. Explain why $\overline{XY}$ is NOT a midsegment of
the triangle.

2. GET ORGANIZED Copy and complete
the graphic organizer. Write the definition
of a triangle midsegment and list
its properties. Then draw an example
and a nonexample.

Definition	Properties
Triangle Midsegment	
Example	Nonexample

6-4 Exercises

my.hrw.com
Homework Help

GUIDED PRACTICE

1. Vocabulary The *midsegment of a triangle* joins the ___?___ of two sides of the
triangle. (*endpoints* or *midpoints*)

SEE EXAMPLE **1**

2. The vertices of $\triangle PQR$ are $P(-4, -1)$, $Q(2, 9)$, and $R(6, 3)$. S is the midpoint of $\overline{PQ}$,
and T is the midpoint of $\overline{QR}$. Show that $\overline{ST} \parallel \overline{PR}$ and $ST = \frac{1}{2}PR$.

SEE EXAMPLE **2**

Find each measure.

3. NM

4. XZ

5. NZ

6. $m\angle LMN$

7. $m\angle YXZ$

8. $m\angle XLM$

SEE EXAMPLE **3**

9. Architecture In this A-frame house,
the width of the first floor $\overline{XZ}$ is 30 feet.
The second floor $\overline{CD}$ is slightly above
and parallel to the midsegment of $\triangle XYZ$.
Is the width of the second floor more
or less than 5 yards? Explain.

PRACTICE AND PROBLEM SOLVING

10. The vertices of $\triangle ABC$ are $A(-6, 11)$, $B(6, -3)$, and $C(-2, -5)$. D is the midpoint
of $\overline{AC}$, and E is the midpoint of $\overline{AB}$. Show that $\overline{DE} \parallel \overline{CB}$ and $DE = \frac{1}{2}CB$.

Independent Practice	
For Exercises	See Example
10	1
11–16	2
17	3

Find each measure.

11. GJ

12. RQ

13. RJ

14. $m\angle PQR$

15. $m\angle HGJ$

16. $m\angle GPQ$

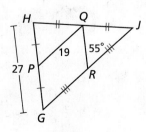

my.hrw.com

Online Extra Practice

17. Carpentry In each support for the garden swing, the crossbar $\overline{DE}$ is attached at the midpoints of legs $\overline{BA}$ and $\overline{BC}$. The distance AC is $4\frac{1}{2}$ feet. The carpenter has a timber that is 30 inches long. Is this timber long enough to be used as one of the crossbars? Explain.

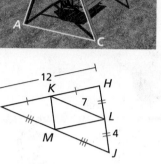

$\triangle KLM$ **is the midsegment triangle of** $\triangle GHJ$.

18. What is the perimeter of $\triangle GHJ$?

19. What is the perimeter of $\triangle KLM$?

20. What is the relationship between the perimeter of $\triangle GHJ$ and the perimeter of $\triangle KLM$?

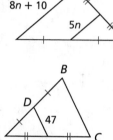

Algebra Find the value of n in each triangle.

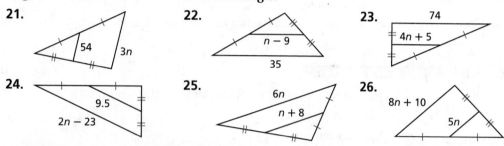

21.

54   3n

22.

$n - 9$

35

23.

74

$4n + 5$

24.

9.5

$2n - 23$

25.

6n

$n + 8$

26.

$8n + 10$

5n

27. ///**ERROR ANALYSIS**/// Below are two solutions for finding BC. Which is incorrect? Explain the error.

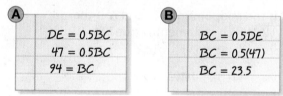

A
$DE = 0.5BC$
$47 = 0.5BC$
$94 = BC$

B
$BC = 0.5DE$
$BC = 0.5(47)$
$BC = 23.5$

28. Critical Thinking Draw scalene $\triangle DEF$. Label X as the midpoint of $\overline{DE}$, Y as the midpoint of $\overline{EF}$, and Z as the midpoint of $\overline{DF}$. Connect the three midpoints. List all of the congruent angles in your drawing.

H.O.T. 29. Estimation The diagram shows the sketch for a new street. Parallel parking spaces will be painted on both sides of the street. Each parallel parking space is 23 feet long. About how many parking spaces can the city accommodate on both sides of the new street? Explain your answer.

$\overline{CG}$, $\overline{EH}$, **and** $\overline{FJ}$ **are midsegments of** $\triangle ABD$, $\triangle GCD$, **and** $\triangle GHE$, **respectively. Find each measure.**

30. CG **31.** EH **32.** FJ

33. m$\angle DCG$ **34.** m$\angle GHE$ **35.** m$\angle FJH$

H.O.T. 36. Write About It An isosceles triangle has two congruent sides. Does it also have two congruent midsegments? Explain.

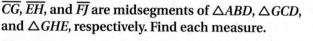

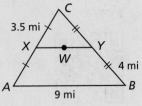

37. The figure shows the roads connecting towns *A*, *B*, and *C*. A music company has a store in each town and a distribution warehouse *W* at the midpoint of road $\overline{XY}$.
    a. What is the distance from the warehouse to point *X*?
    b. A truck starts at the warehouse, delivers instruments to the stores in towns *A*, *B*, and *C* (in this order) and then returns to the warehouse. What is the total length of the trip, assuming the driver takes the shortest possible route?

38. Use coordinates to prove the Triangle Midsegment Theorem. 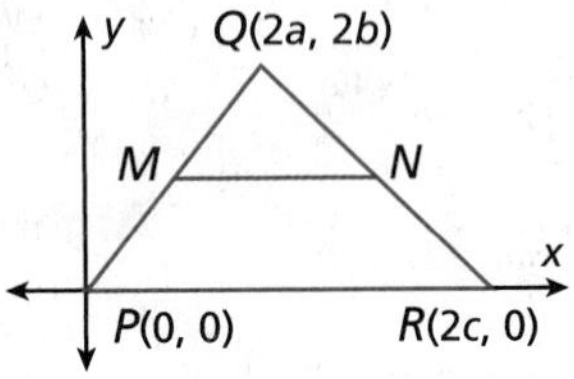
    a. *M* is the midpoint of $\overline{PQ}$. What are its coordinates?
    b. *N* is the midpoint of $\overline{QR}$. What are its coordinates?
    c. Find the slopes of $\overline{PR}$ and $\overline{MN}$. What can you conclude?
    d. Find *PR* and *MN*. What can you conclude?

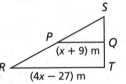

TEST PREP

39. $\overline{PQ}$ is a midsegment of $\triangle RST$. What is the length of $\overline{RT}$?
    Ⓐ 9 meters
    Ⓑ 21 meters
    Ⓒ 45 meters
    Ⓓ 63 meters

40. In $\triangle UVW$, *M* is the midpoint of $\overline{VU}$, and *N* is the midpoint of $\overline{VW}$. Which statement is true?
    Ⓕ $VM = VN$ Ⓗ $VU = 2VM$
    Ⓖ $MN = UV$ Ⓙ $VW = \frac{1}{2}VN$

41. $\triangle XYZ$ is the midsegment triangle of $\triangle JKL$, $XY = 8$, $YK = 14$, and $m\angle YKZ = 67°$. Which of the following measures CANNOT be determined? 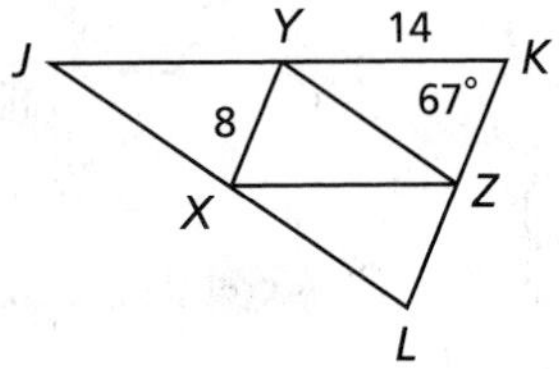
    Ⓐ KL Ⓒ $m\angle XZL$
    Ⓑ JY Ⓓ $m\angle KZY$

CHALLENGE AND EXTEND

42. **Multi-Step** The midpoints of the sides of a triangle are $A(-6, 3)$, $B(2, 1)$, and $C(0, -3)$. Find the coordinates of the vertices of the triangle.

43. **Critical Thinking** Classify the midsegment triangle of an equilateral triangle by its side lengths and angle measures.

H.O.T. **Algebra** Find the value of *n* in each triangle.

44.
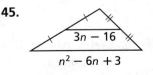

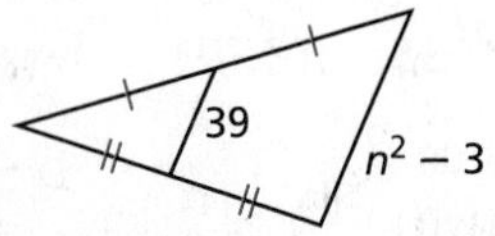

45.

© Creatas/Getty Images

46. $\triangle XYZ$ is the midsegment triangle of $\triangle PQR$. Write a congruence statement involving all four of the smaller triangles. What is the relationship between the area of $\triangle XYZ$ and $\triangle PQR$?

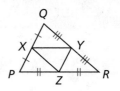

47. $\overline{AB}$ is a midsegment of $\triangle XYZ$. $\overline{CD}$ is a midsegment of $\triangle ABZ$. $\overline{EF}$ is a midsegment of $\triangle CDZ$, and $\overline{GH}$ is a midsegment of $\triangle EFZ$.

a. Copy and complete the table.

Number of Midsegment	1	2	3	4
Length of Midsegment	▨	▨	▨	▨

b. If this pattern continues, what will be the length of midsegment 8?

c. Write an algebraic expression to represent the length of midsegment n. (*Hint*: Think of the midsegment lengths as powers of 2.)

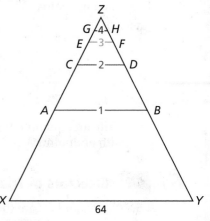

FOCUS ON MATHEMATICAL PRACTICES

H.O.T. **48. Problem Solving** $\triangle FGH$ is an equilateral triangle. The perimeter of the midsegment triangle of $\triangle FGH$ is 60 centimeters. Find FH.

H.O.T. **49. Communication** What information about measures of angles and segments does a midsegment imply that can be used in a proof?

H.O.T. **50. Precision** In $\triangle ABC$, $AB = 6$, $AC = 8$, and $BC = 10$. A midsegment $\overline{MN}$ of the triangle measures 4. What sides contain the endpoints of $\overline{MN}$?

H.O.T. **51. Modeling** The midsegment of a triangle divides the triangle into two regions, a triangle and a trapezoid. What is the ratio of their areas?

Construction Midsegment of a Triangle

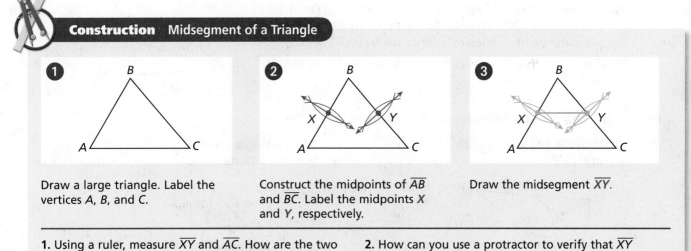

Draw a large triangle. Label the vertices A, B, and C.

Construct the midpoints of $\overline{AB}$ and $\overline{BC}$. Label the midpoints X and Y, respectively.

Draw the midsegment $\overline{XY}$.

1. Using a ruler, measure $\overline{XY}$ and $\overline{AC}$. How are the two lengths related?

2. How can you use a protractor to verify that $\overline{XY}$ is parallel to $\overline{AC}$?

Ready to Go On?

my.hrw.com
Assessment and Intervention

 6-1 Perpendicular and Angle Bisectors

Find each measure.

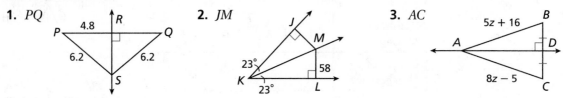

1. PQ

2. JM

3. AC

4. Write an equation in point-slope form for the perpendicular bisector of the segment with endpoints $M(-1, -3)$ and $N(7, 1)$.

 6-2 Bisectors of Triangles

5. $\overline{PX}$, $\overline{PY}$, and $\overline{PZ}$ are the perpendicular bisectors of $\triangle RST$. Find PS and XT.

6. $\overline{JK}$ and $\overline{HK}$ are angle bisectors of $\triangle GHJ$. Find $m\angle GJK$ and the distance from K to $\overline{HJ}$.

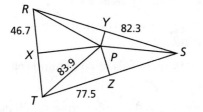

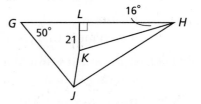

7. Find the circumcenter of $\triangle TVO$ with vertices $T(9, 0)$, $V(0, -4)$, and $O(0, 0)$.

 6-3 Medians and Altitudes of Triangles

8. In $\triangle DEF$, $BD = 87$, and $WE = 38$. Find BW, CW, and CE.

9. Paula cuts a triangle with vertices at coordinates $(0, 4)$, $(8, 0)$, and $(10, 8)$ from grid paper. At what coordinates should she place the tip of a pencil to balance the triangle?

10. Find the orthocenter of $\triangle PSV$ with vertices $P(2, 4)$, $S(8, 4)$, and $V(4, 0)$.

 6-4 The Triangle Midsegment Theorem

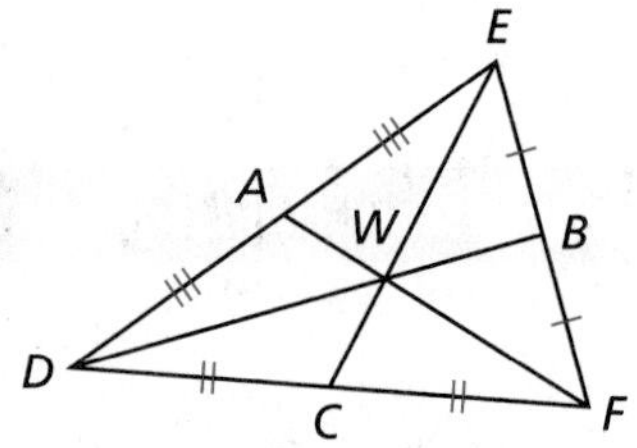

11. Find ZV, PM, and $m\angle RZV$ in $\triangle JMP$.

12. What is the distance XZ across the pond?

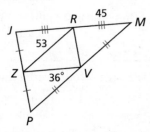

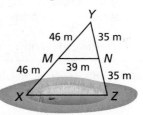

PARCC Assessment Readiness

COMMON CORE GPS

Selected Response

1. Find the measures *BC* and *AC*.

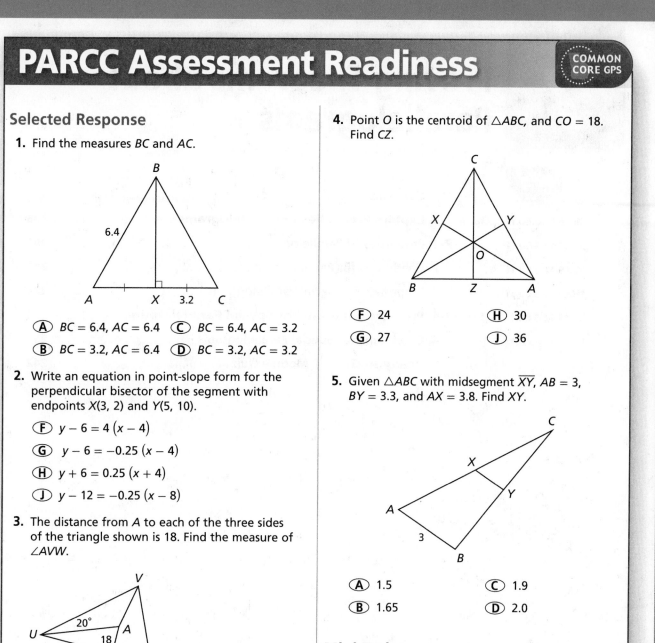

Ⓐ $BC = 6.4, AC = 6.4$ Ⓒ $BC = 6.4, AC = 3.2$

Ⓑ $BC = 3.2, AC = 6.4$ Ⓓ $BC = 3.2, AC = 3.2$

2. Write an equation in point-slope form for the perpendicular bisector of the segment with endpoints *X*(3, 2) and *Y*(5, 10).

Ⓕ $y - 6 = 4 \left(x - 4 \right)$

Ⓖ $y - 6 = -0.25 \left(x - 4 \right)$

Ⓗ $y + 6 = 0.25 \left(x + 4 \right)$

Ⓙ $y - 12 = -0.25 \left(x - 8 \right)$

3. The distance from *A* to each of the three sides of the triangle shown is 18. Find the measure of ∠*AVW*.

Ⓐ 20°   Ⓒ 33°

Ⓑ 24°   Ⓓ 37°

4. Point *O* is the centroid of △*ABC*, and *CO* = 18. Find *CZ*.

Ⓕ 24   Ⓗ 30

Ⓖ 27   Ⓙ 36

5. Given △*ABC* with midsegment $\overline{XY}$, *AB* = 3, *BY* = 3.3, and *AX* = 3.8. Find *XY*.

Ⓐ 1.5   Ⓒ 1.9

Ⓑ 1.65   Ⓓ 2.0

Mini-Tasks

6. Write an equation for the perpendicular bisector of the segment with endpoints *A*(−4, 5) and *B*(6, −5).

7. Find the circumcenter of △*ABC* with vertices *A*(−2, 4), *B*(−2, −2), and *C*(4, −2).

8. The coordinates of the vertices of a triangular piece of a mobile are (0, 4), (3, 8), and (6, 0). The piece will hang from a chain that is attached at the intersection of the medians of the triangle. At what coordinates should the chain be attached?

9. The vertices of △*GHJ* are *G*(−4, −7), *H*(2, 5), and *J*(10, −3). *V* is the midpoint of $\overline{GH}$, and *W* is the midpoint of $\overline{HJ}$. Show that $\overline{VW} \parallel \overline{GJ}$ and $VW = \frac{1}{2}GJ$.

COMMON CORE GPS

Contents

MATHEMATICAL PRACTICES The Common Core Georgia Performance Standards for Mathematical Practice describe varieties of expertise that all students should seek to develop. Opportunities to develop these practices are integrated throughout this program.

1 Make sense of problems and persevere in solving them.

2 Reason abstractly and quantitatively.

3 Construct viable arguments and critique the reasoning of others.

4 Model with mathematics.

5 Use appropriate tools strategically.

6 Attend to precision.

7 Look for and make use of structure.

8 Look for and express regularity in repeated reasoning.

Unpacking the Standards

my.hrw.com
Multilingual Glossary

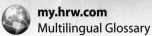

Understanding the standards and the vocabulary terms in the standards will help you know exactly what you are expected to learn in this chapter.

COMMON CORE GPS **MCC9-12.G.CO.11**

Prove theorems about parallelograms.

Key Vocabulary

parallelogram (paralelogramo)
A quadrilateral with two pairs of parallel sides.

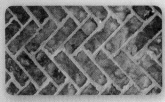

What It Means For You

Parallelograms, including rectangles and squares, are everywhere around you. You can prove the many special relationships about their sides and angles that make them so important.

EXAMPLE

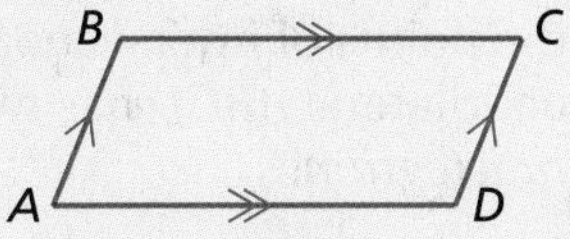

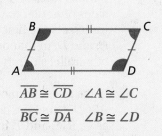

$\overline{AB} \parallel \overline{CD}$, $\overline{BC} \parallel \overline{DA}$

$\overline{AB} \cong \overline{CD}$ $\angle A \cong \angle C$

$\overline{BC} \cong \overline{DA}$ $\angle B \cong \angle D$

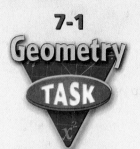

7-1
Geometry
TASK

Use with Properties of Parallelograms

Explore Properties of Parallelograms

In this task, you will investigate the relationships among the angles and sides of a special type of quadrilateral called a *parallelogram*. You will need to apply the Transitive Property of Congruence. That is, if figure $A \cong$ figure B and figure $B \cong$ figure C, then figure $A \cong$ figure C.

 MATHEMATICAL PRACTICES Use appropriate tools strategically.

MCC9-12.G.CO.11 Prove theorems about parallelograms.

Activity

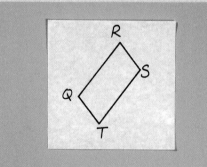

1 Use opposite sides of an index card to draw a set of parallel lines on a piece of patty paper. Then use opposite sides of a ruler to draw a second set of parallel lines that intersects the first. Label the points of intersection A, B, C, and D, in that order. Quadrilateral $ABCD$ has two pairs of parallel sides. It is a *parallelogram*.

2 Place a second piece of patty paper over the first and trace $ABCD$. Label the points that correspond to A, B, C, and D as Q, R, S, and T, in that order. The parallelograms $ABCD$ and $QRST$ are congruent. Name all the pairs of congruent corresponding sides and angles.

3 Lay $ABCD$ over $QRST$ so that $\overline{AB}$ overlays $\overline{ST}$. What do you notice about their lengths? What does this tell you about $\overline{AB}$ and $\overline{CD}$? Now move $ABCD$ so that $\overline{DA}$ overlays $\overline{RS}$. What do you notice about their lengths? What does this tell you about $\overline{DA}$ and $\overline{BC}$?

4 Lay $ABCD$ over $QRST$ so that $\angle A$ overlays $\angle S$. What do you notice about their measures? What does this tell you about $\angle A$ and $\angle C$? Now move $ABCD$ so that $\angle B$ overlays $\angle T$. What do you notice about their measures? What does this tell you about $\angle B$ and $\angle D$?

5 Arrange the pieces of patty paper so that $\overline{RS}$ overlays $\overline{AD}$. What do you notice about $\overline{QR}$ and $\overline{AB}$? What does this tell you about $\angle A$ and $\angle R$? What can you conclude about $\angle A$ and $\angle B$?

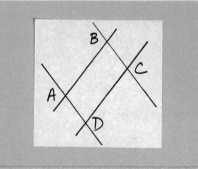

6 Draw diagonals $\overline{AC}$ and $\overline{BD}$. Fold $ABCD$ so that A matches C, making a crease. Unfold the paper and fold it again so that B matches D, making another crease. What do you notice about the creases? What can you conclude about the diagonals?

Try This

1. Repeat the above steps with a different parallelogram. Do you get the same results?

2. **Make a Conjecture** How do you think the sides of a parallelogram are related to each other? the angles? the diagonals? Write your conjectures as conditional statements.

© HMH

7-1 Properties of Parallelograms

Essential Question: If a quadrilateral is a parallelogram, what are some conclusions you can make about its angles, sides, and diagonals?

Objectives
Prove and apply properties of parallelograms.

Use properties of parallelograms to solve problems.

Vocabulary
parallelogram

Who uses this?
Race car designers can use a parallelogram-shaped linkage to keep the wheels of the car vertical on uneven surfaces. (See Example 1.)

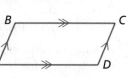

Any polygon with four sides is a quadrilateral. However, some quadrilaterals have special properties. These *special quadrilaterals* are given their own names.

Helpful Hint

Opposite sides of a quadrilateral do not share a vertex. Opposite angles do not share a side.

A quadrilateral with two pairs of parallel sides is a **parallelogram**. To write the name of a parallelogram, you use the symbol $\square$.

Parallelogram *ABCD*
$\square ABCD$

$\overline{AB} \parallel \overline{CD}, \overline{BC} \parallel \overline{DA}$

Theorem 7-1-1 **Properties of Parallelograms**

THEOREM	HYPOTHESIS	CONCLUSION
If a quadrilateral is a parallelogram, then its opposite sides are congruent. $(\square \rightarrow \text{opp. sides} \cong)$		$\overline{AB} \cong \overline{CD}$ $\overline{BC} \cong \overline{DA}$

PROOF **Theorem 7-1-1**

Given: *JKLM* is a parallelogram.
Prove: $\overline{JK} \cong \overline{LM}, \overline{KL} \cong \overline{MJ}$

Proof:

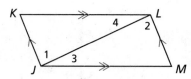

Statements	Reasons
1. *JKLM* is a parallelogram.	1. Given
2. $\overline{JK} \parallel \overline{LM}, \overline{KL} \parallel \overline{MJ}$	2. Def. of $\square$
3. $\angle 1 \cong \angle 2, \angle 3 \cong \angle 4$	3. Alt. Int. $\angle$ Thm.
4. $\overline{JL} \cong \overline{JL}$	4. Reflex. Prop. of $\cong$
5. $\triangle JKL \cong \triangle LMJ$	5. ASA *Steps 3, 4*
6. $\overline{JK} \cong \overline{LM}, \overline{KL} \cong \overline{MJ}$	6. CPCTC

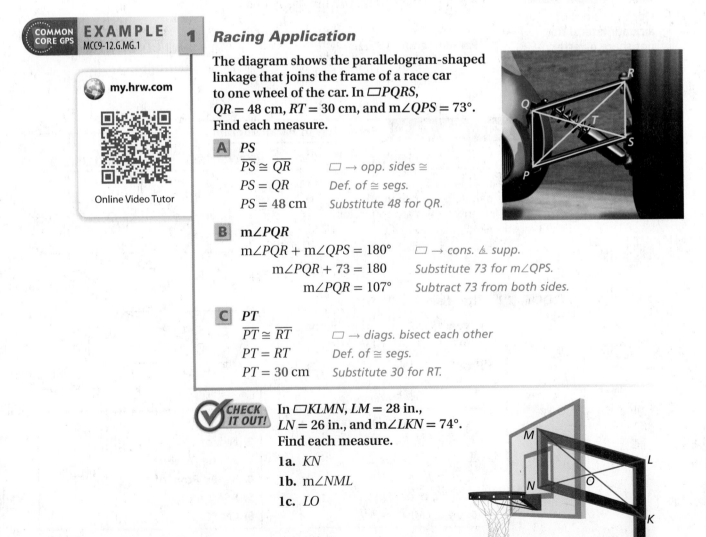

Know it! Note

Theorems — Properties of Parallelograms

THEOREM	HYPOTHESIS	CONCLUSION
7-1-2 If a quadrilateral is a parallelogram, then its opposite angles are congruent. ($\square \rightarrow$ opp. $\angle$s $\cong$)		$\angle A \cong \angle C$ $\angle B \cong \angle D$
7-1-3 If a quadrilateral is a parallelogram, then its consecutive angles are supplementary. ($\square \rightarrow$ cons. $\angle$s supp.)		$m\angle A + m\angle B = 180°$ $m\angle B + m\angle C = 180°$ $m\angle C + m\angle D = 180°$ $m\angle D + m\angle A = 180°$
7-1-4 If a quadrilateral is a parallelogram, then its diagonals bisect each other. ($\square \rightarrow$ diags. bisect each other)		$\overline{AZ} \cong \overline{CZ}$ $\overline{BZ} \cong \overline{DZ}$

You will prove Theorems 7-1-3 and 7-1-4 in Exercises 45 and 44.

COMMON CORE GPS MCC9-12.G.MG.1

EXAMPLE 1

my.hrw.com

Online Video Tutor

Racing Application

The diagram shows the parallelogram-shaped linkage that joins the frame of a race car to one wheel of the car. In $\square PQRS$, $QR = 48$ cm, $RT = 30$ cm, and $m\angle QPS = 73°$. Find each measure.

A PS

$\overline{PS} \cong \overline{QR}$ $\square \rightarrow$ opp. sides $\cong$

$PS = QR$ Def. of $\cong$ segs.

$PS = 48$ cm   Substitute 48 for QR.

B $m\angle PQR$

$m\angle PQR + m\angle QPS = 180°$ $\square \rightarrow$ cons. $\angle$s supp.

$m\angle PQR + 73 = 180$ Substitute 73 for m∠QPS.

$m\angle PQR = 107°$ Subtract 73 from both sides.

C PT

$\overline{PT} \cong \overline{RT}$ $\square \rightarrow$ diags. bisect each other

$PT = RT$ Def. of $\cong$ segs.

$PT = 30$ cm   Substitute 30 for RT.

CHECK IT OUT! In $\square KLMN$, $LM = 28$ in., $LN = 26$ in., and $m\angle LKN = 74°$. Find each measure.

1a. KN

1b. $m\angle NML$

1c. LO

Art Reference: BasketballHoopsUnlimited

EXAMPLE 2

Using Properties of Parallelograms to Find Measures

ABCD is a parallelogram. Find each measure.

A *AD*

$\overline{AD} \cong \overline{BC}$	$\square \rightarrow$ opp. sides $\cong$
$AD = BC$	*Def. of $\cong$ segs.*
$7x = 5x + 19$	*Substitute the given values.*
$2x = 19$	*Subtract 5x from both sides.*
$x = 9.5$	*Divide both sides by 2.*

$AD = 7x = 7(9.5) = 66.5$

B m∠*B*

$m\angle A + m\angle B = 180°$	$\square \rightarrow$ cons. $\angle$s supp.
$(10y - 1) + (6y + 5) = 180$	*Substitute the given values.*
$16y + 4 = 180$	*Combine like terms.*
$16y = 176$	*Subtract 4 from both sides.*
$y = 11$	*Divide both sides by 16.*

$m\angle B = (6y + 5)° = [6(11) + 5]° = 71°$

CHECK IT OUT!

EFGH is a parallelogram.
Find each measure.

2a. *JG*

2b. *FH*

EXAMPLE 3

Parallelograms in the Coordinate Plane

Three vertices of $\square ABCD$ are $A(1, -2)$, $B(-2, 3)$, and $D(5, -1)$. Find the coordinates of vertex C.

Since *ABCD* is a parallelogram, both pairs of opposite sides must be parallel.

Step 1 Graph the given points.

Step 2 Find the slope of $\overline{AB}$ by counting the units from *A* to *B*.
The rise from -2 to 3 is 5.
The run from 1 to -2 is -3.

Step 3 Start at *D* and count the same number of units.
A rise of 5 from -1 is 4.
A run of -3 from 5 is 2. Label $(2, 4)$ as vertex *C*.

Step 4 Use the slope formula to verify that $\overline{BC} \parallel \overline{AD}$.

$$\text{slope of } \overline{BC} = \frac{4 - 3}{2 - (-2)} = \frac{1}{4}$$

$$\text{slope of } \overline{AD} = \frac{-1 - (-2)}{5 - 1} = \frac{1}{4}$$

The coordinates of vertex *C* are $(2, 4)$.

Remember!

When you are drawing a figure in the coordinate plane, the name *ABCD* gives the order of the vertices.

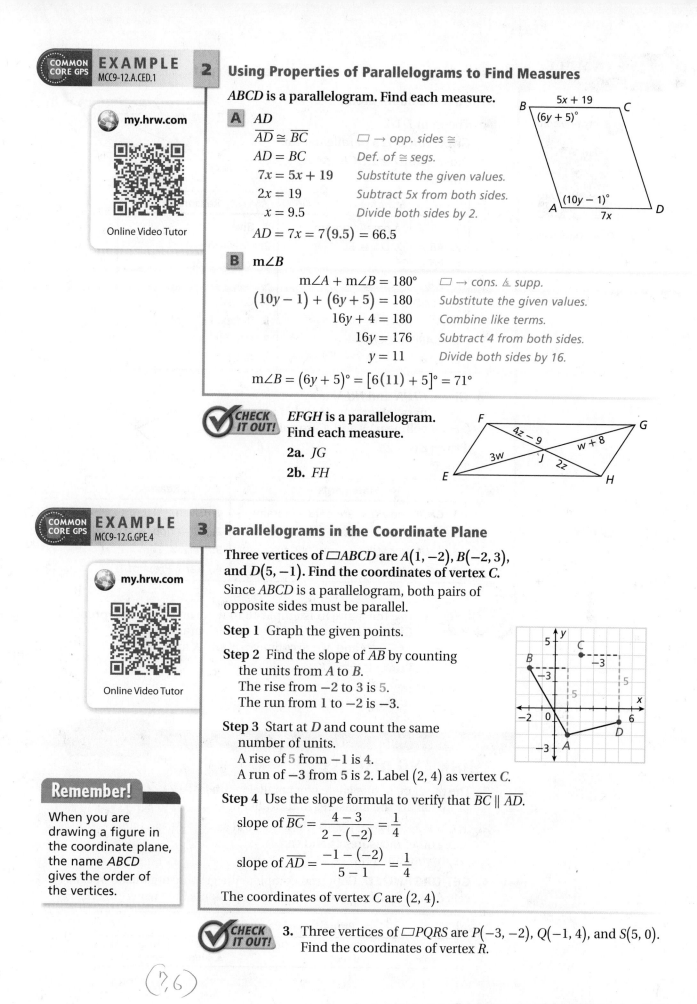

CHECK IT OUT!

3. Three vertices of $\square PQRS$ are $P(-3, -2)$, $Q(-1, 4)$, and $S(5, 0)$.
Find the coordinates of vertex *R*.

$(7,6)$

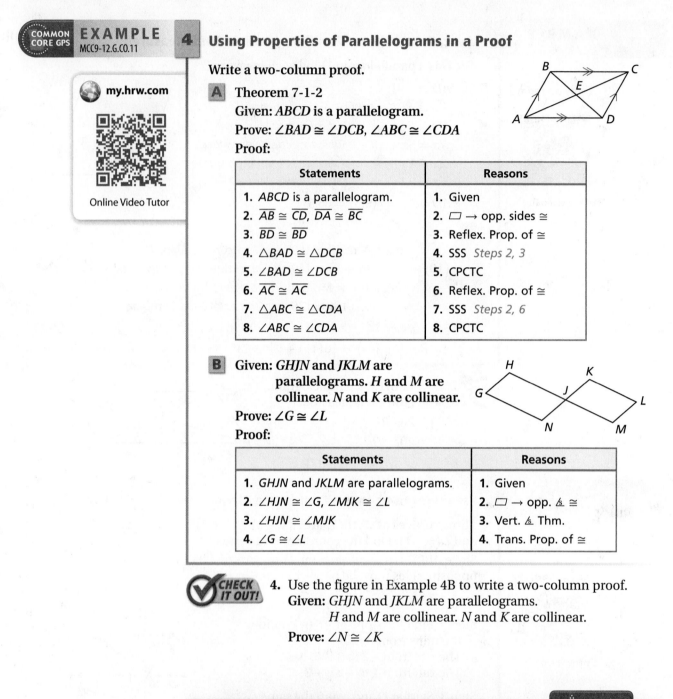

EXAMPLE 4 Using Properties of Parallelograms in a Proof

MCC9-12.G.CO.11

my.hrw.com

Online Video Tutor

Write a two-column proof.

A Theorem 7-1-2

Given: *ABCD* is a parallelogram.

Prove: ∠*BAD* ≅ ∠*DCB*, ∠*ABC* ≅ ∠*CDA*

Proof:

Statements	Reasons
1. *ABCD* is a parallelogram.	1. Given
2. $\overline{AB} \cong \overline{CD}$, $\overline{DA} \cong \overline{BC}$	2. ▱ → opp. sides ≅
3. $\overline{BD} \cong \overline{BD}$	3. Reflex. Prop. of ≅
4. △*BAD* ≅ △*DCB*	4. SSS *Steps 2, 3*
5. ∠*BAD* ≅ ∠*DCB*	5. CPCTC
6. $\overline{AC} \cong \overline{AC}$	6. Reflex. Prop. of ≅
7. △*ABC* ≅ △*CDA*	7. SSS *Steps 2, 6*
8. ∠*ABC* ≅ ∠*CDA*	8. CPCTC

B Given: *GHJN* and *JKLM* are parallelograms. *H* and *M* are collinear. *N* and *K* are collinear.

Prove: ∠*G* ≅ ∠*L*

Proof:

Statements	Reasons
1. *GHJN* and *JKLM* are parallelograms.	1. Given
2. ∠*HJN* ≅ ∠*G*, ∠*MJK* ≅ ∠*L*	2. ▱ → opp. ≜ ≅
3. ∠*HJN* ≅ ∠*MJK*	3. Vert. ≜ Thm.
4. ∠*G* ≅ ∠*L*	4. Trans. Prop. of ≅

CHECK IT OUT!

4. Use the figure in Example 4B to write a two-column proof.

Given: *GHJN* and *JKLM* are parallelograms.

H and *M* are collinear. *N* and *K* are collinear.

Prove: ∠*N* ≅ ∠*K*

MCC.MP.3

MATHEMATICAL PRACTICES

THINK AND DISCUSS

1. The measure of one angle of a parallelogram is 71°. What are the measures of the other angles?

2. In ▱*VWXY*, *VW* = 21, and *WY* = 36. Find as many other measures as you can. Justify your answers.

Know it! Note

3. GET ORGANIZED Copy and complete the graphic organizer. In each cell, draw a figure with markings that represents the given property.

Properties of Parallelograms				
Opp. sides ∥	Opp. sides ≅	Opp. ≜ ≅	Cons. ≜ supp.	Diags. bisect each other.

GUIDED PRACTICE

Vocabulary Apply the vocabulary from this lesson to answer each question.

1. Explain why the figure at right is NOT a *parallelogram*.

2. Draw ▱*PQRS*. Name the opposite sides and opposite angles.

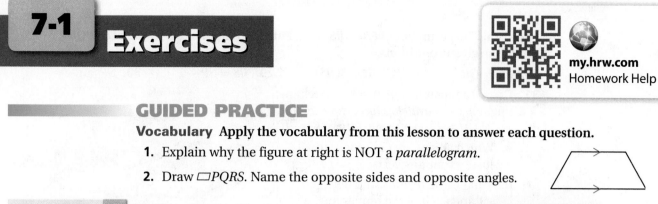

SEE EXAMPLE **1**

Safety The handrail is made from congruent parallelograms. In ▱*ABCD*, *AB* = 17.5, *DE* = 18, and m∠*BCD* = 110°. Find each measure.

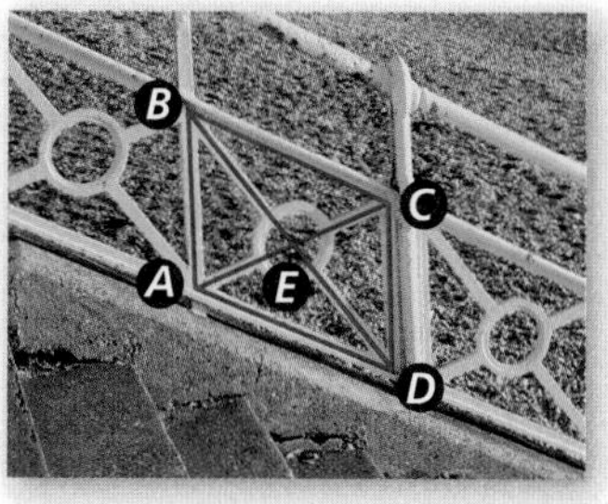

3. *BD*   4. *CD*

5. *BE*   6. m∠*ABC*

7. m∠*ADC*   8. m∠*DAB*

SEE EXAMPLE **2**

JKLM is a parallelogram. Find each measure.

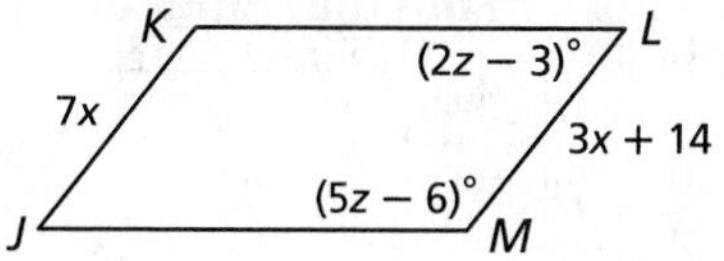

9. *JK*   10. *LM*

11. m∠*L*   12. m∠*M*

SEE EXAMPLE **3**

13. **Multi-Step** Three vertices of ▱*DFGH* are *D*(−9, 4), *F*(−1, 5), and *G*(2, 0). Find the coordinates of vertex *H*.

SEE EXAMPLE **4**

14. Write a two-column proof.
    Given: *PSTV* is a parallelogram. $\overline{PQ} \cong \overline{RQ}$
    Prove: ∠*STV* ≅ ∠*R*

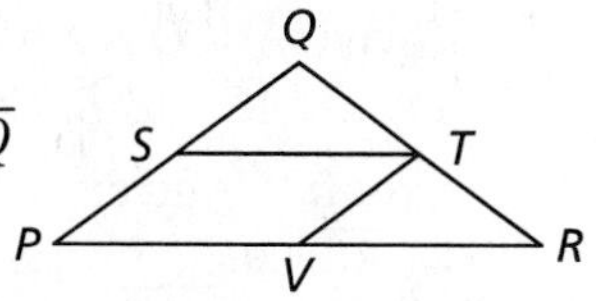

PRACTICE AND PROBLEM SOLVING

Independent Practice	
For Exercises	See Example
15–20	1
21–24	2
25	3
26	4

my.hrw.com

Online Extra Practice

Shipping Cranes can be used to load cargo onto ships. In ▱*JKLM*, *JL* = 165.8, *JK* = 110, and m∠*JML* = 50°. Find the measure of each part of the crane.

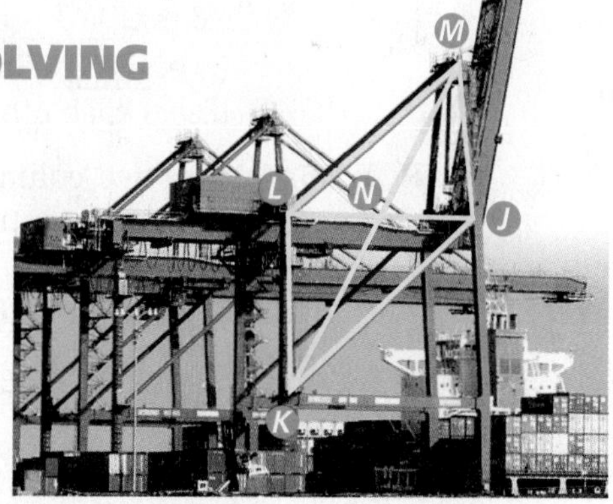

15. *JN*   16. *LM*

17. *LN*   18. m∠*JKL*

19. m∠*KLM*   20. m∠*MJK*

WXYZ is a parallelogram. Find each measure.

21. *WV*   22. *YW*

23. *XZ*   24. *ZV*

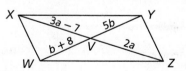

25. **Multi-Step** Three vertices of ▱*PRTV* are *P*(−4, −4), *R*(−10, 0), and *V*(5, −1). Find the coordinates of vertex *T*.

26. Write a two-column proof.
    Given: *ABCD* and *AFGH* are parallelograms.
    Prove: ∠*C* ≅ ∠*G*

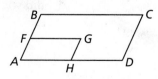

Algebra The perimeter of ▱*PQRS* is 84. Find the length of each side of ▱*PQRS* under the given conditions.

27. $PQ = QR$ **28.** $QR = 3(RS)$ **29.** $RS = SP - 7$ **30.** $SP = RS^2$

31. Cars To repair a large truck, a mechanic might use a *parallelogram lift*. In the lift, $\overline{FG} \cong \overline{GH} \cong \overline{LK} \cong \overline{KJ}$, and $\overline{FL} \cong \overline{GK} \cong \overline{HJ}$.

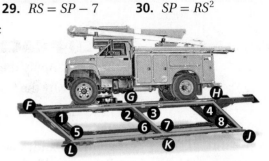

   a. Which angles are congruent to ∠1? Justify your answer.

   b. What is the relationship between ∠1 and each of the remaining labeled angles? Justify your answer.

Complete each statement about ▱*KMPR*. Justify your answer.

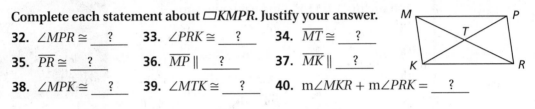

32. ∠*MPR* ≅ ___?___ **33.** ∠*PRK* ≅ ___?___ **34.** $\overline{MT}$ ≅ ___?___

35. $\overline{PR}$ ≅ ___?___ **36.** $\overline{MP}$ ∥ ___?___ **37.** $\overline{MK}$ ∥ ___?___

38. ∠*MPK* ≅ ___?___ **39.** ∠*MTK* ≅ ___?___ **40.** m∠*MKR* + m∠*PRK* = ___?___

Find the values of *x*, *y*, and *z* in each parallelogram.

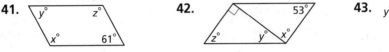

41. **42.** **43.**

44. Complete the paragraph proof of Theorem 7-1-4 by filling in the blanks.

   Given: *ABCD* is a parallelogram.
   Prove: $\overline{AC}$ and $\overline{BD}$ bisect each other at *E*.

   Proof: It is given that *ABCD* is a parallelogram. By the definition of a parallelogram, $\overline{AB}$ ∥ **a.** ___?___ . By the Alternate Interior Angles Theorem, ∠1 ≅ **b.** ___?___ , and ∠3 ≅ **c.** ___?___ . $\overline{AB}$ ≅ $\overline{CD}$ because **d.** ___?___ . This means that △*ABE* ≅ △*CDE* by **e.** ___?___ . So by **f.** ___?___ , $\overline{AE}$ ≅ $\overline{CE}$, and $\overline{BE}$ ≅ $\overline{DE}$. Therefore $\overline{AC}$ and $\overline{BD}$ bisect each other at *E* by the definition of **g.** ___?___ .

H.O.T. **45.** Write a two-column proof of Theorem 7-1-3: If a quadrilateral is a parallelogram, then its consecutive angles are supplementary.

Algebra Find the values of *x* and *y* in each parallelogram.

46. **47.**

48. In this calcite crystal, the face *ABCD* is a parallelogram.

   a. In ▱*ABCD*, m∠*B* = $(6x + 12)°$, and m∠*D* = $(9x - 33)°$. Find m∠*B*.

   b. Find m∠*A* and m∠*C*. Which theorem or theorems did you use to find these angle measures?

H.O.T. 49. Critical Thinking Draw any parallelogram. Draw a second parallelogram whose corresponding sides are congruent to the sides of the first parallelogram but whose corresponding angles are not congruent to the angles of the first.

    a. Is there an SSSS congruence postulate for parallelograms? Explain.

    b. Remember the meaning of triangle rigidity. Is a parallelogram rigid? Explain.

50. Write About It Explain why every parallelogram is a quadrilateral but every quadrilateral is not necessarily a parallelogram.

TEST PREP

51. What is the value of x in $\square PQRS$?

    Ⓐ 15   Ⓒ 30

    Ⓑ 20   Ⓓ 70

52. The diagonals of $\square JKLM$ intersect at Z. Which statement is true?

    Ⓕ $JL = KM$ Ⓖ $JL = \frac{1}{2}KM$ Ⓗ $JL = \frac{1}{2}JZ$ Ⓙ $JL = 2JZ$

53. Gridded Response In $\square ABCD$, $BC = 8.2$, and $CD = 5$. What is the perimeter of $\square ABCD$?

CHALLENGE AND EXTEND

H.O.T. The coordinates of three vertices of a parallelogram are given. Give the coordinates for all possible locations of the fourth vertex.

54. $(0, 5), (4, 0), (8, 5)$ **55.** $(-2, 1), (3, -1), (-1, -4)$

H.O.T. 56. The feathers on an arrow form two congruent parallelograms that share a common side. Each parallelogram is the reflection of the other across the line they share. Show that $y = 2x$.

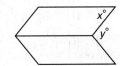

H.O.T. 57. Prove that the bisectors of two consecutive angles of a parallelogram are perpendicular.

FOCUS ON MATHEMATICAL PRACTICES

H.O.T. 58. Problem Solving A fence uses a pattern of quadrilaterals that are parallelograms like the one shown at the right. Find the value of x and the angle measures of the parallelogram.

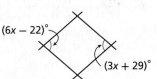

H.O.T. 59. Modeling A parallelogram has one right angle. What is a more specific name for the parallelogram? Justify your answer.

H.O.T. 60. Error Analysis Tony said the diagonals of a parallelogram are always congruent. Do you agree with Tony? If you disagree, correct his statement.

7-2 Conditions for Parallelograms

Essential Question: What information about the angles, sides, or diagonals of a quadrilateral allows you to conclude it is a parallelogram?

Objective
Prove that a given quadrilateral is a parallelogram.

Who uses this?
A bird watcher can use a *parallelogram mount* to adjust the height of a pair of binoculars without changing the viewing angle. (See Example 4.)

You have learned to identify the properties of a parallelogram. Now you will be given the properties of a quadrilateral and will have to tell if the quadrilateral is a parallelogram. To do this, you can use the definition of a parallelogram or the conditions below.

Know it! Note

Theorems | Conditions for Parallelograms

THEOREM	EXAMPLE
7-2-1 If one pair of opposite sides of a quadrilateral are parallel and congruent, then the quadrilateral is a parallelogram. (quad. with pair of opp. sides ‖ and ≅ → ▱)	
7-2-2 If both pairs of opposite sides of a quadrilateral are congruent, then the quadrilateral is a parallelogram. (quad. with opp. sides ≅ → ▱)	
7-2-3 If both pairs of opposite angles of a quadrilateral are congruent, then the quadrilateral is a parallelogram. (quad. with opp. ∠ ≅ → ▱)	

Remember!

In the converse of a theorem, the hypothesis and conclusion are exchanged.

You will prove Theorems 7-2-2 and 7-2-3 in Exercises 26 and 29.

PROOF **Theorem 7-2-1**

Given: $\overline{KL} \parallel \overline{MJ}$, $\overline{KL} \cong \overline{MJ}$
Prove: *JKLM* is a parallelogram.

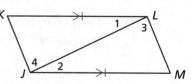

Proof:
It is given that $\overline{KL} \cong \overline{MJ}$. Since $\overline{KL} \parallel \overline{MJ}$, $\angle 1 \cong \angle 2$ by the Alternate Interior Angles Theorem. By the Reflexive Property of Congruence, $\overline{JL} \cong \overline{JL}$. So $\triangle JKL \cong \triangle LMJ$ by SAS. By CPCTC, $\angle 3 \cong \angle 4$, and $\overline{JK} \parallel \overline{LM}$ by the Converse of the Alternate Interior Angles Theorem. Since the opposite sides of *JKLM* are parallel, *JKLM* is a parallelogram by definition.

HMH Photo by Sam Dudgeon

The two theorems below can also be used to show that a given quadrilateral is a parallelogram.

Know it! Note

Theorems: Conditions for Parallelograms

THEOREM	EXAMPLE
7-2-4 If an angle of a quadrilateral is supplementary to both of its consecutive angles, then the quadrilateral is a parallelogram. (quad. with ∠ supp. to cons. ▵ → ▱)	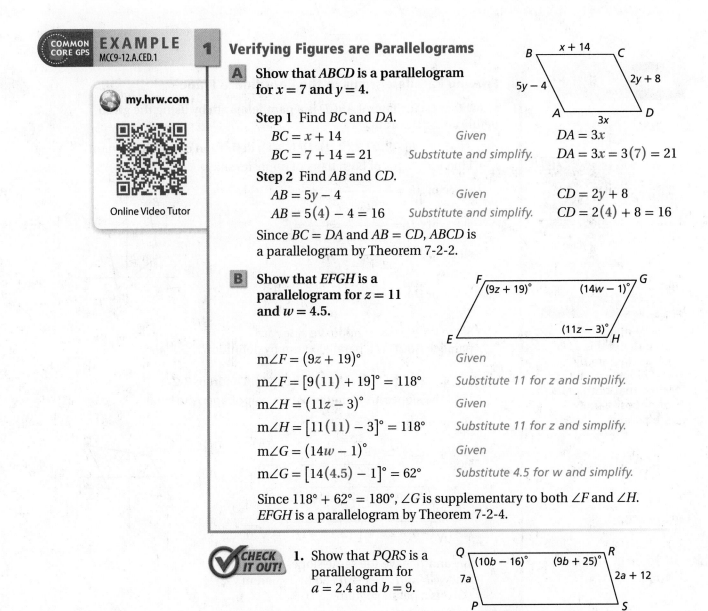
7-2-5 If the diagonals of a quadrilateral bisect each other, then the quadrilateral is a parallelogram. (quad. with diags. bisecting each other → ▱)	

You will prove Theorems 7-2-4 and 7-2-5 in Exercises 27 and 30.

COMMON CORE GPS
MCC9-12.A.CED.1

EXAMPLE 1

my.hrw.com

Online Video Tutor

Verifying Figures are Parallelograms

A Show that *ABCD* is a parallelogram for $x = 7$ and $y = 4$.

Step 1 Find *BC* and *DA*.

| $BC = x + 14$ | *Given* | $DA = 3x$ |
| $BC = 7 + 14 = 21$ | *Substitute and simplify.* | $DA = 3x = 3(7) = 21$ |

Step 2 Find *AB* and *CD*.

| $AB = 5y - 4$ | *Given* | $CD = 2y + 8$ |
| $AB = 5(4) - 4 = 16$ | *Substitute and simplify.* | $CD = 2(4) + 8 = 16$ |

Since $BC = DA$ and $AB = CD$, *ABCD* is a parallelogram by Theorem 7-2-2.

B Show that *EFGH* is a parallelogram for $z = 11$ and $w = 4.5$.

$m\angle F = (9z + 19)^\circ$	*Given*
$m\angle F = [9(11) + 19]^\circ = 118^\circ$	*Substitute 11 for z and simplify.*
$m\angle H = (11z - 3)^\circ$	*Given*
$m\angle H = [11(11) - 3]^\circ = 118^\circ$	*Substitute 11 for z and simplify.*
$m\angle G = (14w - 1)^\circ$	*Given*
$m\angle G = [14(4.5) - 1]^\circ = 62^\circ$	*Substitute 4.5 for w and simplify.*

Since $118^\circ + 62^\circ = 180^\circ$, $\angle G$ is supplementary to both $\angle F$ and $\angle H$. *EFGH* is a parallelogram by Theorem 7-2-4.

CHECK IT OUT!

1. Show that *PQRS* is a parallelogram for $a = 2.4$ and $b = 9$.

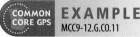

EXAMPLE 2
MCC9-12.G.CO.11

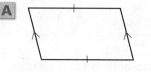

Applying Conditions for Parallelograms

Determine if each quadrilateral must be a parallelogram. Justify your answer.

A

No. One pair of opposite sides are parallel. A different pair of opposite sides are congruent. The conditions for a parallelogram are not met.

B

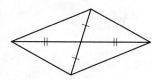

Yes. The diagonals bisect each other. By Theorem 7-2-5, the quadrilateral is a parallelogram.

CHECK IT OUT! **Determine if each quadrilateral must be a parallelogram. Justify your answer.**

2a. 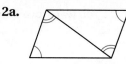   **2b.**

EXAMPLE 3
MCC9-12.G.GPE.4

Proving Parallelograms in the Coordinate Plane

Show that quadrilateral _ABCD_ is a parallelogram by using the given definition or theorem.

A $A(-3, 2)$, $B(-2, 7)$, $C(2, 4)$, $D(1, -1)$; definition of parallelogram

Find the slopes of both pairs of opposite sides.

$$\text{slope of } \overline{AB} = \frac{7 - 2}{-2 - (-3)} = \frac{5}{1} = 5$$

$$\text{slope of } \overline{CD} = \frac{-1 - 4}{1 - 2} = \frac{-5}{-1} = 5$$

$$\text{slope of } \overline{BC} = \frac{4 - 7}{2 - (-2)} = \frac{-3}{4} = -\frac{3}{4}$$

$$\text{slope of } \overline{DA} = \frac{2 - (-1)}{-3 - 1} = \frac{3}{-4} = -\frac{3}{4}$$

Since both pairs of opposite sides are parallel, _ABCD_ is a parallelogram by definition.

Helpful Hint

To say that a quadrilateral is a parallelogram _by definition_, you must show that both pairs of opposite sides are parallel.

B $F(-4, -2)$, $G(-2, 2)$, $H(4, 3)$, $J(2, -1)$; Theorem 7-2-1

Find the slopes and lengths of one pair of opposite sides.

$$\text{slope of } \overline{GH} = \frac{3 - 2}{4 - (-2)} = \frac{1}{6}$$

$$\text{slope of } \overline{JF} = \frac{-2 - (-1)}{-4 - 2} = \frac{-1}{-6} = \frac{1}{6}$$

$$GH = \sqrt{[4 - (-2)]^2 + (3 - 2)^2} = \sqrt{37}$$

$$JF = \sqrt{(-4 - 2)^2 + [-2 - (-1)]^2} = \sqrt{37}$$

$\overline{GH}$ and $\overline{JF}$ have the same slope, so $\overline{GH} \parallel \overline{JF}$. Since $GH = JF$, $\overline{GH} \cong \overline{JF}$. So by Theorem 7-2-1, _FGHJ_ is a parallelogram.

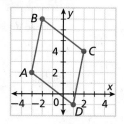

3. Use the definition of a parallelogram to show that the quadrilateral with vertices $K(-3, 0)$, $L(-5, 7)$, $M(3, 5)$, and $N(5, -2)$ is a parallelogram.

You have learned several ways to determine whether a quadrilateral is a parallelogram. You can use the given information about a figure to decide which condition is best to apply.

Helpful Hint

To show that a quadrilateral is a parallelogram, you only have to show that it satisfies one of these sets of conditions.

Conditions for Parallelograms
Both pairs of opposite sides are parallel. (definition)
One pair of opposite sides are parallel and congruent. (Theorem 7-2-1)
Both pairs of opposite sides are congruent. (Theorem 7-2-2)
Both pairs of opposite angles are congruent. (Theorem 7-2-3)
One angle is supplementary to both of its consecutive angles. (Theorem 7-2-4)
The diagonals bisect each other. (Theorem 7-2-5)

COMMON CORE GPS MCC9-12.G.MG.1

EXAMPLE 4

Bird-Watching Application

my.hrw.com

Online Video Tutor

In the parallelogram mount, there are bolts at P, Q, R, and S such that $PQ = RS$ and $QR = SP$. The frame $PQRS$ moves when you raise or lower the binoculars. Why is $PQRS$ always a parallelogram?

When you move the binoculars, the angle measures change, but PQ, QR, RS, and SP stay the same. So it is always true that $PQ = RS$ and $QR = SP$. Since both pairs of opposite sides of the quadrilateral are congruent, $PQRS$ is always a parallelogram.

4. The frame is attached to the tripod at points A and B such that $AB = RS$ and $BR = SA$. So $ABRS$ is also a parallelogram. How does this ensure that the angle of the binoculars stays the same?

MCC.MP.2 **MATHEMATICAL PRACTICES**

THINK AND DISCUSS

1. What do all the theorems in this lesson have in common?

2. How are the theorems in this lesson different from the theorems in the lesson *Properties of Parallelograms*?

3. GET ORGANIZED Copy and complete the graphic organizer. In each box, write one of the six conditions for a parallelogram. Then sketch a parallelogram and label it to show how it meets the condition.

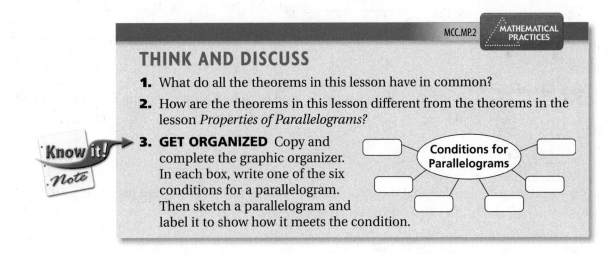

Conditions for Parallelograms

GUIDED PRACTICE

SEE EXAMPLE 1

1. Show that *EFGH* is a parallelogram for $s = 5$ and $t = 6$.

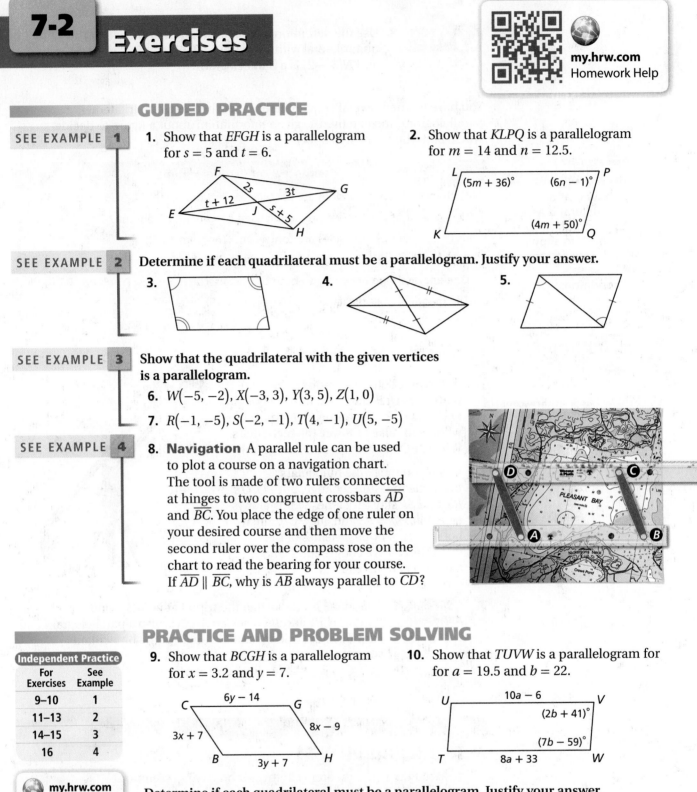

2. Show that *KLPQ* is a parallelogram for $m = 14$ and $n = 12.5$.

$(5m + 36)°$ $(6n - 1)°$

$(4m + 50)°$

SEE EXAMPLE 2

Determine if each quadrilateral must be a parallelogram. Justify your answer.

3.

4.

5.

SEE EXAMPLE 3

Show that the quadrilateral with the given vertices is a parallelogram.

6. $W(-5, -2), X(-3, 3), Y(3, 5), Z(1, 0)$

7. $R(-1, -5), S(-2, -1), T(4, -1), U(5, -5)$

SEE EXAMPLE 4

8. **Navigation** A parallel rule can be used to plot a course on a navigation chart. The tool is made of two rulers connected at hinges to two congruent crossbars $\overline{AD}$ and $\overline{BC}$. You place the edge of one ruler on your desired course and then move the second ruler over the compass rose on the chart to read the bearing for your course. If $\overline{AD} \parallel \overline{BC}$, why is $\overline{AB}$ always parallel to $\overline{CD}$?

PRACTICE AND PROBLEM SOLVING

Independent Practice	
For Exercises	See Example
9–10	1
11–13	2
14–15	3
16	4

my.hrw.com

Online Extra Practice

9. Show that *BCGH* is a parallelogram for $x = 3.2$ and $y = 7$.

$6y - 14$

$3x + 7$ $8x - 9$

$3y + 7$

10. Show that *TUVW* is a parallelogram for for $a = 19.5$ and $b = 22$.

$10a - 6$

$(2b + 41)°$

$(7b - 59)°$

$8a + 33$

Determine if each quadrilateral must be a parallelogram. Justify your answer.

11.

12.

13.

Show that the quadrilateral with the given vertices is a parallelogram.

14. $J(-1, 0), K(-3, 7), L(2, 6), M(4, -1)$

15. $P(-8, -4), Q(-5, 1), R(1, -5), S(-2, -10)$

16. Design The toolbox has cantilever trays that pull away from the box so that you can reach the items beneath them. Two congruent brackets connect each tray to the box. Given that $AD = BC$, how do the brackets $\overline{AB}$ and $\overline{CD}$ keep the tray horizontal?

Determine if each quadrilateral must be a parallelogram. Justify your answer.

17.

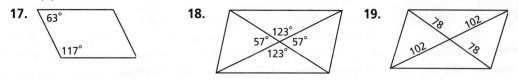

18.

19.

H.O.T. Algebra Find the values of a and b that would make the quadrilateral a parallelogram.

20.

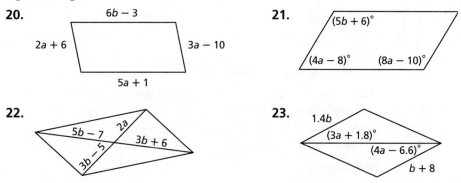

$6b - 3$

$2a + 6$ $3a - 10$

$5a + 1$

21.

$(5b + 6)°$

$(4a - 8)°$ $(8a - 10)°$

22.

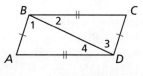

$5b - 7$ $2a$

$3b + 6$

$3b - 5$

23.

$1.4b$

$(3a + 1.8)°$

$(4a - 6.6)°$

$b + 8$

24. Critical Thinking Draw a quadrilateral that has congruent diagonals but is not a parallelogram. What can you conclude about using congruent diagonals as a condition for a parallelogram?

25. Social Studies The angles at the corners of the flag of the Republic of the Congo are right angles. The red and green triangles are congruent isosceles right triangles. Why is the shape of the yellow stripe a parallelogram?

26. Complete the two-column proof of Theorem 7-2-2 by filling in the blanks.

Given: $\overline{AB} \cong \overline{CD}$,
   $\overline{BC} \cong \overline{DA}$
Prove: $ABCD$ is a parallelogram.
Proof:

Statements	Reasons
1. $\overline{AB} \cong \overline{CD}$, $\overline{BC} \cong \overline{DA}$	1. Given
2. $\overline{BD} \cong \overline{BD}$	2. a. ___?___
3. $\triangle DAB \cong$ b. ___?___	3. c. ___?___
4. $\angle 1 \cong$ d. ___?___ , $\angle 4 \cong$ e. ___?___	4. CPCTC
5. $\overline{AB} \parallel \overline{CD}$, $\overline{BC} \parallel \overline{DA}$	5. f. ___?___
6. $ABCD$ is a parallelogram.	6. g. ___?___

27. Complete the paragraph proof of Theorem 7-2-4 by filling in the blanks.
   Given: $\angle P$ is supplementary to $\angle Q$.
   $\angle P$ is supplementary to $\angle S$.
   Prove: $PQRS$ is a parallelogram.

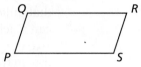

   Proof:
   It is given that $\angle P$ is supplementary to **a.** _____?_____ and **b.** _____?_____ .
   By the Converse of the Same-Side Interior Angles Theorem,
   $\overline{QR} \parallel$ **c.** _____?_____ and $\overline{PQ} \parallel$ **d.** _____?_____ . So $PQRS$ is a parallelogram
   by the definition of **e.** _____?_____ .

28. **Measurement** In the eighteenth century, Gilles Personne de Roberval designed a scale with two beams and two hinges. In $\square ABCD$, E is the midpoint of $\overline{AB}$, and F is the midpoint of $\overline{CD}$. Write a paragraph proof that $AEFD$ and $EBCF$ are parallelograms.

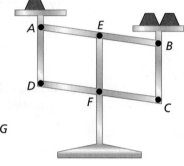

Prove each theorem.

29. Theorem 7-2-3
   Given: $\angle E \cong \angle G$, $\angle F \cong \angle H$
   Prove: $EFGH$ is a parallelogram.

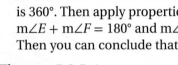

   Plan: Show that the sum of the interior angles of $EFGH$ is 360°. Then apply properties of equality to show that $m\angle E + m\angle F = 180°$ and $m\angle E + m\angle H = 180°$. Then you can conclude that $\overline{EF} \parallel \overline{GH}$ and $\overline{FG} \parallel \overline{HE}$.

30. Theorem 7-2-5
   Given: $\overline{JL}$ and $\overline{KM}$ bisect each other.
   Prove: $JKLM$ is a parallelogram.

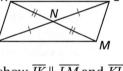

   Plan: Show that $\triangle JNK \cong \triangle LNM$ and $\triangle KNL \cong \triangle MNJ$. Then use the fact that the corresponding angles are congruent to show $\overline{JK} \parallel \overline{LM}$ and $\overline{KL} \parallel \overline{MJ}$.

H.O.T. **31.** Prove that the figure formed by two midsegments of a triangle and their corresponding bases is a parallelogram.

32. **Write About It** Use the theorems about properties of parallelograms to write three biconditional statements about parallelograms.

H.O.T. **33.** **Construction** Explain how you can construct a parallelogram based on the conditions of Theorem 7-2-1. Use your method to construct a parallelogram.

34. A geologist made the following observations while examining this amethyst crystal. Tell whether each set of observations allows the geologist to conclude that $PQRS$ is a parallelogram. If so, explain why.

   a. $\overline{PQ} \cong \overline{SR}$, and $\overline{PS} \parallel \overline{QR}$.

   b. $\angle S$ and $\angle R$ are supplementary, and $\overline{PS} \cong \overline{QR}$.

   c. $\angle S \cong \angle Q$, and $\overline{PQ} \parallel \overline{SR}$.

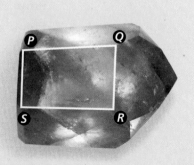

TEST PREP

35. What additional information would allow you to conclude that *WXYZ* is a parallelogram?

Ⓐ $\overline{XY} \cong \overline{ZW}$ Ⓒ $\overline{WY} \cong \overline{WZ}$

Ⓑ $\overline{WX} \cong \overline{YZ}$ Ⓓ $\angle XWY \cong \angle ZYW$

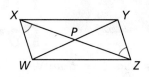

36. Which could be the coordinates of the fourth vertex of □*ABCD* with $A(-1, -1)$, $B(1, 3)$, and $C(6, 1)$?

Ⓕ $D(8, 5)$ Ⓖ $D(4, -3)$ Ⓗ $D(13, 3)$ Ⓙ $D(3, 7)$

37. Short Response The vertices of quadrilateral *RSTV* are $R(-5, 0)$, $S(-1, 3)$, $T(5, 1)$, and $V(2, -2)$. Is *RSTV* a parallelogram? Justify your answer.

CHALLENGE AND EXTEND

38. Write About It As the upper platform of the movable staircase is raised and lowered, the height of each step changes. How does the upper platform remain parallel to the ground?

H.O.T. 39. Multi-Step The diagonals of a parallelogram intersect at $(-2, 1.5)$. Two vertices are located at $(-7, 2)$ and $(2, 6.5)$. Find the coordinates of the other two vertices.

H.O.T. 40. Given: *D* is the midpoint of $\overline{AC}$, and *E* is the midpoint of $\overline{BC}$.

Prove: $\overline{DE} \parallel \overline{AB}$, $DE = \frac{1}{2}AB$

(*Hint:* Extend $\overline{DE}$ to form $\overline{DF}$ so that $\overline{EF} \cong \overline{DE}$. Then show that *DFBA* is a parallelogram.)

FOCUS ON MATHEMATICAL PRACTICES

H.O.T. 41. Proof A precision ice skating team with 10 members formed the figure shown. The skaters positioned themselves along four lines, and the space between each pair of adjacent skaters was 3 feet. Prove that the skaters formed a parallelogram.

H.O.T. 42. Problem Solving The figure shows a parallelogram.

a. Find the coordinates of the fourth vertex.

b. Find the midpoints of the sides of the parallelogram.

c. Show that the quadrilateral formed by connecting the midpoints of adjacent sides is also a parallelogram.

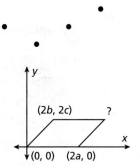

7-3 Properties of Special Parallelograms

Essential Question: What are the geometric properties of rectangles, rhombuses, and squares?

Objectives
Prove and apply properties of rectangles, rhombuses, and squares.

Use properties of rectangles, rhombuses, and squares to solve problems.

Vocabulary
rectangle
rhombus
square

Who uses this?
Artists who work with stained glass can use properties of rectangles to cut materials to the correct sizes.

A second type of special quadrilateral is a *rectangle*. A **rectangle** is a quadrilateral with four right angles.

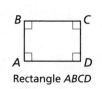
Rectangle *ABCD*

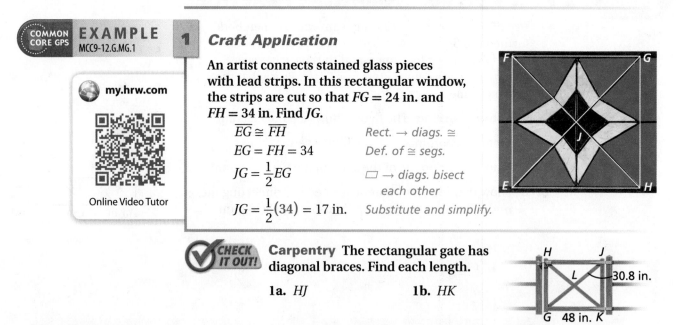

> **Know it! Note**

Theorems — Properties of Rectangles

THEOREM	HYPOTHESIS	CONCLUSION
7-3-1 If a quadrilateral is a rectangle, then it is a parallelogram. (rect. → ▱)		*ABCD* is a parallelogram.
7-3-2 If a parallelogram is a rectangle, then its diagonals are congruent. (rect. → diags. ≅)		$\overline{AC} \cong \overline{BD}$

You will prove Theorems 7-3-1 and 7-3-2 in Exercises 38 and 35.

Since a rectangle is a parallelogram by Theorem 7-3-1, a rectangle "inherits" all the properties of parallelograms.

COMMON CORE GPS MCC9-12.G.MG.1

EXAMPLE 1 *Craft Application*

my.hrw.com

Online Video Tutor

An artist connects stained glass pieces with lead strips. In this rectangular window, the strips are cut so that $FG = 24$ in. and $FH = 34$ in. Find JG.

$\overline{EG} \cong \overline{FH}$ *Rect. → diags. ≅*

$EG = FH = 34$ *Def. of ≅ segs.*

$JG = \frac{1}{2}EG$ *▱ → diags. bisect each other*

$JG = \frac{1}{2}(34) = 17$ in.   *Substitute and simplify.*

> **CHECK IT OUT!**
> **Carpentry** The rectangular gate has diagonal braces. Find each length.
>
> **1a.** *HJ*   **1b.** *HK*

Courtesy of Wimberley Stain Glass/HMH Photo by Peter Van Steen

A *rhombus* is another special quadrilateral. A **rhombus** is a quadrilateral with four congruent sides.

Rhombus *ABCD*

Theorems — Properties of Rhombuses

	THEOREM	HYPOTHESIS	CONCLUSION
7-3-3	If a quadrilateral is a rhombus, then it is a parallelogram. (rhombus → ▱)		*ABCD* is a parallelogram.
7-3-4	If a parallelogram is a rhombus, then its diagonals are perpendicular. (rhombus → diags. ⊥)		$\overline{AC} \perp \overline{BD}$
7-3-5	If a parallelogram is a rhombus, then each diagonal bisects a pair of opposite angles. (rhombus → each diag. bisects opp. ∡)		$\angle 1 \cong \angle 2$ $\angle 3 \cong \angle 4$ $\angle 5 \cong \angle 6$ $\angle 7 \cong \angle 8$

You will prove Theorems 7-3-3 and 7-3-4 in Exercises 34 and 37.

PROOF | **Theorem 7-3-5**

Given: *JKLM* is a rhombus.
Prove: $\overline{JL}$ bisects $\angle KJM$ and $\angle KLM$.
$\overline{KM}$ bisects $\angle JKL$ and $\angle JML$.

Proof:
Since *JKLM* is a rhombus, $\overline{JK} \cong \overline{JM}$, and $\overline{KL} \cong \overline{ML}$ by the definition of a rhombus. By the Reflexive Property of Congruence, $\overline{JL} \cong \overline{JL}$. Thus $\triangle JKL \cong \triangle JML$ by SSS. Then $\angle 1 \cong \angle 2$, and $\angle 3 \cong \angle 4$ by CPCTC. So $\overline{JL}$ bisects $\angle KJM$ and $\angle KLM$ by the definition of an angle bisector. By similar reasoning, $\overline{KM}$ bisects $\angle JKL$ and $\angle JML$.

Like a rectangle, a rhombus is a parallelogram. So you can apply the properties of parallelograms to rhombuses.

COMMON CORE GPS
MCC9-12.A.CED.1

EXAMPLE 2 | **Using Properties of Rhombuses to Find Measures**

RSTV is a rhombus. Find each measure.

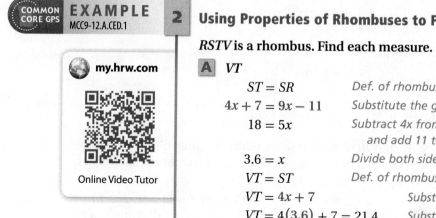

A *VT*

$ST = SR$	*Def. of rhombus*
$4x + 7 = 9x - 11$	*Substitute the given values.*
$18 = 5x$	*Subtract 4x from both sides and add 11 to both sides.*
$3.6 = x$	*Divide both sides by 5.*
$VT = ST$	*Def. of rhombus*
$VT = 4x + 7$	*Substitute 4x + 7 for ST.*
$VT = 4(3.6) + 7 = 21.4$	*Substitute 3.6 for x and simplify.*

my.hrw.com

Online Video Tutor

RSTV is a rhombus. Find each measure.

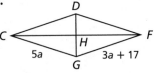

B m∠*WSR*

m∠*SWT* = 90°	*Rhombus → diags.* ⊥
2*y* + 10 = 90	*Substitute 2y + 10 for m∠SWT.*
y = 40	*Subtract 10 from both sides and divide both sides by 2.*
m∠*WSR* = m∠*TSW*	*Rhombus → each diag. bisects opp. ∠.*
m∠*WSR* = (*y* + 2)°	*Substitute y + 2 for m∠TSW.*
m∠*WSR* = (40 + 2)° = 42°	*Substitute 40 for y and simplify.*

 CHECK IT OUT! *CDFG* is a rhombus. Find each measure.

2a. *CD*

2b. m∠*GCH* if m∠*GCD* = (*b* + 3)° and m∠*CDF* = (6*b* − 40)°

A **square** is a quadrilateral with four right angles and four congruent sides. In the exercises, you will show that a square is a parallelogram, a rectangle, and a rhombus. So a square has the properties of all three.

Square *ABCD*

COMMON CORE GPS MCC9-12.G.GPE.4

3 EXAMPLE

my.hrw.com

Online Video Tutor

Verifying Properties of Squares

Show that the diagonals of square *ABCD* are congruent perpendicular bisectors of each other.

Step 1 Show that $\overline{AC}$ and $\overline{BD}$ are congruent.

$$AC = \sqrt{[2 - (-1)]^2 + (7 - 0)^2} = \sqrt{58}$$

$$BD = \sqrt{[4 - (-3)]^2 + (2 - 5)^2} = \sqrt{58}$$

Since $AC = BD$, $\overline{AC} \cong \overline{BD}$.

Step 2 Show that $\overline{AC}$ and $\overline{BD}$ are perpendicular.

slope of $\overline{AC} = \dfrac{7 - 0}{2 - (-1)} = \dfrac{7}{3}$

slope of $\overline{BD} = \dfrac{2 - 5}{4 - (-3)} = \dfrac{-3}{7} = -\dfrac{3}{7}$

Since $\left(\dfrac{7}{3}\right)\left(-\dfrac{3}{7}\right) = -1$, $\overline{AC} \perp \overline{BD}$.

Step 3 Show that $\overline{AC}$ and $\overline{BD}$ bisect each other.

mdpt. of $\overline{AC}$: $\left(\dfrac{-1 + 2}{2}, \dfrac{0 + 7}{2}\right) = \left(\dfrac{1}{2}, \dfrac{7}{2}\right)$

mdpt. of $\overline{BD}$: $\left(\dfrac{-3 + 4}{2}, \dfrac{5 + 2}{2}\right) = \left(\dfrac{1}{2}, \dfrac{7}{2}\right)$

Since $\overline{AC}$ and $\overline{BD}$ have the same midpoint, they bisect each other. The diagonals are congruent perpendicular bisectors of each other.

CHECK IT OUT! **3.** The vertices of square *STVW* are *S*(−5, −4), *T*(0, 2), *V*(6, −3), and *W*(1, −9). Show that the diagonals of square *STVW* are congruent perpendicular bisectors of each other.

Taylor Gallinghouse
Central High School

Special Parallelograms

To remember the properties of rectangles, rhombuses, and squares, I start with a **square**, which has all the properties of the others.

To get a **rectangle** that is not a square, I stretch the square in one direction. Its diagonals are still congruent, but they are no longer perpendicular.

To get a **rhombus** that is not a square, I go back to the square and slide the top in one direction. Its diagonals are still perpendicular and bisect the opposite angles, but they aren't congruent.

COMMON CORE GPS
MCC9-12.G.CO.11

EXAMPLE 4

my.hrw.com

Online Video Tutor

Using Properties of Special Parallelograms in Proofs

Given: *EFGH* is a rectangle. *J* is the midpoint of $\overline{EH}$.
Prove: $\triangle FJG$ is isosceles.

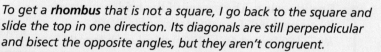

Proof:

Statements	Reasons
1. *EFGH* is a rectangle. *J* is the midpoint of $\overline{EH}$.	1. Given
2. $\angle E$ and $\angle H$ are right angles.	2. Def. of rect.
3. $\angle E \cong \angle H$	3. Rt. $\angle \cong$ Thm.
4. *EFGH* is a parallelogram.	4. Rect. → ▱
5. $\overline{EF} \cong \overline{HG}$	5. ▱ → opp. sides ≅
6. $\overline{EJ} \cong \overline{HJ}$	6. Def. of mdpt.
7. $\triangle FJE \cong \triangle GJH$	7. SAS *Steps 3, 5, 6*
8. $\overline{FJ} \cong \overline{GJ}$	8. CPCTC
9. $\triangle FJG$ is isosceles.	9. Def. of isosc. $\triangle$

 4. **Given:** *PQTS* is a rhombus with diagonal $\overline{PR}$.
Prove: $\overline{RQ} \cong \overline{RS}$

MCC.MP.7   MATHEMATICAL PRACTICES

THINK AND DISCUSS

1. Which theorem means "The diagonals of a rectangle are congruent"? Why do you think the theorem is written as a conditional?

2. What properties of a rhombus are the same as the properties of all parallelograms? What special properties does a rhombus have?

3. GET ORGANIZED Copy and complete the graphic organizer. Write the missing terms in the three unlabeled sections. Then write a definition of each term.

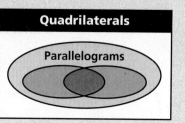

Gareth Brown/CORBIS

GUIDED PRACTICE

1. **Vocabulary** What is another name for an *equilateral quadrilateral?* an *equiangular quadrilateral?* a *regular quadrilateral?*

SEE EXAMPLE 1 **Engineering** The braces of the bridge support lie along the diagonals of rectangle *PQRS*. $RS = 160$ ft, and $QS = 380$ ft. Find each length.

2. *TQ*   3. *PQ*

4. *ST*   5. *PR*

SEE EXAMPLE 2 *ABCD* is a rhombus. Find each measure.

6. *AB*   7. m∠*ABC*

SEE EXAMPLE 3 8. **Multi-Step** The vertices of square *JKLM* are $J(-3, -5)$, $K(-4, 1)$, $L(2, 2)$, and $M(3, -4)$. Show that the diagonals of square *JKLM* are congruent perpendicular bisectors of each other.

SEE EXAMPLE 4 9. **Given:** *RECT* is a rectangle. $\overline{RX} \cong \overline{TY}$
Prove: $\triangle REY \cong \triangle TCX$

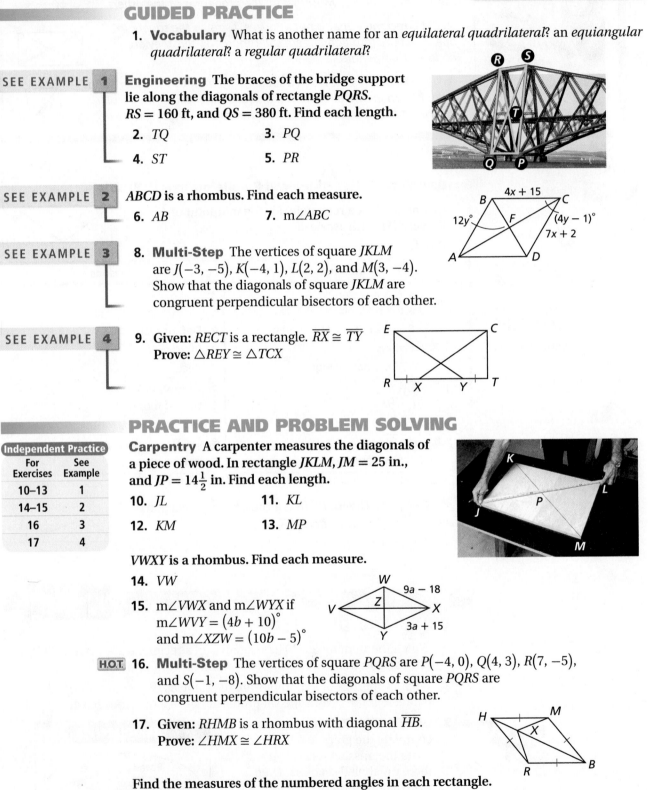

PRACTICE AND PROBLEM SOLVING

Independent Practice	
For Exercises	See Example
10–13	1
14–15	2
16	3
17	4

Carpentry A carpenter measures the diagonals of a piece of wood. In rectangle *JKLM*, $JM = 25$ in., and $JP = 14\frac{1}{2}$ in. Find each length.

10. *JL*   11. *KL*

12. *KM*   13. *MP*

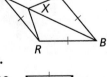

VWXY is a rhombus. Find each measure.

14. *VW*

15. m∠*VWX* and m∠*WYX* if
m∠*WVY* = $(4b + 10)°$
and m∠*XZW* = $(10b - 5)°$

H.O.T. 16. **Multi-Step** The vertices of square *PQRS* are $P(-4, 0)$, $Q(4, 3)$, $R(7, -5)$, and $S(-1, -8)$. Show that the diagonals of square *PQRS* are congruent perpendicular bisectors of each other.

17. **Given:** *RHMB* is a rhombus with diagonal $\overline{HB}$.
Prove: ∠*HMX* ≅ ∠*HRX*

Find the measures of the numbered angles in each rectangle.

18.   19.   20.

Find the measures of the numbered angles in each rhombus.

21.

27° with angles 1, 2, 3, 4, 5

22.

70° with angles 1, 2, 3, 4, 5

23.

26° with angles 1, 2, 3, 4, 5

Tell whether each statement is *sometimes*, *always*, or *never* true.
(*Hint:* Refer to your graphic organizer for this lesson.)

24. A rectangle is a parallelogram.

25. A rhombus is a square.

26. A parallelogram is a rhombus.

27. A rhombus is a rectangle.

28. A square is a rhombus.

29. A rectangle is a quadrilateral.

30. A square is a rectangle.

31. A rectangle is a square.

H.O.T. 32. Critical Thinking A triangle is equilateral if and only if the triangle is equiangular. Can you make a similar statement about a quadrilateral? Explain your answer.

33. **History** There are five shapes of clay tiles in this tile mosaic from the ruins of Pompeii.

   a. Make a sketch of each shape of tile and tell whether the shape is a polygon.

   b. Name each polygon by its number of sides. Does each shape appear to be regular or irregular?

   c. Do any of the shapes appear to be special parallelograms? If so, identify them by name.

   d. Find the measure of each interior angle of the center polygon.

H.O.T. 34. ///ERROR ANALYSIS/// Find and correct the error in this proof of Theorem 7-3-3.

Given: *JKLM* is a rhombus.
Prove: *JKLM* is a parallelogram.

Proof:

   It is given that *JKLM* is a rhombus. So by the definition of a rhombus, $\overline{JK} \cong \overline{LM}$, and $\overline{KL} \cong \overline{MJ}$. If a quadrilateral is a parallelogram, then its opposite sides are congruent. So *JKLM* is a parallelogram.

35. Complete the two-column proof of Theorem 7-3-2 by filling in the blanks.

   Given: *EFGH* is a rectangle.
   Prove: $\overline{FH} \cong \overline{GE}$

   Proof:

Statements	Reasons
1. *EFGH* is a rectangle.	1. Given
2. *EFGH* is a parallelogram.	2. a. ___?___
3. $\overline{EF} \cong$ **b.** ___?___	3. ▱ → opp. sides ≅
4. $\overline{EH} \cong \overline{EH}$	4. c. ___?___
5. ∠*FEH* and ∠*GHE* are right angles.	5. d. ___?___
6. ∠*FEH* ≅ **e.** ___?___	6. Rt. ∠ ≅ Thm.
7. △*FEH* ≅ △*GHE*	7. f. ___?___
8. $\overline{FH} \cong \overline{GE}$	8. g. ___?___

Real-World Connections

36. The organizers of a fair plan to fence off a plot of land given by the coordinates $A(2, 4)$, $B(4, 2)$, $C(-1, -3)$, and $D(-3, -1)$.

  a. Find the slope of each side of quadrilateral *ABCD*.

  b. What type of quadrilateral is formed by the fences? Justify your answer.

  c. The organizers plan to build a straight path connecting *A* and *C* and another path connecting *B* and *D*. Explain why these two paths will have the same length.

37. Use this plan to write a proof of Theorem 7-3-4.

  Given: *VWXY* is a rhombus.

  Prove: $\overline{VX} \perp \overline{WY}$

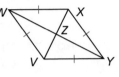

  Plan: Use the definition of a rhombus and the properties of parallelograms to show that $\triangle WZX \cong \triangle YZX$. Then use CPCTC to show that $\angle WZX$ and $\angle YZX$ are right angles.

38. Write a paragraph proof of Theorem 7-3-1.

  Given: *ABCD* is a rectangle.

  Prove: *ABCD* is a parallelogram.

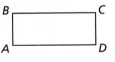

39. Write a two-column proof.

  Given: *ABCD* is a rhombus. *E, F, G,* and *H* are the midpoints of the sides.

  Prove: *EFGH* is a parallelogram.

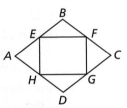

H.O.T. **Multi-Step** Find the perimeter and area of each figure. Round to the nearest hundredth, if necessary.

40.
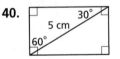

41.
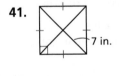

42.
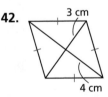

H.O.T. **43.** **Write About It** Explain why each of these conditional statements is true.

  a. If a quadrilateral is a square, then it is a parallelogram.

  b. If a quadrilateral is a square, then it is a rectangle.

  c. If a quadrilateral is a square, then it is a rhombus.

44. **Write About It** List the properties that a square "inherits" because it is (1) a parallelogram, (2) a rectangle, and (3) a rhombus.

TEST PREP

45. Which expression represents the measure of $\angle J$ in rhombus *JKLM*?

  (A) $x°$

  (B) $2x°$

  (C) $(180 - x)°$

  (D) $(180 - 2x)°$

46. **Short Response** The diagonals of rectangle *QRST* intersect at point *P*. If $QR = 1.8$ cm, $QP = 1.5$ cm, and $QT = 2.4$ cm, find the perimeter of $\triangle RST$. Explain how you found your answer.

47. Which statement is NOT true of a rectangle?

  (F) Both pairs of opposite sides are congruent and parallel.

  (G) Both pairs of opposite angles are congruent and supplementary.

  (H) All pairs of consecutive sides are congruent and perpendicular.

  (J) All pairs of consecutive angles are congruent and supplementary.

CHALLENGE AND EXTEND

48. Algebra Find the value of x in the rhombus.

H.O.T. 49. Prove that the segment joining the midpoints of two consecutive sides of a rhombus is perpendicular to one diagonal and parallel to the other.

50. Extend the definition of a triangle midsegment to write a definition for the midsegment of a rectangle. Prove that a midsegment of a rectangle divides the rectangle into two congruent rectangles.

51. The figure is formed by joining eleven congruent squares. How many rectangles are in the figure?

FOCUS ON MATHEMATICAL PRACTICES

H.O.T. 52. Reasoning Explain the relationship between the two labeled angles in the rhombus shown and their relationship to ∠BAD, then find the value of x and m∠BAD.

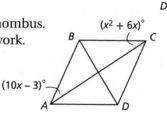

H.O.T. 53. Problem Solving ABCD is a rhombus. Find x and m∠DAC. Show your work.

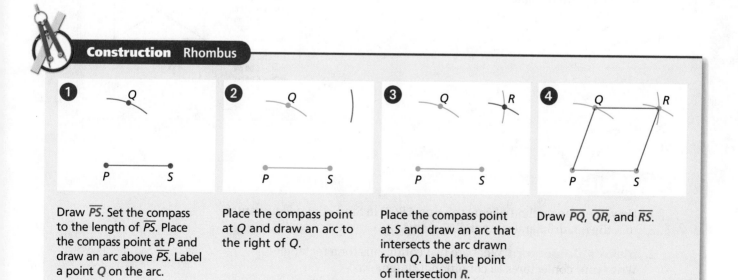

Construction Rhombus

① Draw $\overline{PS}$. Set the compass to the length of $\overline{PS}$. Place the compass point at P and draw an arc above $\overline{PS}$. Label a point Q on the arc.

② Place the compass point at Q and draw an arc to the right of Q.

③ Place the compass point at S and draw an arc that intersects the arc drawn from Q. Label the point of intersection R.

④ Draw $\overline{PQ}$, $\overline{QR}$, and $\overline{RS}$.

7-4

Predict Conditions for Special Parallelograms

In this task, you will use geometry software to predict the conditions that are sufficient to prove that a parallelogram is a rectangle, rhombus, or square.

Use with *Conditions for Special Parallelograms*

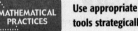

Use appropriate tools strategically.

MCC9-12.G.CO.11 Prove theorems about parallelograms.

Activity 1

1. Construct $\overline{AB}$ and $\overline{AD}$ with a common endpoint A. Construct a line through D parallel to $\overline{AB}$. Construct a line through B parallel to $\overline{AD}$.

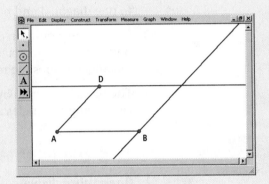

2. Construct point C at the intersection of the two lines. Hide the lines and construct $\overline{BC}$ and $\overline{CD}$ to complete the parallelogram.

3. Measure the four sides and angles of the parallelogram.

4. Move A so that m∠ABC = 90°. What type of special parallelogram results?

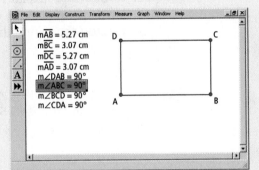

5. Move A so that m∠ABC ≠ 90°.

6. Construct $\overline{AC}$ and $\overline{BD}$ and measure their lengths. Move A so that AC = BD. What type of special parallelogram results?

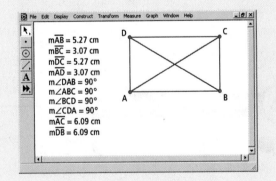

Try This

1. How does the method of constructing ABCD in Steps 1 and 2 guarantee that the quadrilateral is a parallelogram?

2. **Make a Conjecture** What are two conditions for a rectangle? Write your conjectures as conditional statements.

Activity 2

① Use the parallelogram you constructed in Activity 1. Move *A* so that *AB* = *BC*. What type of special parallelogram results?

② Move *A* so that *AB* ≠ *BC*.

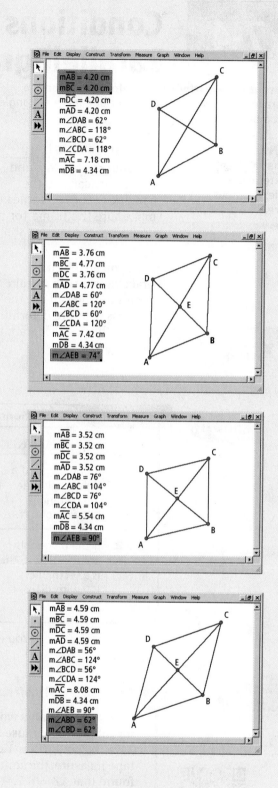

③ Label the intersection of the diagonals as *E*. Measure ∠*AEB*.

④ Move *A* so that m∠*AEB* = 90°. What type of special parallelogram results?

⑤ Move *A* so that m∠*AEB* ≠ 90°.

⑥ Measure ∠*ABD* and ∠*CBD*. Move *A* so that m∠*ABD* = m∠*CBD*. What type of special parallelogram results?

Try This

3. **Make a Conjecture** What are three conditions for a rhombus? Write your conjectures as conditional statements.

4. **Make a Conjecture** A square is both a rectangle and a rhombus. What conditions do you think must hold for a parallelogram to be a square?

7-4 Conditions for Special Parallelograms

Essential Question: What information about a parallelogram allows you to conclude it is a rectangle, rhombus, or square?

Objective
Prove that a given quadrilateral is a rectangle, rhombus, or square.

Who uses this?
Building contractors and carpenters can use the conditions for rectangles to make sure the frame for a house has the correct shape.

When you are given a parallelogram with certain properties, you can use the theorems below to determine whether the parallelogram is a rectangle.

X **Animated Math**

Know it!
Note

| Theorems | Conditions for Rectangles |

THEOREM	EXAMPLE
7-4-1 If one angle of a parallelogram is a right angle, then the parallelogram is a rectangle. (▱ with one rt. ∠ → rect.)	B C A D
7-4-2 If the diagonals of a parallelogram are congruent, then the parallelogram is a rectangle. (▱ with diags. ≅ → rect.)	B C A D $\overline{AC} \cong \overline{BD}$

You will prove Theorems 7-4-1 and 7-4-2 in Exercises 31 and 28.

COMMON CORE GPS
EXAMPLE **1**
MCC9-12.G.MG.1

Carpentry Application

🌐 **my.hrw.com**

Online Video Tutor

A contractor built a wood frame for the side of a house so that $\overline{XY} \cong \overline{WZ}$ and $\overline{XW} \cong \overline{YZ}$. Using a tape measure, the contractor found that $XZ = WY$. Why must the frame be a rectangle?

Both pairs of opposite sides of *WXYZ* are congruent, so *WXYZ* is a parallelogram. Since $XZ = WY$, the diagonals of ▱*WXYZ* are congruent. Therefore the frame is a rectangle by Theorem 7-4-2.

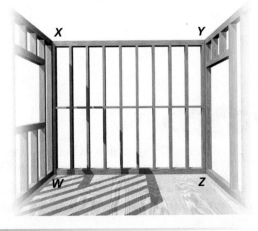

David Papazian/Getty Images

1. A carpenter's square can be used to test that an angle is a right angle. How could the contractor use a carpenter's square to check that the frame is a rectangle?

Below are some conditions you can use to determine whether a parallelogram is a rhombus.

Know it! Note

Theorems	Conditions for Rhombuses	
	THEOREM	**EXAMPLE**
7-4-3	If one pair of consecutive sides of a parallelogram are congruent, then the parallelogram is a rhombus. (▱ with one pair cons. sides ≅ → rhombus)	
7-4-4	If the diagonals of a parallelogram are perpendicular, then the parallelogram is a rhombus. (▱ with diags. ⊥ → rhombus)	
7-4-5	If one diagonal of a parallelogram bisects a pair of opposite angles, then the parallelogram is a rhombus. (▱ with diag. bisecting opp. ∡ → rhombus)	

Caution!

In order to apply Theorems 7-5-1 through 7-5-5, the quadrilateral must be a parallelogram.

You will prove Theorems 7-4-3 and 7-4-4 in Exercises 32 and 30.

PROOF   **Theorem 7-4-5**

Given: *JKLM* is a parallelogram.
    $\overline{JL}$ bisects ∠*KJM* and ∠*KLM*.
Prove: *JKLM* is a rhombus.
Proof:

Statements	Reasons
1. *JKLM* is a parallelogram. $\overline{JL}$ bisects ∠*KJM* and ∠*KLM*.	1. Given
2. ∠1 ≅ ∠2, ∠3 ≅ ∠4	2. Def. of ∠ bisector
3. $\overline{JL} \cong \overline{JL}$	3. Reflex. Prop. of ≅
4. △*JKL* ≅ △*JML*	4. ASA *Steps 2, 3*
5. $\overline{JK} \cong \overline{JM}$	5. CPCTC
6. *JKLM* is a rhombus.	6. ▱ with one pair cons. sides ≅ → rhombus

To prove that a given quadrilateral is a square, it is sufficient to show that the figure is both a rectangle and a rhombus. You will explain why this is true in Exercise 43.

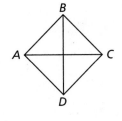
EXAMPLE 2 Applying Conditions for Special Parallelograms

Determine if the conclusion is valid. If not, tell what additional information is needed to make it valid.

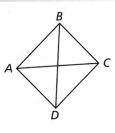

A Given: $\overline{AB} \cong \overline{CD}$, $\overline{BC} \cong \overline{AD}$,
$\overline{AD} \perp \overline{DC}$, $\overline{AC} \perp \overline{BD}$

Conclusion: *ABCD* is a square.

Step 1 Determine if *ABCD* is a parallelogram.

$\overline{AB} \cong \overline{CD}$, $\overline{BC} \cong \overline{AD}$	*Given*
ABCD is a parallelogram.	*Quad. with opp. sides $\cong \rightarrow \square$*

Step 2 Determine if *ABCD* is a rectangle.

$\overline{AD} \perp \overline{DC}$, so $\angle ADC$ is a right angle.	*Def. of $\perp$*
ABCD is a rectangle.	*$\square$ with one rt. $\angle \rightarrow$ rect.*

Step 3 Determine if *ABCD* is a rhombus.

$\overline{AC} \perp \overline{BD}$	*Given*
ABCD is a rhombus.	*$\square$ with diags. $\perp \rightarrow$ rhombus*

Step 4 Determine if *ABCD* is a square.

Since *ABCD* is a rectangle and a rhombus, it has four right angles and four congruent sides. So *ABCD* is a square by definition. The conclusion is valid.

B Given: $\overline{AB} \cong \overline{BC}$

Conclusion: *ABCD* is a rhombus.

The conclusion is not valid. By Theorem 7-4-3, if one pair of consecutive sides of a parallelogram are congruent, then the parallelogram is a rhombus. To apply this theorem, you must first know that *ABCD* is a parallelogram.

Remember!

You can also prove that a given quadrilateral is a rectangle, rhombus, or square by using the definitions of the special quadrilaterals.

CHECK IT OUT!

2. Determine if the conclusion is valid. If not, tell what additional information is needed to make it valid.
Given: $\angle ABC$ is a right angle.
Conclusion: *ABCD* is a rectangle.

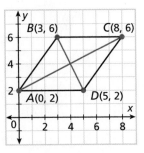

EXAMPLE 3 Identifying Special Parallelograms in the Coordinate Plane

Use the diagonals to determine whether a parallelogram with the given vertices is a rectangle, rhombus, or square. Give all the names that apply.

A $A(0, 2)$, $B(3, 6)$, $C(8, 6)$, $D(5, 2)$

Step 1 Graph $\square ABCD$.

Step 2 Determine if *ABCD* is a rectangle.

$$AC = \sqrt{(8-0)^2 + (6-2)^2}$$
$$= \sqrt{80} = 4\sqrt{5}$$

$$BD = \sqrt{(5-3)^2 + (2-6)^2}$$
$$= \sqrt{20} = 2\sqrt{5}$$

Since $4\sqrt{5} \neq 2\sqrt{5}$, *ABCD* is not a rectangle. Thus *ABCD* is not a square.

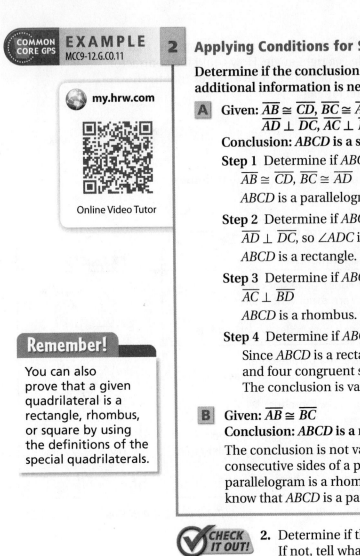

Step 3 Determine if *ABCD* is a rhombus.

slope of $\overline{AC} = \dfrac{6-2}{8-0} = \dfrac{1}{2}$ \qquad slope of $\overline{BD} = \dfrac{2-6}{5-3} = -2$

Since $\left(\dfrac{1}{2}\right)(-2) = -1$, $\overline{AC} \perp \overline{BD}$. *ABCD* is a rhombus.

B $E(-4, -1), F(-3, 2), G(3, 0), H(2, -3)$

Step 1 Graph $\square EFGH$.

Step 2 Determine if *EFGH* is a rectangle.

$EG = \sqrt{[3-(-4)]^2 + [0-(-1)]^2}$

$\quad = \sqrt{50} = 5\sqrt{2}$

$FH = \sqrt{[2-(-3)]^2 + (-3-2)^2}$

$\quad = \sqrt{50} = 5\sqrt{2}$

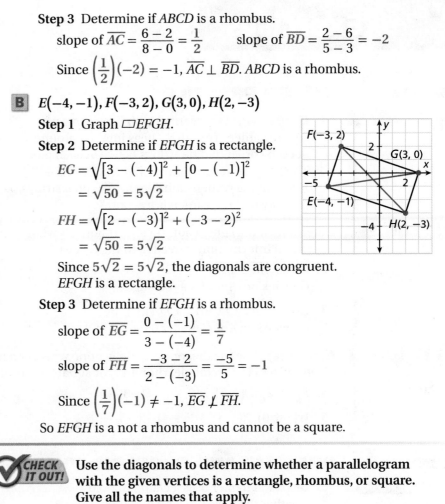

Since $5\sqrt{2} = 5\sqrt{2}$, the diagonals are congruent. *EFGH* is a rectangle.

Step 3 Determine if *EFGH* is a rhombus.

slope of $\overline{EG} = \dfrac{0-(-1)}{3-(-4)} = \dfrac{1}{7}$

slope of $\overline{FH} = \dfrac{-3-2}{2-(-3)} = \dfrac{-5}{5} = -1$

Since $\left(\dfrac{1}{7}\right)(-1) \neq -1$, $\overline{EG} \not\perp \overline{FH}$.

So *EFGH* is a not a rhombus and cannot be a square.

CHECK IT OUT! Use the diagonals to determine whether a parallelogram with the given vertices is a rectangle, rhombus, or square. Give all the names that apply.

3a. $K(-5, -1), L(-2, 4), M(3, 1), N(0, -4)$

3b. $P(-4, 6), Q(2, 5), R(3, -1), S(-3, 0)$

MCC.MP.6   MATHEMATICAL PRACTICES

THINK AND DISCUSS

1. What special parallelogram is formed when the diagonals of a parallelogram are congruent? when the diagonals are perpendicular? when the diagonals are both congruent and perpendicular?

2. Draw a figure that shows why this statement is not necessarily true: If one angle of a quadrilateral is a right angle, then the quadrilateral is a rectangle.

3. A rectangle can also be defined as a parallelogram with a right angle. Explain why this definition is accurate.

4. GET ORGANIZED Copy and complete the graphic organizer. In each box, write at least three conditions for the given parallelogram.

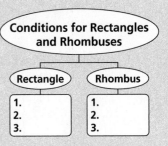

Conditions for Rectangles and Rhombuses

Rectangle
1.
2.
3.

Rhombus
1.
2.
3.

Know it! Note

GUIDED PRACTICE

SEE EXAMPLE **1**

1. **Gardening** A city garden club is planting a square garden. They drive pegs into the ground at each corner and tie strings between each pair. The pegs are spaced so that $\overline{WX} \cong \overline{XY} \cong \overline{YZ} \cong \overline{ZW}$. How can the garden club use the diagonal strings to verify that the garden is a square?

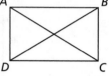

SEE EXAMPLE **2**

Determine if the conclusion is valid. If not, tell what additional information is needed to make it valid.

2. Given: $\overline{AC} \cong \overline{BD}$
   Conclusion: *ABCD* is a rectangle.

3. Given: $\overline{AB} \parallel \overline{CD}$, $\overline{AB} \cong \overline{CD}$, $\overline{AB} \perp \overline{BC}$
   Conclusion: *ABCD* is a rectangle.

SEE EXAMPLE **3**

Multi-Step Use the diagonals to determine whether a parallelogram with the given vertices is a rectangle, rhombus, or square. Give all the names that apply.

4. $P(-5, 2)$, $Q(4, 5)$, $R(6, -1)$, $S(-3, -4)$

5. $W(-6, 0)$, $X(1, 4)$, $Y(2, -4)$, $Z(-5, -8)$

PRACTICE AND PROBLEM SOLVING

my.hrw.com

Online Extra Practice

6. **Crafts** A framer uses a clamp to hold together the pieces of a picture frame. The pieces are cut so that $\overline{PQ} \cong \overline{RS}$ and $\overline{QR} \cong \overline{SP}$. The clamp is adjusted so that *PZ*, *QZ*, *RZ*, and *SZ* are all equal. Why must the frame be a rectangle?

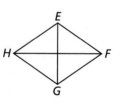

Determine if the conclusion is valid. If not, tell what additional information is needed to make it valid.

7. Given: $\overline{EG}$ and $\overline{FH}$ bisect each other. $\overline{EG} \perp \overline{FH}$
   Conclusion: *EFGH* is a rhombus.

8. Given: $\overline{FH}$ bisects $\angle EFG$ and $\angle EHG$.
   Conclusion: *EFGH* is a rhombus.

Multi-Step Use the diagonals to determine whether a parallelogram with the given vertices is a rectangle, rhombus, or square. Give all the names that apply.

9. $A(-10, 4)$, $B(-2, 10)$, $C(4, 2)$, $D(-4, -4)$

10. $J(-9, -7)$, $K(-4, -2)$, $L(3, -3)$, $M(-2, -8)$

Tell whether each quadrilateral is a parallelogram, rectangle, rhombus, or square. Give all the names that apply.

11. 12. 13.

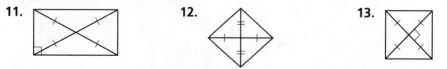

Peter Van Steen/HMH Photo

Tell whether each quadrilateral is a parallelogram, rectangle, rhombus, or square. Give all the names that apply.

14.

15.

16.

17. ///**ERROR ANALYSIS**/// In □ABCD, $\overline{AC} \cong \overline{BD}$. Which conclusion is incorrect? Explain the error.

Ⓐ ABCD is a rectangle.

Ⓑ ABCD is a square.

H.O.T. Give one characteristic of the diagonals of each figure that would make the conclusion valid.

18. Conclusion: *JKLM* is a rhombus.

19. Conclusion: *PQRS* is a square.

The coordinates of three vertices of □*ABCD* are given. Find the coordinates of *D* so that the given type of figure is formed.

20. $A(4, -2)$, $B(-5, -2)$, $C(4, 4)$; rectangle

21. $A(-5, 5)$, $B(0, 0)$, $C(7, 1)$; rhombus

22. $A(0, 2)$, $B(4, -2)$, $C(0, -6)$; square

23. $A(2, 1)$, $B(-1, 5)$, $C(-5, 2)$; square

Find the value of *x* that makes each parallelogram the given type.

24. rectangle

$(5x - 3)°$

25. rhombus

$14 - x$

$2x + 5$

26. square

$(13x + 5.5)°$

27. Critical Thinking The diagonals of a quadrilateral are perpendicular bisectors of each other. What is the best name for this quadrilateral? Explain your answer.

28. Complete the two-column proof of Theorem 7-4-2 by filling in the blanks.

Given: *EFGH* is a parallelogram.
$\overline{EG} \cong \overline{HF}$

Prove: *EFGH* is a rectangle.

Proof:

Statements	Reasons
1. *EFGH* is a parallelogram. $\overline{EG} \cong \overline{HF}$	1. Given
2. $\overline{EF} \cong \overline{HG}$	2. a. ___?___
3. b. ___?___	3. Reflex. Prop. of $\cong$
4. △*EFH* $\cong$ △*HGE*	4. c. ___?___
5. ∠*FEH* $\cong$ d. ___?___	5. e. ___?___
6. ∠*FEH* and ∠*GHE* are supplementary.	6. f. ___?___
7. g. ___?___	7. $\cong$ ⦞ supp. → rt. ⦞
8. *EFGH* is a rectangle.	8. h. ___?___

29. A state fair takes place on a plot of land given by the coordinates
$A(-2, 3)$, $B(1, 2)$, $C(2, -1)$, and $D(-1, 0)$.

  a. Show that the opposite sides of quadrilateral $ABCD$ are parallel.

  b. A straight path connects A and C, and another path connects B and D. Use slopes to prove that these two paths are perpendicular.

  c. What can you conclude about $ABCD$? Explain your answer.

30. Complete the paragraph proof of Theorem 7-4-4 by filling in the blanks.

  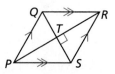

  Given: $PQRS$ is a parallelogram. $\overline{PR} \perp \overline{QS}$
  Prove: $PQRS$ is a rhombus.

  Proof:
  It is given that $PQRS$ is a parallelogram. The diagonals of a parallelogram bisect each other, so $\overline{PT} \cong$ **a.** __?__ . By the Reflexive Property of Congruence, $\overline{QT} \cong$ **b.** __?__ . It is given that $\overline{PR} \perp \overline{QS}$, so $\angle QTP$ and $\angle QTR$ are right angles by the definition of **c.** __?__ . Then $\angle QTP \cong \angle QTR$ by the **d.** __?__ . So $\triangle QTP \cong \triangle QTR$ by **e.** __?__ , and $\overline{QP} \cong$ **f.** __?__ , by CPCTC. By Theorem 7-5-3, if one pair of consecutive sides of a parallelogram are congruent, then the parallelogram is a **g.** __?__ . Therefore $PQRS$ is rhombus.

H.O.T. 31. Write a two-column proof of Theorem 7-4-1.

  Given: $ABCD$ is a parallelogram. $\angle A$ is a right angle.
  Prove: $ABCD$ is a rectangle.

  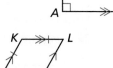

H.O.T. 32. Write a paragraph proof of Theorem 7-4-3.

  Given: $JKLM$ is a parallelogram. $\overline{JK} \cong \overline{KL}$
  Prove: $JKLM$ is a rhombus.

H.O.T. 33. **Algebra** Four lines are represented by the equations below.

  $\ell: y = -x + 1$ $m: y = -x + 7$ $n: y = 2x + 1$ $p: y = 2x + 7$

  a. Graph the four lines in the coordinate plane.

  b. Classify the quadrilateral formed by the lines.

  c. **What if...?** Suppose the slopes of lines n and p change to 1. Reclassify the quadrilateral.

H.O.T. 34. Write a two-column proof.

  Given: $FHJN$ and $GLMF$ are parallelograms. $\overline{FG} \cong \overline{FN}$
  Prove: $FGKN$ is a rhombus.

  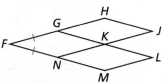

35. **Write About It** Write a biconditional statement based on the theorems about the diagonals of rectangles. Write a biconditional statement based on the theorems about the diagonals of rhombuses. Can you write a biconditional statement based on the theorems about opposite angles in parallelograms? Explain your answer.

Construction Use the diagonals to construct each figure. Then use the theorems from this lesson to explain why your method works.

36. rectangle   37. rhombus   38. square

39. In □*PQRS*, $\overline{PR}$ and $\overline{QS}$ intersect at *T*. What additional information is needed to conclude that *PQRS* is a rectangle?

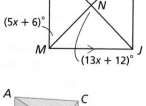

Ⓐ $\overline{PT} \cong \overline{QT}$ Ⓒ $\overline{PT} \perp \overline{QT}$

Ⓑ $\overline{PT} \cong \overline{RT}$ Ⓓ $\overline{PT}$ bisects ∠*QPS*.

40. Which of the following is the best name for figure *WXYZ* with vertices *W*(−3, 1), *X*(1, 5), *Y*(8, −2), and *Z*(4, −6)?

Ⓕ Parallelogram   Ⓖ Rectangle   Ⓗ Rhombus   Ⓙ Square

41. Extended Response

   a. Write and solve an equation to find the value of *x*.

   b. Is *JKLM* a parallelogram? Explain.

   c. Is *JKLM* a rectangle? Explain.

   d. Is *JKLM* a rhombus? Explain.

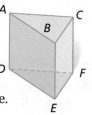

CHALLENGE AND EXTEND

42. Given: $\overline{AC} \cong \overline{DF}$, $\overline{AB} \cong \overline{DE}$, $\overline{AB} \perp \overline{BC}$, $\overline{DE} \perp \overline{EF}$,
   $\overline{BE} \perp \overline{EF}$, $\overline{BC} \parallel \overline{EF}$
   Prove: *EBCF* is a rectangle.

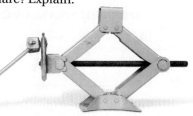

43. Critical Thinking Consider the following statement: If a quadrilateral is a rectangle and a rhombus, then it is a square.

   a. Explain why the statement is true.

   b. If a quadrilateral is a rectangle, is it necessary to show that all four sides are congruent in order to conclude that it is a square? Explain.

   c. If a quadrilateral is a rhombus, is it necessary to show that all four angles are right angles in order to conclude that it is a square? Explain.

44. Cars As you turn the crank of a car jack, the platform that supports the car rises. Use the diagonals of the parallelogram to explain whether the jack forms a rectangle, rhombus, or square.

FOCUS ON MATHEMATICAL PRACTICES

H.O.T. 45. Properties Give the most specific name for the parallelogram with the given properties.

   a. diagonals are congruent and perpendicular

   b. diagonals bisect each other and are congruent

   c. diagonals are perpendicular

H.O.T. 46. Justify Coco made a skating rink in her back yard. The rink is a quadrilateral *PQRS* where $\overline{PQ}$ is parallel to $\overline{RS}$, $\overline{PQ}$ is congruent to $\overline{RS}$, and $\overline{PR}$ is congruent to $\overline{QS}$. What type of quadrilateral is her rink? Justify your answer.

Ready to Go On?

my.hrw.com
Assessment and Intervention

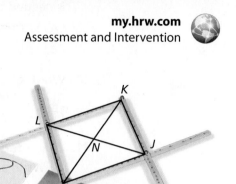

7-1 Properties of Parallelograms

A pantograph is used to copy drawings. Its legs form a parallelogram. In ▱*JKLM*, *LM* = 17 cm, *KN* = 13.5 cm, and m∠*KJM* = 102°. Find each measure.

1. *KM*　　　　2. *KJ*　　　　3. *MN*

4. m∠*JKL*　　5. m∠*JML*　　6. m∠*KLM*

7. Three vertices of ▱*ABCD* are *A*(−3, 1), *B*(5, 7), and *C*(6, 2). Find the coordinates of vertex *D*.

WXYZ is a parallelogram.
Find each measure.

8. *WX*　　　　9. *YZ*

10. m∠*X*　　11. m∠*W*

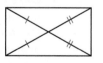

7-2 Conditions for Parallelograms

12. Show that *RSTV* is a parallelogram for *x* = 6 and *y* = 4.5.

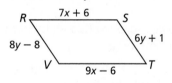

13. Show that *GHJK* is a parallelogram for *m* = 12 and *n* = 9.5.

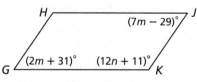

Determine if each quadrilateral must be a parallelogram. Justify your answer.

14.　　　　　　15.　　　　　　16.

17. Show that a quadrilateral with vertices *C*(−9, 4), *D*(−4, 8), *E*(2, 6), and *F*(−3, 2) is a parallelogram.

7-3 Properties of Special Parallelograms

The flag of Jamaica is a rectangle with stripes along the diagonals. In rectangle *QRST*, *QS* = 80.5, and *RS* = 36. Find each length.

18. *SP*　　19. *QT*　　20. *TR*　　21. *TP*

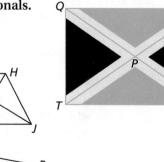

GHJK is a rhombus. Find each measure.

22. *HJ*

23. m∠*HJG* and m∠*GHJ* if m∠*JLH* = (4*b* − 6)° and m∠*JKH* = (2*b* + 11)°

24. **Given:** *QSTV* is a rhombus. $\overline{PT} \cong \overline{RT}$
    Prove: $\overline{PQ} \cong \overline{RQ}$

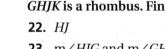

☑ 7-4 Conditions for Special Parallelograms

Determine if the conclusion is valid. If not, tell what additional information is needed to make it valid.

25. Given: $\overline{AC} \perp \overline{BD}$
Conclusion: $ABCD$ is a rhombus.

26. Given: $\overline{AB} \cong \overline{CD}$, $\overline{AC} \cong \overline{BD}$, $\overline{AB} \parallel \overline{CD}$
Conclusion: $ABCD$ is a rectangle.

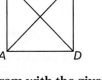

Use the diagonals to determine whether a parallelogram with the given vertices is a rectangle, rhombus, or square. Give all the names that apply.

27. $W(-2, 2)$, $X(1, 5)$, $Y(7, -1)$, $Z(4, -4)$

28. $M(-4, 5)$, $N(1, 7)$, $P(3, 2)$, $Q(-2, 0)$

29. Given: $\overline{VX}$ and $\overline{ZX}$ are midsegments of $\triangle TWY$. $\overline{TW} \cong \overline{TY}$
Prove: $TVXZ$ is a rhombus.

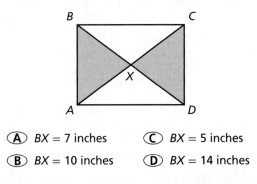

PARCC Assessment Readiness

Selected Response

1. The diagram shows the parallelogram-shaped component that attaches a car's rearview mirror to the car. In parallelogram $RSTU$, $UR = 25$, $RX = 16$, and m$\angle STU = 42.4°$. Find ST, XT, and m$\angle RST$.

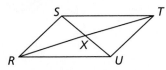

- Ⓐ $ST = 16$, $XT = 25$, m$\angle RST = 42.4°$
- Ⓑ $ST = 25$, $XT = 16$, m$\angle RST = 47.8°$
- Ⓒ $ST = 25$, $XT = 16$, m$\angle RST = 137.6°$
- Ⓓ $ST = 5$, $XT = 4$, m$\angle RST = 137.6°$

2. Use the diagonals to determine whether a parallelogram with vertices $A(-1, -2)$, $B(-2, 0)$, $C(0, 1)$, and $D(1, -1)$ is a rectangle, rhombus, or square. Give all the names that apply.

- Ⓕ rectangle, rhombus, square
- Ⓖ rectangle, rhombus
- Ⓗ rectangle
- Ⓙ square

3. An artist designs a rectangular quilt piece with different types of ribbon that go from the corner to the center of the quilt. The dimensions of the rectangle are $AB = 10$ inches and $AC = 14$ inches. Find BX.

- Ⓐ $BX = 7$ inches
- Ⓒ $BX = 5$ inches
- Ⓑ $BX = 10$ inches
- Ⓓ $BX = 14$ inches

Mini-Task

4. Two vertices of a parallelogram are $A(2, 3)$ and $B(8, 11)$, and the intersection of the diagonals is $X(7, 6)$. Find the coordinates of the other two vertices.

Similarity

COMMON CORE GPS

Contents

MATHEMATICAL PRACTICES The Common Core Georgia Performance Standards for Mathematical Practice describe varieties of expertise that all students should seek to develop. Opportunities to develop these practices are integrated throughout this program.

1 Make sense of problems and persevere in solving them.

2 Reason abstractly and quantitatively.

3 Construct viable arguments and critique the reasoning of others.

4 Model with mathematics.

5 Use appropriate tools strategically.

6 Attend to precision.

7 Look for and make use of structure.

8 Look for and express regularity in repeated reasoning.

Unpacking the Standards

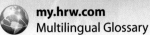

Understanding the standards and the vocabulary terms in the standards will help you know exactly what you are expected to learn in this chapter.

 MCC9-12.G.SRT.2

Given two figures, … decide if they are similar; explain using similarity transformations the meaning of similarity for triangles as the equality of all corresponding pairs of angles and the proportionality of all corresponding pairs of sides.

Key Vocabulary

similar polygons (polígonos semejantes) Two polygons whose corresponding angles are congruent and whose corresponding side lengths are proportional.

similarity transformation (transformación de semejanza) A transformation that produces similar figures.

triangle (triángulo) A three-sided polygon.

corresponding angles of polygons (ángulos correspondientes de los polígonos) Angles in the same position in two different polygons that have the same number of angles.

corresponding sides of polygons (lados correspondientes de los polígonos) Sides in the same position in two different polygons that have the same number of sides.

What It Means For You

Two figures are similar if they have the same shape but not necessarily the same size. When two figures are similar, you can dilate one of them and then slide, flip, and/or rotate it so that it coincides with the other. As a result, corresponding angles of similar figures are congruent and corresponding side lengths are proportional.

EXAMPLE   **Similar figures**

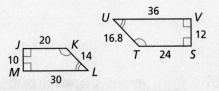

The figures are similar because you can multiply all the side lengths of the smaller figure by 1.2, rotate it 180°, and slide it so that it coincides with the larger figure.

NON-EXAMPLE   **Non-similar figures**

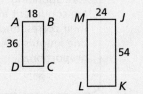

The rectangles are not similar. There is no combination of dilations, slides, flips, and/or rotations that will cause the two figures to coincide.

8-1 Ratios in Similar Polygons

? *Essential Question:* How are ratios and corresponding parts used to solve problems about similar polygons?

Objectives
Identify similar polygons.

Apply properties of similar polygons to solve problems.

Vocabulary
similar
similar polygons
similarity ratio

Why learn this?
Similar polygons are used to build models of actual objects. (See Example 3.)

Figures that are **similar** (~) have the same shape but not necessarily the same size.

△1 is similar to △2(△1 ~ △2).   △1 is not similar to △3(△1 ≁ △3).

Know it! Note

Similar Polygons

DEFINITION	DIAGRAM	STATEMENTS
Two polygons are **similar polygons** if and only if their corresponding angles are congruent and their corresponding side lengths are proportional.	*diagram of ABCD with sides 6, 5, 5.4, 4 and EFGH with sides 12, 10, 10.8, 8* ABCD ~ EFGH	$\angle A \cong \angle E$ $\angle B \cong \angle F$ $\angle C \cong \angle G$ $\angle D \cong \angle H$ $\frac{AB}{EF} = \frac{BC}{FG} = \frac{CD}{GH} = \frac{DA}{HE} = \frac{1}{2}$

COMMON CORE GPS MCC9-12.G.SRT.2

EXAMPLE 1 Describing Similar Polygons

my.hrw.com

Online Video Tutor

Identify the pairs of congruent angles and corresponding sides.

$\angle Z \cong \angle R$ and $\angle Y \cong \angle Q$. By the Third Angles Theorem, $\angle X \cong \angle S$.

$\frac{XY}{SQ} = \frac{6}{9} = \frac{2}{3}$, $\frac{YZ}{QR} = \frac{12}{18} = \frac{2}{3}$,

$\frac{XZ}{SR} = \frac{9}{13.5} = \frac{2}{3}$

CHECK IT OUT!

1. Identify the pairs of congruent angles and corresponding sides.

Jens Meyer/AP/Wide World Photos

A **similarity ratio** is the ratio of the lengths of the corresponding sides of two similar polygons. The similarity ratio of $\triangle ABC$ to $\triangle DEF$ is $\frac{3}{6}$, or $\frac{1}{2}$. The similarity ratio of $\triangle DEF$ to $\triangle ABC$ is $\frac{6}{3}$, or 2.

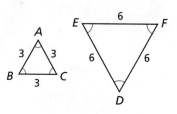

EXAMPLE 2
MCC9-12.G.SRT.2

Identifying Similar Polygons

Determine whether the polygons are similar. If so, write the similarity ratio and a similarity statement.

A rectangles *PQRS* and *TUVW*

Step 1 Identify pairs of congruent angles.
$\angle P \cong \angle T$, $\angle Q \cong \angle U$, $\angle R \cong \angle V$, and $\angle S \cong \angle W$ *All ∠ of a rect. are rt. ∠ and are ≅.*

Step 2 Compare corresponding sides.
$$\frac{PQ}{TU} = \frac{12}{16} = \frac{3}{4}, \quad \frac{PS}{TW} = \frac{4}{6} = \frac{2}{3}$$

Since corresponding sides are not proportional, the rectangles are not similar.

B $\triangle ABC$ and $\triangle DEF$

Step 1 Identify pairs of congruent angles.
$\angle A \cong \angle D$, $\angle B \cong \angle E$ *Given*
$\angle C \cong \angle F$ *Third ∠ Thm.*

Step 2 Compare corresponding sides.
$$\frac{AB}{DE} = \frac{20}{15} = \frac{4}{3}, \quad \frac{BC}{EF} = \frac{24}{18} = \frac{4}{3}, \quad \frac{AC}{DF} = \frac{16}{12} = \frac{4}{3}$$

Thus the similarity ratio is $\frac{4}{3}$, and $\triangle ABC \sim \triangle DEF$.

Writing Math

Writing a similarity statement is like writing a congruence statement—be sure to list corresponding vertices in the same order.

CHECK IT OUT!

2. Determine if $\triangle JLM \sim \triangle NPS$. If so, write the similarity ratio and a similarity statement.

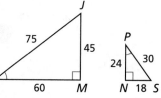

Student to Student   *Proportions with Similar Figures*

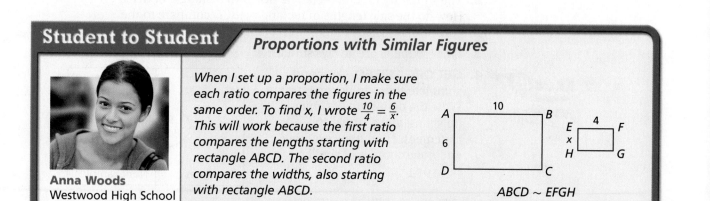

When I set up a proportion, I make sure each ratio compares the figures in the same order. To find x, I wrote $\frac{10}{4} = \frac{6}{x}$. This will work because the first ratio compares the lengths starting with rectangle ABCD. The second ratio compares the widths, also starting with rectangle ABCD.

Anna Woods
Westwood High School

ABCD ~ EFGH

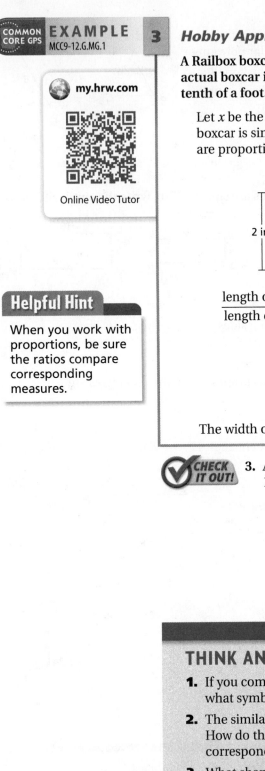

COMMON CORE GPS **EXAMPLE** **3**
MCC9-12.G.MG.1

my.hrw.com

Online Video Tutor

Hobby Application

A Railbox boxcar can be used to transport auto parts. If the length of the actual boxcar is 50 ft, find the width of the actual boxcar to the nearest tenth of a foot.

Let x be the width of the actual boxcar in feet. The rectangular model of a boxcar is similar to the rectangular boxcar, so the corresponding lengths are proportional.

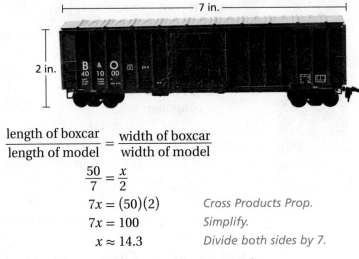

$$\frac{\text{length of boxcar}}{\text{length of model}} = \frac{\text{width of boxcar}}{\text{width of model}}$$

$$\frac{50}{7} = \frac{x}{2}$$

$7x = (50)(2)$	*Cross Products Prop.*
$7x = 100$	*Simplify.*
$x \approx 14.3$	*Divide both sides by 7.*

The width of the model is approximately 14.3 ft.

Helpful Hint

When you work with proportions, be sure the ratios compare corresponding measures.

CHECK IT OUT!

3. A boxcar has the dimensions shown. A model of the boxcar is 1.25 in. wide. Find the length of the model to the nearest inch.

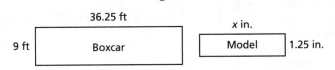

MCC.MP.2   **MATHEMATICAL PRACTICES**

THINK AND DISCUSS

1. If you combine the symbol for similarity with the equal sign, what symbol is formed?

2. The similarity ratio of rectangle *ABCD* to rectangle *EFGH* is $\frac{1}{9}$. How do the side lengths of rectangle *ABCD* compare to the corresponding side lengths of rectangle *EFGH*?

3. What shape(s) are always similar?

4. GET ORGANIZED Copy and complete the graphic organizer. Write the definition of similar polygons, and a similarity statement. Then draw examples and nonexamples of similar polygons.

Definition	Similarity statement
	Similar Polygons
Examples	Nonexamples

©Nathan Keay/HMH

my.hrw.com
Homework Help

GUIDED PRACTICE

1. **Vocabulary** Give an example of similar figures in your classroom.

SEE EXAMPLE **1** Identify the pairs of congruent angles and corresponding sides.

2.

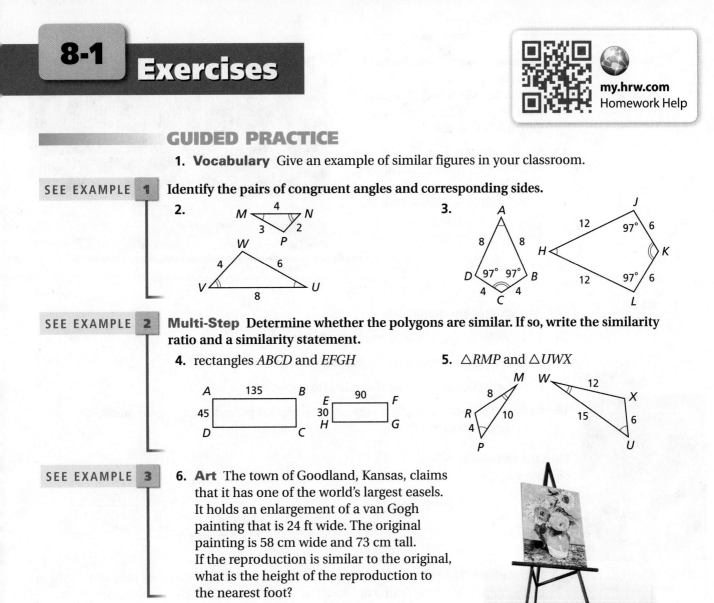

3.

SEE EXAMPLE **2** **Multi-Step** Determine whether the polygons are similar. If so, write the similarity ratio and a similarity statement.

4. rectangles *ABCD* and *EFGH*

5. △*RMP* and △*UWX*

SEE EXAMPLE **3** 6. **Art** The town of Goodland, Kansas, claims that it has one of the world's largest easels. It holds an enlargement of a van Gogh painting that is 24 ft wide. The original painting is 58 cm wide and 73 cm tall. If the reproduction is similar to the original, what is the height of the reproduction to the nearest foot?

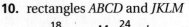
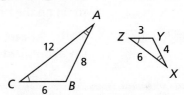

PRACTICE AND PROBLEM SOLVING

Independent Practice	
For Exercises	See Example
7–8	1
9–10	2
11	3

my.hrw.com

Online Extra Practice

Identify the pairs of congruent angles and corresponding sides.

7.

8.

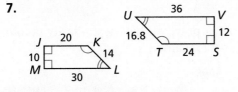

Multi-Step Determine whether the polygons are similar. If so, write the similarity ratio and a similarity statement.

9. △*RSQ* and △*UXZ*

10. rectangles *ABCD* and *JKLM*

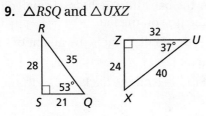
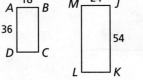

H.O.T. 11. Hobbies The ratio of the model car's dimensions to the actual car's dimensions is $\frac{1}{56}$. The model has a length of 3 in. What is the length of the actual car?

12. Square *ABCD* has an area of 4 m². Square *PQRS* has an area of 36 m². What is the similarity ratio of square *ABCD* to square *PQRS*? What is the similarity ratio of square *PQRS* to square *ABCD*?

Tell whether each statement is sometimes, always, or never true.

13. Two right triangles are similar.

14. Two squares are similar.

15. A parallelogram and a trapezoid are similar.

16. If two polygons are congruent, they are also similar.

17. If two polygons are similar, they are also congruent.

18. Critical Thinking Explain why any two regular polygons having the same number of sides are similar.

Find the value of x.

19. *ABCD* ~ *EFGH*

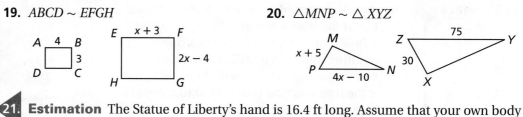

20. $\triangle MNP \sim \triangle XYZ$

Monument

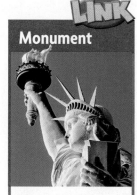

The height of the Statue of Liberty from the foundation of the pedestal to the torch is 305 ft. Her index finger measures 8 ft, and the fingernail is 13 in. by 10 in.

Source: libertystatepark.org

21. Estimation The Statue of Liberty's hand is 16.4 ft long. Assume that your own body is similar to that of the Statue of Liberty and estimate the length of the Statue of Liberty's nose. (*Hint:* Use a ruler to measure your own hand and nose. Then set up a proportion.)

22. Write the definition of similar polygons as two conditional statements.

23. □*JKLM* ~ □*NOPQ*. If m∠*K* = 75°, name two 75° angles in □*NOPQ*.

24. A dining room is 18 ft long and 14 ft wide. On a blueprint for the house, the dining room is 3.5 in. long. To the nearest tenth of an inch, what is the width of the dining room on the blueprint?

H.O.T. 25. Write About It Two similar polygons have a similarity ratio of 1 : 1. What can you say about the two polygons? Explain.

Real-World Connections

26. A stage set consists of a painted backdrop with some wooden flats in front of it. One of the flats shows a tree that has a similarity ratio of $\frac{1}{2}$ to an actual tree. To give an illusion of distance, the backdrop includes a small painted tree that has a similarity ratio of $\frac{1}{10}$ to the tree on the flat.

a. The tree on the backdrop is 0.9 ft tall. What is the height of the tree on the flat?

b. What is the height of the actual tree?

c. Find the similarity ratio of the tree on the backdrop to the actual tree.

TEST PREP

27. Which value of y makes the two rectangles similar?

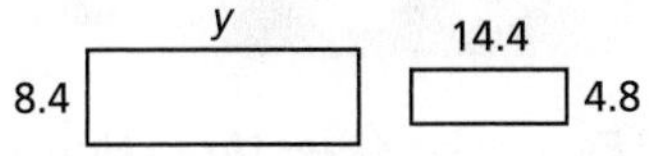

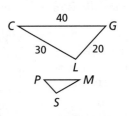

Ⓐ 3   Ⓒ 25.2

Ⓑ 8.2   Ⓓ 28.8

28. △CGL ~ △MPS. The similarity ratio of △CGL to △MPS is $\frac{5}{2}$. What is the length of $\overline{PS}$?

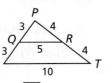

Ⓕ 8   Ⓗ 50

Ⓖ 12   Ⓙ 75

29. **Short Response** Explain why 1.5, 2.5, 3.5 and 6, 10, 12 cannot be corresponding sides of similar triangles.

CHALLENGE AND EXTEND

30. **Architecture** An architect is designing a building that is 200 ft long and 140 ft wide. She builds a model so that the similarity ratio of the model to the building is $\frac{1}{500}$. What is the length and width of the model in inches?

H.O.T. 31. Write a paragraph proof.

Given: $\overline{QR} \parallel \overline{ST}$

Prove: △PQR ~ △PST

H.O.T. 32. In the figure, D is the midpoint of $\overline{AC}$.

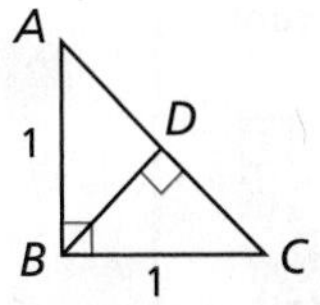

a. Find AC, DC, and DB.

b. Use your results from part **a** to help you explain why △ABC ~ △CDB.

H.O.T. 33. A golden rectangle has the following property: If a square is cut from one end of the rectangle, the rectangle that remains is similar to the original rectangle.

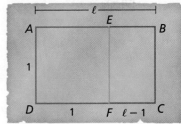

a. Rectangle ABCD is a golden rectangle. Write a similarity statement for rectangle ABCD and rectangle BCFE.

b. Write a proportion using the corresponding sides of these rectangles.

c. Solve the proportion for ℓ. (*Hint:* Use the Quadratic Formula.)

d. The value of ℓ is known as the golden ratio. Use a calculator to find ℓ to the nearest tenth.

FOCUS ON MATHEMATICAL PRACTICES

H.O.T. 34. **Precision** △MNO ~ △XYZ, and $\overline{XY}$ is the hypotenuse of a right triangle. Name two acute angles in △MNO.

H.O.T. 35. **Reasoning** △FGH ~ △RST. The similarity ratio of △FGH to △RST is $\frac{2}{5}$. The area of △RST is 275 square units. Find the area of △FGH and explain your work.

H.O.T. 36. **Problem Solving** Rectangle EFGH has side lengths of 2 and 7. The longer side of rectangle QRST has a length of 3y − 22 and the shorter side has a length of 2x + 4. Describe the relation of y in terms of x that will make the two rectangles similar. If the rectangles are similar and x = 6, what are the two side lengths of rectangle QRST?

8-2 Similarity and Transformations

Essential Question: How can you use properties of transformations to determine whether figures are similar?

Objectives
Draw and describe similarity transformations in the coordinate plane.

Use properties of similarity transformations to determine whether polygons are similar and to prove circles are similar.

Vocabulary
dilation
scale factor
similarity transformation

Who uses this?

A sign maker can use a similarity transformation to create a banner showing state flags. (See Example 4.)

A transformation that maps (x, y) to (kx, ky), where $k > 0$, is a **dilation** with center $(0, 0)$ and **scale factor** k. If $0 < k < 1$, the dilation is a *reduction*. If $k > 1$, the dilation is an *enlargement*.

COMMON CORE GPS
MCC9-12.G.SRT.1

EXAMPLE 1

my.hrw.com

Online Video Tutor

Drawing and Describing Dilations

Apply the dilation D to the polygon with the given vertices. Describe the dilation.

A $D : (x, y) \rightarrow (2x, 2y)$

$A(2, 1)$, $B(2, 3)$, $C(5, 1)$

B $D : (x, y) \rightarrow \left(\dfrac{2}{3}x, \dfrac{2}{3}y\right)$

$P(-6, 3)$, $Q(-3, 9)$, $R(3, 6)$

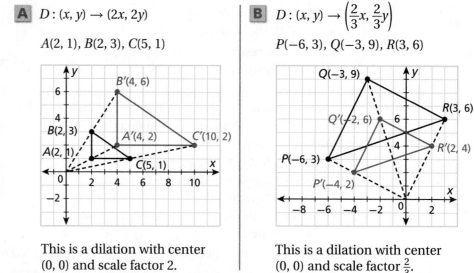

This is a dilation with center $(0, 0)$ and scale factor 2.

This is a dilation with center $(0, 0)$ and scale factor $\dfrac{2}{3}$.

CHECK IT OUT!

1. Apply the dilation $D : (x, y) \rightarrow \left(\dfrac{1}{4}x, \dfrac{1}{4}y\right)$ to the polygon with vertices $D(-8, 0)$, $E(-8, -4)$, and $F(-4, -8)$. Name the coordinates of the image points. Describe the dilation.

Remember!

Translations, reflections, and rotations are congruence transformations.

In a dilation, the image and the preimage are similar because they have the same shape. When the figures in a dilation are polygons, the image and preimage are similar polygons, so corresponding side lengths are proportional and corresponding angles are congruent. That is, dilations preserve angle measure.

A transformation that produces similar figures is a *similarity transformation*. A **similarity transformation** is a dilation or a composite of one or more dilations and one or more congruence transformations. Two figures are similar if and only if there is a similarity transformation that maps one figure to the other figure.

Jürgen Priewe/Alamy

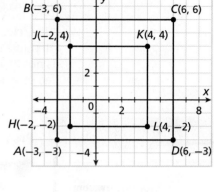
Determining Whether Polygons are Similar

Determine whether the polygons with the given vertices are similar.

A $A(-3, -3)$, $B(-3, 6)$, $C(6, 6)$, $D(6, -3)$
$H(-2, -2)$, $J(-2, 4)$, $K(4, 4)$, $L(4, -2)$

Yes; $ABCD$ can be mapped to $HJKL$ by a dilation: $(x, y) \rightarrow \left(\frac{2}{3}x, \frac{2}{3}y\right)$.

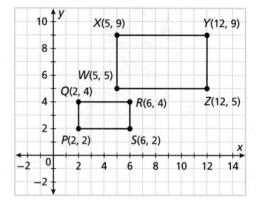

Helpful Hint

Every dilation has an inverse, and the scale factors are reciprocals. In Example 2A, you can say $HJKL$ is mapped to $ABCD$ using the scale factor $\frac{3}{2}$.

B $P(2, 2)$, $Q(2, 4)$, $R(6, 4)$, $S(6, 2)$
$W(5, 5)$, $X(5, 9)$, $Y(12, 9)$, $Z(12, 5)$

No;

The rule $(x, y) \rightarrow (2.5x, 2.5y)$ maps P to W, but not Q to X. No similarity transformation maps $PQRS$ to $WXYZ$.

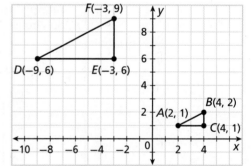

C $A(2, 1)$, $B(4, 2)$, $C(4, 1)$
$D(-9, 6)$, $E(-3, 6)$, $F(-3, 9)$

Yes; Translate $\triangle ABC$ to the left and up. Then enlarge the image to obtain $\triangle DFE$.

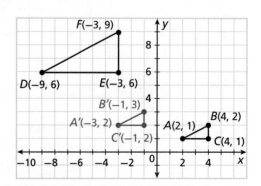

Yes; $\triangle ABC$ can be mapped to $\triangle A'B'C'$ by a translation: $(x, y) \rightarrow (x - 5, y + 1)$. Then $\triangle A'B'C'$ can be mapped to $\triangle DFE$ by a dilation: $(x, y) \rightarrow (3x, 3y)$.

2. Determine whether the polygons with the given vertices are similar: $A(2, -1)$, $B(3, -1)$, $C(3, -4)$ and $P(3, 6)$, $Q(3, 9)$, $R(12, 9)$.

All circles are similar because they all have the same shape. To prove this, it is helpful to use a dilation whose center is not (0, 0). In general, a dilation with center C and scale factor k maps P to P' so that P' is on $\overline{CP}$ and $CP' = k \cdot CP$.

COMMON CORE GPS

EXAMPLE 3
MCC9-12.G.C.1

my.hrw.com

Online Video Tutor

Proving Circles Similar

A Prove that circle A with center (0, 0) and radius 1 is similar to circle B with center (5, 0) and radius 2.

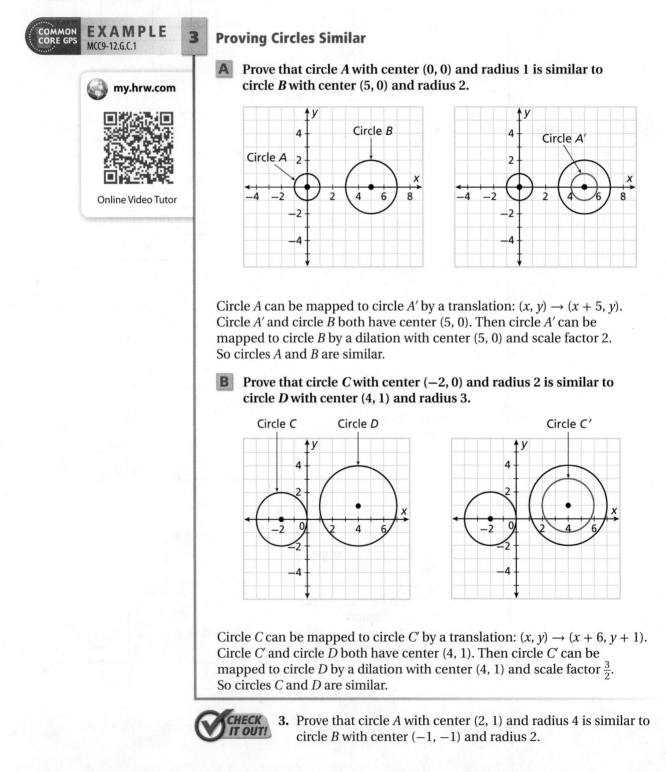

Circle A can be mapped to circle A' by a translation: $(x, y) \rightarrow (x + 5, y)$. Circle A' and circle B both have center (5, 0). Then circle A' can be mapped to circle B by a dilation with center (5, 0) and scale factor 2. So circles A and B are similar.

B Prove that circle C with center (−2, 0) and radius 2 is similar to circle D with center (4, 1) and radius 3.

Circle C can be mapped to circle C' by a translation: $(x, y) \rightarrow (x + 6, y + 1)$. Circle C' and circle D both have center (4, 1). Then circle C' can be mapped to circle D by a dilation with center (4, 1) and scale factor $\frac{3}{2}$. So circles C and D are similar.

3. Prove that circle A with center (2, 1) and radius 4 is similar to circle B with center (−1, −1) and radius 2.

EXAMPLE MCC9-12.G.CO.2 **4**

Business Application

Tia makes signs and banners. She is making a banner that shows five Texas flags. The middle flag is 3 times the size of each of the other flags. Tia will first draw the lower left flag and then the middle flag. How can she draw those flags?

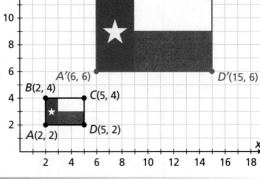

Place the lower left flag on a coordinate plane in a convenient position, such as that shown by rectangle *ABCD*.

Apply the dilation with center (0, 0) and scale factor 3: $(x, y) \rightarrow (3x, 3y)$.

The image, $A'B'C'D'$, represents the middle flag.

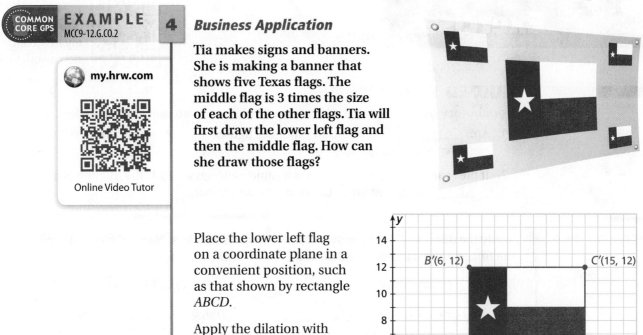

CHECK IT OUT!

4. What if...? How could Tia draw the middle flag to make it 4 times the size of each of the other flags?

MCC.MP.1   MATHEMATICAL PRACTICES

THINK AND DISCUSS

1. Consider this dilation applied to a polygon: $(x, y) \rightarrow (1.5x, 1.5y)$. Describe the corresponding side lengths, corresponding angle measures, and position of the image compared to the preimage.

2. Explain why the rules $(x, y) \rightarrow (y, -x)$ and then $(x, y) \rightarrow (2x, 2y)$ form a similarity transformation.

3. GET ORGANIZED Copy and complete the graphic organizer.

Determining if polygons are similar	
Proving circles are similar	

my.hrw.com
Homework Help

GUIDED PRACTICE

Vocabulary Apply the vocabulary from this lesson to answer each question.

1. A(n) ____?____ transformation produces figures that are similar. (*similarity*, *congruence*, or *scale factor*)

2. If the scale factor *k* in a dilation is a value between 0 and 1, the dilation is a(n) ____?____ . (*enlargement*, *reduction*, or *translation*)

SEE EXAMPLE 1

Apply the dilation *D* to the polygon with the given vertices. Name the coordinates of the image points. Identify and describe the transformation.

3. $D: (x, y) \rightarrow (4x, 4y)$

$A(-1, -1), B(2, 1), C(-2, 1)$

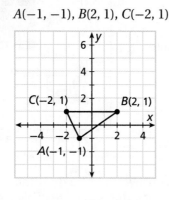

4. $D: (x, y) \rightarrow \left(\dfrac{1}{3}x, \dfrac{1}{3}y\right)$

$A(3, 9), B(-6, 3), C(3, -3)$

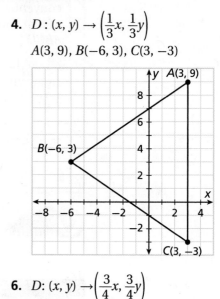

5. $D: (x, y) \rightarrow (2.5x, 2.5y)$

$A(2, 3), B(5, -2), C(-4, -2)$

6. $D: (x, y) \rightarrow \left(\dfrac{3}{4}x, \dfrac{3}{4}y\right)$

$A(4, 8), B(-8, 4), C(8, -4)$

SEE EXAMPLE 2

Determine whether the polygons with the given vertices are similar. Support your answer by describing a transformation.

7. $L(1, -4), M(1, -9), N(5, -2), O(9, -5)$
$P(2, 5), Q(2, -5), R(10, 9), S(18, 3)$

8. $W(-4, 2), X(-4, 6), Y(6, 2), Z(6, 6)$
$D(-2, 1), E(-8, 12), F(3, 10), G(3, 3)$

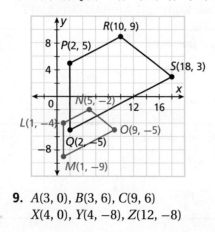

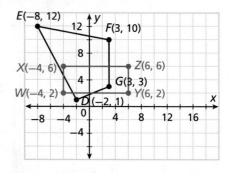

9. $A(3, 0), B(3, 6), C(9, 6)$
$X(4, 0), Y(4, -8), Z(12, -8)$

10. $L(-10, 5), M(-5, 0), N(0, 0), O(5, 5)$
$D(4, 2), E(2, 0), F(0, 0), G(-2, 2)$

SEE EXAMPLE 3

11. Prove that circle A with center $(4, 0)$ and radius 5 is similar to circle B with center $(-6, -3)$ and radius 3.

12. Prove that circle A with center $(6, -9)$ and radius 4 is similar to circle B with center $(3, -8)$ and radius 5.

SEE EXAMPLE 4

13. Hector is making an art project by cutting and gluing shapes to a wooden board. His design includes two similar triangles, with one 4 times the size of the other. He cuts and traces the small triangle first onto grid paper. Describe how he can use the tracing to make a pattern for the large fabric triangle.

PRACTICE AND PROBLEM SOLVING

For Exercises	See Example
14–15	1
16–17	2
22	3
23	4

Independent Practice

my.hrw.com

Online Extra Practice

Apply the dilation D to the polygon with the given vertices. Name the coordinates of the image points. Identify and describe the transformation.

14. $D : (x, y) \rightarrow (0.5x, 0.5y)$

$A(1, -2)$, $B(1, -4)$, $C(5, -2)$ $D(5, -4)$

15. $D : (x, y) \rightarrow \left(\dfrac{3}{10}x, \dfrac{3}{10}y\right)$

$A(20, 10)$, $B(0, -20)$, $C(10, 30)$

H.O.T. **Determine whether the polygons with the given vertices are similar. Support your answer by describing a transformation.**

16. $V(3, 2)$, $W(8, 2)$, $X(1, 5)$

$R(6, 4)$, $S(16, 4)$, $T(3, 15)$

17. $A(-2, -3)$, $B(-2, 0)$, $C(10, -3)$

$P(-4, 2)$, $Q(-4, 4)$, $R(4, 2)$

18. **Write About It** Triangle ABC is dilated by a scale factor of 5. The image is $A'B'C'$. Compare the angle measures and side lengths of the original triangle and its image after dilation.

Determine whether the polygons shown are similar. If they are similar, describe the transformation in two different ways, from the larger to the smaller figure, and from the smaller to the larger figure.

19.
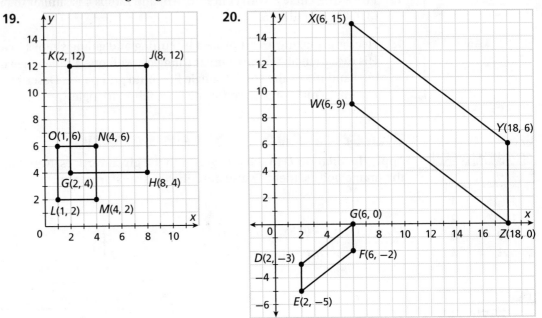

20.

21. **//ERROR ANALYSIS///** Triangle ABC has vertices at $A(-12, -6)$, $B(-6, 12)$, and $C(6, 12)$. The images of A and B after the similarity transformation D are $A'(-8, -4)$ and $B'(-4, 8)$. Reggie and Hillary find different coordinates for C', the image of C. Their work is shown below. Who made an error? Describe the error.

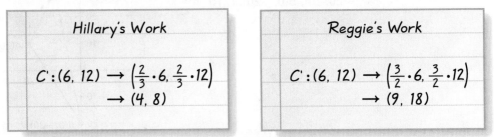

Hillary's Work	Reggie's Work
$C': (6, 12) \rightarrow \left(\frac{2}{3} \cdot 6, \frac{2}{3} \cdot 12\right)$ $\rightarrow (4, 8)$	$C': (6, 12) \rightarrow \left(\frac{3}{2} \cdot 6, \frac{3}{2} \cdot 12\right)$ $\rightarrow (9, 18)$

H.O.T. 22. A baby pool with radius 2 meters is being built near a larger pool with radius 4 meters at a recreation center. The plans for the construction are laid out on the coordinate system shown. Prove that the baby pool is similar to the larger pool.

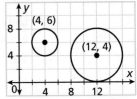

23. **Architecture** An architect is making a scale drawing of two buildings whose floor plans are to be similar rectangles. He has already drawn the smaller building. The larger building will be located to the upper right and will have dimensions 5 times those of the smaller building. How can he draw the larger building?

H.O.T. 24. **Critical Thinking** To map a figure A to a similar figure B, first A is mapped to A' by a dilation: $(x, y) \rightarrow \left(\frac{5}{3}x, \frac{5}{3}y\right)$. Then A' is mapped to B by a translation $(x, y) \rightarrow (x - 2, y + 1)$. The vertices of A' are $W(-10, 0)$, $X(-5, 10)$, $Y(5, 10)$, and $Z(-5, 0)$. Find the vertices of A and B.

25. Triangle *ABC* undergoes a transformation *T* to produce the image *EFG*. Given the vertices of the triangles below, which is a true statement about *T*?

$$A(4, 8), B(0, 4), C(4, 0)$$
$$E(3, 6), F(0, 3), G(3, 0)$$

(A) *T* is a similarity transformation in which *ABC* is dilated by a scale factor of $\frac{3}{4}$.

(B) *T* is a congruence transformation in which *ABC* is dilated by a scale factor of $\frac{3}{4}$.

(C) *T* is a similarity transformation in which *ABC* is dilated by a scale factor of of $\frac{4}{3}$.

(D) *T* is a congruence transformation in which *ABC* is dilated by a scale factor of $\frac{4}{3}$.

26. Figure *ABCD* with the vertices given below is translated 6 units left and 7 units down. It is then dilated to produce the similar figure *EFGH* with the vertices given below. By what scale is the figure dilated?

$$A(10, 15), B(14, 7), C(6, 7), D(6, 11)$$
$$E(5, 10), F(10, 0), G(0, 0), H(0, 5)$$

(A) 0.5

(B) 0.8

(C) 1.25

(D) 1.5

27. The area of a square is 16 square units. Its sides are horizontal and vertical, and its lower left vertex is (2, 0). After a similarity transformation, the image of the lower left vertex is (−8, 0). Name the other three vertices of the image and find its area.

H.O.T. **28.** The hypotenuse of a right triangle *ABC* in a coordinate plane is $\overline{AB}$, with *A* at (1, 2) and *B* at (3, 6). The image of the hypotenuse after a rotation of 180° and a dilation is $\overline{A'B'}$, with *A′* at (−3.5, −7) and *B′* at (−10.5, −21). Give two possible locations of *C′*, the image of *C*.

MATHEMATICAL
PRACTICES

FOCUS ON MATHEMATICAL PRACTICES

H.O.T. **29. Reasoning** A circle has center (3, −4) and radius 2. The circle undergoes a dilation with center (3, −4) so that the image passes through the origin.

a. Is the dilation an enlargement or a reduction? Explain your answer.

b. What is the scale factor of the dilation?

H.O.T. **30. Justify** A triangle undergoes a 180° rotation about the origin. It is then translated 4 units to the left and 6 units upward. Finally the triangle is dilated with center (0, 0) and scale factor 2.5. Is the net result a similarity transformation? Describe how the transformations change the triangle's appearance.

H.O.T. **31. Analysis** A square with vertices *A*(1, 1), *B*(1, 3), *C*(3, 3), and *D*(3, 1) undergoes a congruence transformation followed by a dilation with center (0, 0) and scale factor 3. The resulting square has vertices *A′*(−3, 3), *B′*(−9, 3), *C′*(−9, 9), and *D′*(−3, 9). What is the congruence transformation?

8-3
Technology
TASK

Predict Triangle Similarity Relationships

You have found shortcuts for determining that two triangles are congruent. Now you will use geometry software to find ways to determine that triangles are similar.

Use with Triangle Similarity: AA, SSS, and SAS

Use appropriate tools strategically.

MCC9-12.G.SRT.3 Use the properties of similarity transformations to establish the AA criterion for two triangles to be similar.

Activity 1

1 Construct △ABC. Construct $\overline{DE}$ longer than any of the sides of △ABC. Rotate $\overline{DE}$ around D by rotation ∠BAC. Rotate $\overline{DE}$ around E by rotation ∠ABC. Label the intersection point of the two rotated segments as F.

2 Measure angles to confirm that ∠BAC ≅ ∠EDF and ∠ABC ≅ ∠DEF. Drag a vertex of △ABC or an endpoint of $\overline{DE}$ to show that the two triangles have two pairs of congruent angles.

3 Measure the side lengths of both triangles. Divide each side length of △ABC by the corresponding side length of △DEF. Compare the resulting ratios. What do you notice?

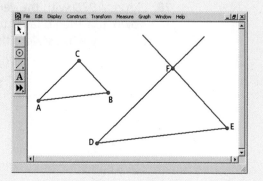

Try This

1. What theorem guarantees that the third pair of angles in the triangles are also congruent?

2. Will the ratios of corresponding sides found in Step 3 always be equal? Drag a vertex of △ABC or an endpoint of $\overline{DE}$ to investigate this question. State a conjecture based on your results.

Activity 2

1 Construct a new △ABC. Create P in the interior of the triangle. Create △DEF by enlarging △ABC around P by a multiple of 2 using the Dilation command. Drag P outside of △ABC to separate the triangles.

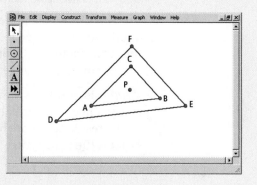

Know it! Note

Theorem 8-3-3 — Side-Angle-Side (SAS) Similarity

THEOREM	HYPOTHESIS	CONCLUSION
If two sides of one triangle are proportional to two sides of another triangle and their included angles are congruent, then the triangles are similar.	$\angle B \cong \angle E$	$\triangle ABC \sim \triangle DEF$

You will prove Theorem 8-3-3 in Exercise 39.

COMMON CORE GPS MCC9-12.G.SRT.5

EXAMPLE 2 Verifying Triangle Similarity

my.hrw.com

Online Video Tutor

Verify that the triangles are similar.

A $\triangle PQR$ and $\triangle PRS$

$\dfrac{PQ}{PR} = \dfrac{4}{6} = \dfrac{2}{3}, \dfrac{QR}{RS} = \dfrac{4}{6} = \dfrac{2}{3}, \dfrac{PR}{PS} = \dfrac{6}{9} = \dfrac{2}{3}$

Therefore $\triangle PQR \sim \triangle PRS$ by SSS ~.

B $\triangle JKL$ and $\triangle JMN$

$\angle J \cong \angle J$ by the Reflexive Property of $\cong$.

$\dfrac{JK}{JM} = \dfrac{2}{6} = \dfrac{1}{3}, \dfrac{JL}{JN} = \dfrac{3}{9} = \dfrac{1}{3}$

Therefore $\triangle JKL \sim \triangle JMN$ by SAS ~.

CHECK IT OUT! **2.** Verify that $\triangle TXU \sim \triangle VXW$.

COMMON CORE GPS MCC9-12.G.SRT.5

EXAMPLE 3 Finding Lengths in Similar Triangles

my.hrw.com

Online Video Tutor

Explain why $\triangle ABC \sim \triangle DBE$ and then find BE.

Step 1 Prove triangles are similar.

As shown $\overline{AC} \parallel \overline{ED}$, $\angle A \cong \angle D$, and $\angle C \cong \angle E$ by the Alternate Interior Angles Theorem. Therefore $\triangle ABC \sim \triangle DBE$ by AA ~.

Step 2 Find BE.

$\dfrac{AB}{DB} = \dfrac{BC}{BE}$ *Corr. sides are proportional.*

$\dfrac{36}{54} = \dfrac{54}{BE}$ *Substitute 36 for AB, 54 for DB, and 54 for BC.*

$36(BE) = 54^2$ *Cross Products Prop.*

$36(BE) = 2916$ *Simplify.*

$BE = 81$ *Divide both sides by 36.*

CHECK IT OUT! **3.** Explain why $\triangle RSV \sim \triangle RTU$ and then find RT.

EXAMPLE **4**

Writing Proofs with Similar Triangles

Given: *A* is the midpoint of $\overline{BC}$.
D is the midpoint of $\overline{BE}$.

Prove: $\triangle BDA \sim \triangle BEC$

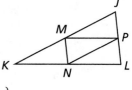

Proof:

Statements	Reasons
1. *A* is the mdpt. of $\overline{BC}$. *D* is the mdpt. of $\overline{BE}$.	1. Given
2. $\overline{BA} \cong \overline{AC}$, $\overline{BD} \cong \overline{DE}$	2. Def. of mdpt.
3. $BA = AC$, $BD = DE$	3. Def. of $\cong$ seg.
4. $BC = BA + AC$, $BE = BD + DE$	4. Seg. Add. Post.
5. $BC = BA + BA$, $BE = BD + BD$	5. Subst. Prop.
6. $BC = 2BA$, $BE = 2BD$	6. Simplify.
7. $\frac{BC}{BA} = 2$, $\frac{BE}{BD} = 2$	7. Div. Prop. of $=$
8. $\frac{BC}{BA} = \frac{BE}{BD}$	8. Trans. Prop. of $=$
9. $\angle B \cong \angle B$	9. Reflex. Prop. of $\cong$
10. $\triangle BDA \sim \triangle BEC$	10. SAS ~ *Steps 8, 9*

4. **Given:** *M* is the midpoint of $\overline{JK}$.
N is the midpoint of $\overline{KL}$,
and *P* is the midpoint of $\overline{JL}$.

Prove: $\triangle JKL \sim \triangle NPM$
(*Hint:* Use the Triangle
Midsegment Theorem and SSS ~.)

EXAMPLE **5**

Engineering Application

The photo shows a gable roof. $\overline{AC} \parallel \overline{FG}$. Use similar triangles to prove
$\triangle ABC \sim \triangle FBG$ and then find *BF* to the nearest tenth of a foot.

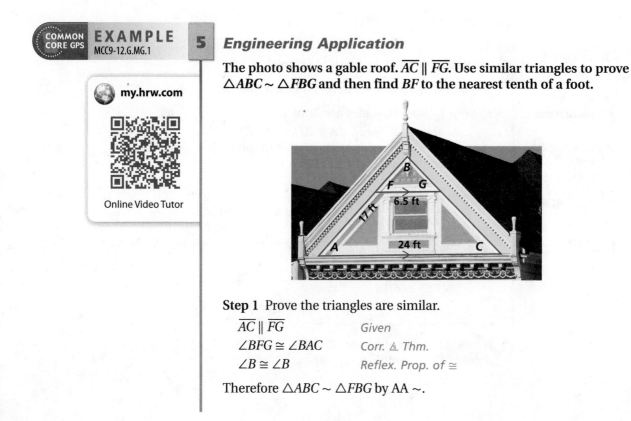

Step 1 Prove the triangles are similar.

$\overline{AC} \parallel \overline{FG}$ *Given*

$\angle BFG \cong \angle BAC$ *Corr. $\angle$ Thm.*

$\angle B \cong \angle B$ *Reflex. Prop. of $\cong$*

Therefore $\triangle ABC \sim \triangle FBG$ by AA ~.

PhotoDisc/gettyimages

Step 2 Find BF.

$$\frac{BA}{AC} = \frac{BF}{FG}$$ *Corr. sides are proportional.*

$$\frac{x + 17}{24} = \frac{x}{6.5}$$ *Substitute the given values.*

$$6.5(x + 17) = 24x$$ *Cross Products Prop.*

$$6.5x + 110.5 = 24x$$ *Distrib. Prop.*

$$110.5 = 17.5x$$ *Subtract 6.5x from both sides.*

$$6.3 \approx x \text{ or } BF$$ *Divide both sides by 17.5.*

CHECK IT OUT! **5. What if...?** If $AB = 4x$, $AC = 5x$, and $BF = 4$, find FG.

The Reflexive, Symmetric, and Transitive Properties of Equality have corresponding properties of congruence. These properties also hold true for similarity of triangles.

Properties of Similarity

Reflexive Property of Similarity

$\triangle ABC \sim \triangle ABC$ (Reflex. Prop. of $\sim$)

Symmetric Property of Similarity

If $\triangle ABC \sim \triangle DEF$, then $\triangle DEF \sim \triangle ABC$. (Sym. Prop. of $\sim$)

Transitive Property of Similarity

If $\triangle ABC \sim \triangle DEF$ and $\triangle DEF \sim \triangle XYZ$, then $\triangle ABC \sim \triangle XYZ$.
(Trans. Prop. of $\sim$)

MCC.MP.3 | **MATHEMATICAL PRACTICES**

THINK AND DISCUSS

1. What additional information, if any, would you you need in order to show that $\triangle ABC \sim \triangle DEF$ by the AA Similarity Postulate?

2. What additional information, if any, would you need in order to show that $\triangle ABC \sim \triangle DEF$ by the SAS Similarity Theorem?

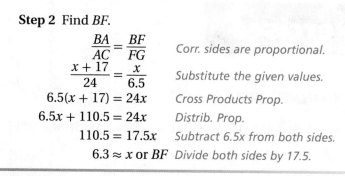

3. Do corresponding sides of similar triangles need to be proportional and congruent? Explain.

4. GET ORGANIZED Copy and complete the graphic organizer. If possible, write a congruence or similarity theorem or postulate in each section of the table. Include a marked diagram for each.

	Congruence	Similarity
SSS		
SAS		
AA		

my.hrw.com
Homework Help

GUIDED PRACTICE

SEE EXAMPLE 1 Explain why the triangles are similar and write a similarity statement.

1.

2.

SEE EXAMPLE 2 Verify that the triangles are similar.

3. △DEF and △JKL

4. △MNP and △MRQ

SEE EXAMPLE 3 **Multi-Step** Explain why the triangles are similar and then find each length.

5. AB

6. WY

SEE EXAMPLE 4

7. **Given:** $\overleftrightarrow{MN} \parallel \overline{KL}$
   Prove: △JMN ~ △JKL

8. **Given:** SQ = 2QP, TR = 2RP
   Prove: △PQR ~ △PST

9. The coordinates of A, B, and C are A(0, 0), B(2, 6), and C(8, −2). What theorem or postulate justifies the statement △ABC ~ △ADE, if the coordinates of D and E are twice the coordinates of B and C?

SEE EXAMPLE 5 10. **Surveying** In order to measure the distance AB across the meteorite crater, a surveyor at S locates points A, B, C, and D as shown. What is AB to the nearest meter? nearest kilometer?

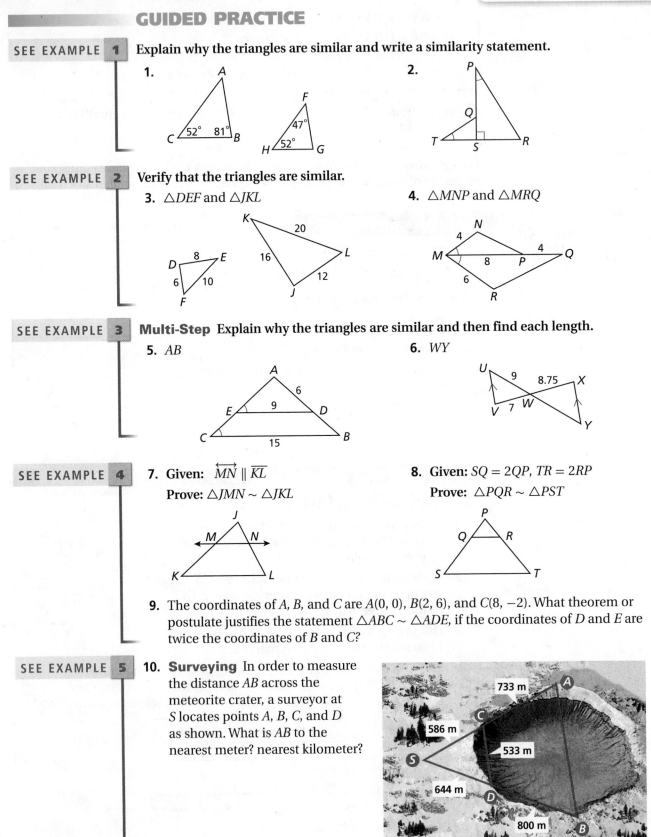

PRACTICE AND PROBLEM SOLVING

Independent Practice

For Exercises	See Example
11–12	1
13–14	2
15–16	3
17–18	4
19	5

my.hrw.com

Online Extra Practice

Explain why the triangles are similar and write a similarity statement.

11.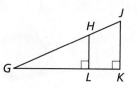

12.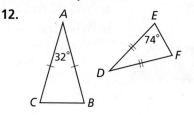

Verify that the given triangles are similar.

13. △*KLM* and △*KNL*

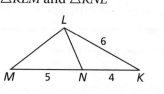

14. △*UVW* and △*XYZ*

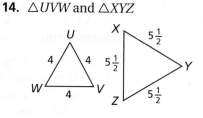

Multi-Step Explain why the triangles are similar and then find each length.

15. *AB*

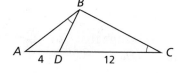

16. *PS*

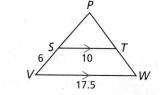

17. **Given:** $CD = 3AC, CE = 3BC$

    Prove: △*ABC* ~ △*DEC*

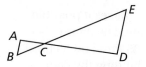

18. **Given:** $\dfrac{PR}{MR} = \dfrac{QR}{NR}$

    Prove: ∠1 ≅ ∠2

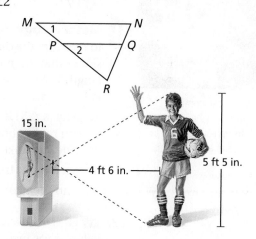

19. **Photography** The picture shows a person taking a pinhole photograph of himself. Light entering the opening reflects his image on the wall, forming similar triangles. What is the height of the image to the nearest tenth of a foot?

15 in. 4 ft 6 in. 5 ft 5 in.

Draw △*JKL* and △*MNP*. Determine if you can conclude that △*JKL* ~ △*MNP* based on the given information. If so, which postulate or theorem justifies your response?

20. ∠*K* ≅ ∠*N*, $\dfrac{JK}{MN} = \dfrac{KL}{NP}$

21. $\dfrac{JK}{MN} = \dfrac{KL}{NP} = \dfrac{JL}{MP}$

22. ∠*J* ≅ ∠*M*, $\dfrac{JL}{MP} = \dfrac{KL}{NP}$

Find the value of *x*.

23.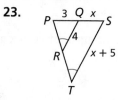

24.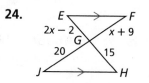

25. The set for an animated film includes three small triangles that represent pyramids.

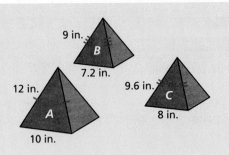

    a. Which pyramids are similar? Why?

    b. What is the similarity ratio of the similar pyramids?

H.O.T. 26. Critical Thinking △*ABC* is not similar to △*DEF*, and △*DEF* is not similar to △*XYZ*. Could △*ABC* be similar to △*XYZ*? Why or why not? Make a sketch to support your answer.

27. Recreation To play shuffleboard, two teams take turns sliding disks on a court. The dimensions of the scoring area for a standard shuffleboard court are shown. What are *JK* and *MN*?

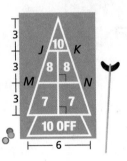

28. Prove the Transitive Property of Similarity.
    Given: △*ABC* ~ △*DEF*,
              △*DEF* ~ △*XYZ*
    Prove: △*ABC* ~ △*XYZ*

29. Draw and label △*PQR* and △*STU* such that $\frac{PQ}{ST} = \frac{QR}{TU}$ but △*PQR* is NOT similar to △*STU*.

30. Given: △*KNJ* is isosceles with ∠*N* as the vertex angle.
             ∠*H* ≅ ∠*L*
    Prove: △*GHJ* ~ △*MLK*

31. Meteorology Satellite photography makes it possible to measure the diameter of a hurricane. The figure shows that a camera's aperture *YX* is 35 mm and its focal length *WZ* is 50 mm. The satellite *W* holding the camera is 150 mi above the hurricane, centered at *C*.

    a. Why is △*XYZ* ~ △*ABZ*? What assumption must you make about the position of the camera in order to make this conclusion?

    b. What other triangles in the figure must be similar? Why?

    c. Find the diameter *AB* of the hurricane.

32. ///ERROR ANALYSIS/// Which solution for the value of *y* is incorrect? Explain the error.

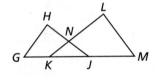

A	**B**
△*ABE* ~ △*CDE* by AA ~ , so $\frac{14}{8+y} = \frac{10}{8}$. Then 10(8 + *y*) = 8(14), or 80 + 10*y* = 112. So 10*y* = 32 and *y* = 3.2.	△*ABE* ~ △*CDE* by AA ~ , so $\frac{8}{10} = \frac{y}{14}$. Therefore 8(14) = 10*y*, which means 10*y* = 112 and *y* = 11.2.

H.O.T. 33. Write About It Two isosceles triangles have congruent vertex angles. Explain why the two triangles must be similar.

34. What is the length of $\overline{TU}$?

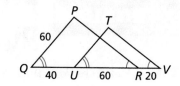

Ⓐ 36   Ⓒ 48

Ⓑ 40   Ⓓ 90

35. Which dimensions guarantee that $\triangle BCD \sim \triangle FGH$?

Ⓕ $FG = 11.6$, $GH = 8.4$

Ⓖ $FG = 12$, $GH = 14$

Ⓗ $FG = 11.4$, $GH = 11.4$

Ⓙ $FG = 10.5$, $GH = 14.5$

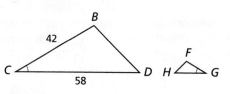

36. $\square ABCD \sim \square EFGH$. Which similarity postulate or theorem lets you conclude that $\triangle BCD \sim \triangle FGH$?

Ⓐ AA   Ⓒ SAS

Ⓑ SSS   Ⓓ None of these

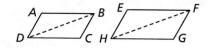

37. Gridded Response If 6, 8, and 12 and 15, 20, and x are the lengths of the corresponding sides of two similar triangles, what is the value of x?

CHALLENGE AND EXTEND

H.O.T. 38. Prove the SSS Similarity Theorem.

Given: $\dfrac{AB}{DE} = \dfrac{BC}{EF} = \dfrac{AC}{DF}$

Prove: $\triangle ABC \sim \triangle DEF$

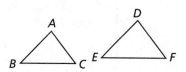

(*Hint:* Assume that $AB < DE$ and choose point X on $\overline{DE}$ so that $\overline{AB} \cong \overline{DX}$. Then choose point Y on $\overline{DF}$ so that $\overleftrightarrow{XY} \parallel \overline{EF}$. Show that $\triangle DXY \sim \triangle DEF$ and that $\triangle ABC \cong \triangle DXY$.)

H.O.T. 39. Prove the SAS Similarity Theorem.

Given: $\angle B \cong \angle E$, $\dfrac{AB}{DE} = \dfrac{BC}{EF}$

Prove: $\triangle ABC \sim \triangle DEF$

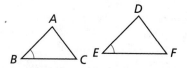

(*Hint:* Assume that $AB < DE$ and choose point X on $\overline{DE}$ so that $\overline{EX} \cong \overline{BA}$. Then choose point Y on $\overline{EF}$ so that $\angle EXY \cong \angle EDF$. Show that $\triangle XEY \sim \triangle DEF$ and that $\triangle ABC \cong \triangle XEF$.)

H.O.T. 40. Given $\triangle ABC \sim \triangle XYZ$, $m\angle A = 50°$, $m\angle X = (2x + 5y)°$, $m\angle Z = (5x + y)°$, and that $m\angle B = (102 - x)°$, find $m\angle Z$.

MATHEMATICAL PRACTICES

FOCUS ON MATHEMATICAL PRACTICES

H.O.T. 41. Reasoning Explain why angle-side-angle (ASA) is not given as a relationship that proves two triangles are similar.

H.O.T. 42. Justify $\triangle ABC$ and $\triangle JKL$ are isosceles triangles with congruent legs. $\angle B$ and $\angle K$ are both 40° angles. Must the two triangles be similar? Explain.

H.O.T. 43. Problem Solving $\triangle EFG \sim \triangle PQR$. The following side lengths are given: $PQ = 3$, $QR = 5$, and $EG = 24$. The perimeter of $\triangle EFG$ is 56. Find the unknown side lengths of each triangle.

Proving the Pythagorean Theorem

Essential Question: How can similar triangles be used in a proof of the Pythagorean Theorem?

Objective
Prove the Pythagorean Theorem using similar triangles.

The Pythagorean Theorem is one of the most widely used and well-known mathematical theorems. The theorem has been proven in many different ways, some of which involve subdividing the triangle in some way. The following proof uses similar triangles.

COMMON CORE GPS MCC9-12.G.SRT.4 **EXAMPLE 1** **Proving the Pythagorean Theorem Using Similar Triangles**

Prove the Pythagorean Theorem using similar triangles.
Given: $\triangle ABC$ with right $\angle C$
Prove: $a^2 + b^2 = c^2$

Proof: Draw an altitude from vertex C to side c as shown. By the Reflexive Property of Congruence, $\angle A \cong \angle A$ and $\angle B \cong \angle B$. All right angles are congruent, so $\angle ADC \cong \angle ACB$ and $\angle BDC \cong \angle ACB$. Therefore, $\triangle ACD \sim \triangle ABC$ and $\triangle CBD \sim \triangle ABC$ by the AA Similarity Postulate.

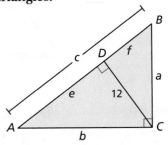

By the Transitive Property of Similarity, $\triangle ACD \sim \triangle CBD$.

Corresponding sides of similar triangles are proportional, so $\dfrac{c}{a} = \dfrac{a}{f}$ and $\dfrac{c}{b} = \dfrac{b}{e}$.

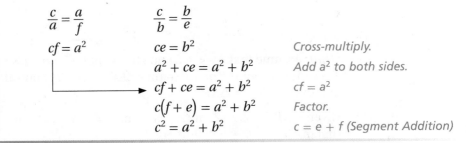

$\dfrac{c}{a} = \dfrac{a}{f}$	$\dfrac{c}{b} = \dfrac{b}{e}$	
$cf = a^2$	$ce = b^2$	*Cross-multiply.*
	$a^2 + ce = a^2 + b^2$	*Add a^2 to both sides.*
	$cf + ce = a^2 + b^2$	*$cf = a^2$*
	$c(f + e) = a^2 + b^2$	*Factor.*
	$c^2 = a^2 + b^2$	*$c = e + f$ (Segment Addition)*

 1. In the figure, find c, e, and f.

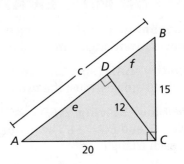

Applying the Pythagorean Theorem

Mike places a 20-foot ladder diagonally against the wall of the building. The bottom of the ladder is 3.5 feet from the building. The top of the ladder reaches how many feet above the ground?

Use the Pythagorean Theorem. The ladder is the hypotenuse of the triangle.

$$a^2 + b^2 = c^2$$
$$3.5^2 + b^2 = 20^2$$
$$12.25 + b^2 = 400$$
$$b^2 = 387.75$$
$$b \approx 19.7$$

The ladder reaches approximately 19.7 ft above the ground.

CHECK IT OUT!

2. Jackie drives 5 miles east and 3 miles north from home to school. What is the shortest distance from Jackie's home to school?

EXTENSION

Exercises

my.hrw.com
Homework Help

Find the unknown values in each figure. Give your answers in simplest radical form.

1.

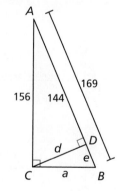

2.

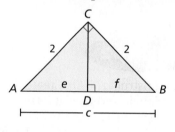

3. Critical Thinking Explain why any triple a, $2a$, $a\sqrt{3}$ are possible side lengths of a right triangle for any constant a.

4. The figure shows a loading dock with a ramp used to unload packages. What is the length of the ramp?

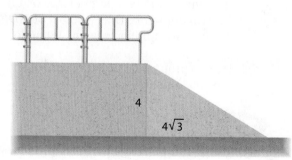

8-4 Technology TASK

Investigate Angle Bisectors of a Triangle

In a triangle, an angle bisector divides the opposite side into two segments. You will use geometry software to explore the relationships between these segments.

Use with Applying Properties of Similar Triangles

 MATHEMATICAL PRACTICES

Use appropriate tools strategically.

Activity 1

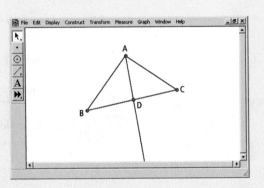

1 Construct △ABC. Bisect ∠BAC and create the point of intersection of the angle bisector and $\overline{BC}$. Label the intersection D.

2 Measure $\overline{AB}$, $\overline{AC}$, $\overline{BD}$, and $\overline{CD}$. Use these measurements to write ratios. What are the results? Drag a vertex of △ABC and examine the ratios again. What do you notice?

Try This

1. Choose Tabulate and create a table using the four lengths and the ratios from Step 2. Drag a vertex of △ABC and add the new measurements to the table. What conjecture can you make about the segments created by an angle bisector?

2. Write a proportion based on your conjecture.

Activity 2

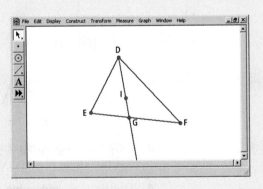

1 Construct △DEF. Create the *incenter* of the triangle and label it *I*. Hide the angle bisectors of ∠E and ∠F. Find the point of intersection of $\overline{EF}$ and the bisector of ∠D. Label the intersection G.

2 Find *DI*, *DG*, and the perimeter of △DEF.

3 Divide the length of $\overline{DI}$ by the length of *DG*. Add the lengths of $\overline{DE}$ and $\overline{DF}$. Then divide this sum by the perimeter of △DEF. Compare the two quotients. Drag a vertex of △DEF and examine the quotients again. What do you notice?

4 Write a proportion based on your quotients. What conjecture can you make about this relationship?

Try This

3. Show the hidden angle bisector of ∠E or ∠F. Confirm that your conjecture is true for this bisector. Drag a vertex of △DEF and observe the results.

4. Choose Tabulate and create a table with the measurements you used in your proportion in Step 4.

8-4

Applying Properties of Similar Triangles

? Essential Question: What proportional relationships are formed when parallel lines or segments intersect other lines or segments?

Objectives
Use properties of similar triangles to find segment lengths.

Apply proportionality and triangle angle bisector theorems.

Who uses this?
Artists use similarity and proportionality to give paintings an illusion of depth. (See Example 3.)

Artists use mathematical techniques to make two-dimensional paintings appear three-dimensional. The invention of *perspective* was based on the observation that far away objects look smaller and closer objects look larger.

Mathematical theorems like the Triangle Proportionality Theorem are important in making perspective drawings.

Know it! Note

Theorem 8-4-1 | **Triangle Proportionality Theorem**

THEOREM	HYPOTHESIS	CONCLUSION
If a line parallel to a side of a triangle intersects the other two sides, then it divides those sides proportionally.	$\overline{EF} \parallel \overline{BC}$	$\dfrac{AE}{EB} = \dfrac{AF}{FC}$

You can use a compass-and-straightedge construction to verify this theorem. Although the construction is not a proof, it should help convince you that the theorem is true. After you have completed the construction, use a ruler to measure $\overline{AE}$, $\overline{EB}$, $\overline{AF}$, and $\overline{FC}$ to see that $\frac{AE}{EB} = \frac{AF}{FC}$.

Construction Triangle Proportionality Theorem

Construct a line parallel to a side of a triangle.

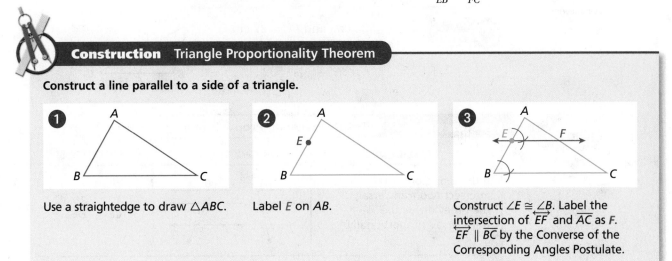

1 Use a straightedge to draw △ABC.

2 Label *E* on *AB*.

3 Construct ∠E ≅ ∠B. Label the intersection of $\overleftrightarrow{EF}$ and $\overline{AC}$ as *F*. $\overleftrightarrow{EF} \parallel \overline{BC}$ by the Converse of the Corresponding Angles Postulate.

©Christie's Images/CORBIS

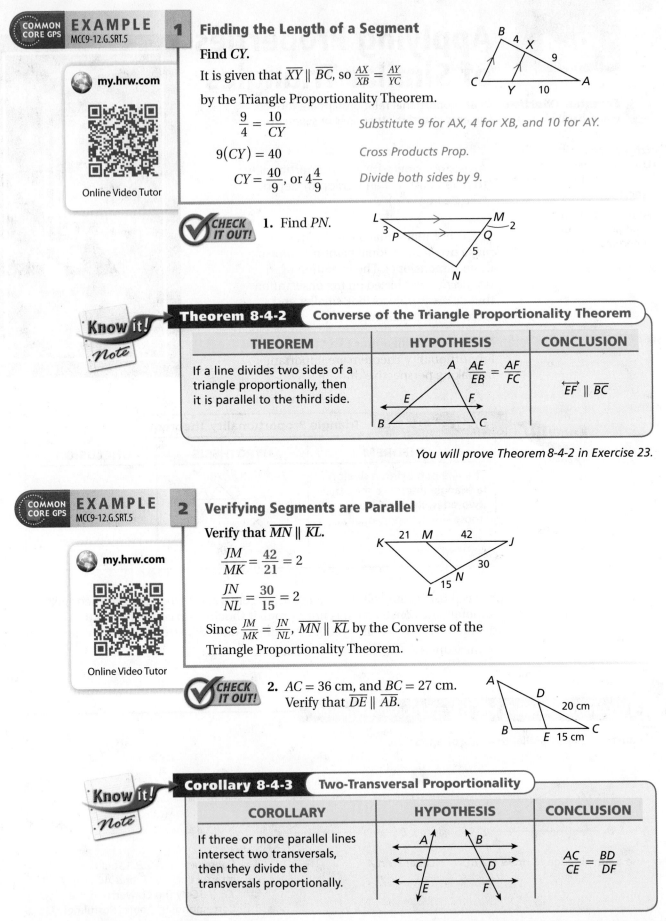

EXAMPLE **1** MCC9-12.G.SRT.5

Finding the Length of a Segment

Find CY.

It is given that $\overline{XY} \parallel \overline{BC}$, so $\frac{AX}{XB} = \frac{AY}{YC}$

by the Triangle Proportionality Theorem.

$$\frac{9}{4} = \frac{10}{CY}$$ *Substitute 9 for AX, 4 for XB, and 10 for AY.*

$$9(CY) = 40$$ *Cross Products Prop.*

$$CY = \frac{40}{9}, \text{ or } 4\frac{4}{9}$$ *Divide both sides by 9.*

CHECK IT OUT! **1.** Find *PN*.

Know it! *.Note*

Theorem 8-4-2 **Converse of the Triangle Proportionality Theorem**

THEOREM	HYPOTHESIS	CONCLUSION
If a line divides two sides of a triangle proportionally, then it is parallel to the third side.	$\frac{AE}{EB} = \frac{AF}{FC}$	$\overleftrightarrow{EF} \parallel \overline{BC}$

You will prove Theorem 8-4-2 in Exercise 23.

EXAMPLE **2** MCC9-12.G.SRT.5

Verifying Segments are Parallel

Verify that $\overline{MN} \parallel \overline{KL}$.

$$\frac{JM}{MK} = \frac{42}{21} = 2$$

$$\frac{JN}{NL} = \frac{30}{15} = 2$$

Since $\frac{JM}{MK} = \frac{JN}{NL}$, $\overline{MN} \parallel \overline{KL}$ by the Converse of the Triangle Proportionality Theorem.

CHECK IT OUT! **2.** $AC = 36$ cm, and $BC = 27$ cm. Verify that $\overline{DE} \parallel \overline{AB}$.

Know it! *.Note*

Corollary 8-4-3 **Two-Transversal Proportionality**

COROLLARY	HYPOTHESIS	CONCLUSION
If three or more parallel lines intersect two transversals, then they divide the transversals proportionally.		$\frac{AC}{CE} = \frac{BD}{DF}$

You will prove Corollary 8-4-3 in Exercise 24.

EXAMPLE **3**

Art Application

An artist used perspective to draw guidelines to help her sketch a row of parallel trees. She then checked the drawing by measuring the distances between the trees. What is *LN*?

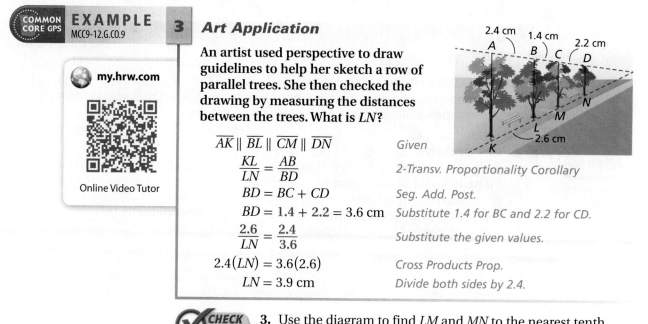

2.4 cm   1.4 cm   2.2 cm

$\overline{AK} \parallel \overline{BL} \parallel \overline{CM} \parallel \overline{DN}$	*Given*
$\dfrac{KL}{LN} = \dfrac{AB}{BD}$	*2-Transv. Proportionality Corollary*
$BD = BC + CD$	*Seg. Add. Post.*
$BD = 1.4 + 2.2 = 3.6$ cm	*Substitute 1.4 for BC and 2.2 for CD.*
$\dfrac{2.6}{LN} = \dfrac{2.4}{3.6}$	*Substitute the given values.*
$2.4(LN) = 3.6(2.6)$	*Cross Products Prop.*
$LN = 3.9$ cm	*Divide both sides by 2.4.*

CHECK IT OUT!   **3.** Use the diagram to find *LM* and *MN* to the nearest tenth.

The previous theorems and corollary lead to the following conclusion.

Know it! Note

Theorem 8-4-4   **Triangle Angle Bisector Theorem**

THEOREM	HYPOTHESIS	CONCLUSION
An angle bisector of a triangle divides the opposite side into two segments whose lengths are proportional to the lengths of the other two sides. ($\triangle \angle$ Bisector Thm.)		$\dfrac{BD}{DC} = \dfrac{AB}{AC}$

You will prove Theorem 8-4-4 in Exercise 38.

EXAMPLE **4**

Using the Triangle Angle Bisector Theorem

Find *RV* and *VT*.

$\dfrac{RV}{VT} = \dfrac{SR}{ST}$ by the $\triangle \angle$ Bisector Thm.

$\dfrac{x + 2}{2x + 1} = \dfrac{10}{14}$	*Substitute the given values.*
$14(x + 2) = 10(2x + 1)$	*Cross Products Prop.*
$14x + 28 = 20x + 10$	*Dist. Prop.*
$18 = 6x$	*Simplify.*
$x = 3$	*Divide both sides by 6.*

$RV = x + 2 \qquad\qquad VT = 2x + 1$ *Substitute 3 for x.*
$\quad = 3 + 2 = 5 \qquad\quad\; = 2(3) + 1 = 7$

CHECK IT OUT!   **4.** Find *AC* and *DC*.

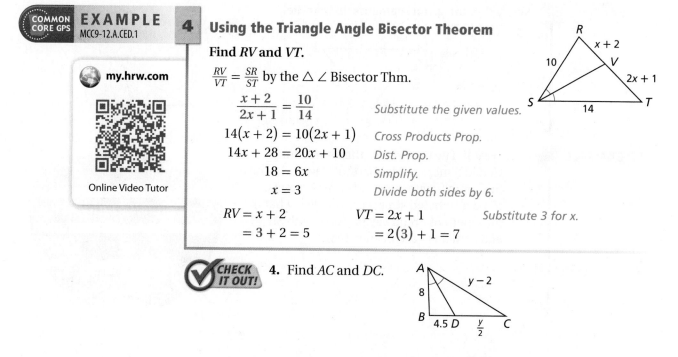

THINK AND DISCUSS

1. $\overline{XY} \parallel \overline{BC}$. Use what you know about similarity and proportionality to state as many different proportions as possible.

Know it! Note

2. GET ORGANIZED Copy and complete the graphic organizer. Draw a figure for each proportionality theorem or corollary and then measure it. Use your measurements to write an if-then statement about each figure.

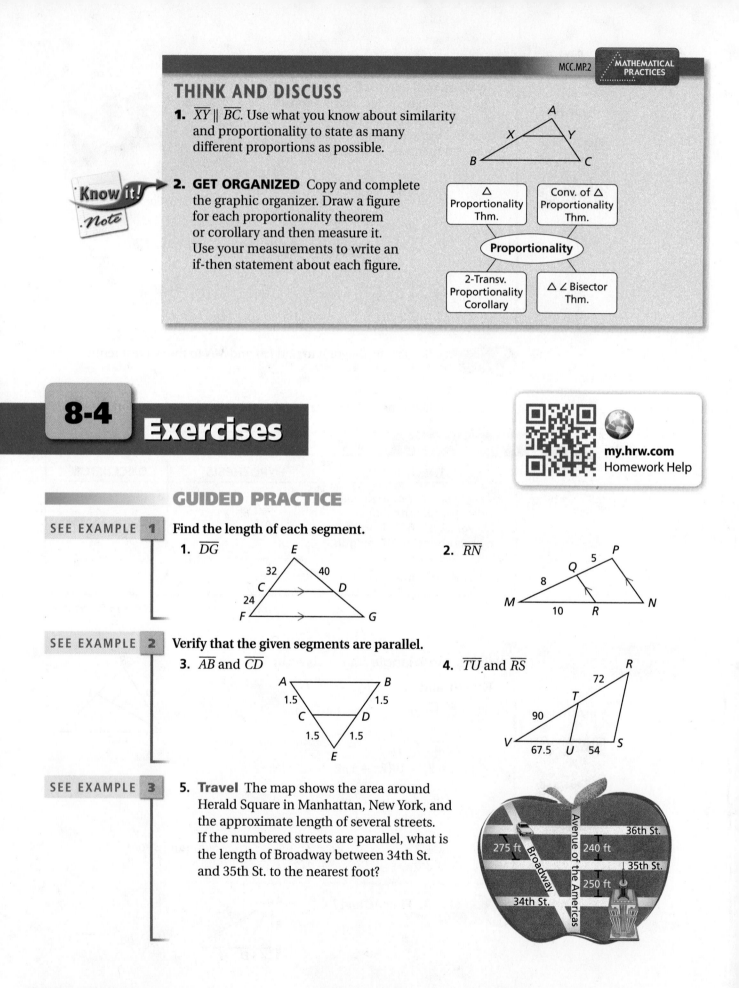

△ Proportionality Thm.

Conv. of △ Proportionality Thm.

Proportionality

2-Transv. Proportionality Corollary

△ ∠ Bisector Thm.

8-4 Exercises

my.hrw.com
Homework Help

GUIDED PRACTICE

SEE EXAMPLE 1

Find the length of each segment.

1. $\overline{DG}$

2. $\overline{RN}$

SEE EXAMPLE 2

Verify that the given segments are parallel.

3. $\overline{AB}$ and $\overline{CD}$

4. $\overline{TU}$ and $\overline{RS}$

SEE EXAMPLE 3

5. Travel The map shows the area around Herald Square in Manhattan, New York, and the approximate length of several streets. If the numbered streets are parallel, what is the length of Broadway between 34th St. and 35th St. to the nearest foot?

Find the length of each segment.

6. $\overline{QR}$ and $\overline{RS}$

7. $\overline{CD}$ and $\overline{AD}$

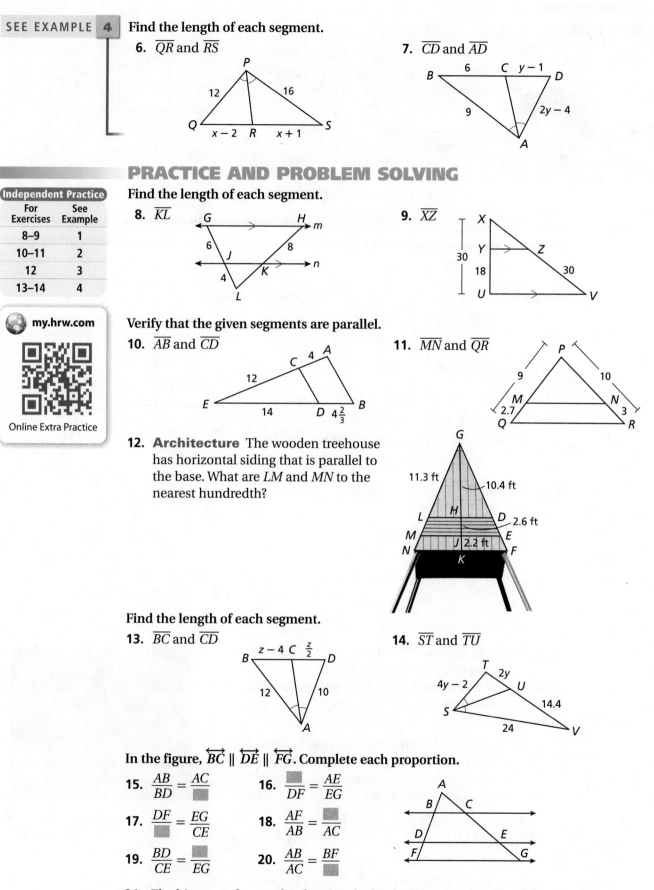

PRACTICE AND PROBLEM SOLVING

Find the length of each segment.

Independent Practice

For Exercises	See Example
8–9	1
10–11	2
12	3
13–14	4

my.hrw.com

Online Extra Practice

8. $\overline{KL}$

9. $\overline{XZ}$

Verify that the given segments are parallel.

10. $\overline{AB}$ and $\overline{CD}$

11. $\overline{MN}$ and $\overline{QR}$

12. Architecture The wooden treehouse has horizontal siding that is parallel to the base. What are LM and MN to the nearest hundredth?

Find the length of each segment.

13. $\overline{BC}$ and $\overline{CD}$

14. $\overline{ST}$ and $\overline{TU}$

In the figure, $\overleftrightarrow{BC} \parallel \overleftrightarrow{DE} \parallel \overleftrightarrow{FG}$. Complete each proportion.

15. $\dfrac{AB}{BD} = \dfrac{AC}{\blacksquare}$

16. $\dfrac{\blacksquare}{DF} = \dfrac{AE}{EG}$

17. $\dfrac{DF}{\blacksquare} = \dfrac{EG}{CE}$

18. $\dfrac{AF}{AB} = \dfrac{\blacksquare}{AC}$

19. $\dfrac{BD}{CE} = \dfrac{\blacksquare}{EG}$

20. $\dfrac{AB}{AC} = \dfrac{BF}{\blacksquare}$

21. The bisector of an angle of a triangle divides the opposite side of the triangle into segments that are 12 in. and 16 in. long. Another side of the triangle is 20 in. long. What are two possible lengths for the third side?

22. Jaclyn is building a slide rail, the narrow, slanted beam found in skateboard parks.

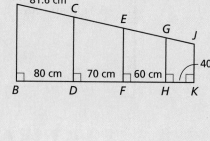

   a. Write a proportion that Jaclyn can use to calculate the length of $\overline{CE}$.

   b. Find *CE*.

   c. What is the overall length of the slide rail *AJ*?

H.O.T. 23. Prove the Converse of the Triangle Proportionality Theorem.

   Given: $\dfrac{AE}{EB} = \dfrac{AF}{FC}$

   Prove: $\overleftrightarrow{EF} \parallel \overline{BC}$

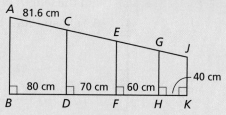

H.O.T. 24. Prove the Two-Transversal Proportionality Corollary.

   Given: $\overleftrightarrow{AB} \parallel \overleftrightarrow{CD},\ \overleftrightarrow{CD} \parallel \overleftrightarrow{EF}$

   Prove: $\dfrac{AC}{CE} = \dfrac{BD}{DF}$

   (*Hint:* Draw $\overleftrightarrow{BE}$ through *X*.)

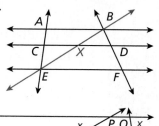

25. Given that $\overleftrightarrow{PQ} \parallel \overleftrightarrow{RS} \parallel \overleftrightarrow{TU}$

   a. Find *PR*, *RT*, *QS*, and *SU*.

   b. Use your results from part **b** to write a proportion relating the segment lengths.

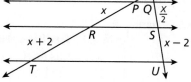

H.O.T. Find the length of each segment.

26. $\overline{EF}$

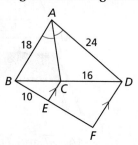

27. $\overline{ST}$

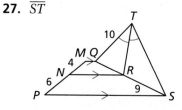

H.O.T. 28. Real Estate A developer is laying out lots along Grant Rd. whose total width is 500 ft. Given the width of each lot along Chavez St., what is the width of each of the lots along Grant Rd. to the nearest foot?

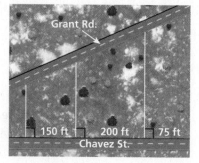

29. Critical Thinking Explain how to use a sheet of lined notebook paper to divide a segment into five congruent segments. Which theorem or corollary do you use?

30. Given that $\overline{DE} \parallel \overline{BC},\ \overline{XY} \parallel \overline{AD}$
Find *EC*.

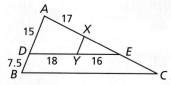

31. Write About It In $\triangle ABC,\ \overrightarrow{AD}$ bisects $\angle BAC$. Write a proportionality statement for the triangle. What theorem supports your conclusion?

32. Which dimensions let you conclude that $\overline{UV} \parallel \overline{ST}$?

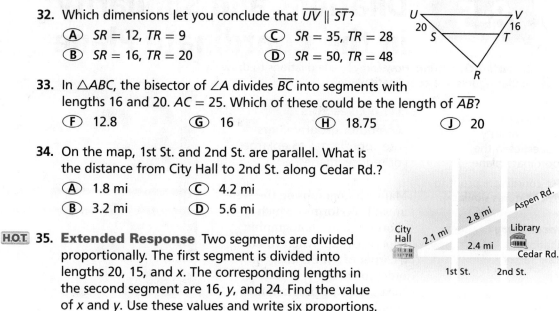

   (A) $SR = 12$, $TR = 9$ **(C)** $SR = 35$, $TR = 28$

   (B) $SR = 16$, $TR = 20$ **(D)** $SR = 50$, $TR = 48$

33. In $\triangle ABC$, the bisector of $\angle A$ divides $\overline{BC}$ into segments with lengths 16 and 20. $AC = 25$. Which of these could be the length of $\overline{AB}$?

   (F) 12.8   **(G)** 16   **(H)** 18.75   **(J)** 20

34. On the map, 1st St. and 2nd St. are parallel. What is the distance from City Hall to 2nd St. along Cedar Rd.?

   (A) 1.8 mi   **(C)** 4.2 mi

   (B) 3.2 mi   **(D)** 5.6 mi

H.O.T. 35. Extended Response Two segments are divided proportionally. The first segment is divided into lengths 20, 15, and x. The corresponding lengths in the second segment are 16, y, and 24. Find the value of x and y. Use these values and write six proportions.

CHALLENGE AND EXTEND

36. The perimeter of $\triangle ABC$ is 29 cm. $\overline{AD}$ bisects $\angle A$. Find AB and AC.

H.O.T. 37. Prove that if two triangles are similar, then the ratio of their corresponding angle bisectors is the same as the ratio of their corresponding sides.

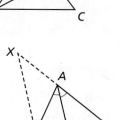

H.O.T. 38. Prove the Triangle Angle Bisector Theorem.

   Given: In $\triangle ABC$, $\overline{AD}$ bisects $\angle A$.

   Prove: $\dfrac{BD}{DC} = \dfrac{AB}{AC}$

   Plan: Draw $\overline{BX} \parallel \overline{AD}$ and extend $\overline{AC}$ to X. Use properties of parallel lines and the Converse of the Isosceles Triangle Theorem to show that $\overline{AX} \cong \overline{AB}$. Then apply the Triangle Proportionality Theorem.

39. Construction Construct three parallel lines cut by a transversal. Construct a second transversal that forms line segments twice the length of the corresponding segments on the first transversal.

FOCUS ON MATHEMATICAL PRACTICES

H.O.T. 40. Justify In the figure shown, does $\overline{KM}$ bisect $\angle LKN$? If not, which is larger, $m\angle LKM$ or $m\angle MKN$? Justify your answer.

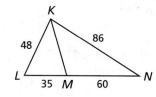

H.O.T. 41. Problem Solving $\triangle WXY$ is isosceles with $\angle X$ as its vertex angle. Find YZ and WX. Show your work.

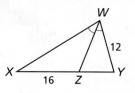

Dilations and Similarity in the Coordinate Plane

 Essential Question: How can you use dilations to draw similar figures in a coordinate plane?

Objectives
Apply similarity properties in the coordinate plane.

Use coordinate proof to prove figures similar.

Vocabulary
dilation
scale factor

Who uses this?
Computer programmers use coordinates to enlarge or reduce images.

Many photographs on the Web are in JPEG format, which is short for Joint Photographic Experts Group. When you drag a corner of a JPEG image in order to enlarge it or reduce it, the underlying program uses coordinates and similarity to change the image's size.

A **dilation** is a transformation that changes the size of a figure but not its shape. The preimage and the image are always similar. A **scale factor** describes how much the figure is enlarged or reduced. For a dilation with scale factor k, you can find the image of a point by multiplying each coordinate by k: $(a, b) \rightarrow (ka, kb)$.

COMMON CORE GPS
EXAMPLE 1
MCC9-12.G.CO.2

Computer Graphics Application

my.hrw.com

Online Video Tutor

The figure shows the position of a JPEG photo. Draw the border of the photo after a dilation with scale factor $\frac{3}{2}$.

Step 1 Multiply the vertices of the photo $A(0, 0)$, $B(0, 4)$, $C(3, 4)$, and $D(3, 0)$ by $\frac{3}{2}$.

Rectangle ABCD	Rectangle A′B′C′D′

$$A(0, 0) \rightarrow A'\left(0 \cdot \frac{3}{2}, 0 \cdot \frac{3}{2}\right) \rightarrow A'(0, 0)$$

$$B(0, 4) \rightarrow B'\left(0 \cdot \frac{3}{2}, 4 \cdot \frac{3}{2}\right) \rightarrow B'(0, 6)$$

$$C(3, 4) \rightarrow C'\left(3 \cdot \frac{3}{2}, 4 \cdot \frac{3}{2}\right) \rightarrow C'(4.5, 6)$$

$$D(3, 0) \rightarrow D'\left(3 \cdot \frac{3}{2}, 0 \cdot \frac{3}{2}\right) \rightarrow D'(4.5, 0)$$

Step 2 Plot points $A'(0, 0)$, $B'(0, 6)$, $C'(4.5, 6)$, and $D'(4.5, 0)$. Draw the rectangle.

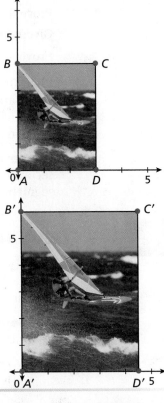

Helpful Hint

If the scale factor of a dilation is greater than 1 ($k > 1$), it is an *enlargement*. If the scale factor is less than 1 ($k < 1$), it is a *reduction*.

 CHECK IT OUT!
1. **What if...?** Draw the border of the original photo after a dilation with scale factor $\frac{1}{2}$.

(tr), © moodboard/Corbis; (cr), ©Photodisc/gettyimages; (b), Photodisc/gettyimages

Finding Coordinates of Similar Triangles

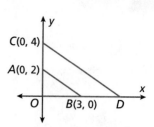
Given that $\triangle AOB \sim \triangle COD$, find the coordinates of D and the scale factor.

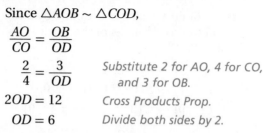

Since $\triangle AOB \sim \triangle COD$,

$\dfrac{AO}{CO} = \dfrac{OB}{OD}$

$\dfrac{2}{4} = \dfrac{3}{OD}$ *Substitute 2 for AO, 4 for CO, and 3 for OB.*

$2OD = 12$ *Cross Products Prop.*

$OD = 6$ *Divide both sides by 2.*

D lies on the x-axis, so its y-coordinate is 0. Since $OD = 6$, its x-coordinate must be 6. The coordinates of D are $(6, 0)$.

$(3, 0) \rightarrow (3 \cdot 2, 0 \cdot 2) \rightarrow (6, 0)$, so the scale factor is 2.

CHECK IT OUT!

2. Given that $\triangle MON \sim \triangle POQ$ and coordinates $P(-15, 0)$, $M(-10, 0)$, and $Q(0, -30)$, find the coordinates of N and the scale factor.

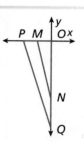

Proving Triangles Are Similar

Given: $A(1, 5)$, $B(-1, 3)$, $C(3, 4)$, $D(-3, 1)$, and $E(5, 3)$

Prove: $\triangle ABC \sim \triangle ADE$

Step 1 Plot the points and draw the triangles.

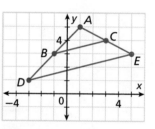

Step 2 Use the Distance Formula to find the side lengths.

$AB = \sqrt{(-1-1)^2 + (3-5)^2}$ $AC = \sqrt{(3-1)^2 + (4-5)^2}$

$\quad = \sqrt{8} = 2\sqrt{2}$ $= \sqrt{5}$

$AD = \sqrt{(-3-1)^2 + (1-5)^2}$ $AE = \sqrt{(5-1)^2 + (3-5)^2}$

$\quad = \sqrt{32} = 4\sqrt{2}$ $= \sqrt{20} = 2\sqrt{5}$

Step 3 Find the similarity ratio.

$\dfrac{AB}{AD} = \dfrac{2\sqrt{2}}{4\sqrt{2}}$ $\dfrac{AC}{AE} = \dfrac{\sqrt{5}}{2\sqrt{5}}$

$\quad = \dfrac{2}{4}$ $= \dfrac{1}{2}$

$\quad = \dfrac{1}{2}$

Since $\dfrac{AB}{AD} = \dfrac{AC}{AE}$ and $\angle A \cong \angle A$ by the Reflexive Property, $\triangle ABC \sim \triangle ADE$ by SAS $\sim$.

CHECK IT OUT!

3. Given: $R(-2, 0)$, $S(-3, 1)$, $T(0, 1)$, $U(-5, 3)$, and $V(4, 3)$
Prove: $\triangle RST \sim \triangle RUV$

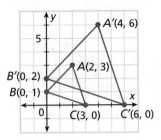

COMMON CORE GPS MCC9-12.G.SRT.5

EXAMPLE 4

my.hrw.com

Online Video Tutor

Using the SSS Similarity Theorem

Graph the image of $\triangle ABC$ after a dilation with scale factor 2.
Verify that $\triangle A'B'C' \sim \triangle ABC$.

Step 1 Multiply each coordinate by 2 to
find the coordinates of the vertices
of $\triangle A'B'C'$.

$$A(2, 3) \rightarrow A'(2 \cdot 2, 3 \cdot 2) = A'(4, 6)$$
$$B(0, 1) \rightarrow B'(0 \cdot 2, 1 \cdot 2) = B'(0, 2)$$
$$C(3, 0) \rightarrow C'(3 \cdot 2, 0 \cdot 2) = C'(6, 0)$$

Step 2 Graph $\triangle A'B'C'$.

Step 3 Use the Distance Formula to find the side lengths.

$$AB = \sqrt{(2-0)^2 + (3-1)^2} \qquad A'B' = \sqrt{(4-0)^2 + (6-2)^2}$$
$$= \sqrt{8} = 2\sqrt{2} \qquad\qquad = \sqrt{32} = 4\sqrt{2}$$

$$BC = \sqrt{(3-0)^2 + (0-1)^2} \qquad B'C' = \sqrt{(6-0)^2 + (0-2)^2}$$
$$= \sqrt{10} \qquad\qquad\qquad = \sqrt{40} = 2\sqrt{10}$$

$$AC = \sqrt{(3-2)^2 + (0-3)^2} \qquad A'C' = \sqrt{(6-4)^2 + (0-6)^2}$$
$$= \sqrt{10} \qquad\qquad\qquad = \sqrt{40} = 2\sqrt{10}$$

Step 4 Find the similarity ratio.

$$\frac{A'B'}{AB} = \frac{4\sqrt{2}}{2\sqrt{2}} = 2, \ \frac{B'C'}{BC} = \frac{2\sqrt{10}}{\sqrt{10}} = 2, \ \frac{A'C'}{AC} = \frac{2\sqrt{10}}{\sqrt{10}} = 2$$

Since $\dfrac{A'B'}{AB} = \dfrac{B'C'}{BC} = \dfrac{A'C'}{AC}$, $\triangle ABC \sim \triangle A'B'C'$ by SSS ~.

CHECK IT OUT!

4. Graph the image of $\triangle MNP$ after
a dilation with scale factor 3.
Verify that $\triangle M'N'P' \sim \triangle MNP$.

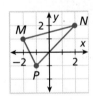

MCC.MP.8 **MATHEMATICAL PRACTICES**

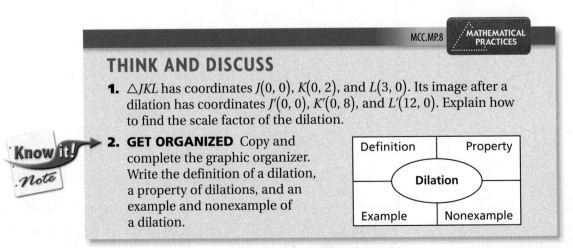

THINK AND DISCUSS

1. $\triangle JKL$ has coordinates $J(0, 0)$, $K(0, 2)$, and $L(3, 0)$. Its image after a
dilation has coordinates $J'(0, 0)$, $K'(0, 8)$, and $L'(12, 0)$. Explain how
to find the scale factor of the dilation.

Know it! Note

2. GET ORGANIZED Copy and
complete the graphic organizer.
Write the definition of a dilation,
a property of dilations, and an
example and nonexample of
a dilation.

Definition	Property
Dilation	
Example	Nonexample

GUIDED PRACTICE

Vocabulary Apply the vocabulary from this lesson to answer each question.

1. A ___?___ is a transformation that proportionally reduces or enlarges a figure, such as the pupil of an eye. (*dilation* or *scale factor*)

2. A ratio that describes or determines the dimensional relationship of a figure to that which it represents, such as a map scale of 1 in. : 45 ft, is called a ___?___. (*dilation* or *scale factor*)

SEE EXAMPLE 1

3. **Graphic Design** A designer created this logo for a real estate agent but needs to make the logo twice as large for use on a sign. Draw the logo after a dilation with scale factor 2.

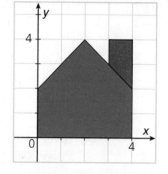

SEE EXAMPLE 2

4. Given that △AOB ~ △COD, find the coordinates of *C* and the scale factor.

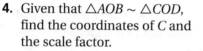

5. Given that △ROS ~ △POQ, find the coordinates of *S* and the scale factor.

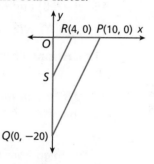

SEE EXAMPLE 3

6. **Given:** $A(0, 0)$, $B(-1, 1)$, $C(3, 2)$, $D(-2, 2)$, and $E(6, 4)$
   Prove: △ABC ~ △ADE

7. **Given:** $J(-1, 0)$, $K(-3, -4)$, $L(3, -2)$, $M(-4, -6)$, and $N(5, -3)$
   Prove: △JKL ~ △JMN

SEE EXAMPLE 4

Multi-Step Graph the image of each triangle after a dilation with the given scale factor. Then verify that the image is similar to the given triangle.

8. scale factor 2

9. scale factor $\frac{3}{2}$

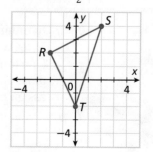

PRACTICE AND PROBLEM SOLVING

Independent Practice	
For Exercises	See Example
10	1
11–12	2
13–14	3
15–16	4

my.hrw.com

Online Extra Practice

10. Advertising A promoter produced this design for a street festival. She now wants to make the design smaller to use on postcards. Sketch the design after a dilation with scale factor $\frac{1}{2}$.

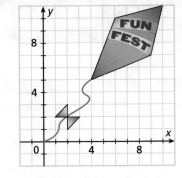

11. Given that $\triangle UOV \sim \triangle XOY$, find the coordinates of X and the scale factor.

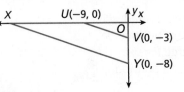

12. Given that $\triangle MON \sim \triangle KOL$, find the coordinates of K and the scale factor.

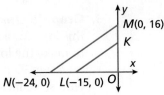

13. Given: $D(-1, 3)$, $E(-3, -1)$, $F(3, -1)$, $G(-4, -3)$, and $H(5, -3)$
Prove: $\triangle DEF \sim \triangle DGH$

14. Given: $M(0, 10)$, $N(5, 0)$, $P(15, 15)$, $Q(10, -10)$, and $R(30, 20)$
Prove: $\triangle MNP \sim \triangle MQR$

H.O.T. Multi-Step Graph the image of each triangle after a dilation with the given scale factor. Then verify that the image is similar to the given triangle.

15. $J(-2, 0)$ and $K(-1, -1)$, and $L(-3, -2)$ with scale factor 3

16. $M(0, 4)$, $N(4, 2)$, and $P(2, -2)$ with scale factor $\frac{1}{2}$

H.O.T. 17. Critical Thinking Consider the transformation given by the mapping $(x, y) \rightarrow (2x, 4y)$. Is this transformation a dilation? Why or why not?

18. ///ERROR ANALYSIS/// Which solution to find the scale factor of the dilation that maps $\triangle RST$ to $\triangle UVW$ is incorrect? Explain the error.

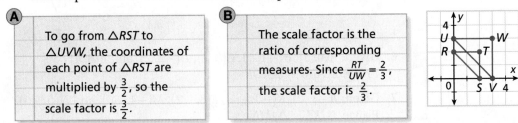

A To go from $\triangle RST$ to $\triangle UVW$, the coordinates of each point of $\triangle RST$ are multiplied by $\frac{3}{2}$, so the scale factor is $\frac{3}{2}$.

B The scale factor is the ratio of corresponding measures. Since $\frac{RT}{UW} = \frac{2}{3}$, the scale factor is $\frac{2}{3}$.

H.O.T. 19. Write About It A dilation maps $\triangle ABC$ to $\triangle A'B'C'$. How is the scale factor of the dilation related to the similarity ratio of $\triangle ABC$ to $\triangle A'B'C'$? Explain.

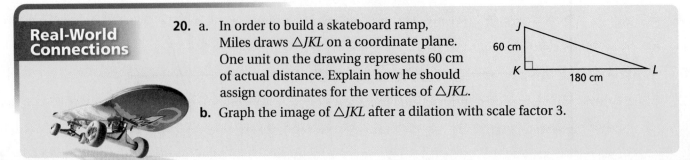

Real-World Connections

20. a. In order to build a skateboard ramp, Miles draws $\triangle JKL$ on a coordinate plane. One unit on the drawing represents 60 cm of actual distance. Explain how he should assign coordinates for the vertices of $\triangle JKL$.

b. Graph the image of $\triangle JKL$ after a dilation with scale factor 3.

TEST PREP

21. Which coordinates for *C* make △*COD* similar to △*AOB*?

    Ⓐ (0, 2.4)   Ⓒ (0, 3)

    Ⓑ (0, 2.5)   Ⓓ (0, 3.6)

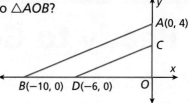

22. A dilation with scale factor 2 maps △*RST* to △*R'S'T'*. The perimeter of △*RST* is 60. What is the perimeter of △*R'S'T'*?

    Ⓕ 30   Ⓖ 60   Ⓗ 120   Ⓙ 240

23. Which triangle with vertices *D*, *E*, and *F* is similar to △*ABC*?

    Ⓐ *D*(1, 2), *E*(3, 2), *F*(2, 0)

    Ⓑ *D*(−1, −2), *E*(2, −2), *F*(1, −5)

    Ⓒ *D*(1, 2), *E*(5, 2), *F*(3, 0)

    Ⓓ *D*(−2, −2), *E*(0, 2), *F*(−1, 0)

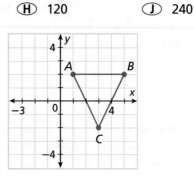

24. Gridded Resonse $\overline{AB}$ with endpoints *A*(3, 2) and *B*(7, 5) is dilated by a scale factor of 3. Find the length of $\overline{A'B'}$.

CHALLENGE AND EXTEND

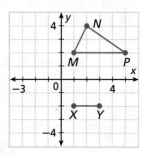

H.O.T. 25. How many different triangles having $\overline{XY}$ as a side are similar to △*MNP*?

26. △*XYZ* ~ △*MPN*. Find the coordinates of *Z*.

27. A rectangle has two of its sides on the *x*- and *y*-axes, a vertex at the origin, and a vertex on the line *y* = 2*x*. Prove that any two such rectangles are similar.

28. △*ABC* has vertices *A*(0, 1), *B*(3, 1), and *C*(1, 3). △*DEF* has vertices *D*(1, −1) and *E*(7, −1). Find two different locations for vertex *F* so that △*ABC* ~ △*DEF*.

FOCUS ON MATHEMATICAL PRACTICES

H.O.T. 29. Error Analysis Jonah says that △*RST* shown is similar to a triangle in the coordinate plane with vertices *D*(6, 6), *E*(1, 6), and *F*(1, 10). Charles says that the two triangles are not similar. Who is correct? Explain your answer.

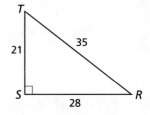

H.O.T. 30. Problem Solving $\overline{JK}$ has length 10. $\overline{J'K'}$ is a dilation of $\overline{JK}$ and has endpoints *J'*(5, 16) and *K'*(12, −8). Find the scale factor of the dilation and show your work. Is the dilation an enlargement or a reduction? How do you know?

Ready to Go On?

my.hrw.com
Assessment and Intervention

✓ 8-1 Ratios in Similar Polygons

Determine whether the two polygons are similar. If so, write the similarity ratio and a similarity statement.

1. rectangles *ABCD* and *WXYZ*

2. △*JMR* and △*NPK*

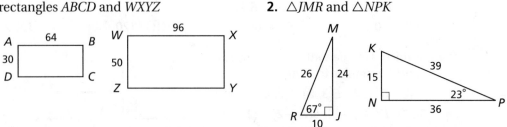

3. Leonardo da Vinci's famous portrait the *Mona Lisa* is 30 in. long and 21 in. wide. Janelle has a refrigerator magnet of the painting that is 3.5 cm wide. What is the length of the magnet?

✓ 8-2 Similarity and Transformations

Apply the dilation to the polygon with the given vertices. Name the coordinates of the points. Identify and describe the transformation.

4. *D* : (*x*, *y*) →(3*x*, 3*y*); *A*(0, 0), *B*(1, 2), *C*(3, −2)

5. *D* : (*x*, *y*) →(0.5*x*, 0.5*y*); *A*(10, 6), *B*(8, −4), *C*(−2, 0)

Determine whether the polygons with the given vertices are similar. Support your answer by describing a transformation.

6. *A*(0, 0), *B*(−2, 0), *C*(−2, 1)
   X(10, 0), *Y*(6, 0), *Z*(6, 2)

7. *A*(0, 0), *B*(1, 3), *C*(−1, 4)
   X(0, 0), *Y*(3, 9), *Z*(−2, 8)

✓ 8-3 Triangle Similarity: AA, SSS, and SAS

8. Given: ▱*ABCD*
   Prove: △*EDG* ~ △*FBG*

9. Given: $MQ = \frac{1}{3}MN$, $MR = \frac{1}{3}MP$
   Prove: △*MQR* ~ △*MNP*

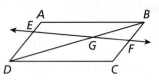

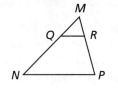

✓ 8-4 Applying Properties of Similar Triangles

Find the length of each segment.

10. $\overline{ST}$

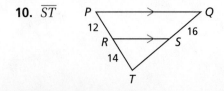

11. $\overline{AB}$ and $\overline{AC}$

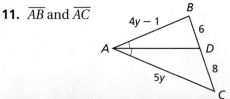

12. Given: $A(-1, 2)$, $B(-3, -2)$, $C(3, 0)$, $D(-2, 0)$, and $E(1, 1)$
Prove: $\triangle ADE \sim \triangle ABC$

13. Given: $R(0, 0)$, $S(-2, -1)$, $T(0, -3)$, $U(4, 2)$, and $V(0, 6)$
Prove: $\triangle RST \sim \triangle RUV$

Graph the image of each triangle after a dilation with the given scale factor. Then verify that the image is similar to the given triangle.

14. scale factor 3

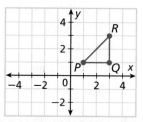

15. scale factor 1.5

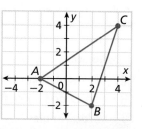

PARCC Assessment Readiness

COMMON CORE GPS

Selected Response

1. A video game designer is modeling a tower that is 320 ft high and 260 ft wide. She creates a model so that the similarity ratio of the model to the tower is $\frac{1}{500}$. What are the height and the width of the model in inches?

Ⓐ height = 0.64 in.; width = 0.52 in.

Ⓑ height = 3840 in.; width = 3120 in.

Ⓒ height = 7.68 in.; width = 6.24 in.

Ⓓ height = 160,000 in.; width = 130,000 in.

2. Find *NP*.

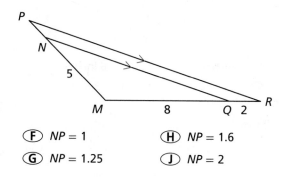

Ⓕ *NP* = 1   Ⓗ *NP* = 1.6

Ⓖ *NP* = 1.25   Ⓙ *NP* = 2

Mini-Tasks

3. Given: $\overline{BD} \parallel \overline{CE}$
Prove: $AB(CE) = AC(BD)$

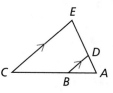

4. Apply the dilation *D* to the polygon with the given vertices. Name the coordinates of the image points. Identify and describe the transformation.

$D:(x, y) \rightarrow (4x, 4y)$

$A(2, 1), B(4, 1), C(4, -3)$

PARCC Assessment Readiness

COMMON CORE GPS

Selected Response

1. $\triangle ABC \cong \triangle DEF$, $EF = x^2 - 7$, and $BC = 4x - 2$. Find the values of x.

   (A) −1 and 5 (C) 1 and 5
   (B) −1 and 6 (D) 2 and 3

2. For two lines and a transversal, $\angle 1$ and $\angle 2$ are same-side interior angles, $\angle 2$ and $\angle 3$ are vertical angles, and $\angle 3$ and $\angle 4$ are alternate exterior angles. Which classification best describes the angle pair $\angle 2$ and $\angle 4$?

   (F) Adjacent angles
   (G) Alternate interior angles
   (H) Corresponding angles
   (J) Vertical angles

3. If $\triangle ABC \cong \triangle PQR$ and $\triangle RPQ \cong \triangle XYZ$, which of the following angles is congruent to $\angle CAB$?

   (A) $\angle QRP$ (C) $\angle YXZ$
   (B) $\angle XZY$ (D) $\angle XYZ$

4. For $\triangle ABC$ and $\triangle DEF$, $\angle A \cong \angle F$, and $\overline{AC} \cong \overline{EF}$. Which of the following would allow you to conclude that these triangles are congruent by AAS?

   (F) $\angle ABC \cong \angle EDF$
   (G) $\angle ACB \cong \angle EDF$
   (H) $\angle BAC \cong \angle FDE$
   (J) $\angle CBA \cong \angle FED$

5. The measure of $\angle 1$ is 4 times the measure of its supplement. What is the measure, in degrees, of $\angle 1$?

   (A) 36 (C) 135
   (B) 45 (D) 144

6. R has coordinates $(-4, 9)$. S has coordinates $(4, -6)$. What is RS?

   (F) 8 (H) 17
   (G) 15 (J) 23

Use the figure below for Items 7 and 8.

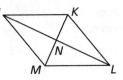

7. If $\overline{JK} \parallel \overline{ML}$, what additional information do you need to prove that quadrilateral $JKLM$ is a parallelogram?

   (A) $\overline{JM} \cong \overline{KL}$
   (B) $\overline{MN} \cong \overline{LN}$
   (C) $\angle MLK$ and $\angle LKJ$ are right angles.
   (D) $\angle JML$ and $\angle KLM$ are supplementary.

8. Given that $JKLM$ is a parallelogram and that $m\angle KLN = 25°$, $m\angle JMN = 65°$, and $m\angle JML = 130°$, which term best describes quadrilateral $JKLM$?

   (F) Rectangle
   (G) Rhombus
   (H) Square
   (J) Trapezoid

9. The vertices of $\square ABCD$ are $A(1, 4)$, $B(4, y)$, $C(3, -2)$, and $D(0, -3)$. What is the value of y?

   (A) 3 (C) 5
   (B) 4 (D) 6

10. Quadrilateral $RSTU$ is a kite. What is the length of $\overline{RV}$?

   (F) 4 inches (H) 6 inches
   (G) 5 inches (J) 13 inches

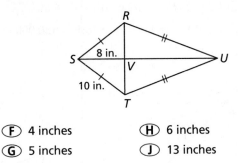

11. Which of the following is NOT valid for proving that triangles are congruent?

Ⓐ AAA Ⓒ SAS

Ⓑ ASA Ⓓ HL

12. Which condition guarantees that $r \parallel s$?

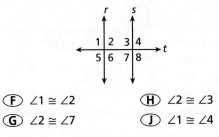

Ⓕ $\angle 1 \cong \angle 2$ Ⓗ $\angle 2 \cong \angle 3$

Ⓖ $\angle 2 \cong \angle 7$ Ⓙ $\angle 1 \cong \angle 4$

13. Two lines a and b are cut by a transversal so that $\angle 1$ and $\angle 2$ are same-side interior angles. If $m\angle 1 = (2x + 30)°$ and $m\angle 2 = (4x - 75)°$, what value of x proves that $a \parallel b$?

Ⓐ 22.5 Ⓒ 45

Ⓑ 37.5 Ⓓ 67.5

14. Heather is 1.6 m tall and casts a shadow of 3.5 m. At the same time, a barn casts a shadow of 17.5 m. Find the height of the barn in meters.

Ⓕ 5 Ⓗ 14

Ⓖ 8 Ⓙ 38

15. What is the measure, in degrees, of $\angle H$?

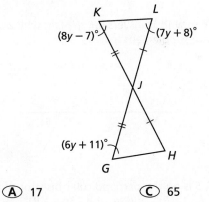

Ⓐ 17 Ⓒ 65

Ⓑ 44 Ⓓ 71

16. $\triangle JKL \cong \triangle XYZ$, and $JK = 10 - 2n$. $XY = 2$, and $YZ = n^2$. What is KL?

Ⓕ 2 Ⓗ 8

Ⓖ 4 Ⓙ 16

Use the diagram for Items 17 and 18.

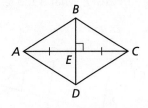

17. Which of these congruence statements can be proved from the information given in the figure?

Ⓐ $\triangle AEB \cong \triangle CED$

Ⓑ $\triangle BAC \cong \triangle DAC$

Ⓒ $\triangle ABD \cong \triangle BCA$

Ⓓ $\triangle DEC \cong \triangle DEA$

18. What other information is needed to prove that $\triangle CEB \cong \triangle AED$ by the HL Congruence Theorem?

Ⓕ $\overline{AD} \cong \overline{AB}$

Ⓖ $\overline{BE} \cong \overline{AE}$

Ⓗ $\overline{CB} \cong \overline{AD}$

Ⓙ $\overline{DE} \cong \overline{CE}$

19. What is the measure of $\angle ACD$?

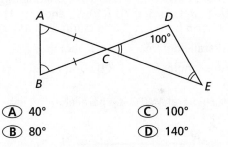

Ⓐ 40° Ⓒ 100°

Ⓑ 80° Ⓓ 140°

20. Congruent segments have equal measures. A segment bisector divides a segment into two congruent segments. $\overrightarrow{XY}$ intersects $\overline{DE}$ at X and bisects $\overline{DE}$. Which conjecture is valid?

Ⓕ $m\angle YXD = m\angle YXE$

Ⓖ Y is between D and E.

Ⓗ $DX = XE$

Ⓙ $DE = YE$

21. $\overline{GJ}$ is a midsegment of $\triangle DEF$, and $\overline{HK}$ is a midsegment of $\triangle GFJ$. What is the length of $\overline{HK}$?

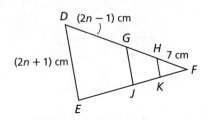

    Ⓐ 2.25 centimeters

    Ⓑ 4 centimeters

    Ⓒ 7.5 centimeters

    Ⓓ 9 centimeters

22. In $\triangle ABC$ and $\triangle DEF$, $\overline{AC} \cong \overline{DE}$, and $\angle A \cong \angle E$. Which of the following would allow you to conclude by SAS that these triangles are congruent?

    Ⓕ $\overline{AB} \cong \overline{DF}$

    Ⓖ $\overline{AC} \cong \overline{EF}$

    Ⓗ $\overline{BA} \cong \overline{FE}$

    Ⓙ $\overline{CB} \cong \overline{DF}$

23. The coordinates of the vertices of quadrilateral $RSTU$ are $R(1, 3)$, $S(2, 7)$, $T(10, 5)$, and $U(9, 1)$. Which term best describes quadrilateral $RSTU$?

    Ⓐ Parallelogram   Ⓒ Rhombus

    Ⓑ Rectangle   Ⓓ Trapezoid

24. If quadrilateral $MNPQ$ is a parallelogram, what is the value of x?

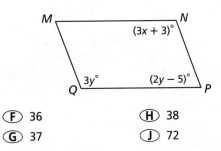

    Ⓕ 36   Ⓗ 38

    Ⓖ 37   Ⓙ 72

25. Quadrilateral $RSTU$ is a rectangle with diagonals $\overline{RT}$ and $\overline{SU}$. If $RT = 4a + 2$ and $SU = 6a - 25$, what is the value of a?

    Ⓐ 2.7   Ⓒ 13.5

    Ⓑ 11.5   Ⓓ 20.5

Use the diagram for Items 26 and 27.

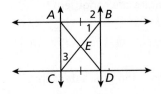

26. Given that $\overline{AB} \cong \overline{CD}$, which additional information would be sufficient to prove that $ABCD$ is a parallelogram?

    Ⓕ $\overline{AB} \parallel \overline{CD}$

    Ⓖ $\overline{AC} \parallel \overline{BD}$

    Ⓗ $\angle CAB \cong \angle CDB$

    Ⓙ E is the midpoint of $\overline{AD}$.

27. If $\overleftrightarrow{AC}$ is parallel to $\overleftrightarrow{BD}$ and $m\angle 1 + m\angle 2 = 140°$, what is the measure of $\angle 3$?

    Ⓐ 20°   Ⓒ 50°

    Ⓑ 40°   Ⓓ 70°

Mini-Tasks

28. $\triangle ABC$ has vertices $A(-2, 0)$, $B(2, 2)$, and $C(2, -2)$. $\triangle DEC$ has vertices $D(0, -1)$, $E(2, 0)$, and $C(2, -2)$. Prove that $\triangle ABC \sim \triangle DEC$.

29. $\triangle ABC$ and $\triangle ABD$ share side $\overline{AB}$. Given that $\triangle ABC \sim \triangle ABD$, use AAS to explain why these two triangles must also be congruent.

30. Given $\ell \parallel m$ with transversal t, explain why $\angle 1$ and $\angle 8$ are supplementary.

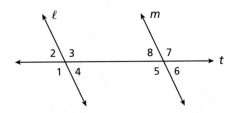

31. In $\triangle RST$, S is on the perpendicular bisector of $\overline{RT}$, $m\angle S = (4n + 16)°$, and $m\angle R = (3n - 18)°$. Find $m\angle R$. Show your work and explain how you determined your answer.

32. Use the given two-column proof to write a flowchart proof.

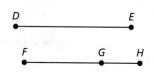

Given: $\overline{DE} \cong \overline{FH}$
Prove: $DE = FG + GH$

Two-column proof:

Statements	Reasons
1. $\overline{DE} \cong \overline{FH}$	**1.** Given
2. $DE = FH$	**2.** Def. of ≅ segs.
3. $FG + GH = FH$	**3.** Seg. Add. Post.
4. $DE = FG + GH$	**4.** Subst.

Performance Tasks

33. a. Complete the following proof by filling in the missing statements and reasons.

Given: $\overline{WY}$ bisects $\angle XWZ$,
$\overline{WX} \cong \overline{WZ}$
Prove: $\overline{WY}$ bisects $\overline{XZ}$

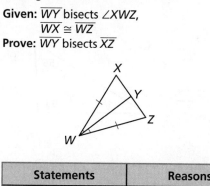

Statements	Reasons
1. ?	**1.** Given
2. $\overline{WX} \cong \overline{WZ}$	**2.** ?
3. $\overline{WY} \cong \overline{WY}$	**3.** ?
4. $\angle XWY \cong \angle ZWY$	**4.** Def. of angle bisector
5. ?	**5.** SAS
6. $\overline{XY} \cong \overline{ZY}$	**6.** ?
7. ?	**7.** ?

b. Another student claims that you don't need SAS to prove this result. Is the student correct? Which congruence theorem could you use? Rewrite the proof using that theorem.

34. Abstract Furnishings is a company that specializes in designing and making unusual furniture. The diagram shows one of their bookshelf designs.

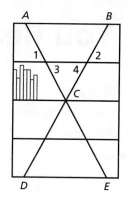

a. Complete the two-column proof.

Given: $\angle 1 \cong \angle 2$
Prove: $\angle 3 \cong \angle 4$

Statements	Reasons
1. $\angle 1 \cong \angle 2$	**1.** Given
2. $m\angle 1 = m\angle 2$	**2.** Def. of ≅ ∠s
3. $\angle 1 \cong$?	**3.** Vert. ∠s Thm.
4. $m\angle 1 = m\angle 3$	**4.** Def. of ≅ ∠s
5. $\angle 2 \cong \angle 4$	**5.** ?
6. $m\angle 2 = m\angle 4$	**6.** Def. of ≅ ∠s
7. $m\angle 1 = m\angle 4$	**7.** ?
8. $m\angle 3 =$?	**8.** Substitution
9. $\angle 3 \cong \angle 4$	**9.** Def. of ≅ ∠s

b. The designer wants to change the design so that AB is smaller, while keeping C fixed in place. How will this affect the numbered angle measures? Include a sketch with your answer.

c. If $\angle 1 \cong \angle 2$ is still true in the new design, can you still conclude $\angle 3 \cong \angle 4$? Explain why or why not.

my.hrw.com
Online Assessment

Go online for updated, PARCC-aligned assessment readiness.

Are You Ready?

my.hrw.com
Assessment and Intervention

✓ Vocabulary

Match each term on the left with a definition on the right.

1. angle bisector
2. conclusion
3. hypotenuse
4. leg of a right triangle
5. perpendicular bisector of a segment

A. the side opposite the right angle in a right triangle

B. a line that is perpendicular to a segment at its midpoint

C. the phrase following the word *then* in a conditional statement

D. one of the two sides that form the right angle in a right triangle

E. a line or ray that divides an angle into two congruent angles

F. the phrase following the word *if* in a conditional statement

✓ Classify Triangles

Tell whether each triangle is acute, right, or obtuse.

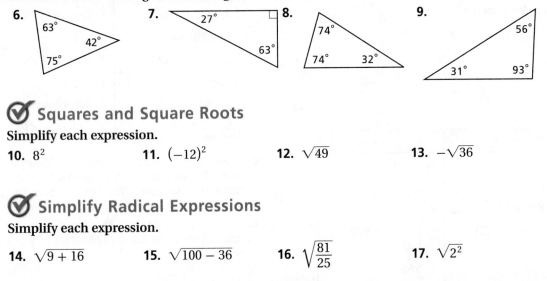

6. (63°, 42°, 75°)
7. (27°, 63°, right angle)
8. (74°, 74°, 32°)
9. (56°, 31°, 93°)

✓ Squares and Square Roots

Simplify each expression.

10. 8^2

11. $(-12)^2$

12. $\sqrt{49}$

13. $-\sqrt{36}$

✓ Simplify Radical Expressions

Simplify each expression.

14. $\sqrt{9 + 16}$

15. $\sqrt{100 - 36}$

16. $\sqrt{\dfrac{81}{25}}$

17. $\sqrt{2^2}$

Career Readiness Air Traffic Controllers

Air traffic controllers coordinate movement of air traffic using radar and visual observation. They observe takeoffs and landings (including angles of elevation and depression), handle flight data, and monitor the movement of all planes for which they are responsible. Training of air traffic controllers varies but includes certification by the Federal Aviation Administration (FAA). Air traffic controllers may be employed by the FAA, the Department of Defense, or private air traffic control companies.

Right Triangle Trigonometry

Online Edition

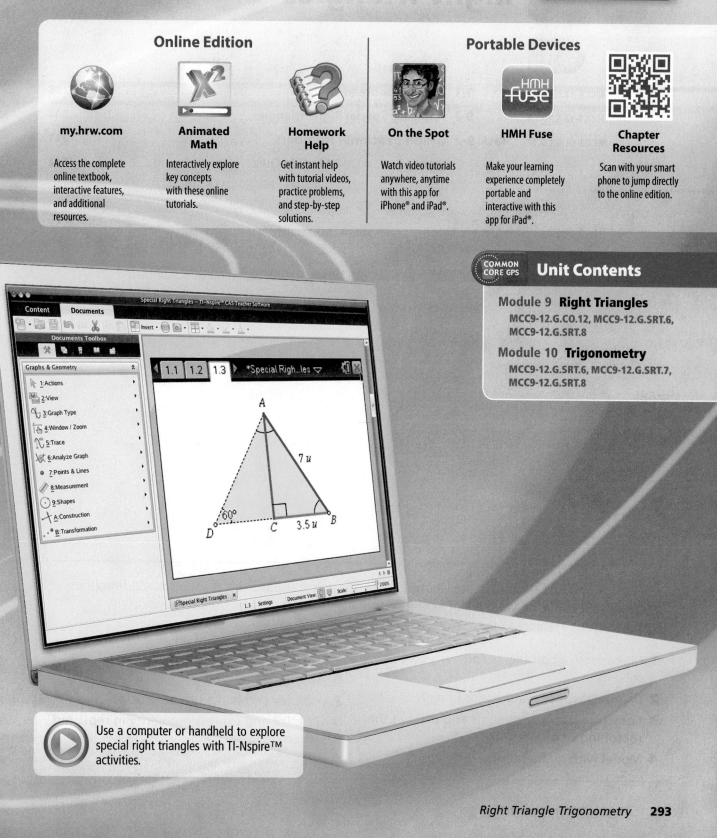

my.hrw.com

Access the complete online textbook, interactive features, and additional resources.

Animated Math

Interactively explore key concepts with these online tutorials.

Homework Help

Get instant help with tutorial videos, practice problems, and step-by-step solutions.

Portable Devices

On the Spot

Watch video tutorials anywhere, anytime with this app for iPhone® and iPad®.

HMH Fuse

Make your learning experience completely portable and interactive with this app for iPad®.

Chapter Resources

Scan with your smart phone to jump directly to the online edition.

Use a computer or handheld to explore special right triangles with TI-Nspire™ activities.

9 Right Triangles

COMMON CORE GPS

Contents

MATHEMATICAL PRACTICES   The Common Core Georgia Performance Standards for Mathematical Practice describe varieties of expertise that all students should seek to develop. Opportunities to develop these practices are integrated throughout this program.

1 Make sense of problems and persevere in solving them.

2 Reason abstractly and quantitatively.

3 Construct viable arguments and critique the reasoning of others.

4 Model with mathematics.

5 Use appropriate tools strategically.

6 Attend to precision.

7 Look for and make use of structure.

8 Look for and express regularity in repeated reasoning.

Unpacking the Standards

my.hrw.com
Multilingual Glossary

Understanding the standards and the vocabulary terms in the standards will help you know exactly what you are expected to learn in this chapter.

 MCC9-12.G.SRT.8

Use ... the Pythagorean Theorem to solve right triangles in applied problems.

Key Vocabulary

Pythagorean Theorem (Teorema de Pitágoras) If a right triangle has legs of lengths a and b and a hypotenuse of length c, then $a^2 + b^2 = c^2$.

right triangle (triángulo rectángulo) A triangle with one right angle.

What It Means For You

You can use the relationship between the side lengths of a right triangle to solve real-world problems.

EXAMPLE

The diagram shows the recommended position for placing a ladder. Given the length L of the ladder, you can use the Pythagorean Theorem to find x, the distance from the base of the wall to place the foot of the ladder.

$$L^2 = x^2 + (4x)^2$$
$$L^2 = 17x^2$$
$$\frac{L^2}{17} = x^2$$
$$\frac{L}{\sqrt{17}} = x$$

©PhotoDisc/Getty Images

The Pythagorean Theorem

Essential Question: How can you use side lengths to determine whether a triangle is acute, right, or obtuse?

Objectives
Use the Pythagorean Theorem and its converse to solve problems.

Use Pythagorean inequalities to classify triangles.

Vocabulary
Pythagorean triple

Why learn this?

You can use the Pythagorean Theorem to determine whether a ladder is in a safe position. (See Example 2.)

The Pythagorean Theorem is probably the most famous mathematical relationship. The theorem states that in a right triangle, the sum of the squares of the lengths of the legs equals the square of the length of the hypotenuse.

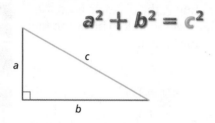

$$a^2 + b^2 = c^2$$

The Pythagorean Theorem is named for the Greek mathematician Pythagoras, who lived in the sixth century B.C.E. However, this relationship was known to earlier people, such as the Babylonians, Egyptians, and Chinese.

There are many different proofs of the Pythagorean Theorem. The one below uses area and algebra.

PROOF   **Pythagorean Theorem**

Given: A right triangle with leg lengths a and b and hypotenuse of length c
Prove: $a^2 + b^2 = c^2$

> **Remember!**
>
> The area A of a square with side length s is given by the formula $A = s^2$.
>
> The area A of a triangle with base b and height h is given by the formula $A = \frac{1}{2}bh$.

Proof: Arrange four copies of the triangle as shown. The sides of the triangles form two squares.

The area of the outer square is $(a + b)^2$. The area of the inner square is c^2. The area of each blue triangle is $\frac{1}{2}ab$.

area of outer square = area of 4 blue triangles + area of inner square

$$(a + b)^2 = 4\left(\frac{1}{2}ab\right) + c^2 \quad \text{Substitute the areas.}$$

$$a^2 + 2ab + b^2 = 2ab + c^2 \quad \text{Simplify.}$$

$$a^2 + b^2 = c^2 \quad \text{Subtract 2ab from both sides.}$$

The Pythagorean Theorem gives you a way to find unknown side lengths when you know a triangle is a right triangle.

EXAMPLE **1** MCC9-12.G.SRT.8

Using the Pythagorean Theorem

Find the value of x. Give your answer in simplest radical form.

A

6, x, 4

$a^2 + b^2 = c^2$ *Pythagorean Theorem*

$6^2 + 4^2 = x^2$ *Substitute 6 for a, 4 for b, and x for c.*

$52 = x^2$ *Simplify.*

$\sqrt{52} = x$ *Find the positive square root.*

$x = \sqrt{(4)(13)} = 2\sqrt{13}$ *Simplify the radical.*

B

5, $x - 1$, x

$a^2 + b^2 = c^2$ *Pythagorean Theorem*

$5^2 + (x - 1)^2 = x^2$ *Substitute 5 for a, x − 1 for b, and x for c.*

$25 + x^2 - 2x + 1 = x^2$ *Multiply.*

$-2x + 26 = 0$ *Combine like terms.*

$26 = 2x$ *Add 2x to both sides.*

$x = 13$ *Divide both sides by 2.*

✓ **CHECK IT OUT!** **Find the value of x. Give your answer in simplest radical form.**

1a. 8, 4, x

1b. $x + 4$, x, 12

EXAMPLE **2** MCC9-12.G.SRT.8

Safety Application

To prevent a ladder from shifting, safety experts recommend that the ratio of $a:b$ be 4:1. How far from the base of the wall should you place the foot of a 10-foot ladder? Round to the nearest inch.

Let x be the distance in feet from the foot of the ladder to the base of the wall. Then $4x$ is the distance in feet from the top of the ladder to the base of the wall.

$a^2 + b^2 = c^2$ *Pythagorean Theorem*

$(4x)^2 + x^2 = 10^2$ *Substitute.*

$17x^2 = 100$ *Multiply and combine like terms.*

$x^2 = \dfrac{100}{17}$ *Divide both sides by 17.*

$x = \sqrt{\dfrac{100}{17}} \approx 2$ ft 5 in.   *Find the positive square root and round it.*

✓ **CHECK IT OUT!** **2. What if...?** According to the recommended ratio, how high will a 30-foot ladder reach when placed against a wall? Round to the nearest inch.

A set of three nonzero whole numbers a, b, and c such that $a^2 + b^2 = c^2$ is called a **Pythagorean triple**.

Common Pythagorean Triples			
3, 4, 5	5, 12, 13	8, 15, 17	7, 24, 25

Identifying Pythagorean Triples

Find the missing side length. Tell if the side lengths form a Pythagorean triple. Explain.

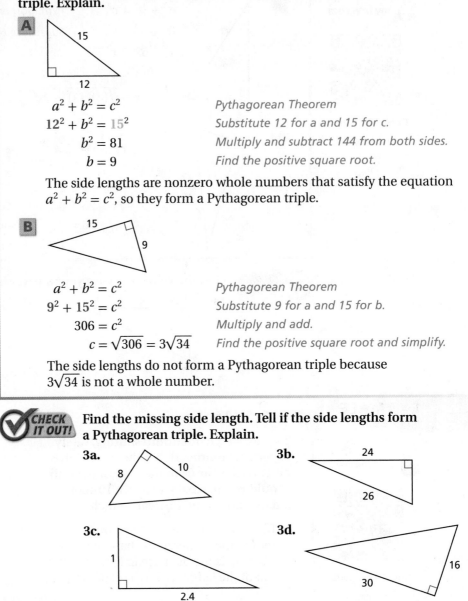

A

$$a^2 + b^2 = c^2 \qquad \text{\textit{Pythagorean Theorem}}$$
$$12^2 + b^2 = 15^2 \qquad \text{\textit{Substitute 12 for a and 15 for c.}}$$
$$b^2 = 81 \qquad \text{\textit{Multiply and subtract 144 from both sides.}}$$
$$b = 9 \qquad \text{\textit{Find the positive square root.}}$$

The side lengths are nonzero whole numbers that satisfy the equation $a^2 + b^2 = c^2$, so they form a Pythagorean triple.

B

$$a^2 + b^2 = c^2 \qquad \text{\textit{Pythagorean Theorem}}$$
$$9^2 + 15^2 = c^2 \qquad \text{\textit{Substitute 9 for a and 15 for b.}}$$
$$306 = c^2 \qquad \text{\textit{Multiply and add.}}$$
$$c = \sqrt{306} = 3\sqrt{34} \qquad \text{\textit{Find the positive square root and simplify.}}$$

The side lengths do not form a Pythagorean triple because $3\sqrt{34}$ is not a whole number.

my.hrw.com

Online Video Tutor

CHECK IT OUT! Find the missing side length. Tell if the side lengths form a Pythagorean triple. Explain.

3a. 8, 10

3b. 24, 26

3c. 1, 2.4

3d. 30, 16

The converse of the Pythagorean Theorem gives you a way to tell if a triangle is a right triangle when you know the side lengths.

Know it!
Note

Theorems 9-1-1	Converse of the Pythagorean Theorem	
THEOREM	**HYPOTHESIS**	**CONCLUSION**
If the sum of the squares of the lengths of two sides of a triangle is equal to the square of the length of the third side, then the triangle is a right triangle.	$a^2 + b^2 = c^2$	$\triangle ABC$ is a right triangle.

You will prove Theorem 9-1-1 in Exercise 45.

You can also use side lengths to classify a triangle as acute or obtuse.

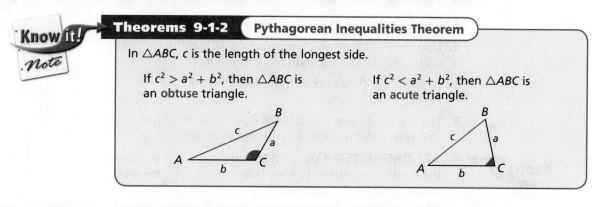

Theorems 9-1-2 (**Pythagorean Inequalities Theorem**)

In $\triangle ABC$, c is the length of the longest side.

If $c^2 > a^2 + b^2$, then $\triangle ABC$ is an **obtuse** triangle.

If $c^2 < a^2 + b^2$, then $\triangle ABC$ is an **acute** triangle.

To understand why the Pythagorean inequalities are true, consider $\triangle ABC$.

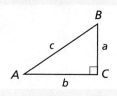

If $c^2 = a^2 + b^2$, then $\triangle ABC$ is a right triangle by the Converse of the Pythagorean Theorem. So $m\angle C = 90°$.

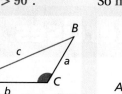

If $c^2 > a^2 + b^2$, then c has increased. By the Converse of the Hinge Theorem, $m\angle C$ has also increased. So $m\angle C > 90°$.

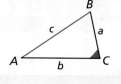

If $c^2 < a^2 + b^2$, then c has decreased. By the Converse of the Hinge Theorem, $m\angle C$ has also decreased. So $m\angle C < 90°$.

COMMON CORE GPS MCC9-12.A.CED.3

EXAMPLE 4

Classifying Triangles

my.hrw.com

Online Video Tutor

Tell if the measures can be the side lengths of a triangle. If so, classify the triangle as acute, obtuse, or right.

A 8, 11, 13

Step 1 Determine if the measures form a triangle.

By the Triangle Inequality Theorem, 8, 11, and 13 can be the side lengths of a triangle.

Step 2 Classify the triangle.

$c^2 \stackrel{?}{=} a^2 + b^2$ *Compare c^2 to $a^2 + b^2$.*

$13^2 \stackrel{?}{=} 8^2 + 11^2$ *Substitute the longest side length for c.*

$169 \stackrel{?}{=} 64 + 121$ *Multiply.*

$169 < 185$ *Add and compare.*

Since $c^2 < a^2 + b^2$, the triangle is **acute**.

B 5.8, 9.3, 15.6

Step 1 Determine if the measures form a triangle.

Since $5.8 + 9.3 = 15.1$ and $15.1 \not> 15.6$, these cannot be the side lengths of a triangle.

CHECK IT OUT! Tell if the measures can be the side lengths of a triangle. If so, classify the triangle as acute, obtuse, or right.

4a. 7, 12, 16   **4b.** 11, 18, 34   **4c.** 3.8, 4.1, 5.2

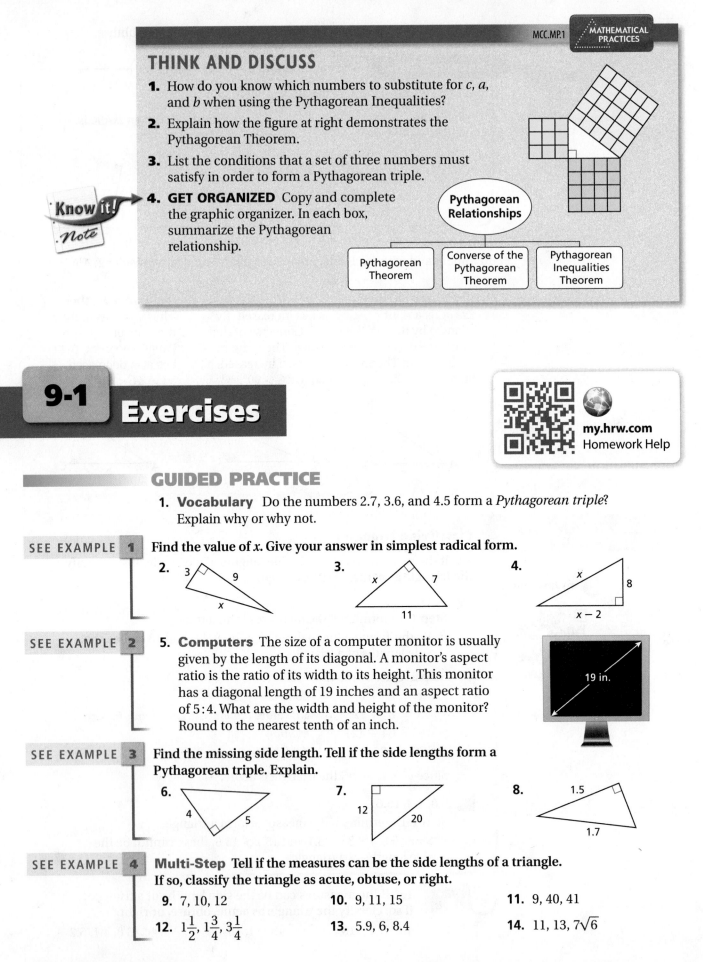

THINK AND DISCUSS

1. How do you know which numbers to substitute for c, a, and b when using the Pythagorean Inequalities?

2. Explain how the figure at right demonstrates the Pythagorean Theorem.

3. List the conditions that a set of three numbers must satisfy in order to form a Pythagorean triple.

4. GET ORGANIZED Copy and complete the graphic organizer. In each box, summarize the Pythagorean relationship.

Pythagorean Relationships
- Pythagorean Theorem
- Converse of the Pythagorean Theorem
- Pythagorean Inequalities Theorem

Know it! Note

9-1 Exercises

my.hrw.com
Homework Help

GUIDED PRACTICE

1. Vocabulary Do the numbers 2.7, 3.6, and 4.5 form a *Pythagorean triple*? Explain why or why not.

SEE EXAMPLE 1 Find the value of x. Give your answer in simplest radical form.

2. 3, 9, x

3. x, 7, 11

4. x, 8, $x-2$

SEE EXAMPLE 2 **5. Computers** The size of a computer monitor is usually given by the length of its diagonal. A monitor's aspect ratio is the ratio of its width to its height. This monitor has a diagonal length of 19 inches and an aspect ratio of 5:4. What are the width and height of the monitor? Round to the nearest tenth of an inch.

19 in.

SEE EXAMPLE 3 Find the missing side length. Tell if the side lengths form a Pythagorean triple. Explain.

6. 4, 5

7. 12, 20

8. 1.5, 1.7

SEE EXAMPLE 4 **Multi-Step** Tell if the measures can be the side lengths of a triangle. If so, classify the triangle as acute, obtuse, or right.

9. 7, 10, 12

10. 9, 11, 15

11. 9, 40, 41

12. $1\frac{1}{2}$, $1\frac{3}{4}$, $3\frac{1}{4}$

13. 5.9, 6, 8.4

14. 11, 13, $7\sqrt{6}$

PRACTICE AND PROBLEM SOLVING

Independent Practice

For Exercises	See Example
15–17	1
18	2
19–21	3
22–27	4

my.hrw.com

Online Extra Practice

Find the value of *x*. Give your answer in simplest radical form.

15.

8

6

x

16.

13

9

x

17.

x

7

x + 1

18. Safety The safety rules for a playground state that the height of the slide and the distance from the base of the ladder to the front of the slide must be in a ratio of 3 : 5. If a slide is about 8 feet long, what are the height of the slide and the distance from the base of the ladder to the front of the slide? Round to the nearest inch.

8 ft
3*x* ft
5*x* ft

Find the missing side length. Tell if the side lengths form a Pythagorean triple. Explain.

19.

6.5

2.5

20.

20

15

21.

7

2

Multi-Step Tell if the measures can be the side lengths of a triangle. If so, classify the triangle as acute, obtuse, or right.

22. 10, 12, 15

23. 8, 13, 23

24. 9, 14, 17

25. $1\frac{1}{2}$, 2, $2\frac{1}{2}$

26. 0.7, 1.1, 1.7

27. 7, 12, $6\sqrt{5}$

28. Surveying It is believed that surveyors in ancient Egypt laid out right angles using a rope divided into twelve sections by eleven equally spaced knots. How could the surveyors use this rope to make a right angle?

Surveying

Ancient Egyptian surveyors were referred to as *rope-stretchers*. The standard surveying rope was 100 royal cubits. A cubit is 52.4 cm long.

29. ///**ERROR ANALYSIS**/// Below are two solutions for finding *x*. Which is incorrect? Explain the error.

13

x + 3

4

A
$a^2 + 4^2 = 13^2$
$a^2 = 169 - 16 = 153$
$a \approx 12.4$
$x + 3 \approx 12.4$
$x \approx 9.4$

B
$(x + 3)^2 + 4^2 = 13^2$
$x^2 + 9 + 16 = 169$
$x^2 = 144$
$x = 12$

Find the value of *x*. Give your answer in simplest radical form.

30.

x

9

15

25

31.

10

6

7

x

32.

5

7

2

x

33.

$\sqrt{34}$

11

3

x

34.

13

20

5

x

35.

30

18

x

H.O.T. 36. Space Exploration The International Space Station orbits at an altitude of about 250 miles above Earth's surface. The radius of Earth is approximately 3963 miles. How far can an astronaut in the space station see to the horizon? Round to the nearest mile.

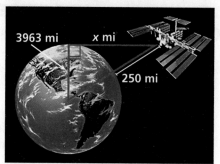

37. Critical Thinking In the proof of the Pythagorean Theorem on the first page of this lesson, how do you know the outer figure is a square? How do you know the inner figure is a square?

Not drawn to scale

Multi-Step Find the perimeter and the area of each figure. Give your answer in simplest radical form.

38.

39.

40.

41.

42.

43.

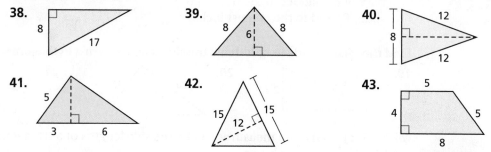

44. Write About It When you apply both the Pythagorean Theorem and its converse, you use the equation $a^2 + b^2 = c^2$. Explain in your own words how the two theorems are different.

45. Use this plan to write a paragraph proof of the Converse of the Pythagorean Theorem.

Given: $\triangle ABC$ with $a^2 + b^2 = c^2$
Prove: $\triangle ABC$ is a right triangle.

Plan: Draw $\triangle PQR$ with $\angle R$ as the right angle, leg lengths of a and b, and a hypotenuse of length x. By the Pythagorean Theorem, $a^2 + b^2 = x^2$. Use substitution to compare x and c. Show that $\triangle ABC \cong \triangle PQR$ and thus $\angle C$ is a right angle.

H.O.T. 46. Complete these steps to prove the Distance Formula.

Given: $J(x_1, y_1)$ and $K(x_2, y_2)$ with $x_1 \neq x_2$ and $y_1 \neq y_2$
Prove: $JK = \sqrt{(x_2 - x_1)^2 + (y_2 - y_1)^2}$

a. Locate L so that $\overline{JK}$ is the hypotenuse of right $\triangle JKL$. What are the coordinates of L?

b. Find JL and LK.

c. By the Pythagorean Theorem, $JK^2 = JL^2 + LK^2$. Find JK.

Real-World Connections

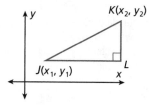

47. The figure shows an airline's routes between four cities.

a. A traveler wants to go from Sanak (*S*) to Manitou (*M*). To minimize the total number of miles traveled, should she first fly to King City (*K*) or to Rice Lake (*R*)?

b. The airline decides to offer a direct flight from Sanak (*S*) to Manitou (*M*). Given that the length of this flight is more than 1360 mi, what can you say about m$\angle SRM$?

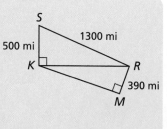

Transtock Inc./Alamy Images

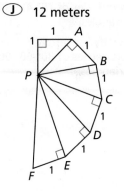

48. Gridded Response $\overline{KX}$, $\overline{LX}$, and $\overline{MX}$ are the perpendicular bisectors of $\triangle GHJ$. Find GJ to the nearest tenth of a unit.

49. Which number forms a Pythagorean triple with 24 and 25?

   A 1   **B** 7   **C** 26   **D** 49

50. The lengths of two sides of an obtuse triangle are 7 meters and 9 meters. Which could NOT be the length of the third side?

   F 4 meters   **G** 5 meters   **H** 11 meters   **J** 12 meters

H.O.T. 51. Extended Response The figure shows the first six triangles in a pattern of triangles.

   a. Find PA, PB, PC, PD, PE, and PF in simplest radical form.

   b. If the pattern continues, what would be the length of the hypotenuse of the ninth triangle? Explain your answer.

   c. Write a rule for finding the length of the hypotenuse of the nth triangle in the pattern. Explain your answer.

CHALLENGE AND EXTEND

52. Algebra Find all values of k so that $(-1, 2)$, $(-10, 5)$, and $(-4, k)$ are the vertices of a right triangle.

H.O.T. 53. Critical Thinking Use a diagram of a right triangle to explain why $a + b > \sqrt{a^2 + b^2}$ for any positive numbers a and b.

54. In a right triangle, the leg lengths are a and b, and the length of the altitude to the hypotenuse is h. Write an expression for h in terms of a and b. (*Hint:* Think of the area of the triangle.)

H.O.T. 55. Critical Thinking Suppose the numbers a, b, and c form a Pythagorean triple. Is each of the following also a Pythagorean triple? Explain.

   a. $a + 1, b + 1, c + 1$ **b.** $2a, 2b, 2c$

   c. a^2, b^2, c^2 **d.** $\sqrt{a}, \sqrt{b}, \sqrt{c}$

MATHEMATICAL
PRACTICES

FOCUS ON MATHEMATICAL PRACTICES

H.O.T. 56. Reasoning Joe rides his bicycle 9 blocks north, then 22 blocks east, then 3 blocks north, and then 12 blocks east. The blocks are square.

   a. How many blocks north did Joe ride? How many blocks east?

   b. Each block is 0.5 mile long. To the nearest tenth of a mile, how far is Joe from his starting point?

H.O.T. 57. Problem Solving A dog pen in the shape of a right isosceles triangle will be placed in the corner of a yard. The owner wants the pen to have an area of 200 square feet. About how much fencing will the owner need?

H.O.T. 58. Analysis $BC = 120$ and the perimeter of $ABCD$ is 458.

   a. Find AB.

   b. Explain why $\triangle AXD$ is a right triangle.

   c. Find the perimeter of $\triangle AXD$.

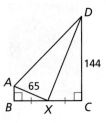

9-2

Applying Special Right Triangles

? Essential Question: What are the proportions of the side lengths in 30°-60°-90° triangles and 45°-45°-90° triangles?

Objectives
Justify and apply properties of 45°-45°-90° triangles.

Justify and apply properties of 30°-60°-90° triangles.

Who uses this?
You can use properties of special right triangles to calculate the correct size of a bandana for your dog. (See Example 2.)

A diagonal of a square divides it into two congruent isosceles right triangles. Since the base angles of an isosceles triangle are congruent, the measure of each acute angle is 45°. So another name for an isosceles right triangle is a 45°-45°-90° triangle.

Animated Math

A 45°-45°-90° triangle is one type of *special right triangle.* You can use the Pythagorean Theorem to find a relationship among the side lengths of a 45°-45°-90° triangle.

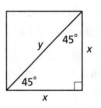

$$a^2 + b^2 = c^2 \quad \text{Pythagorean Theorem}$$
$$x^2 + x^2 = y^2 \quad \text{Substitute the given values.}$$
$$2x^2 = y^2 \quad \text{Simplify.}$$
$$\sqrt{2x^2} = \sqrt{y^2} \quad \text{Find the square root of both sides.}$$
$$x\sqrt{2} = y \quad \text{Simplify.}$$

Know it!
·Note

| Theorem 9-2-1 | 45°-45°-90° Triangle Theorem |

In a 45°-45°-90° triangle, both legs are congruent, and the length of the hypotenuse is the length of a leg times $\sqrt{2}$.

$$AC = BC = \ell \qquad AB = \ell\sqrt{2}$$

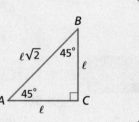

COMMON CORE GPS
MCC9-12.G.SRT.6

EXAMPLE 1 Finding Side Lengths in a 45°-45°-90° Triangle

Find the value of *x*. Give your answer in simplest radical form.

🌐 my.hrw.com

Online Video Tutor

A
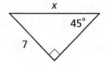

By the Triangle Sum Theorem, the measure of the third angle of the triangle is 45°. So it is a 45°-45°-90° triangle with a leg length of 7.

$$x = 7\sqrt{2} \qquad \text{Hypotenuse} = leg\sqrt{2}$$

Taxi/Getty Images

Find the value of *x*. Give your answer in simplest radical form.

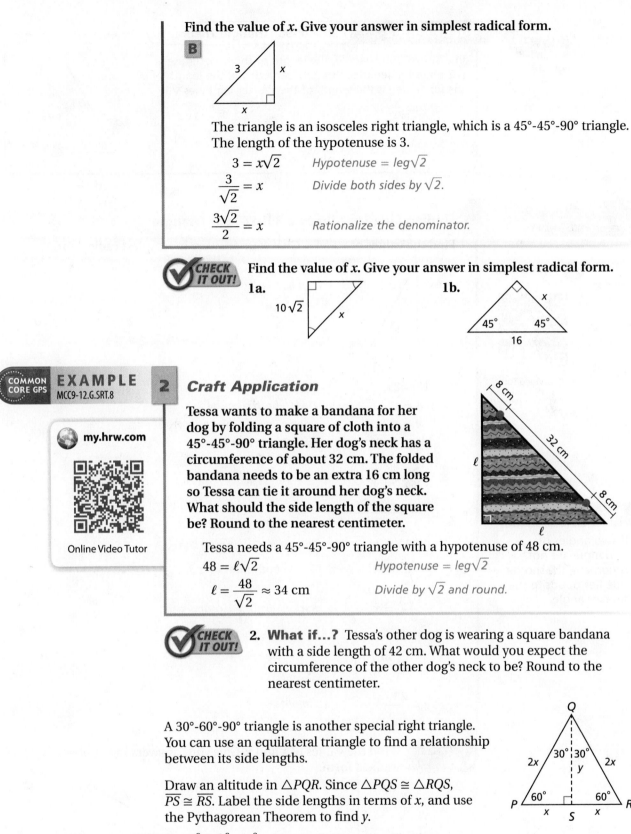

B

The triangle is an isosceles right triangle, which is a 45°-45°-90° triangle. The length of the hypotenuse is 3.

$$3 = x\sqrt{2} \qquad \textit{Hypotenuse = leg}\sqrt{2}$$

$$\frac{3}{\sqrt{2}} = x \qquad \textit{Divide both sides by } \sqrt{2}.$$

$$\frac{3\sqrt{2}}{2} = x \qquad \textit{Rationalize the denominator.}$$

CHECK IT OUT! **Find the value of *x*. Give your answer in simplest radical form.**

1a. **1b.**

COMMON CORE GPS **EXAMPLE** **2** *Craft Application*
MCC9-12.G.SRT.8

my.hrw.com

Online Video Tutor

Tessa wants to make a bandana for her dog by folding a square of cloth into a 45°-45°-90° triangle. Her dog's neck has a circumference of about 32 cm. The folded bandana needs to be an extra 16 cm long so Tessa can tie it around her dog's neck. What should the side length of the square be? Round to the nearest centimeter.

Tessa needs a 45°-45°-90° triangle with a hypotenuse of 48 cm.

$$48 = \ell\sqrt{2} \qquad \textit{Hypotenuse = leg}\sqrt{2}$$

$$\ell = \frac{48}{\sqrt{2}} \approx 34 \text{ cm} \qquad \textit{Divide by } \sqrt{2} \textit{ and round.}$$

CHECK IT OUT! **2. What if...?** Tessa's other dog is wearing a square bandana with a side length of 42 cm. What would you expect the circumference of the other dog's neck to be? Round to the nearest centimeter.

A 30°-60°-90° triangle is another special right triangle. You can use an equilateral triangle to find a relationship between its side lengths.

Draw an altitude in △*PQR*. Since △*PQS* ≅ △*RQS*, $\overline{PS} \cong \overline{RS}$. Label the side lengths in terms of *x*, and use the Pythagorean Theorem to find *y*.

$$a^2 + b^2 = c^2 \qquad \textit{Pythagorean Theorem}$$

$$x^2 + y^2 = (2x)^2 \qquad \textit{Substitute x for a, y for b, and 2x for c.}$$

$$y^2 = 3x^2 \qquad \textit{Multiply and combine like terms.}$$

$$\sqrt{y^2} = \sqrt{3x^2} \qquad \textit{Find the square root of both sides.}$$

$$y = x\sqrt{3} \qquad \textit{Simplify.}$$

HMH Photo

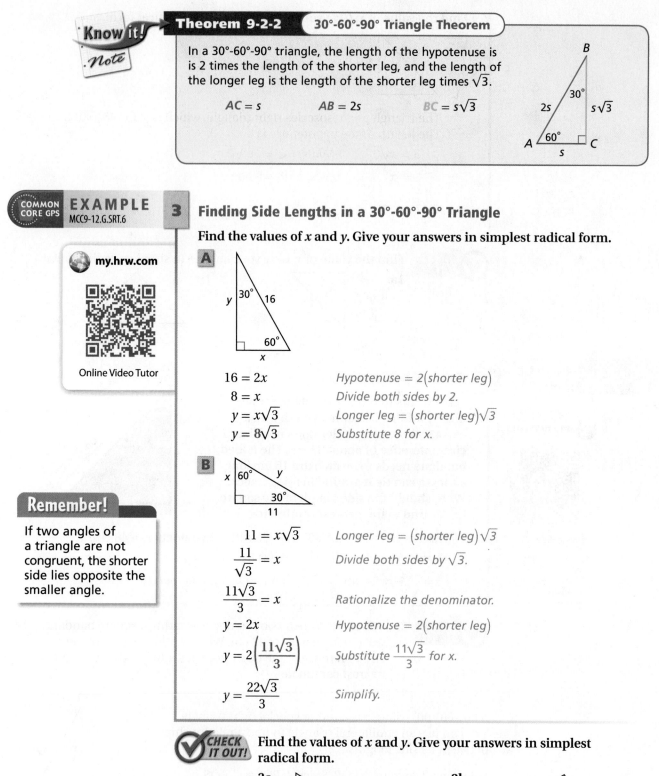

Know it! Note

Theorem 9-2-2 **30°-60°-90° Triangle Theorem**

In a 30°-60°-90° triangle, the length of the hypotenuse is is 2 times the length of the shorter leg, and the length of the longer leg is the length of the shorter leg times $\sqrt{3}$.

$$AC = s \qquad AB = 2s \qquad BC = s\sqrt{3}$$

COMMON CORE GPS
MCC9-12.G.SRT.6

EXAMPLE **3** Finding Side Lengths in a 30°-60°-90° Triangle

Find the values of x and y. Give your answers in simplest radical form.

A

$$16 = 2x \qquad \text{Hypotenuse} = 2(\text{shorter leg})$$
$$8 = x \qquad \text{Divide both sides by 2.}$$
$$y = x\sqrt{3} \qquad \text{Longer leg} = (\text{shorter leg})\sqrt{3}$$
$$y = 8\sqrt{3} \qquad \text{Substitute 8 for } x.$$

B

Remember!

If two angles of a triangle are not congruent, the shorter side lies opposite the smaller angle.

$$11 = x\sqrt{3} \qquad \text{Longer leg} = (\text{shorter leg})\sqrt{3}$$
$$\frac{11}{\sqrt{3}} = x \qquad \text{Divide both sides by } \sqrt{3}.$$
$$\frac{11\sqrt{3}}{3} = x \qquad \text{Rationalize the denominator.}$$
$$y = 2x \qquad \text{Hypotenuse} = 2(\text{shorter leg})$$
$$y = 2\left(\frac{11\sqrt{3}}{3}\right) \qquad \text{Substitute } \frac{11\sqrt{3}}{3} \text{ for } x.$$
$$y = \frac{22\sqrt{3}}{3} \qquad \text{Simplify.}$$

my.hrw.com

Online Video Tutor

CHECK IT OUT! Find the values of x and y. Give your answers in simplest radical form.

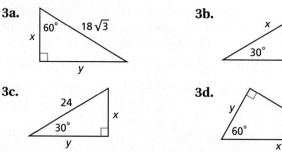

3a.

3b.

3c.

3d.

30°-60°-90° Triangles

Marcus Maiello
Johnson High School

To remember the side relationships in a 30°-60°-90° triangle, I draw a simple "1-2-$\sqrt{3}$" triangle like this.

$2 = 2(1)$, so
hypotenuse = 2(shorter leg).

$\sqrt{3} = \sqrt{3}(1)$, so
longer leg = $\sqrt{3}$(*shorter leg*).

COMMON CORE GPS

EXAMPLE 4
MCC9-12.G.SRT.8

my.hrw.com

Online Video Tutor

Using the 30°-60°-90° Triangle Theorem

The frame of the clock shown is an equilateral triangle. The length of one side of the frame is 20 cm. Will the clock fit on a shelf that is 18 cm below the shelf above it?

Step 1 Divide the equilateral triangle into two 30°-60°-90° triangles.

The height of the frame is the length of the longer leg.

Step 2 Find the length x of the shorter leg.

$20 = 2x$ Hypotenuse = 2(shorter leg)
$10 = x$ Divide both sides by 2.

Step 3 Find the length h of the longer leg.

$h = 10\sqrt{3} \approx 17.3$ cm   Longer leg = (shorter leg)$\sqrt{3}$

The frame is approximately 17.3 centimeters tall.
So the clock will fit on the shelf.

CHECK IT OUT!

4. What if...? A manufacturer wants to make a larger clock with a height of 30 centimeters. What is the length of each side of the frame? Round to the nearest tenth.

MCC.MP.6

MATHEMATICAL PRACTICES

THINK AND DISCUSS

1. Explain why an isosceles right triangle is a 45°-45°-90° triangle.

2. Describe how finding x in triangle I is different from finding x in triangle II.

I.

II.

Know it! Note

3. GET ORGANIZED Copy and complete the graphic organizer. In each box, sketch the special right triangle and label its side lengths in terms of s.

Special Right Triangles

45°-45°-90° triangle

30°-60°-90° triangle

Exercises

GUIDED PRACTICE

SEE EXAMPLE **1**   Find the value of x. Give your answer in simplest radical form.

1. $45°$ 14 x

2. 12 x x

3. x $45°$ $9\sqrt{2}$

SEE EXAMPLE **2**   **4. Transportation** The two arms of the railroad sign are perpendicular bisectors of each other. In Pennsylvania, the lengths marked in red must be 19.5 inches. What is the distance labeled d? Round to the nearest tenth of an inch.

RAIL CROSSING ROAD
19.5 in. d

SEE EXAMPLE **3**   Find the values of x and y. Give your answers in simplest radical form.

5. y $30°$ x $60°$ 6

6. y x $30°$ 15

7. x $7\sqrt{3}$ $30°$ $60°$ y

SEE EXAMPLE **4**   **8. Entertainment** Regulation billiard balls are $2\frac{1}{4}$ inches in diameter. The rack used to group 15 billiard balls is in the shape of an equilateral triangle. What is the approximate height of the triangle formed by the rack? Round to the nearest quarter of an inch.

PRACTICE AND PROBLEM SOLVING

Independent Practice	
For Exercises	See Example
9–11	1
12	2
13–15	3
16	4

Find the value of x. Give your answer in simplest radical form.

9. x $45°$ 15

10. x $45°$ $45°$ $4\sqrt{2}$

11. $18\sqrt{2}$ x

12. Design This tabletop is an isosceles right triangle. The length of the front edge of the table is 48 inches. What is the length w of each side edge? Round to the nearest tenth of an inch.

w w 48 in.

Find the value of x and y. Give your answers in simplest radical form.

13. 24 y $60°$ x

14. y $30°$ x $10\sqrt{3}$

15. y $60°$ $30°$ x 2

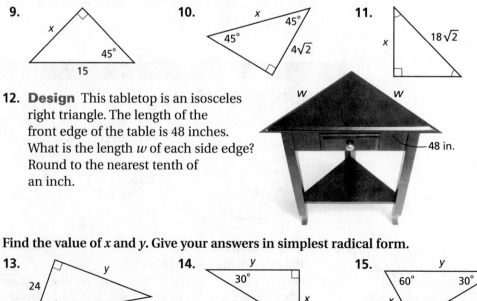

16. Pets A dog walk is used in dog agility competitions. In this dog walk, each ramp makes an angle of 30° with the ground.

  a. How long is one ramp?

  b. How long is the entire dog walk, including both ramps?

Multi-Step Find the perimeter and area of each figure. Give your answers in simplest radical form.

17. a 45°-45°-90° triangle with hypotenuse length 12 inches

18. a 30°-60°-90° triangle with hypotenuse length 28 centimeters

19. a square with diagonal length 18 meters

20. an equilateral triangle with side length 4 feet

21. an equilateral triangle with height 30 yards

H.O.T. 22. Estimation The triangle loom is made from wood strips shaped into a 45°-45°-90° triangle. Pegs are placed every $\frac{1}{2}$ inch along the hypotenuse and every $\frac{1}{4}$ inch along each leg. Suppose you make a loom with an 18-inch hypotenuse. Approximately how many pegs will you need?

H.O.T. 23. Critical Thinking The angle measures of a triangle are in the ratio 1:2:3. Are the side lengths also in the ratio 1:2:3? Explain your answer.

Find the coordinates of point P under the given conditions. Give your answers in simplest radical form.

24. $\triangle PQR$ is a 45°-45°-90° triangle with vertices $Q(4, 6)$ and $R(-6, -4)$, and m$\angle P = 90°$. P is in Quadrant II.

25. $\triangle PST$ is a 45°-45°-90° triangle with vertices $S(4, -3)$ and $T(-2, 3)$, and m$\angle S = 90°$. P is in Quadrant I.

26. $\triangle PWX$ is a 30°-60°-90° triangle with vertices $W(-1, -4)$ and $X(4, -4)$, and m$\angle W = 90°$. P is in Quadrant II.

27. $\triangle PYZ$ is a 30°-60°-90° triangle with vertices $Y(-7, 10)$ and $Z(5, 10)$, and m$\angle Z = 90°$. P is in Quadrant IV.

28. Write About It Why do you think 30°-60°-90° triangles and 45°-45°-90° triangles are called *special right triangles*?

Real-World Connections

29. The figure shows an airline's routes among four cities. The airline offers one frequent-flier mile for each mile flown (rounded to the nearest mile). How many frequent-flier miles do you earn for each flight?

  a. Nelson (*N*) to Belton (*B*)

  b. Idria (*I*) to Nelson (*N*)

  c. Belton (*B*) to Idria (*I*)

TEST PREP

30. Which is a true statement?

    Ⓐ $AB = BC\sqrt{2}$ Ⓒ $AC = BC\sqrt{3}$

    Ⓑ $AB = BC\sqrt{3}$ Ⓓ $AC = AB\sqrt{2}$

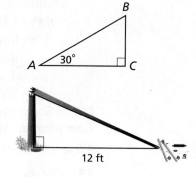

31. An 18-foot pole is broken during a storm. The top of the pole touches the ground 12 feet from the base of the pole. How tall is the part of the pole left standing?

    Ⓕ 5 feet   Ⓗ 13 feet

    Ⓖ 6 feet   Ⓙ 22 feet

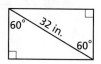

32. The length of the hypotenuse of an isosceles right triangle is 24 inches. What is the length of one leg of the triangle, rounded to the nearest tenth of an inch?

    Ⓐ 13.9 inches   Ⓒ 33.9 inches

    Ⓑ 17.0 inches   Ⓓ 41.6 inches

33. **Gridded Response** Find the area of the rectangle to the nearest tenth of a square inch.

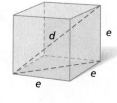

CHALLENGE AND EXTEND

H.O.T. **Multi-Step** Find the value of x in each figure.

34.

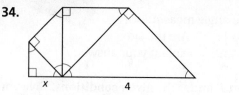

35.

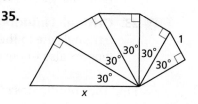

36. Each edge of the cube has length e.

  a. Find the diagonal length d when $e = 1$, $e = 2$, and $e = 3$. Give the answers in simplest radical form.

  b. Write a formula for d for any positive value of e.

H.O.T. **37.** Write a paragraph proof to show that the altitude to the hypotenuse of a 30°-60°-90° triangle divides the hypotenuse into two segments, one of which is 3 times as long as the other.

FOCUS ON MATHEMATICAL PRACTICES

H.O.T. **38.** **Number Sense** The lengths of the sides of a triangle, rounded to the nearest ten, are 60 cm, 100 cm, and 120 cm. Could the triangle be a special right triangle? If so, which one could it be?

H.O.T. **39.** **Make a Conjecture** Three clocks with identical heights are shaped like isosceles triangles. They have base angles of 30°, 45°, and 60°. Order the lengths of the bases from least to greatest. Make a conjecture about the relationship between the measures of the base angles and the lengths of the bases of isosceles triangles with equal heights.

H.O.T. **40.** **Reasoning** The perimeter of a 45°-45°-90° triangle is P. Write an expression for the length of one leg in terms of P.

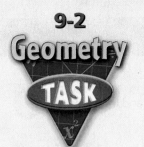

9-2
Geometry TASK

Graph Irrational Numbers

Numbers such as $\sqrt{2}$ and $\sqrt{3}$ are irrational. That is, they cannot be written as the ratio of two integers. In decimal form, they are infinite nonrepeating decimals. You can round the decimal form to estimate the location of these numbers on a number line, or you can use right triangles to construct their locations exactly.

Use with Applying Special Right Triangles

 **Use appropriate tools strategically.**

Activity

① Draw a line. Mark two points near the left side of the line and label them 0 and 1. The distance from 0 to 1 is 1 unit.

② Set your compass to 1 unit and mark increments at 2, 3, 4, and 5 units to construct a number line.

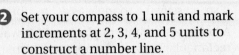

③ Construct a perpendicular to the line through 1.

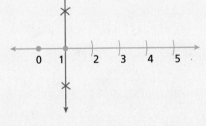

④ Using your compass, mark 1 unit up from the number line and then draw a right triangle. The legs both have length 1, so by the Pythagorean Theorem, the hypotenuse has a length of $\sqrt{2}$.

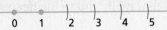

⑤ Set your compass to the length of the hypotenuse. Draw an arc centered at 0 that intersects the number line at $\sqrt{2}$.

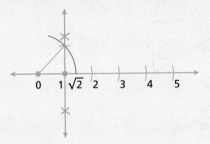

⑥ Repeat Steps 3 through 5, starting at $\sqrt{2}$, to construct a segment of length $\sqrt{3}$.

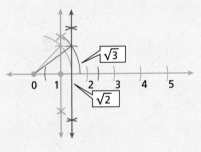

Try This

1. Sketch the two right triangles from Step 6. Label the side lengths and use the Pythagorean Theorem to show why the construction is correct.

2. Construct $\sqrt{4}$ and verify that it is equal to 2.

3. Construct $\sqrt{5}$ through $\sqrt{9}$ and verify that $\sqrt{9}$ is equal to 3.

4. Set your compass to the length of the segment from 0 to $\sqrt{2}$. Mark off another segment of length $\sqrt{2}$ to show that $\sqrt{8}$ is equal to $2\sqrt{2}$.

Ready to Go On?

my.hrw.com
Assessment and Intervention

9-1 The Pythagorean Theorem

1. Find the value of x. Give the answer in simplest radical form.

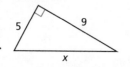

2. Find the missing side length. Tell if the side lengths form a Pythagorean triple. Explain.

3. Tell if the measures 10, 12, and 16 can be the side lengths of a triangle. If so, classify the triangle as acute, obtuse, or right.

4. A landscaper wants to place a stone walkway from one corner of the rectangular lawn to the opposite corner. What will be the length of the walkway? Round to the nearest inch.

Find the missing side length. Tell if the sides form a Pythagorean triple. Explain.

5.

6.

Tell if the measures can be the side lengths of a triangle. If so, classify the triangle as acute, obtuse, or right.

7. 9, 12, 16

8. 11, 14, 27

9. 1.5, 3.6, 3.9

10. 2, 3.7, 4.1

9-2 Applying Special Right Triangles

Find the values of the variables. Give your answers in simplest radical form.

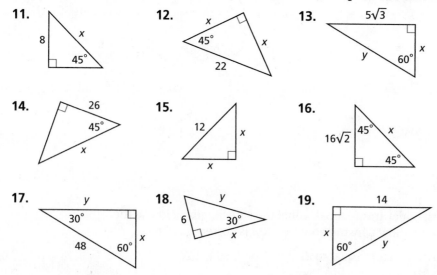

11.

12.

13.

14.

15.

16.

17.

18.

19.

PARCC Assessment Readiness

Selected Response

1. Find the value of *x*. Express your answer in simplest radical form.

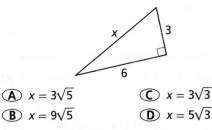

- **(A)** $x = 3\sqrt{5}$
- **(B)** $x = 9\sqrt{5}$
- **(C)** $x = 3\sqrt{3}$
- **(D)** $x = 5\sqrt{3}$

2. Find the value of *x*. Express your answer in simplest radical form.

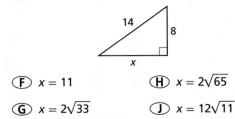

- **(F)** $x = 11$
- **(G)** $x = 2\sqrt{33}$
- **(H)** $x = 2\sqrt{65}$
- **(J)** $x = 12\sqrt{11}$

3. Tell if the measures 9, 11, and 15 can be side lengths of a triangle. If so, classify the triangle as acute, right, or obtuse.

- **(A)** Yes; acute triangle
- **(B)** Yes; right triangle
- **(C)** Yes; obtuse triangle
- **(D)** No; the measures cannot be side lengths of a triangle.

4. The length of the hypotenuse of a right triangle is three times the length of the shorter leg. The length of the longer leg is 12. What is the length of the shorter leg?

- **(F)** $2\sqrt{3}$
- **(G)** $\sqrt{14.4}$
- **(H)** $3\sqrt{2}$
- **(J)** $6\sqrt{2}$

5. What is an expression in simplest form for the perimeter of the 30°-60°-90° triangle shown?

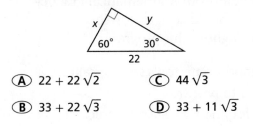

- **(A)** $22 + 22\sqrt{2}$
- **(B)** $33 + 22\sqrt{3}$
- **(C)** $44\sqrt{3}$
- **(D)** $33 + 11\sqrt{3}$

6. Each triangle is a 45°-45°-90° triangle. Find the value of *x*.

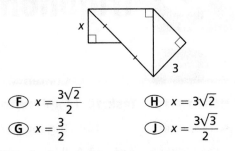

- **(F)** $x = \dfrac{3\sqrt{2}}{2}$
- **(G)** $x = \dfrac{3}{2}$
- **(H)** $x = 3\sqrt{2}$
- **(J)** $x = \dfrac{3\sqrt{3}}{2}$

7. The size of a TV screen is given by the length of its diagonal. The screen aspect ratio is the ratio of its width to its height. The screen aspect ratio of a standard TV screen is 4:3. What are the width and height of a 27″ TV screen?

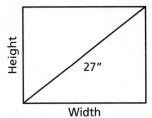

- **(A)** width: 21.6 in., height: 16.2 in.
- **(B)** width: 16.2 in., height: 21.6 in.
- **(C)** width: 21.6 in., height: 5.4 in.
- **(D)** width: 5.4 in., height: 21.6 in.

Mini-Task

8. The yield sign has the shape of an equilateral triangle with a side length of 36 inches. What is the height of the sign? Will a rectangular metal sheet 36 inches wide and 32 inches tall be big enough to make one sign?

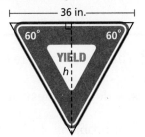

10 Trigonometry

COMMON
CORE GPS

Contents

MATHEMATICAL PRACTICES — The Common Core Georgia Performance Standards for Mathematical Practice describe varieties of expertise that all students should seek to develop. Opportunities to develop these practices are integrated throughout this program.

1 Make sense of problems and persevere in solving them.

2 Reason abstractly and quantitatively.

3 Construct viable arguments and critique the reasoning of others.

4 Model with mathematics.

5 Use appropriate tools strategically.

6 Attend to precision.

7 Look for and make use of structure.

8 Look for and express regularity in repeated reasoning.

Unpacking the Standards

Understanding the standards and the vocabulary terms in the standards will help you know exactly what you are expected to learn in this chapter.

 MCC9-12.G.SRT.6

Understand that by similarity, side ratios in right triangles are properties of the angles in the triangle, leading to definitions of trigonometric ratios for acute angles.

Key Vocabulary

similar (semejantes)
Two figures are similar if they have the same shape but not necessarily the same size.

ratio (razón)
A comparison of two quantities by division.

right triangle (triángulo rectángulo)
A triangle with one right (90°) angle.

angle (ángulo)
A figure formed by two rays with a common endpoint.

trigonometric ratio (razón trigonométrica)
A ratio of two sides of a right triangle.

acute angle (ángulo agudo)
An angle that measures greater than 0° and less than 90°.

What It Means For You

All right triangles with the same angle measures are similar, and similar triangles have proportional side lengths. So the measures of the acute angles in a given right triangle determine the ratios of the side lengths of that triangle and of all similar triangles. These ratios, called *trigonometric ratios*, can be used to solve problems.

EXAMPLE

The sine of $\angle R$ is $\dfrac{\text{opposite leg}}{\text{hypotenuse}} = \dfrac{12}{13}$.

The cosine of $\angle R$ is $\dfrac{\text{adjacent leg}}{\text{hypotenuse}} = \dfrac{5}{13}$.

The tangent of $\angle R$ is $\dfrac{\text{opposite leg}}{\text{adjacent leg}} = \dfrac{12}{5}$.

10-1
Technology TASK

Explore Trigonometric Ratios

In a right triangle, the ratio of two side lengths is known as a *trigonometric ratio*.

Use with Trigonometric Ratios

Use appropriate tools strategically.

MCC9-12.G.SRT.6 Understand that … side ratios in right triangles are properties of the angles in the triangle, leading to definitions of trigonometric ratios …

Activity

1. Construct three points and label them *A*, *B*, and *C*. Construct rays $\overrightarrow{AB}$ and $\overrightarrow{AC}$ with common endpoint *A*. Move *C* so that ∠*A* is an acute angle.

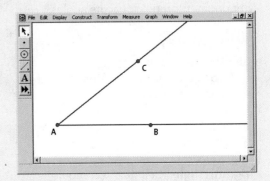

2. Construct point *D* on $\overrightarrow{AC}$. Construct a line through *D* perpendicular to $\overrightarrow{AB}$. Label the intersection of the perpendicular line and $\overrightarrow{AB}$ as *E*.

3. Measure ∠*A*. Measure *DE*, *AE*, and *AD*, the side lengths of △*AED*.

4. Calculate the ratios $\dfrac{DE}{AD}$, $\dfrac{AE}{AD}$, and $\dfrac{DE}{AE}$.

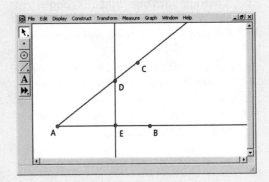

Try This

1. Drag *D* along $\overrightarrow{AC}$. What happens to the measure of ∠*A* as *D* moves? What postulate or theorem guarantees that the different triangles formed are similar to each other?

2. As you move *D*, what happens to the values of the three ratios you calculated? Use the properties of similar triangles to explain this result.

3. Move *C*. What happens to the measure of ∠*A*? With a new value for m∠*A*, note the values of the three ratios. What happens to the ratios if you drag *D*?

4. Move *C* until $\dfrac{DE}{AD} = \dfrac{AE}{AD}$. What is the value of $\dfrac{DE}{AE}$? What is the measure of ∠*A*? Use the properties of special right triangles to justify this result.

10-1 Trigonometric Ratios

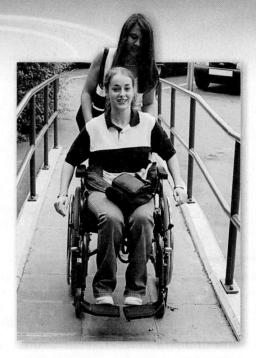

 Essential Question: How do side ratios in right triangles define trigonometric ratios?

Objectives
Find the sine, cosine, and tangent of an acute angle.

Use trigonometric ratios to find side lengths in right triangles and to solve real-world problems.

Vocabulary
trigonometric ratio
sine
cosine
tangent

Animated Math

Who uses this?

Contractors use trigonometric ratios to build ramps that meet legal requirements.

According to the Americans with Disabilities Act (ADA), the maximum slope allowed for a wheelchair ramp is $\frac{1}{12}$, which is an angle of about 4.8°. Properties of right triangles help builders construct ramps that meet this requirement.

By the AA Similarity Postulate, a right triangle with a given acute angle is similar to every other right triangle with that same acute angle measure. So $\triangle ABC \sim \triangle DEF \sim \triangle XYZ$, and $\frac{BC}{AC} = \frac{EF}{DF} = \frac{YZ}{XZ}$. These are *trigonometric ratios*. A **trigonometric ratio** is a ratio of two sides of a right triangle.

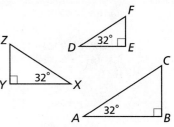

Know it! Note

Writing Math

In trigonometry, the letter of the vertex of the angle is often used to represent the measure of that angle. For example, the sine of $\angle A$ is written as sin A.

Trigonometric Ratios

DEFINITION	SYMBOLS	DIAGRAM
The **sine** of an angle is the ratio of the length of the leg opposite the angle to the length of the hypotenuse.	$\sin A = \dfrac{\text{opposite leg}}{\text{hypotenuse}} = \dfrac{a}{c}$ $\sin B = \dfrac{\text{opposite leg}}{\text{hypotenuse}} = \dfrac{b}{c}$	
The **cosine** of an angle is the ratio of the length of the leg adjacent to the angle to the length of the hypotenuse.	$\cos A = \dfrac{\text{adjacent leg}}{\text{hypotenuse}} = \dfrac{b}{c}$ $\cos B = \dfrac{\text{adjacent leg}}{\text{hypotenuse}} = \dfrac{a}{c}$	
The **tangent** of an angle is the ratio of the length of the leg opposite the angle to the length of the leg adjacent to the angle.	$\tan A = \dfrac{\text{opposite leg}}{\text{adjacent leg}} = \dfrac{a}{b}$ $\tan B = \dfrac{\text{opposite leg}}{\text{adjacent leg}} = \dfrac{b}{a}$	

COMMON CORE GPS
MCC9-12.G.SRT.6

EXAMPLE 1 **Finding Trigonometric Ratios**

Write each trigonometric ratio as a fraction and as a decimal rounded to the nearest hundredth.

A $\sin R$

$\sin R = \dfrac{12}{13} \approx 0.92$ *The sine of an $\angle$ is $\dfrac{\text{opp. leg}}{\text{hyp.}}$.*

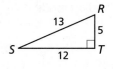

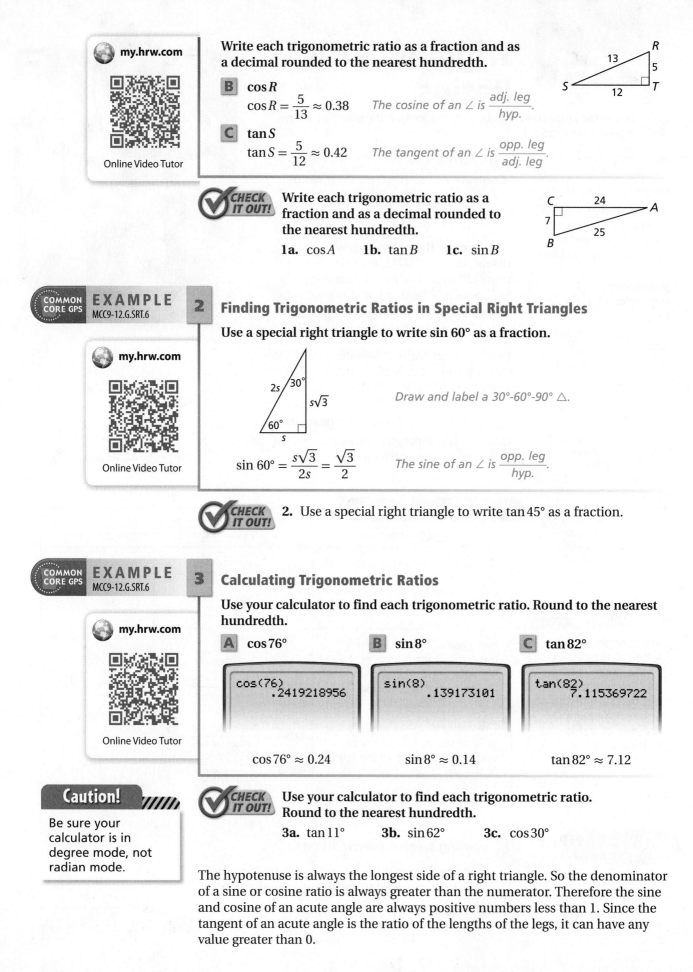

Write each trigonometric ratio as a fraction and as a decimal rounded to the nearest hundredth.

B $\cos R$

$\cos R = \dfrac{5}{13} \approx 0.38$ *The cosine of an $\angle$ is $\dfrac{adj.\ leg}{hyp.}$.*

C $\tan S$

$\tan S = \dfrac{5}{12} \approx 0.42$ *The tangent of an $\angle$ is $\dfrac{opp.\ leg}{adj.\ leg}$.*

CHECK IT OUT! Write each trigonometric ratio as a fraction and as a decimal rounded to the nearest hundredth.

1a. $\cos A$ **1b.** $\tan B$ **1c.** $\sin B$

EXAMPLE 2 Finding Trigonometric Ratios in Special Right Triangles

Use a special right triangle to write $\sin 60°$ as a fraction.

Draw and label a 30°-60°-90° $\triangle$.

$\sin 60° = \dfrac{s\sqrt{3}}{2s} = \dfrac{\sqrt{3}}{2}$ *The sine of an $\angle$ is $\dfrac{opp.\ leg}{hyp.}$.*

CHECK IT OUT! **2.** Use a special right triangle to write $\tan 45°$ as a fraction.

EXAMPLE 3 Calculating Trigonometric Ratios

Use your calculator to find each trigonometric ratio. Round to the nearest hundredth.

A $\cos 76°$ **B** $\sin 8°$ **C** $\tan 82°$

```
cos(76)
       .2419218956
```
```
sin(8)
       .139173101
```
```
tan(82)
       7.115369722
```

$\cos 76° \approx 0.24$ $\sin 8° \approx 0.14$ $\tan 82° \approx 7.12$

Caution!

Be sure your calculator is in degree mode, not radian mode.

CHECK IT OUT! Use your calculator to find each trigonometric ratio. Round to the nearest hundredth.

3a. $\tan 11°$ **3b.** $\sin 62°$ **3c.** $\cos 30°$

The hypotenuse is always the longest side of a right triangle. So the denominator of a sine or cosine ratio is always greater than the numerator. Therefore the sine and cosine of an acute angle are always positive numbers less than 1. Since the tangent of an acute angle is the ratio of the lengths of the legs, it can have any value greater than 0.

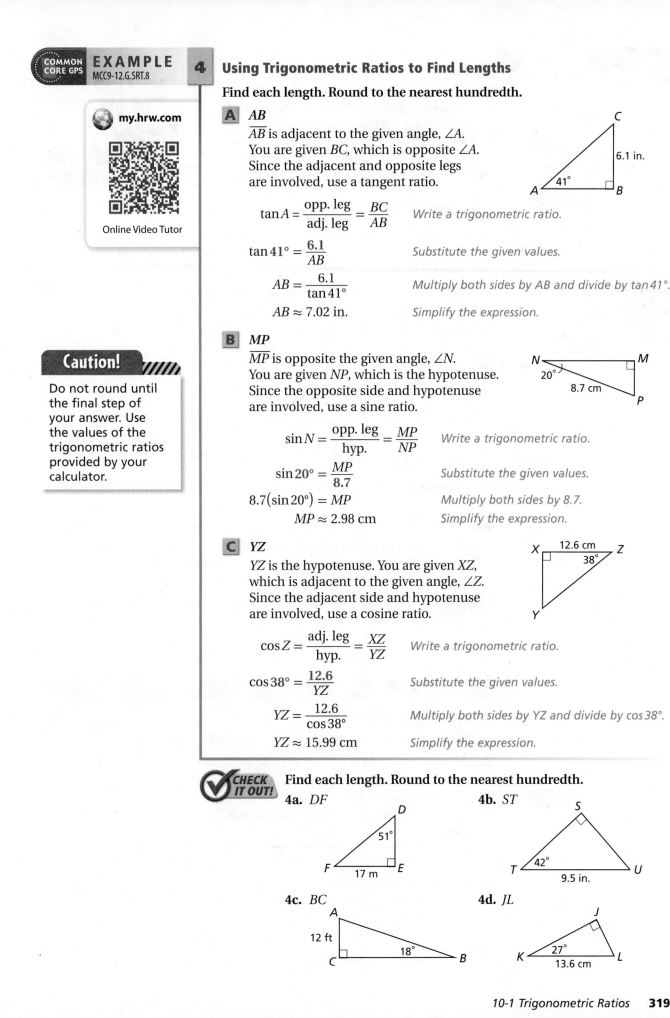

EXAMPLE 4

Using Trigonometric Ratios to Find Lengths

Find each length. Round to the nearest hundredth.

A *AB*

$\overline{AB}$ is adjacent to the given angle, ∠A.
You are given *BC*, which is opposite ∠A.
Since the adjacent and opposite legs
are involved, use a tangent ratio.

$$\tan A = \frac{\text{opp. leg}}{\text{adj. leg}} = \frac{BC}{AB} \qquad \text{Write a trigonometric ratio.}$$

$$\tan 41° = \frac{6.1}{AB} \qquad \text{Substitute the given values.}$$

$$AB = \frac{6.1}{\tan 41°} \qquad \text{Multiply both sides by } AB \text{ and divide by } \tan 41°.$$

$$AB \approx 7.02 \text{ in.} \qquad \text{Simplify the expression.}$$

B *MP*

$\overline{MP}$ is opposite the given angle, ∠N.
You are given *NP*, which is the hypotenuse.
Since the opposite side and hypotenuse
are involved, use a sine ratio.

$$\sin N = \frac{\text{opp. leg}}{\text{hyp.}} = \frac{MP}{NP} \qquad \text{Write a trigonometric ratio.}$$

$$\sin 20° = \frac{MP}{8.7} \qquad \text{Substitute the given values.}$$

$$8.7(\sin 20°) = MP \qquad \text{Multiply both sides by 8.7.}$$

$$MP \approx 2.98 \text{ cm} \qquad \text{Simplify the expression.}$$

C *YZ*

YZ is the hypotenuse. You are given *XZ*,
which is adjacent to the given angle, ∠Z.
Since the adjacent side and hypotenuse
are involved, use a cosine ratio.

$$\cos Z = \frac{\text{adj. leg}}{\text{hyp.}} = \frac{XZ}{YZ} \qquad \text{Write a trigonometric ratio.}$$

$$\cos 38° = \frac{12.6}{YZ} \qquad \text{Substitute the given values.}$$

$$YZ = \frac{12.6}{\cos 38°} \qquad \text{Multiply both sides by } YZ \text{ and divide by } \cos 38°.$$

$$YZ \approx 15.99 \text{ cm} \qquad \text{Simplify the expression.}$$

my.hrw.com

Online Video Tutor

Caution!

Do not round until
the final step of
your answer. Use
the values of the
trigonometric ratios
provided by your
calculator.

CHECK IT OUT! **Find each length. Round to the nearest hundredth.**

4a. *DF*

4b. *ST*

4c. *BC*

4d. *JL*

Problem Solving Application

A contractor is building a wheelchair ramp for a doorway that is 1.2 ft above the ground. To meet ADA guidelines, the ramp will make an angle of 4.8° with the ground. To the nearest hundredth of a foot, what is the horizontal distance covered by the ramp?

MATHEMATICAL PRACTICES

Make sense of problems and persevere in solving them.

1 **Understand the Problem**

Make a sketch. The **answer** is BC.

2 **Make a Plan**

$\overline{BC}$ is the leg adjacent to $\angle C$. You are given AB, which is the leg opposite $\angle C$. Since the opposite and adjacent legs are involved, write an equation using the tangent ratio.

3 **Solve**

$\tan C = \dfrac{AB}{BC}$ *Write a trigonometric ratio.*

$\tan 4.8° = \dfrac{1.2}{BC}$ *Substitute the given values.*

$BC = \dfrac{1.2}{\tan 4.8°}$ *Multiply both sides by BC and divide by $\tan 4.8°$.*

$BC \approx 14.2904$ ft   *Simplify the expression.*

4 **Look Back**

The problem asks for BC rounded to the nearest hundredth, so round the length to 14.29. The ramp covers a horizontal distance of 14.29 ft.

 5. Find AC, the length of the ramp in Example 5, to the nearest hundredth of a foot.

MCC.MP.4   MATHEMATICAL PRACTICES

THINK AND DISCUSS

1. Tell how you could use a sine ratio to find AB.

2. Tell how you could use a cosine ratio to find AB.

3. GET ORGANIZED Copy and complete the graphic organizer. In each cell, write the meaning of each abbreviation and draw a diagram for each.

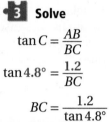

Know it!
.Note

Abbreviation	Words	Diagram
$\sin = \dfrac{\text{opp. leg}}{\text{hyp.}}$		
$\cos = \dfrac{\text{adj. leg}}{\text{hyp.}}$		
$\tan = \dfrac{\text{opp. leg}}{\text{adj. leg}}$		

GUIDED PRACTICE

Vocabulary Apply the vocabulary from this lesson to answer each question.

1. In $\triangle JKL$, $\angle K$ is a right angle. Write the *sine* of $\angle J$ as a ratio of side lengths.

2. In $\triangle MNP$, $\angle M$ is a right angle. Write the *tangent* of $\angle N$ as a ratio of side lengths.

SEE EXAMPLE 1 Write each trigonometric ratio as a fraction and as a decimal rounded to the nearest hundredth.

3. $\sin C$ 4. $\tan A$ 5. $\cos A$

6. $\cos C$ 7. $\tan C$ 8. $\sin A$

SEE EXAMPLE 2 Use a special right triangle to write each trigonometric ratio as a fraction.

9. $\cos 60°$ 10. $\tan 30°$ 11. $\sin 45°$

SEE EXAMPLE 3 Use your calculator to find each trigonometric ratio. Round to the nearest hundredth.

12. $\tan 67°$ 13. $\sin 23°$ 14. $\sin 49°$

15. $\cos 88°$ 16. $\cos 12°$ 17. $\tan 9°$

SEE EXAMPLE 4 Find each length. Round to the nearest hundredth.

18. BC 19. QR 20. KL

SEE EXAMPLE 5 21. **Architecture** A pediment has a pitch of 15°, as shown. If the width of the pediment, WZ, is 56 ft, what is XY to the nearest inch?

PRACTICE AND PROBLEM SOLVING

Independent Practice	
For Exercises	See Example
22–27	1
28–30	2
31–36	3
37–42	4
43	5

Write each trigonometric ratio as a fraction and as a decimal rounded to the nearest hundredth.

22. $\cos D$ 23. $\tan D$ 24. $\tan F$

25. $\cos F$ 26. $\sin F$ 27. $\sin D$

Use a special right triangle to write each trigonometric ratio as a fraction.

28. $\tan 60°$ 29. $\sin 30°$ 30. $\cos 45°$

Use your calculator to find each trigonometric ratio. Round to the nearest hundredth.

31. $\tan 51°$ 32. $\sin 80°$ 33. $\cos 77°$

34. $\tan 14°$ 35. $\sin 55°$ 36. $\cos 48°$

Alamy Images

Find each length. Round to the nearest hundredth.

37. *PQ*

38. *AC*

39. *GH*

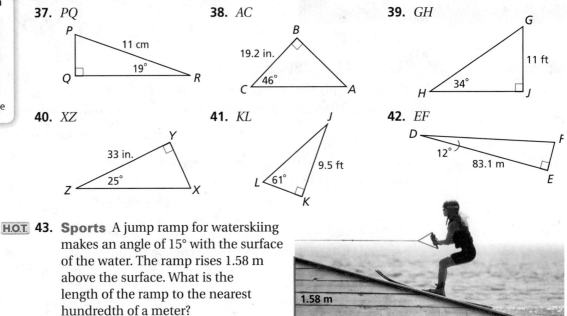

P
11 cm
19°
Q   R

B
19.2 in.
46°
C   A

G
11 ft
34°
H   J

40. *XZ*

41. *KL*

42. *EF*

Y
33 in.
25°
Z   X

J
9.5 ft
61°
L   K

D
12°
83.1 m
F
E

H.O.T. 43. Sports A jump ramp for waterskiing makes an angle of 15° with the surface of the water. The ramp rises 1.58 m above the surface. What is the length of the ramp to the nearest hundredth of a meter?

1.58 m

15°

Use special right triangles to complete each statement.

44. An angle that measures ___?___ has a tangent of 1.

45. For a 45° angle, the ___?___ and ___?___ ratios are equal.

46. The sine of a ___?___ angle is 0.5.

47. The cosine of a 30° angle is equal to the sine of a ___?___ angle.

H.O.T. 48. Safety According to the Occupational Safety and Health Administration (OSHA), a ladder that is placed against a wall should make a 75.5° angle with the ground for optimal safety. To the nearest tenth of a foot, what is the maximum height that a 10-ft ladder can safely reach?

Find the indicated length in each rectangle. Round to the nearest tenth.

49. *BC*

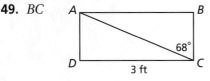

A   B
68°
D   3 ft   C

50. *SU*

R   S
49°
U   9.4 in.   T

H.O.T. 51. Critical Thinking For what angle measures is the tangent ratio less than 1? greater than 1? Explain.

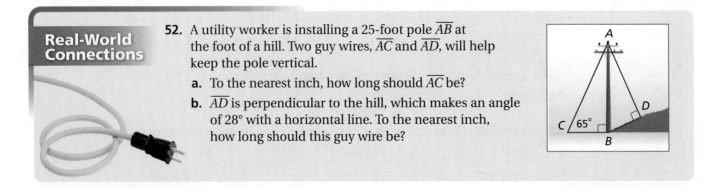

52. A utility worker is installing a 25-foot pole $\overline{AB}$ at the foot of a hill. Two guy wires, $\overline{AC}$ and $\overline{AD}$, will help keep the pole vertical.

a. To the nearest inch, how long should $\overline{AC}$ be?

b. $\overline{AD}$ is perpendicular to the hill, which makes an angle of 28° with a horizontal line. To the nearest inch, how long should this guy wire be?

Real-World Connections

A
D
C   65°
B

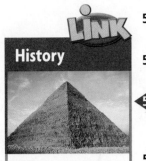
53. Find the sine of the smaller acute angle in a triangle with side lengths of 3, 4, and 5 inches.

54. Find the tangent of the greater acute angle in a triangle with side lengths of 7, 24, and 25 centimeters.

55. **History** The Great Pyramid of Cheops in Giza, Egypt, was completed around 2566 B.C.E. Its original height was 482 ft. Each face of the pyramid forms a 52° angle with the ground. To the nearest foot, how long is the base of the pyramid?

56. **Measurement** Follow these steps to calculate trigonometric ratios.
    a. Use a centimeter ruler to find AB, BC, and AC.
    b. Use your measurements from part **a** to find the sine, cosine, and tangent of $\angle A$.
    c. Use a protractor to find $m\angle A$.
    d. Use a calculator to find the sine, cosine, and tangent of $\angle A$.
    e. How do the values in part **d** compare to the ones you found in part **b**?

H.O.T. 57. **Algebra** Recall from Algebra I that an *identity* is an equation that is true for all values of the variables.
    a. Show that the identity $\tan A = \dfrac{\sin A}{\cos A}$ is true when $m\angle A = 30°$.
    b. Write $\tan A$, $\sin A$, and $\cos A$ in terms of a, b, and c.
    c. Use your results from part **b** to prove the identity $\tan A = \dfrac{\sin A}{\cos A}$.

Verify that $(\sin A)^2 + (\cos A)^2 = 1$ for each angle measure.

58. $m\angle A = 45°$

59. $m\angle A = 30°$

60. $m\angle A = 60°$

H.O.T. 61. **Multi-Step** The equation $(\sin A)^2 + (\cos A)^2 = 1$ is known as a Pythagorean identity.
    a. Write $\sin A$ and $\cos A$ in terms of a, b, and c.
    b. Use your results from part **a** to prove the identity $(\sin A)^2 + (\cos A)^2 = 1$.
    c. **Write About It** Why do you think the identity is called a Pythagorean identity?

Find the perimeter and area of each triangle. Round to the nearest hundredth.

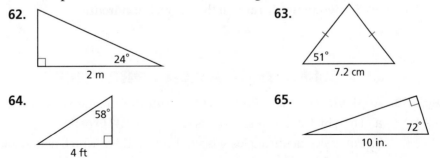

62. 24° 2 m

63. 51° 7.2 cm

64. 58° 4 ft

65. 72° 10 in.

66. **Critical Thinking** Draw $\triangle ABC$ with $\angle C$ a right angle. Write $\sin A$ and $\cos B$ in terms of the side lengths of the triangle. What do you notice? How are $\angle A$ and $\angle B$ related? Make a conjecture based on your observations.

67. **Write About It** Explain how the tangent of an acute angle changes as the angle measure increases.

68. Which expression can be used to find *AB*?

Ⓐ 7.1(sin 25°)   Ⓒ 7.1(sin 65°)

Ⓑ 7.1(cos 25°)   Ⓓ 7.1(tan 65°)

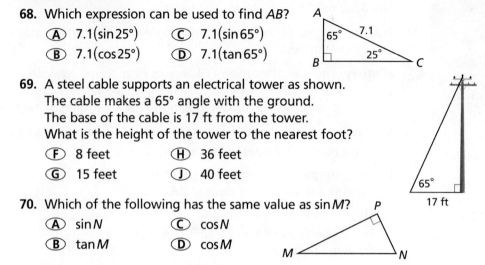

69. A steel cable supports an electrical tower as shown.
The cable makes a 65° angle with the ground.
The base of the cable is 17 ft from the tower.
What is the height of the tower to the nearest foot?

Ⓕ   8 feet   Ⓗ 36 feet

Ⓖ 15 feet   Ⓙ 40 feet

70. Which of the following has the same value as sin *M*?

Ⓐ sin *N*   Ⓒ cos *N*

Ⓑ tan *M*   Ⓓ cos *M*

CHALLENGE AND EXTEND

Algebra Find the value of *x*. Then find *AB*, *BC*, and *AC*. Round each to the nearest unit.

71.

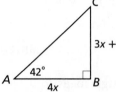

72.

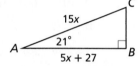

H.O.T. 73. Multi-Step Prove the identity $(\tan A)^2 + 1 = \dfrac{1}{(\cos A)^2}$.

74. A regular pentagon with 1 in. sides is inscribed in a circle.
Find the radius of the circle rounded to the nearest hundredth.

1 in.

Each of the three trigonometric ratios has a reciprocal ratio,
as defined below. These ratios are *cosecant* (csc), *secant* (sec),
and *cotangent* (cot).

$$\csc A = \dfrac{1}{\sin A} \qquad \sec A = \dfrac{1}{\cos A} \qquad \cot A = \dfrac{1}{\tan A}$$

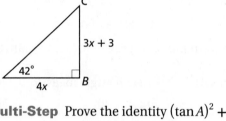

Find each trigonometric ratio to the nearest hundredth.

75. csc *Y*   **76.** sec *Z*   **77.** cot *Y*

MATHEMATICAL
PRACTICES

FOCUS ON MATHEMATICAL PRACTICES

H.O.T. 78. Analysis Use the definitions of the sine and cosine ratios for acute angles.

a. For which acute angle *A* does sin *A* = cos *A*? Explain.

b. For which acute angles *A* is sin *A* > cos *A*? For which acute angles *A* is
sin *A* < cos *A*? Explain.

H.O.T. 79. Error Analysis For the question, "If ∠*A* is an acute angle of a right triangle, which
is greater, sin *A* or tan *A*?" Danielle wrote the answer shown. Is she correct? If not,
explain her error and correct her work.

> sin *A* = $\dfrac{a}{c}$ and tan *A* = $\dfrac{a}{b}$. Since the hypotenuse is the longest side
> of a right triangle, *c* > *b*, so $\dfrac{a}{c}$ > $\dfrac{a}{b}$. Therefore sin *A* > tan *A*.

EXTENSION Trigonometric Ratios and Complementary Angles

Essential Question: How is the sine ratio of one acute angle in a right triangle related to the cosine ratio of the other acute angle?

Objectives
Use the relationship between the sine and cosine of complementary angles.

The acute angles of a right triangle are complementary angles. If the measure of one of the two acute angles is given, the measure of the second acute angle can be found by subtracting the given measure from 90°.

COMMON CORE GPS MCC9-12.G.SRT.7

EXAMPLE 1

Finding the Sine and Cosine of Acute Angles

Vocabulary
cofunction

Find the sine and cosine of the acute angles in the right triangle shown.

Start with the sine and cosine of ∠A.

$$\sin A = \frac{\text{opposite}}{\text{hypotenuse}} = \frac{6}{10} = \frac{3}{5}$$

$$\cos A = \frac{\text{adjacent}}{\text{hypotenuse}} = \frac{8}{10} = \frac{4}{5}$$

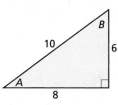

Then, find the sine and cosine of ∠B.

$$\sin B = \frac{\text{opposite}}{\text{hypotenuse}} = \frac{8}{10} = \frac{4}{5}$$

$$\cos B = \frac{\text{adjacent}}{\text{hypotenuse}} = \frac{6}{10} = \frac{3}{5}$$

 1. Find the sine and cosine of the acute angles of a right triangle with sides 10, 24, 26. (Use A for the angle opposite the side with length 10 and B for the angle opposite the side with length 24.)

In Example 1, notice that $\sin A = \cos B$ and $\cos A = \sin B$. In general, the sine of an acute angle is equal to the cosine of the complement of that angle.

The trigonometric function of the complement of an angle is called a **cofunction.** The sine and cosines are cofunctions of each other.

COMMON CORE GPS MCC9-12.G.SRT.7

EXAMPLE 2

Writing Sine in Cosine Terms and Cosine in Sine Terms

A Write sin 42° in terms of the cosine.

$$\sin 42° = \cos(90 - 42)°$$
$$= \cos 48°$$

B Write cos 36° in terms of the sine.

$$\cos 36° = \sin(90 - 36)°$$
$$= \sin 54°$$

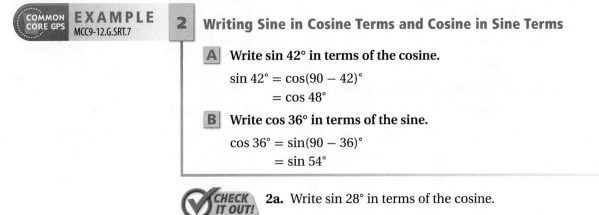 **2a.** Write sin 28° in terms of the cosine.

2b. Write cos 51° in terms of the sine.

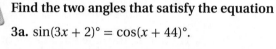

COMMON CORE GPS MCC9-12.G.SRT.7

EXAMPLE 3 Finding Unknown Angles

Find two angles that satisfy the equation.

$$\sin(2x - 4)° = \cos(3x + 9)°$$

If $\sin(2x - 4)° = \cos(3x + 9)°$, then $(2x - 4)°$ and $(3x + 9)°$ are the measures of complementary angles. The sum of the measures must be 90°.

$$(2x - 4) + (3x + 9) = 90$$
$$5x + 5 = 90$$
$$5x = 85$$
$$x = 17$$

Substitute the value of x into the original expression to find the angle measures.

$$2x - 4 = 2(17) - 4$$
$$= 30°$$

$$3x + 9 = 3(17) + 9$$
$$= 60°$$

The measurements of the two angles are 30° and 60°.

CHECK IT OUT! Find the two angles that satisfy the equation

3a. $\sin(3x + 2)° = \cos(x + 44)°$.

3b. $\sin(2x + 20)° = \cos(3x + 30)°$.

EXTENSION

Exercises

my.hrw.com
Homework Help

Find the cosine and sine of the acute angles in the triangles shown.

1.
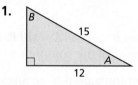

2.
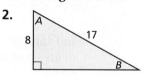

Write each trigonometric function in terms of its cofunction.

3. sin 64°

4. cos 84°

5. cos 38°

6. sin 24°

7. cos 72°

8. sin 45°

Find two angles that satisfy each equation.

9. $\sin(4x + 30)° = \cos(-2x + 54)°$

10. $\sin(-2x + 92)° = \cos(x + 8)°$

11. $\cos(5x + 49)° = \sin(3x + 57)°$

12. $\cos(-3x + 106)° = \sin(7x - 64)°$

13. $\sin(2x + 30)° = \cos(3x + 5)°$

14. $\sin(5x - 12)° = \cos(x + 54)°$

15. $\cos(3x - 10)° = \sin(3x - 20)°$

16. $\cos(7x - 68)° = \sin(-3x + 110)°$

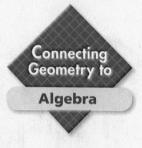

Inverse Functions

Connecting Geometry to Algebra

In Algebra, you learned that a function is a relation in which each element of the domain is paired with exactly one element of the range. If you switch the domain and range of a one-to-one function, you create an *inverse function*.

The function $y = \sin^{-1} x$ is the inverse of the function $y = \sin x$.

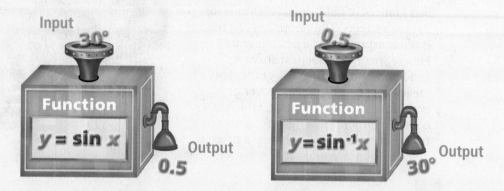

If you know the value of a trigonometric ratio, you can use the inverse trigonometric function to find the angle measure. You can do this either with a calculator or by looking at the graph of the function.

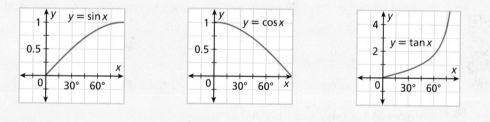

Example

Use the graphs above to find the value of x for $1 = \sin x$. Then write this expression using an inverse trigonometric function.

$1 = \sin x$ *Look at the graph of $y = \sin x$. Find where the graph intersects the line $y = 1$ and read the corresponding x-coordinate.*

$x = 90°$

$90° = \sin^{-1}(1)$ *Switch the x- and y-values.*

Try This

Use the graphs above to find the value of x for each of the following. Then write each expression using an inverse trigonometric function.

1. $0 = \sin x$

2. $\dfrac{1}{2} = \cos x$

3. $1 = \tan x$

4. $0 = \cos x$

5. $0 = \tan x$

6. $\dfrac{1}{2} = \sin x$

Solving Right Triangles

? **Essential Question:** How can you use inverse trigonometric functions to solve for the angles in a right triangle?

Objective
Use trigonometric ratios to find angle measures in right triangles and to solve real-world problems.

Why learn this?
You can convert the percent grade of a road to an angle measure by solving a right triangle.

San Francisco, California, is famous for its steep streets. The steepness of a road is often expressed as a *percent grade*. Filbert Street, the steepest street in San Francisco, has a 31.5% grade. This means the road rises 31.5 ft over a horizontal distance of 100 ft, which is equivalent to a 17.5° angle. You can use trigonometric ratios to change a percent grade to an angle measure.

 **EXAMPLE 1**
MCC9-12.G.SRT.8

Identifying Angles from Trigonometric Ratios

Use the trigonometric ratio $\cos A = 0.6$ to determine which angle of the triangle is $\angle A$.

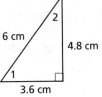

$$\cos A = \frac{\text{adj. leg}}{\text{hyp.}}$$ *Cosine is the ratio of the adjacent leg to the hypotenuse.*

$$\cos \angle 1 = \frac{3.6}{6} = 0.6$$ *The leg adjacent to $\angle 1$ is 3.6. The hypotenuse is 6.*

$$\cos \angle 2 = \frac{4.8}{6} = 0.8$$ *The leg adjacent to $\angle 2$ is 4.8. The hypotenuse is 6.*

Since $\cos A = \cos \angle 1$, $\angle 1$ is $\angle A$.

 **my.hrw.com**

Online Video Tutor

 CHECK IT OUT! Use the given trigonometric ratio to determine which angle of the triangle is $\angle A$.

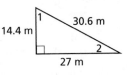

1a. $\sin A = \dfrac{8}{17}$ **1b.** $\tan A = 1.875$

You have learned that $\sin 30° = 0.5$. Conversely, if you know that the sine of an acute angle is 0.5, you can conclude that the angle measures 30°. This is written as $\sin^{-1}(0.5) = 30°$.

If you know the sine, cosine, or tangent of an acute angle measure, you can use the inverse trigonometric functions to find the measure of the angle.

 **Reading Math**

The expression $\sin^{-1}x$ is read "the inverse sine of x." It does *not* mean $\frac{1}{\sin x}$. You can think of $\sin^{-1}x$ as "the angle whose sine is x."

Inverse Trigonometric Functions
If $\sin A = x$, then $\sin^{-1}x = m\angle A$.
If $\cos A = x$, then $\cos^{-1}x = m\angle A$.
If $\tan A = x$, then $\tan^{-1}x = m\angle A$.

Photo Edit Inc.

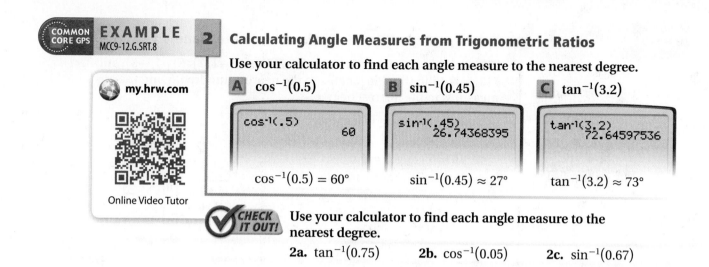

COMMON CORE GPS **EXAMPLE** MCC9-12.G.SRT.8 **2** | **Calculating Angle Measures from Trigonometric Ratios**

Use your calculator to find each angle measure to the nearest degree.

A $\cos^{-1}(0.5)$ **B** $\sin^{-1}(0.45)$ **C** $\tan^{-1}(3.2)$

my.hrw.com

Online Video Tutor

```
cos⁻¹(.5)
              60
```

```
sin⁻¹(.45)
      26.74368395
```

```
tan⁻¹(3.2)
      72.64597536
```

$\cos^{-1}(0.5) = 60°$ $\sin^{-1}(0.45) \approx 27°$ $\tan^{-1}(3.2) \approx 73°$

CHECK IT OUT! Use your calculator to find each angle measure to the nearest degree.

2a. $\tan^{-1}(0.75)$ **2b.** $\cos^{-1}(0.05)$ **2c.** $\sin^{-1}(0.67)$

Using given measures to find the unknown angle measures or side lengths of a triangle is known as *solving a triangle*. To solve a right triangle, you need to know two side lengths or one side length and an acute angle measure.

COMMON CORE GPS **EXAMPLE** MCC9-12.G.SRT.8 **3** | **Solving Right Triangles**

Find the unknown measures. Round lengths to the nearest hundredth and angle measures to the nearest degree.

my.hrw.com

Online Video Tutor

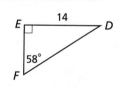

Method 1:
By the Pythagorean Theorem,
$AC^2 = AB^2 + BC^2$.

$$= (7.5)^2 + 5^2 = 81.25$$

So $AC = \sqrt{81.25} \approx 9.01$.

$$m\angle A = \tan^{-1}\left(\frac{5}{7.5}\right) \approx 34°$$

Since the acute angles of a right triangle are complementary,
$m\angle C \approx 90° - 34° \approx 56°$.

Method 2:

$$m\angle A = \tan^{-1}\left(\frac{5}{7.5}\right) \approx 34°$$

Since the acute angles of a right triangle are complementary,
$m\angle C \approx 90° - 34° \approx 56°$.

$$\sin A = \frac{5}{AC}, \text{ so } AC = \frac{5}{\sin A}.$$

$$AC \approx \frac{5}{\sin\left[\tan^{-1}\left(\frac{5}{7.5}\right)\right]} \approx 9.01$$

Helpful Hint

When using your calculator to find the value of an inverse trigonometric expression, you may need to press the [arc], [inv], or [2nd] key.

CHECK IT OUT! **3.** Find the unknown measures. Round lengths to the nearest hundredth and angle measures to the nearest degree.

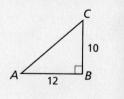

Student to Student | *Solving Right Triangles*

Kendell Waters
Marshall High School

Rounding can really make a difference! To find AC, I used the Pythagorean Theorem and got 15.62.

Then I did it a different way. I used $m\angle A = \tan^{-1}\left(\frac{10}{12}\right)$ to find $m\angle A = 39.8056°$, which I rounded to 40°. $\sin 40° = \frac{10}{AC}$, so $AC = \frac{10}{\sin 40°} \approx 15.56$.

The difference in the two answers reminded me not to round values until the last step.

EXAMPLE **4**
MCC9-12.G.SRT.8

my.hrw.com

Solving a Right Triangle in the Coordinate Plane

The coordinates of the vertices of $\triangle JKL$ are $J(-1, 2)$, $K(-1, -3)$, and $L(3, -3)$. Find the side lengths to the nearest hundredth and the angle measures to the nearest degree.

Step 1 Find the side lengths.

Plot points J, K, and L.

$JK = 5$ $KL = 4$

By the Distance Formula,

$JL = \sqrt{[3 - (-1)]^2 + (-3 - 2)^2}$.

$= \sqrt{4^2 + (-5)^2}$

$= \sqrt{16 + 25} = \sqrt{41} \approx 6.40$

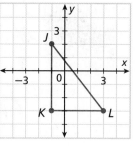

Step 2 Find the angle measures.

$m\angle K = 90°$ *$\overline{JK}$ and $\overline{KL}$ are $\perp$.*

$m\angle J = \tan^{-1}\left(\dfrac{4}{5}\right) \approx 39°$ *$\overline{KL}$ is opp. $\angle J$, and $\overline{JK}$ is adj. to $\angle J$.*

$m\angle L \approx 90° - 39° \approx 51°$ *The acute $\angle$ of a rt. $\triangle$ are comp.*

CHECK IT OUT!

4. The coordinates of the vertices of $\triangle RST$ are $R(-3, 5)$, $S(4, 5)$, and $T(4, -2)$. Find the side lengths to the nearest hundredth and the angle measures to the nearest degree.

EXAMPLE **5**
MCC9-12.G.SRT.8

my.hrw.com

Travel Application

San Francisco's Lombard Street is known as one of "the crookedest streets in the world." The road's eight switchbacks were built in the 1920s to make the steep hill passable by cars. If the hill has a percent grade of 84%, what angle does the hill make with a horizontal line? Round to the nearest degree.

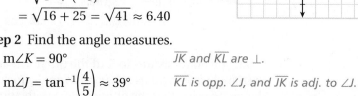

$84\% = \dfrac{84}{100}$ *Change the percent grade to a fraction.*

An 84% grade means the hill rises 84 ft for every 100 ft of horizontal distance.

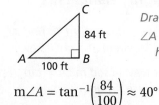

Draw a right triangle to represent the hill.
$\angle A$ is the angle the hill makes with a horizontal line.

$m\angle A = \tan^{-1}\left(\dfrac{84}{100}\right) \approx 40°$

CHECK IT OUT!

5. Baldwin St. in Dunedin, New Zealand, is the steepest street in the world. It has a grade of 38%. To the nearest degree, what angle does Baldwin St. make with a horizontal line?

THINK AND DISCUSS

1. Describe the steps you would use to solve △RST.

2. Given that cos Z = 0.35, write an equivalent statement using an inverse trigonometric function.

3. GET ORGANIZED Copy and complete the graphic organizer. In each box, write a trigonometric ratio for ∠A. Then write an equivalent statement using an inverse trigonometric function.

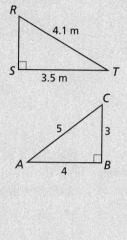

	Trigonometric Ratio	Inverse Trigonometric Function
Sine		
Cosine		
Tangent		

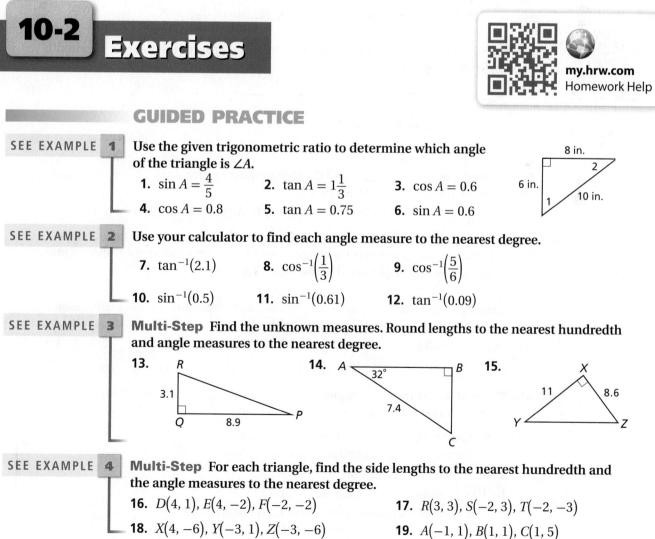

10-2 Exercises

my.hrw.com
Homework Help

GUIDED PRACTICE

SEE EXAMPLE 1

Use the given trigonometric ratio to determine which angle of the triangle is ∠A.

1. $\sin A = \dfrac{4}{5}$ **2.** $\tan A = 1\dfrac{1}{3}$ **3.** $\cos A = 0.6$

4. $\cos A = 0.8$ **5.** $\tan A = 0.75$ **6.** $\sin A = 0.6$

SEE EXAMPLE 2

Use your calculator to find each angle measure to the nearest degree.

7. $\tan^{-1}(2.1)$ **8.** $\cos^{-1}\left(\dfrac{1}{3}\right)$ **9.** $\cos^{-1}\left(\dfrac{5}{6}\right)$

10. $\sin^{-1}(0.5)$ **11.** $\sin^{-1}(0.61)$ **12.** $\tan^{-1}(0.09)$

SEE EXAMPLE 3

Multi-Step Find the unknown measures. Round lengths to the nearest hundredth and angle measures to the nearest degree.

13. **14.** **15.**

SEE EXAMPLE 4

Multi-Step For each triangle, find the side lengths to the nearest hundredth and the angle measures to the nearest degree.

16. $D(4, 1)$, $E(4, -2)$, $F(-2, -2)$ **17.** $R(3, 3)$, $S(-2, 3)$, $T(-2, -3)$

18. $X(4, -6)$, $Y(-3, 1)$, $Z(-3, -6)$ **19.** $A(-1, 1)$, $B(1, 1)$, $C(1, 5)$

20. Cycling A hill in the Tour de France bike race has a grade of 8%. To the nearest degree, what is the angle that this hill makes with a horizontal line?

PRACTICE AND PROBLEM SOLVING

Independent Practice

For Exercises	See Example
21–26	1
27–32	2
33–35	3
36–37	4
38	5

my.hrw.com

Online Extra Practice

Use the given trigonometric ratio to determine which angle of the triangle is $\angle A$.

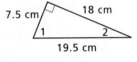

21. $\tan A = \dfrac{5}{12}$ **22.** $\tan A = 2.4$ **23.** $\sin A = \dfrac{12}{13}$

24. $\sin A = \dfrac{5}{13}$ **25.** $\cos A = \dfrac{12}{13}$ **26.** $\cos A = \dfrac{5}{13}$

Use your calculator to find each angle measure to the nearest degree.

27. $\sin^{-1}(0.31)$ **28.** $\tan^{-1}(1)$ **29.** $\cos^{-1}(0.8)$

30. $\cos^{-1}(0.72)$ **31.** $\tan^{-1}(1.55)$ **32.** $\sin^{-1}\left(\dfrac{9}{17}\right)$

Multi-Step Find the unknown measures. Round lengths to the nearest hundredth and angle measures to the nearest degree.

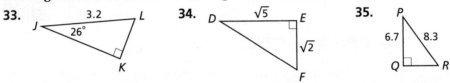

33.   **34.**   **35.**

Multi-Step For each triangle, find the side lengths to the nearest hundredth and the angle measures to the nearest degree.

36. $A(2, 0)$, $B(2, -5)$, $C(1, -5)$ **37.** $M(3, 2)$, $N(3, -2)$, $P(-1, -2)$

H.O.T. 38. Building For maximum accessibility, a wheelchair ramp should have a slope between $\dfrac{1}{16}$ and $\dfrac{1}{20}$. What is the range of angle measures that a ramp should make with a horizontal line? Round to the nearest degree.

Complete each statement. If necessary, round angle measures to the nearest degree. Round other values to the nearest hundredth.

39. $\tan \underline{\ \ ?\ \ } \approx 3.5$ **40.** $\sin \underline{\ \ ?\ \ } \approx \dfrac{2}{3}$ **41.** $\underline{\ \ ?\ \ }\ 42° \approx 0.74$

42. $\cos^{-1}\left(\underline{\ \ ?\ \ }\right) \approx 12°$ **43.** $\sin^{-1}\left(\underline{\ \ ?\ \ }\right) \approx 69°$ **44.** $\underline{\ \ ?\ \ }\ 60° = \dfrac{1}{2}$

H.O.T. 45. Critical Thinking Use trigonometric ratios to explain why the diagonal of a square forms a 45° angle with each of the sides.

46. Estimation You can use trigonometry to find angle measures when a protractor is not available.

  a. Estimate the measure of $\angle P$.

  b. Use a centimeter ruler to find RQ and PQ.

  c. Use your measurements from part **b** and an inverse trigonometric function to find m$\angle P$ to the nearest degree.

  d. How does your result in part **c** compare to your estimate in part **a**?

47. An electric company wants to install a vertical utility pole at the base of a hill that has an 8% grade.

    a. To the nearest degree, what angle does the hill make with a horizontal line?

    b. What is the measure of the angle between the pole and the hill? Round to the nearest degree.

    c. A utility worker installs a 31-foot guy wire from the top of the pole to the hill. Given that the guy wire is perpendicular to the hill, find the height of the pole to the nearest inch.

The side lengths of a right triangle are given below. Find the measures of the acute angles in the triangle. Round to the nearest degree.

48. 3, 4, 5   **49.** 5, 12, 13   **50.** 8, 15, 17

51. What if...? A right triangle has leg lengths of 28 and 45 inches. Suppose the length of the longer leg doubles. What happens to the measure of the acute angle opposite that leg?

Fitness

52. Fitness As part of off-season training, the Houston Texans football team must sprint up a ramp with a 28% grade. To the nearest degree, what angle does this ramp make with a horizontal line?

53. The coordinates of the vertices of a triangle are $A(-1, 0)$, $B(6, 1)$, and $C(0, 3)$.

    a. Use the Distance Formula to find AB, BC, and AC.

    b. Use the Converse of the Pythagorean Theorem to show that $\triangle ABC$ is a right triangle. Identify the right angle.

    c. Find the measures of the acute angles of $\triangle ABC$. Round to the nearest degree.

Running on a treadmill is slightly easier than running outdoors, since you don't have to overcome wind resistance. Set the treadmill to a 1% grade to match the intensity of an outdoor run.

Find the indicated measure in each rectangle. Round to the nearest degree.

54. m∠BDC

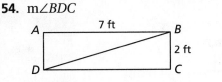

55. m∠STV

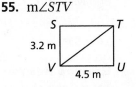

Find the indicated measure in each rhombus. Round to the nearest degree.

56. m∠DGF

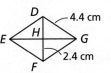

57. m∠LKN

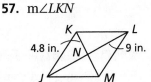

58. Critical Thinking Without using a calculator, compare the values of tan 60° and tan 70°. Explain your reasoning.

The measure of an acute angle formed by a line with slope m and the x-axis can be found by using the expression $\tan^{-1}(m)$. Find the measure of the acute angle that each line makes with the x-axis. Round to the nearest degree.

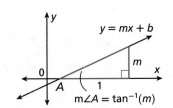

59. $y = 3x + 5$ **60.** $y = \frac{2}{3}x + 1$ **61.** $5y = 4x + 3$

H.O.T. 62. ///ERROR ANALYSIS/// A student was asked to find m∠C. Explain the error in the student's solution.

> Since tan C = $\frac{3}{4}$, m∠C = tan⁻¹($\frac{3}{4}$), and tan⁻¹(0.75) ≈ 37°. So m∠C ≈ 37°.

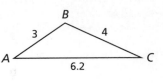

H.O.T. 63. Write About It A student claims that you must know the three side lengths of a right triangle before you can use trigonometric ratios to find the measures of the acute angles. Do you agree? Why or why not?

64. $\overline{DC}$ is an altitude of right △ABC. Use trigonometric ratios to find the missing lengths in the figure. Then use these lengths to verify the three relationships in the Geometric Mean Corollaries.

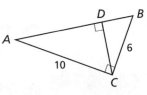

TEST PREP

65. Which expression can be used to find m∠A?

   (A) tan⁻¹(0.75)   (C) cos⁻¹(0.8)

   (B) sin⁻¹($\frac{3}{5}$)   (D) tan⁻¹($\frac{4}{3}$)

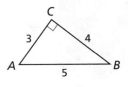

66. Which expression is NOT equivalent to cos 60°?

   (F) $\frac{1}{2}$ (H) $\frac{\sin 60°}{\tan 60°}$

   (G) sin 30°   (J) cos⁻¹($\frac{1}{2}$)

67. To the nearest degree, what is the measure of the acute angle formed by Jefferson St. and Madison St.?

   (A) 27°   (C) 59°

   (B) 31°   (D) 63°

68. Gridded Response A highway exit ramp has a slope of $\frac{3}{20}$. To the nearest degree, find the angle that the ramp makes with a horizontal line.

CHALLENGE AND EXTEND

Find each angle measure. Round to the nearest degree.

69. m∠J

70. m∠A

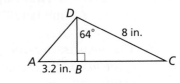

H.O.T. Simplify each expression.

71. cos⁻¹(cos 34°)   **72.** tan[tan⁻¹(1.5)]   **73.** sin(sin⁻¹ x)

74. A ramp has a 6% grade. The ramp is 40 ft long. Find the vertical distance that the ramp rises. Round your answer to the nearest hundredth.

75. **Critical Thinking** Explain why the expression $\sin^{-1}(1.5)$ does not make sense.

76. If you are given the lengths of two sides of $\triangle ABC$ and the measure of the included angle, you can use the formula $\frac{1}{2}bc \sin A$ to find the area of the triangle. Derive this formula. (*Hint:* Draw an altitude from B to $\overline{AC}$. Use trigonometric ratios to find the length of this altitude.)

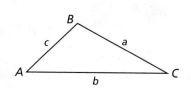

MATHEMATICAL PRACTICES

FOCUS ON MATHEMATICAL PRACTICES

H.O.T. 77. Problem Solving Find x to the nearest degree. What do you need to find out to solve for x?

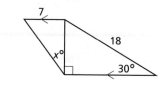

H.O.T. 78. Communication Is it possible to solve a right triangle if you know only its angle measures? Explain in terms of trigonometric ratios.

H.O.T. 79. Analysis Zach was puzzled by a problem because he had never seen one like it before: "Evaluate $\tan\left[\cos^{-1}\left(\frac{5}{13}\right)\right]$."

   a. Explain in words what the problem is asking Zach to find.

   b. A right triangle can be used to solve this problem without calculating any angle measures. What are its side lengths?

   c. Find the answer to the problem.

Using Technology

Use a spreadsheet to complete the following.

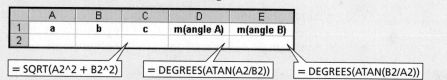

1. In cells A2 and B2, enter values for the leg lengths of a right triangle.

2. In cell C2, write a formula to calculate c, the length of the hypotenuse.

3. Write a formula to calculate the measure of $\angle A$ in cell D2. Be sure to use the Degrees function so that the answer is given in degrees. Format the value to include no decimal places.

4. Write a formula to calculate the measure of $\angle B$ in cell E2. Again, be sure to use the Degrees function and format the value to include no decimal places.

5. Use your spreadsheet to check your answers for Exercises 48–50.

10-3 Angles of Elevation and Depression

? **Essential Question:** How can trigonometric ratios be used to estimate distances when you know an angle of elevation or depression?

Objective
Solve problems involving angles of elevation and angles of depression.

Vocabulary
angle of elevation
angle of depression

Who uses this?
Pilots and air traffic controllers use angles of depression to calculate distances.

An **angle of elevation** is the angle formed by a horizontal line and a line of sight to a point *above* the line. In the diagram, ∠1 is the angle of elevation from the tower *T* to the plane *P*.

An **angle of depression** is the angle formed by a horizontal line and a line of sight to a point *below* the line. ∠2 is the angle of depression from the plane to the tower.

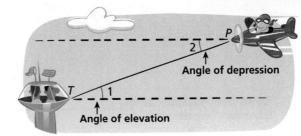

Angle of depression

Angle of elevation

Since horizontal lines are parallel, ∠1 ≅ ∠2 by the Alternate Interior Angles Theorem. Therefore the angle of elevation from one point is congruent to the angle of depression from the other point.

COMMON CORE GPS

EXAMPLE 1
Prep for MCC9-12.G.SRT.8

my.hrw.com

Online Video Tutor

Classifying Angles of Elevation and Depression

Classify each angle as an angle of elevation or angle of depression.

A ∠3

∠3 is formed by a horizontal line and a line of sight to a point below the line. It is an angle of depression.

B ∠4

∠4 is formed by a horizontal line and a line of sight to a point above the line. It is an angle of elevation.

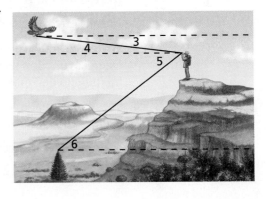

CHECK IT OUT! Use the diagram above to classify each angle as an angle of elevation or angle of depression.

1a. ∠5   **1b.** ∠6

Stone/Getty Images

COMMON
CORE GPS | EXAMPLE | 2
MCC9-12.G.SRT.8

Finding Distance by Using Angle of Elevation

An air traffic controller at an airport sights a plane at an angle of elevation of 41°. The pilot reports that the plane's altitude is 4000 ft. What is the horizontal distance between the plane and the airport? Round to the nearest foot.

Draw a sketch to represent the given information. Let A represent the airport and let P represent the plane. Let x be the horizontal distance between the plane and the airport.

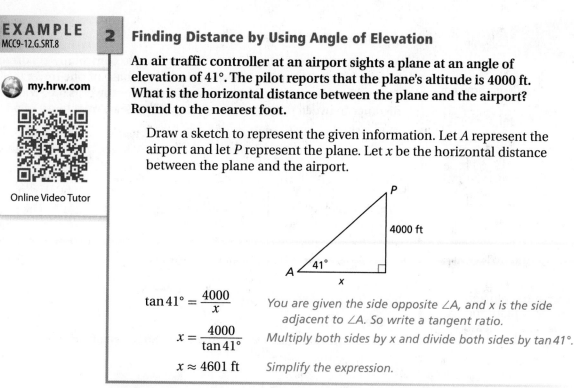

$\tan 41° = \dfrac{4000}{x}$ *You are given the side opposite $\angle A$, and x is the side adjacent to $\angle A$. So write a tangent ratio.*

$x = \dfrac{4000}{\tan 41°}$ *Multiply both sides by x and divide both sides by $\tan 41°$.*

$x \approx 4601$ ft   *Simplify the expression.*

CHECK IT OUT!

2. What if...? Suppose the plane is at an altitude of 3500 ft and the angle of elevation from the airport to the plane is 29°. What is the horizontal distance between the plane and the airport? Round to the nearest foot.

COMMON
CORE GPS | EXAMPLE | 3
MCC9-12.G.SRT.8

Finding Distance by Using Angle of Depression

A forest ranger in a 90-foot observation tower sees a fire. The angle of depression to the fire is 7°. What is the horizontal distance between the tower and the fire? Round to the nearest foot.

Draw a sketch to represent the given information. Let T represent the top of the tower and let F represent the fire. Let x be the horizontal distance between the tower and the fire.

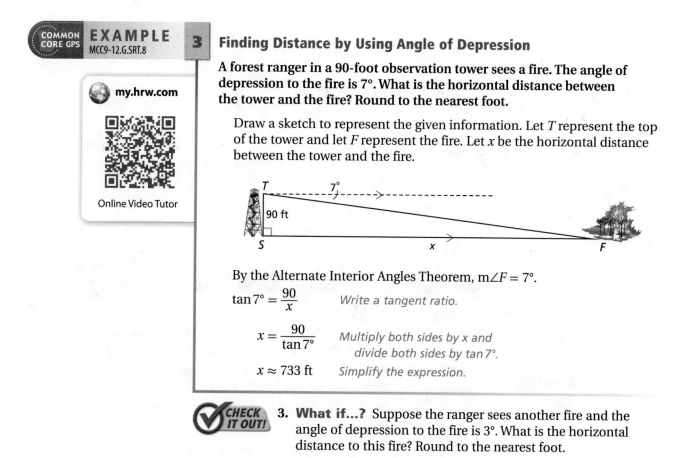

By the Alternate Interior Angles Theorem, $m\angle F = 7°$.

$\tan 7° = \dfrac{90}{x}$ *Write a tangent ratio.*

$x = \dfrac{90}{\tan 7°}$ *Multiply both sides by x and divide both sides by $\tan 7°$.*

$x \approx 733$ ft   *Simplify the expression.*

CHECK IT OUT!

3. What if...? Suppose the ranger sees another fire and the angle of depression to the fire is 3°. What is the horizontal distance to this fire? Round to the nearest foot.

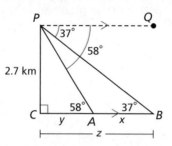

Aviation Application

A pilot flying at an altitude of 2.7 km sights two control towers directly in front of her. The angle of depression to the base of one tower is 37°. The angle of depression to the base of the other tower is 58°. What is the distance between the two towers? Round to the nearest tenth of a kilometer.

Step 1 Draw a sketch. Let P represent the plane and let A and B represent the two towers. Let x be the distance between the towers.

Helpful Hint

Always make a sketch to help you correctly place the given angle measure.

Step 2 Find y.

By the Alternate Interior Angles Theorem, m∠CAP = 58°.

In △APC, $\tan 58° = \dfrac{2.7}{y}$.

So $y = \dfrac{2.7}{\tan 58°} \approx 1.6871$ km.

Step 3 Find z.

By the Alternate Interior Angles Theorem, m∠CBP = 37°.

In △BPC, $\tan 37° = \dfrac{2.7}{z}$.

So $z = \dfrac{2.7}{\tan 37°} \approx 3.5830$ km.

Step 4 Find x.

$x = z - y$

$x \approx 3.5830 - 1.6871 \approx 1.9$ km

So the two towers are about 1.9 km apart.

CHECK IT OUT!

4. A pilot flying at an altitude of 12,000 ft sights two airports directly in front of him. The angle of depression to one airport is 78°, and the angle of depression to the second airport is 19°. What is the distance between the two airports? Round to the nearest foot.

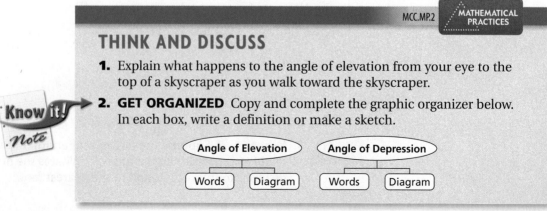

MCC.MP.2 **MATHEMATICAL PRACTICES**

THINK AND DISCUSS

1. Explain what happens to the angle of elevation from your eye to the top of a skyscraper as you walk toward the skyscraper.

2. GET ORGANIZED Copy and complete the graphic organizer below. In each box, write a definition or make a sketch.

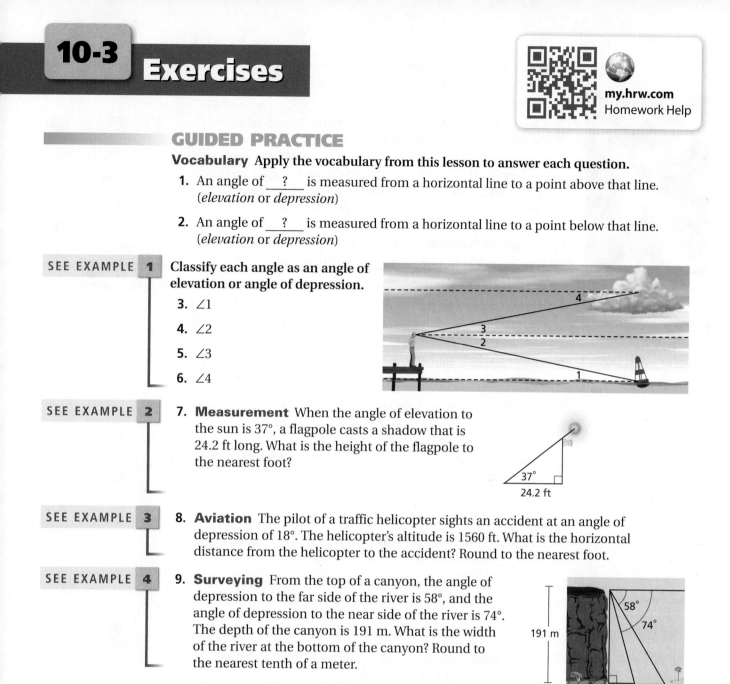

GUIDED PRACTICE

Vocabulary Apply the vocabulary from this lesson to answer each question.

1. An angle of ___?___ is measured from a horizontal line to a point above that line. (*elevation* or *depression*)

2. An angle of ___?___ is measured from a horizontal line to a point below that line. (*elevation* or *depression*)

SEE EXAMPLE 1 Classify each angle as an angle of elevation or angle of depression.

3. ∠1

4. ∠2

5. ∠3

6. ∠4

SEE EXAMPLE 2 7. **Measurement** When the angle of elevation to the sun is 37°, a flagpole casts a shadow that is 24.2 ft long. What is the height of the flagpole to the nearest foot?

37°
24.2 ft

SEE EXAMPLE 3 8. **Aviation** The pilot of a traffic helicopter sights an accident at an angle of depression of 18°. The helicopter's altitude is 1560 ft. What is the horizontal distance from the helicopter to the accident? Round to the nearest foot.

SEE EXAMPLE 4 9. **Surveying** From the top of a canyon, the angle of depression to the far side of the river is 58°, and the angle of depression to the near side of the river is 74°. The depth of the canyon is 191 m. What is the width of the river at the bottom of the canyon? Round to the nearest tenth of a meter.

58°
74°
191 m

PRACTICE AND PROBLEM SOLVING

Independent Practice	
For Exercises	See Example
10–13	1
14	2
15	3
16	4

my.hrw.com

Online Extra Practice

Classify each angle as an angle of elevation or angle of depression.

10. ∠1

11. ∠2

12. ∠3

13. ∠4

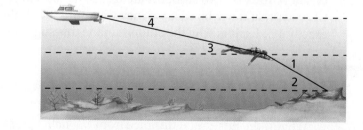

14. **Geology** To measure the height of a rock formation, a surveyor places her transit 100 m from its base and focuses the transit on the top of the formation. The angle of elevation is 67°. The transit is 1.5 m above the ground. What is the height of the rock formation? Round to the nearest meter.

Space Shuttle

During its launch, a space shuttle accelerates to more than 27,359 km/h in just over 8 minutes. So the shuttle travels 3219 km/h faster each minute.

15. Forestry A forest ranger in a 120 ft observation tower sees a fire. The angle of depression to the fire is 3.5°. What is the horizontal distance between the tower and the fire? Round to the nearest foot.

16. Space Shuttle Marion is observing the launch of a space shuttle from the command center. When she first sees the shuttle, the angle of elevation to it is 16°. Later, the angle of elevation is 74°. If the command center is 1 mi from the launch pad, how far did the shuttle travel while Marion was watching? Round to the nearest tenth of a mile.

Tell whether each statement is true or false. If false, explain why.

17. The angle of elevation from your eye to the top of a tree increases as you walk toward the tree.

18. If you stand at street level, the angle of elevation to a building's tenth-story window is greater than the angle of elevation to one of its ninth-story windows.

19. As you watch a plane fly above you, the angle of elevation to the plane gets closer to 0° as the plane approaches the point directly overhead.

20. An angle of depression can never be more than 90°.

Use the diagram for Exercises 21 and 22.

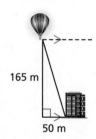

21. Which angles are not angles of elevation or angles of depression?

22. The angle of depression from the helicopter to the car is 30°. Find m∠1, m∠2, m∠3, and m∠4.

23. Critical Thinking Describe a situation in which the angle of depression to an object is decreasing.

24. An observer in a hot-air balloon sights a building that is 50 m from the balloon's launch point. The balloon has risen 165 m. What is the angle of depression from the balloon to the building? Round to the nearest degree.

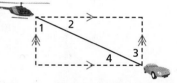

25. Multi-Step A surveyor finds that the angle of elevation to the top of a 1000 ft tower is 67°.

a. To the nearest foot, how far is the surveyor from the base of the tower?

b. How far back would the surveyor have to move so that the angle of elevation to the top of the tower is 55°? Round to the nearest foot.

H.O.T. 26. Write About It Two students are using shadows to calculate the height of a pole. One says that it will be easier if they wait until the angle of elevation to the sun is exactly 45°. Explain why the student made this suggestion.

Real-World Connections

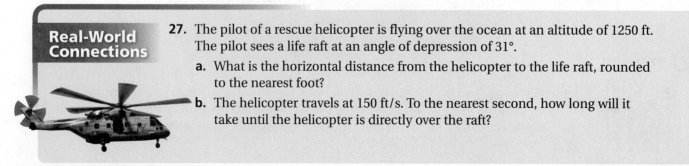

27. The pilot of a rescue helicopter is flying over the ocean at an altitude of 1250 ft. The pilot sees a life raft at an angle of depression of 31°.

a. What is the horizontal distance from the helicopter to the life raft, rounded to the nearest foot?

b. The helicopter travels at 150 ft/s. To the nearest second, how long will it take until the helicopter is directly over the raft?

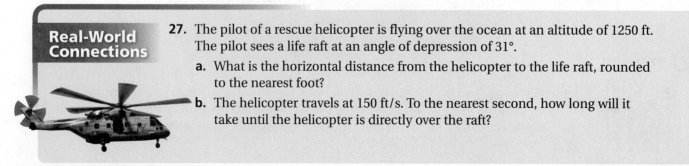

(tl), The Image Bank/Getty Images; (bl), Pete Ryan/National Geographic/Getty

TEST PREP

28. Mai is flying a plane at an altitude of 1600 ft. She sights a stadium at an angle of depression of 35°. What is Mai's approximate horizontal distance from the stadium?

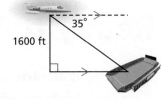

Ⓐ 676 feet   Ⓒ 1450 feet

Ⓑ 1120 feet   Ⓓ 2285 feet

29. Jeff finds that an office building casts a shadow that is 93 ft long when the angle of elevation to the sun is 60°. What is the height of the building?

Ⓕ 54 feet   Ⓖ 81 feet   Ⓗ 107 feet   Ⓙ 161 feet

30. **Short Response** Jim is rafting down a river that runs through a canyon. He sees a trail marker ahead at the top of the canyon and estimates the angle of elevation from the raft to the marker as 45°. Draw a sketch to represent the situation. Explain what happens to the angle of elevation as Jim moves closer to the marker.

CHALLENGE AND EXTEND

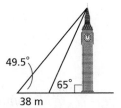

H.O.T. 31. Susan and Jorge stand 38 m apart. From Susan's position, the angle of elevation to the top of Big Ben is 65°. From Jorge's position, the angle of elevation to the top of Big Ben is 49.5°. To the nearest meter, how tall is Big Ben?

H.O.T. 32. A plane is flying at a constant altitude of 14,000 ft and a constant speed of 500 mi/h. The angle of depression from the plane to a lake is 6°. To the nearest minute, how much time will pass before the plane is directly over the lake?

H.O.T. 33. A skyscraper stands between two school buildings. The two schools are 10 mi apart. From school A, the angle of elevation to the top of the skyscraper is 5°. From school B, the angle of elevation is 2°. What is the height of the skyscraper to the nearest foot?

H.O.T. 34. Katie and Kim are attending a theater performance. Katie's seat is at floor level. She looks down at an angle of 18° to see the orchestra pit. Kim's seat is in the balcony directly above Katie. Kim looks down at an angle of 42° to see the pit. The horizontal distance from Katie's seat to the pit is 46 ft. What is the vertical distance between Katie's seat and Kim's seat? Round to the nearest inch.

FOCUS ON MATHEMATICAL PRACTICES

H.O.T. 35. **Analysis** If you are given the measure of the angle of depression from Q to P, what information can you find about the triangle?

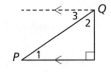

H.O.T. 36. **Modeling** A radio antenna is supported by guy wires, cables that run from the top of the antenna to the ground. How can you find the length of a guy wire if you can measure distance on the flat ground as well as angles from the ground?

H.O.T. 37. **Problem Solving** The angle of elevation from the top of a 55-ft tall building to the top of a nearby taller building is 43°. The angle of depression to the base of the taller building is 21°.

a. Make a sketch illustrating this situation. Include all the given measurements. Label the unknown distances with variables.

b. Describe in words how to calculate the height of the taller building.

c. What is the height of the taller building to the nearest foot?

Ready to Go On?

my.hrw.com
Assessment and Intervention

✓ 10-1 Trigonometric Ratios

Use a special right triangle to write each trigonometric ratio as a fraction.

1. $\tan 45°$

2. $\sin 30°$

3. $\cos 30°$

Use your calculator to find each trigonometric ratio. Round to the nearest hundredth.

4. $\sin 16°$

5. $\cos 79°$

6. $\tan 27°$

Find each length. Round to the nearest hundredth.

7. *QR*

8. *AB*

9. *LM*

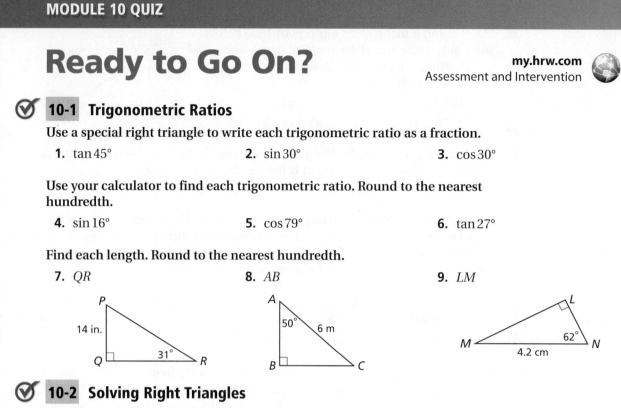

✓ 10-2 Solving Right Triangles

Find the unknown measures. Round lengths to the nearest hundredth and angle measures to the nearest degree.

10.

11.

12.

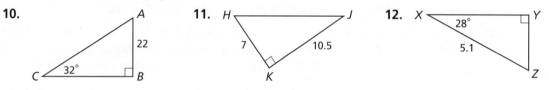

13. The wheelchair ramp at the entrance of the Mission Bay Library has a slope of $\frac{1}{18}$. What angle does the ramp make with the sidewalk? Round to the nearest degree.

✓ 10-3 Angles of Elevation and Depression

14. An observer in a blimp sights a football stadium at an angle of depression of 34°. The blimp's altitude is 1600 ft. What is the horizontal distance from the blimp to the stadium? Round to the nearest foot.

15. When the angle of elevation of the sun is 78°, a building casts a shadow that is 6 m long. What is the height of the building to the nearest tenth of a meter?

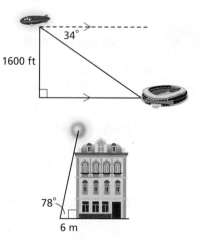

PARCC Assessment Readiness

Selected Response

1. Write cos 16° in terms of the sine.

    A sin 164°

    B sin 74°

    C sin 84°

    D sin 16°

2. Use the trigonometric ratio sin $A = 0.38$ to determine which angle of the triangle is $\angle A$.

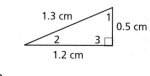

    F ∠2

    G ∠1

    H ∠3

    J No solution

3. A pilot flying at an altitude of 1.8 km sights the runway directly in front of her. The angle of depression to the beginning of the runway is 31°. The angle of depression to the end of the runway is 23°. What is the length of the runway? Round to the nearest tenth of a kilometer.

    A 1.2 km

    B 0.9 km

    C 1.3 km

    D 1.0 km

4. Find the perimeter of the right triangle. Round to the nearest tenth of a centimeter.

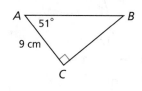

    F 27.9 cm

    G 30.7 cm

    H 34.4 cm

    J 36.0 cm

5. Nate built a skateboard ramp that covers a horizontal distance of 10 ft. The ramp rises a total of 3.5 ft. What angle does the ramp make with the ground? Round to the nearest degree.

    A 19°

    B 20°

    C 28°

    D 35°

6. The largest Egyptian pyramid is 146.5 m high. When Rowena stands far away from the pyramid, her line of sight to the top of the pyramid forms an angle of elevation of 20° with the ground. What is the horizontal distance between the center of the pyramid and Rowena? Round to the nearest meter.

    F 402 m

    G 427 m

    H 156 m

    J 65 m

7. The coordinates of the vertices of △RPQ are $R(2, -1)$, $P(2, 2)$, and $Q(-2, -1)$. Find m∠P.

    A m∠$P = 53°$

    B m∠$P = 37°$

    C m∠$P = 93°$

    D m∠$P = 42°$

Mini-Tasks

8. Jessie is building a ramp for loading motorcycles onto a trailer. The trailer is 2.8 feet off of the ground. To avoid making it too difficult to push a motorcycle up the ramp, Jessie decides to make the angle between the ramp and the ground 15°. To the nearest hundredth of a foot, find the length of the ramp.

9. An observer at the top of a skyscraper sights a tour bus at an angle of depression of 61°. The skyscraper is 910 ft tall. What is the horizontal distance from the base of the skyscraper to the tour bus? Round to the nearest foot.

Selected Response

1. The length of one leg of a right triangle is 3 times the length of the other, and the length of the hypotenuse is 10. What is the length of the longest leg?

(A) 3

(B) $3\sqrt{10}$

(C) $\sqrt{10}$

(D) $12\sqrt{5}$

2. Which of the following is NOT equivalent to $\sin 60°$?

(F) $\cos 30°$

(G) $\dfrac{\sqrt{3}}{2}$

(H) $(\cos 60°)(\tan 60°)$

(J) $\dfrac{\tan 30°}{\sin 30°}$

3. $\triangle ABC$ is a right triangle. $m\angle A = 20°$, $m\angle B = 90°$, $AC = 8$, and $AB = 3$. Which expression can be used to find BC?

(A) $\dfrac{3}{\tan 70°}$

(B) $\dfrac{8}{\sin 20°}$

(C) $8 \tan 20°$

(D) $3 \cos 70°$

4. A slide at a park is 25 ft long, and the top of the slide is 10 ft above the ground. What is the approximate measure of the angle the slide makes with the ground?

(F) 21.8°

(G) 23.6°

(H) 66.4°

(J) 68.2°

5. Tell if the measures 6, 13, and 14 can be side lengths of a triangle. If so, classify the triangle as acute, right, or obtuse.

(A) Yes; acute triangle

(B) Yes; obtuse triangle

(C) Yes; right triangle

(D) No.

6. Find all the values of k so that $(-3, 4)$, $(-8, 5)$, and $(-5, k)$ are the vertices of a right triangle.

(F) $k = -6, 1, 9, 20$

(G) $k = -5, 2, 7, 19$

(H) $k = -5, 1, 9, 19$

(J) $k = -6, 2, 7, 20$

7. $\triangle ABC$ is a right triangle in which $m\angle A = 30°$ and $m\angle B = 60°$. Which of the following are possible lengths for the sides of this triangle?

(A) $AB = \sqrt{3}$, $AC = \sqrt{2}$, and $BC = 1$

(B) $AB = 4$, $AC = 2$, and $BC = 2\sqrt{3}$

(C) $AB = 6\sqrt{3}$, $AC = 27$, and $BC = 3\sqrt{3}$

(D) $AB = 8$, $AC = 4\sqrt{3}$, and $BC = 4$

8. Find the values of x and y. Express your answers in simplest radical form.

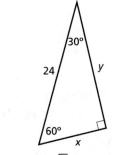

(F) $x = 12$, $y = 12\sqrt{3}$

(G) $x = 12\sqrt{3}$, $y = 12$

(H) $x = 12$, $y = 12\sqrt{2}$

(J) $x = 12\sqrt{2}$, $y = 12$

9. An architect designs the front view of a house with a gable roof that has a 45°-45°-90° triangle shape. The overhangs are 0.5 meter each from the exterior walls, and the width of the house is 16 meters. What should the side length *l* of the triangle be? Round your answer to the nearest meter.

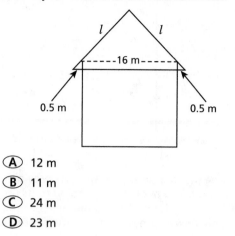

(A) 12 m

(B) 11 m

(C) 24 m

(D) 23 m

10. Write the trigonometric ratio for cos *X* as a fraction and as a decimal rounded to the nearest hundredth.

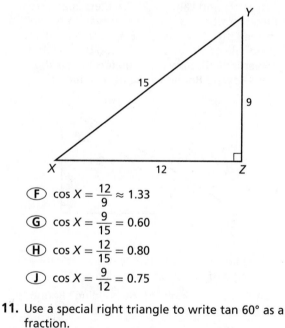

(F) $\cos X = \dfrac{12}{9} \approx 1.33$

(G) $\cos X = \dfrac{9}{15} = 0.60$

(H) $\cos X = \dfrac{12}{15} = 0.80$

(J) $\cos X = \dfrac{9}{12} = 0.75$

11. Use a special right triangle to write tan 60° as a fraction.

(A) $\dfrac{\sqrt{3}}{1}$

(B) $\dfrac{1}{\sqrt{3}}$

(C) $\dfrac{\sqrt{2}}{1}$

(D) $\dfrac{\sqrt{3}}{2}$

12. Use your calculator to find the trigonometric ratios sin 79°, cos 47°, and tan 77°. Round to the nearest hundredth.

(F) sin 79° = −0.99,
cos 47° = −0.44,
tan 77° = −32.27

(G) sin 79° = −0.44,
cos 47° = −0.99,
tan 77° = −32.27

(H) sin 79° = 0.68,
cos 47° = 0.98,
tan 77° = 4.33

(J) sin 79° = 0.98,
cos 47° = 0.68,
tan 77° = 4.33

13. Find sin ∠*A* to the nearest hundredth.

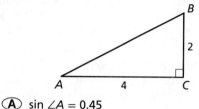

(A) sin ∠*A* = 0.45

(B) sin ∠*A* = 0.50

(C) sin ∠*A* = 2.24

(D) sin ∠*A* = 0.89

14. Some mountains in the Alps are very steep and have a grade of 42.7%. To the nearest degree, what angle do these mountains make with a horizontal line?

(F) 23°

(G) 67°

(H) 47°

(J) 32°

15. Classify each angle in the diagram as an angle of elevation or an angle of depression.

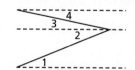

(A) Angles of elevation: ∠1, ∠3
Angles of depression: ∠2, ∠4

(B) Angles of elevation: ∠2, ∠4
Angles of depression: ∠1, ∠3

(C) Angles of elevation: ∠1, ∠4
Angles of depression: ∠2, ∠3

(D) Angles of elevation: ∠2, ∠3
Angles of depression: ∠1, ∠4

16. Find the missing side length. Tell if the side lengths form a Pythagorean triple. Explain.

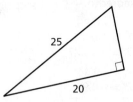

- **F** The missing side length is 15. The side lengths form a Pythagorean triple because they are nonzero whole numbers that satisfy the equation $a^2 + b^2 = c^2$.

- **G** The missing side length is 32.02. The side lengths do not form a Pythagorean triple because one of them is not a nonzero whole number.

- **H** The missing side length is 5. The side lengths form a Pythagorean triple because they are nonzero whole numbers that satisfy the equation $a^2 + b^2 = c^2$.

- **J** The missing side length is 32.02. The side lengths form a Pythagorean triple because they satisfy the equation $a^2 + b^2 = c^2$.

17. Find the value of x. Express your answer in simplest radical form.

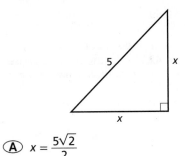

- **A** $x = \dfrac{5\sqrt{2}}{2}$

- **B** $x = 5\sqrt{2}$

- **C** $x = \dfrac{\sqrt{5}\sqrt{2}}{2}$

- **D** $x = \dfrac{5\sqrt{3}}{2}$

18. Find the value of x that satisfies the equation $\sin(4x + 14)° = \cos(-3x + 73)°$.

- **F** $x = \dfrac{3}{7}$
- **G** $x = 3$
- **H** $x = \dfrac{59}{7}$
- **J** $x = 93$

Mini-Tasks

19. Find the sine and cosine of the acute angles in the right triangle.

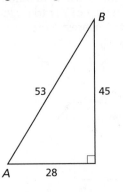

20. An eagle 300 feet in the air spots its prey on the ground. The angle of depression to its prey is 15°. What is the horizontal distance between the eagle and its prey? Round to the nearest foot.

21. Mike is standing between Lani and the Eiffel Tower. He and Lani are 21.2 meters apart. From Mike's position, the angle of elevation to the top of the Eiffel Tower is 40°. From Lani's position, the angle of elevation to the top of the Eiffel Tower is 38.5°. How many meters high is the Eiffel Tower? Round to the nearest meter.

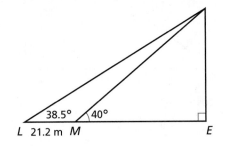

22. A building casts a shadow that is 85 ft long when the angle of elevation to the sun is 34°.

- **a.** What is the height of the building? Round to the nearest inch and show your work.

- **b.** What is the angle of elevation to the sun when the shadow is 42 ft 6 in. long? Round to the nearest tenth of a degree and show your work.

Performance Tasks

23. A 30°-60°-90° triangle is shown below. Draw another triangle similar to the given triangle, indicating the lengths of the sides. Show that the values of the sine, cosine, and tangent of the 30° and 60° angles of your triangle are the same as those for the given triangle.

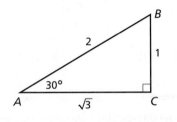

24. A new street is going to be constructed to connect Main Street, which runs in the east-west direction, and North Boulevard, which runs in the north-south direction, as shown in the diagram below. The construction cost has been estimated at $110 per linear foot, excluding the new intersections. The intersections are estimated to cost $1,450,000 each.

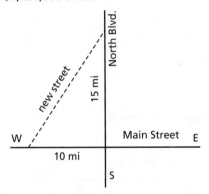

Part A: What type of triangle is bounded by the new street, North Boulevard, and Main Street? How do you know?

Part B: Let x represent the length of the new street. What is the name of the formula that can be used to find the value of x? Use that formula to write an equation that can be solved for x.

Part C: What is the length of the new street to the nearest thousandth of a mile? Convert that distance to the nearest foot. Show your work.

Part D: Estimate the cost of constructing the new street. Be sure to include the costs for intersections. Show your work and round the cost to the nearest thousand dollars.

Are You Ready?

my.hrw.com
Assessment and Intervention

✓ Vocabulary

Match each term on the left with a definition on the right.

1. equilateral
2. parallelogram
3. apothem
4. composite figure

A. the distance from the center of a regular polygon to a side of the polygon

B. a quadrilateral with four right angles

C. a quadrilateral with two pairs of parallel sides

D. having all sides congruent

E. a figure made up of simple shapes, such as triangles, rectangles, trapezoids, and circles

✓ Find Area in the Coordinate Plane

Find the area of each figure with the given vertices.

5. $\triangle ABC$ with $A(0, 3)$, $B(5, 3)$, and $C(2, -1)$

6. rectangle $KLMN$ with $K(-2, 3)$, $L(-2, 7)$, $M(6, 7)$, and $N(6, 3)$

7. $\odot P$ with center $P(2, 3)$ that passes through the point $Q(-6, 3)$

✓ Circumference and Area of Circles

Find the circumference and area of each circle. Give your answers in terms of π.

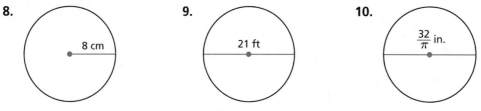

8.

8 cm

9.

21 ft

10.

$\frac{32}{\pi}$ in.

✓ Distance and Midpoint Formulas

Find the length and midpoint of the segment with the given endpoints.

11. $A(-3, 2)$ and $B(5, 6)$

12. $C(-4, -4)$ and $D(2, -3)$

Career Readiness Transportation Engineer

Transportation engineers are civil engineers who specialize in highways, rail and bus systems, and airports. Some transportation engineers develop entire systems or supervise construction or repair of systems. They need to find areas of composite figures or volumes of composite solids to determine construction costs. A college degree in civil engineering is required. Most transportation engineers work for construction or engineering companies or government agencies.

UNIT

3

Circles and Volume

Online Edition

my.hrw.com

Access the complete online textbook, interactive features, and additional resources.

Multilingual Glossary

Enhance your math vocabulary with this illustrated online glossary in 13 languages.

Homework Help

Get instant help with tutorial videos, practice problems, and step-by-step solutions.

Portable Devices

eTextbook

Access your full textbook on your tablet or e-reader.

HMH Fuse

Make your learning experience completely portable and interactive with this app for iPad®.

Chapter Resources

Scan with your smart phone to jump directly to the online edition.

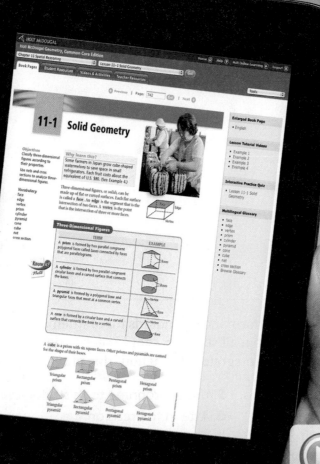

The online edition of your textbook is enhanced with videos and interactive features for every lesson.

UNIT 3

Module

11 Area and Volume

Contents

MATHEMATICAL PRACTICES The Common Core Georgia Performance Standards for Mathematical Practice describe varieties of expertise that all students should seek to develop. Opportunities to develop these practices are integrated throughout this program.

1 Make sense of problems and persevere in solving them.

2 Reason abstractly and quantitatively.

3 Construct viable arguments and critique the reasoning of others.

4 Model with mathematics.

5 Use appropriate tools strategically.

6 Attend to precision.

7 Look for and make use of structure.

8 Look for and express regularity in repeated reasoning.

Unpacking the Standards

my.hrw.com
Multilingual Glossary

Understanding the standards and the vocabulary terms in the standards will help you know exactly what you are expected to learn in this chapter.

COMMON CORE GPS **MCC9-12.G.GMD.3**

Use volume formulas for cylinders, pyramids, cones, and spheres to solve problems.

Key Vocabulary

volume (volumen)
The number of nonoverlapping unit cubes of a given size that will exactly fill the interior of a three-dimensional figure.

formula (formula)
A literal equation that states a rule for a relationship among quantities.

cylinder (cilindro)
A three-dimensional figure with two parallel congruent circular bases and a curved surface that connects the bases.

pyramid (pirámide)
A polyhedron formed by a polygonal base and triangular lateral faces that meet at a common vertex.

cone (cono)
A three-dimensional figure with a circular base and a curved surface that connects the base to a point called the vertex.

sphere (esfera)
The set of points in space that are a fixed distance from a given point called the center of the sphere.

What It Means For You

Volume problems appear frequently in real-world contexts. Learning the relationships among volume formulas helps you understand, remember, and apply them.

EXAMPLE **Volume of a cylinder**

A grain silo at a port has the dimensions shown. The volume is the base area B times the height h. Because the base is a circle, this gives:

$$V = Bh = \pi r^2 h$$
$$= \pi (15^2)(42)$$
$$\approx 30,000 \text{ ft}^3$$

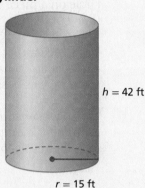
$h = 42$ ft

$r = 15$ ft

EXAMPLE **Volume of a cone**

The silo above contains just enough grain so that the grain reaches to the outer edge of the floor, forming a cone. The volume is one third the base area times the height. This gives:

$$V = \frac{1}{3}Bh = \frac{1}{3}\pi r^2 h = \frac{1}{3}\pi(15^2)(8) \approx 1900 \text{ ft}^3$$

8 ft

15 ft

EXAMPLE **Volume of a sphere**

A liquefied natural gas tank at the port is in the shape of a sphere with the radius shown. The volume is:

$$V = \frac{4}{3}\pi r^3 = \frac{4}{3}\pi(16^3) \approx 17,000 \text{ ft}^3$$

16 ft

EXAMPLE **Volume of a pyramid**

A customs building at the port has a roof in the shape of a pyramid with the dimensions shown. As with a cone, the volume is one third the base area times the height. Because the base is a rectangle, this gives:

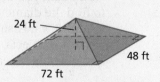
24 ft

48 ft

72 ft

$$V = \frac{1}{3}Bh = \frac{1}{3}(72)(48)(24) \approx 28,000 \text{ ft}^3$$

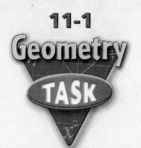

Geometry TASK

Develop π

The ratio of the circumference of a circle to its diameter is defined as π. All circles are similar, so this ratio is the same for all circles:

$$\pi = \frac{\text{circumference}}{\text{diameter}}.$$

Use with Developing Formulas for Circles and Regular Polygons

MATHEMATICAL PRACTICES

Use appropriate tools strategically.

MCC9-12.G.GMD.1 Give an informal argument for the formulas for the circumference of a circle, area of a circle …

Activity 1

1 Use your compass to draw a large circle on a piece of cardboard and then cut it out.

2 Use a measuring tape to measure the circle's diameter and circumference as accurately as possible.

3 Use the results from your circle to estimate π. Compare your answers with the results of the rest of the class.

Try This

1. Do you think it is possible to draw a circle whose ratio of circumference to diameter is not π? Why or why not?

2. How does knowing the relationship between circumference, diameter, and π help you determine the formula for circumference?

3. Use a ribbon to make a π measuring tape. Mark off increments of π inches or π cm on your ribbon as accurately as possible. How could you use this π measuring tape to find the diameter of a circular object? Use your π measuring tape to measure 5 circular objects. Give the circumference and diameter of each object.

Sam Dudgeon/HMH Photo

Archimedes used inscribed and circumscribed polygons to estimate the value of π. His "method of exhaustion" is considered to be an early version of calculus. In the figures below, the circumference of the circle is less than the perimeter of the larger polygon and greater than the perimeter of the smaller polygon. This fact is used to estimate π.

1 Construct a large square. Construct the perpendicular bisectors of two adjacent sides.

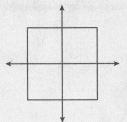

2 Use your compass to draw an inscribed circle as shown.

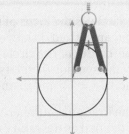

3 Connect the midpoints of the sides to form a square that is inscribed in the circle.

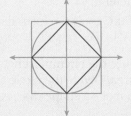

4 Let P_1 represent the perimeter of the smaller square, P_2 represent the perimeter of the larger square, and C represent the circumference of the circle. Measure the squares to find P_1 and P_2 and substitute the values into the inequality below.

$$P_1 < C < P_2$$

5 Divide each expression in the inequality by the diameter of the circle. Why does this give you an inequality in terms of π? Complete the inequality below.

$$\underline{\quad ? \quad} < \pi < \underline{\quad ? \quad}$$

4. Use the perimeters of the inscribed and circumscribed regular hexagons to write an inequality for π. Assume the diameter of each circle is 2 units.

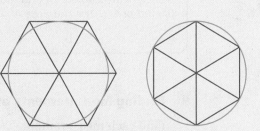

5. Compare the inequalities you found for π. What do you think would be true about your inequality if you used regular polygons with more sides? How could you use inscribed and circumscribed regular polygons to estimate π?

6. An alternate definition of π is the area of a circle with radius 1. How could you use this definition and the figures above to estimate the value of π?

Developing Formulas for Circles and Regular Polygons

Essential Question: How do you find the area of a regular polygon?

Objectives
Develop and apply the formulas for the area and circumference of a circle.

Develop and apply the formula for the area of a regular polygon.

Vocabulary
circle
center of a circle
center of a regular polygon
apothem
central angle of a regular polygon

Who uses this?
Drummers use drums of different sizes to produce different notes. The pitch is related to the area of the top of the drum. (See Example 2.)

A **circle** is the locus of points in a plane that are a fixed distance from a point called the **center of the circle**. A circle is named by the symbol $\odot$ and its center. $\odot A$ has radius $r = AB$ and diameter $d = CD$.

The irrational number π is defined as the ratio of the circumference C to the diameter d, or $\pi = \frac{C}{d}$. Solving for C gives the formula $C = \pi d$. Also $d = 2r$, so $C = 2\pi r$.

You can use the circumference of a circle to find its area. Divide the circle and rearrange the pieces to make a shape that resembles a parallelogram.

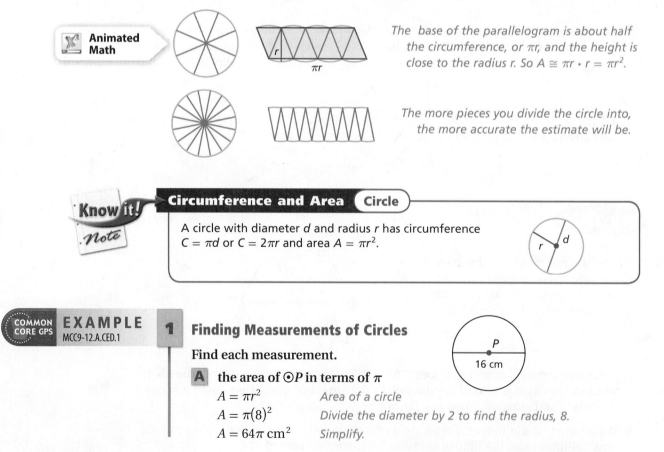

Animated Math

The base of the parallelogram is about half the circumference, or πr, and the height is close to the radius r. So $A \cong \pi r \cdot r = \pi r^2$.

The more pieces you divide the circle into, the more accurate the estimate will be.

Know it! Note

Circumference and Area — Circle

A circle with diameter d and radius r has circumference $C = \pi d$ or $C = 2\pi r$ and area $A = \pi r^2$.

COMMON CORE GPS MCC9-12.A.CED.1

EXAMPLE 1 Finding Measurements of Circles

Find each measurement.

A the area of $\odot P$ in terms of π

$A = \pi r^2$ *Area of a circle*

$A = \pi(8)^2$ *Divide the diameter by 2 to find the radius, 8.*

$A = 64\pi \text{ cm}^2$ *Simplify.*

Find each measurement.

B the radius of $\odot X$ in which $C = 24\pi$ in.

$C = 2\pi r$ — *Circumference of a circle*

$24\pi = 2\pi r$ — *Substitute 24π for C.*

$r = 12$ in. — *Divide both sides by 2π.*

C the circumference of $\odot S$ in which $A = 9x^2 \pi$ cm^2

Step 1 Use the given area to solve for r.

$A = \pi r^2$ — *Area of a circle*

$9x^2\pi = \pi r^2$ — *Substitute $9x^2\pi$ for A.*

$9x^2 = r^2$ — *Divide both sides by π.*

$3x = r$ — *Take the square root of both sides.*

Step 2 Use the value of r to find the circumference.

$C = 2\pi r$

$C = 2\pi(3x)$ — *Substitute $3x$ for r.*

$C = 6x\pi$ cm — *Simplify.*

CHECK IT OUT!

1. Find the area of $\odot A$ in terms of π in which $C = (4x - 6)\pi$ m.

EXAMPLE 2

Music Application

A drum kit contains three drums with diameters of 10 in., 12 in., and 14 in. Find the area of the top of each drum. Round to the nearest tenth.

10 in. diameter	12 in. diameter	14 in. diameter
$A = \pi(5^2)$ $r = \dfrac{10}{2} = 5$	$A = \pi(6^2)$ $r = \dfrac{12}{2} = 6$	$A = \pi(7)^2$ $r = \dfrac{14}{2} = 7$
$\cong 78.5$ in^2	$\cong 113.1$ in^2	$\cong 153.9$ in^2

CHECK IT OUT!

2. Use the information above to find the circumference of each drum.

The **center of a regular polygon** is equidistant from the vertices. The **apothem** is the distance from the center to a side. A **central angle of a regular polygon** has its vertex at the center, and its sides pass through consecutive vertices. Each central angle measure of a regular n-gon is $\frac{360°}{n}$.

To find the area of a regular n-gon with side length s and apothem a, divide it into n congruent isosceles triangles.

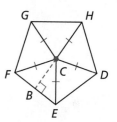

Regular pentagon *DEFGH* has center *C*, apothem *BC*, and central angle $\angle DCE$.

area of each triangle: $\frac{1}{2}as$

total area of the polygon: $A = n\left(\frac{1}{2}as\right)$, or $A = \frac{1}{2}aP$ — *The perimeter is $P = ns$.*

Know it! Note

Area — **Regular Polygon**

The area of a regular polygon with apothem a and perimeter P is $A = \frac{1}{2}aP$.

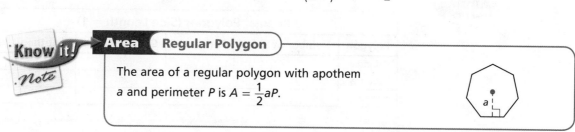

COMMON CORE GPS **EXAMPLE** **3**
MCC9-12.G.SRT.8

Finding the Area of a Regular Polygon

Find the area of each regular polygon. Round to the nearest tenth.

A **a regular hexagon with side length 6 m**

The perimeter is $6(6) = 36$ m. The hexagon can be divided into 6 equilateral triangles with side length 6 m. By the 30°-60°-90° Triangle Theorem, the apothem is $3\sqrt{3}$ m.

$A = \frac{1}{2}aP$ *Area of a regular polygon*

$A = \frac{1}{2}(3\sqrt{3})(36)$ *Substitute $3\sqrt{3}$ for a and 36 for P.*

$A = 54\sqrt{3} \cong 93.5$ m^2 *Simplify.*

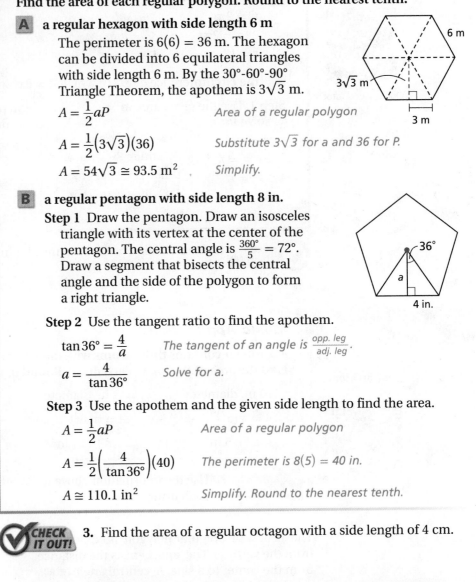

6 m

$3\sqrt{3}$ m

3 m

my.hrw.com

Online Video Tutor

Remember!

The tangent of an angle in a right triangle is the ratio of the opposite leg length to the adjacent leg length.

B **a regular pentagon with side length 8 in.**

Step 1 Draw the pentagon. Draw an isosceles triangle with its vertex at the center of the pentagon. The central angle is $\frac{360°}{5} = 72°$. Draw a segment that bisects the central angle and the side of the polygon to form a right triangle.

Step 2 Use the tangent ratio to find the apothem.

$\tan 36° = \frac{4}{a}$ *The tangent of an angle is $\frac{\text{opp. leg}}{\text{adj. leg}}$.*

$a = \frac{4}{\tan 36°}$ *Solve for a.*

Step 3 Use the apothem and the given side length to find the area.

$A = \frac{1}{2}aP$ *Area of a regular polygon*

$A = \frac{1}{2}\left(\frac{4}{\tan 36°}\right)(40)$ *The perimeter is $8(5) = 40$ in.*

$A \cong 110.1$ in^2 *Simplify. Round to the nearest tenth.*

36°

a

4 in.

CHECK IT OUT! **3.** Find the area of a regular octagon with a side length of 4 cm.

MCC.MP.7 **MATHEMATICAL PRACTICES**

THINK AND DISCUSS

1. Describe the relationship between the circumference of a circle and π.

2. Explain how you would find the central angle of a regular polygon with n sides.

3. **GET ORGANIZED** Copy and complete the graphic organizer.

Regular Polygons (Side Length = 1)					
Polygon	Number of Sides	Perimeter	Central Angle	Apothem	Area
Triangle					
Square					
Hexagon					

GUIDED PRACTICE

1. **Vocabulary** Describe how to find the *apothem* of a square with side length *s*.

SEE EXAMPLE **1** Find each measurement.

2. the circumference of ⊙*C*

3. the area of ⊙*A* in terms of π

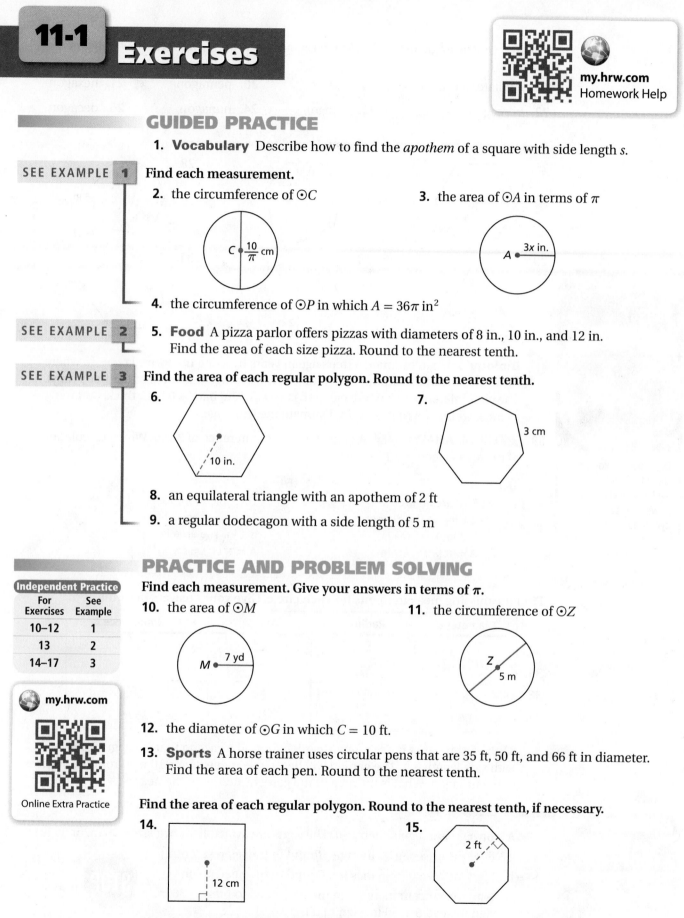

4. the circumference of ⊙*P* in which $A = 36\pi$ in²

SEE EXAMPLE **2**

5. **Food** A pizza parlor offers pizzas with diameters of 8 in., 10 in., and 12 in. Find the area of each size pizza. Round to the nearest tenth.

SEE EXAMPLE **3** Find the area of each regular polygon. Round to the nearest tenth.

6.

7.

8. an equilateral triangle with an apothem of 2 ft

9. a regular dodecagon with a side length of 5 m

PRACTICE AND PROBLEM SOLVING

Independent Practice	
For Exercises	See Example
10–12	1
13	2
14–17	3

my.hrw.com

Online Extra Practice

Find each measurement. Give your answers in terms of π.

10. the area of ⊙*M*

11. the circumference of ⊙*Z*

12. the diameter of ⊙*G* in which $C = 10$ ft.

13. **Sports** A horse trainer uses circular pens that are 35 ft, 50 ft, and 66 ft in diameter. Find the area of each pen. Round to the nearest tenth.

Find the area of each regular polygon. Round to the nearest tenth, if necessary.

14.

15.

16. a regular nonagon with a perimeter of 144 in.

17. a regular pentagon with an apothem of 2 ft.

Find the central angle measure of each regular polygon. (*Hint:* To review polygon names.)

18. equilateral triangle
19. square
20. pentagon
21. hexagon
22. heptagon
23. octagon
24. nonagon
25. decagon

Find the area of each regular polygon. Round to the nearest tenth.

26.

14 in.

27.

5 cm

28.

6 in.

29.

3 m

30.

2 cm

31.

5 ft

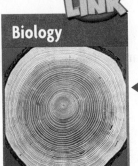

Biology

Dendroclimatologists study tree rings for evidence of changes in weather patterns over time.

32. **Biology** You can estimate a tree's age in years by using the formula $a = \frac{r}{w}$, where r is the tree's radius without bark and w is the average thickness of the tree's rings. The circumference of a white oak tree is 100 in. The bark is 0.5 in. thick, and the average width of a ring is 0.2 in. Estimate the tree's age.

33. ///**ERROR ANALYSIS**/// A circle has a circumference of 2π in. Which calculation of the area is incorrect? Explain.

A
The circumference is 2π in., so the diameter is 2 in. The area is $A = \pi (2^2) = 4\pi$ in².

B
The circumference is 2π in., so the radius is 1 in. The area is $A = \pi (1^2) = 2\pi$ in².

Find the missing measurements for each circle. Give your answers in terms of π.

	Diameter d	Radius r	Area A	Circumference C
34.	6			
35.			100	
36.		17		
37.				36π

H.O.T. 38. **Multi-Step** Janet is designing a garden around a gazebo that is a regular hexagon with side length 6 ft. The garden will be a circle that extends 10 feet from the vertices of the hexagon. What is the area of the garden? Round to the nearest square foot.

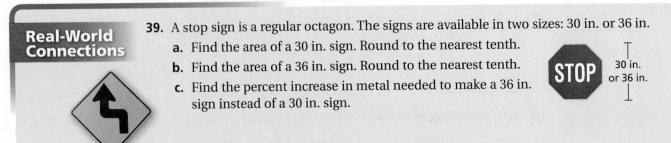

Real-World Connections

39. A stop sign is a regular octagon. The signs are available in two sizes: 30 in. or 36 in.
   a. Find the area of a 30 in. sign. Round to the nearest tenth.
   b. Find the area of a 36 in. sign. Round to the nearest tenth.
   c. Find the percent increase in metal needed to make a 36 in. sign instead of a 30 in. sign.

STOP 30 in. or 36 in.

40. Measurement A *trundle wheel* is used to measure distances by rolling it on the ground and counting its number of turns. If the circumference of a trundle wheel is 1 meter, what is its diameter?

H.O.T. 41. Critical Thinking Which do you think would seat more people, a 4 ft by 6 ft rectangular table or a circular table with a diameter of 6 ft? How many people would you sit at each table? Explain your reasoning.

H.O.T. 42. Write About It The center of each circle in the figure lies on the number line. Describe the relationship between the circumference of the largest circle and the circumferences of the four smaller circles.

TEST PREP

43. Find the perimeter of the regular octagon to the nearest centimeter.

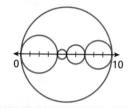

   Ⓐ 5   Ⓑ 40   Ⓒ 20   Ⓓ 68

44. Which of the following ratios comparing a circle's circumference C to its diameter d gives the value of π?

   Ⓕ $\dfrac{C}{d}$ Ⓖ $\dfrac{4C}{d^2}$ Ⓗ $\dfrac{d}{C}$ Ⓙ $\dfrac{d}{2C}$

45. Alisa has a circular tabletop with a 2-foot diameter. She wants to paint a pattern on the table top that includes a 2-foot-by-1-foot rectangle and 4 squares with sides 0.5 foot long. Which information makes this scenario impossible?

   Ⓐ There will be no room left on the tabletop after the rectangle has been painted.

   Ⓑ A 2-foot-long rectangle will not fit on the circular tabletop.

   Ⓒ Squares cannot be painted on the circle.

   Ⓓ There will not be enough room on the table to fit all the 0.5-foot squares.

CHALLENGE AND EXTEND

H.O.T. 46. Two circles have the same center. The radius of the larger circle is 5 units longer than the radius of the smaller circle. Find the difference in the circumferences of the two circles.

47. Algebra Write the formula for the area of a circle in terms of its circumference.

48. Critical Thinking Show that the formula for the area of a regular n-gon approaches the formula for the area of a circle as n gets very large.

FOCUS ON MATHEMATICAL PRACTICES

H.O.T. 49. Reasoning A circle inscribed in a regular polygon touches each side of the polygon at its midpoint. What does the radius of the inscribed circle represent in the regular polygon?

H.O.T. 50. Communication The center of a circle is located at $(-5, 10)$. The point $(7, 15)$ is on the circle. Find the other point on the circle that lies on the same diameter as $(7, 15)$. Explain your solution process.

H.O.T. 51. Problem Solving The area of a regular hexagon is 500 square units. Find its perimeter to the nearest tenth of a unit. Show your work.

H.O.T. 52. Number Sense What is the radius of the circle whose numerical circumference is the same as its numerical area?

Triangle Area Formulas

You've used the formula $A = \frac{1}{2}bh$ to find the area of a triangle, and you've used trigonometric ratios to find missing lengths in right triangles. You can combine the two techniques to find the area of a triangle when you don't know the value of h.

MATHEMATICAL PRACTICES   **Reason abstractly and quantitatively.**   **MCC9-12.G.SRT.9(+)** Derive the formula $A = 1/2\ ab\ \sin(C)$ for the area of a triangle by drawing an auxiliary line from a vertex perpendicular to the opposite side.

If you are given the lengths of two sides and the included angle, you can use this information to find the area of the triangle

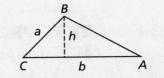

$\dfrac{h}{a} = \sin C$ *Write the sine of C in terms of h and a.*

$h = a \sin C$ *Multiply both sides by a to isolate h.*

$A = \dfrac{1}{2} ba \sin C$ *Substitute the expression for h into the area formula.*

Example

Find the area of the triangle shown.

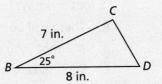

$A = \dfrac{1}{2} ba \sin B$

$A = \dfrac{1}{2}(7)(8) \sin 25°$ *Substitute the values for the side lengths and the measure of the included angle.*

$A \approx 11.8$ *Simplify.*

The area is approximately 11.8 in.^{2}.

Try This

Find the area of each triangle. Round to the nearest tenth.

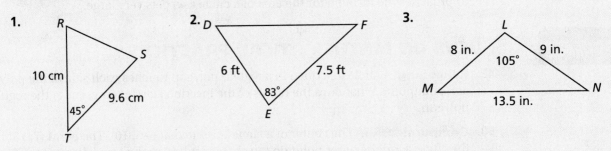

1.
2.
3.

4. You can also find the area of a triangle if you only know the lengths of the sides. Heron's formula is $A = \sqrt{s(s-a)(s-b)(s-c)}$, where s is one-half of the perimeter of the triangle and a, b, and c are the side lengths of the triangle. Find *s* for the triangle in Exercise 3, and use Heron's formula to find the area. Round to the nearest tenth.

11-2

Volume of Prisms and Cylinders

? **Essential Question:** What are the volume formulas for prisms and cylinders?

Objectives
Learn and apply the formula for the volume of a prism.

Learn and apply the formula for the volume of a cylinder.

Vocabulary
volume

Who uses this?
Marine biologists must ensure that aquariums are large enough to accommodate the number of fish inside them. (See Example 2.)

The **volume** of a three-dimensional figure is the number of nonoverlapping unit cubes of a given size that will exactly fill the interior.

A cube built out of 27 unit cubes has a volume of 27 cubic units.

Cavalieri's principle says that if two three-dimensional figures have the same height and have the same cross-sectional area at every level, they have the same volume.

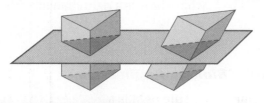

A right prism and an oblique prism with the same base and height have the same volume.

Know it! **Note**

Volume of a Prism

The volume of a prism with base area B and height h is $V = Bh$.

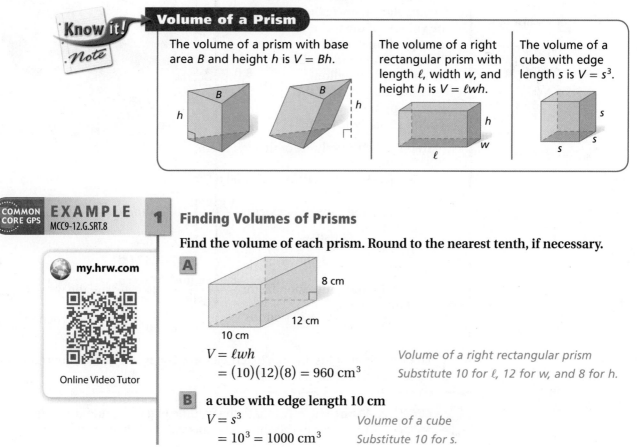

The volume of a right rectangular prism with length ℓ, width w, and height h is $V = \ell wh$.

The volume of a cube with edge length s is $V = s^3$.

COMMON CORE GPS MCC9-12.G.SRT.8

EXAMPLE **1**

Finding Volumes of Prisms

Find the volume of each prism. Round to the nearest tenth, if necessary.

A

8 cm
12 cm
10 cm

$V = \ell wh$ *Volume of a right rectangular prism*
$\ \ = (10)(12)(8) = 960 \text{ cm}^3$ *Substitute 10 for ℓ, 12 for w, and 8 for h.*

B a cube with edge length 10 cm

$V = s^3$ *Volume of a cube*
$\ \ = 10^3 = 1000 \text{ cm}^3$ *Substitute 10 for s.*

my.hrw.com

Online Video Tutor

Find the volume of each prism. Round to the nearest tenth, if necessary.

C a right regular pentagonal prism with base edge length 5 m and height 7 m

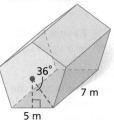

36°

7 m

5 m

Step 1 Find the apothem *a* of the base. First draw a right triangle on one base as shown. The measure of the angle with its vertex at the center is $\frac{360°}{10} = 36°$.

$\tan 36° = \frac{2.5}{a}$ *The leg of the triangle is half the side length, or 2.5 m.*

$a = \frac{2.5}{\tan 36°}$ *Solve for a.*

Step 2 Use the value of *a* to find the base area.

$B = \frac{1}{2}aP = \frac{1}{2}\left(\frac{2.5}{\tan 36°}\right)(25) = \frac{31.25}{\tan 36°}$ $P = 5(5) = 25$ m

Step 3 Use the base area to find the volume.

$V = Bh = \frac{31.25}{\tan 36°} \cdot 7 \approx 301.1 \text{ m}^3$

CHECK IT OUT!

1. Find the volume of a triangular prism with a height of 9 yd whose base is a right triangle with legs 7 yd and 5 yd long.

COMMON CORE GPS   **EXAMPLE**   **2**
MCC9-12.G.MG.2

my.hrw.com

Online Video Tutor

Marine Biology Application

The aquarium at the right is a rectangular prism. Estimate the volume of the water in the aquarium in gallons. The density of water is about 8.33 pounds per gallon. Estimate the weight of the water in pounds.
(*Hint:* 1 gallon ≈ 0.134 ft³)

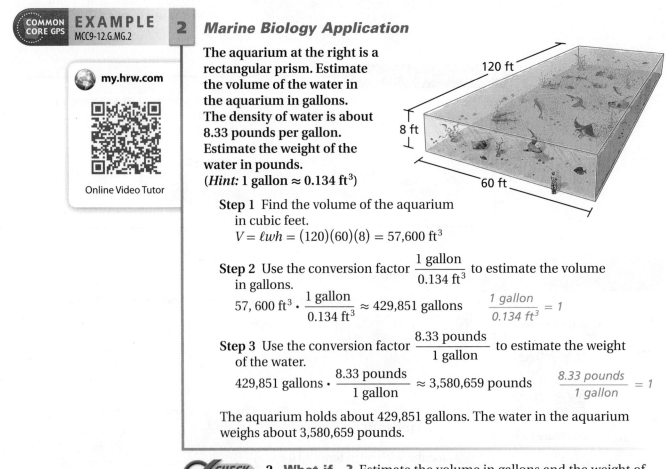

120 ft

8 ft

60 ft

Step 1 Find the volume of the aquarium in cubic feet.
$V = \ell wh = (120)(60)(8) = 57,600 \text{ ft}^3$

Step 2 Use the conversion factor $\frac{1 \text{ gallon}}{0.134 \text{ ft}^3}$ to estimate the volume in gallons.

$57,600 \text{ ft}^3 \cdot \frac{1 \text{ gallon}}{0.134 \text{ ft}^3} \approx 429,851 \text{ gallons}$ $\frac{1 \text{ gallon}}{0.134 \text{ ft}^3} = 1$

Step 3 Use the conversion factor $\frac{8.33 \text{ pounds}}{1 \text{ gallon}}$ to estimate the weight of the water.

$429,851 \text{ gallons} \cdot \frac{8.33 \text{ pounds}}{1 \text{ gallon}} \approx 3,580,659 \text{ pounds}$ $\frac{8.33 \text{ pounds}}{1 \text{ gallon}} = 1$

The aquarium holds about 429,851 gallons. The water in the aquarium weighs about 3,580,659 pounds.

CHECK IT OUT!

2. What if...? Estimate the volume in gallons and the weight of the water in the aquarium above if the height were doubled.

Cavalieri's principle also relates to cylinders. The two stacks have the same number of CDs, so they have the same volume.

Volume of a Cylinder

The volume of a cylinder with base area B, radius r, and height h is $V = Bh$, or $V = \pi r^2 h$.

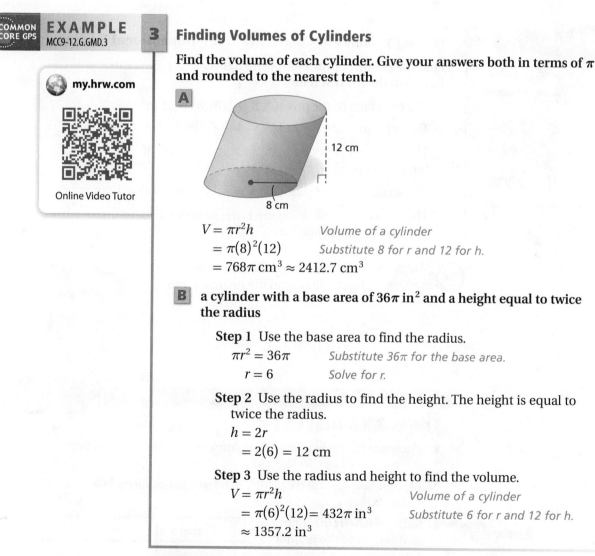

EXAMPLE 3
MCC9-12.G.GMD.3

Finding Volumes of Cylinders

Find the volume of each cylinder. Give your answers both in terms of π and rounded to the nearest tenth.

A

12 cm

8 cm

$$V = \pi r^2 h \qquad \text{Volume of a cylinder}$$
$$= \pi(8)^2(12) \qquad \text{Substitute 8 for r and 12 for h.}$$
$$= 768\pi \text{ cm}^3 \approx 2412.7 \text{ cm}^3$$

B a cylinder with a base area of 36π in² and a height equal to twice the radius

Step 1 Use the base area to find the radius.
$$\pi r^2 = 36\pi \qquad \text{Substitute } 36\pi \text{ for the base area.}$$
$$r = 6 \qquad \text{Solve for r.}$$

Step 2 Use the radius to find the height. The height is equal to twice the radius.
$$h = 2r$$
$$= 2(6) = 12 \text{ cm}$$

Step 3 Use the radius and height to find the volume.
$$V = \pi r^2 h \qquad \text{Volume of a cylinder}$$
$$= \pi(6)^2(12) = 432\pi \text{ in}^3 \qquad \text{Substitute 6 for r and 12 for h.}$$
$$\approx 1357.2 \text{ in}^3$$

3. Find the volume of a cylinder with a diameter of 16 in. and a height of 17 in. Give your answer both in terms of π and rounded to the nearest tenth.

my.hrw.com

Online Video Tutor

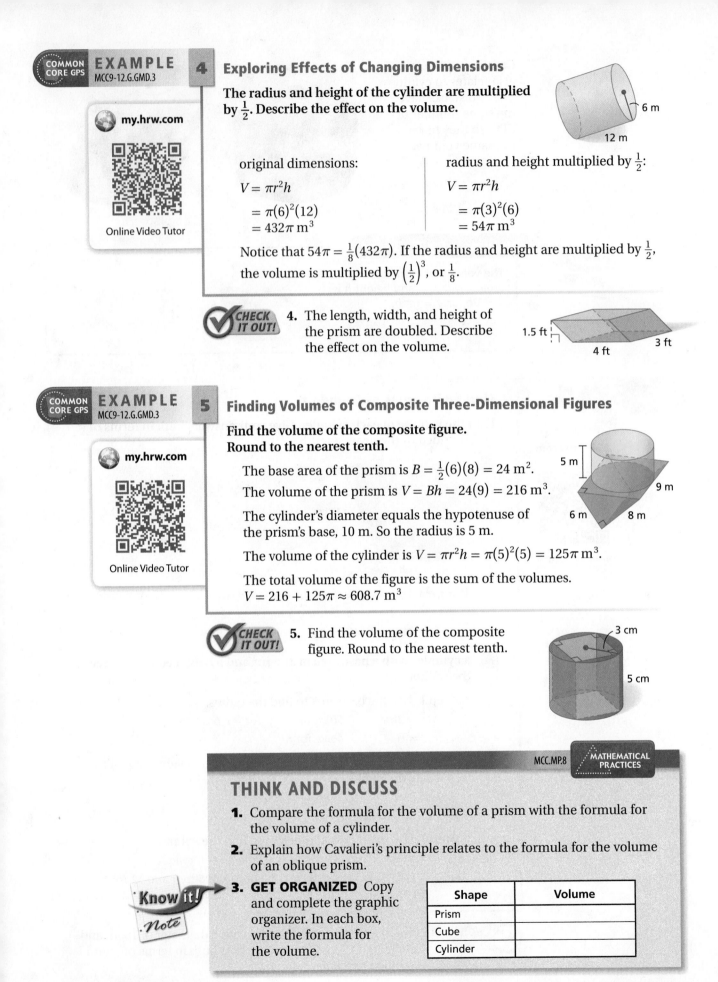

EXAMPLE 4

Exploring Effects of Changing Dimensions

The radius and height of the cylinder are multiplied by $\frac{1}{2}$. Describe the effect on the volume.

6 m

12 m

original dimensions:

$V = \pi r^2 h$

$= \pi(6)^2(12)$

$= 432\pi \text{ m}^3$

radius and height multiplied by $\frac{1}{2}$:

$V = \pi r^2 h$

$= \pi(3)^2(6)$

$= 54\pi \text{ m}^3$

Notice that $54\pi = \frac{1}{8}(432\pi)$. If the radius and height are multiplied by $\frac{1}{2}$, the volume is multiplied by $\left(\frac{1}{2}\right)^3$, or $\frac{1}{8}$.

CHECK IT OUT!

4. The length, width, and height of the prism are doubled. Describe the effect on the volume.

1.5 ft

4 ft

3 ft

EXAMPLE 5

Finding Volumes of Composite Three-Dimensional Figures

Find the volume of the composite figure.
Round to the nearest tenth.

The base area of the prism is $B = \frac{1}{2}(6)(8) = 24 \text{ m}^2$.

The volume of the prism is $V = Bh = 24(9) = 216 \text{ m}^3$.

5 m

9 m

6 m   8 m

The cylinder's diameter equals the hypotenuse of the prism's base, 10 m. So the radius is 5 m.

The volume of the cylinder is $V = \pi r^2 h = \pi(5)^2(5) = 125\pi \text{ m}^3$.

The total volume of the figure is the sum of the volumes.
$V = 216 + 125\pi \approx 608.7 \text{ m}^3$

CHECK IT OUT!

5. Find the volume of the composite figure. Round to the nearest tenth.

3 cm

5 cm

THINK AND DISCUSS

1. Compare the formula for the volume of a prism with the formula for the volume of a cylinder.

2. Explain how Cavalieri's principle relates to the formula for the volume of an oblique prism.

3. GET ORGANIZED Copy and complete the graphic organizer. In each box, write the formula for the volume.

Shape	Volume
Prism	
Cube	
Cylinder	

Know it!
Note

GUIDED PRACTICE

1. **Vocabulary** In a right cylinder, the *altitude* is ___?___ the axis. (*longer than, shorter than,* or *the same length as*)

SEE EXAMPLE 1 **Find the volume of each prism.**

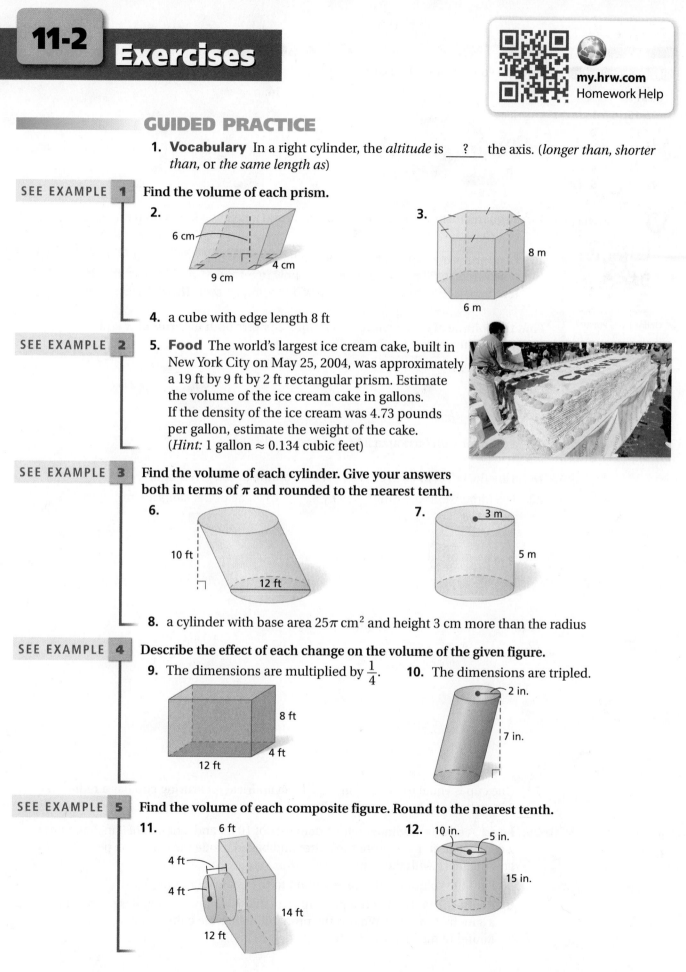

2.
6 cm
9 cm
4 cm

3.
8 m
6 m

4. a cube with edge length 8 ft

SEE EXAMPLE 2 5. **Food** The world's largest ice cream cake, built in New York City on May 25, 2004, was approximately a 19 ft by 9 ft by 2 ft rectangular prism. Estimate the volume of the ice cream cake in gallons. If the density of the ice cream was 4.73 pounds per gallon, estimate the weight of the cake. (*Hint:* 1 gallon ≈ 0.134 cubic feet)

SEE EXAMPLE 3 **Find the volume of each cylinder. Give your answers both in terms of π and rounded to the nearest tenth.**

6.
10 ft
12 ft

7.
3 m
5 m

8. a cylinder with base area 25π cm² and height 3 cm more than the radius

SEE EXAMPLE 4 **Describe the effect of each change on the volume of the given figure.**

9. The dimensions are multiplied by $\frac{1}{4}$.
8 ft
4 ft
12 ft

10. The dimensions are tripled.
2 in.
7 in.

SEE EXAMPLE 5 **Find the volume of each composite figure. Round to the nearest tenth.**

11.
6 ft
4 ft
4 ft
14 ft
12 ft

12.
10 in.
5 in.
15 in.

PRACTICE AND PROBLEM SOLVING

Find the volume of each prism.

my.hrw.com

Online Extra Practice

13.

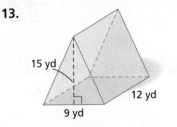

15 yd

12 yd

9 yd

14.

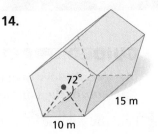

72°

15 m

10 m

15. a square prism with a base area of 49 ft² and a height 2 ft less than the base edge length

16. Landscaping Colin is buying dirt to fill a garden bed that is a 9 ft by 16 ft rectangle. If he wants to fill it to a depth of 4 in., how many cubic yards of dirt does he need? If dirt costs $25 per yd³, how much will the project cost? (*Hint:* 1 yd³ = 27 ft³)

Find the volume of each cylinder. Give your answers both in terms of π and rounded to the nearest tenth.

17.

14 cm

9 cm

18. 6 in.

3 in.

19. a cylinder with base area 24π cm² and height 16 cm

H.O.T. Describe the effect of each change on the volume of the given figure.

20. The dimensions are multiplied by 5.

2 yd

3 yd

21. The dimensions are multiplied by $\frac{3}{5}$.

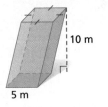

10 m

5 m

Find the volume of each composite figure.

22.

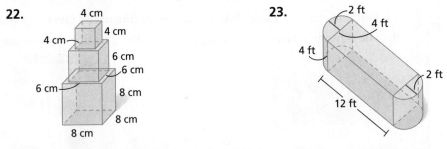

4 cm

4 cm

4 cm

6 cm

6 cm

6 cm

8 cm

8 cm

8 cm

23.

2 ft

4 ft

4 ft

2 ft

12 ft

24. One cup is equal to 14.4375 in³. If a 1 c cylindrical measuring cup has a radius of 2 in., what is its height? If the radius is 1.5 in., what is its height?

H.O.T. 25. Food A cake is a cylinder with a diameter of 10 in. and a height of 3 in. For a party, a coin has been mixed into the batter and baked inside the cake. The person who gets the piece with the coin wins a prize.

   a. Find the volume of the cake. Round to the nearest tenth.

   b. Probability Keka gets a piece of cake that is a right rectangular prism with a 3 in. by 1 in. base. What is the probability that the coin is in her piece? Round to the nearest hundredth.

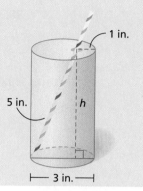

26. A cylindrical juice container with a 3 in. diameter has a hole for a straw that is 1 in. from the side. Up to 5 in. of a straw can be inserted.

   a. Find the height h of the container to the nearest tenth.

   b. Find the volume of the container to the nearest tenth.

   c. How many ounces of juice does the container hold? (*Hint:* $1 \text{ in}^3 \approx 0.55 \text{ oz}$)

27. Find the height of a rectangular prism with length 5 ft, width 9 ft, and volume 495 ft^3.

28. Find the area of the base of a rectangular prism with volume 360 in^3 and height 9 in.

29. Find the volume of a cylinder with surface area $210\pi \text{ m}^2$ and height 8 m.

30. Find the volume of a rectangular prism with vertices $(0, 0, 0)$, $(0, 3, 0)$, $(7, 0, 0)$, $(7, 3, 0)$, $(0, 0, 6)$, $(0, 3, 6)$, $(7, 0, 6)$, and $(7, 3, 6)$.

31. You can use *displacement* to find the volume of an irregular object, such as a stone. Suppose the tank shown is filled with water to a depth of 8 in. A stone is placed in the tank so that it is completely covered, causing the water level to rise by 2 in. Find the volume of the stone.

32. Food A 1 in. cube of cheese is one serving. How many servings are in a 4 in. by 4 in. by $\frac{1}{4}$ in. slice?

33. History In 1919, a cylindrical tank containing molasses burst and flooded the city of Boston, Massachusetts. The tank had a 90 ft diameter and a height of 52 ft. How many gallons of molasses were in the tank? (*Hint:* $1 \text{ gal} \approx 0.134 \text{ ft}^3$)

34. Meteorology If 3 in. of rain fall on the property shown, what is the volume in cubic feet? In gallons? The density of water is 8.33 pounds per gallon. What is the weight of the rain in pounds? (*Hint:* $1 \text{ gal} \approx 0.134 \text{ ft}^3$)

H.O.T. 35. Critical Thinking The dimensions of a prism with volume V and surface area S are multiplied by a scale factor of k to form a similar prism. Make a conjecture about the ratio of the surface area of the new prism to its volume. Test your conjecture using a cube with an edge length of 1 and a scale factor of 2.

H.O.T. 36. Write About It How can you change the edge length of a cube so that its volume is doubled?

TEST PREP

37. Abigail has a cylindrical candle mold with the dimensions shown. If Abigail has a rectangular block of wax measuring 15 cm by 12 cm by 18 cm, about how many candles can she make after melting the block of wax?

   Ⓐ 14   Ⓑ 31   Ⓒ 35   Ⓓ 76

38. A 96-inch piece of wire was cut into equal segments that were then connected to form the edges of a cube. What is the volume of the cube?

   Ⓕ 512 in³   Ⓖ 576 in³   Ⓗ 729 in³   Ⓙ 1728 in³

39. One juice container is a rectangular prism with a height of 9 in. and a 3 in. by 3 in. square base. Another juice container is a cylinder with a radius of 1.75 in. and a height of 9 in. Which best describes the relationship between the two containers?

   Ⓐ The prism has the greater volume.

   Ⓑ The cylinder has the greater volume.

   Ⓒ The volumes are equivalent.

   Ⓓ The volumes cannot be determined.

40. What is the volume of the three-dimensional object with the dimensions shown in the three views below?

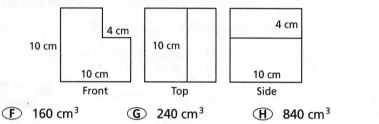

   Ⓕ 160 cm³   Ⓖ 240 cm³   Ⓗ 840 cm³   Ⓙ 1000 cm³

CHALLENGE AND EXTEND

Algebra Find the volume of each three-dimensional figure in terms of x.

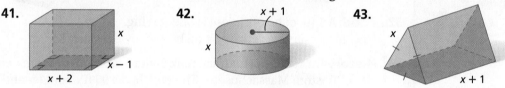

41.   **42.**   **43.**

H.O.T. **44.** The volume in cubic units of a cylinder is equal to its surface area in square units. Prove that the radius and height must both be greater than 2.

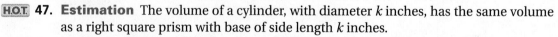

MATHEMATICAL PRACTICES

FOCUS ON MATHEMATICAL PRACTICES

H.O.T. **45. Problem Solving** The floor layout of a hotel suite is shown. The ceiling is 8.5 feet high. What is the volume of the suite?

H.O.T. **46. Number Sense** The volume of a right square prism is 432 cubic centimeters. Every dimension is a whole number of centimeters. One of the dimensions is 6 centimeters. Find the other two dimensions.

H.O.T. **47. Estimation** The volume of a cylinder, with diameter k inches, has the same volume as a right square prism with base of side length k inches.

   a. For what values of k is the area of the cylinder's base greater than, or equal to, the area of the prism's base? Explain.

   b. What can you conclude from part **a**?

   c. Which figure is taller? Why?

   d. Find the ratio of the taller figure to the shorter figure.

   e. The height of the prism is 22 centimeters. What is the height of the cylinder to the nearest tenth of an inch?

Volume of Pyramids and Cones

? **Essential Question:** What are the volume formulas for pyramids and cones?

Objectives
Learn and apply the formula for the volume of a pyramid.

Learn and apply the formula for the volume of a cone.

Who uses this?
The builders of the Rainforest Pyramid in Galveston, Texas, needed to calculate the volume of the pyramid to plan the climate control system. (See Example 2.)

The volume of a pyramid is related to the volume of a prism with the same base and height. The relationship can be verified by dividing a cube into three congruent square pyramids, as shown.

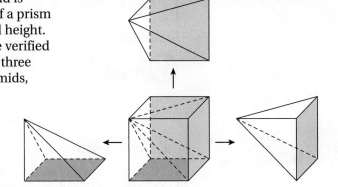

The square pyramids are congruent, so they have the same volume. The volume of each pyramid is one third the volume of the cube.

Know it!
Note

Volume of a Pyramid

The volume of a pyramid with base area B and height h is $V = \frac{1}{3}Bh$.

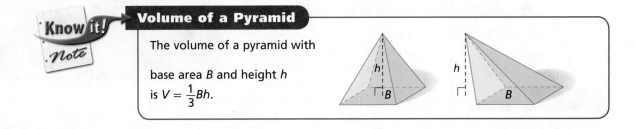

COMMON CORE GPS MCC9-12.G.GMD.3

EXAMPLE 1 **Finding Volumes of Pyramids**

Find the volume of each pyramid.

my.hrw.com

Online Video Tutor

A a rectangular pyramid with length 7 ft, width 9 ft, and height 12 ft

$$V = \frac{1}{3}Bh = \frac{1}{3}(7 \cdot 9)(12) = 252 \text{ ft}^3$$

B the square pyramid

The base is a square with a side length of 4 in., and the height is 6 in.

$$V = \frac{1}{3}Bh = \frac{1}{3}(4^2)(6) = 32 \text{ in}^3$$

6 in.

4 in.

4 in.

Find the volume of the pyramid.

C the trapezoidal pyramid with base $ABCD$, where $\overline{AB} \parallel \overline{CD}$ and $\overline{AE} \perp$ plane ABC

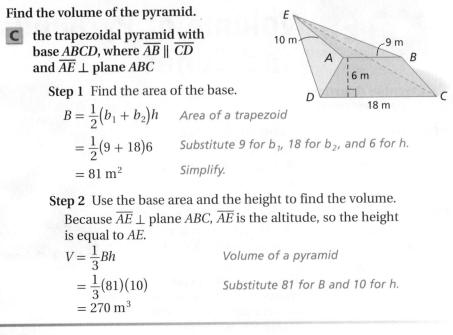

Step 1 Find the area of the base.

$B = \dfrac{1}{2}(b_1 + b_2)h$ *Area of a trapezoid*

$\quad = \dfrac{1}{2}(9 + 18)6$ *Substitute 9 for b_1, 18 for b_2, and 6 for h.*

$\quad = 81 \text{ m}^2$ *Simplify.*

Step 2 Use the base area and the height to find the volume. Because $\overline{AE} \perp$ plane ABC, $\overline{AE}$ is the altitude, so the height is equal to AE.

$V = \dfrac{1}{3}Bh$ *Volume of a pyramid*

$\quad = \dfrac{1}{3}(81)(10)$ *Substitute 81 for B and 10 for h.*

$\quad = 270 \text{ m}^3$

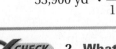

1. Find the volume of a regular hexagonal pyramid with a base edge length of 2 cm and a height equal to the area of the base.

COMMON CORE GPS
MCC9-12.G.MG.1

EXAMPLE **2**

Architecture Application

The Rainforest Pyramid in Galveston, Texas, is a square pyramid with a base area of about 1 acre and a height of 10 stories. Estimate the volume in cubic yards and in cubic feet. (*Hint:* 1 acre = 4840 yd^2, 1 story ≈ 10 ft)

my.hrw.com

Online Video Tutor

Remember!

A *regular pyramid* has a base that is a regular polygon. Its lateral faces are congruent isosceles triangles. In a regular pyramid, the *slant height* is the distance from the vertex to the midpoint of an edge of the base.

The base is a square with an area of about 4840 yd^2. The base edge length is $\sqrt{4840} \approx 70$ yd. The height is about $10(10) = 100$ ft, or about 33 yd.

First find the volume in cubic yards.

$V = \dfrac{1}{3}Bh$ *Volume of a regular pyramid*

$\quad = \dfrac{1}{3}(70^2)(33) = 53{,}900 \text{ yd}^3$ *Substitute 70^2 for B and 33 for h.*

Then convert your answer to find the volume in cubic feet. The volume of one cubic yard is $(3 \text{ ft})(3 \text{ ft})(3 \text{ ft}) = 27 \text{ ft}^3$. Use the conversion factor $\dfrac{27 \text{ ft}^3}{1 \text{ yd}^3}$ to find the volume in cubic feet.

$53{,}900 \text{ yd}^3 \cdot \dfrac{27 \text{ ft}^3}{1 \text{ yd}^3} \approx 1{,}455{,}300 \text{ ft}^3$

2. What if...? What would be the volume of the Rainforest Pyramid if the height were doubled?

Volume of Cones

The volume of a cone with base area B, radius r, and height h is $V = \frac{1}{3}Bh$, or $V = \frac{1}{3}\pi r^2 h$.

COMMON CORE GPS
MCC9-12.G.GMD.3

EXAMPLE 3 Finding Volumes of Cones

my.hrw.com

Online Video Tutor

Find the volume of each cone. Give your answers both in terms of π and rounded to the nearest tenth.

A a cone with radius 5 cm and height 12 cm

$V = \frac{1}{3}\pi r^2 h$ *Volume of a cone*

$= \frac{1}{3}\pi(5)^2(12)$ *Substitute 5 for r and 12 for h.*

$= 100\pi \text{ cm}^3 \approx 314.2 \text{ cm}^3$ *Simplify.*

B a cone with a base circumference of 21π cm and a height 3 cm less than twice the radius

Step 1 Use the circumference to find the radius.

$2\pi r = 21\pi$ *Substitute 21π for C.*

$r = 10.5 \text{ cm}$ *Divide both sides by 2π.*

Step 2 Use the radius to find the height.

$2(10.5) - 3 = 18 \text{ cm}$ *The height is 3 cm less than twice the radius.*

Step 3 Use the radius and height to find the volume.

$V = \frac{1}{3}\pi r^2 h$ *Volume of a cone*

$= \frac{1}{3}\pi(10.5)^2(18)$ *Substitute 10.5 for r and 18 for h.*

$= 661.5\pi \text{ cm}^3 \approx 2078.2 \text{ cm}^3$ *Simplify.*

C

25 ft
7 ft

Step 1 Use the Pythagorean Theorem to find the height.

$7^2 + h^2 = 25^2$ *Pythagorean Theorem*

$h^2 = 576$ *Subtract 7² from both sides.*

$h = 24$ *Take the square root of both sides.*

Step 2 Use the radius and height to find the volume.

$V = \frac{1}{3}\pi r^2 h$ *Volume of a cone*

$= \frac{1}{3}\pi(7)^2(24)$ *Substitute 7 for r and 24 for h.*

$= 392\pi \text{ ft}^3 \approx 1231.5 \text{ ft}^3$ *Simplify.*

Remember!

A *right cone* has an axis perpendicular to the base. In a right cone, the *slant height* is the distance from the vertex of the cone to a point on the edge of the base. If ℓ is the *slant height* in a right cone with radius r and height h, then $r^2 + h^2 = \ell^2$ by the Pythagorean Theorem.

CHECK IT OUT! 3. Find the volume of the cone.

18 m
8 m

Exploring Effects of Changing Dimensions

The length, width, and height of the rectangular pyramid are multiplied by $\frac{1}{4}$. Describe the effect on the volume.

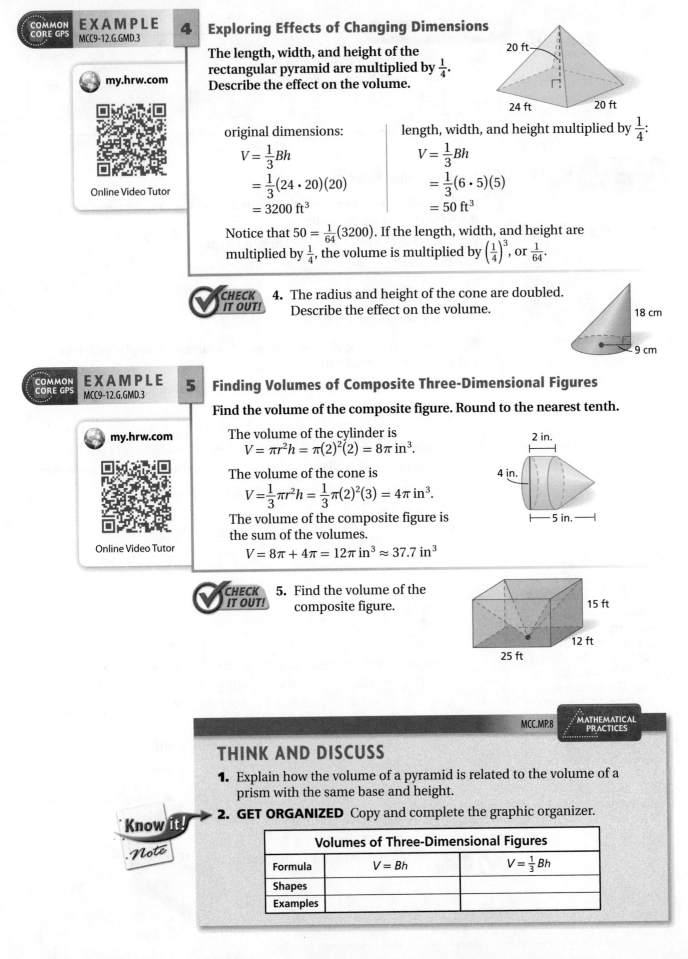

20 ft

24 ft   20 ft

original dimensions:

$V = \frac{1}{3}Bh$

$= \frac{1}{3}(24 \cdot 20)(20)$

$= 3200 \text{ ft}^3$

length, width, and height multiplied by $\frac{1}{4}$:

$V = \frac{1}{3}Bh$

$= \frac{1}{3}(6 \cdot 5)(5)$

$= 50 \text{ ft}^3$

Notice that $50 = \frac{1}{64}(3200)$. If the length, width, and height are multiplied by $\frac{1}{4}$, the volume is multiplied by $\left(\frac{1}{4}\right)^3$, or $\frac{1}{64}$.

CHECK IT OUT!

4. The radius and height of the cone are doubled. Describe the effect on the volume.

18 cm

9 cm

Finding Volumes of Composite Three-Dimensional Figures

Find the volume of the composite figure. Round to the nearest tenth.

The volume of the cylinder is
$V = \pi r^2 h = \pi(2)^2(2) = 8\pi \text{ in}^3$.

The volume of the cone is
$V = \frac{1}{3}\pi r^2 h = \frac{1}{3}\pi(2)^2(3) = 4\pi \text{ in}^3$.

The volume of the composite figure is the sum of the volumes.

$V = 8\pi + 4\pi = 12\pi \text{ in}^3 \approx 37.7 \text{ in}^3$

2 in.

4 in.

5 in.

CHECK IT OUT!

5. Find the volume of the composite figure.

15 ft

12 ft

25 ft

MCC.MP.8

MATHEMATICAL PRACTICES

THINK AND DISCUSS

1. Explain how the volume of a pyramid is related to the volume of a prism with the same base and height.

2. GET ORGANIZED Copy and complete the graphic organizer.

Know it!
Note

Volumes of Three-Dimensional Figures		
Formula	$V = Bh$	$V = \frac{1}{3}Bh$
Shapes		
Examples		

GUIDED PRACTICE

1. **Vocabulary** The *altitude* of a pyramid is ___?___ to the base. (*perpendicular, parallel,* or *oblique*)

SEE EXAMPLE 1 Find the volume of each pyramid. Round to the nearest tenth, if necessary.

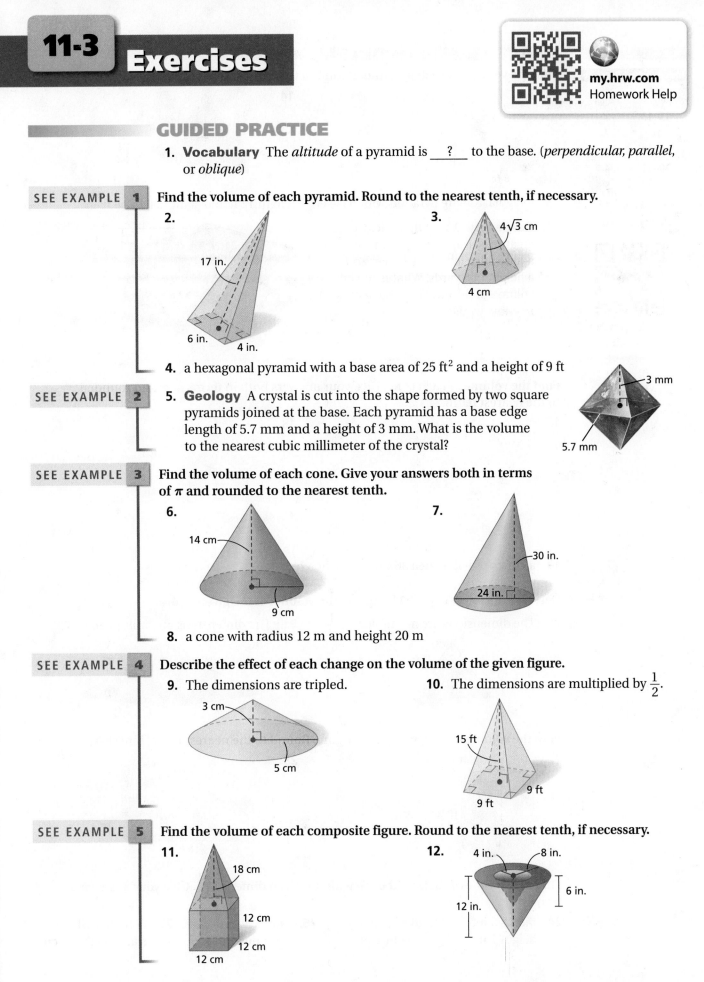

2.

17 in.

6 in.   4 in.

3.

$4\sqrt{3}$ cm

4 cm

4. a hexagonal pyramid with a base area of 25 ft² and a height of 9 ft

SEE EXAMPLE 2
5. **Geology** A crystal is cut into the shape formed by two square pyramids joined at the base. Each pyramid has a base edge length of 5.7 mm and a height of 3 mm. What is the volume to the nearest cubic millimeter of the crystal?

3 mm

5.7 mm

SEE EXAMPLE 3 Find the volume of each cone. Give your answers both in terms of π and rounded to the nearest tenth.

6.

14 cm

9 cm

7.

30 in.

24 in.

8. a cone with radius 12 m and height 20 m

SEE EXAMPLE 4 Describe the effect of each change on the volume of the given figure.

9. The dimensions are tripled.

3 cm

5 cm

10. The dimensions are multiplied by $\frac{1}{2}$.

15 ft

9 ft

9 ft

SEE EXAMPLE 5 Find the volume of each composite figure. Round to the nearest tenth, if necessary.

11.

18 cm

12 cm

12 cm

12 cm

12.

4 in.   8 in.

12 in.   6 in.

PRACTICE AND PROBLEM SOLVING

Independent Practice

For Exercises	See Example
13–15	1
16	2
17–19	3
20–21	4
22–23	5

my.hrw.com

Online Extra Practice

Find the volume of each pyramid. Round to the nearest tenth, if necessary.

13.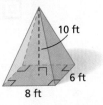

14.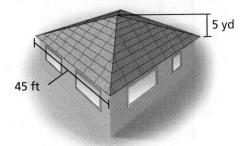

15. a regular square pyramid with base edge length 12 ft and slant height 10 ft

16. **Carpentry** A roof that encloses an attic is a square pyramid with a base edge length of 45 feet and a height of 5 yards. What is the volume of the attic in cubic feet? In cubic yards?

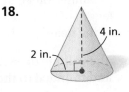

Find the volume of each cone. Give your answers both in terms of π and rounded to the nearest tenth.

17.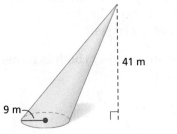

18.

19. a cone with base area 36π ft^2 and a height equal to twice the radius

H.O.T. **Describe the effect of each change on the volume of the given figure.**

20. The dimensions are multiplied by $\frac{1}{3}$.

21. The dimensions are multiplied by 6.

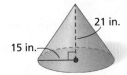

Find the volume of each composite figure. Round to the nearest tenth, if necessary.

22.

23.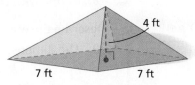

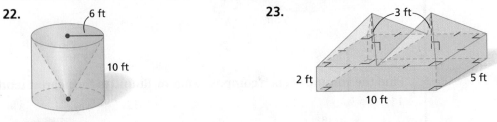

Find the volume of each right cone with the given dimensions. Give your answers in terms of π.

24. radius 3 in. height 7 in.

25. diameter 5 m height 2 m

26. radius 28 ft slant height 53 ft

27. diameter 24 cm slant height 13 cm

Find the volume of each regular pyramid with the given dimensions. Round to the nearest tenth, if necessary.

	Number of sides of base	Base edge length	Height	Volume
28.	3	10 ft	6 ft	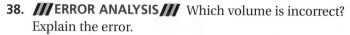
29.	4	15 m	18 m	
30.	5	9 in.	12 in.	
31.	6	8 cm	3 cm	

32. Find the height of a rectangular pyramid with length 3 m, width 8 m, and volume 112 m³.

33. Find the base circumference of a cone with height 5 cm and volume 125π cm³.

34. Find the volume of a cone with slant height 10 ft and height 8 ft.

35. Find the volume of a square pyramid with slant height 17 in. and surface area 800 in².

36. Find the surface area of a cone with height 20 yd and volume 1500π yd³. The surface area of a right cone with base radius r, height h, and slant height ℓ is $\pi r\ell + \pi r^2$.

37. Find the volume of a triangular pyramid with vertices $(0, 0, 0)$, $(5, 0, 0)$, $(0, 3, 0)$, and $(0, 0, 7)$.

38. ///ERROR ANALYSIS/// Which volume is incorrect? Explain the error.

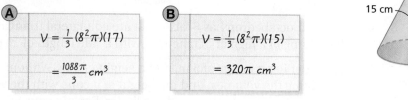

A
$$V = \frac{1}{3}(8^2\pi)(17)$$
$$= \frac{1088\pi}{3} \ cm^3$$

B
$$V = \frac{1}{3}(8^2\pi)(15)$$
$$= 320\pi \ cm^3$$

15 cm   17 cm
8 cm

H.O.T. 39. Critical Thinking Write a ratio comparing the volume of the prism to the volume of the composite figure. Explain your answer.

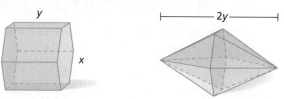

y
x
├──── 2y ────┤

H.O.T. 40. Write About It Explain how you would find the volume of a cone, given the radius and the surface area.

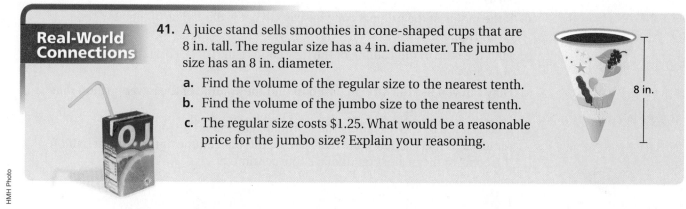

Real-World Connections

41. A juice stand sells smoothies in cone-shaped cups that are 8 in. tall. The regular size has a 4 in. diameter. The jumbo size has an 8 in. diameter.

   a. Find the volume of the regular size to the nearest tenth.

   b. Find the volume of the jumbo size to the nearest tenth.

   c. The regular size costs $1.25. What would be a reasonable price for the jumbo size? Explain your reasoning.

8 in.

TEST PREP

42. Find the volume of the cone.

  (A) 432π cm^3 (C) 1296π cm^3

  (B) 720π cm^3 (D) 2160π cm^3

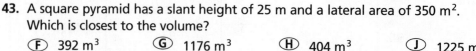

15 cm

12 cm

43. A square pyramid has a slant height of 25 m and a lateral area of 350 m^2. Which is closest to the volume?

  (F) 392 m^3 (G) 1176 m^3 (H) 404 m^3 (J) 1225 m^3

44. A cone has a volume of 18π in^3. Which are possible dimensions of the cone?

  (A) Diameter 1 in., height 18 in.   (C) Diameter 3 in., height 6 in.

  (B) Diameter 6 in., height 6 in.   (D) Diameter 6 in., height 3 in.

45. Gridded Response Find the height in centimeters of a square pyramid with a volume of 243 cm^3 and a base edge length equal to the height.

CHALLENGE AND EXTEND

H.O.T. Each cone is inscribed in a regular pyramid with a base edge length of 2 ft and a height of 2 ft. Find the volume of each cone.

46.

47.

48.

49. A regular octahedron has 8 faces that are equilateral triangles. Find the volume of a regular octahedron with a side length of 10 cm.

50. A cylinder has a radius of 5 in. and a height of 3 in. Without calculating the volumes, find the height of a cone with the same base and the same volume as the cylinder. Explain your reasoning.

FOCUS ON MATHEMATICAL PRACTICES

H.O.T. 51. Communication How can Cavalieri's principle regarding the volume of prisms and cylinders be related to finding the area of triangles and parallelograms?

H.O.T. 52. Justify Two tents each have a volume of 1350 cubic feet. One is in the shape of a cone and the other is in the shape of a square pyramid. They are both 9 feet tall. Which is greater, the diagonal of the base of the pyramid or the diameter of the base of the cone? Justify your answer.

H.O.T. 53. Problem Solving The top portion of a cone is removed to make a new cone half as tall as the original.

  a. If the radius of the original cone base is r, what is the radius of the new cone base? Explain.

  b. Find the ratio of the volume of the new cone to that of the original cone. Justify your answer.

  c. How can you use the ratio in part **b** to find the volume of the lower portion that was removed from the original cone?

  d. A cone has a base with radius 10 cm and height 9 cm. The top portion is removed to make a new cone half as tall. Find the volume of the bottom half of the cone, to the nearest tenth of a cubic centimeter.

Cube Roots

If you know the area of a square, you can find the length of a side by taking the square root of the area. How can you find the length of a side of a cube if you know the volume?

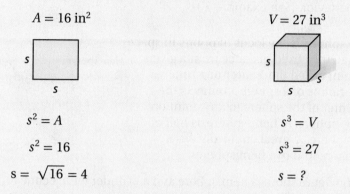

$$A = 16 \text{ in}^2$$

$$s^2 = A$$
$$s^2 = 16$$
$$s = \sqrt{16} = 4$$

$$V = 27 \text{ in}^3$$

$$s^3 = V$$
$$s^3 = 27$$
$$s = ?$$

To find the side length, you need to find the *cube root* of 27. The cube root of 27 is 3 because $3^3 = 27$, so the side length of the cube above is 3 in. "The cube root of 27" can also be written as $\sqrt[3]{27}$.

Example

The volume of a cube is 64 m³. Find the side length of the cube.

$$s^3 = V$$
$$s^3 = 64 \qquad \text{\textit{Substitute 64 for V.}}$$
$$s = \sqrt[3]{64} = 4 \qquad \text{\textit{$4^3 = 64$, so the cube root of 64 is 4.}}$$

The side length of the cube is 4 m.

Try This

Given the volume, find the side length of each cube.

1. $V = 8 \text{ cm}^3$ **2.** $V = 125 \text{ ft}^3$ **3.** $V = 216 \text{ in.}^3$

4. $V = 1{,}000 \text{ yd}^3$ **5.** $V = 1 \text{ cm}^3$ **6.** $V = 0.064 \text{ m}^3$

7. Carlos wants to buy an angelfish for a pet. The pet store recommends a fish tank that holds 2,197 in³ of water. If the tank is in the shape of a cube, how long is each side?

For an integer $n > 1$, an *n*th root of *x* is a number *a* such that $a^n = x$. If *n* is also even and $x > 0$, *x* has both positive and negative *n*th roots, written as $\sqrt[n]{x}$ and $-\sqrt[n]{x}$. For example, the 4th roots of 16 are 2 and -2, because $2^4 = 16$ and $(-2)^4 = 16$. So, $\sqrt[4]{16} = 2$, and $-\sqrt[4]{16} = -2$. Simplify each expression.

8. $\sqrt[4]{81}$ **9.** $\sqrt[5]{32}$ **10.** $\sqrt[3]{729}$

11. $\sqrt[5]{243}$ **12.** $\sqrt[7]{1}$ **13.** $\sqrt[4]{0.0016}$

11-4 Spheres

? **Essential Question:** How do you find the volume and surface area of a sphere?

Objectives
Learn and apply the formula for the volume of a sphere.

Learn and apply the formula for the surface area of a sphere.

Vocabulary
sphere
center of a sphere
radius of a sphere
hemisphere
great circle

Who uses this?
Biologists study the eyes of deep-sea predators such as the giant squid to learn about their behavior. (See Example 2.)

A **sphere** is the locus of points in space that are a fixed distance from a given point called the **center of a sphere**. A **radius of a sphere** connects the center of the sphere to any point on the sphere. A **hemisphere** is half of a sphere. A **great circle** divides a sphere into two hemispheres.

The figure shows a hemisphere and a cylinder with a cone removed from its interior. The cross sections have the same area at every level, so the volumes are equal by Cavalieri's Principle. You will prove that the cross sections have equal areas in Exercise 39.

$$V(\text{hemisphere}) = V(\text{cylinder}) - V(\text{cone})$$
$$= \pi r^2 h - \frac{1}{3}\pi r^2 h$$
$$= \frac{2}{3}\pi r^2 h$$
$$= \frac{2}{3}\pi r^2(r) \quad \text{\textit{The height of the hemisphere is equal to the radius.}}$$
$$= \frac{2}{3}\pi r^3$$

Animated Math

The volume of a sphere with radius r is twice the volume of the hemisphere, or $V = \frac{4}{3}\pi r^3$.

Volume of a Sphere

The volume of a sphere with radius r is $V = \frac{4}{3}\pi r^3$.

COMMON CORE GPS MCC9-12.G.GMD.3

EXAMPLE 1 **Finding Volumes of Spheres**

Find each measurement. Give your answer in terms of π.

A the volume of the sphere

$$V = \frac{4}{3}\pi r^3$$

$$V = \frac{4}{3}\pi(9)^3 \quad \text{\textit{Substitute 9 for r.}}$$

$$= 972\pi \text{ cm}^3 \quad \text{\textit{Simplify.}}$$

9 cm

Find each measurement. Give your answer in terms of π.

B the diameter of a sphere with volume 972π in^3

$972\pi = \dfrac{4}{3}\pi r^3$ *Substitute 972π for V.*

$729 = r^3$ *Divide both sides by $\dfrac{4}{3}\pi$.*

$r = 9$ *Take the cube root of both sides.*

$d = 18$ in.   *d = 2r*

C the volume of the hemisphere

$V = \dfrac{2}{3}\pi r^3$ *Volume of a hemisphere*

$= \dfrac{2}{3}\pi(4)^3 = \dfrac{128\pi}{3}$ m^3 *Substitute 4 for r.*

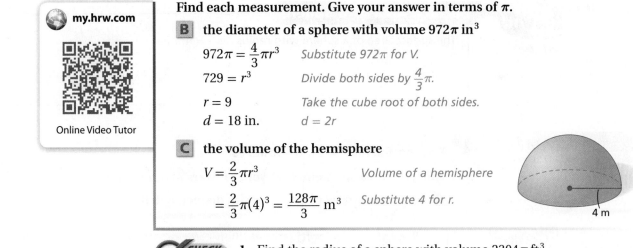

4 m

CHECK IT OUT!   **1.** Find the radius of a sphere with volume 2304π ft^3.

EXAMPLE 2   *Biology Application*

Giant squid need large eyes to see their prey in low light. The eyeball of a giant squid is approximately a sphere with a diameter of 25 cm, which is bigger than a soccer ball. A human eyeball is approximately a sphere with a diameter of 2.5 cm. How many times as great is the volume of a giant squid eyeball as the volume of a human eyeball?

human eyeball:	giant squid eyeball:
$V = \dfrac{4}{3}\pi r^3$	$V = \dfrac{4}{3}\pi r^3$
$= \dfrac{4}{3}\pi(1.25)^3 \approx 8.18$ cm^3	$= \dfrac{4}{3}\pi(12.5)^3 \approx 8181.23$ cm^3

A giant squid eyeball is about 1000 times as great in volume as a human eyeball.

CHECK IT OUT!   **2.** A hummingbird eyeball has a diameter of approximately 0.6 cm. How many times as great is the volume of a human eyeball as the volume of a hummingbird eyeball?

In the figure, the vertex of the pyramid is at the center of the sphere. The height of the pyramid is approximately the radius r of the sphere. Suppose the entire sphere is filled with n pyramids that each have base area B and height r.

$V(\text{sphere}) \approx \dfrac{1}{3}Br + \dfrac{1}{3}Br + \ldots + \dfrac{1}{3}Br$ *The sphere's volume is close to the sum of the volumes of the pyramids.*

$\dfrac{4}{3}\pi r^3 \approx n\left(\dfrac{1}{3}Br\right)$

$4\pi r^2 \approx nB$ *Divide both sides by $\dfrac{1}{3}\pi r$.*

If the pyramids fill the sphere, the total area of the bases is approximately equal to the surface area of the sphere S, so $4\pi r^2 \approx S$. As the number of pyramids increases, the approximation gets closer to the actual surface area.

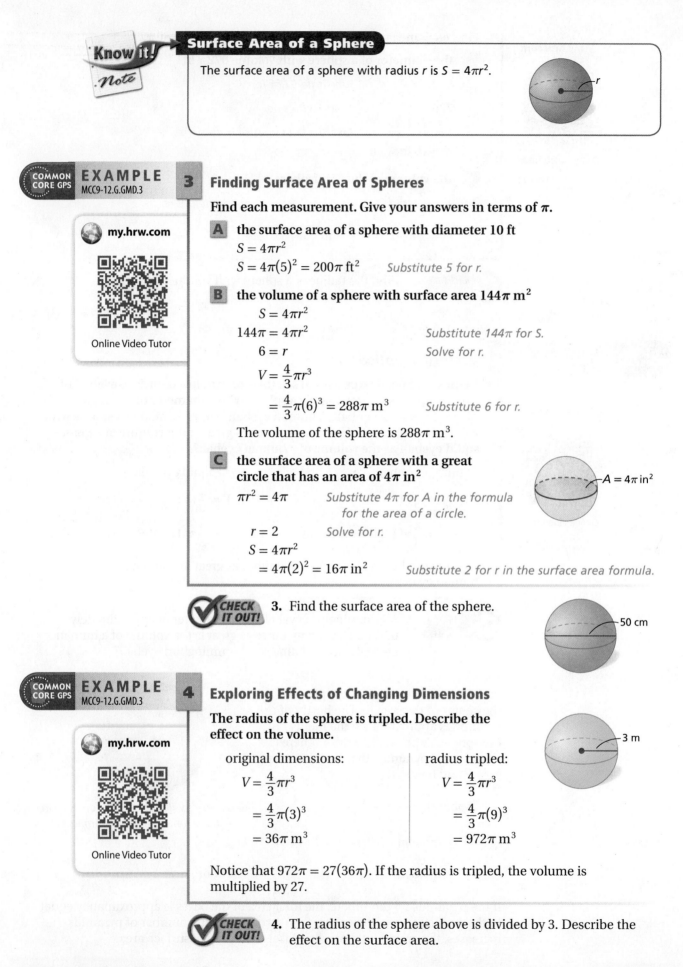

Know it!

Note

Surface Area of a Sphere

The surface area of a sphere with radius r is $S = 4\pi r^2$.

COMMON CORE GPS
MCC9-12.G.GMD.3

EXAMPLE 3

my.hrw.com

Online Video Tutor

Finding Surface Area of Spheres

Find each measurement. Give your answers in terms of π.

A the surface area of a sphere with diameter 10 ft

$S = 4\pi r^2$

$S = 4\pi(5)^2 = 200\pi \text{ ft}^2$ *Substitute 5 for r.*

B the volume of a sphere with surface area $144\pi \text{ m}^2$

$S = 4\pi r^2$

$144\pi = 4\pi r^2$ *Substitute 144π for S.*

$6 = r$ *Solve for r.*

$V = \dfrac{4}{3}\pi r^3$

$= \dfrac{4}{3}\pi(6)^3 = 288\pi \text{ m}^3$ *Substitute 6 for r.*

The volume of the sphere is $288\pi \text{ m}^3$.

C the surface area of a sphere with a great circle that has an area of $4\pi \text{ in}^2$

$\pi r^2 = 4\pi$ *Substitute 4π for A in the formula for the area of a circle.*

$r = 2$ *Solve for r.*

$S = 4\pi r^2$

$= 4\pi(2)^2 = 16\pi \text{ in}^2$ *Substitute 2 for r in the surface area formula.*

$A = 4\pi \text{ in}^2$

CHECK IT OUT!
3. Find the surface area of the sphere.

50 cm

COMMON CORE GPS
MCC9-12.G.GMD.3

EXAMPLE 4

my.hrw.com

Online Video Tutor

Exploring Effects of Changing Dimensions

The radius of the sphere is tripled. Describe the effect on the volume.

3 m

original dimensions:	radius tripled:
$V = \dfrac{4}{3}\pi r^3$	$V = \dfrac{4}{3}\pi r^3$
$= \dfrac{4}{3}\pi(3)^3$	$= \dfrac{4}{3}\pi(9)^3$
$= 36\pi \text{ m}^3$	$= 972\pi \text{ m}^3$

Notice that $972\pi = 27(36\pi)$. If the radius is tripled, the volume is multiplied by 27.

CHECK IT OUT!
4. The radius of the sphere above is divided by 3. Describe the effect on the surface area.

EXAMPLE 5 **Finding Surface Areas and Volumes of Composite Figures**

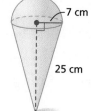

Find the surface area and volume of the composite figure. Give your answers in terms of π.

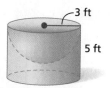

Step 1 Find the surface area of the composite figure.

The surface area of the composite figure is the sum of the surface area of the hemisphere and the lateral area of the cone.

$$S \text{ (hemisphere)} = \frac{1}{2}(4\pi r^2) = 2\pi(7)^2 = 98\pi \text{ cm}^2$$

$$L \text{ (cone)} = \pi r \ell = \pi(7)(25) = 175\pi \text{ cm}^2$$

The surface area of the composite figure is $98\pi + 175\pi = 273\pi \text{ cm}^2$.

Step 2 Find the volume of the composite figure.

First find the height of the cone.

$$h = \sqrt{25^2 - 7^2} \qquad \textit{Pythagorean Theorem}$$

$$= \sqrt{576} = 24 \text{ cm} \qquad \textit{Simplify.}$$

The volume of the composite figure is the sum of the volume of the hemisphere and the volume of the cone.

$$V \text{ (hemisphere)} = \frac{1}{2}\left(\frac{4}{3}\pi r^3\right) = \frac{2}{3}\pi(7)^3 = \frac{686\pi}{3} \text{ cm}^3$$

$$V \text{ (cone)} = \frac{1}{3}\pi r^2 h = \frac{1}{3}\pi(7)^2(24) = 392\pi \text{ cm}^3$$

The volume of the composite figure is $\frac{686\pi}{3} + 392\pi = \frac{1862\pi}{3} \text{ cm}^3$.

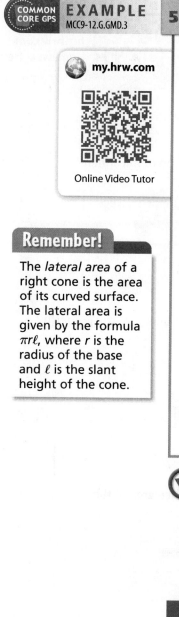

Remember!

The *lateral area* of a right cone is the area of its curved surface. The lateral area is given by the formula $\pi r \ell$, where r is the radius of the base and ℓ is the slant height of the cone.

CHECK IT OUT!

5. Find the surface area and volume of the composite figure.

─3 ft

5 ft

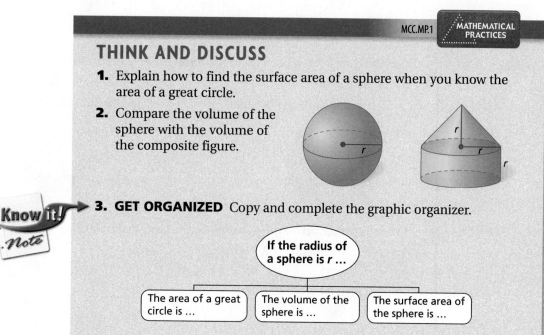

MCC.MP.1 **MATHEMATICAL PRACTICES**

THINK AND DISCUSS

1. Explain how to find the surface area of a sphere when you know the area of a great circle.

2. Compare the volume of the sphere with the volume of the composite figure.

3. GET ORGANIZED Copy and complete the graphic organizer.

If the radius of a sphere is r ...

- The area of a great circle is ...
- The volume of the sphere is ...
- The surface area of the sphere is ...

GUIDED PRACTICE

1. **Vocabulary** Describe the endpoints of a *radius of a sphere*.

SEE EXAMPLE 1 **Find each measurement. Give your answers in terms of π.**

2. the volume of the hemisphere

3. the volume of the sphere

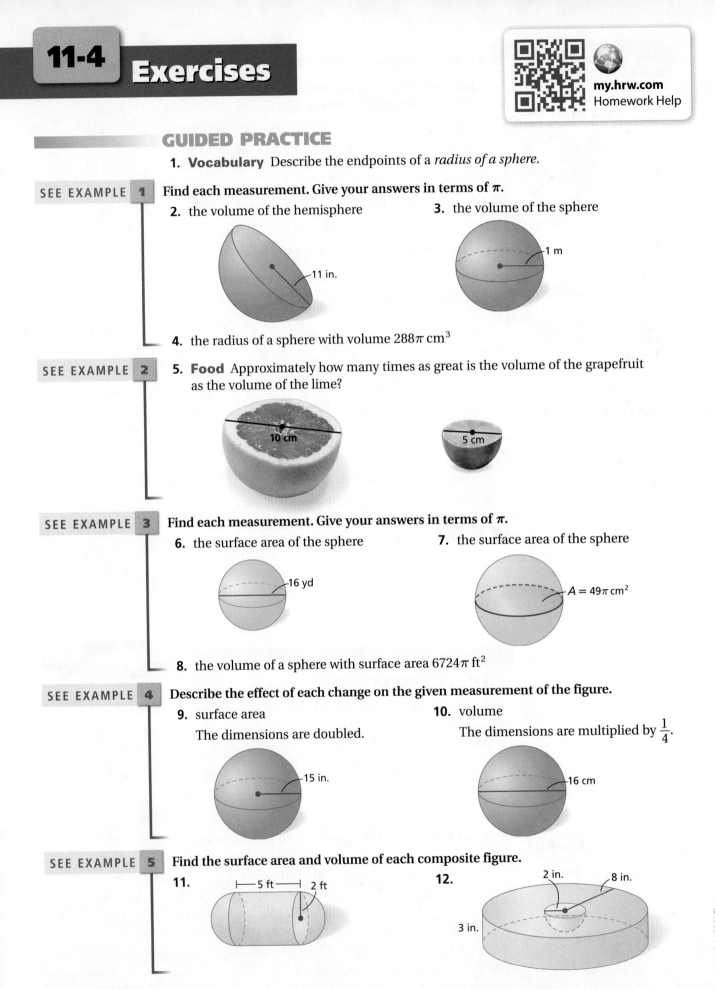

4. the radius of a sphere with volume 288π cm^3

SEE EXAMPLE 2

5. **Food** Approximately how many times as great is the volume of the grapefruit as the volume of the lime?

SEE EXAMPLE 3 **Find each measurement. Give your answers in terms of π.**

6. the surface area of the sphere

7. the surface area of the sphere

8. the volume of a sphere with surface area 6724π ft^2

SEE EXAMPLE 4 **Describe the effect of each change on the given measurement of the figure.**

9. surface area

The dimensions are doubled.

10. volume

The dimensions are multiplied by $\frac{1}{4}$.

SEE EXAMPLE 5 **Find the surface area and volume of each composite figure.**

11.

12.

Victoria Smith/HMH Photo

PRACTICE AND PROBLEM SOLVING

Independent Practice

For Exercises	See Example
13–15	1
16	2
17–19	3
20–21	4
22–23	5

my.hrw.com

Online Extra Practice

Find each measurement. Give your answers in terms of π.

13. the volume of the sphere

18 cm

14. the volume of the hemisphere

7 ft

15. the diameter of a sphere with volume 7776π in^3

16. Jewelry The size of a cultured pearl is typically indicated by its diameter in mm. How many times as great is the volume of the 9 mm pearl as the volume of the 6 mm pearl?

6 mm

9 mm

Find each measurement. Give your answers in terms of π.

17. the surface area of the sphere

21 in.

18. the surface area of the sphere

$A = 81\pi$ in^2

19. the volume of a sphere with surface area 625π m^2

H.O.T. **Describe the effect of each change on the given measurement of the figure.**

20. surface area
The dimensions are multiplied by $\frac{1}{5}$.

1.2 ft

21. volume
The dimensions are multiplied by 6.

14 mm

Find the surface area and volume of each composite figure.

22.

3 cm

4 cm

5 cm

10 cm

23.

10 mm

24 mm

8 mm

24. Find the radius of a hemisphere with a volume of 144π cm^3.

25. Find the circumference of a sphere with a surface area of 60π in^2.

26. Find the volume of a sphere with a circumference of 36π ft.

27. Find the surface area and volume of a sphere centered at $(0, 0, 0)$ that passes through the point $(2, 3, 6)$.

H.O.T. **28. Estimation** A bead is formed by drilling a cylindrical hole with a 2 mm diameter through a sphere with an 8 mm diameter. Estimate the surface area and volume of the bead.

© Susan Van Etten/Photo Edit

Sports Find the unknown dimensions of the ball for each sport.

	Sport	Ball	Diameter	Circumference	Surface Area	Volume
29.	Golf		1.68 in.			
30.	Cricket			9 in.		
31.	Tennis		2.5 in.			
32.	Petanque		74 mm			

Marine Biology

In 1934, the bathysphere reached a record depth of 3028 feet. The pressure on the hull was about half a ton per square inch.

33. Marine Biology The *bathysphere* was an early version of a submarine, invented in the 1930s. The inside diameter of the bathysphere was 54 inches, and the steel used to make the sphere was 1.5 inches thick. It had three 8-inch diameter windows. Estimate the volume of steel used to make the bathysphere.

34. Geography Earth's radius is approximately 4000 mi. About two-thirds of Earth's surface is covered by water. Estimate the land area on Earth.

Astronomy Use the table for Exercises 35–38.

35. How many times as great is the volume of Jupiter as the volume of Earth?

36. The sum of the volumes of Venus and Mars is about equal to the volume of which planet?

37. Which is greater, the sum of the surface areas of Uranus and Neptune or the surface area of Saturn?

38. How many times as great is the surface area of Earth as the surface area of Mars?

Planet	Diameter (mi)
Mercury	3,032
Venus	7,521
Earth	7,926
Mars	4,222
Jupiter	88,846
Saturn	74,898
Uranus	31,763
Neptune	30,775

H.O.T. 39. Critical Thinking In the figure, the hemisphere and the cylinder both have radius and height r. Prove that the shaded cross sections have equal areas.

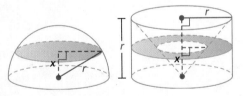

H.O.T. 40. Write About It Suppose a sphere and a cube have equal surface areas. Using r for the radius of the sphere and s for the side of a cube, write an equation to show the relationship between r and s.

Real-World Connections

41. A company sells orange juice in spherical containers that look like oranges. Each container has a surface area of approximately 50.3 in^2.

a. What is the volume of the container? Round to the nearest tenth.

b. The company decides to increase the radius of the container by 10%. What is the volume of the new container?

TEST PREP

42. A sphere with radius 8 cm is inscribed in a cube. Find the ratio of the volume of the cube to the volume of the sphere.

(A) $2:\frac{1}{3}\pi$ (B) $2:3\pi$ (C) $1:\frac{4}{3}\pi$ (D) $1:\frac{2}{3}\pi$

43. What is the surface area of a sphere with volume $10\frac{2}{3}\pi$ in^3?

(F) 8π in^2 (G) $10\frac{2}{3}\pi$ in^2 (H) 16π in^2 (J) 32π in^2

44. Which expression represents the volume of the composite figure formed by a hemisphere with radius r and a cube with side length $2r$?

(A) $r^3\left(\frac{2}{3}\pi + 8\right)$ (C) $2r^2(2\pi + 12)$

(B) $\frac{4}{3}\pi r^3 + 2r^3$ (D) $\frac{4}{3}\pi r^3 + 8r^3$

CHALLENGE AND EXTEND

45. Food The top of a gumball machine is an 18 in. sphere. The machine holds a maximum of 3300 gumballs, which leaves about 43% of the space in the machine empty. Estimate the diameter of each gumball.

H.O.T. 46. The surface area of a sphere can be used to determine its volume.

    a. Solve the surface area formula of a sphere to get an expression for r in terms of S.

    b. Substitute your result from part **a** into the volume formula to find the volume V of a sphere in terms of its surface area S.

    c. Graph the relationship between volume and surface area with S on the horizontal axis and V on the vertical axis. What shape is the graph?

Use the diagram of a sphere inscribed in a cylinder for Exercises 47 and 48.

47. What is the relationship between the volume of the sphere and the volume of the cylinder?

48. What is the relationship between the surface area of the sphere and the lateral area of the cylinder?

FOCUS ON MATHEMATICAL PRACTICES

H.O.T. 49. Estimation The volume of a tennis ball is 157.5 cm^3. What whole number of centimeters is the best approximation for its radius? Explain.

H.O.T. 50. Problem Solving A spherical scoop of frozen yogurt with a 6 cm diameter is placed in a cone with the same diameter. If left to melt, the yogurt exactly fills the cone, without overflowing. What is the height of the cone? Explain your reasoning.

H.O.T. 51. Justify The surface area of a sphere has the same numerical value as its volume. Find the diameter of this sphere. Justify your answer.

H.O.T. 52. Analysis A spherical piece of ice melts, and the water is poured into identical cylindrical buckets that have diameters and heights equal to the radius of the sphere. How many buckets are needed?

Ready to Go On?

my.hrw.com
Assessment and Intervention

11-1 Developing Formulas for Circles and Regular Polygons

Find each measurement.

1. the circumference of ⊙*R* in terms of π

2. the area of ⊙*E* in terms of π

3. A store sells circular rugs in three different sizes. The rugs come in diameters of 8 ft, 12 ft, and 16 ft. Find the areas of the three different sizes of rugs. Use 3.14 for π and round answers to the nearest tenth.

Find the area of each regular polygon. Round to the nearest tenth.

4. a regular hexagon with apothem 6 ft

5. a regular pentagon with side length 12 m

11-2 Volume of Prisms and Cylinders

Find the volume of each figure. Round to the nearest tenth, if necessary.

6. a regular hexagonal prism with base area 23 in^2 and height 9 in.

7. a cylinder with radius 8 yd and height 14 yd

8. A brick patio measures 10 ft by 12 ft by 4 in. Find the volume of the bricks. If the density of brick is 130 pounds per cubic foot, what is the weight of the patio in pounds?

9. The dimensions of a cylinder with diameter 2 ft and height 1 ft are doubled. Describe the effect on the volume.

11-3 Volume of Pyramids and Cones

Find the volume of each figure. Round to the nearest tenth, if necessary.

10.

11.

12.

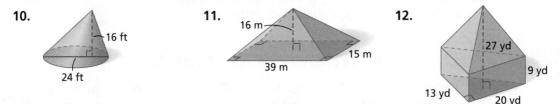

11-4 Spheres

Find the surface area and volume of each figure.

13. a sphere with diameter 20 in.

14. a hemisphere with radius 12 in.

15. A baseball has a diameter of approximately 3 in., and a softball has a diameter of approximately 5 in. About how many times as great is the volume of a softball as the volume of a baseball?

PARCC Assessment Readiness

Selected Response

1. The radius and height of the cylinder are multiplied by 4. Describe the effect on the volume.

   Ⓐ The volume is multiplied by 4.

   Ⓑ The volume is multiplied by 8.

   Ⓒ The volume is multiplied by 16.

   Ⓓ The volume is multiplied by 64.

2. A human's eyeball is shaped like a sphere with a diameter of 2.5 cm. A dog's eyeball is shaped like a sphere with a diameter of 1.75 cm. About how many times greater is the volume of a human's eyeball than the volume of a dog's eyeball?

   Ⓕ about 1.5 times greater

   Ⓖ about 3 times greater

   Ⓗ about 8 times greater

   Ⓙ about 23 times greater

3. Find the volume of a cone with a base circumference of 19π cm and a height 6 cm less than twice the radius. Give your answer both in terms of π and rounded to the nearest tenth.

   Ⓐ 752.1π cm³ ≈ 2,362.7 cm³

   Ⓑ $1,173.3\pi$ cm³ ≈ 3,685.9 cm³

   Ⓒ 391.1π cm³ ≈ 1,228.6 cm³

   Ⓓ 17.2π cm³ ≈ 54.1 cm³

4. Two circles have the same center. The radius of the larger circle is 3 units longer than the radius of the smaller circle. Find the difference in the circumferences of the two circles. Round to the nearest hundredth.

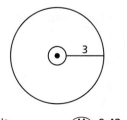

   Ⓕ 6.00 units   Ⓗ 9.42 units

   Ⓖ 18.84 units   Ⓙ 28.26 units

5. Find the surface area of a sphere with volume 288π m³. Give your answer in terms of π.

   Ⓐ 144 m²   Ⓒ 144π m²

   Ⓑ 6π m²   Ⓓ 864 m²

6. Find the volume of the composite figure. Round to the nearest tenth.
(*Hint*: Volume of a cone is $V = \frac{1}{3}\pi r^2 h$.)

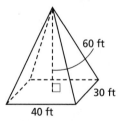

   Ⓕ 88.0 cm³   Ⓗ 75.4 cm³

   Ⓖ 12.6 cm³   Ⓙ 28.0 cm³

7. The length, width, and height of the rectangular pyramid are multiplied by $\frac{1}{3}$. Describe the effect on the volume.

   Ⓐ The volume is multiplied by $\frac{1}{81}$.

   Ⓑ The volume is multiplied by $\frac{1}{27}$.

   Ⓒ The volume is multiplied by $\frac{1}{9}$.

   Ⓓ The volume is multiplied by $\frac{1}{3}$.

Mini-Task

8. Find the height in centimeters of a square pyramid with a volume of 72 cm³ and a base edge length equal to the height.

12 Circles

Contents

MATHEMATICAL PRACTICES   The Common Core Georgia Performance Standards for Mathematical Practice describe varieties of expertise that all students should seek to develop. Opportunities to develop these practices are integrated throughout this program.

1 Make sense of problems and persevere in solving them.

2 Reason abstractly and quantitatively.

3 Construct viable arguments and critique the reasoning of others.

4 Model with mathematics.

5 Use appropriate tools strategically.

6 Attend to precision.

7 Look for and make use of structure.

8 Look for and express regularity in repeated reasoning.

Unpacking the Standards

my.hrw.com
Multilingual Glossary

Understanding the standards and the vocabulary terms in the standards will help you know exactly what you are expected to learn in this chapter.

 MCC9-12.G.C.5

Derive using similarity the fact that the length of the arc intercepted by an angle is proportional to the radius, and define the radian measure of the angle as the constant of proportionality; derive the formula for the area of a sector.

Key Vocabulary

similar (semejantes)
Two figures are similar if they have the same shape but not necessarily the same size.

intercepted arc (arco abarcado)
An arc that consists of endpoints that lie on the sides of an inscribed angle and all the points of the circle between the endpoints.

radian (radian)
A unit of angle measure based on arc length. In a circle of radius r, if a central angle has a measure of 1 radian, then the length of the intercepted arc is r units.
2π radians = 360°
1 radian ≈ 57°

sector of a circle (sector de un círculo)
A region inside a circle bounded by two radii of the circle and their intercepted arc.

What It Means For You

You can find the length of an arc with central angle m by multiplying the circumference by $\dfrac{m°}{360°}$ if m is in degrees or by $\dfrac{m\text{ radians}}{2\pi\text{ radians}}$ if m is in radians. You can also find the area of a sector by multiplying the area of the circle by $\dfrac{m°}{360°}$ or by $\dfrac{m\text{ radians}}{2\pi\text{ radians}}$.

EXAMPLE **Finding Arc Length**

Find the length of $\overset{\frown}{CD}$.

$$\text{Arc length} = \text{Circumference} \times \frac{m°}{360°}$$
$$= 2\pi r \times \frac{m°}{360°}$$
$$= 2\pi(10)\left(\frac{90°}{360°}\right)$$
$$= 5\pi \approx 16 \text{ feet}$$

The radian measure of the central angle is

$$90°\left(\frac{2\pi\text{ radians}}{360°}\right) = \frac{\pi}{2}\text{ radians, and } 2\pi r\left(\frac{\frac{\pi}{2}}{2\pi}\right) = 5\pi \approx 16\text{ feet,}$$

which is the same as the answer above.

EXAMPLE **Finding the Area of a Sector**

A farmer uses a rotating sprayer to irrigate a circular plot with radius 660 feet. What is the area that is irrigated as the sprayer moves through an angle of 60°?

$$\text{Area of sector} = \text{Area of plot} \times \frac{m°}{360°}$$
$$= \pi r^2 \times \frac{m°}{360°}$$
$$= \pi(660)^2 \times \left(\frac{60°}{360°}\right)$$
$$= 72{,}600\pi$$
$$\approx 228{,}000 \text{ square feet}$$

Lines That Intersect Circles

 Essential Question: What are various ways that lines and circles can intersect?

Objectives
Identify tangents, secants, and chords.

Use properties of tangents to solve problems.

Vocabulary
interior of a circle
exterior of a circle
chord
secant
tangent of a circle
point of tangency
congruent circles
concentric circles
tangent circles
common tangent

Why learn this?
You can use circle theorems to solve problems about Earth. (See Example 3.)

This photograph was taken 216 miles above Earth. From this altitude, it is easy to see the curvature of the horizon. Facts about circles can help us understand details about Earth.

Recall that a circle is the set of all points in a plane that are equidistant from a given point, called the center of the circle. A circle with center C is called circle C, or $\odot C$.

The **interior of a circle** is the set of all points inside the circle. The **exterior of a circle** is the set of all points outside the circle.

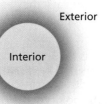

Exterior

Interior

Lines and Segments That Intersect Circles	
TERM	**DIAGRAM**
A **chord** is a segment whose endpoints lie on a circle.	
A **secant** is a line that intersects a circle at two points.	
A **tangent** is a line in the same plane as a circle that intersects it at exactly one point.	
The point where the tangent and a circle intersect is called the **point of tangency**.	

COMMON CORE GPS
Prep for MCC9-12.G.C.2

EXAMPLE 1 **Identifying Lines and Segments That Intersect Circles**

Identify each line or segment that intersects $\odot$A.

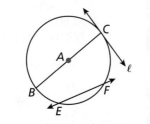

my.hrw.com

Online Video Tutor

chords: $\overline{EF}$ and $\overline{BC}$

tangent: ℓ

radii: $\overline{AC}$ and $\overline{AB}$

secant: $\overleftrightarrow{EF}$

diameter: $\overline{BC}$

PhotoDisc/Getty Images

1. Identify each line or segment that intersects $\odot P$.

Remember that the terms *radius* and *diameter* may refer to line segments, or to the lengths of segments.

Pairs of Circles

TERM	DIAGRAM
Two circles are **congruent circles** if and only if they have congruent radii.	$\odot A \cong \odot B$ if $\overline{AC} \cong \overline{BD}$. $\overline{AC} \cong \overline{BD}$ if $\odot A \cong \odot B$.
Concentric circles are coplanar circles with the same center.	
Two coplanar circles that intersect at exactly one point are called **tangent circles**.	Internally tangent circles · · · Externally tangent circles

EXAMPLE Prep for MCC9-12.G.C.4(+)

2 Identifying Tangents of Circles

my.hrw.com

Online Video Tutor

Find the length of each radius. Identify the point of tangency and write the equation of the tangent line at this point.

radius of $\odot A$: 4   *Center is (–1, 0). Pt. on $\odot$ is (3, 0). Dist. between the 2 pts. is 4.*

radius of $\odot B$: 2   *Center is (1, 0). Pt. on $\odot$ is (3, 0). Dist. between the 2 pts. is 2.*

point of tangency: $(3, 0)$ *Pt. where the $\odot$s and tangent line intersect*

equation of tangent line: $x = 3$ *Vert. line through (3, 0)*

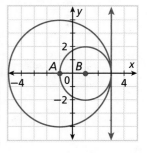

2. Find the length of each radius. Identify the point of tangency and write the equation of the tangent line at this point.

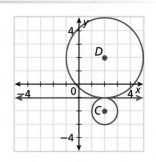

A **common tangent** is a line that is tangent to two circles.

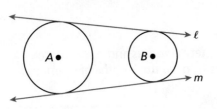

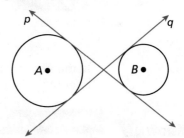

Lines ℓ and m are common external tangents to $\odot A$ and $\odot B$.

Lines p and q are common internal tangents to $\odot A$ and $\odot B$.

Construction Tangent to a Circle at a Point

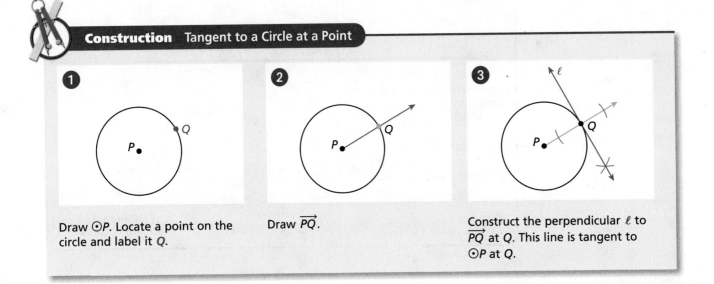

① Draw $\odot P$. Locate a point on the circle and label it Q.

② Draw $\overrightarrow{PQ}$.

③ Construct the perpendicular ℓ to $\overrightarrow{PQ}$ at Q. This line is tangent to $\odot P$ at Q.

Notice that in the construction, the tangent line is perpendicular to the radius at the point of tangency. This fact is the basis for the following theorems.

Know It! Note

Theorems

	THEOREM	HYPOTHESIS	CONCLUSION
12-1-1	If a line is tangent to a circle, then it is perpendicular to the radius drawn to the point of tangency. (line tangent to $\odot$ → line ⊥ to radius)	ℓ is tangent to $\odot A$	$\ell \perp \overline{AB}$
12-1-2	If a line is perpendicular to a radius of a circle at a point on the circle, then the line is tangent to the circle. (line ⊥ to radius → line tangent to $\odot$)	m is ⊥ to $\overline{CD}$ at D	m is tangent to $\odot C$.

Reading Math

Theorem 12-1-2 is the converse of Theorem 12-1-1.

You will prove Theorems 12-1-1 and 12-1-2 in Exercises 28 and 29.

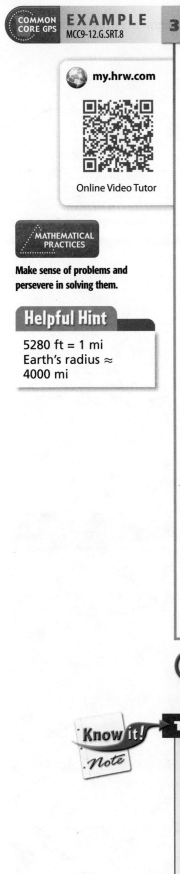

EXAMPLE MCC9-12.G.SRT.8 **3**

COMMON CORE GPS

my.hrw.com

Online Video Tutor

MATHEMATICAL PRACTICES

Make sense of problems and persevere in solving them.

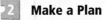
Helpful Hint

5280 ft = 1 mi
Earth's radius ≈ 4000 mi

Problem Solving Application

The summit of Mount Everest is approximately 29,000 ft above sea level. What is the distance from the summit to the horizon to the nearest mile?

1 Understand the Problem

The **answer** will be the length of an imaginary segment from the summit of Mount Everest to Earth's horizon.

2 Make a Plan

Draw a sketch. Let C be the center of Earth, E be the summit of Mount Everest, and H be a point on the horizon. You need to find the length of $\overline{EH}$, which is tangent to $\odot C$ at H. By Theorem 12-1-1, $\overline{EH} \perp \overline{CH}$. So $\triangle CHE$ is a right triangle.

3 Solve

$ED = 29{,}000$ ft	*Given*
$= \dfrac{29{,}000}{5280} \approx 5.49$ mi	*Change ft to mi.*
$EC = CD + ED$	*Seg. Add. Post.*
$= 4000 + 5.49 = 4005.49$ mi	*Substitute 4000 for CD and 5.49 for ED.*
$EC^2 = EH^2 + CH^2$	*Pyth. Thm.*
$4005.49^2 = EH^2 + 4000^2$	*Substitute the given values.*
$43{,}950.14 \approx EH^2$	*Subtract 4000^2 from both sides.*
210 mi $\approx EH$	*Take the square root of both sides.*

4 Look Back

The problem asks for the distance to the nearest mile. Check if your answer is reasonable by using the Pythagorean Theorem. Is $210^2 + 4000^2 \approx 4005^2$? Yes, $16{,}044{,}100 \approx 16{,}040{,}025$.

CHECK IT OUT!

3. Kilimanjaro, the tallest mountain in Africa, is 19,340 ft tall. What is the distance from the summit of Kilimanjaro to the horizon to the nearest mile?

Know it!
Note

Theorem 12-1-3

THEOREM	HYPOTHESIS	CONCLUSION
If two segments are tangent to a circle from the same external point, then the segments are congruent. (2 segs. tangent to $\odot$ from same ext. pt. → segs. $\cong$)	$\overline{AB}$ and $\overline{AC}$ are tangent to $\odot P$.	$\overline{AB} \cong \overline{AC}$

You will prove Theorem 12-1-3 in Exercise 30.

You can use Theorem 12-1-3 to find the length of segments drawn tangent to a circle from an exterior point.

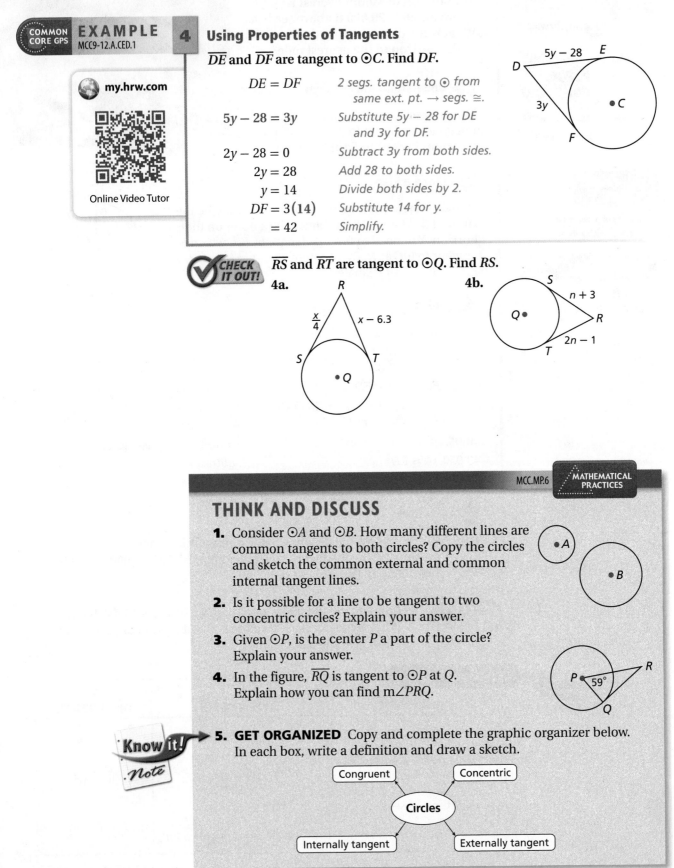

COMMON CORE GPS MCC9-12.A.CED.1

EXAMPLE 4

Using Properties of Tangents

$\overline{DE}$ and $\overline{DF}$ are tangent to $\odot C$. Find DF.

$DE = DF$	*2 segs. tangent to $\odot$ from same ext. pt. → segs. ≅.*
$5y - 28 = 3y$	*Substitute $5y - 28$ for DE and $3y$ for DF.*
$2y - 28 = 0$	*Subtract $3y$ from both sides.*
$2y = 28$	*Add 28 to both sides.*
$y = 14$	*Divide both sides by 2.*
$DF = 3(14)$	*Substitute 14 for y.*
$= 42$	*Simplify.*

my.hrw.com

Online Video Tutor

CHECK IT OUT!

$\overline{RS}$ and $\overline{RT}$ are tangent to $\odot Q$. Find RS.

4a.

4b.

MCC.MP.6   **MATHEMATICAL PRACTICES**

THINK AND DISCUSS

1. Consider $\odot A$ and $\odot B$. How many different lines are common tangents to both circles? Copy the circles and sketch the common external and common internal tangent lines.

2. Is it possible for a line to be tangent to two concentric circles? Explain your answer.

3. Given $\odot P$, is the center P a part of the circle? Explain your answer.

4. In the figure, $\overline{RQ}$ is tangent to $\odot P$ at Q. Explain how you can find m∠PRQ.

Know it! Note

5. **GET ORGANIZED** Copy and complete the graphic organizer below. In each box, write a definition and draw a sketch.

Congruent   Concentric

Circles

Internally tangent   Externally tangent

GUIDED PRACTICE

Vocabulary Apply the vocabulary from this lesson to answer each question.

1. A ___?___ is a line in the plane of a circle that intersects the circle at two points. (*secant* or *tangent*)

2. Coplanar circles that have the same center are called ___?___ . (*concentric* or *congruent*)

3. $\odot Q$ and $\odot R$ both have a radius of 3 cm. Therefore the circles are ___?___ . (*concentric* or *congruent*)

SEE EXAMPLE 1 Identify each line or segment that intersects each circle.

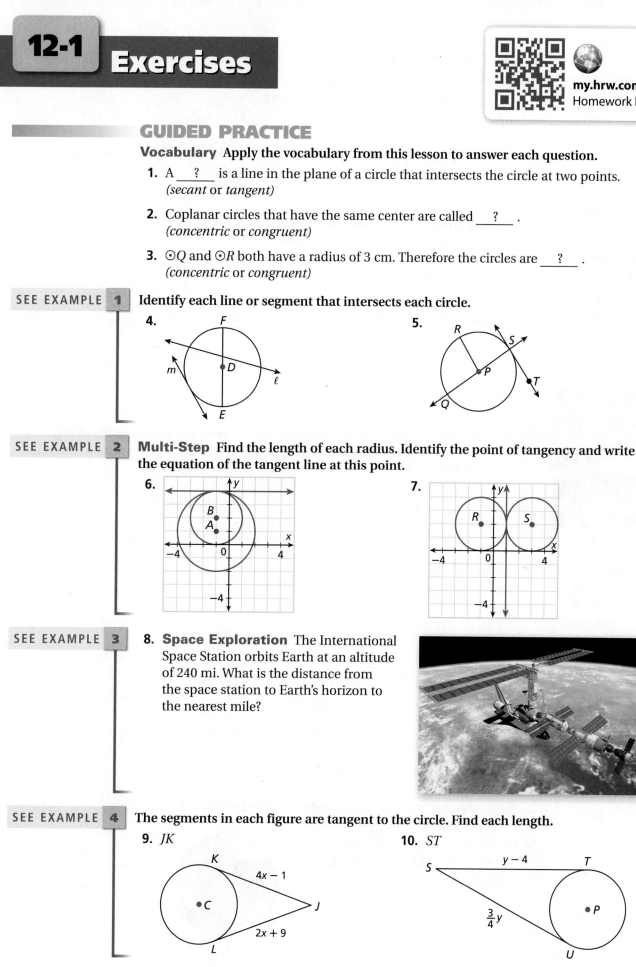

4.

5.

SEE EXAMPLE 2 **Multi-Step** Find the length of each radius. Identify the point of tangency and write the equation of the tangent line at this point.

6.

7.

SEE EXAMPLE 3

8. **Space Exploration** The International Space Station orbits Earth at an altitude of 240 mi. What is the distance from the space station to Earth's horizon to the nearest mile?

SEE EXAMPLE 4 The segments in each figure are tangent to the circle. Find each length.

9. *JK*

10. *ST*

PRACTICE AND PROBLEM SOLVING

Independent Practice

For Exercises	See Example
11–12	1
13–14	2
15	3
16–17	4

my.hrw.com

Online Extra Practice

Identify each line or segment that intersects each circle.

11.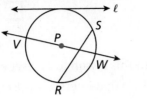

12.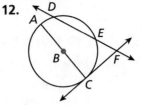

Multi-Step Find the length of each radius. Identify the point of tangency and write the equation of the tangent line at this point.

13.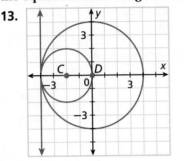

14.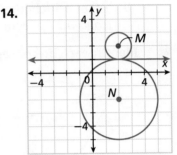

Astronomy

Olympus Mons, located on Mars, is the tallest known volcano in the solar system.

15. Astronomy Olympus Mons's peak rises 25 km above the surface of the planet Mars. The diameter of Mars is approximately 6794 km. What is the distance from the peak of Olympus Mons to the horizon to the nearest kilometer?

The segments in each figure are tangent to the circle. Find each length.

16. AB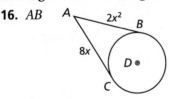

17. RT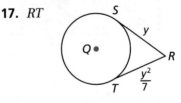

Tell whether each statement is sometimes, always, or never true.

18. Two circles with the same center are congruent.

19. A tangent to a circle intersects the circle at two points.

20. Tangent circles have the same center.

21. A tangent to a circle will form a right angle with a radius that is drawn to the point of tangency.

22. A chord of a circle is a diameter.

Graphic Design Use the following diagram for Exercises 23–25.

The peace symbol was designed in 1958 by Gerald Holtom, a professional artist and designer. Identify the following.

23. diameter

24. radii

25. chord

In each diagram, $\overline{PR}$ and $\overline{PS}$ are tangent to $\odot Q$. Find each angle measure.

26. m∠Q

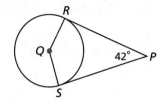

27. m∠P

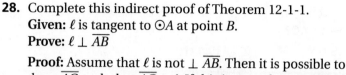

28. Complete this indirect proof of Theorem 12-1-1.
Given: ℓ is tangent to $\odot A$ at point B.
Prove: $\ell \perp \overline{AB}$

Proof: Assume that ℓ is not $\perp \overline{AB}$. Then it is possible to draw $\overline{AC}$ such that $\overline{AC} \perp \ell$. If this is true, then $\triangle ACB$ is a right triangle. $AC < AB$ because **a.** __?__ . Since ℓ is a tangent line, it can only intersect $\odot A$ at **b.** __?__ , and C must be in the exterior of $\odot A$. That means that $AC > AB$ since $\overline{AB}$ is a **c.** __?__ . This contradicts the fact that $AC < AB$. Thus the assumption is false, and **d.** __?__ .

H.O.T. 29. Prove Theorem 12-1-2.
Given: $m \perp \overline{CD}$
Prove: m is tangent to $\odot C$.

(*Hint:* Choose a point on m. Then use the Pythagorean Theorem to prove that if the point is not D, then it is not on the circle.)

H.O.T. 30. Prove Theorem 12-1-3.
Given: $\overline{AB}$ and $\overline{AC}$ are tangent to $\odot P$.
Prove: $\overline{AB} \cong \overline{AC}$

Plan: Draw auxiliary segments $\overline{PA}$, $\overline{PB}$, and $\overline{PC}$. Show that the triangles formed are congruent. Then use CPCTC.

Algebra Assume the segments that appear to be tangent are tangent. Find each length.

31. ST

32. DE

33. JL

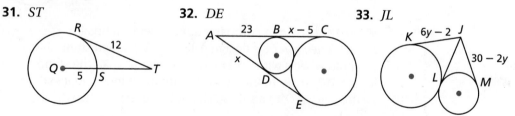

34. $\odot M$ has center $M(2, 2)$ and radius 3. $\odot N$ has center $N(-3, 2)$ and is tangent to $\odot M$. Find the coordinates of the possible points of tangency of the two circles.

35. The diagram shows the gears of a bicycle. $AD = 5$ in., and $BC = 3$ in. CD, the length of the chain between the gears, is 17 in.

a. What type of quadrilateral is $BCDE$? Why?

b. Find BE and AE.

c. What is AB to the nearest tenth of an inch?

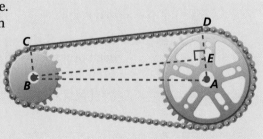

H.O.T. 36. Critical Thinking Given a circle with diameter $\overline{BC}$, is it possible to draw tangents to B and C from an external point X? If so, make a sketch. If not, explain why it is not possible.

37. Write About It $\overline{PR}$ and $\overline{PS}$ are tangent to $\odot Q$ at points R and S. Explain why $\angle RPS$ and $\angle SQR$ are supplementary.

TEST PREP

38. $\overline{AB}$ and $\overline{AC}$ are tangent to $\odot D$. Which of these is closest to AD?

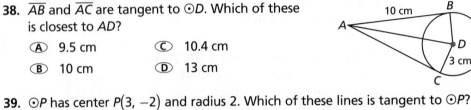

- Ⓐ 9.5 cm
- Ⓒ 10.4 cm
- Ⓑ 10 cm
- Ⓓ 13 cm

39. $\odot P$ has center $P(3, -2)$ and radius 2. Which of these lines is tangent to $\odot P$?

- Ⓕ $x = 0$
- Ⓖ $y = -4$
- Ⓗ $y = -2$
- Ⓙ $x = 4$

40. $\odot A$ has radius 5. $\odot B$ has radius 6. What is the ratio of the area of $\odot A$ to that of $\odot B$?

- Ⓐ $\dfrac{125}{216}$
- Ⓑ $\dfrac{25}{36}$
- Ⓒ $\dfrac{5}{6}$
- Ⓓ $\dfrac{36}{25}$

CHALLENGE AND EXTEND

H.O.T. 41. Given: $\odot G$ with $\overline{GH} \perp \overline{JK}$
Prove: $\overline{JH} \cong \overline{KH}$

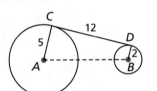

H.O.T. 42. Multi-Step $\odot A$ has radius 5, $\odot B$ has radius 2, and $\overline{CD}$ is a common tangent. What is AB? (*Hint:* Draw a perpendicular segment from B to E, a point on $\overline{AC}$.)

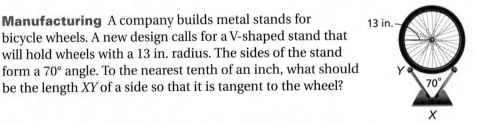

H.O.T. 43. Manufacturing A company builds metal stands for bicycle wheels. A new design calls for a V-shaped stand that will hold wheels with a 13 in. radius. The sides of the stand form a 70° angle. To the nearest tenth of an inch, what should be the length XY of a side so that it is tangent to the wheel?

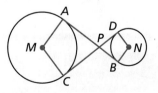

FOCUS ON MATHEMATICAL PRACTICES

H.O.T. 44. Proof $\overline{AB}$ and $\overline{CD}$ are common internal tangents to $\odot M$ and $\odot N$, and they intersect at point P. Prove that $\angle M \cong \angle N$.

H.O.T. 45. Problem Solving Three circles, R, S, and T are tangent to each other. $RS = 13$, $RT = 14$, and $ST = 11$. Find the length of each radius. (*Hint:* Represent the radius of one circle with x. Represent each of the other radii in terms of x.)

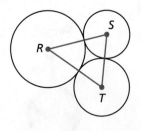

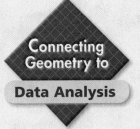

Circle Graphs

A circle graph compares data that are parts of a whole unit. When you make a circle graph, you find the measure of each *central angle*. A *central angle* is an angle whose vertex is the center of the circle.

Example

Make a circle graph to represent the following data.

Step 1 Add all the amounts. $110 + 40 + 300 + 150 = 600$

Step 2 Write each part as a fraction of the whole.

fiction: $\frac{110}{600}$; nonfiction: $\frac{40}{600}$; children's: $\frac{300}{600}$; audio books: $\frac{150}{600}$

Step 3 Multiply each fraction by 360° to calculate the central angle measure.

$\frac{110}{600}(360°) = 66°$; $\frac{40}{600}(360°) = 24°$; $\frac{300}{600}(360°) = 180°$; $\frac{150}{600}(360°) = 90°$

Step 4 Make a circle graph. Then color each section of the circle to match the data.

The section with a central angle of 66° is green, 24° is orange, 180° is purple, and 90° is yellow.

Books in the Bookmobile	
Fiction	110
Nonfiction	40
Children's	300
Audio books	150

Try This

Choose the circle graph that best represents the data. Show each step.

A	B	C	D

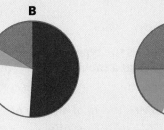

1.
Books in Linda's Library	
Novels	18
Reference	10
Textbooks	8

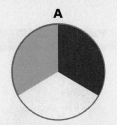

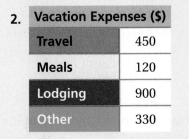

2.
Vacation Expenses ($)	
Travel	450
Meals	120
Lodging	900
Other	330

3.
Puppy Expenses ($)	
Food	190
Health	375
Training	120
Other	50

12-2 Arcs and Chords

Essential Question: How are arcs of circles measured in relation to central angles?

Objectives
Apply properties of arcs.

Apply properties of chords.

Vocabulary
central angle
arc
minor arc
major arc
semicircle
adjacent arcs
congruent arcs

Who uses this?
Market analysts use circle graphs to compare sales of different products.

A **central angle** is an angle whose vertex is the center of a circle. An **arc** is an unbroken part of a circle consisting of two points called the endpoints and all the points on the circle between them.

Know it!
Note

Writing Math

Minor arcs may be named by two points. Major arcs and semicircles must be named by three points.

Arcs and Their Measure

ARC	MEASURE	DIAGRAM
A **minor arc** is an arc whose points are on or in the interior of a central angle.	The measure of a minor arc is equal to the measure of its central angle. $$m\widehat{AC} = m\angle ABC = x°$$	
A **major arc** is an arc whose points are on or in the exterior of a central angle.	The measure of a major arc is equal to 360° minus the measure of its central angle. $$m\widehat{ADC} = 360° - m\angle ABC$$ $$= 360° - x°$$	
If the endpoints of an arc lie on a diameter, the arc is a **semicircle**.	The measure of a semicircle is equal to 180°. $$m\widehat{EFG} = 180°$$	

COMMON CORE GPS
Prep for MCC9-12.G.C.2

EXAMPLE 1

Data Application

my.hrw.com

Online Video Tutor

The circle graph shows the types of music sold during one week at a music store. Find $m\widehat{BC}$.

$$m\widehat{BC} = m\angle BMC \qquad \text{m of arc = m of central } \angle.$$

$$m\angle BMC = 0.13(360°) \qquad \text{Central } \angle \text{ is 13\%}$$
$$= 46.8° \qquad \text{of the } \odot.$$

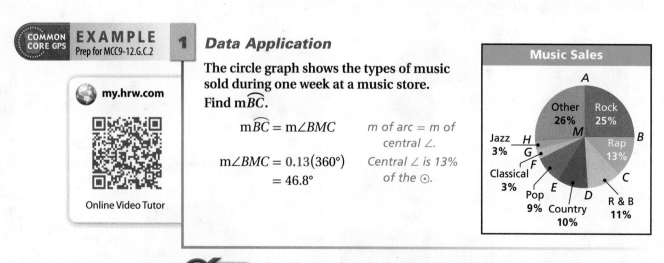

CHECK IT OUT! Use the graph to find each of the following.
1a. $m\angle FMC$ **1b.** $m\widehat{AHB}$ **1c.** $m\angle EMD$

Adjacent arcs are arcs of the same circle that intersect at exactly one point. $\overset{\frown}{RS}$ and $\overset{\frown}{ST}$ are adjacent arcs.

Know it! Note

Postulate 12-2-1 | **Arc Addition Postulate**

The measure of an arc formed by two adjacent arcs is the sum of the measures of the two arcs.

$$m\overset{\frown}{ABC} = m\overset{\frown}{AB} + m\overset{\frown}{BC}$$

COMMON CORE GPS Prep for MCC9-12.G.C.2

EXAMPLE 2 **Using the Arc Addition Postulate**

Find $m\overset{\frown}{CDE}$

$m\overset{\frown}{CD} = 90°$	$m\angle CFD = 90°$
$m\angle DFE = 18°$	Vert. $\angle$s Thm.
$m\overset{\frown}{DE} = 18°$	$m\angle DFE = 18°$
$m\overset{\frown}{CE} = m\overset{\frown}{CD} + m\overset{\frown}{DE}$	Arc Add. Post.
$= 90° + 18° = 108°$	Substitute and simplify.

my.hrw.com

Online Video Tutor

CHECK IT OUT! Find each measure.
2a. $m\overset{\frown}{JKL}$ **2b.** $m\overset{\frown}{LJN}$

Within a circle or congruent circles, **congruent arcs** are two arcs that have the same measure. In the figure, $\overset{\frown}{ST} \cong \overset{\frown}{UV}$.

Know it! Note

Theorem 12-2-2

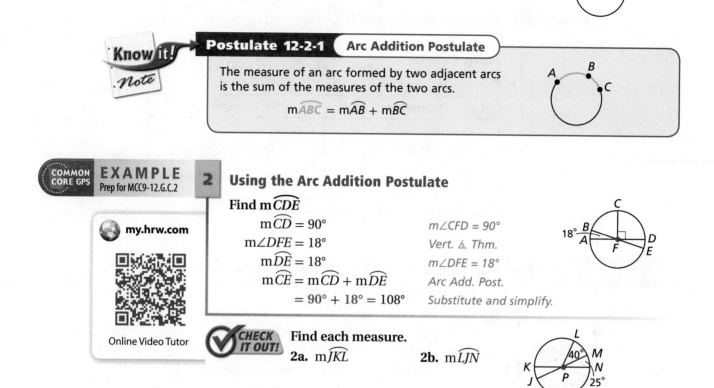

THEOREM	HYPOTHESIS	CONCLUSION
In a circle or congruent circles:		
(1) Congruent central angles have congruent chords.	$\angle EAD \cong \angle BAC$	$\overline{DE} \cong \overline{BC}$
(2) Congruent chords have congruent arcs.	$\overline{ED} \cong \overline{BC}$	$\overset{\frown}{DE} \cong \overset{\frown}{BC}$
(3) Congruent arcs have congruent central angles.	$\overset{\frown}{ED} \cong \overset{\frown}{BC}$	$\angle DAE \cong \angle BAC$

You will prove parts 2 and 3 of Theorem 12-2-2 in Exercises 40 and 41.

The converses of the parts of Theorem 12-2-2 are also true. For example, with part 1, congruent chords have congruent central angles.

PROOF **Theorem 12-2-2 (Part 1)**

Given: $\angle BAC \cong \angle DAE$
Prove: $\overline{BC} \cong \overline{DE}$

Proof:

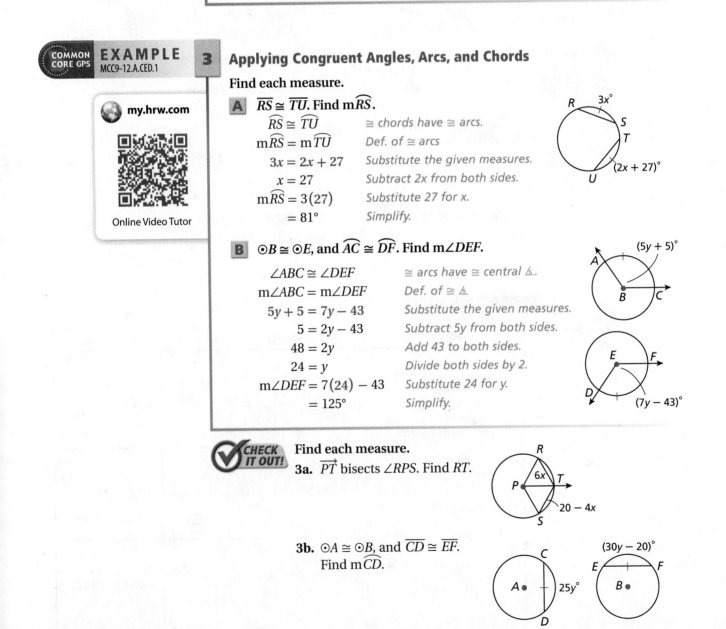

Statements	Reasons
1. $\angle BAC \cong \angle DAE$	1. Given
2. $\overline{AB} \cong \overline{AD}, \overline{AC} \cong \overline{AE}$	2. All radii of a $\odot$ are $\cong$.
3. $\triangle BAC \cong \triangle DAE$	3. SAS *Steps 2, 1*
4. $\overline{BC} \cong \overline{DE}$	4. CPCTC

COMMON CORE GPS
MCC9-12.A.CED.1

EXAMPLE 3 Applying Congruent Angles, Arcs, and Chords

Find each measure.

my.hrw.com

Online Video Tutor

A $\overline{RS} \cong \overline{TU}$. Find m$\overarc{RS}$.

$\overarc{RS} \cong \overarc{TU}$ $\cong$ chords have $\cong$ arcs.
m$\overarc{RS}$ = m$\overarc{TU}$ *Def. of $\cong$ arcs*
$3x = 2x + 27$ *Substitute the given measures.*
$x = 27$ *Subtract 2x from both sides.*
m$\overarc{RS}$ = 3(27)   *Substitute 27 for x.*
$= 81°$ *Simplify.*

B $\odot B \cong \odot E$, and $\overarc{AC} \cong \overarc{DF}$. Find m$\angle DEF$.

$\angle ABC \cong \angle DEF$ $\cong$ arcs have $\cong$ central $\angle$.
m$\angle ABC$ = m$\angle DEF$ *Def. of $\cong$ $\angle$*
$5y + 5 = 7y - 43$ *Substitute the given measures.*
$5 = 2y - 43$ *Subtract 5y from both sides.*
$48 = 2y$ *Add 43 to both sides.*
$24 = y$ *Divide both sides by 2.*
m$\angle DEF$ = 7(24) - 43   *Substitute 24 for y.*
$= 125°$ *Simplify.*

CHECK IT OUT! **Find each measure.**

3a. $\overrightarrow{PT}$ bisects $\angle RPS$. Find RT.

3b. $\odot A \cong \odot B$, and $\overline{CD} \cong \overline{EF}$. Find m$\overarc{CD}$.

Theorems

THEOREM	HYPOTHESIS	CONCLUSION
12-2-3 In a circle, if a radius (or diameter) is perpendicular to a chord, then it bisects the chord and its arc.	$\overline{CD} \perp \overline{EF}$	$\overline{CD}$ bisects $\overline{EF}$ and $\widehat{EF}$.
12-2-4 In a circle, the perpendicular bisector of a chord is a radius (or diameter).	$\overline{JK}$ is $\perp$ bisector of $\overline{GH}$.	$\overline{JK}$ is a diameter of $\odot A$.

You will prove Theorems 12-2-3 and 12-2-4 in Exercises 42 and 43.

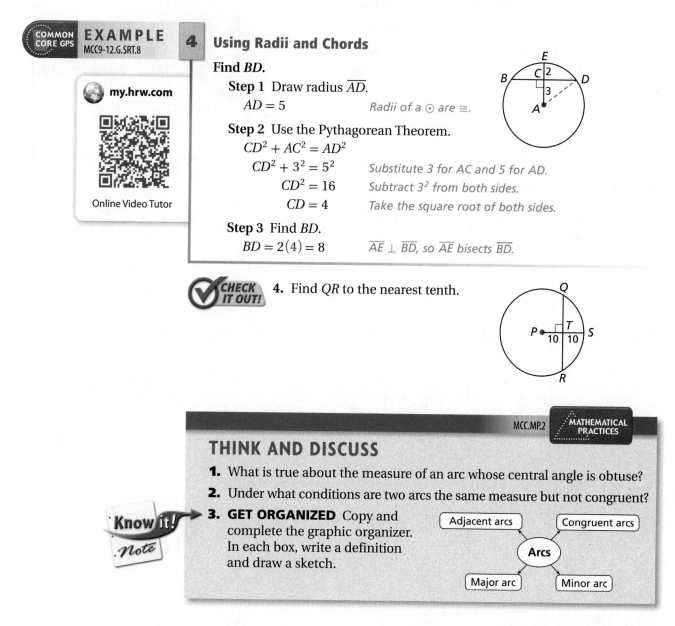

COMMON CORE GPS
EXAMPLE **4**
MCC9-12.G.SRT.8

Using Radii and Chords

Find *BD*.

Step 1 Draw radius $\overline{AD}$.

$AD = 5$ *Radii of a ⊙ are ≅.*

Step 2 Use the Pythagorean Theorem.

$CD^2 + AC^2 = AD^2$

$CD^2 + 3^2 = 5^2$ *Substitute 3 for AC and 5 for AD.*

$CD^2 = 16$ *Subtract 3^2 from both sides.*

$CD = 4$ *Take the square root of both sides.*

Step 3 Find *BD*.

$BD = 2(4) = 8$ $\overline{AE} \perp \overline{BD}$, so $\overline{AE}$ bisects $\overline{BD}$.

my.hrw.com

Online Video Tutor

CHECK IT OUT!

4. Find *QR* to the nearest tenth.

MCC.MP.2   MATHEMATICAL PRACTICES

THINK AND DISCUSS

1. What is true about the measure of an arc whose central angle is obtuse?

2. Under what conditions are two arcs the same measure but not congruent?

3. GET ORGANIZED Copy and complete the graphic organizer. In each box, write a definition and draw a sketch.

Know it!
.Note

Adjacent arcs   Congruent arcs

Arcs

Major arc   Minor arc

GUIDED PRACTICE

Vocabulary Apply the vocabulary from this lesson to answer each question.

1. An arc that joins the endpoints of a diameter is called a __?__ . (*semicircle* or *major arc*)

2. How do you recognize a *central angle* of a circle?

3. In ⊙*P* m$\widehat{ABC}$ = 205°. Therefore $\widehat{ABC}$ is a __?__ . (*major arc* or *minor arc*)

4. In a circle, an arc that is less than a semicircle is a __?__ . (*major arc* or *minor arc*)

SEE EXAMPLE 1

Consumer Application Use the following information for Exercises 5–10.

The circle graph shows how a typical household spends money on energy. Find each of the following.

5. m∠*PAQ*

6. m∠*VAU*

7. m∠*SAQ*

8. m$\widehat{UT}$

9. m$\widehat{RQ}$

10. m$\widehat{UPT}$

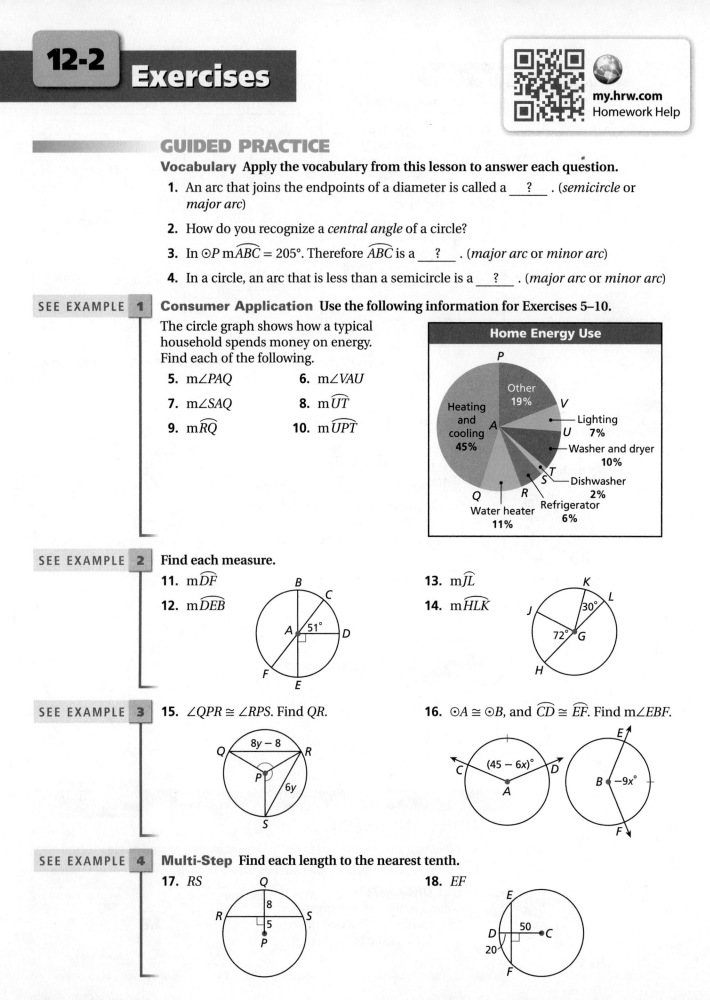

Home Energy Use

Other 19%
Heating and cooling 45%
Lighting 7%
Washer and dryer 10%
Dishwasher 2%
Refrigerator 6%
Water heater 11%

SEE EXAMPLE 2

Find each measure.

11. m$\widehat{DF}$

12. m$\widehat{DEB}$

13. m$\widehat{JL}$

14. m$\widehat{HLK}$

SEE EXAMPLE 3

15. ∠*QPR* ≅ ∠*RPS*. Find *QR*.

16. ⊙*A* ≅ ⊙*B*, and $\widehat{CD}$ ≅ $\widehat{EF}$. Find m∠*EBF*.

SEE EXAMPLE 4

Multi-Step Find each length to the nearest tenth.

17. *RS*

18. *EF*

PRACTICE AND PROBLEM SOLVING

Independent Practice

For Exercises	See Example
19–24	1
25–28	2
29–30	3
31–32	4

my.hrw.com

Online Extra Practice

Sports Use the following information for Exercises 19–24.

The key shows the number of medals won by U.S. athletes at the 2004 Olympics in Athens. Find each of the following to the nearest tenth.

19. m∠ADB

20. m∠ADC

21. m$\overset{\frown}{AB}$

22. m$\overset{\frown}{BC}$

23. m$\overset{\frown}{ACB}$

24. m$\overset{\frown}{CAB}$

Medals	
Gold	35
Silver	39
Bronze	29

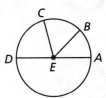

Find each measure.

25. m$\overset{\frown}{MP}$

26. m$\overset{\frown}{QNL}$

27. m$\overset{\frown}{WT}$

28. m$\overset{\frown}{WTV}$

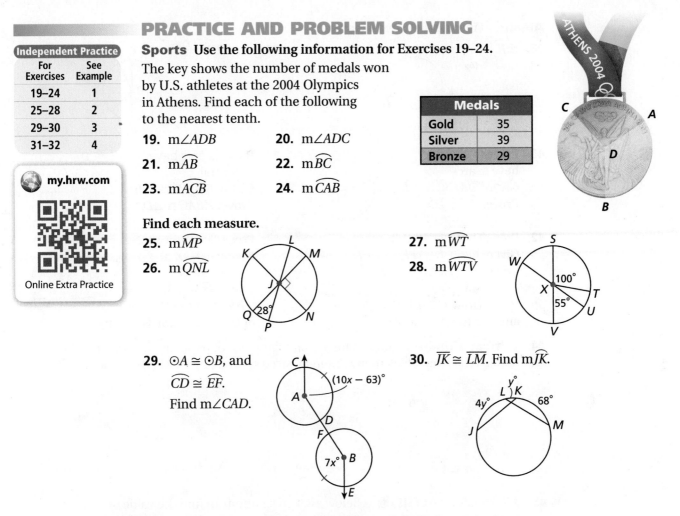

29. $\odot A \cong \odot B$, and $\overset{\frown}{CD} \cong \overset{\frown}{EF}$. Find m∠CAD.

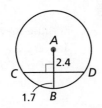

30. $\overline{JK} \cong \overline{LM}$. Find m$\overset{\frown}{JK}$.

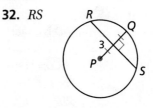

H.O.T. Multi-Step Find each length to the nearest tenth.

31. CD

32. RS

H.O.T. Determine whether each statement is true or false. If false, explain why.

33. The central angle of a minor arc is an acute angle.

34. Any two points on a circle determine a minor arc and a major arc.

35. In a circle, the perpendicular bisector of a chord must pass through the center of the circle.

H.O.T. 36. Data Collection Use a graphing calculator, a pH probe, and a data-collection device to collect information about the pH levels of ten different liquids. Then create a circle graph with the following sectors: strong basic $(9 < \text{pH} < 14)$, weak basic $(7 < \text{pH} < 9)$, neutral $(\text{pH} = 7)$, weak acidic $(5 < \text{pH} < 7)$, and strong acidic $(0 < \text{pH} < 5)$.

37. In $\odot E$, the measures of ∠AEB, ∠BEC, and ∠CED are in the ratio 3:4:5. Find m$\overset{\frown}{AB}$, m$\overset{\frown}{BC}$, and m$\overset{\frown}{CD}$.

Algebra Find the indicated measure.

38. m$\widehat{JL}$

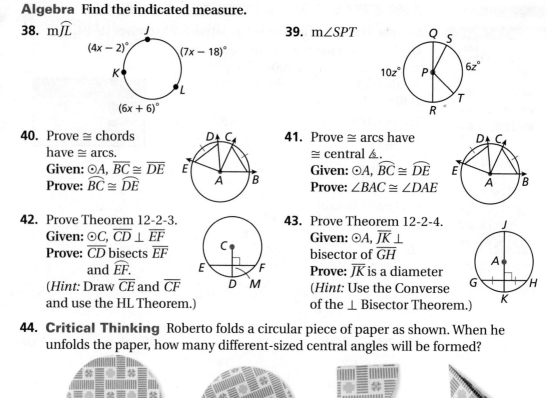

39. m∠*SPT*

40. Prove ≅ chords
have ≅ arcs.
Given: ⊙*A*, $\overline{BC} \cong \overline{DE}$
Prove: $\widehat{BC} \cong \widehat{DE}$

41. Prove ≅ arcs have
≅ central ∡.
Given: ⊙*A*, $\widehat{BC} \cong \widehat{DE}$
Prove: ∠*BAC* ≅ ∠*DAE*

42. Prove Theorem 12-2-3.
Given: ⊙*C*, $\overline{CD} \perp \overline{EF}$
Prove: $\overline{CD}$ bisects $\overline{EF}$
and $\widehat{EF}$.
(*Hint:* Draw $\overline{CE}$ and $\overline{CF}$
and use the HL Theorem.)

43. Prove Theorem 12-2-4.
Given: ⊙*A*, $\overline{JK} \perp$
bisector of $\overline{GH}$
Prove: $\overline{JK}$ is a diameter
(*Hint:* Use the Converse
of the ⊥ Bisector Theorem.)

44. Critical Thinking Roberto folds a circular piece of paper as shown. When he
unfolds the paper, how many different-sized central angles will be formed?

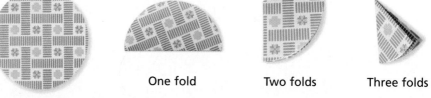

One fold   Two folds   Three folds

H.O.T. 45. ///**ERROR ANALYSIS**/// Below are two solutions to find the value of *x*. Which
solution is incorrect? Explain the error.

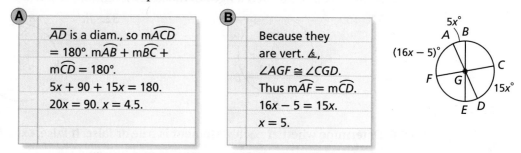

A

$\overline{AD}$ is a diam., so m$\widehat{ACD}$
= 180°. m$\widehat{AB}$ + m$\widehat{BC}$ +
m$\widehat{CD}$ = 180°.
5*x* + 90 + 15*x* = 180.
20*x* = 90. *x* = 4.5.

B

Because they
are vert. ∡,
∠*AGF* ≅ ∠*CGD*.
Thus m$\widehat{AF}$ = m$\widehat{CD}$.
16*x* − 5 = 15*x*.
x = 5.

46. Write About It According to a school survey, 40% of the students take a bus
to school, 35% are driven to school, 15% ride a bike, and the remainder walk.
Explain how to use central angles to create a circle graph from this data.

Real-World Connections

47. Chantal's bike has wheels with a 27 in. diameter.
  a. What are *AC* and *AD* if *DB* is 7 in.?
  b. What is *CD* to the nearest tenth of an inch?
  c. What is *CE*, the length of the top of the bike stand?

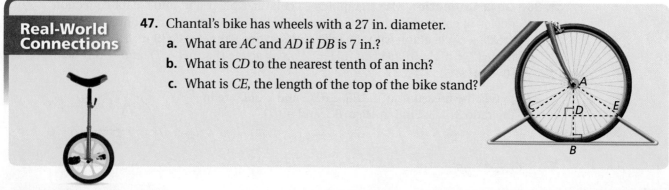

48. Which of these arcs of ⊙Q has the greatest measure?

Ⓐ $\overset{\frown}{WT}$ Ⓒ $\overset{\frown}{VR}$

Ⓑ $\overset{\frown}{UW}$ Ⓓ $\overset{\frown}{TV}$

49. In ⊙A, CD = 10. Which of these is closest to the length of $\overline{AE}$?

Ⓕ 3.3 cm   Ⓗ 5 cm

Ⓖ 4 cm   Ⓙ 7.8 cm

50. Gridded Response ⊙P has center P(2, 1) and radius 3. What is the measure, in degrees, of the minor arc with endpoints A(−1, 1) and B(2, −2)?

CHALLENGE AND EXTEND

51. In the figure, $\overline{AB} \perp \overline{CD}$. Find m$\overset{\frown}{BD}$ to the nearest tenth of a degree.

52. Two points on a circle determine two distinct arcs. How many arcs are determined by *n* points on a circle? (*Hint:* Make a table and look for a pattern.)

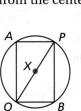

H.O.T. 53. An angle measure other than degrees is *radian* measure. 360° converts to 2π radians, or 180° converts to π radians.

    a. Convert the following radian angle measures to degrees: $\frac{\pi}{2}, \frac{\pi}{3}, \frac{\pi}{4}$.

    b. Convert the following angle measures to radians: 135°, 270°.

FOCUS ON MATHEMATICAL PRACTICES

H.O.T. 54. Reasoning In a circle, two chords are the same distance from the center of the circle. Are the chords necessarily congruent? Explain.

H.O.T. 55. Proof In ⊙X, $\overset{\frown}{AP} \cong \overset{\frown}{QB}$ and $\overset{\frown}{AQ} \cong \overset{\frown}{PB}$. Prove $\overline{AP} \parallel \overline{QB}$.

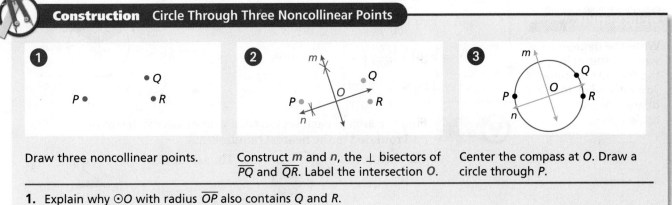

Construction   Circle Through Three Noncollinear Points

❶ Draw three noncollinear points.

❷ Construct *m* and *n*, the ⊥ bisectors of $\overline{PQ}$ and $\overline{QR}$. Label the intersection *O*.

❸ Center the compass at *O*. Draw a circle through *P*.

1. Explain why ⊙O with radius $\overline{OP}$ also contains Q and R.

Sector Area and Arc Length

Essential Question: How is proportional reasoning used to find areas of circle sectors and lengths of arcs?

Objectives
Find the area of sectors.
Find arc lengths.

Vocabulary
sector of a circle
segment of a circle
arc length

Who uses this?
Farmers use irrigation radii to calculate areas of sectors. (See Example 2.)

The area of a sector is a fraction of the circle containing the sector. To find the area of a sector whose central angle measures $m°$, multiply the area of the circle by $\frac{m°}{360°}$.

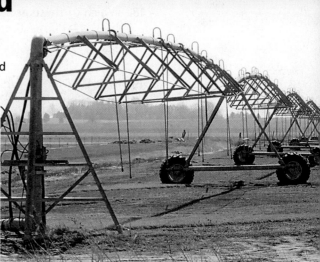

Know it! Note

Animated Math

Sector of a Circle

TERM	NAME	DIAGRAM	AREA
A **sector of a circle** is a region bounded by two radii of the circle and their intercepted arc.	sector *ACB*		$A = \pi r^2\left(\dfrac{m°}{360°}\right)$

COMMON CORE GPS MCC9-12.G.C.5

EXAMPLE **1** Finding the Area of a Sector

my.hrw.com

Online Video Tutor

Find the area of each sector. Give your answer in terms of π and rounded to the nearest hundredth.

A sector *MPN*

$A = \pi r^2\left(\dfrac{m°}{360°}\right)$ *Use formula for area of a sector.*

$= \pi(3)^2\left(\dfrac{80°}{360°}\right)$ *Substitute 3 for r and 80 for m.*

$= 2\pi \text{ in}^2 \approx 6.28 \text{ in}^2$ *Simplify.*

B sector *EFG*

$A = \pi r^2\left(\dfrac{m°}{360°}\right)$ *Use formula for area of a sector.*

$= \pi(6)^2\left(\dfrac{120°}{360°}\right)$ *Substitute 6 for r and 120 for m.*

$= 12\pi \approx 37.70 \text{ cm}^2$ *Simplify.*

Helpful Hint

Write the degree symbol after *m* in the formula to help you remember to use degree measure not arc length.

CHECK IT OUT! Find the area of each sector. Give your answer in terms of π and rounded to the nearest hundredth.

1a. sector *ACB*

1b. sector *JKL*

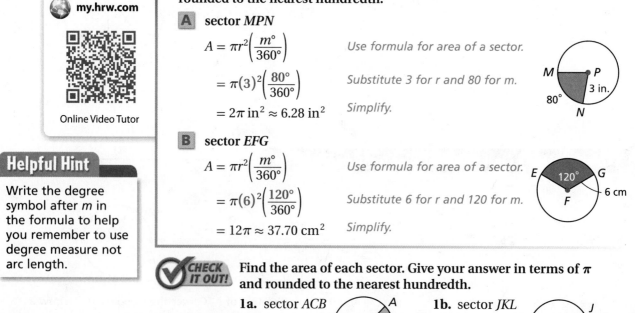

AP/Wide World Photos.

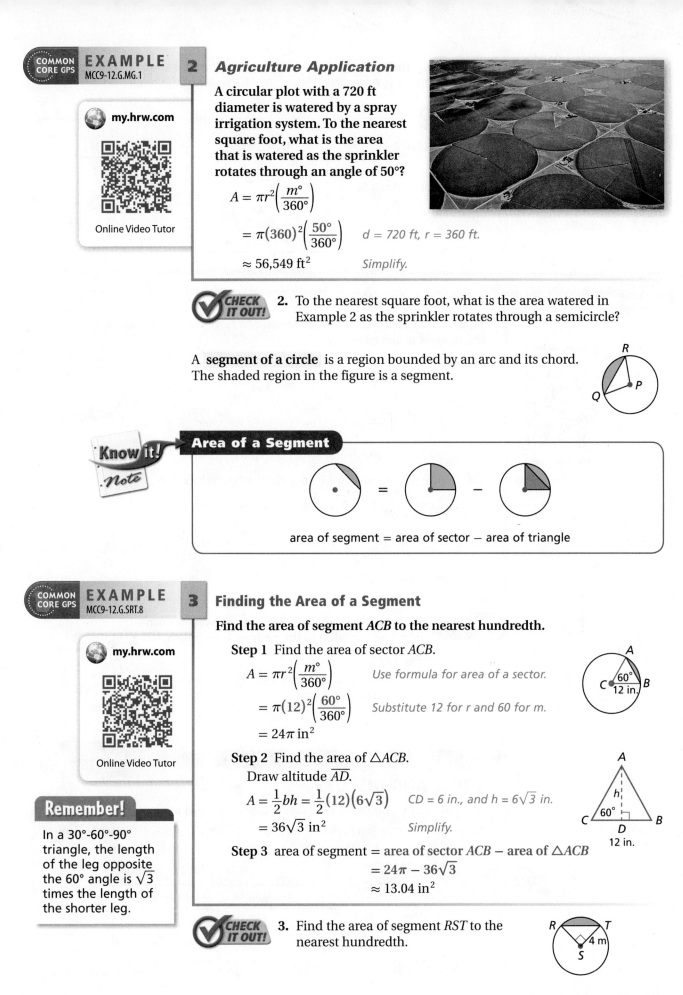

COMMON CORE GPS **EXAMPLE 2**
MCC9-12.G.MG.1

my.hrw.com

Online Video Tutor

Agriculture Application

A circular plot with a 720 ft diameter is watered by a spray irrigation system. To the nearest square foot, what is the area that is watered as the sprinkler rotates through an angle of 50°?

$$A = \pi r^2 \left(\frac{m°}{360°} \right)$$

$$= \pi (360)^2 \left(\frac{50°}{360°} \right) \quad \textit{d = 720 ft, r = 360 ft.}$$

$$\approx 56{,}549 \text{ ft}^2 \quad \textit{Simplify.}$$

CHECK IT OUT!

2. To the nearest square foot, what is the area watered in Example 2 as the sprinkler rotates through a semicircle?

A **segment of a circle** is a region bounded by an arc and its chord. The shaded region in the figure is a segment.

Area of a Segment

Know it! Note

area of segment = area of sector − area of triangle

COMMON CORE GPS **EXAMPLE 3**
MCC9-12.G.SRT.8

my.hrw.com

Online Video Tutor

Finding the Area of a Segment

Find the area of segment ACB to the nearest hundredth.

Step 1 Find the area of sector ACB.

$$A = \pi r^2 \left(\frac{m°}{360°} \right) \quad \textit{Use formula for area of a sector.}$$

$$= \pi (12)^2 \left(\frac{60°}{360°} \right) \quad \textit{Substitute 12 for r and 60 for m.}$$

$$= 24\pi \text{ in}^2$$

Step 2 Find the area of △ACB.
Draw altitude $\overline{AD}$.

$$A = \frac{1}{2}bh = \frac{1}{2}(12)\left(6\sqrt{3}\right) \quad \textit{CD = 6 in., and h = 6}\sqrt{3} \textit{ in.}$$

$$= 36\sqrt{3} \text{ in}^2 \quad \textit{Simplify.}$$

Step 3 area of segment = area of sector ACB − area of △ACB

$$= 24\pi - 36\sqrt{3}$$

$$\approx 13.04 \text{ in}^2$$

Remember!

In a 30°-60°-90° triangle, the length of the leg opposite the 60° angle is $\sqrt{3}$ times the length of the shorter leg.

CHECK IT OUT!

3. Find the area of segment RST to the nearest hundredth.

In the same way that the area of a sector is a fraction of the area of the circle, the length of an arc is a fraction of the circumference of the circle.

Arc Length		
TERM	**DIAGRAM**	**LENGTH**
Arc length is the distance along an arc measured in linear units.	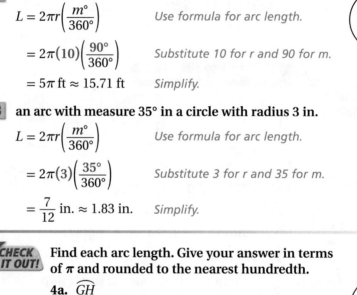	$L = 2\pi r\left(\dfrac{m^\circ}{360^\circ}\right)$

COMMON CORE GPS
MCC9-12.G.C.5

EXAMPLE **4**

Finding Arc Length

Find each arc length. Give your answer in terms of π and rounded to the nearest hundredth.

A $\overset{\frown}{CD}$

$L = 2\pi r\left(\dfrac{m^\circ}{360^\circ}\right)$ *Use formula for arc length.*

$= 2\pi(10)\left(\dfrac{90^\circ}{360^\circ}\right)$ *Substitute 10 for r and 90 for m.*

$= 5\pi$ ft ≈ 15.71 ft   *Simplify.*

B an arc with measure 35° in a circle with radius 3 in.

$L = 2\pi r\left(\dfrac{m^\circ}{360^\circ}\right)$ *Use formula for arc length.*

$= 2\pi(3)\left(\dfrac{35^\circ}{360^\circ}\right)$ *Substitute 3 for r and 35 for m.*

$= \dfrac{7}{12}$ in. ≈ 1.83 in.   *Simplify.*

my.hrw.com

Online Video Tutor

CHECK IT OUT! Find each arc length. Give your answer in terms of π and rounded to the nearest hundredth.

4a. $\overset{\frown}{GH}$

4b. an arc with measure 135° in a circle with radius 4 cm

MCC.MP.4

MATHEMATICAL PRACTICES

THINK AND DISCUSS

1. What is the difference between arc measure and arc length?

2. A slice of pizza is a sector of a circle. Explain what measurements you would need to make in order to calculate the area of the slice.

3. GET ORGANIZED Copy and complete the graphic organizer.

	Formula	Diagram
Area of a Sector		
Area of a Segment		
Arc Length		

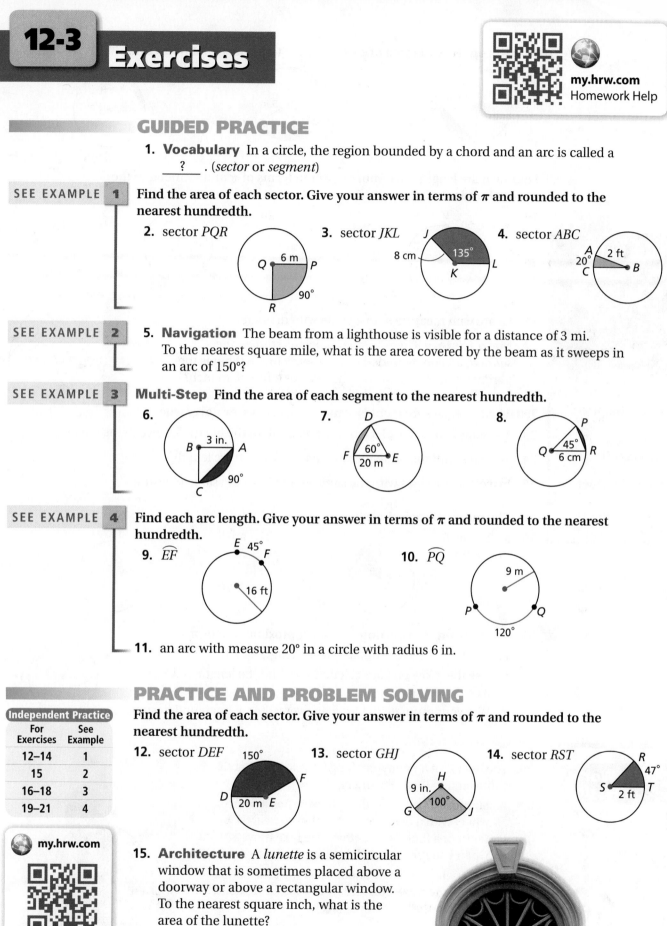

GUIDED PRACTICE

1. **Vocabulary** In a circle, the region bounded by a chord and an arc is called a
   ___?___ . (*sector* or *segment*)

SEE EXAMPLE 1 Find the area of each sector. Give your answer in terms of π and rounded to the nearest hundredth.

2. sector *PQR*

3. sector *JKL*

4. sector *ABC*

SEE EXAMPLE 2

5. **Navigation** The beam from a lighthouse is visible for a distance of 3 mi. To the nearest square mile, what is the area covered by the beam as it sweeps in an arc of 150°?

SEE EXAMPLE 3 **Multi-Step** Find the area of each segment to the nearest hundredth.

6.

7.

8.

SEE EXAMPLE 4 Find each arc length. Give your answer in terms of π and rounded to the nearest hundredth.

9. $\overarc{EF}$

10. $\overarc{PQ}$

11. an arc with measure 20° in a circle with radius 6 in.

PRACTICE AND PROBLEM SOLVING

Find the area of each sector. Give your answer in terms of π and rounded to the nearest hundredth.

12. sector *DEF*

13. sector *GHJ*

14. sector *RST*

15. **Architecture** A *lunette* is a semicircular window that is sometimes placed above a doorway or above a rectangular window. To the nearest square inch, what is the area of the lunette?

40 in.

H.O.T. Multi-Step Find the area of each segment to the nearest hundredth.

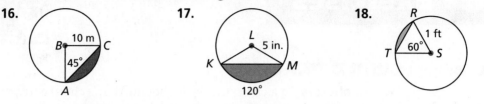

16.

17.

18.

Find each arc length. Give your answer in terms of π and rounded to the nearest hundredth.

19. $\overarc{UV}$

20. $\overarc{AB}$

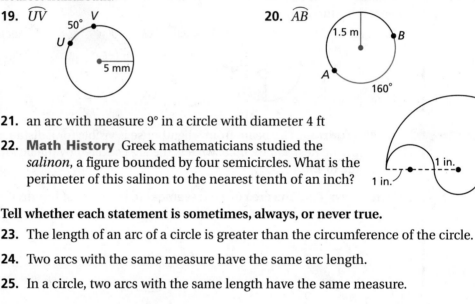

21. an arc with measure 9° in a circle with diameter 4 ft

22. **Math History** Greek mathematicians studied the *salinon*, a figure bounded by four semicircles. What is the perimeter of this salinon to the nearest tenth of an inch?

Tell whether each statement is sometimes, always, or never true.

23. The length of an arc of a circle is greater than the circumference of the circle.

24. Two arcs with the same measure have the same arc length.

25. In a circle, two arcs with the same length have the same measure.

Find the radius of each circle.

26. area of sector
$ABC = 9\pi$

27. arc length of
$\overarc{EF} = 8\pi$

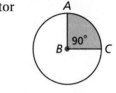

H.O.T. 28. Estimation The fraction $\frac{22}{7}$ is an approximation for π.

  a. Use this value to estimate the arc length of $\overarc{XY}$.

  b. Use the π key on your calculator to find the length of $\overarc{XY}$ to 8 decimal places.

  c. Was your estimate in part **a** an overestimate or an underestimate?

29. The pedals of a penny-farthing bicycle are directly connected to the front wheel.

  a. Suppose a penny-farthing bicycle has a front wheel with a diameter of 5 ft. To the nearest tenth of a foot, how far does the bike move when you turn the pedals through an angle of 90°?

  b. Through what angle should you turn the pedals in order to move forward by a distance of 4.5 ft? Round to the nearest degree.

H.O.T. 30. Critical Thinking What is the length of the radius that makes the area of $\odot A = 24$ in^2 and the area of sector $BAC = 3$ in^2? Explain.

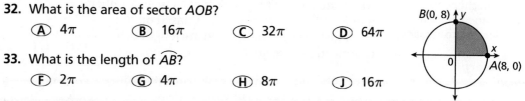

31. Write About It Given the length of an arc of a circle and the measure of the arc, explain how to find the radius of the circle.

TEST PREP

32. What is the area of sector AOB?

    Ⓐ 4π Ⓑ 16π Ⓒ 32π Ⓓ 64π

33. What is the length of $\overset{\frown}{AB}$?

    Ⓕ 2π Ⓖ 4π Ⓗ 8π Ⓙ 16π

34. Gridded Response To the nearest hundredth, what is the area of the sector determined by an arc with measure 35° in a circle with radius 12?

CHALLENGE AND EXTEND

H.O.T. 35. In the diagram, the larger of the two concentric circles has radius 5, and the smaller circle has radius 2. What is the area of the shaded region in terms of π?

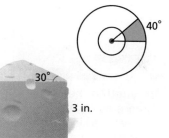

36. A wedge of cheese is a sector of a cylinder.

    a. To the nearest tenth, what is the volume of the wedge with the dimensions shown?

    b. What is the surface area of the wedge of cheese to the nearest tenth?

30°
3 in.
4 in.

37. Probability The central angles of a target measure 45°. The inner circle has a radius of 1 ft, and the outer circle has a radius of 2 ft. Assuming that all arrows hit the target at random, find the following probabilities.

    a. hitting a red region

    b. hitting a blue region

    c. hitting a red or blue region

FOCUS ON MATHEMATICAL PRACTICES

H.O.T. 38. Number Sense Two congruent circles have a regular hexagon and a regular octagon inscribed in them, respectively. Which figure has segments with greater area? Explain.

H.O.T. 39. Problem Solving The circumference of a circle is 15.6 inches. The length of an arc in the circle is 5.2 inches.

    a. Find the measure of the central angle m.

    b. Explain how to find the length of the radius. Then find it to the nearest tenth of an inch.

    c. Find the length of the intercepted chord to the nearest tenth.

    d. Find the area of the sector to the nearest tenth.

    e. Find the area of the segment to the nearest tenth.

H.O.T. 40. Draw Conclusions Two sectors are in the same circle. The area of one is greater than the area of the other. What conclusions can you draw?

EXTENSION Measuring Angles in Radians

Essential Question: How does the direct variation relationship between arc length and radius lead to the definition of radian measure?

Objective
Use proportions to convert angle measures from degrees to radians.

Vocabulary
radian

One unit of measurement for angles is degrees, which are based on a fraction of a circle. Another unit is called a *radian*, which is based on the relationship of the radius and arc length of a central angle in a circle.

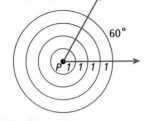

Four concentric circles are shown, with radius 1, 2, 3, and 4. The measure of each arc is 60°.

Radius	Arc Length
1	$2\pi(1)\left(\dfrac{60°}{360°}\right) = \dfrac{\pi}{3}$
2	$2\pi(2)\left(\dfrac{60°}{360°}\right) = \dfrac{2\pi}{3}$
3	$2\pi(3)\left(\dfrac{60°}{360°}\right) = \pi$
4	$2\pi(4)\left(\dfrac{60°}{360°}\right) = \dfrac{4\pi}{3}$

Remember!

Arc length is the distance along an arc measured in linear units. In a circle of radius r, the length of an arc with a central angle measure m is $L = 2\pi r\left(\dfrac{m°}{360°}\right)$.

The relationship between the radius and arc length is linear, with a slope of $2\pi\left(\dfrac{60°}{360°}\right) = \dfrac{\pi}{3}$, or about 1.05. The slope represents the ratio of the arc length to the radius. This ratio is the *radian* measure of the angle, so 60° is the same as $\dfrac{\pi}{3}$ radians.

If a central angle θ in a circle of radius r intercepts an arc of length r, the measure of θ is defined as 1 **radian.** Since the circumference of a circle of radius r is $2\pi r$, an angle representing one complete rotation measures 2π radians, or 360°.

2π radians $= 360°$ and π radians $= 180°$

$1° = \left(\dfrac{\pi \text{ radians}}{180°}\right)$ and 1 radian $= \left(\dfrac{180°}{\pi \text{ radians}}\right)$

Use these facts to convert between radians and degrees.

Converting Angle Measures	
DEGREES TO RADIANS	**RADIANS TO DEGREES**
Multiply the number of degrees by	Multiply the number of radians by
$\left(\dfrac{\pi \text{ radians}}{180°}\right)$	$\left(\dfrac{180°}{\pi \text{ radians}}\right)$

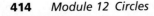

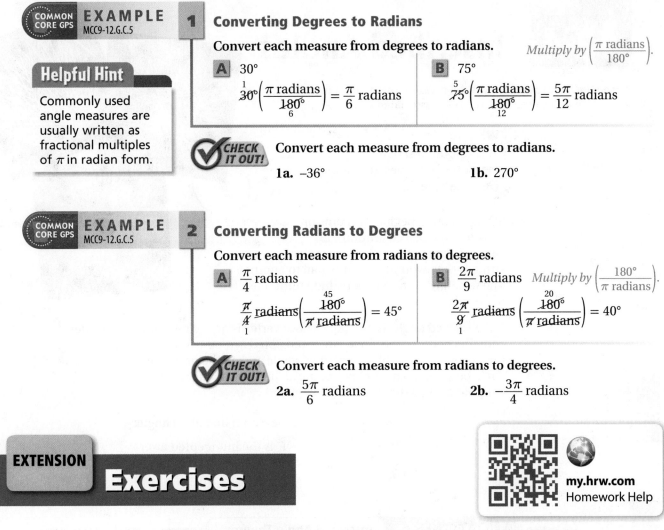

COMMON CORE GPS MCC9-12.G.C.5 **EXAMPLE 1** Converting Degrees to Radians

Convert each measure from degrees to radians. *Multiply by* $\left(\dfrac{\pi \text{ radians}}{180°}\right)$.

A 30°

$$\overset{1}{\cancel{30°}}\left(\dfrac{\pi \text{ radians}}{\underset{6}{\cancel{180°}}}\right) = \dfrac{\pi}{6} \text{ radians}$$

B 75°

$$\overset{5}{\cancel{75°}}\left(\dfrac{\pi \text{ radians}}{\underset{12}{\cancel{180°}}}\right) = \dfrac{5\pi}{12} \text{ radians}$$

CHECK IT OUT! Convert each measure from degrees to radians.

1a. −36°   **1b.** 270°

COMMON CORE GPS MCC9-12.G.C.5 **EXAMPLE 2** Converting Radians to Degrees

Convert each measure from radians to degrees.

A $\dfrac{\pi}{4}$ radians

$$\dfrac{\cancel{\pi}}{\underset{1}{\cancel{4}}} \text{ radians}\left(\dfrac{\overset{45}{\cancel{180°}}}{\cancel{\pi} \text{ radians}}\right) = 45°$$

B $\dfrac{2\pi}{9}$ radians   *Multiply by* $\left(\dfrac{180°}{\pi \text{ radians}}\right)$.

$$\dfrac{2\cancel{\pi}}{\underset{1}{\cancel{9}}} \text{ radians}\left(\dfrac{\overset{20}{\cancel{180°}}}{\cancel{\pi} \text{ radians}}\right) = 40°$$

CHECK IT OUT! Convert each measure from radians to degrees.

2a. $\dfrac{5\pi}{6}$ radians   **2b.** $-\dfrac{3\pi}{4}$ radians

EXTENSION

Exercises

my.hrw.com
Homework Help

1. Convert each measure from degrees to radians to complete the table.

0°	30°	45°	60°	90°	180°	270°	360°

Convert each measure from degrees to radians.

2. 215°   **3.** 25°   **4.** −180°   **5.** 35°

6. 120°   **7.** −315°   **8.** 400°   **9.** −60°

Convert each measure from radians to degrees.

10. $\dfrac{6\pi}{5}$ radians   **11.** $\dfrac{3\pi}{5}$ radians   **12.** $-\dfrac{\pi}{3}$ radians   **13.** $\dfrac{5\pi}{9}$ radians

14. $\dfrac{\pi}{6}$ radians   **15.** $\dfrac{2\pi}{3}$ radians   **16.** $\dfrac{5\pi}{8}$ radians   **17.** $\dfrac{7\pi}{2}$ radians

18. Electronics A DVD rotates through an angle of 20π radians in 1 second. At this speed, how many revolutions does the DVD make in 2 minutes?

19. Clocks Find the measure of the angle in radians formed by the minute hand on a clock at 7:35 and its position 15 minutes later.

20. Wheels A bicycle's wheel spins backwards, making 2 complete counterclockwise revolutions. What is the measure of the wheel's rotation angle in radians?

12-4 Inscribed Angles

Essential Question: How is the measure of an angle inscribed in a circle related to the measure of its associated central angle?

Objectives
Find the measure of an inscribed angle.

Use inscribed angles and their properties to solve problems.

Vocabulary
inscribed angle
intercepted arc
subtend

Why learn this?
You can use inscribed angles to find measures of angles in string art. (See Example 2.)

String art often begins with pins or nails that are placed around the circumference of a circle. A long piece of string is then wound from one nail to another. The resulting pattern may include hundreds of *inscribed angles*.

An **inscribed angle** is an angle whose vertex is on a circle and whose sides contain chords of the circle. An **intercepted arc** consists of endpoints that lie on the sides of an inscribed angle and all the points of the circle between them. A chord or arc **subtends** an angle if its endpoints lie on the sides of the angle.

∠*DEF* is an inscribed angle.

$\overset{\frown}{DF}$ is the intercepted arc.

$\overset{\frown}{DF}$ subtends ∠*DEF*.

Know it!
.Note

| **Theorem 12-4-1** | **Inscribed Angle Theorem** |

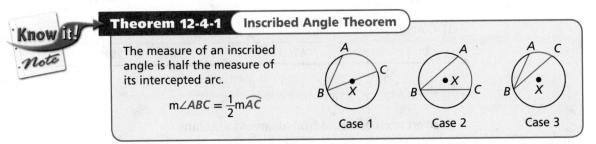

The measure of an inscribed angle is half the measure of its intercepted arc.

$$m\angle ABC = \tfrac{1}{2}m\overset{\frown}{AC}$$

Case 1   Case 2   Case 3

You will prove Cases 2 and 3 of Theorem 12-4-1 in Exercises 30 and 31.

PROOF | **Inscribed Angle Theorem**

Given: ∠*ABC* is inscribed in ⊙*X*.
Prove: $m\angle ABC = \tfrac{1}{2}m\overset{\frown}{AC}$

Proof Case 1:
∠*ABC* is inscribed in ⊙*X* with *X* on $\overline{BC}$. Draw $\overline{XA}$. $m\overset{\frown}{AC} = m\angle AXC$. By the Exterior Angle Theorem $m\angle AXC = m\angle ABX + m\angle BAX$. Since $\overline{XA}$ and $\overline{XB}$ are radii of the circle, $\overline{XA} \cong \overline{XB}$. Then by definition △*AXB* is isosceles. Thus $m\angle ABX = m\angle BAX$.

By the Substitution Property, $m\overset{\frown}{AC} = 2m\angle ABX$ or $2m\angle ABC$. Thus $\tfrac{1}{2}m\overset{\frown}{AC} = m\angle ABC$.

Victoria Smith/HMH

EXAMPLE 1
MCC9-12.G.C.2

Finding Measures of Arcs and Inscribed Angles

Find each measure.

my.hrw.com

Online Video Tutor

A $m\angle RST$

$m\angle RST = \frac{1}{2}m\overset{\frown}{RT}$ *Inscribed ∠ Thm.*

$= \frac{1}{2}(120°) = 60°$ *Substitute 120 for m$\overset{\frown}{RT}$.*

B $m\overset{\frown}{SU}$

$m\angle SRU = \frac{1}{2}m\overset{\frown}{SU}$ *Inscribed ∠ Thm.*

$40° = \frac{1}{2}m\overset{\frown}{SU}$ *Substitute 40 for m∠SRU.*

$m\overset{\frown}{SU} = 80°$ *Mult. both sides by 2.*

CHECK IT OUT!

Find each measure.
1a. $m\overset{\frown}{ADC}$
1b. $m\angle DAE$

Know it! Note

Corollary 12-4-2

COROLLARY	HYPOTHESIS	CONCLUSION
If inscribed angles of a circle intercept the same arc or are subtended by the same chord or arc, then the angles are congruent.	$\angle ACB, \angle ADB,$ and $\angle AEB$ intercept $\overset{\frown}{AB}$.	$\angle ACB \cong \angle ADB \cong \angle AEB$ (and $\angle CAE \cong \angle CBE$)

You will prove Corollary 12-4-2 in Exercise 32.

EXAMPLE 2
MCC9-12.G.C.2

Hobby Application

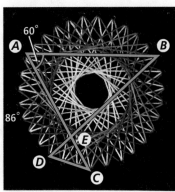

my.hrw.com

Online Video Tutor

Find $m\angle DEC$, if $m\overset{\frown}{AD} = 86°$.

$\angle BAC \cong \angle BDC$ *∠BAC and ∠BDC intercept $\overset{\frown}{BC}$.*

$m\angle BAC = m\angle BDC$ *Def. of ≅*

$m\angle BDC = 60°$ *Substitute 60 for m∠BDC.*

$m\angle ACD = \frac{1}{2}m\overset{\frown}{AD}$ *Inscribed ∠ Thm.*

$= \frac{1}{2}(86°)$ *Substitute 86 for m$\overset{\frown}{AD}$.*

$= 43°$ *Simplify.*

$m\angle DEC + 60 + 43 = 180$ *△ Sum Theorem*

$m\angle DEC = 77°$ *Simplify.*

CHECK IT OUT!

2. Find $m\angle ABD$ and $m\overset{\frown}{BC}$ in the string art.

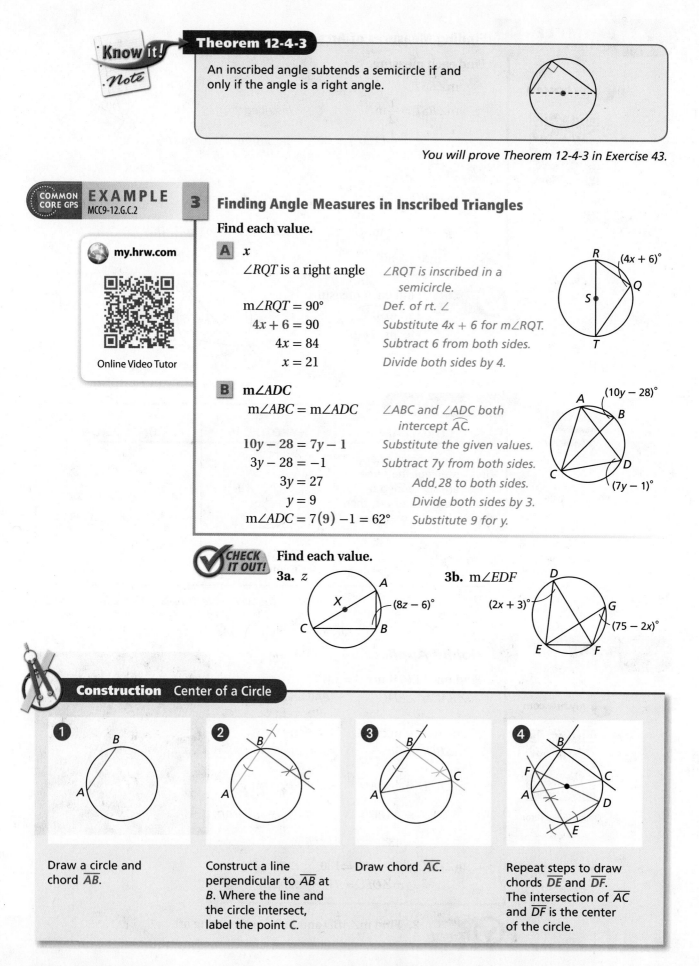

Know it! Note

Theorem 12-4-3

An inscribed angle subtends a semicircle if and only if the angle is a right angle.

You will prove Theorem 12-4-3 in Exercise 43.

COMMON CORE GPS MCC9-12.G.C.2 **EXAMPLE 3**

Finding Angle Measures in Inscribed Triangles

Find each value.

A *x*

$\angle RQT$ is a right angle ⟶ *∠RQT is inscribed in a semicircle.*

$m\angle RQT = 90°$ ⟶ *Def. of rt. ∠*

$4x + 6 = 90$ ⟶ *Substitute 4x + 6 for m∠RQT.*

$4x = 84$ ⟶ *Subtract 6 from both sides.*

$x = 21$ ⟶ *Divide both sides by 4.*

B $m\angle ADC$

$m\angle ABC = m\angle ADC$ ⟶ *∠ABC and ∠ADC both intercept $\overset{\frown}{AC}$.*

$10y - 28 = 7y - 1$ ⟶ *Substitute the given values.*

$3y - 28 = -1$ ⟶ *Subtract 7y from both sides.*

$3y = 27$ ⟶ *Add 28 to both sides.*

$y = 9$ ⟶ *Divide both sides by 3.*

$m\angle ADC = 7(9) - 1 = 62°$ ⟶ *Substitute 9 for y.*

my.hrw.com

Online Video Tutor

CHECK IT OUT! Find each value.

3a. *z*

3b. $m\angle EDF$

Construction Center of a Circle

1 Draw a circle and chord $\overline{AB}$.

2 Construct a line perpendicular to $\overline{AB}$ at *B*. Where the line and the circle intersect, label the point *C*.

3 Draw chord $\overline{AC}$.

4 Repeat steps to draw chords $\overline{DE}$ and $\overline{DF}$. The intersection of $\overline{AC}$ and $\overline{DF}$ is the center of the circle.

Theorem 12-4-4

THEOREM	HYPOTHESIS	CONCLUSION
If a quadrilateral is inscribed in a circle, then its opposite angles are supplementary.	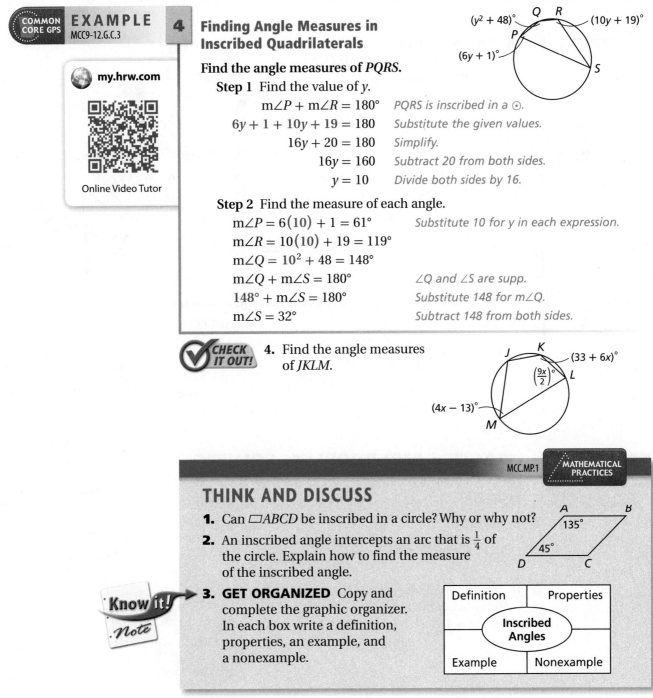 *ABCD* is inscribed in ⊙*E*.	∠*A* and ∠*C* are supplementary. ∠*B* and ∠*D* are supplementary.

You will prove Theorem 12-4-4 in Exercise 44.

EXAMPLE 4
MCC9-12.G.C.3

Finding Angle Measures in Inscribed Quadrilaterals

Find the angle measures of *PQRS*.

Step 1 Find the value of *y*.

$m\angle P + m\angle R = 180°$	*PQRS is inscribed in a ⊙.*
$6y + 1 + 10y + 19 = 180$	*Substitute the given values.*
$16y + 20 = 180$	*Simplify.*
$16y = 160$	*Subtract 20 from both sides.*
$y = 10$	*Divide both sides by 16.*

Step 2 Find the measure of each angle.

$m\angle P = 6(10) + 1 = 61°$	*Substitute 10 for y in each expression.*
$m\angle R = 10(10) + 19 = 119°$	
$m\angle Q = 10^2 + 48 = 148°$	
$m\angle Q + m\angle S = 180°$	*∠Q and ∠S are supp.*
$148° + m\angle S = 180°$	*Substitute 148 for m∠Q.*
$m\angle S = 32°$	*Subtract 148 from both sides.*

CHECK IT OUT!

4. Find the angle measures of *JKLM*.

THINK AND DISCUSS

1. Can ▱*ABCD* be inscribed in a circle? Why or why not?

2. An inscribed angle intercepts an arc that is $\frac{1}{4}$ of the circle. Explain how to find the measure of the inscribed angle.

3. GET ORGANIZED Copy and complete the graphic organizer. In each box write a definition, properties, an example, and a nonexample.

Definition	Properties
	Inscribed Angles
Example	Nonexample

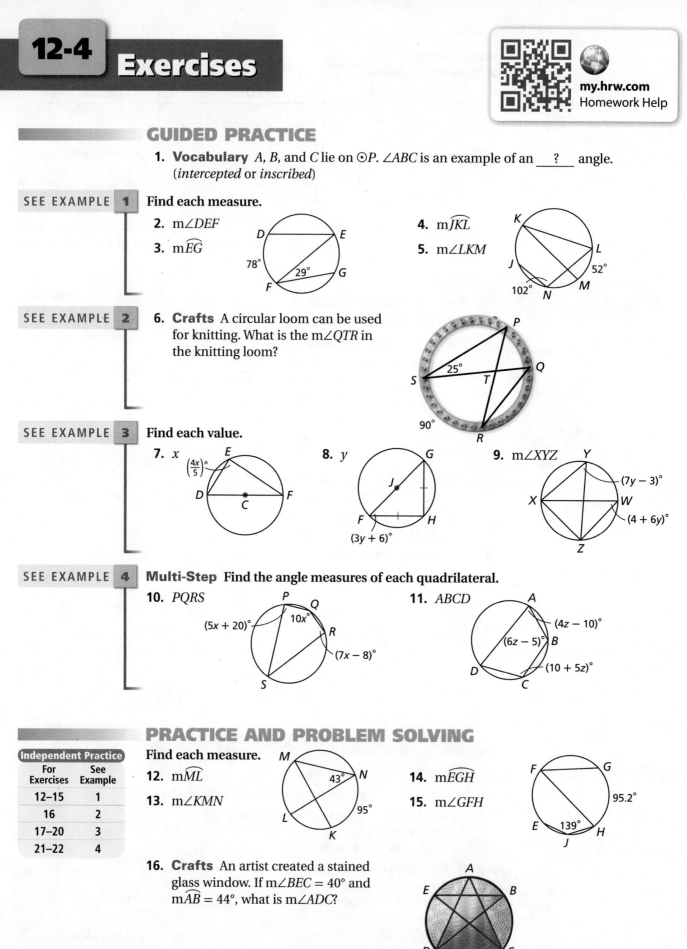

GUIDED PRACTICE

1. **Vocabulary** *A*, *B*, and *C* lie on ⊙*P*. ∠*ABC* is an example of an ____?____ angle. (*intercepted* or *inscribed*)

SEE EXAMPLE 1   **Find each measure.**

2. m∠*DEF*

3. m$\widehat{EG}$

4. m$\widehat{JKL}$

5. m∠*LKM*

SEE EXAMPLE 2

6. **Crafts** A circular loom can be used for knitting. What is the m∠*QTR* in the knitting loom?

SEE EXAMPLE 3   **Find each value.**

7. *x*

8. *y*

9. m∠*XYZ*

SEE EXAMPLE 4   **Multi-Step** Find the angle measures of each quadrilateral.

10. *PQRS*

11. *ABCD*

PRACTICE AND PROBLEM SOLVING

Find each measure.

12. m$\widehat{ML}$

13. m∠*KMN*

14. m$\widehat{EGH}$

15. m∠*GFH*

16. **Crafts** An artist created a stained glass window. If m∠*BEC* = 40° and m$\widehat{AB}$ = 44°, what is m∠*ADC*?

Algebra Find each value.

17. y

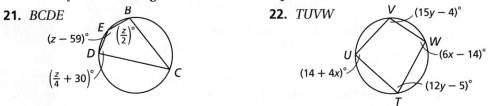

$(3y^2 - 18)°$

18. z

$30°$

$(6z - 4)°$

19. $m\widehat{AB}$

$(2x^2)°$

$10x°$

20. $m\angle MPN$

$(3x - 10)°$

$\left(\frac{11x}{3}\right)°$

H.O.T. Multi-Step Find the angle measures of each quadrilateral.

21. *BCDE*

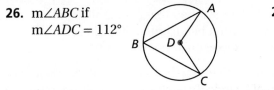

$(z - 59)°$

$\left(\frac{z}{2}\right)°$

$\left(\frac{z}{4} + 30\right)°$

22. *TUVW*

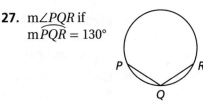

$(15y - 4)°$

$(6x - 14)°$

$(14 + 4x)°$

$(12y - 5)°$

Tell whether each statement is sometimes, always, or never true.

23. Two inscribed angles that intercept the same arc of a circle are congruent.

24. When a right triangle is inscribed in a circle, one of the legs of the triangle is a diameter of the circle.

25. A trapezoid can be inscribed in a circle.

H.O.T. Multi-Step Find each angle measure.

26. $m\angle ABC$ if
$m\angle ADC = 112°$

27. $m\angle PQR$ if
$m\widehat{PQR} = 130°$

28. Prove that the measure of a central angle subtended by a chord is twice the measure of the inscribed angle subtended by the chord.
Given: In $\odot H$ $\overline{JK}$ subtends $\angle JHK$ and $\angle JLK$.
Prove: $m\angle JHK = 2m\angle JLK$

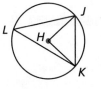

Real-World Connections

29. A Native American sand painting could be used to indicate the direction of sunrise on the winter and summer solstices. You can make this design by placing six equally spaced points around the circumference of a circle and connecting them as shown.

a. Find $m\angle BAC$.

b. Find $m\angle CDE$.

c. What type of triangle is $\triangle FBC$? Why?

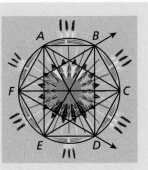

H.O.T. 30. **Given:** $\angle ABC$ is inscribed in $\odot X$ with X in the interior of $\angle ABC$.
Prove: $m\angle ABC = \frac{1}{2}m\widehat{AC}$
(*Hint:* Draw $\overrightarrow{BX}$ and use Case 1 of the Inscribed Angle Theorem.)

H.O.T. 31. **Given:** $\angle ABC$ is inscribed in $\odot X$ with X in the exterior of $\angle ABC$.
Prove: $m\angle ABC = \frac{1}{2}m\widehat{AC}$

H.O.T. 32. Prove Corollary 12-4-2.
Given: $\angle ACB$ and $\angle ADB$ intercept $\widehat{AB}$.
Prove: $\angle ACB \cong \angle ADB$

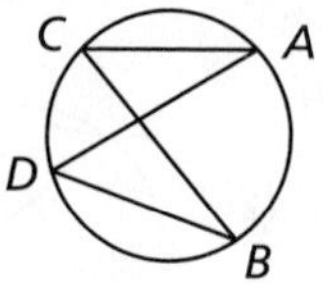

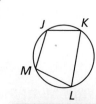

33. **Multi-Step** In the diagram, $m\widehat{JKL} = 198°$,
and $m\widehat{KLM} = 216°$. Find the measures of the angles
of quadrilateral $JKLM$.

34. **Critical Thinking** A rectangle $PQRS$ is inscribed
in a circle. What can you conclude about $\overline{PR}$? Explain.

35. **History** The diagram shows the Winchester Round
Table with inscribed $\triangle ABC$. The table may
have been made at the request of King Edward III,
who created the Order of the Garter as a return to
the Round Table and an order of chivalry.

a. Explain why $\overline{BC}$ must be a diameter of
the circle.

b. Find $m\widehat{AC}$.

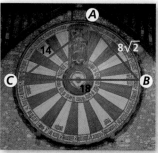

36. To inscribe an equilateral triangle in a circle, draw a
diameter $\overline{BC}$. Open the compass to the radius of the circle.
Place the point of the compass at C and make arcs
on the circle at D and E, as shown. Draw $\overline{BD}$, $\overline{BE}$, and
$\overline{DE}$. Explain why $\triangle BDE$ is an equilateral triangle.

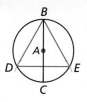

37. **Write About It** A student claimed that if a parallelogram
contains a 30° angle, it cannot be inscribed in a circle.
Do you agree or disagree? Explain.

38. **Construction** Circumscribe a circle about a triangle. (*Hint:* Follow the steps
for the construction of a circle through three given noncollinear points.)

TEST PREP

39. What is $m\angle BAC$?

(A) 38°   (C) 66°

(B) 43°   (D) 81°

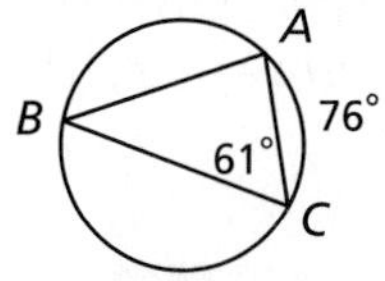

40. Equilateral $\triangle XCZ$ is inscribed in a circle.
If $\overline{CY}$ bisects $\angle C$, what is $m\widehat{XY}$?

(F) 15°   (G) 30°   (H) 60°   (J) 120°

41. Quadrilateral $ABCD$ is inscribed in a circle. The ratio of
$m\angle A$ to $m\angle C$ is 4:5. What is $m\angle A$?

(A) 20°   (B) 40°   (C) 80°   (D) 100°

42. Which of these angles has the greatest measure?

(F) $\angle STR$ (G) $\angle QPR$ (H) $\angle QSR$ (J) $\angle PQS$

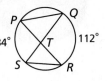

43. Prove that an inscribed angle subtends a semicircle if and only if the angle is a right angle. (*Hint:* There are two parts.)

44. Prove that if a quadrilateral is inscribed in a circle, then its opposite angles are supplementary. (*Hint:* There are two parts.)

45. Find m$\overarc{PQ}$ to the nearest degree.

46. Find m∠*ABD*.

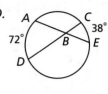

47. Construction To circumscribe an equilateral triangle about a circle, construct $\overline{AB}$ parallel to the horizontal diameter of the circle and tangent to the circle. Then use a 30°-60°-90° triangle to draw $\overline{AC}$ and $\overline{BC}$ so that they form 60° angles with $\overline{AB}$ and are tangent to the circle.

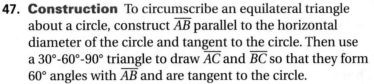

FOCUS ON MATHEMATICAL PRACTICES

48. Reasoning Solve for *x*. Explain your reasoning.

49. Precision A quadrilateral is inscribed in a circle. Its two diagonals are diameters of the circle. Classify the quadrilateral by its most precise name. Explain.

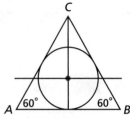

50. Analysis The inscribed angle has measure *x*°, *O* is the center of the circle, and $\overline{AP}$ and $\overline{BP}$ are tangent to the circle at *A* and *B*.

  a. What is m∠*O* in terms of *x*? Explain.

  b. What is m∠*P*? Explain.

  c. In ⊙*O*, *x* = 63. Find m∠*P*.

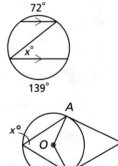

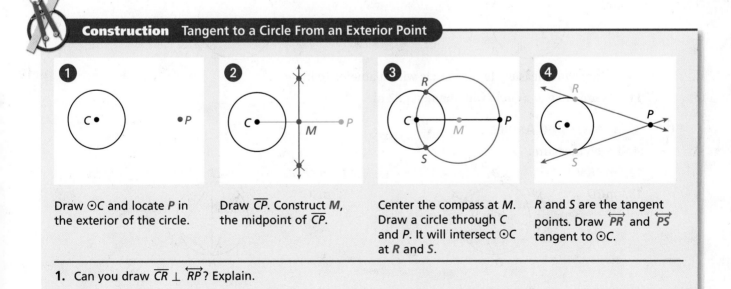

Construction Tangent to a Circle From an Exterior Point

1 Draw ⊙*C* and locate *P* in the exterior of the circle.

2 Draw $\overline{CP}$. Construct *M*, the midpoint of $\overline{CP}$.

3 Center the compass at *M*. Draw a circle through *C* and *P*. It will intersect ⊙*C* at *R* and *S*.

4 *R* and *S* are the tangent points. Draw $\overleftrightarrow{PR}$ and $\overleftrightarrow{PS}$ tangent to ⊙*C*.

1. Can you draw $\overline{CR} \perp \overleftrightarrow{RP}$? Explain.

Ready to Go On?

my.hrw.com
Assessment and Intervention

12-1 Lines That Intersect Circles

Identify each line or segment that intersects each circle.

1.

2.

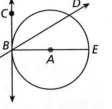

12-2 Arcs and Chords

Find each measure.

3. $\overset{\frown}{BC}$

4. $\overset{\frown}{BED}$

Find each length to the nearest tenth.

5. JK

6. NK

12-3 Sector Area and Arc Length

7. As part of an art project, Peter buys a circular piece of fabric and then cuts out the sector shown. What is the area of the sector to the nearest square centimeter?

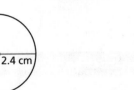

22 cm

Find each arc length. Give your answer in terms of π and rounded to the nearest hundredth.

8. $\overset{\frown}{AB}$

150°

4 ft

9. $\overset{\frown}{EF}$

75°

2.4 cm

10. an arc with measure 44° in a circle with diameter 10 in.

11. a semicircle in a circle with diameter 92 m

12-4 Inscribed Angles

Find each measure.

12. m∠BAC

13. m$\overset{\frown}{CD}$

102°

38°

14. m∠FGH

15. m$\overset{\frown}{JGF}$

25°

Selected Response

1. Find m$\widehat{CFB}$.

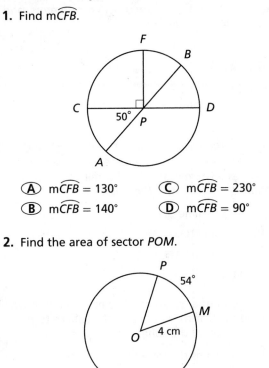

- **A** m$\widehat{CFB} = 130°$
- **C** m$\widehat{CFB} = 230°$
- **B** m$\widehat{CFB} = 140°$
- **D** m$\widehat{CFB} = 90°$

2. Find the area of sector *POM*.

- **F** 0.6π cm^2
- **H** 2.4π cm^2
- **G** 1.2π cm^2
- **J** 864π cm^2

3. Carlos plays vinyl records on a turntable that rotates through an angle of $\frac{3}{2}\pi$ radians in 1 second. How many revolutions does the turntable make in one minute?

- **A** $33\frac{1}{3}$ revolutions per minute
- **B** 45 revolutions per minute
- **C** 78 revolutions per minute
- **D** $16\frac{2}{3}$ revolutions per minute

4. A satellite orbits 50 miles above Earth's atmosphere. An astronaut works on the satellite and sees the sun rise over Earth. To the nearest mile, what is the distance from the astronaut to the horizon? (*Hint*: Earth's radius is about 4,000 miles.)

- **F** 634 mi
- **H** 630 mi
- **G** 402,500 mi
- **J** 397,500 mi

5. Solve for *x*.

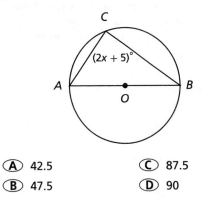

- **A** 42.5
- **C** 87.5
- **B** 47.5
- **D** 90

6. Identify the secant.

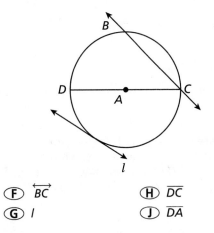

- **F** $\overleftrightarrow{BC}$
- **H** $\overline{DC}$
- **G** *l*
- **J** $\overline{DA}$

Mini-Task

7. $\overline{GK}$ is a diameter of the circle. Find m$\widehat{HK}$ to the nearest degree.

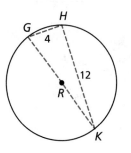

PARCC Assessment Readiness

Selected Response

1. The floor of a tent is a regular hexagon. If the side length of the tent floor is 5 feet, what is the area of the floor? Round to the nearest tenth.

- (A) 32.5 square feet
- (B) 65.0 square feet
- (C) 75.0 square feet
- (D) 129.9 square feet

2. Find the area of ⊙Q in terms of π.

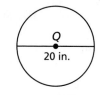

- (F) 400π in.²
- (G) 100 in.²
- (H) 200π in.²
- (J) 100π in.²

3. Find the area of a regular hexagon with side length 4 m. Round to the nearest tenth.

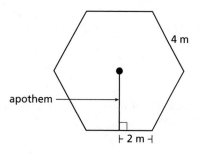

- (A) 83.1 m²
- (B) 24 m²
- (C) 41.6 m²
- (D) 20.8 m²

4. How many cubes with edge length 3 centimeters will fit in a box that is a rectangular prism with length 12 centimeters, width 15 centimeters, and height 24 centimeters?

- (F) 160
- (G) 480
- (H) 1440
- (J) 4320

5. Right △ABC with legs AB = 9 millimeters and BC = 12 millimeters is the base of a prism that has a volume of 513 cubic millimeters. What is the height of the prism?

- (A) 4.75 millimeters
- (B) 6 millimeters
- (C) 9.5 millimeters
- (D) 11 millimeters

6. The radius of a sphere is doubled. What happens to the ratio of the volume of the sphere to the surface area of the sphere?

- (F) It remains the same.
- (G) It is doubled.
- (H) It is increased by a factor of 4.
- (J) It is increased by a factor of 8.

7. To the nearest tenth of a cubic centimeter, what is the volume of a right regular octagonal prism with base edge length 4 centimeters and height 7 centimeters?

- (A) 180.3 cubic centimeters
- (B) 224.0 cubic centimeters
- (C) 270.4 cubic centimeters
- (D) 540.8 cubic centimeters

8. A square pyramid has a base area of 225 square meters and a volume of 2925 cubic meters. To the nearest meter, what is the height of the pyramid?

- Ⓕ 13 meters
- Ⓖ 26 meters
- Ⓗ 39 meters
- Ⓙ 52 meters

9. A cylinder has a height of 10 inches. The circumference of the base is 28.3 inches. To the nearest cubic inch, what is the volume of this cylinder?

- Ⓐ 141 cubic inches
- Ⓑ 283 cubic inches
- Ⓒ 637 cubic inches
- Ⓓ 2545 cubic inches

10. The volume of the smaller sphere is 288 cubic centimeters. Find the volume of the larger sphere.

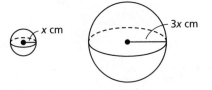

- Ⓕ 864 cubic centimeters
- Ⓖ 2,592 cubic centimeters
- Ⓗ 7,776 cubic centimeters
- Ⓙ 23,328 cubic centimeters

11. A cylinder has a volume of 24 cubic centimeters. The height of a cone with the same radius is two times the height of the cylinder. What is the volume of the cone?

- Ⓐ 8 cubic centimeters
- Ⓑ 12 cubic centimeters
- Ⓒ 16 cubic centimeters
- Ⓓ 48 cubic centimeters

12. The volume of a sphere is 288π cubic centimeters. What is its surface area, rounded to the nearest hundredth?

- Ⓕ 113.10 square centimeters
- Ⓖ 452.39 square centimeters
- Ⓗ 2842.45 square centimeters
- Ⓙ 8527.34 square centimeters

13. The circle graph shows the colors of automobiles sold at a car dealership. Find m$\overset{\frown}{CD}$.

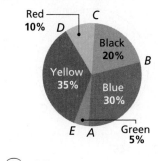

- Ⓐ m$\overset{\frown}{CD}$ = 36°
- Ⓑ m$\overset{\frown}{CD}$ = 10°
- Ⓒ m$\overset{\frown}{CD}$ = 170°
- Ⓓ m$\overset{\frown}{CD}$ = 20°

Use the diagram for Items 14–16.

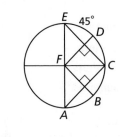

14. What is m$\overset{\frown}{BC}$?

- Ⓕ 36°
- Ⓖ 45°
- Ⓗ 54°
- Ⓙ 72°

15. If the length of $\overset{\frown}{ED}$ is 6π centimeters, what is the area of sector *EFD*?

- Ⓐ 20π square centimeters
- Ⓑ 72π square centimeters
- Ⓒ 120π square centimeters
- Ⓓ 240π square centimeters

16. Which of these line segments is NOT a chord of ⊙*F*?

- Ⓕ $\overline{EC}$
- Ⓖ $\overline{CA}$
- Ⓗ $\overline{AF}$
- Ⓙ $\overline{AE}$

17. A wheel from a motor has springs arranged as in the figure. Find m∠DOC.

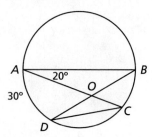

(A) m∠DOC = 145°

(B) m∠DOC = 150°

(C) m∠DOC = 140°

(D) m∠DOC = 130°

18. What is the arc length, rounded to the nearest hundredth, of a semicircle in a circle with radius 5 millimeters?

(F) 3.14 millimeters

(G) 6.28 millimeters

(H) 15.71 millimeters

(J) 31.42 millimeters

19. △ABC is inscribed in a circle with center P. Side $\overline{BC}$ passes through point P. Which of the following is true?

(A) $\overline{BC}$ is a radius of the circle.

(B) PA < PC

(C) m$\widehat{BAC}$ = 90°

(D) ∠BAC is a right angle.

20. A circle of radius r units has a central angle whose measure is 30°. What do you multiply r by to find the length of the arc intercepted by this central angle?

(F) 2π

(G) $\frac{\pi}{6}$

(H) $\frac{\pi}{12}$

(J) $\frac{1}{12}$

21. Circumscribed ∠ABC is tangent to ⊙P at points A and C. Which statement is not always true?

(A) $\overline{BC} \perp \overline{PC}$

(B) $\overline{BA} \perp \overline{PA}$

(C) $\overline{BC} \cong \overline{PC}$

(D) $\overline{BA} \cong \overline{BC}$

22. Which steps can you take to construct the tangent to ⊙M at point N on the circle?

(F) Draw $\overrightarrow{MN}$. Then construct the line through N that is perpendicular to $\overrightarrow{MN}$.

(G) Draw $\overrightarrow{MN}$. Then construct the line through M that is perpendicular to $\overrightarrow{MN}$.

(H) Draw $\overrightarrow{MN}$. Then construct the perpendicular bisector of $\overline{MN}$.

(J) Draw $\overleftrightarrow{MN}$ so that it intersects ⊙M at points P and N. Then construct the line through P that is perpendicular to $\overleftrightarrow{MN}$.

23. The illustration shows a fragment of a circular plate. AB = 8 in., and CD = 2 in. What is the diameter of the plate?

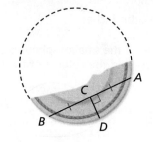

(A) 4 in.

(B) 5 in.

(C) 8 in.

(D) 10 in.

24. Which line of reasoning can be used to begin to derive the formula for the area of a circle with radius r and circumference C?

(F) Divide the circle into eight congruent sectors and treat each sector as a triangle with base $\frac{1}{8}C$ and height $\frac{1}{2}r$.

(G) Divide the circle into eight congruent sectors and arrange them to approximate a parallelogram with base C and height r.

(H) Divide the circle into eight congruent sectors and arrange them to approximate a parallelogram with base $\frac{1}{8}C$ and height r.

(J) Divide the circle into nine congruent sectors and arrange them to approximate a trapezoid with bases $\frac{5}{9}C$ and $\frac{4}{9}C$ and height r.

Mini-Tasks

25. Use the diagram to find the value of *x*. Show your work or explain in words how you determined your answer.

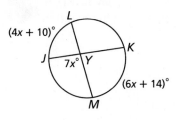

26. The figure shows the top view of a stack of cubes. The number on each cube represents the number of stacked cubes. The volume of each cube is 4 cubic inches. What is the volume of the three-dimensional figure formed by the cubes?

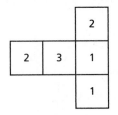

27. Find the volume of a cone with a base circumference of 15π m and a height 3 m less than twice the radius. Give your answer both in terms of π and rounded to the nearest tenth.

28. Find the area of segment *POM*. Round to the nearest tenth.

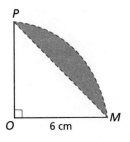

29. Find the volume of a sphere with diameter 24 ft. Give your answer in terms of π.

Performance Tasks

30. Zachary works for an outdoor supply company and is in charge of creating the specs for the tent shown below.

The tent will be in the shape of a regular hexagonal pyramid.

a. Zachary decides the distance from the center of the tent's base to any vertex of the base will be 8 feet and the distance from any vertex of the base to the top of the pyramid will be 10 feet. What is the height of the tent?

b. The base of the tent is a regular hexagon. What is the area of the base? Show your work, and round your answer to the nearest tenth of a square foot.

c. What is the volume of the tent? Show your work, and round your answer to the nearest cubic foot.

d. Zachary's boss says that if they keep the distance from the center to any vertex of the base 8 feet, and they keep the height of the tent the same, but they change the base of the tent to a regular polygon with 8 sides instead of 6 sides, the volume of the tent will increase by 33%. Is Zachary's boss correct? Explain why or why not.

31. The length of $\overline{TJ}$ is 10 inches and $m\widehat{JMB}$ is 225°.

Part A: Find the measure of $\angle JTB$. Find the circumference of circle *T*. Find the arc length of $\widehat{JB}$. Find the area of circle *T*. Find the area of sector *JTB*.

Part B: If the radius of circle *T* is doubled, will the area of sector *JTB* also double? Explain your reasoning by finding the area of sector *JTB* when the radius is doubled.

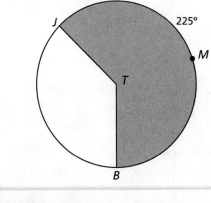

my.hrw.com
Online Assessment

Go online for updated, PARCC-aligned assessment readiness.

Are You Ready?

my.hrw.com
Assessment and Intervention

✓ Vocabulary

Match each term on the left with a definition on the right.

1. linear equation

2. solution set

3. transformation

4. x-intercept

A. a change in a function rule and its graph

B. the x-coordinate of the point where a graph crosses the x-axis

C. the group of values that make an equation or inequality true

D. a letter or symbol that represents a number

E. an equation whose graph is a line

✓ Squares and Square Roots

Simplify each expression.

5. 3.2^2

6. $\left(\dfrac{2}{5}\right)^2$

7. $\sqrt{121}$

8. $\sqrt{\dfrac{1}{16}}$

✓ Simplify Radical Expressions

Simplify each expression.

9. $\sqrt{72}$

10. $2\left(\sqrt{144} - 4\right)$

11. $\sqrt{33} \cdot \sqrt{75}$

12. $\dfrac{\sqrt{54}}{\sqrt{3}}$

✓ Multiply Binomials

Multiply.

13. $(x - 2)(x - 6)$

14. $(x + 9)(x - 9)$

15. $(x + 2)(x + 7)$

16. $(2x - 3)(5x + 1)$

✓ Solve Multi-Step Equations

Solve each equation.

17. $2x + 10 = -32$

18. $2x - (1 - x) = 2$

19. $\dfrac{2}{3}(x - 1) = 11$

20. $2(x + 5) - 5x = 1$

Career Readiness Mechanical Engineers

Mechanical engineers design, test, build, and maintain all sorts of mechanical devices, including engines, vehicles, and tools. They use their knowledge of physics and math, including quadratic functions, to design products to meet a given need. Most mechanical engineers have college degrees in mechanical engineering. They work in many different businesses from small machine shops to huge corporations, and may also work as consultants or in research.

UNIT 4

Extending the Number System

Online Edition

my.hrw.com

Access the complete online textbook, interactive features, and additional resources.

Multilingual Glossary

Enhance your math vocabulary with this illustrated online glossary in 13 languages.

Homework Help

Get instant help with tutorial videos, practice problems, and step-by-step solutions.

Portable Devices

On the Spot

Watch video tutorials anywhere, anytime with this app for iPhone® and iPad®.

eTextbook

Access your full textbook on your tablet or e-reader.

Chapter Resources

Scan with your smart phone to jump directly to the online edition.

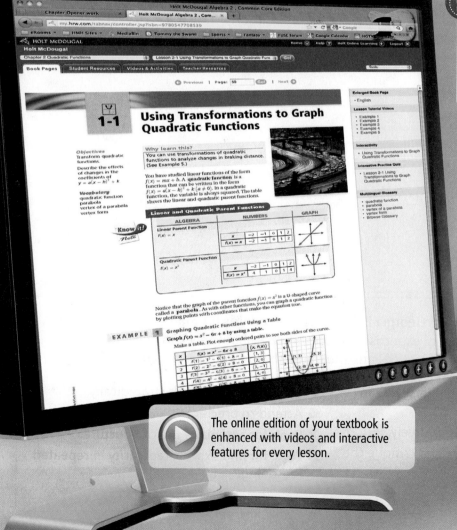

The online edition of your textbook is enhanced with videos and interactive features for every lesson.

UNIT 4

Module

13 Complex Numbers, Rational Exponents, and Closure

MCC9-12.N.CN.1

MCC9-12.N.CN.2,
MCC9-12.N.CN.3(+)

MCC9-12.N.RN.1, MCC9-12.N.RN.2

MCC9-12.N.RN.3, MCC9-12.A.APR.1

Contents

MATHEMATICAL PRACTICES
The Common Core Georgia Performance Standards for Mathematical Practice describe varieties of expertise that all students should seek to develop. Opportunities to develop these practices are integrated throughout this program.

1 Make sense of problems and persevere in solving them.

2 Reason abstractly and quantitatively.

3 Construct viable arguments and critique the reasoning of others.

4 Model with mathematics.

5 Use appropriate tools strategically.

6 Attend to precision.

7 Look for and make use of structure.

8 Look for and express regularity in repeated reasoning.

Unpacking the Standards

Understanding the standards and the vocabulary terms in the standards will help you know exactly what you are expected to learn in this chapter.

 MCC9-12.N.CN.2

Use the relation $i^2 = -1$ and the commutative, associative, and distributive properties to add, subtract, and multiply complex numbers.

Key Vocabulary

complex number (número complejo)
Any number that can be written as $a + bi$, where a and b are real numbers and $i = \sqrt{-1}$.

What It Means For You

Whole numbers, integers, real numbers, and so on, are all members of a larger set called the complex numbers. You can use the same properties of operations with all of them.

EXAMPLE

$$(4 + i)(3 - 2i)$$

$$= 4(3 - 2i) + i(3 - 2i) \qquad \textit{Distributive Property}$$

$$= 12 - 8i + 3i - 2i^2 \qquad \textit{Distributive Property}$$

$$= 12 - 8i + 3i + 2 \qquad \textit{i}^2 = -1$$

$$= (12 + 2) + (-8i + 3i) \qquad \textit{Associative/Commutative Properties}$$

$$= 14 - 5i \qquad \textit{Add real parts and imaginary parts.}$$

13-1 Complex Numbers and Roots

 Essential Question: How can you use complex numbers to solve quadratic equations that have no real-number solutions?

Objectives
Define and use imaginary and complex numbers.

Solve quadratic equations with complex roots.

Vocabulary
imaginary unit
imaginary number
complex number
real part
imaginary part
complex conjugate

Why learn this?

Complex numbers can be used to describe the zeros of quadratic functions that have no real zeros. (See Example 4.)

You can see in the graph of $f(x) = x^2 + 1$ below that f has no real zeros. If you solve the corresponding equation $0 = x^2 + 1$, you find that $x = \pm\sqrt{-1}$, which has no *real* solutions.

However, you can find solutions if you define the square root of negative numbers, which is why *imaginary numbers* were invented. The **imaginary unit** i is defined as $\sqrt{-1}$. You can use the imaginary unit to write the square root of any negative number.

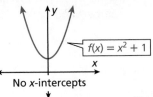

No x-intercepts

Know it!
Note

Imaginary Numbers

WORDS	NUMBERS	ALGEBRA
An **imaginary number** is the square root of a negative number.	$\sqrt{-1} = i$	If b is a positive real number,
Imaginary numbers can be written in the form bi, where b is a real number and i is the imaginary unit.	$\sqrt{-2} = \sqrt{-1}\sqrt{2} = i\sqrt{2}$ $\sqrt{-4} = \sqrt{-1}\sqrt{4} = 2i$	then $\sqrt{-b} = i\sqrt{b}$ and $\sqrt{-b^2} = bi$.
The square of an imaginary number is the original negative number.	$\left(\sqrt{-1}\right)^2 = i^2 = -1$	$\left(\sqrt{-b}\right)^2 = -b$

COMMON CORE GPS
MCC9-12.N.CN.1

EXAMPLE **1** **Simplifying Square Roots of Negative Numbers**

Express each number in terms of i.

A $3\sqrt{-16}$

$\quad 3\sqrt{(16)(-1)}$ — *Factor out −1.*

$\quad 3\sqrt{16}\sqrt{-1}$ — *Product Property*

$\quad 3 \cdot 4\sqrt{-1}$ — *Simplify.*

$\quad 12\sqrt{-1}$ — *Multiply.*

$\quad 12i$ — *Express in terms of i.*

B $-\sqrt{-75}$

$\quad -\sqrt{(75)(-1)}$ — *Factor out −1.*

$\quad -\sqrt{75}\sqrt{-1}$ — *Product Property*

$\quad -\sqrt{25}\sqrt{3}\sqrt{-1}$ — *Product Property*

$\quad -5\sqrt{3}\sqrt{-1}$ — *Simplify.*

$\quad -5\sqrt{3}i = -5i\sqrt{3}$ — *Express in terms of i.*

my.hrw.com

Online Video Tutor

CHECK IT OUT! Express each number in terms of i.

1a. $\sqrt{-12}$ **1b.** $2\sqrt{-36}$ **1c.** $-\frac{1}{3}\sqrt{-63}$

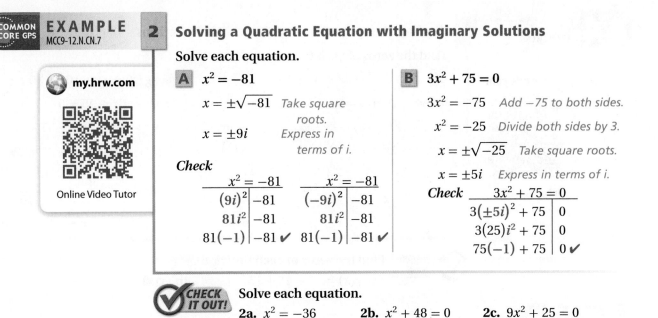

COMMON CORE GPS EXAMPLE **2** MCC9-12.N.CN.7

Solving a Quadratic Equation with Imaginary Solutions

Solve each equation.

my.hrw.com

Online Video Tutor

A $x^2 = -81$

$x = \pm\sqrt{-81}$ *Take square roots.*

$x = \pm 9i$ *Express in terms of i.*

Check

$x^2 = -81$		$x^2 = -81$	
$(9i)^2$	-81	$(-9i)^2$	-81
$81i^2$	-81	$81i^2$	-81
$81(-1)$	-81 ✔	$81(-1)$	-81 ✔

B $3x^2 + 75 = 0$

$3x^2 = -75$ *Add −75 to both sides.*

$x^2 = -25$ *Divide both sides by 3.*

$x = \pm\sqrt{-25}$ *Take square roots.*

$x = \pm 5i$ *Express in terms of i.*

Check

$3x^2 + 75 = 0$	
$3(\pm 5i)^2 + 75$	0
$3(25)i^2 + 75$	0
$75(-1) + 75$	0 ✔

CHECK IT OUT! Solve each equation.

2a. $x^2 = -36$ 　　　　 **2b.** $x^2 + 48 = 0$ 　　　　 **2c.** $9x^2 + 25 = 0$

A **complex number** is a number that can be written in the form $a + bi$, where a and b are real numbers and $i = \sqrt{-1}$. The set of real numbers is a subset of the set of complex numbers $\mathbb{C}$.

Every complex number has a **real part** a and an **imaginary part** b.

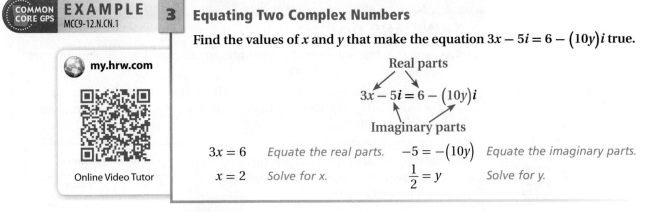

Real numbers are complex numbers where $b = 0$. Imaginary numbers are complex numbers where $a = 0$ and $b \neq 0$. These are sometimes called *pure imaginary numbers*.

Two complex numbers are equal if and only if their real parts are equal and their imaginary parts are equal.

COMMON CORE GPS EXAMPLE **3** MCC9-12.N.CN.1

Equating Two Complex Numbers

Find the values of x and y that make the equation $3x - 5i = 6 - (10y)i$ true.

my.hrw.com

Online Video Tutor

Real parts

$$3x - 5i = 6 - (10y)i$$

Imaginary parts

$3x = 6$ *Equate the real parts.* 　　 $-5 = -(10y)$ *Equate the imaginary parts.*

$x = 2$ *Solve for x.* 　　 $\dfrac{1}{2} = y$ *Solve for y.*

CHECK IT OUT! Find the values of x and y that make each equation true.

3a. $2x - 6i = -8 + (20y)i$ 　　　　 **3b.** $-8 + (6y)i = 5x - i\sqrt{6}$

13-1 Complex Numbers and Roots　**435**

EXAMPLE **4**

Finding Complex Zeros of Quadratic Functions

Find the zeros of each function.

A $f(x) = x^2 - 2x + 5$

$x^2 - 2x + 5 = 0$	*Set equal to 0.*
$x^2 - 2x + \blacksquare = -5 + \blacksquare$	*Rewrite.*
$x^2 - 2x + 1 = -5 + 1$	*Add $\left(\frac{b}{2}\right)^2$.*
$(x - 1)^2 = -4$	*Factor.*
$x - 1 = \pm\sqrt{-4}$	*Take square roots.*
$x = 1 \pm 2i$	*Simplify.*

B $g(x) = x^2 + 10x + 35$

$x^2 + 10x + 35 = 0$

$x^2 + 10x + \blacksquare = -35 + \blacksquare$

$x^2 + 10x + 25 = -35 + 25$

$(x + 5)^2 = -10$

$x + 5 = \pm\sqrt{-10}$

$x = -5 \pm i\sqrt{10}$

my.hrw.com

Online Video Tutor

CHECK IT OUT! Find the zeros of each function.

4a. $f(x) = x^2 + 4x + 13$ **4b.** $g(x) = x^2 - 8x + 18$

Helpful Hint

When given one complex root, you can always find the other by finding its conjugate.

The solutions $-5 + i\sqrt{10}$ and $-5 - i\sqrt{10}$ in Example 4B are related. These solutions are a *complex conjugate* pair. Their real parts are equal and their imaginary parts are opposites. The **complex conjugate** of any complex number $a + bi$ is the complex number $a - bi$.

If a quadratic equation with real coefficients has nonreal roots, those roots are complex conjugates.

EXAMPLE **5**

Finding Complex Conjugates

Find each complex conjugate.

A $2i - 15$

$-15 + 2i$	*Write as $a + bi$.*
$-15 - 2i$	*Find $a - bi$.*

B $-4i$

$0 + (-4)i$ *Write as $a + bi$.*

$0 - (-4)i$ *Find $a - bi$.*

$4i$ *Simplify.*

my.hrw.com

Online Video Tutor

CHECK IT OUT! Find each complex conjugate.

5a. $9 - i$ **5b.** $i + \sqrt{3}$ **5c.** $-8i$

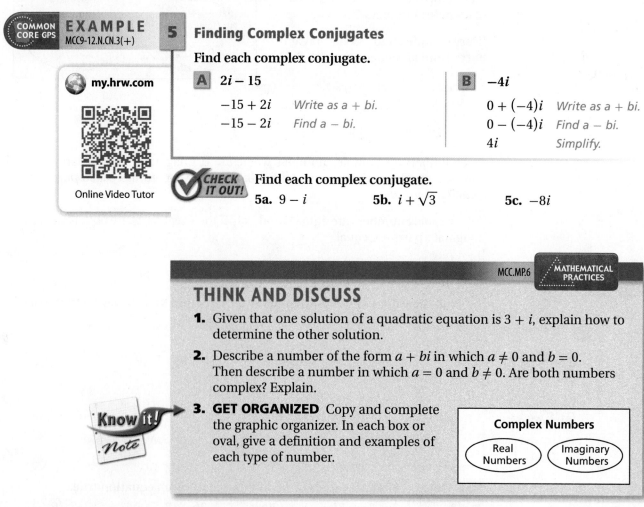

MCC.MP.6   MATHEMATICAL PRACTICES

THINK AND DISCUSS

1. Given that one solution of a quadratic equation is $3 + i$, explain how to determine the other solution.

2. Describe a number of the form $a + bi$ in which $a \neq 0$ and $b = 0$. Then describe a number in which $a = 0$ and $b \neq 0$. Are both numbers complex? Explain.

3. GET ORGANIZED Copy and complete the graphic organizer. In each box or oval, give a definition and examples of each type of number.

Know it! Note

Complex Numbers

Real Numbers   Imaginary Numbers

GUIDED PRACTICE

1. **Vocabulary** The number 7 is the ___?___ part of the complex number $\sqrt{5} + 7i$. (*real* or *imaginary*)

SEE EXAMPLE 1

Express each number in terms of i.

2. $5\sqrt{-100}$ 3. $\frac{1}{2}\sqrt{-16}$ 4. $-\sqrt{-32}$ 5. $\sqrt{-144}$

SEE EXAMPLE 2

Solve each equation.

6. $x^2 = -9$ 7. $2x^2 + 72 = 0$ 8. $4x^2 = -16$ 9. $x^2 + 121 = 0$

SEE EXAMPLE 3

Find the values of x and y that make each equation true.

10. $-2x + 6i = (-24y)i - 14$ 11. $-4 + (y)i = -12x - i + 8$

SEE EXAMPLE 4

Find the zeros of each function.

12. $f(x) = x^2 - 12x + 45$ 13. $g(x) = x^2 + 6x + 34$

SEE EXAMPLE 5

Find each complex conjugate.

14. $-9i$ 15. $\sqrt{5} + 5i$ 16. $8i - 3$ 17. $6 + i\sqrt{2}$

PRACTICE AND PROBLEM SOLVING

Independent Practice	
For Exercises	See Example
18–21	1
22–25	2
26–27	3
28–31	4
32–35	5

my.hrw.com

Online Extra Practice

Express each number in terms of i.

18. $8\sqrt{-4}$ 19. $-\frac{1}{3}\sqrt{-90}$ 20. $6\sqrt{-12}$ 21. $\sqrt{-50}$

Solve each equation.

22. $x^2 + 49 = 0$ 23. $5x^2 = -80$ 24. $3x^2 + 27 = 0$ 25. $\frac{1}{2}x^2 = -32$

Find the values of x and y that make each equation true.

26. $9x + (y)i - 5 = -12i + 4$ 27. $5(x - 1) + (3y)i = -15i - 20$

Find the zeros of each function.

28. $f(x) = x^2 + 2x + 3$ 29. $g(x) = 4x^2 - 3x + 1$

30. $f(x) = x^2 + 4x + 8$ 31. $g(x) = 3x^2 - 6x + 10$

Find each complex conjugate.

32. i 33. $-\frac{\sqrt{3}}{2} - 2i$ 34. $-2.5i + 1$ 35. $\frac{i}{10} - 1$

H.O.T. 36. **What if...?** A carnival game asks participants to strike a spring with a hammer. The spring shoots a puck upward toward a bell. If the puck strikes the bell, the participant wins a prize. Suppose that a participant strikes the spring and shoots the puck according to the model $d(t) = 16t^2 - 32t + 18$, where d is the distance in feet between the puck and the bell and t is the time in seconds since the puck was struck. Is it possible for the participant to win a prize? Explain your answer.

18 ft

Given each solution to a quadratic equation, find the other solution.

37. $1 + 14i$ **38.** $\frac{5}{7}i$ **39.** $4i - 2\sqrt{5}$

40. $-12 - i$ **41.** $9 - i\sqrt{2}$ **42.** $-\frac{17i}{3}$

Find the values of c and d that make each equation true.

43. $2ci + 1 = -d + 6 - ci$ **44.** $c + 3ci = 4 + di$ **45.** $c^2 + 4i = d + di$

Solve each equation.

46. $8x^2 = -8$ **47.** $\frac{1}{3}x^2 = -27$ **48.** $2x^2 + 12.5 = 0$

49. $\frac{1}{2}x^2 + 72 = 0$ **50.** $x^2 = -30$ **51.** $2x^2 + 16 = 0$

52. $x^2 - 4x + 8 = 0$ **53.** $x^2 + 10x + 29 = 0$ **54.** $x^2 - 12x + 44 = 0$

55. $x^2 + 2x = -5$ **56.** $x^2 + 18 = -6x$ **57.** $-149 = x^2 - 24x$

Tell whether each statement is always, sometimes, or never true. If sometimes true, give examples to support your answer.

58. A real number is an imaginary number.

59. An imaginary number is a complex number.

60. A rational number is a complex number.

61. A complex number is an imaginary number.

62. An integer is a complex number.

63. Quadratic equations have no real solutions.

64. Quadratic equations have roots that are real and complex.

65. Roots of quadratic equations are conjugate pairs.

Find the zeros of each function.

66. $f(x) = x^2 - 10x + 26$ **67.** $g(x) = x^2 + 2x + 17$ **68.** $h(x) = x^2 - 10x + 50$

69. $f(x) = x^2 + 16x + 73$ **70.** $g(x) = x^2 - 10x + 37$ **71.** $h(x) = x^2 - 16x + 68$

72. Critical Thinking Can you determine the zeros of $f(x) = x^2 + 64$ by using a graph? Explain why or why not.

73. Critical Thinking What is the complex conjugate of a real number?

H.O.T. **74. Write About It** Explain the procedures you can use to solve for nonreal complex roots.

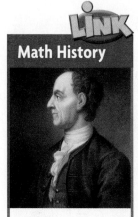
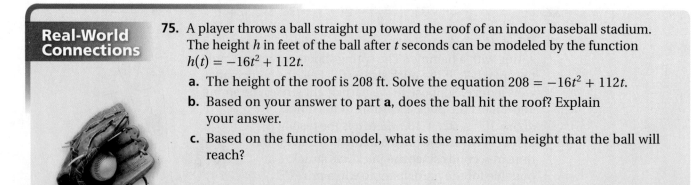

Real-World Connections

75. A player throws a ball straight up toward the roof of an indoor baseball stadium. The height h in feet of the ball after t seconds can be modeled by the function $h(t) = -16t^2 + 112t$.

   a. The height of the roof is 208 ft. Solve the equation $208 = -16t^2 + 112t$.

   b. Based on your answer to part **a**, does the ball hit the roof? Explain your answer.

   c. Based on the function model, what is the maximum height that the ball will reach?

76. What is the complex conjugate of $-2 + i$?

    Ⓐ $2 + i$ Ⓑ $2 - i$ Ⓒ $i - 2$ Ⓓ $-2 - i$

77. Express $\sqrt{-225}$ in terms of i.

    Ⓕ $15i$ Ⓖ $-15i$ Ⓗ $i\sqrt{15}$ Ⓙ $-i\sqrt{15}$

78. Find the zeros of $f(x) = x^2 - 2x + 17$.

    Ⓐ $1 \pm 4i$ Ⓑ $4 \pm i$ Ⓒ $-1 \pm 4i$ Ⓓ $-4 \pm i$

79. What value of c makes the equation $3 - 4i - 5 = (9 + ci) - 11$ true?

    Ⓕ -2 Ⓖ -4 Ⓗ 2 Ⓙ 4

80. Which of the following equations has roots of $-6i$ and $6i$?

    Ⓐ $-\dfrac{1}{6}x^2 = 6$ Ⓒ $\dfrac{1}{4}x^2 = 9$

    Ⓑ $x^2 - 30 = 6$ Ⓓ $20 - x^2 = -16$

81. Short Response Explain the types of solutions that equations of the form $x^2 = a$ have when $a < 0$ and when $a > 0$.

CHALLENGE AND EXTEND

82. Find the complex number $a + bi$ such that $5a + 3b = 1$ and $-5b = 7 + 4a$.

H.O.T. 83. Can a quadratic equation have only one real number root? only one imaginary root? only one complex root? Explain.

H.O.T. 84. Given the general form of a quadratic equation $x^2 + bx + c = 0$, determine the effect of each condition on the solutions.

    a. $b = 0$ **b.** $c \le 0$ **c.** $c > 0$

    d. What is needed for the solutions to have imaginary parts?

FOCUS ON MATHEMATICAL PRACTICES

H.O.T. 85. Analysis A quadratic equation has two complex solutions and the y-coordinate of its vertex is negative. From this information, what else do you know about the equation?

H.O.T. 86. Patterns For each of the following graphs, find the number of zeros it has and type of number each zero is. If it has real solutions, are they positive or negative?

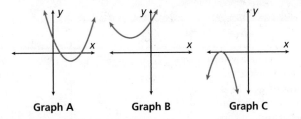

    Graph A   **Graph B**   **Graph C**

H.O.T. 87. Make a Conjecture Find the zeros and axes of symmetry of the functions $f(x) = x^2 - 4x + 6$, $g(x) = 3x^2 + x + 1$, and $h(x) = -x^2 - 2x - 5$. What relationship do you notice?

13-2 Operations with Complex Numbers

 Essential Question: How do you add, subtract, multiply, and divide complex numbers?

Objective
Perform operations with complex numbers.

Vocabulary
complex plane
absolute value of a
   complex number

> **Why learn this?**
> Complex numbers can be used in formulas to create patterns called fractals. (See Exercise 84.)

Just as you can represent real numbers graphically as points on a number line, you can represent complex numbers in a special coordinate plane.

The **complex plane** is a set of coordinate axes in which the horizontal axis represents real numbers and the vertical axis represents imaginary numbers.

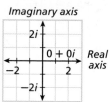

COMMON CORE GPS
EXAMPLE 1
MCC9-12.N.CN.4(+)

Graphing Complex Numbers

Graph each complex number.

A $-3 + 0i$

B $-3i$

C $4 + 3i$

D $-2 + 4i$

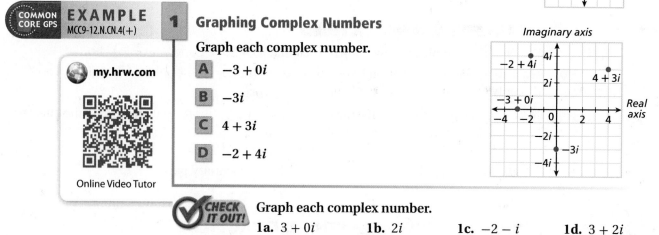

my.hrw.com

Online Video Tutor

CHECK IT OUT! Graph each complex number.

1a. $3 + 0i$ **1b.** $2i$ **1c.** $-2 - i$ **1d.** $3 + 2i$

Recall that the absolute value of a real number is its distance from 0 on the real axis, which is also a number line. Similarly, the absolute value of an imaginary number is its distance from 0 along the imaginary axis.

Know it! Note

Helpful Hint

The real axis corresponds to the x-axis, and the imaginary axis corresponds to the y-axis. Think of $a + bi$ as $x + yi$.

Absolute Value of a Complex Number

WORDS	ALGEBRA	EXAMPLE
The **absolute value** of a complex number $a + bi$ is the distance from the origin to the point (a, b) in the complex plane, and is denoted $\lvert a + bi \rvert$.	$\lvert a + bi \rvert = \sqrt{a^2 + b^2}$	*Imaginary axis* $\lvert 3 + 4i \rvert = \sqrt{3^2 + 4^2}$ $= \sqrt{9 + 16}$ $= 5$

© Gregory Sams/SPL/Photo Researchers, Inc

EXAMPLE 2

Determining the Absolute Value of Complex Numbers

Find each absolute value.

A $|-9 + i|$

$|-9 + 1i|$

$\sqrt{(-9)^2 + 1^2}$

$\sqrt{81 + 1}$

$\sqrt{82}$

B $|6|$

$|6 + 0i|$

$\sqrt{6^2 + 0^2}$

$\sqrt{36}$

6

C $|-4i|$

$|0 + (-4)i|$

$\sqrt{0^2 + (-4)^2}$

$\sqrt{16}$

4

CHECK IT OUT!

Find each absolute value.

2a. $|1 - 2i|$ **2b.** $\left|-\dfrac{1}{2}\right|$ **2c.** $|23i|$

Adding and subtracting complex numbers is similar to adding and subtracting variable expressions with like terms. Simply combine the real parts, and combine the imaginary parts.

The set of complex numbers has all the properties of the set of real numbers. So you can use the Commutative, Associative, and Distributive Properties to simplify complex number expressions.

EXAMPLE 3

Adding and Subtracting Complex Numbers

Add or subtract. Write the result in the form $a + bi$.

A $(-2 + 4i) + (3 - 11i)$

$(-2 + 3) + (4i - 11i)$ *Associative and Commutative Properties*

$1 - 7i$ *Add real parts and imaginary parts.*

B $(4 - i) - (5 + 8i)$

$(4 - i) - 5 - 8i$ *Distributive Property*

$(4 - 5) + (-i - 8i)$ *Associative and Commutative Properties*

$-1 - 9i$ *Add real parts and imaginary parts.*

C $(6 - 2i) + (-6 + 2i)$

$(6 - 6) + (-2i + 2i)$ *Associative and Commutative Properties*

$0 + 0i$ *Add real parts and imaginary parts.*

0

D $(10 + 3i) - (10 - 4i)$

$(10 + 3i) - 10 - (-4i)$ *Distributive Property*

$(10 - 10) + (3i + 4i)$ *Associative and Commutative Properties*

$0 + 7i$ *Add real parts and imaginary parts.*

$7i$

Helpful Hint

Complex numbers also have additive inverses. The additive inverse of $a + bi$ is $-(a + bi)$, or $-a - bi$.

CHECK IT OUT!

Add or subtract. Write the result in the form $a + bi$.

3a. $(-3 + 5i) + (-6i)$ **3b.** $2i - (3 + 5i)$ **3c.** $(4 + 3i) + (4 - 3i)$

You can also add complex numbers by using coordinate geometry.

EXAMPLE 4

Adding Complex Numbers on the Complex Plane

Find $(4 + 3i) + (-2 + i)$ by graphing on the complex plane.

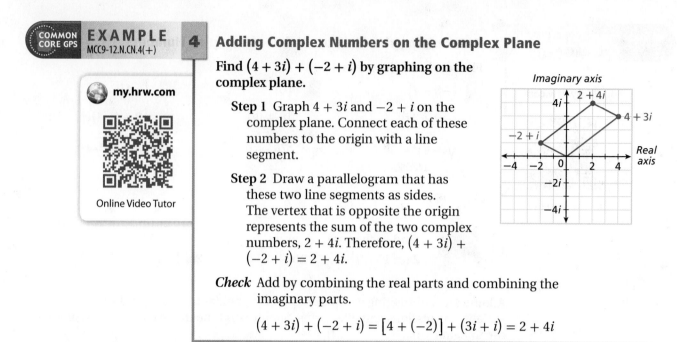

Step 1 Graph $4 + 3i$ and $-2 + i$ on the complex plane. Connect each of these numbers to the origin with a line segment.

Step 2 Draw a parallelogram that has these two line segments as sides. The vertex that is opposite the origin represents the sum of the two complex numbers, $2 + 4i$. Therefore, $(4 + 3i) + (-2 + i) = 2 + 4i$.

Check Add by combining the real parts and combining the imaginary parts.

$$(4 + 3i) + (-2 + i) = [4 + (-2)] + (3i + i) = 2 + 4i$$

CHECK IT OUT! Find each sum by graphing on the complex plane.
4a. $(3 + 4i) + (1 - 3i)$ **4b.** $(-4 - i) + (2 - 2i)$

my.hrw.com

Online Video Tutor

You can multiply complex numbers by using the Distributive Property and treating the imaginary parts as like terms. Simplify by using the fact $i^2 = -1$.

EXAMPLE 5

Multiplying Complex Numbers

Multiply. Write the result in the form $a + bi$.

A $2i(3 - 5i)$

$6i - 10i^2$ *Distribute.*

$6i - 10(-1)$ *Use $i^2 = -1$.*

$10 + 6i$ *Write in a + bi form.*

B $(5 - 6i)(4 - 3i)$

$20 - 15i - 24i + 18i^2$ *Multiply.*

$20 - 39i + 18(-1)$ *Use $i^2 = -1$.*

$2 - 39i$

C $(7 + 2i)(7 - 2i)$

$49 - 14i + 14i - 4i^2$ *Multiply.*

$49 - 4(-1)$ *Use $i^2 = -1$.*

53

D $(6i)(6i)$

$36i^2$

$36(-1)$ *Use $i^2 = -1$.*

-36

my.hrw.com

Online Video Tutor

CHECK IT OUT! Multiply. Write the result in the form $a + bi$.
5a. $2i(3 - 5i)$ **5b.** $(4 - 4i)(6 - i)$ **5c.** $(3 + 2i)(3 - 2i)$

Helpful Hint

Notice the repeating pattern in each row of the table. The pattern allows you to express any power of i as one of four possible values: i, -1, $-i$, or 1.

The imaginary unit i can be raised to higher powers as shown below.

Powers of i		
$i^1 = i$	$i^5 = i^4 \cdot i = 1 \cdot i = i$	$i^9 = i$
$i^2 = -1$	$i^6 = i^4 \cdot i^2 = 1 \cdot (-1) = -1$	$i^{10} = -1$
$i^3 = i^2 \cdot i = -1 \cdot i = -i$	$i^7 = i^4 \cdot i^3 = 1 \cdot (-i) = -i$	$i^{11} = -i$
$i^4 = i^2 \cdot i^2 = -1 \cdot (-1) = 1$	$i^8 = i^4 \cdot i^4 = 1 \cdot 1 = 1$	$i^{12} = 1$

EXAMPLE **6** MCC9-12.N.CN.2

Evaluating Powers of *i*

A **Simplify** $-3i^{12}$.

$$-3i^{12} = -3(i^2)^6$$ *Rewrite i^{12} as a power of i^2.*

$$= -3(-1)^6 = -3(1) = -3$$ *Simplify.*

B **Simplify** i^{25}.

$$i^{25} = i \cdot i^{24}$$ *Rewrite as a product of i and an even power of i.*

$$= i \cdot (i^2)^{12}$$ *Rewrite i^{24} as a power of i^2.*

$$= i \cdot (-1)^{12} = i \cdot 1 = i$$ *Simplify.*

CHECK IT OUT!   **6a.** Simplify $\frac{1}{2}i^7$.   **6b.** Simplify i^{42}.

Remember!

The complex conjugate of a complex number $a + bi$ is $a - bi$.

Recall that expressions in simplest form cannot have square roots in the denominator. Because the imaginary unit represents a square root, you must rationalize any denominator that contains an imaginary unit. To do this, multiply the numerator and denominator by the complex conjugate of the denominator.

EXAMPLE **7** MCC9-12.N.CN.3(+)

Dividing Complex Numbers

A **Simplify** $\dfrac{3 + 7i}{8i}$.

$$\frac{3 + 7i}{8i}\left(\frac{-8i}{-8i}\right)$$ *Multiply by the conjugate.*

$$\frac{-24i - 56i^2}{-64i^2}$$ *Distribute.*

$$\frac{-24i + 56}{64}$$ *Use $i^2 = -1$.*

$$\frac{-3i + 7}{8} = \frac{7}{8} - \frac{3}{8}i$$ *Simplify.*

B **Simplify** $\dfrac{5 + i}{2 - 4i}$.

$$\frac{5 + i}{2 - 4i}\left(\frac{2 + 4i}{2 + 4i}\right)$$

$$\frac{10 + 20i + 2i + 4i^2}{4 + 8i - 8i - 16i^2}$$

$$\frac{10 + 22i - 4}{4 + 16}$$

$$\frac{6 + 22i}{20} = \frac{3}{10} + \frac{11}{10}i$$

CHECK IT OUT!   **7a.** Simplify $\dfrac{3 + 8i}{-i}$.   **7b.** Simplify $\dfrac{3 - i}{2 - i}$.

MCC.MP.2   MATHEMATICAL PRACTICES

THINK AND DISCUSS

1. Explain when a complex number $a + bi$ and its conjugate are equal.

2. Find the product $(a + bi)(c + di)$, and identify which terms in the product are real and which are imaginary.

3. **GET ORGANIZED** Copy and complete the graphic organizer. In each box, give an example.

Know it! Note

Absolute value	Adding
Complex Numbers	
Multiplying	Conjugates

GUIDED PRACTICE

1. **Vocabulary** In the complex number plane, the horizontal axis represents __?__ numbers, and the vertical axis represents __?__ numbers. (*real, irrational, or imaginary*)

SEE EXAMPLE 1 Graph each complex number.

2. 4 　　　　　　3. $-i$ 　　　　　　4. $3 + 2i$ 　　　　　　5. $-2 - 3i$

SEE EXAMPLE 2 Find each absolute value.

6. $|4 - 5i|$ 　　　　7. $|-33.3|$ 　　　　8. $|-9i|$

9. $|5 + 12i|$ 　　　10. $|-1 + i|$ 　　　11. $|15i|$

SEE EXAMPLE 3 Add or subtract. Write the result in the form $a + bi$.

12. $(2 + 5i) + (-2 + 5i)$ 　　13. $(-1 - 8i) + (4 + 3i)$ 　　14. $(1 - 3i) - (7 + i)$

15. $(4 - 8i) + (-13 + 23i)$ 　　16. $(6 + 17i) - (18 - 9i)$ 　　17. $(-30 + i) - (-2 + 20i)$

SEE EXAMPLE 4 Find each sum by graphing on the complex plane.

18. $(3 + 4i) + (-2 - 4i)$ 　　19. $(-2 - 5i) + (-1 + 4i)$ 　　20. $(-4 - 4i) + (4 + 2i)$

SEE EXAMPLE 5 Multiply. Write the result in the form $a + bi$.

21. $(1 - 2i)(1 + 2i)$ 　　22. $3i(5 + 2i)$ 　　23. $(9 + i)(4 - i)$

24. $(6 + 8i)(5 - 4i)$ 　　25. $(3 + i)^2$ 　　26. $(-4 - 5i)(2 + 10i)$

SEE EXAMPLE 6 Simplify.

27. $-i^9$ 　　　　28. $2i^{15}$ 　　　　29. i^{30}

SEE EXAMPLE 7 30. $\dfrac{5 - 4i}{i}$ 　　31. $\dfrac{11 - 5i}{2 - 4i}$ 　　32. $\dfrac{8 + 2i}{5 + i}$

33. $\dfrac{17}{4 + i}$ 　　34. $\dfrac{45 - 3i}{7 - 8i}$ 　　35. $\dfrac{-3 - 12i}{6i}$

PRACTICE AND PROBLEM SOLVING

Independent Practice	
For Exercises	See Example
36–39	1
40–45	2
46–51	3
52–54	4
55–60	5
61–63	6
64–69	7

Graph each complex number.

36. -3 　　　　37. $-2.5i$ 　　　　38. $1 + i$ 　　　　39. $4 - 3i$

Find each absolute value.

40. $|2 + 3i|$ 　　　41. $|-18|$ 　　　42. $\left|\dfrac{4}{5}i\right|$

43. $|6 - 8i|$ 　　　44. $|-0.5i|$ 　　　45. $|10 - 4i|$

Add or subtract. Write the result in the form $a + bi$.

46. $(8 - 9i) - (-2 - i)$ 　　47. $4i - (11 - 3i)$ 　　48. $(4 - 2i) + (-9 - 5i)$

49. $(13 + 6i) + (15 + 35i)$ 　　50. $(3 - i) - (-3 + i)$ 　　51. $-16 + (12 + 9i)$

Find each sum by graphing on the complex plane.

52. $(4 + i) + (-3i)$ 　　53. $(5 + 4i) + (-1 + 2i)$ 　　54. $(-3 - 3i) + (4 - 3i)$

my.hrw.com

Online Extra Practice

Multiply. Write the result in the form $a + bi$.

55. $-12i(-1 + 4i)$ **56.** $(3 - 5i)(2 + 9i)$ **57.** $(7 + 2i)(7 - 2i)$

58. $(5 + 6i)^2$ **59.** $(7 - 5i)(-3 + 9i)$ **60.** $-4(8 + 12i)$

Simplify.

61. i^{27} **62.** $-i^{11}$ **63.** $5i^{10}$

64. $\dfrac{2 - 3i}{i}$ **65.** $\dfrac{5 - 2i}{3 + i}$ **66.** $\dfrac{3}{-1 - 5i}$

67. $\dfrac{19 + 9i}{5 + i}$ **68.** $\dfrac{8 + 4i}{7 + i}$ **69.** $\dfrac{6 + 3i}{2 - 2i}$

Write the complex number represented by each point on the graph.

70. A

71. B

72. C

73. D

74. E

Imaginary axis

Real axis

Find the absolute value of each complex number.

75. $3 - i$ **76.** $7i$ **77.** $-2 - 6i$

78. $-1 - 8i$ **79.** 0 **80.** $5 + 4i$

81. $\dfrac{3}{2} - \dfrac{1}{2}i$ **82.** $5 - i\sqrt{3}$ **83.** $2\sqrt{2} - i\sqrt{3}$

Fractals

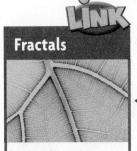

Fractals are self-similar, which means that smaller parts of a fractal are similar to the fractal as a whole. Many objects in nature, such as the veins of leaves and snow crystals, also exhibit self-similarity. As a result, scientists can use fractals to model these objects.

84. Fractals Fractals are patterns produced using complex numbers and the repetition of a mathematical formula. Substitute the first number into the formula. Then take the result, put it back into the formula, and so on. Each complex number produced by the formula can be used to assign a color to a pixel on a computer screen. The result is an image such as the one at right. Many common fractals are based on the Julia Set, whose formula is $Z_{n+1} = (Z_n)^2 + c$, where c is a constant.

a. Find Z_2 using $Z_2 = (Z_1)^2 + 0.25$. Let $Z_1 = 0.5 + 0.6i$.

b. Find Z_3 using $Z_3 = (Z_2)^2 + 0.25$. Use Z_2 that you obtained in part **a**.

c. Find Z_4 using $Z_4 = (Z_3)^2 + 0.25$. Use Z_3 that you obtained in part **b**.

Simplify. Write the result in the form $a + bi$.

85. $(3.5 + 5.2i) + (6 - 2.3i)$ **86.** $6i - (4 + 5i)$ **87.** $(-2.3 + i) - (7.4 - 0.3i)$

88. $(-8 - 11i) + (-1 + i)$ **89.** $i(4 + i)$ **90.** $(6 - 5i)^2$

91. $(-2 - 3i)^2$ **92.** $(5 + 7i)(5 - 7i)$ **93.** $(2 - i)(2 + i)(2 - i)$

94. $3 - i^{11}$ **95.** $i^{52} - i^{48}$ **96.** $i^{35} - i^{24} + i^{18}$

97. $\dfrac{12 + i}{i}$ **98.** $\dfrac{18 - 3i}{i}$ **99.** $\dfrac{4 + 2i}{6 + i}$

100. $\dfrac{1 + i}{-2 + 4i}$ **101.** $\dfrac{4}{2 - 3i}$ **102.** $\dfrac{6}{\sqrt{2} - i}$

HOT **Multi-Step** *Impedance* is a measure of the opposition of a circuit to an electric current. Electrical engineers find it convenient to model impedance Z with complex numbers. In a parallel AC circuit with two impedances Z_1 and Z_2, the *equivalent* or total impedance in ohms can be determined by using the formula $Z_{eq} = \dfrac{Z_1 Z_2}{Z_1 + Z_2}$.

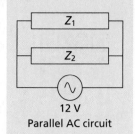

12 V
Parallel AC circuit

103. Find the equivalent impedance Z_{eq} for $Z_1 = 3 + 2i$ and $Z_2 = 1 - 2i$ arranged in a parallel AC circuit.

104. Find the equivalent impedance Z_{eq} for $Z_1 = 2 + 2i$ and $Z_2 = 4 - i$ arranged in a parallel AC circuit.

Tell whether each statement is sometimes, always, or never true. If the statement is sometimes true, give an example and a counterexample. If the statement is never true, give a counterexample.

105. The sum of any complex number $a + bi$ and its conjugate is a real number.

106. The difference between any complex number $a + bi$ $(b \neq 0)$ and its conjugate is a real number.

107. The product of any complex number $a + bi$ $(a \neq 0)$ and its conjugate is a positive real number.

108. The product of any two imaginary numbers bi $(b \neq 0)$ and di $(d \neq 0)$ is a positive real number.

109. ///**ERROR ANALYSIS**/// Two attempts to simplify $\dfrac{3}{2 + i}$ are shown. Which is incorrect? Explain the error.

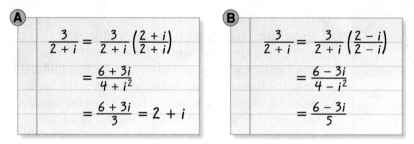

A

$$\frac{3}{2 + i} = \frac{3}{2 + i}\left(\frac{2 + i}{2 + i}\right)$$

$$= \frac{6 + 3i}{4 + i^2}$$

$$= \frac{6 + 3i}{3} = 2 + i$$

B

$$\frac{3}{2 + i} = \frac{3}{2 + i}\left(\frac{2 - i}{2 - i}\right)$$

$$= \frac{6 - 3i}{4 - i^2}$$

$$= \frac{6 - 3i}{5}$$

HOT **110. Critical Thinking** Why are the absolute value of a complex number and the absolute value of its conjugate equal? Use a graph to justify your answer.

111. Write About It Discuss how the difference of two squares, $a^2 - b^2 = (a + b)(a - b)$, relates to the product of a complex number and its conjugate.

112. Multi-Step You have seen how to graph sums of complex numbers on the complex plane.

a. Find three pairs of complex numbers whose sum is $4 + 4i$.

b. Graph each of the sums on the same complex plane.

c. Describe the results of your graph.

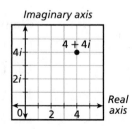

TEST PREP

Use the graph for Exercises 113–114.

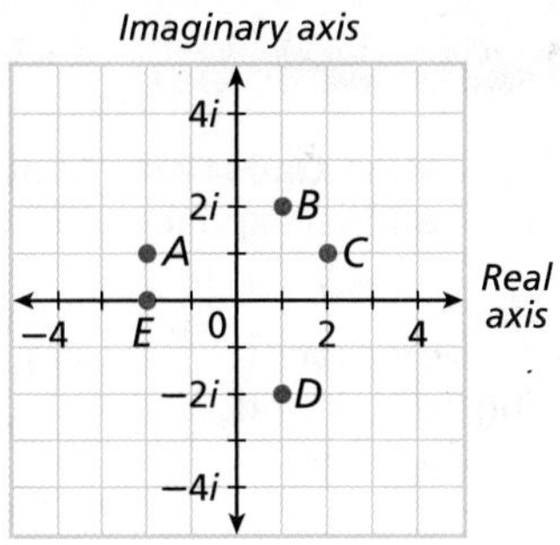

113. Which point on the graph represents $1 - 2i$?

    Ⓐ A   Ⓒ C

    Ⓑ B   Ⓓ D

114. What is the value of the complex number represented in the graph by E?

    Ⓕ -2 Ⓗ $-2i$

    Ⓖ 2 Ⓙ $2i$

Imaginary axis

115. Which expression is equivalent to $(2 - 5i) - (2 + 5i)$?

    Ⓐ $10i$ Ⓑ $4 + 10i$ Ⓒ $-10i$ Ⓓ $4 - 10i$

116. Which expression is equivalent to $(-5 + 3i)^2$?

    Ⓕ $16 - 15i$ Ⓖ $16 - 30i$ Ⓗ $34 - 15i$ Ⓙ $34 - 30i$

CHALLENGE AND EXTEND

117. Consider the powers of i.

    a. Complete the table, and look for a pattern.

$i^1 = $ ▧	$i^0 = $ ▧	$i^{-1} = $ ▧	$i^{-2} = $ ▧	$i^{-3} = $ ▧	$i^{-4} = $ ▧	$i^{-5} = $ ▧

    b. Explain the pattern that you observed for i raised to negative powers. What are the only possible values of i raised to a negative integer power?

    c. Simplify i^{-12}, i^{-37}, and i^{-90}.

H.O.T. Find the general form of the result for each complex operation.

118. $(a + bi)(c + di)$ 119. $\dfrac{a + bi}{c + di}$

MATHEMATICAL PRACTICES

FOCUS ON MATHEMATICAL PRACTICES

H.O.T. 120. **Justify** Lulu said that the sum of a complex number and its conjugate is 0. Do you agree? Justify your answer.

H.O.T. 121. **Modeling** Where is the sum of a complex number and its conjugate located on the complex plane?

H.O.T. 122. **Proof** Use any two complex numbers z and w, such as $z = 2 + 4i$ and $w = 5 - i$, as directed.

    a. Find $z \cdot w$, the product of your complex numbers.

    b. Find the conjugate of the product in part **a**.

    c. Find the conjugate of z and of w.

    d. Find the product of the two conjugates in part **c**. How does this result compare with part **b**?

    e. Using the results in parts **a–d**, make a conjecture. Then prove your conjecture using algebraic representations.

Radicals and Rational Exponents

 Essential Question: What is the connection between radical expressions and rational exponents?

Objective
Simplify expressions involving radicals and rational exponents.

Vocabulary
index
simplest radical form
rational exponent

In general, a is an nth root of b if $a^n = b$. The nth root of a number b can be written with a radical as $\sqrt[n]{b}$, where n is the **index** of the radical and b is the radicand. For example, $6^3 = 216$, so the cube root of 216 is 6 and you write $\sqrt[3]{216} = 6$.

When a number has more than one real root, the radical indicates only the positive, or principal, root. For example, 5 and -5 are both fourth roots of 625, since $5^4 = 625$ and $(-5)^4 = 625$, but $\sqrt[4]{625} = 5$.

 Know it!
·Note

Properties of nth Roots

For positive real numbers a and b:

WORDS	NUMBERS	ALGEBRA
Product Property of Roots The nth root of a product is equal to the product of the nth roots.	$\sqrt[4]{32} = \sqrt[4]{16} \cdot \sqrt[4]{2} = 2\sqrt[4]{2}$	$\sqrt[n]{ab} = \sqrt[n]{a} \cdot \sqrt[n]{b}$
Quotient Property of Roots The nth root of a quotient is equal to the quotient of the nth roots.	$\sqrt[3]{\dfrac{8}{27}} = \dfrac{\sqrt[3]{8}}{\sqrt[3]{27}} = \dfrac{2}{3}$	$\sqrt[n]{\dfrac{a}{b}} = \dfrac{\sqrt[n]{a}}{\sqrt[n]{b}}$

When a problem involves radicals, you may be asked to write your answer in simplest radical form. An expression is in **simplest radical form** if:

• the radicand has no perfect nth-power factors other than 1;

• the radicand contains no fractions;

• there are no radicals in any denominator.

COMMON CORE GPS Prep for MCC9-12.N.RN.2

EXAMPLE **1** **Simplifying Radical Expressions**

Simplify each expression. Assume all variables are positive.

Remember!

A radical sign with no index represents a square root. For example, $\sqrt{x} = \sqrt[2]{x}$.

A $\sqrt[3]{250}$

$\sqrt[3]{125 \cdot 2}$ *Factor out a perfect cube.*

$\sqrt[3]{125} \cdot \sqrt[3]{2}$ *Product Property*

$5\sqrt[3]{2}$ *Simplify.*

B $\sqrt{\dfrac{x^6}{3}}$

$\dfrac{\sqrt{x^6}}{\sqrt{3}}$ *Quotient Property*

$\dfrac{x^3}{\sqrt{3}}$ $\sqrt{x^6} = \sqrt{(x^3)^2} = x^3$

$\dfrac{x^3}{\sqrt{3}} \cdot \dfrac{\sqrt{3}}{\sqrt{3}}$ *Rationalize the denominator.*

$\dfrac{x^3\sqrt{3}}{3}$ *Simplify.*

✓ **CHECK IT OUT!** Simplify each expression. Assume all variables are positive.

1a. $\sqrt[4]{48z^4}$

1b. $\sqrt[3]{\dfrac{x^4}{2}}$

A **rational exponent** is an exponent that can be expressed as $\frac{m}{n}$, where m and n are integers and $n \neq 0$.

In order to understand what is meant by an expression with a rational exponent, such as $4^{\frac{1}{5}}$, notice that the standard properties of exponents should still apply. Therefore,

$$\left(4^{\frac{1}{5}}\right)^5 = 4^{\frac{1}{5} \cdot 5} = 4^1.$$

In other words, $4^{\frac{1}{5}}$ must be the fifth root of 4, or $\sqrt[5]{4}$. By similar reasoning, $4^{\frac{2}{5}}$ should equal $\left(4^{\frac{1}{5}}\right)^2$, or $\left(\sqrt[5]{4}\right)^2$. These ideas are summarized below.

Know it! Note

Rational Exponents

For any natural number n and integer m:

WORDS	NUMBERS	ALGEBRA
The exponent $\frac{1}{n}$ indicates the nth root.	$8^{\frac{1}{3}} = \sqrt[3]{8} = 2$	$a^{\frac{1}{n}} = \sqrt[n]{a}$
The exponent $\frac{m}{n}$ indicates the nth root raised to the mth power.	$16^{\frac{3}{4}} = \left(\sqrt[4]{16}\right)^3 = 2^3 = 8$	$a^{\frac{m}{n}} = \left(\sqrt[n]{a}\right)^m = \sqrt[n]{a^m}$

COMMON CORE GPS MCC9-12.N.RN.2 **EXAMPLE 2**

Writing Expressions in Radical Form

Write each expression in radical form, and simplify.

A $64^{\frac{2}{3}}$

$\left(\sqrt[3]{64}\right)^2$ *Write with a radical.*

$(4)^2$ *Evaluate the root.*

16 *Evaluate the power.*

B $(-8)^{\frac{5}{3}}$

$\left(\sqrt[3]{-8}\right)^5$ *Write with a radical.*

$(-2)^5$ *Evaluate the root.*

-32 *Evaluate the power.*

 CHECK IT OUT! Write each expression in radical form, and simplify.

2a. $(-243)^{\frac{1}{5}}$ **2b.** $17^{\frac{3}{4}}$

COMMON CORE GPS MCC9-12.N.RN.2 **EXAMPLE 3**

Writing Expressions with Rational Exponents

Write each expression by using rational exponents. Assume all variables are positive.

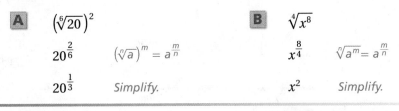

A $\left(\sqrt[6]{20}\right)^2$

$20^{\frac{2}{6}}$ $\left(\sqrt[n]{a}\right)^m = a^{\frac{m}{n}}$

$20^{\frac{1}{3}}$ *Simplify.*

B $\sqrt[4]{x^8}$

$x^{\frac{8}{4}}$ $\sqrt[n]{a^m} = a^{\frac{m}{n}}$

x^2 *Simplify.*

CHECK IT OUT! Write each expression by using rational exponents. Assume all variables are positive.

3a. $\left(\sqrt[4]{x}\right)^2$ **3b.** $\sqrt[5]{13^3}$

Rational exponents have the same properties as integer exponents. These properties are useful when you simplify expressions with rational exponents.

Know it! Note

Properties of Rational Exponents

For all nonzero real numbers a and b and rational numbers m and n:

WORDS	NUMBERS	ALGEBRA
Product of Powers Property To multiply powers with the same base, add the exponents.	$7^{\frac{1}{2}} \cdot 7^{\frac{3}{2}} = 7^{\frac{1}{2}+\frac{3}{2}} = 7^2 = 49$	$a^m \cdot a^n = a^{m+n}$
Quotient of Powers Property To divide powers with the same base, subtract the exponents.	$\dfrac{8^{\frac{2}{3}}}{8^{\frac{1}{3}}} = 8^{\frac{2}{3}-\frac{1}{3}} = 8^{\frac{1}{3}} = 2$	$\dfrac{a^m}{a^n} = a^{m-n}$
Power of a Power Property To raise one power to another, multiply the exponents.	$\left(6^{\frac{3}{4}}\right)^4 = 6^{\frac{3}{4}\cdot 4} = 6^3 = 216$	$(a^m)^n = a^{m \cdot n}$
Power of a Product Property To find the power of a product, distribute the exponent.	$(8 \cdot 125)^{\frac{1}{3}} = 8^{\frac{1}{3}} \cdot 125^{\frac{1}{3}} = 2 \cdot 5 = 10$	$(ab)^m = a^m b^m$
Power of a Quotient Property To find the power of a quotient, distribute the exponent.	$\left(\dfrac{8}{27}\right)^{\frac{1}{3}} = \dfrac{8^{\frac{1}{3}}}{27^{\frac{1}{3}}} = \dfrac{2}{3}$	$\left(\dfrac{a}{b}\right)^m = \dfrac{a^m}{b^m}$

COMMON CORE GPS MCC9-12.N.RN.2

EXAMPLE 4 Simplifying Expressions with Rational Exponents

Simplify each expression. Assume all variables are positive.

A $9^{\frac{1}{4}} \cdot 9^{\frac{7}{4}}$

$9^{\frac{1}{4}+\frac{7}{4}}$ *Product of Powers*

9^2 *Simplify.*

81 *Evaluate the power.*

B $\dfrac{x^{\frac{7}{2}}}{x^{\frac{1}{2}}}$

$x^{\frac{7}{2}-\frac{1}{2}}$ *Quotient of Powers*

x^3 *Simplify.*

C $\dfrac{27^{\frac{1}{3}}}{27^{\frac{2}{3}}}$

$27^{\frac{1}{3}-\frac{2}{3}}$ *Quotient of Powers*

$27^{-\frac{1}{3}}$ *Simplify.*

$\dfrac{1}{27^{\frac{1}{3}}}$ *Negative Exponent Property*

$\dfrac{1}{3}$ $27^{\frac{1}{3}} = \sqrt[3]{27} = 3$

D $\left(x^3 y^{\frac{1}{3}}\right)^3 \sqrt[4]{x^4}$

$\left(x^3 y^{\frac{1}{3}}\right)^3 \cdot x$ $\sqrt[4]{x^4} = x$

$\left(x^{3 \cdot 3}\right) \cdot \left(y^{\frac{1}{3} \cdot 3}\right) \cdot x$ *Power of a Product*

$x^9 \cdot y \cdot x$ *Simplify.*

$x^{9+1} \cdot y$ *Product of Powers*

$x^{10} y$ *Simplify.*

CHECK IT OUT! Simplify each expression. Assume all variables are positive.

4a. $\left(100^{\frac{1}{8}}\right)^4$

4b. $\dfrac{8^{\frac{2}{3}}}{8^{\frac{5}{3}}}$

4c. $x^{\frac{3}{8}} \cdot x^{\frac{1}{2}} \cdot x^{\frac{1}{8}}$

4d. $\left(x^6 y^8\right)^{\frac{1}{2}} \sqrt[3]{y^6}$

Exercises

Simplify each expression. Assume all variables are positive.

1. $\sqrt[4]{32}$ **2.** $\sqrt[5]{64}$ **3.** $\sqrt[3]{24}$ **4.** $\sqrt[3]{32}$

5. $\sqrt{16x^4}$ **6.** $\sqrt[3]{27y^3}$ **7.** $\sqrt[3]{-8x^4}$ **8.** $\sqrt[5]{y^6}$

9. $\sqrt[3]{\dfrac{x^9}{27}}$ **10.** $\sqrt[3]{\dfrac{16}{x^3}}$ **11.** $\sqrt{\dfrac{50}{z}}$ **12.** $\sqrt[3]{\dfrac{x^{15}}{7}}$

Write each expression in radical form, and simplify.

13. $49^{\frac{1}{2}}$ **14.** $8^{\frac{2}{3}}$ **15.** $16^{\frac{3}{4}}$ **16.** $27^{\frac{4}{3}}$

17. $7^{\frac{1}{3}}$ **18.** $5^{\frac{2}{3}}$ **19.** $(-27)^{\frac{2}{3}}$ **20.** $(-32)^{\frac{3}{5}}$

21. $(-1000)^{\frac{2}{3}}$ **22.** $-36^{\frac{3}{2}}$ **23.** $(-1)^{\frac{1}{3}}$ **24.** $4^{\frac{5}{2}}$

Write each expression by using rational exponents. Assume all variables are positive.

25. $\sqrt[5]{11^2}$ **26.** $\sqrt[4]{x^3}$ **27.** $\sqrt[8]{y^2}$ **28.** $\sqrt[5]{7}$

29. $\sqrt[3]{9^6}$ **30.** $\left(\sqrt[4]{2}\right)^2$ **31.** $\sqrt{4^3}$ **32.** $\left(\sqrt{y}\right)^5$

33. $\sqrt[4]{7^8}$ **34.** $\left(\sqrt[6]{z}\right)^2$ **35.** $\sqrt[6]{m^4}$ **36.** $-\sqrt{19^7}$

Simplify each expression. Assume all variables are positive.

37. $8^{\frac{1}{2}} \cdot 8^{\frac{3}{2}}$ **38.** $n^{\frac{1}{3}} \cdot n^{\frac{5}{3}}$ **39.** $16^{\frac{1}{4}} \cdot 16^{\frac{1}{4}} \cdot 16^{\frac{3}{4}}$ **40.** $x^{\frac{1}{2}} \cdot x^3$

41. $\left(5^{\frac{1}{2}}\right)^6$ **42.** $\left(7^{\frac{3}{2}}\right)^{\frac{2}{3}}$ **43.** $\dfrac{49^{\frac{1}{4}}}{49^{\frac{3}{4}}}$ **44.** $\dfrac{25^{\frac{5}{4}}}{25^{\frac{1}{4}}}$

45. $8^{-\frac{1}{3}}$ **46.** $\left(\dfrac{1}{25}\right)^{-\frac{1}{2}}$ **47.** $\left(x^3 z^9\right)^{\frac{2}{3}}$ **48.** $\left(x^{\frac{1}{2}} y^2\right)^4 \sqrt[3]{y^3}$

49. $\left(m^4 n^2\right)^{\frac{1}{2}} \sqrt{m^2 n^2}$ **50.** $\dfrac{7^{\frac{1}{2}}}{\sqrt{7}}$ **51.** $\left(y^{\frac{2}{3}}\right) \sqrt[3]{y^9}$ **52.** $\dfrac{z^{\frac{1}{3}}}{\sqrt[3]{z^2}}$

53. The formula $r = \left(\dfrac{3V}{4\pi}\right)^{\frac{1}{3}}$ gives the radius r, in inches, of a sphere that has a volume of V cubic inches. Use the formula to find the radius of a sphere that has a volume of 36π in³.

54. For which values of n is $2^{\frac{n}{2}}$ an integer? What are the integer values of $2^{\frac{n}{2}}$?

55. **Write About It** Describe two different ways to simplify the expression $\sqrt[3]{7^6}$. Which method is easier? Why?

56. **Critical Thinking** Explain how to solve the equation $16^{\frac{x}{2}} = 64$.

EXTENSION Closure

? **Essential Question:** Under what operations are various sets of numbers and the set of polynomials closed?

Objective
Identify sets and the operations under which they are closed.

Vocabulary
set
element
subset
closure

A **set** is a collection of objects. Each object in a set is called an **element** of the set. A set may have no elements, a finite number of elements, or an infinite number of elements. For example, $N = \{1, 2, 3, \ldots\}$ describes the set of natural numbers.

A **subset** is a set contained entirely within another set. For example, $A = \{2, 6, 11, 50\}$ is a subset of set N above. Also, N is a subset of the set of real numbers. The diagram below shows other subsets of the real numbers.

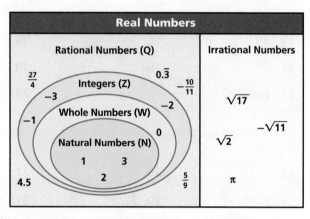

A set of numbers is *closed*, or has **closure**, under a given operation if the result of the operation on any two numbers in the set is also in the set. For example, the set of even numbers is closed under addition, since the sum of two even numbers is also an even number.

Closure Properties of the Real Numbers

WORDS	NUMBERS	ALGEBRA
The real numbers are closed under addition, subtraction, and multiplication.	$6.1 + \sqrt{2}$, $6.1 - \sqrt{2}$, and $6.1 \times \sqrt{2}$ are all real numbers.	For real numbers a and b, $a + b$, $a - b$, and ab are real numbers.

COMMON CORE GPS
Prep. for MCC9-12.N.RN.3

EXAMPLE 1 Determining Closure of Sets of Numbers

A Is the set $\{-1, 0, 1\}$ closed under multiplication?

Multiply each pair of elements in the set. Check whether each product is in the set.

$-1 \times (-1) = 1 \checkmark \qquad -1 \times 1 = -1 \checkmark \qquad 0 \times 1 = 0 \checkmark$
$\qquad -1 \times 0 = 0 \checkmark \qquad 0 \times 0 = 0 \checkmark \qquad 1 \times 1 = 1 \checkmark$

The set $\{-1, 0, 1\}$ is closed under multiplication.

B Show that the set of irrational numbers is not closed under multiplication.

Find two irrational numbers whose product is not an irrational number.

$$\sqrt{2} \times \sqrt{2} = \sqrt{4} = 2 \qquad \text{2 is not irrational.}$$

The set of irrational numbers is not closed under multiplication.

Helpful Hint

Remember the Commutative Property of Multiplication.

If $1 \times (-1) = -1$, then $-1 \times 1 = -1$. Only one instance needs to be tested.

1. Show that the set of whole numbers is not closed under subtraction.

The set of polynomials also has closure under certain operations. The closure properties of polynomials are similar to the closure properties of real numbers.

Closure Properties of Polynomials		
WORDS	**EXAMPLES**	**ALGEBRA**
The set of all polynomials is closed under addition, subtraction, and multiplication.	$x^2 + (x + 1)$, $x^2 - (x + 1)$ and $x^2(x + 1)$ are all polynomials.	For polynomials p and q, $p + q$, $p - q$, and pq are all polynomials.

COMMON CORE GPS
MCC9-12.A.APR.1

EXAMPLE 2 Determining Closure of Sets of Polynomials

A Is the set $\{-x, 0, x\}$ closed under addition?

Add each pair of elements in the set. Check whether each sum is in the set.

$-x + 0 = -x$ ✓ $-x + (-x) = -2x$ ✗ $0 + 0 = 0$ ✓
$-x + x = 0$ ✓ $0 + x = x$ ✓ $x + x = 2x$ ✗

The set $\{-x, 0, x\}$ is not closed under addition.

B Show that the set of polynomials is not closed under division.

Find two polynomials, a and b, such that their quotient, $\frac{a}{b}$, is not a polynomial. Try $a = x + 1$ and $b = 0$.

$$\frac{x + 1}{0} = \text{undefined} \qquad \textit{The result is not a polynomial.}$$

The set of polynomials is not closed under division.

2. Is the set $\{x, x + 1, x^2 - 1\}$ closed under division?

EXTENSION

Exercises

my.hrw.com
Homework Help

Determine whether the following sets are closed under addition, subtraction, multiplication, and division.

1. $\{-1, 0, 1\}$

2. $\{0, 8\}$

3. $\{x^2, 1\}$

4. $\{0, x\}$

5. $\{-x^3, 1, x^3\}$

6. $\{-x, 1, x + 1\}$

7. $\{-1, 1\}$

8. $\{-1, 0, x\}$

9. $\{-1, x + 3, 1\}$

10. The set of whole numbers

11. The set of natural numbers

12. The set of integers

13. Polynomials without a constant term

14. The set of rational numbers

15. The set of real numbers

16. Write About It Compare closure properties under the four operations for the set of rational numbers and the set of irrational numbers.

17. Proof Prove that the sum of a rational number and an irrational number is irrational, and that the product of a nonzero rational number and an irrational number is irrational. (*Hint:* Assume the opposite of what you are trying to prove and show that this leads to a contradiction.)

Ready to Go On?

my.hrw.com
Assessment and Intervention

13-1 Complex Numbers and Roots

Solve each equation.

1. $3x^2 = -48$

2. $x^2 - 20x = -125$

3. $x^2 - 8x + 30 = 0$

4. $x^2 = -81$

5. $6x^2 + 150 = 0$

6. $x^2 + 6x + 10 = 0$

7. $x^2 + 12x + 45 = 0$

8. $x^2 - 14x + 75 = 0$

9. $x^2 - 22x + 133 = 0$

13-2 Operations with Complex Numbers

Find each absolute value.

10. $\left|-6i\right|$

11. $\left|3 + 4i\right|$

12. $\left|2 - i\right|$

Perform each indicated operation, and write the result in the form $a + bi$.

13. $(3 - 5i) - (6 - i)$

14. $(-6 + 4i) + (7 - 2i)$

15. $3i(4 + i)$

16. $(3 + i)(5 - i)$

17. $(1 - 4i)(1 + 4i)$

18. $3i^{15}$

19. $\dfrac{2 - 7i}{-i}$

20. $\dfrac{3 - i}{4 - 2i}$

21. $\left|-3i\right|$

22. $\left|4 - 2i\right|$

23. $\left|12 - 16i\right|$

24. $\left|7i\right|$

25. $(1 + 5i) + (6 - i)$

26. $(9 + 4i) - (3 + 2i)$

27. $(5 - i) - (11 - i)$

28. $-5i(3 - 4i)$

29. $(5 - 2i)(6 + 8i)$

30. $(3 + 2i)(3 - 2i)$

31. $(4 + i)(1 - 5i)$

32. $(-7 + 4i)(3 + 9i)$

33. i^{32}

34. $-5i^{21}$

35. $\dfrac{2 + 9i}{-2i}$

36. $\dfrac{5 + 2i}{3 - 4i}$

37. $\dfrac{8 - 4i}{1 + i}$

38. $\dfrac{-12 + 26i}{2 + 4i}$

PARCC Assessment Readiness

Selected Response

1. Graph the complex number $-2i$.

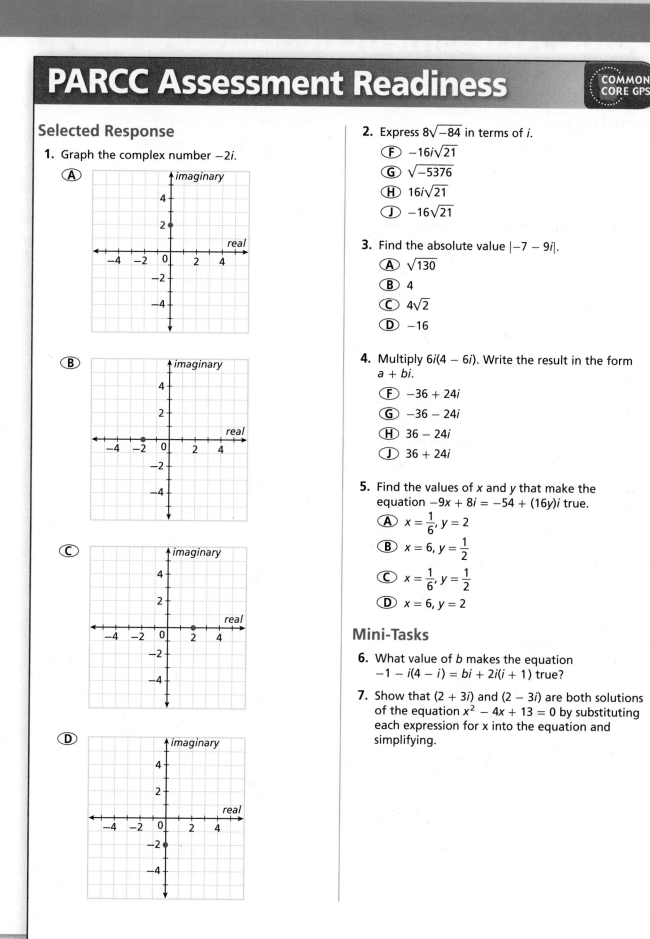

(A)

(B)

(C)

(D)

2. Express $8\sqrt{-84}$ in terms of i.

   (F) $-16i\sqrt{21}$

   (G) $\sqrt{-5376}$

   (H) $16i\sqrt{21}$

   (J) $-16\sqrt{21}$

3. Find the absolute value $|-7 - 9i|$.

   (A) $\sqrt{130}$

   (B) 4

   (C) $4\sqrt{2}$

   (D) -16

4. Multiply $6i(4 - 6i)$. Write the result in the form $a + bi$.

   (F) $-36 + 24i$

   (G) $-36 - 24i$

   (H) $36 - 24i$

   (J) $36 + 24i$

5. Find the values of x and y that make the equation $-9x + 8i = -54 + (16y)i$ true.

   (A) $x = \frac{1}{6}, y = 2$

   (B) $x = 6, y = \frac{1}{2}$

   (C) $x = \frac{1}{6}, y = \frac{1}{2}$

   (D) $x = 6, y = 2$

Mini-Tasks

6. What value of b makes the equation $-1 - i(4 - i) = bi + 2i(i + 1)$ true?

7. Show that $(2 + 3i)$ and $(2 - 3i)$ are both solutions of the equation $x^2 - 4x + 13 = 0$ by substituting each expression for x into the equation and simplifying.

PARCC Assessment Readiness

Selected Response

1. Express $2\sqrt{-97}$ in terms of i.

   Ⓐ $2i\sqrt{97}$ Ⓒ $-2\sqrt{97}$

   Ⓑ $-2i\sqrt{97}$ Ⓓ $\sqrt{-388}$

2. Solve the equation $2x^2 + 72 = 0$.

   Ⓕ $x = \pm 6 + i$ Ⓗ $x = \pm 6i$

   Ⓖ $x = 6 \pm i$ Ⓙ $x = \pm 6$

3. Find the values of x and y that make the equation $5x + 6i = -35 - (24y)i$ true.

   Ⓐ $x = -7, y = -\frac{1}{4}$

   Ⓑ $x = -\frac{1}{7}, y = -\frac{1}{4}$

   Ⓒ $x = -\frac{1}{7}, y = -4$

   Ⓓ $x = -7, y = -4$

4. What value(s) of x satisfy $x^2 + 8x + 32 = 0$?

   Ⓕ $x = -8 + 4i$ or $-8 - 4i$

   Ⓖ $x = -4 + 4i$ or $-4 - 4i$

   Ⓗ $x = 4i$ or $-4i$

   Ⓙ $x = -4 + 4i$

5. Find the complex conjugate of $5i + 7$.

   Ⓐ $7 - 5i$ Ⓒ $7 + 5i$

   Ⓑ $5i - 7$ Ⓓ $-7 - 5i$

6. Find the absolute value $|-6 + 9i|$.

   Ⓕ 3 Ⓗ $3\sqrt{13}$

   Ⓖ $3\sqrt{5}$ Ⓙ $\sqrt{3}$

7. Add. Write the result in the form $a + bi$.
$(4 + 3i) + (5 + 9i)$

   Ⓐ $13 + 8i$ Ⓒ $-1 - 6i$

   Ⓑ $9 + 12i$ Ⓓ $7 + 14i$

8. Graph the complex number $5 - 3i$.

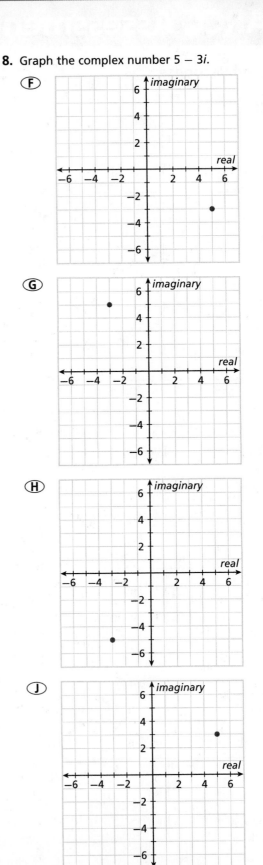

9. Rewrite $\sqrt[3]{x^7}$ in rational exponent form.

(A) x^{10}

(C) $x^{\frac{3}{7}}$

(B) $x^{\frac{7}{3}}$

(D) x^4

10. Rewrite $x^{\frac{9}{5}}$ in radical form.

(F) $\sqrt[9]{x^5}$

(H) $\frac{1}{5}x^9$

(G) x^4

(J) $\sqrt[5]{x^9}$

11. Express $\sqrt{192}$ in simplest radical form.

(A) $\sqrt{32} \cdot \sqrt{6}$

(B) $3\sqrt{64}$

(C) $8\sqrt{3}$

(D) $\sqrt{192}$ is already in simplest radical form.

12. Simplify the expression $\dfrac{x^{\frac{5}{3}}}{x^{\frac{2}{3}}}$. Assume x is positive.

(F) $x^{\frac{7}{3}}$

(H) $x^{\frac{10}{9}}$

(G) $x^{\frac{5}{2}}$

(J) x

13. For any two polynomials m and n, where n is nonzero, which expression might not be a polynomial?

(A) $m + n$

(C) mn

(B) $m - n$

(D) $\dfrac{m}{n}$

14 If a, b, c, and d are integers, and both b and d are nonzero, what conclusion can you draw from the statement $\dfrac{a}{b} \cdot \dfrac{c}{d} = \dfrac{ac}{bd}$ given that the set of integers is closed under multiplication?

(F) The set of nonzero numbers is closed under multiplication.

(G) The set of integers is closed under division.

(H) The set of rational numbers is closed under multiplication.

(J) The set of rational numbers is closed under division.

Mini-Tasks

15. Multiply $4i(3 - 5i)$. Write the result in the form $a + bi$.

16. Subtract. Write the result in the form $a + bi$.
$(5 - 2i) - (6 + 8i)$

17. What value of d makes the equation $-2 + 3i + 12i = 9i - (2 - di)$ true?

Performance Tasks

18. Simplify $\dfrac{-2 + 2i}{5 + 3i}$. Show and describe each step.

19. Find $(-3 - 2i) + (-4 - 6i)$ by graphing on the complex plane. Explain.

Are You Ready?

my.hrw.com
Assessment and Intervention

 Vocabulary

Match each term on the left with a definition on the right.

1. binomial
2. composite number
3. factor
4. multiple
5. prime number

A. a whole number greater than 1 that has more than two positive factors

B. a polynomial with two terms

C. the product of any number and a whole number

D. a number that is written as the product of its prime factors

E. a whole number greater than 1 that has exactly two positive factors, itself and 1

F. a number that is multiplied by another number to get a product

Prime and Composite Numbers

Tell whether each number is prime or composite. If the number is composite, write it as the product of two numbers.

6. 2
7. 7
8. 10
9. 38
10. 115
11. 147
12. 151
13. 93

Multiply Monomials and Polynomials

Multiply.

14. $2(x + 5)$
15. $3h(h + 1)$
16. $xy(x^2 - xy^3)$
17. $6m(m^2 - 4m - 1)$

Multiply Binomials

Find each product.

18. $(x + 3)(x + 8)$
19. $(b - 7)(b + 1)$
20. $(2p - 5)(p - 1)$
21. $(3n + 4)(2n + 3)$

Career Readiness Physicists

Physicists may work on theories of how the natural world works, perform experiments to study the natural world, apply theories to practical problems, or work in research and development. Many of the formulas physicists deal with involve polynomials and factoring. Physicists usually have advanced college degrees with strong math and science backgrounds. They may work in research for scientific companies, for government agencies, or in colleges and universities.

Quadratic Functions

Online Edition

my.hrw.com

Access the complete online textbook, interactive features, and additional resources.

Animated Math

Interactively explore key concepts with these online tutorials.

Online Video Tutor

Watch full explanations of every example in the textbook with these online videos.

Portable Devices

On the Spot

Watch video tutorials anywhere, anytime with this app for iPhone® and iPad®.

eTextbook

Access your full textbook on your tablet or e-reader.

Chapter Resources

Scan with your smart phone to jump directly to the online edition.

Use the Algebra Tiles tool on **HMH Fuse** to explore and factor polynomials.

14 Factoring Quadratic Expressions

Contents

MATHEMATICAL PRACTICES The Common Core Georgia Performance Standards for Mathematical Practice describe varieties of expertise that all students should seek to develop. Opportunities to develop these practices are integrated throughout this program.

1 Make sense of problems and persevere in solving them.

2 Reason abstractly and quantitatively.

3 Construct viable arguments and critique the reasoning of others.

4 Model with mathematics.

5 Use appropriate tools strategically.

6 Attend to precision.

7 Look for and make use of structure.

8 Look for and express regularity in repeated reasoning.

Unpacking the Standards

my.hrw.com
Multilingual Glossary

Understanding the standards and the vocabulary terms in the standards will help you know exactly what you are expected to learn in this chapter.

 MCC9-12.A.SSE.2

Use the structure of an expression to identify ways to rewrite it.

Key Vocabulary

expression (expresión)
A mathematical phrase that contains operations, numbers, and/or variables.

What It Means For You

You will learn to *factor* expressions, which means you will rewrite them as a product of two expressions. Being able to recognize patterns will help you decide which method to use.

EXAMPLE   **Factor $x^2 + 7x + 6$**

The algebra tiles below show that $x^2 + 7x + 6 = (x + 1)(x + 6)$.

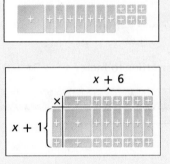

EXAMPLE   **Factor $6x^2 - 11x + 3$**

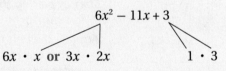

Guess and check: $(6x - 1)(x - 3) = 6x^2 - 18x - x + 3$

$= 6x^2 - 19x + 3$ ✗

Guess and check: $(3x - 1)(2x - 3) = 6x^2 - 9x - 2x + 3$

$= 6x^2 - 11x + 3$ ✓

EXAMPLE   **Factor $x^2 - 49$**

Use the difference of two squares pattern:

$$a^2 - b^2 = (a + b)(a - b)$$

$$x^2 - 49 = (x + 7)(x - 7)$$

14-1
Algebra
TASK

Model Factorization

Some expressions of the form $x^2 + bx + c$ can be rewritten as a product of factors. You can use algebra tiles to model these expressions.

Use with Factoring
$x^2 + bx + c$

KEY

+ = 1
– = –1

| = x | = –x   + = x^2

MATHEMATICAL PRACTICES — **Use appropriate tools strategically.**

MCC9-12.A.SSE.2 Use the structure of an expression to identify ways to rewrite it.

Activity 1

Use algebra tiles to factor $x^2 + 7x + 6$.

MODEL		ALGEBRA
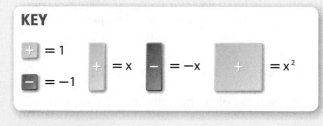	Model $x^2 + 7x + 6$.	$x^2 + 7x + 6$
	Try to arrange all of the tiles in a rectangle. Start by placing the x^2-tile in the upper left corner.	
	Arrange the unit tiles in a rectangle so that the top left corner of this rectangle touches the bottom right corner of the x^2-tile.	$x^2 + 7x + 6 \neq (x + 2)(x + 3)$
	Arrange the x-tiles so that all the tiles together make one large rectangle.	
	This arrangement does not work because two x-tiles are left over.	
	Rearrange the unit tiles to form another rectangle.	
	Fill in the empty spaces with x-tiles. All 7 x-tiles fit. This is the correct arrangement.	$x^2 + 7x + 6 = (x + 1)(x + 6)$
	The total area represents the expression. The length and width represent the factors.	

The rectangle has width $x + 1$ and length $x + 6$. So $x^2 + 7x + 6 = (x + 1)(x + 6)$.

Try This

Use algebra tiles to factor each expression.

1. $x^2 + 2x + 1$ **2.** $x^2 + 3x + 2$ **3.** $x^2 + 6x + 5$ **4.** $x^2 + 6x + 9$

5. $x^2 + 5x + 4$ **6.** $x^2 + 6x + 8$ **7.** $x^2 + 5x + 6$ **8.** $x^2 + 8x + 12$

Activity 2

Use algebra tiles to factor $x^2 + x - 2$.

MODEL		ALGEBRA
	Model $x^2 + x - 2$.	$x^2 + x - 2$
	Start by placing the x^2-tile in the upper left corner. Arrange the unit tiles in a rectangle so that the top left corner of this rectangle touches the bottom right corner of the x^2-tile. To make a rectangle, you need to fill in the empty spaces, but there aren't enough x-tiles to fill in the empty spaces.	
	Add a zero pair. Arrange the x-tiles to complete the rectangle. Remember that the product of two positive values is positive and the product of a positive and a negative value is negative.	
	The total area represents the expression. The length and width represent the factors.	$x^2 + x - 2 = (x - 1)(x + 2)$

The rectangle has width $x - 1$ and length $x + 2$. So, $x^2 + x - 2 = (x - 1)(x + 2)$.

Try This

9. Why can you add one red $-x$-tile and one yellow x-tile?

Use algebra tiles to factor each expression.

10. $x^2 - x - 2$ **11.** $x^2 - 2x - 3$ **12.** $x^2 - 5x + 4$ **13.** $x^2 - 7x + 10$

14. $x^2 - 2x + 1$ **15.** $x^2 - 6x + 5$ **16.** $x^2 + 5x - 6$ **17.** $x^2 + 3x - 4$

18. $x^2 - x - 6$ **19.** $x^2 + 3x - 10$ **20.** $x^2 - 2x - 8$ **21.** $x^2 + x - 12$

Factoring $x^2 + bx + c$

 Essential Question: How can you factor a trinomial with a leading coefficient of 1?

Objective
Factor quadratic trinomials of the form $x^2 + bx + c$.

Vocabulary
monomial
polynomial
binomial
trinomial

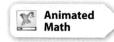 Animated Math

Why learn this?
Factoring will help you find the dimensions of rectangular shapes, such as a fountain. (See Exercise 71.)

A **monomial** is a number, a variable, or a product of numbers and variables with whole-number exponents.

A **polynomial** is a monomial or a sum of monomials. A **binomial** is a polynomial that has two terms. A **trinomial** is a polynomial that has three terms.

Notice that when you multiply $(x + 2)(x + 5)$, the constant term in the trinomial is the product of the constants in the binomials.

$$(x + 2)(x + 5) = x^2 + 7x + 10$$

You can use this fact to factor a trinomial into its binomial factors. Look for two numbers that are factors of the constant term in the trinomial. Write two binomials with those numbers, and then multiply to see if you are correct.

COMMON CORE GPS MCC9-12.A.SSE.2

EXAMPLE 1 Factoring Trinomials by Guess and Check

my.hrw.com

Online Video Tutor

Remember!

When you multiply two binomials, multiply:

First terms
Outer terms
Inner terms
Last terms

Factor $x^2 + 19x + 60$ by guess and check.

$(\blacksquare + \blacksquare)(\blacksquare + \blacksquare)$ *Write two sets of parentheses.*

$(x + \blacksquare)(x + \blacksquare)$ *The first term is x^2, so the variable terms have a coefficient of 1.*

The constant term in the trinomial is 60.

$(x + 1)(x + 60) = x^2 + 61x + 60$ ✗   *Try factors of 60 for the constant terms in the binomials.*

$(x + 2)(x + 30) = x^2 + 32x + 60$ ✗

$(x + 3)(x + 20) = x^2 + 23x + 60$ ✗

$(x + 4)(x + 15) = x^2 + 19x + 60$ ✓

The factors of $x^2 + 19x + 60$ are $(x + 4)$ and $(x + 15)$.

$x^2 + 19x + 60 = (x + 4)(x + 15)$

CHECK IT OUT! Factor each trinomial by guess and check.

1a. $x^2 + 10x + 24$ **1b.** $x^2 + 7x + 12$

Travel-Shots / Alamy

The guess and check method is usually not the most efficient method of factoring a trinomial. Look at the product of $(x + 3)$ and $(x + 4)$.

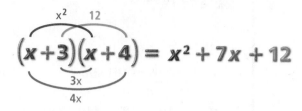

$$(x + 3)(x + 4) = x^2 + 7x + 12$$

The coefficient of the middle term is the sum of 3 and 4. The third term is the product of 3 and 4.

Know it! Note

Factoring $x^2 + bx + c$

WORDS	EXAMPLE
To factor a quadratic trinomial of the form $x^2 + bx + c$, find two factors of c whose sum is b. If no such integers exist, the trinomial is not factorable.	To factor $x^2 + 9x + 18$, look for factors of 18 whose sum is 9. Factors of 18 | Sum 1 and 18 | 19 ✗ 2 and 9 | 11 ✗ 3 and 6 | 9 ✓ $x^2 + 9x + 18 = (x + 3)(x + 6)$

When c is positive, its factors have the same sign. The sign of b tells you whether the factors are positive or negative. When b is positive, the factors are positive, and when b is negative, the factors are negative.

COMMON CORE GPS **EXAMPLE** 2 MCC9-12.A.SSE.2

Factoring $x^2 + bx + c$ When c Is Positive

Factor each trinomial. Check your answer.

my.hrw.com

Online Video Tutor

A $x^2 + 6x + 8$

$(x + \blacksquare)(x + \blacksquare)$ $b = 6$ and $c = 8$; look for factors of 8 whose sum is 6.

Factors of 8	Sum
1 and 8	9 ✗
2 and 4	6 ✓

The factors needed are 2 and 4.

$(x + 2)(x + 4)$

Check $(x + 2)(x + 4) = x^2 + 4x + 2x + 8$ Use the FOIL method.

$= x^2 + 6x + 8$ ✓   The product is the original polynomial.

B $x^2 + 5x + 6$

$(x + \blacksquare)(x + \blacksquare)$ $b = 5$ and $c = 6$; look for factors of 6 whose sum is 5.

Factors of 6	Sum
1 and 6	7 ✗
2 and 3	5 ✓

The factors needed are 2 and 3.

$(x + 2)(x + 3)$

Check $(x + 2)(x + 3) = x^2 + 3x + 2x + 6$ Use the FOIL method.

$= x^2 + 5x + 6$ ✓   The product is the original polynomial.

Factor each trinomial. Check your answer.

C $x^2 - 10x + 16$

   $(x + \blacksquare)(x + \blacksquare)$

b = −10 and c = 16; look for factors of 16 whose sum is −10.

Factors of 16	Sum	
−1 and −16	−17	✗
−2 and −8	−10	✓

The factors needed are −2 and −8.

$(x - 2)(x - 8)$

Check $(x - 2)(x - 8) = x^2 - 8x - 2x + 16$ *Use the FOIL method.*

                          $= x^2 - 10x + 16$ ✓   *The product is the original polynomial.*

CHECK IT OUT!

Factor each trinomial. Check your answer.

2a. $x^2 + 8x + 12$ **2b.** $x^2 - 5x + 6$

2c. $x^2 + 13x + 42$ **2d.** $x^2 - 13x + 40$

When *c* is negative, its factors have opposite signs. The sign of *b* tells you which factor is positive and which is negative. The factor with the greater absolute value has the same sign as *b*.

COMMON CORE GPS
MCC9-12.A.SSE.2

EXAMPLE **3**

Factoring $x^2 + bx + c$ When *c* Is Negative

Factor each trinomial.

A $x^2 + 7x - 18$

   $(x + \blacksquare)(x + \blacksquare)$

b = 7 and c = −18; look for factors of −18 whose sum is 7. The factor with the greater absolute value is positive.

my.hrw.com

Online Video Tutor

Factors of −18	Sum	
−1 and 18	17	✗
−2 and 9	7	✓

The factors needed are −2 and 9.

$(x - 2)(x + 9)$

B $x^2 - 5x - 24$

   $(x + \blacksquare)(x + \blacksquare)$

b = −5 and c = −24; look for factors of −24 whose sum is −5. The factor with the greater absolute value is negative.

Helpful Hint

If you have trouble remembering the rules for which factor is positive and which is negative, you can try all the factor pairs and check their sums.

Factors of −24	Sum	
1 and −24	−23	✗
2 and −12	−10	✗
3 and −8	−5	✓

The factors needed are 3 and −8.

$(x + 3)(x - 8)$

CHECK IT OUT!

Factor each trinomial. Check your answer.

3a. $x^2 + 2x - 15$ **3b.** $x^2 - 6x + 8$ **3c.** $x^2 - 8x - 20$

A polynomial and the factored form of the polynomial are equivalent expressions. When you evaluate these two expressions for the same value of the variable, the results are the same.

EXAMPLE 4

Evaluating Polynomials

Factor $n^2 + 11n + 24$. Show that the original polynomial and the factored form have the same value for $n = 0, 1, 2, 3,$ and 4.

$$n^2 + 11n + 24$$
$$(n + \boxed{})(n + \boxed{})$$

$b = 11$ and $c = 24$; look for factors of 24 whose sum is 11.

Factors of 24	Sum	
1 and 24	25	✗
2 and 12	14	✗
3 and 8	11	✓

The factors needed are 3 and 8.

$$(n + 3)(n + 8)$$

Evaluate the original polynomial and the factored form for $n = 0, 1, 2, 3,$ and 4.

n	$n^2 + 11n + 24$
0	$0^2 + 11(0) + 24 = 24$
1	$1^2 + 11(1) + 24 = 36$
2	$2^2 + 11(2) + 24 = 50$
3	$3^2 + 11(3) + 24 = 66$
4	$4^2 + 11(4) + 24 = 84$

n	$(n + 3)(n + 8)$
0	$(0 + 3)(0 + 8) = 24$
1	$(1 + 3)(1 + 8) = 36$
2	$(2 + 3)(2 + 8) = 50$
3	$(3 + 3)(3 + 8) = 66$
4	$(4 + 3)(4 + 8) = 84$

The original polynomial and the factored form have the same value for the given values of n.

CHECK IT OUT!

4. Factor $n^2 - 7n + 10$. Show that the original polynomial and the factored form have the same value for $n = 0, 1, 2, 3,$ and 4.

MCC.MP.6 — **MATHEMATICAL PRACTICES**

THINK AND DISCUSS

1. Explain in your own words how to factor $x^2 + 9x + 14$. Show how to check your answer.

2. Explain how you can determine the signs of the factors of c when factoring a trinomial of the form $x^2 + bx + c$.

Know it! Note

3. GET ORGANIZED Copy and complete the graphic organizer. In each box, write an example of a trinomial with the given properties and factor it.

Factoring $x^2 + bx + c$

c is positive, and b is positive.	c is negative, and b is positive.
c is positive, and b is negative.	c is negative, and b is negative.

GUIDED PRACTICE

SEE EXAMPLE 1

Factor each trinomial by guess and check.

1. $x^2 + 13x + 36$ **2.** $x^2 + 11x + 24$ **3.** $x^2 + 14x + 40$

Factor each trinomial. Check your answer.

SEE EXAMPLE 2

4. $x^2 + 4x + 3$ **5.** $x^2 + 10x + 16$ **6.** $x^2 + 15x + 44$

7. $x^2 - 7x + 6$ **8.** $x^2 - 9x + 14$ **9.** $x^2 - 11x + 24$

SEE EXAMPLE 3

10. $x^2 - 6x - 7$ **11.** $x^2 + 6x - 27$ **12.** $x^2 + x - 30$

13. $x^2 - x - 2$ **14.** $x^2 - 3x - 18$ **15.** $x^2 - 4x - 45$

SEE EXAMPLE 4

16. Factor $n^2 + 6n - 7$. Show that the original polynomial and the factored form have the same value for $n = 0, 1, 2, 3,$ and 4.

PRACTICE AND PROBLEM SOLVING

Independent Practice

For Exercises	See Example
17–19	1
20–25	2
26–31	3
32	4

my.hrw.com

Online Extra Practice

Factor each trinomial by guess and check.

17. $x^2 + 13x + 30$ **18.** $x^2 + 11x + 28$ **19.** $x^2 + 16x + 48$

Factor each trinomial. Check your answer.

20. $x^2 + 12x + 11$ **21.** $x^2 + 16x + 28$ **22.** $x^2 + 15x + 36$

23. $x^2 - 6x + 5$ **24.** $x^2 - 9x + 18$ **25.** $x^2 - 12x + 32$

26. $x^2 + x - 12$ **27.** $x^2 + 4x - 21$ **28.** $x^2 + 9x - 36$

29. $x^2 - 12x - 13$ **30.** $x^2 - 10x - 24$ **31.** $x^2 - 2x - 35$

32. Factor $n^2 - 12n - 45$. Show that the original polynomial and the factored form have the same value for $n = 0, 1, 2, 3,$ and 4.

Match each trinomial with its correct factorization.

33. $x^2 + 3x - 10$ **A.** $(x - 2)(x - 5)$

34. $x^2 - 7x + 10$ **B.** $(x + 1)(x + 10)$

35. $x^2 - 9x - 10$ **C.** $(x - 2)(x + 5)$

36. $x^2 + 11x + 10$ **D.** $(x + 1)(x - 10)$

H.O.T. **37. Write About It** Compare multiplying binomials with factoring polynomials into binomial factors.

Factor each trinomial. Check your answer.

38. $x^2 + x - 20$ **39.** $x^2 - 11x + 18$ **40.** $x^2 - 4x - 21$

41. $x^2 + 10x + 9$ **42.** $x^2 - 12x + 32$ **43.** $x^2 + 13x + 42$

44. $x^2 - 7x + 12$ **45.** $x^2 + 11x + 18$ **46.** $x^2 - 6x - 27$

47. $x^2 + 5x - 24$ **48.** $x^2 - 10x + 21$ **49.** $x^2 + 4x - 45$

50. Factor $n^2 + 11n + 28$. Show that the original polynomial and the factored form have the same value for $n = 0, 1, 2, 3,$ and 4.

51. **Estimation** The graph shows the areas of rectangles with dimensions $(x + 1)$ yards and $(x + 2)$ yards. Estimate the value of x for a rectangle with area 9 square yards.

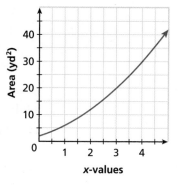

52. **Geometry** The area of a rectangle in square feet can be represented by $x^2 + 8x + 12$. The length is $(x + 6)$ ft. What is the width of the rectangle?

53. **Remodeling** A homeowner wants to enlarge a rectangular closet that has an area of $(x^2 + 3x + 2)$ ft². The length is $(x + 2)$ ft. After construction, the area will be $(x^2 + 8x + 15)$ ft² with a length of $(x + 3)$ ft.

   a. Find the dimensions of the closet before construction.

   b. Find the dimensions of the closet after construction.

   c. By how many feet will the length and width increase after construction?

Art Write the polynomial modeled and then factor.

54.

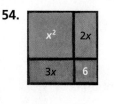

x^2	$2x$
$3x$	6

55.

x^2	$2x$
$4x$	8

56.

x^2	$-2x$
$4x$	-8

Copy and complete the table.

	$x^2 + bx + c$	Sign of c	Binomial Factors	Signs of Numbers in Binomials
	$x^2 + 4x + 3$	Positive	$(x + 1)(x + 3)$	Both positive
57.	$x^2 - 4x + 3$	▨	$(x \blacksquare 1)(x \blacksquare 3)$	▨
58.	$x^2 + 2x - 3$	▨	$(x \blacksquare 1)(x \blacksquare 3)$	▨
59.	$x^2 - 2x - 3$	▨	$(x \blacksquare 1)(x \blacksquare 3)$	▨

H.O.T. 60. **Geometry** A rectangle has area $x^2 + 6x + 8$. The length is $x + 4$. Find the width of the rectangle. Could the rectangle be a square? Explain why or why not.

Real-World Connections

61. The equation for the motion of an object with constant acceleration is $d = vt + \frac{1}{2}at^2$ where d is distance traveled in feet, v is starting velocity in feet per second, a is acceleration in feet per second squared, and t is time in seconds.

   a. Janna has two toy race cars on a track. One starts with a velocity of 0 ft/s and accelerates at 2 ft/s². Write an equation for the distance the car travels in time t.

   b. The second car travels at a constant speed of 4 ft/s. Write an equation for the distance the second car travels in time t. (*Hint:* When speed is constant, the acceleration is 0 ft/s².)

   c. By setting the equations equal to each other you can determine when the cars have traveled the same distance: $t^2 = 4t$. This can be written as $t^2 - 4t = 0$. Factor the left side of the equation.

62. Construction The length of a rectangular porch is $(x + 7)$ ft. The area of the porch is $\left(x^2 + 9x + 14\right)$ ft^2. Find the width of the porch.

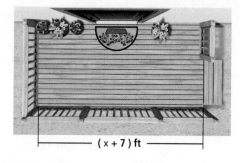

Tell whether each statement is true or false. If false, explain.

63. The third term in a factorable trinomial is equal to the product of the constants in its binomial factors.

64. The constants in the binomial factors of $x^2 + x - 2$ are both negative.

65. The correct factorization of $x^2 - 3x - 4$ is $(x + 4)(x - 1)$.

66. All trinomials of the form $x^2 + bx + c$ can be factored.

Fill in the missing part of each factorization.

67. $x^2 - 6x + 8 = (x - 2)(x - \blacksquare)$

68. $x^2 - 2x - 8 = (x + 2)(x - \blacksquare)$

69. $x^2 + 2x - 8 = (x - 2)(x + \blacksquare)$

70. $x^2 + 6x + 8 = (x + 2)(x + \blacksquare)$

71. Construction The area of a rectangular fountain is $\left(x^2 + 12x + 20\right)$ ft^2. The width is $(x + 2)$ ft.

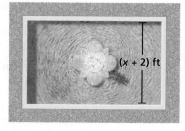

   a. Find the length of the fountain.

   b. A 2-foot walkway is built around the fountain. Find the dimensions of the outside border of the walkway.

   c. Find the total area covered by the fountain and walkway.

H.O.T. 72. Critical Thinking Find all possible values of b so that $x^2 + bx + 6$ can be factored into binomial factors.

TEST PREP

73. Which is the correct factorization of $x^2 - 10x - 24$?

   Ⓐ $(x - 4)(x - 6)$ Ⓒ $(x - 2)(x + 12)$

   Ⓑ $(x + 4)(x - 6)$ Ⓓ $(x + 2)(x - 12)$

74. Which value of b would make $x^2 + bx - 20$ factorable?

   Ⓕ 9   Ⓖ 12   Ⓗ 19   Ⓙ 21

75. Which value of b would NOT make $x^2 + bx - 36$ factorable?

   Ⓐ 5   Ⓑ 9   Ⓒ 15   Ⓓ 16

H.O.T. 76. Short Response What are the factors of $x^2 + 2x - 24$? Show and explain each step of factoring the polynomial.

CHALLENGE AND EXTEND

Factor each expression.

77. $x^4 + 18x^2 + 81$ **78.** $y^4 - 5y^2 - 24$ **79.** $d^4 + 22d^2 + 21$

80. $(u + v)^2 + 2(u + v) - 3$ **81.** $(de)^2 - (de) - 20$ **82.** $(m - n)^2 - 4(m - n) - 45$

83. Find all possible values of b such that, when $x^2 + bx + 28$ is factored, both constants in the binomials are positive.

84. Find all possible values of b such that, when $x^2 + bx + 32$ is factored, both constants in the binomials are negative.

85. The area of Beth's rectangular garden is $(x^2 + 13x + 42)$ ft². The width is $(x + 6)$ ft.

Item	Cost
Fertilizer	0.28 ($/ft²)
Fencing	2.00 ($/ft)

   a. What is the length of the garden?

   b. Find the perimeter in terms of x.

   c. Find the cost to fence the garden when x is 5.

   d. Find the cost of fertilizer when x is 5.

   e. Find the total cost to fence and fertilize Beth's garden when x is 5.

MATHEMATICAL PRACTICES

FOCUS ON MATHEMATICAL PRACTICES

H.O.T. 86. Make a Conjecture Consider the trinomial $x^2 + (p + q)x + pq$.

   a. Substitute $p = 3$ and $q = 5$ into the trinomial and factor it.

   b. Substitute $p = 6$ and $q = -2$ into the trinomial and factor it.

   c. Based on this evidence, make a conjecture about how the trinomial $x^2 + (p + q)x + pq$ can be factored for all values of p and q.

H.O.T. 87. Analysis Suppose that the trinomial $x^2 + bx + 17$ is factorable as $(x + s)(x + t)$ for some positive integer values of s and t.

   a. What is the value of st?

   b. What is the value of $s + t$?

   c. How does knowing the value of $s + t$ help you find the value of b?

Career Path

Jessica Rubino
Environmental Sciences major

Q: What math classes did you take in high school?
A: Algebra 1, Algebra 2, and Geometry

Q: What college math classes have you taken?
A: I took several computer modeling and programming classes as well as Statistics and Probability.

Q: How is math used in some of your projects?
A: Computer applications help me analyze data collected from a local waste disposal site. I used my mathematical knowledge to make recommendations on how to preserve surrounding water supplies.

Q: What plans do you have for the future?
A: I enjoy my studies in the area of water pollution. I would also like to research more efficient uses of natural energy resources.

14-2 Factoring $ax^2 + bx + c$

 Essential Question: How can you factor a trinomial with a leading coefficient other than 1?

Objective
Factor quadratic trinomials of the form $ax^2 + bx + c$.

Why learn this?
The height of a football that has been kicked can be modeled by a factored polynomial. (See Exercise 69.)

You have already factored trinomials of the form $x^2 + bx + c$. Now you will factor trinomials of the form $ax^2 + bx + c$, where $a \neq 0$ or 1.

When you multiply $(3x + 2)(2x + 5)$, the coefficient of the x^2-term is the product of the coefficients of the x-terms. Also, the constant term in the trinomial is the product of the constants in the binomials.

$$(3x+2)(2x+5) = 6x^2 + 19x + 10$$

To factor a trinomial like $ax^2 + bx + c$ into its binomial factors, write two sets of parentheses: $(\blacksquare x + \blacksquare)(\blacksquare x + \blacksquare)$.

Write two numbers that are factors of a next to the x's and two numbers that are factors of c in the other blanks. Then multiply to see if the product is the original trinomial. If there are not two such integers, the trinomial is unfactorable.

COMMON CORE GPS
MCC9-12.A.SSE.2

EXAMPLE 1 Factoring $ax^2 + bx + c$ by Guess and Check

my.hrw.com

Online Video Tutor

Factor $4x^2 + 16x + 15$ by guess and check.

$(\blacksquare + \blacksquare)(\blacksquare + \blacksquare)$ *Write two sets of parentheses.*

$(\blacksquare x + \blacksquare)(\blacksquare x + \blacksquare)$ *The first term is $4x^2$, so at least one variable term has a coefficient other than 1.*

The coefficient of the x^2-term is 4. The constant term in the trinomial is 15.

$(1x + 15)(4x + 1) = 4x^2 + 61x + 15$ ✗

$(1x + 5)(4x + 3) = 4x^2 + 23x + 15$ ✗

$(1x + 3)(4x + 5) = 4x^2 + 17x + 15$ ✗

$(1x + 1)(4x + 15) = 4x^2 + 19x + 15$ ✗

$(2x + 15)(2x + 1) = 4x^2 + 32x + 15$ ✗

$(2x + 5)(2x + 3) = 4x^2 + 16x + 15$ ✓

Try factors of 4 for the coefficients and factors of 15 for the constant terms.

The factors of $4x^2 + 16x + 15$ are $(2x + 5)$ and $(2x + 3)$.

$4x^2 + 16x + 15 = (2x + 5)(2x + 3)$

CHECK IT OUT!

Factor each trinomial by guess and check.

1a. $6x^2 + 11x + 3$ **1b.** $3x^2 - 2x - 8$

AP Photo/Peter Cosgrove

So, to factor $ax^2 + bx + c$, check the factors of a and the factors of c in the binomials. The sum of the products of the outer and inner terms should be b.

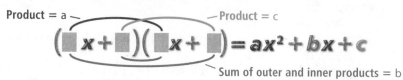

Product = a — — Product = c

$$(\blacksquare x + \blacksquare)(\blacksquare x + \blacksquare) = ax^2 + bx + c$$

Sum of outer and inner products = b

Since you need to check all the factors of a and all the factors of c, it may be helpful to make a table. Then check the products of the outer and inner terms to see if the sum is b. You can multiply the binomials to check your answer.

EXAMPLE 2
MCC9-12.A.SSE.2

Factoring $ax^2 + bx + c$ When c Is Positive

Factor each trinomial. Check your answer.

A $2x^2 + 11x + 12$

$(\blacksquare x + \blacksquare)(\blacksquare x + \blacksquare)$ *a = 2 and c = 12; Outer + Inner = 11*

Factors of 2	Factors of 12	Outer + Inner	
1 and 2	1 and 12	$1(12) + 2(1) = 14$	✗
1 and 2	12 and 1	$1(1) + 2(12) = 25$	✗
1 and 2	2 and 6	$1(6) + 2(2) = 10$	✗
1 and 2	6 and 2	$1(2) + 2(6) = 14$	✗
1 and 2	3 and 4	$1(4) + 2(3) = 10$	✗
1 and 2	4 and 3	$1(3) + 2(4) = 11$	✓

$(x + 4)(2x + 3)$

Check $(x + 4)(2x + 3) = 2x^2 + 3x + 8x + 12$ *Use the FOIL method.*
$= 2x^2 + 11x + 12$ ✓

B $5x^2 - 14x + 8$

$(\blacksquare x + \blacksquare)(\blacksquare x + \blacksquare)$ *a = 5 and c = 8; Outer + Inner = −14*

Factors of 5	Factors of 8	Outer + Inner	
1 and 5	−1 and −8	$1(-8) + 5(-1) = -13$	✗
1 and 5	−8 and −1	$1(-1) + 5(-8) = -41$	✗
1 and 5	−2 and −4	$1(-4) + 5(-2) = -14$	✓

$(x - 2)(5x - 4)$

Check $(x - 2)(5x - 4) = 5x^2 - 4x - 10x + 8$ *Use the FOIL method.*
$= 5x^2 - 14x + 8$ ✓

Remember!

When b is negative and c is positive, the factors of c are both negative.

CHECK IT OUT!   Factor each trinomial. Check your answer.
2a. $6x^2 + 17x + 5$ **2b.** $9x^2 - 15x + 4$ **2c.** $3x^2 + 13x + 12$

When c is negative, one factor of c will be positive and the other factor will be negative. Only some of the factors are shown in the examples, but you may need to check all of the possibilities.

EXAMPLE 3

Factoring $ax^2 + bx + c$ When c Is Negative

Factor each trinomial. Check your answer.

A $4y^2 + 7y - 2$

$\left(\blacksquare y + \blacksquare\right)\left(\blacksquare y + \blacksquare\right)$ *a = 4 and c = −2; Outer + Inner = 7*

Factors of 4	Factors of −2	Outer + Inner	
1 and 4	1 and −2	$1(-2) + 4(1) = 2$	✗
1 and 4	−1 and 2	$1(2) + 4(-1) = -2$	✗
1 and 4	2 and −1	$1(-1) + 4(2) = 7$	✓

$(y + 2)(4y - 1)$

Check $(y + 2)(4y - 1) = 4y^2 - y + 8y - 2$ *Use the FOIL method.*

$= 4y^2 + 7y - 2$ ✓

B $4x^2 + 19x - 5$

$\left(\blacksquare x + \blacksquare\right)\left(\blacksquare x + \blacksquare\right)$ *a = 4 and c = −5; Outer + Inner = 19*

Factors of 4	Factors of −5	Outer + Inner	
1 and 4	1 and −5	$1(-5) + 4(1) = -1$	✗
1 and 4	−1 and 5	$1(5) + 4(-1) = 1$	✗
1 and 4	5 and −1	$1(-1) + 4(5) = 19$	✓

$(x + 5)(4x - 1)$

Check $(x + 5)(4x - 1) = 4x^2 - x + 20x - 5$ *Use the FOIL method.*

$= 4x^2 + 19x - 5$ ✓

C $2x^2 - 7x - 15$

$\left(\blacksquare x + \blacksquare\right)\left(\blacksquare x + \blacksquare\right)$ *a = 2 and c = −15; Outer + Inner = −7*

Factors of 2	Factors of −15	Outer + Inner	
1 and 2	1 and −15	$1(-15) + 2(1) = -13$	✗
1 and 2	−1 and 15	$1(15) + 2(-1) = 13$	✗
1 and 2	3 and −5	$1(-5) + 2(3) = 1$	✗
1 and 2	−3 and 5	$1(5) + 2(-3) = -1$	✗
1 and 2	5 and −3	$1(-3) + 2(5) = 7$	✗
1 and 2	−5 and 3	$1(3) + 2(-5) = -7$	✓

$(x - 5)(2x + 3)$

Check $(x - 5)(2x + 3) = 2x^2 + 3x - 10x - 15$ *Use the FOIL method.*

$= 2x^2 - 7x - 15$ ✓

CHECK IT OUT!

Factor each trinomial. Check your answer.

3a. $6x^2 + 7x - 3$ **3b.** $4n^2 - n - 3$

Factoring $ax^2 + bx + c$

Reggie Wilson
Franklin High School

When a, b, and c are positive, I like to use a box to help me factor. I look for factors of ac that add to b. Then I arrange the terms in a box and factor.

To factor $6x^2 + 7x + 2$, first I find the factors I need.

$$ac = 2(6) = 12 \quad b = 7$$

Factors of 12	Sum
1 and 12	13
2 and 6	8
3 and 4	7

Then I rewrite the trinomial as $6x^2 + 3x + 4x + 2$.

Now I arrange $6x^2 + 3x + 4x + 2$ in a box and factor out the common factors from each row and column.

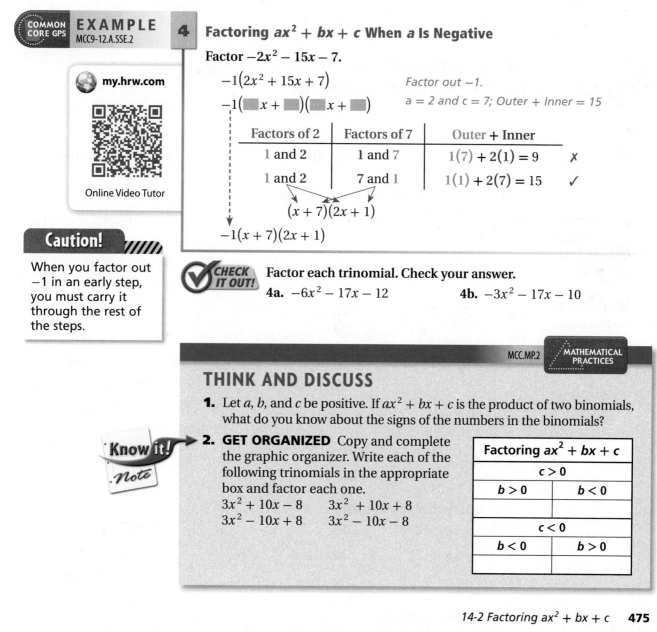

The factors are $(2x + 1)$ and $(3x + 2)$.

When the leading coefficient is negative, factor out -1 from each term before using other factoring methods.

COMMON CORE GPS
EXAMPLE 4
MCC9-12.A.SSE.2

Factoring $ax^2 + bx + c$ When a Is Negative

Factor $-2x^2 - 15x - 7$.

$-1(2x^2 + 15x + 7)$ *Factor out -1.*

$-1(\blacksquare x + \blacksquare)(\blacksquare x + \blacksquare)$ *$a = 2$ and $c = 7$; Outer + Inner = 15*

my.hrw.com

Online Video Tutor

Factors of 2	Factors of 7	Outer + Inner	
1 and 2	1 and 7	$1(7) + 2(1) = 9$	✗
1 and 2	7 and 1	$1(1) + 2(7) = 15$	✓

$(x + 7)(2x + 1)$

$-1(x + 7)(2x + 1)$

Caution!

When you factor out -1 in an early step, you must carry it through the rest of the steps.

CHECK IT OUT! Factor each trinomial. Check your answer.

4a. $-6x^2 - 17x - 12$ **4b.** $-3x^2 - 17x - 10$

MCC.MP.2   MATHEMATICAL PRACTICES

THINK AND DISCUSS

1. Let a, b, and c be positive. If $ax^2 + bx + c$ is the product of two binomials, what do you know about the signs of the numbers in the binomials?

2. GET ORGANIZED Copy and complete the graphic organizer. Write each of the following trinomials in the appropriate box and factor each one.

$3x^2 + 10x - 8$ $3x^2 + 10x + 8$
$3x^2 - 10x + 8$ $3x^2 - 10x - 8$

Know it! Note

Factoring $ax^2 + bx + c$	
$c > 0$	
$b > 0$	$b < 0$
$c < 0$	
$b < 0$	$b > 0$

© Stockbyte

GUIDED PRACTICE

SEE EXAMPLE 1

Factor each trinomial by guess and check.

1. $2x^2 + 9x + 10$　　　**2.** $5x^2 + 31x + 6$　　　**3.** $5x^2 + 7x - 6$

4. $6x^2 + 37x + 6$　　　**5.** $3x^2 - 14x - 24$　　　**6.** $6x^2 + x - 2$

Factor each trinomial. Check your answer.

SEE EXAMPLE 2

7. $5x^2 + 11x + 2$　　　**8.** $2x^2 + 11x + 5$　　　**9.** $4x^2 - 9x + 5$

10. $2y^2 - 11y + 14$　　**11.** $5x^2 + 9x + 4$　　　**12.** $3x^2 + 7x + 2$

SEE EXAMPLE 3

13. $4a^2 + 8a - 5$　　　**14.** $15x^2 + 4x - 3$　　**15.** $2x^2 + x - 6$

16. $6n^2 - 11n - 10$　　**17.** $10x^2 - 9x - 1$　　**18.** $7x^2 - 3x - 10$

SEE EXAMPLE 4

19. $-2x^2 + 5x + 12$　　**20.** $-4n^2 - 16n + 9$　　**21.** $-5x^2 + 7x + 6$

22. $-6x^2 + 13x - 2$　　**23.** $-4x^2 - 8x + 5$　　**24.** $-5x^2 + x + 18$

PRACTICE AND PROBLEM SOLVING

Factor each trinomial by guess and check.

25. $9x^2 + 9x + 2$　　　**26.** $2x^2 + 7x + 5$　　　**27.** $3n^2 + 8n + 4$

28. $10d^2 + 17d + 7$　　**29.** $4c^2 - 17c + 15$　　**30.** $6x^2 + 14x + 4$

31. $8x^2 + 22x + 5$　　　**32.** $6x^2 - 13x + 6$　　**33.** $5x^2 + 9x - 18$

Factor each trinomial. Check your answer.

34. $6x^2 + 23x + 7$　　**35.** $10n^2 - 17n + 7$　　**36.** $3x^2 + 11x + 6$

37. $7x^2 + 15x + 2$　　**38.** $3n^2 + 4n + 1$　　　**39.** $3x^2 - 19x + 20$

40. $6x^2 + 11x + 4$　　**41.** $4x^2 - 31x + 21$　　**42.** $10x^2 + 31x + 15$

43. $12y^2 + 17y - 5$　　**44.** $3x^2 + 10x - 8$　　**45.** $4x^2 + 4x - 3$

46. $2n^2 - 7n - 4$　　　**47.** $3x^2 - 4x - 15$　　**48.** $3n^2 - n - 4$

49. $-4x^2 - 4x + 15$　　**50.** $-3x^2 + 16x - 16$　　**51.** $-3x^2 - x + 2$

Geometry For Exercises 52–54, write the polynomial modeled and then factor.

52.
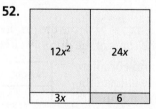

53.
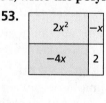

54.

Factor each trinomial, if possible.

55. $9n^2 + 17n + 8$　　**56.** $2x^2 - 7x - 4$　　　**57.** $4x^2 - 12x + 5$

58. $5x^2 - 4x + 12$　　**59.** $3x^2 + 14x + 16$　　**60.** $-3x^2 - 11x + 4$

61. $6x^2 - x - 12$　　　**62.** $10a^2 + 11a + 3$　　**63.** $4x^2 - 12x + 9$

64. Geometry The area of a rectangle is $(6x^2 + 11x + 5)$ cm². The width is $(x + 1)$ cm. What is the length of the rectangle?

$(x + 1)$ cm

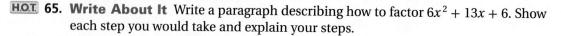

H.O.T. 65. Write About It Write a paragraph describing how to factor $6x^2 + 13x + 6$. Show each step you would take and explain your steps.

Complete each factorization.

66.
$$8x^2 + 18x - 5$$
$$8x^2 + 20x - 2x - 5$$
$$(8x^2 + 20x) - (2x + 5)$$
$$\blacksquare(\blacksquare + \blacksquare) - \blacksquare(2x + 5)$$
$$(\blacksquare - \blacksquare)(2x + 5)$$

67.
$$4x^2 + 9x + 2$$
$$4x^2 + 8x + x + 2$$
$$(4x^2 + 8x) + (x + 2)$$
$$\blacksquare(\blacksquare + \blacksquare) + \blacksquare(x + 2)$$
$$(\blacksquare + \blacksquare)(x + 2)$$

68. Gardening The length of Rebecca's rectangular garden was two times the width w. Rebecca increased the length and width of the garden so that the area of the new garden is $(2w^2 + 7w + 6)$ square yards. By how much did Rebecca increase the length and the width?

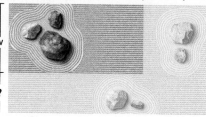

69. Physics The height of a football that has been thrown or kicked can be described by the expression $-16t^2 + vt + h$ where t is the time in seconds, v is the initial upward velocity, and h is the initial height in feet.

a. Write an expression for the height of a football at time t when the initial upward velocity is 20 feet per second and the initial height is 6 feet.

b. Factor your expression from part **a**.

c. Find the height of the football after 1 second.

H.O.T. 70. /// ERROR ANALYSIS /// A student attempted to factor $2x^2 + 11x + 12$ as shown. Find and explain the error.

$2x^2 + 11x + 12$

Factors of 12	Sum	
1 and 12	13	✓
2 and 6	8	✗
3 and 4	7	✗

$(2x + 1)(x + 12)$

Real-World Connections

71. The equation $d = 2t^2$ gives the distance from the start point of a toy boat that starts at rest and accelerates at 4 cm/s². The equation $d = 10t - 8$ gives the distance from the start point of a second boat that starts at rest 8 cm behind the first boat and travels at a constant rate of 10 cm/s.

a. By setting the equations equal to each other, you can determine when the cars are the same distance from the start point: $2t^2 = 10t - 8$. Use properties of algebra to collect all terms on the left side of the equation, leaving 0 on the right side.

b. Factor the expression on the left side of the equation.

c. The boats are the same distance from the start point at $t = 1$ and $t = 4$. Explain how the factors you found in part **b** were used to find these two times.

HMH

Match each trinomial with its correct factorization.

72. $6x^2 - 29x - 5$ **A.** $(x + 5)(6x + 1)$

73. $6x^2 - 31x + 5$ **B.** $(x - 5)(6x - 1)$

74. $6x^2 + 31x + 5$ **C.** $(x + 5)(6x - 1)$

75. $6x^2 + 29x - 5$ **D.** $(x - 5)(6x + 1)$

H.O.T. 76. Critical Thinking The quadratic trinomial $ax^2 + bx + c$ has $a > 0$ and can be factored into the product of two binomials.

   a. Explain what you know about the signs of the constants in the factors if $c > 0$.

   b. Explain what you know about the signs of the constants in the factors if $c < 0$.

TEST PREP

77. What value of b would make $3x^2 + bx - 8$ factorable?

   Ⓐ 3   **Ⓑ** 10   **Ⓒ** 11   **Ⓓ** 25

78. Which product of binomials is represented by the model?

   Ⓕ $(x + 4)(3x + 5)$ **Ⓗ** $(x + 3)(5x + 4)$

   Ⓖ $(x + 4)(5x + 3)$ **Ⓙ** $(x + 5)(3x + 4)$

$5x^2$	$4x$
$15x$	12

79. Which binomial is a factor of $24x^2 - 49x + 2$?

   Ⓐ $x - 2$ **Ⓑ** $x - 1$ **Ⓒ** $x + 1$ **Ⓓ** $x + 2$

80. Which value of c would make $2x^2 + x + c$ NOT factorable?

   Ⓕ -15 **Ⓖ** -9 **Ⓗ** -6 **Ⓙ** -1

CHALLENGE AND EXTEND

Factor each trinomial. Check your answer.

81. $1 + 4x + 4x^2$ **82.** $1 - 14x + 49x^2$ **83.** $1 + 18x + 81x^2$

84. $25 + 30x + 9x^2$ **85.** $4 + 20x + 25x^2$ **86.** $4 - 12x + 9x^2$

87. Find all possible values of b such that $3x^2 + bx + 2$ can be factored.

88. Find all possible values of b such that $3x^2 + bx - 2$ can be factored.

89. Find all possible values of b such that $5x^2 + bx + 1$ can be factored.

FOCUS ON MATHEMATICAL PRACTICES

H.O.T. 90. Problem Solving Suppose that a is a positive integer in the trinomial $ax^2 + x - 1 = (ax - 1)(x + 1)$. What is the value of a?

H.O.T. 91. Analysis Let a and c be prime numbers.

   a. Assuming the trinomial $ax^2 + bx + c$ can be factored, list all possible integer values for b in terms of a and c. Explain your reasoning.

   b. Assuming the trinomial $ax^2 + bx - c$ can be factored, list all possible integer values for b in terms of a and c. Explain your reasoning.

H.O.T. 92. Proof Show that for any integer value of k, the trinomial $kx^2 + kx + k$ has no binomial factors.

14-2 Technology TASK

Use a Graph to Factor Polynomials

You can use a graphing calculator to help factor polynomials.

MATHEMATICAL PRACTICES Use appropriate tools strategically.

Use with Factoring $ax^2 + bx + c$

MCC9-12.A.SSE.3a Factor a quadratic expression to reveal the zeros of the function it defines. *Also* **MCC9-12.A.SSE.2**

Activity

Factor $x^2 - 3x - 4$ using algebra and check your factorization using a graphing calculator.

1 $x^2 - 3x - 4$

$(x + \blacksquare)(x + \blacksquare)$ $b = -3$ and $c = -4$; look for factors of -4 whose sum is -3.

$(x - 4)(x + 1)$ $-4(1) = -4$; $-4 + 1 = -3$

2 Press Y= and enter $x^2 - 3x - 4$ for **Y1**.

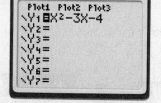

3 Press GRAPH to view the graph of the equation.

4 Press TRACE and use the left and right buttons to move the cursor along the graph. The graph appears to cross the x-axis at $x = -1$ and $x = 4$.

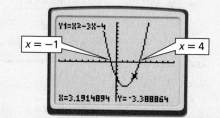

5 To find the value of y at $x = -1$, enter -1 and press ENTER while in *Trace* mode. The calculator gives you a value for y. Then enter 4 to find the value of y at $x = 4$.

The calculator tells you that $y = 0$ at $x = -1$ and at $x = 4$.

Notice that for a function with a binomial factor of the form $(x - a)$, it appears that a is an x-intercept.

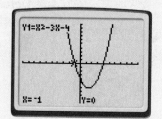

Try This

Graph each trinomial and use the graph to predict the factors. Then factor each trinomial using algebra.

1. $x^2 - x - 2$ **2.** $x^2 + 5x + 6$ **3.** $x^2 + x - 12$

4. $x^2 + 12x - 64$ **5.** $x^2 - 4x - 5$ **6.** $3x^2 + 16x - 12$

Factoring Special Products

 Essential Question: How can you recognize and factor special products?

Objectives
Factor perfect-square trinomials.

Factor the difference of two squares.

Who uses this?
Urban planners can use the area of a square park to find its length and width. (See Example 2.)

You can recognize and use patterns in the coefficients of some polynomials to factor them.

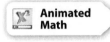 **Animated Math**

A trinomial is a perfect square if:
- The **first** and **last** terms are perfect squares.
- The **middle** term is two times one factor from the first term and one factor from the last term.

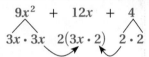

$$9x^2 \;+\; 12x \;+\; 4$$
$$3x \cdot 3x \quad 2(3x \cdot 2) \quad 2 \cdot 2$$

Know it! Note

Perfect-Square Trinomials

PERFECT-SQUARE TRINOMIAL	EXAMPLES
$a^2 + 2ab + b^2 = (a + b)(a + b) = (a + b)^2$	$x^2 + 6x + 9 = (x + 3)(x + 3) = (x + 3)^2$
$a^2 - 2ab + b^2 = (a - b)(a - b) = (a - b)^2$	$x^2 - 2x + 1 = (x - 1)(x - 1) = (x - 1)^2$

COMMON CORE GPS MCC9-12.A.SSE.2

EXAMPLE 1 Recognizing and Factoring Perfect-Square Trinomials

my.hrw.com

Online Video Tutor

Determine whether each trinomial is a perfect square. If so, factor. If not, explain.

A $x^2 + 12x + 36$

$$x^2 + 12x + 36$$
$$x \cdot x \quad 2(x \cdot 6) \quad 6 \cdot 6$$

The trinomial is a perfect square. Factor.

Method 1 Factor.
$x^2 + 12x + 36$

Factors of 36	Sum	
1 and 36	37	✗
2 and 18	20	✗
3 and 12	15	✗
4 and 9	13	✗
6 and 6	12	✓

$(x + 6)(x + 6)$

Method 2 Use the rule.
$x^2 + 12x + 36$ *a = x, b = 6*

$x^2 + 2(x)(6) + 6^2$ *Write the trinomial as $a^2 + 2ab + b^2$.*

$(x + 6)^2$ *Write the trinomial as $(a + b)^2$.*

Helpful Hint

You can check your answer by using the FOIL method.

For Example 1B,
$(2x - 3)^2 =$
$(2x - 3)(2x - 3) =$
$4x^2 - 6x - 6x + 9 =$
$4x^2 - 12x + 9$

Determine whether each trinomial is a perfect square. If so, factor. If not, explain.

B $4x^2 - 12x + 9$

$$4x^2 - 12x + 9$$

$2x \cdot 2x \qquad 2(2x \cdot 3) \qquad 3 \cdot 3$ *The trinomial is a perfect square. Factor.*

$$4x^2 - 12x + 9 \qquad a = 2x, \ b = 3$$
$$(2x)^2 - 2(2x)(3) + 3^2 \qquad a^2 - 2ab + b^2$$
$$(2x - 3)^2 \qquad (a - b)^2$$

C $x^2 + 9x + 16$

$$x^2 + 9x + 16$$

$x \cdot x \qquad 2(x \cdot 4) \qquad 4 \cdot 4 \qquad 2(x \cdot 4) \neq 9x$

$x^2 + 9x + 16$ is not a perfect-square trinomial because $9x \neq 2(x \cdot 4)$.

CHECK IT OUT! Determine whether each trinomial is a perfect square. If so, factor. If not, explain.

1a. $x^2 + 4x + 4$ **1b.** $x^2 - 14x + 49$ **1c.** $9x^2 - 6x + 4$

my.hrw.com

Online Video Tutor

Make sense of problems and persevere in solving them.

Problem-Solving Application

The park in the center of the Place des Vosges in Paris, France, is in the shape of a square. The area of the park is $(25x^2 + 70x + 49)$ ft². The side length of the park is in the form $cx + d$, where c and d are whole numbers. Find an expression in terms of x for the perimeter of the park. Find the perimeter when $x = 8$ ft.

1 Understand the Problem

The **answer** will be an expression for the perimeter of the park and the value of the expression when $x = 8$.

List the **important information:**

- The park is a square with area $(25x^2 + 70x + 49)$ ft².
- The side length of the park is in the form $cx + d$, where c and d are whole numbers.

2 Make a Plan

The formula for the area of a square is area = $(\text{side})^2$.

Factor $25x^2 + 70x + 49$ to find the side length of the park. Write a formula for the perimeter of the park, and evaluate the expression for $x = 8$.

3 Solve

$$25x^2 + 70x + 49 \qquad a = 5x, \, b = 7$$
$$(5x)^2 + 2(5x)(7) + 7^2 \quad \textit{Write the trinomial as } a^2 + 2ab + b^2.$$
$$(5x + 7)^2 \qquad\qquad \textit{Write the trinomial as } (a + b)^2.$$

$$25x^2 + 70x + 49 = (5x + 7)(5x + 7)$$

The side length of the park is $(5x + 7)$ ft.

Write a formula for the perimeter of the park.

$$P = 4s \qquad\qquad \textit{Write the formula for the perimeter of a square.}$$
$$= 4(5x + 7) \qquad \textit{Substitute the side length for s.}$$
$$= 20x + 28 \qquad \textit{Distribute 4.}$$

An expression for the perimeter of the park in feet is $20x + 28$.

Evaluate the expression when $x = 8$.

$$P = 20x + 28$$
$$= 20(8) + 28 \qquad \textit{Substitute 8 for x.}$$
$$= 188$$

When $x = 8$ ft, the perimeter of the park is 188 ft.

4 Look Back

For a square with a perimeter of 188 ft, the side length is $\frac{188}{4} = 47$ ft and the area is $47^2 = 2209$ ft^2.

Evaluate $25x^2 + 70x + 49$ for $x = 8$:
$$25(8)^2 + 70(8) + 49$$
$$1600 + 560 + 49$$
$$2209 \checkmark$$

 2. What if...? A company produces square sheets of aluminum, each of which has an area of $(9x^2 + 6x + 1)$ m^2. The side length of each sheet is in the form $cx + d$, where c and d are whole numbers. Find an expression in terms of x for the perimeter of a sheet. Find the perimeter when $x = 3$ m.

Previously, you learned that the difference of two squares has the form $a^2 - b^2$. The difference of two squares can be written as the product $(a + b)(a - b)$. You can use this pattern to factor some polynomials.

A polynomial is a difference of two squares if:
- There are two terms, one subtracted from the other.
- Both terms are perfect squares.

$$4x^2 - 9$$
$$\overset{\textstyle\diagdown\diagup}{2x \cdot 2x} \quad \overset{\textstyle\diagdown\diagup}{3 \cdot 3}$$

Difference of Two Squares

DIFFERENCE OF TWO SQUARES	EXAMPLE
$a^2 - b^2 = (a + b)(a - b)$	$x^2 - 9 = (x + 3)(x - 3)$

EXAMPLE **3**

Recognizing and Factoring the Difference of Two Squares

Determine whether each binomial is a difference of two squares. If so, factor. If not, explain.

A $x^2 - 81$

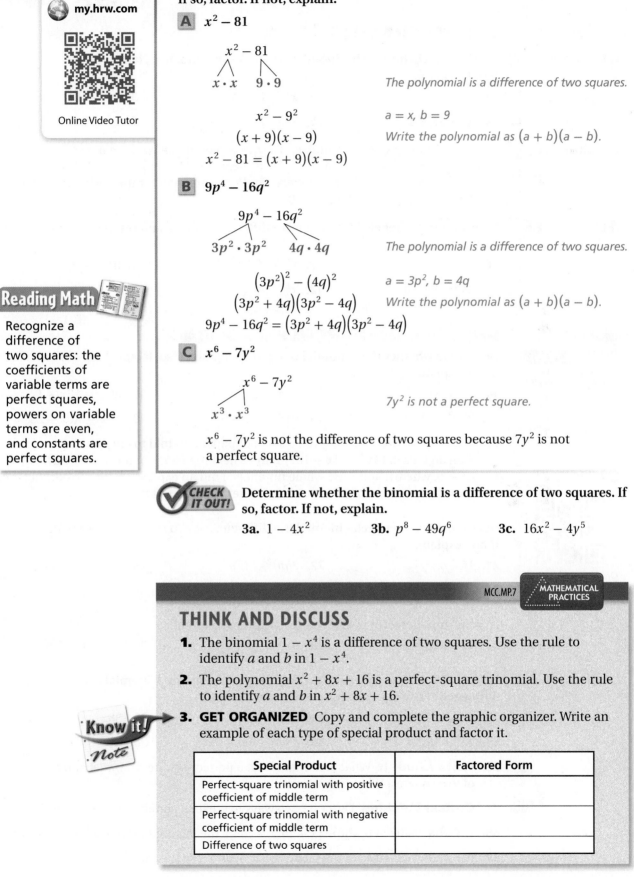

$$x^2 - 81$$
$$x \cdot x \qquad 9 \cdot 9$$

The polynomial is a difference of two squares.

$$x^2 - 9^2 \qquad\qquad a = x, \; b = 9$$
$$(x + 9)(x - 9) \qquad \textit{Write the polynomial as } (a + b)(a - b).$$
$$x^2 - 81 = (x + 9)(x - 9)$$

B $9p^4 - 16q^2$

$$9p^4 - 16q^2$$
$$3p^2 \cdot 3p^2 \qquad 4q \cdot 4q$$

The polynomial is a difference of two squares.

Reading Math

Recognize a difference of two squares: the coefficients of variable terms are perfect squares, powers on variable terms are even, and constants are perfect squares.

$$\left(3p^2\right)^2 - \left(4q\right)^2 \qquad a = 3p^2, \; b = 4q$$
$$\left(3p^2 + 4q\right)\left(3p^2 - 4q\right) \qquad \textit{Write the polynomial as } (a + b)(a - b).$$
$$9p^4 - 16q^2 = \left(3p^2 + 4q\right)\left(3p^2 - 4q\right)$$

C $x^6 - 7y^2$

$$x^6 - 7y^2$$
$$x^3 \cdot x^3$$

$7y^2$ is not a perfect square.

$x^6 - 7y^2$ is not the difference of two squares because $7y^2$ is not a perfect square.

CHECK IT OUT! Determine whether the binomial is a difference of two squares. If so, factor. If not, explain.

3a. $1 - 4x^2$ **3b.** $p^8 - 49q^6$ **3c.** $16x^2 - 4y^5$

MCC.MP.7   **MATHEMATICAL PRACTICES**

THINK AND DISCUSS

1. The binomial $1 - x^4$ is a difference of two squares. Use the rule to identify a and b in $1 - x^4$.

2. The polynomial $x^2 + 8x + 16$ is a perfect-square trinomial. Use the rule to identify a and b in $x^2 + 8x + 16$.

Know it! Note

3. GET ORGANIZED Copy and complete the graphic organizer. Write an example of each type of special product and factor it.

Special Product	Factored Form
Perfect-square trinomial with positive coefficient of middle term	
Perfect-square trinomial with negative coefficient of middle term	
Difference of two squares	

GUIDED PRACTICE

SEE EXAMPLE 1

Determine whether each trinomial is a perfect square. If so, factor. If not, explain.

1. $x^2 - 4x + 4$

2. $x^2 - 4x - 4$

3. $9x^2 - 12x + 4$

4. $x^2 + 2x + 1$

5. $x^2 - 6x + 9$

6. $x^2 - 6x - 9$

SEE EXAMPLE 2

7. City Planning A city purchases a square plot of land with an area of $(x^2 + 24x + 144)$ yd^2 for a park. The dimensions of the plot are of the form $ax + b$, where a and b are whole numbers. Find an expression for the perimeter of the park. Find the perimeter when $x = 10$ yd.

SEE EXAMPLE 3

Determine whether each binomial is a difference of two squares. If so, factor. If not, explain.

8. $1 - 4x^2$

9. $s^2 - 4^2$

10. $81x^2 - 1$

11. $4x^4 - 9y^2$

12. $x^8 - 50$

13. $x^6 - 9$

PRACTICE AND PROBLEM SOLVING

Independent Practice	
For Exercises	See Example
14–19	1
20	2
21–26	3

my.hrw.com

Online Extra Practice

Determine whether the trinomial is a perfect square. If so, factor. If not, explain.

14. $4x^2 - 4x + 1$

15. $4x^2 - 4x - 1$

16. $36x^2 - 12x + 1$

17. $25x^2 + 10x + 4$

18. $9x^2 + 18x + 9$

19. $16x^2 - 40x + 25$

20. Measurement You are given a sheet of paper and told to cut out a square piece with an area of $(4x^2 - 44x + 121)$ mm^2. The dimensions of the square have the form $ax - b$, where a and b are whole numbers. Find an expression for the perimeter of the square you cut out. Find the perimeter when $x = 41$ mm.

Determine whether each binomial is a difference of two squares. If so, factor. If not, explain.

21. $1^2 - 4x^2$

22. $25m^2 - 16n^2$

23. $4x - 9y$

24. $49p^{12} - 9q^6$

25. $9^2 - 100x^4$

26. $x^3 - y^3$

Find the missing term in each perfect-square trinomial.

27. $x^2 + 14x + \blacksquare$

28. $9x^2 + \blacksquare + 25$

29. $\blacksquare - 36y + 81$

Factor each polynomial using the rule for perfect-square trinomials or the rule for a difference of two squares. Tell which rule you used.

30. $x^2 - 8x + 16$

31. $100x^2 - 81y^2$

32. $36x^2 + 24x + 4$

33. $4r^6 - 25s^6$

34. $49x^2 - 70x + 25$

35. $x^{14} - 144$

H.O.T. **36. Write About It** What is similar about a perfect-square trinomial and a difference of two squares? What is different?

H.O.T. **37. Critical Thinking** Describe two ways to create a perfect-square trinomial.

38. For what value of b would $(x + b)(x + b)$ be the factored form of $x^2 - 22x + 121$?

39. For what value of c are the factors of $x^2 + cx + 256$ the same?

40. Juanita designed a vegetable garden in the shape of a square and purchased fencing for that design. Then she decided to change the design to a rectangle.

   a. The square garden had an area of x^2 ft^2. The area of the rectangular garden is $\left(x^2 - 25\right)$ ft^2. Factor this expression.

   b. The rectangular garden must have the same perimeter as the square garden, so Juanita added a number of feet to the length and subtracted the same number of feet from the width. Use your factors from part **a** to determine how many feet were added to the length and subtracted from the width.

   c. If the original length of the square garden was 8 feet, what are the length and width of the new garden?

41. Multi-Step The area of a square is represented by $25z^2 - 40z + 16$.

   a. What expression represents the length of a side of the square?

   b. What expression represents the perimeter of the square?

   c. What are the length of a side, the perimeter, and the area of the square when $z = 3$?

42. Multi-Step A small rectangle is drawn inside a larger rectangle as shown.

   a. What is the area of each rectangle?

   b. What is the area of the green region?

   c. Factor the expression for the area of the green region. (*Hint:* First factor out the common factor of 3 and then factor the binomial.)

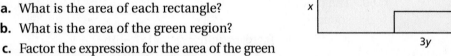

43. Evaluate each expression for the values of x.

	x	$x^2 + 10x + 25$	$(x + 5)^2$	$(x - 5)^2$	$x^2 - 10x + 25$	$x^2 - 25$
a.	-5	■	■	■	■	■
b.	-1	■	■	■	■	■
c.	0	■	■	■	■	■
d.	1	■	■	■	■	■
e.	5	■	■	■	■	■

44. In the table above, which columns have equivalent values? Explain why.

45. Geometry A model for the difference of two squares is shown below. Copy and complete the second figure by writing the missing labels.

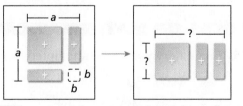

H.O.T. 46. **///ERROR ANALYSIS///** Two students factored $25x^4 - 9y^2$. Which is incorrect? Explain the error.

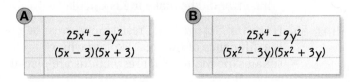

47. A polynomial expression is evaluated for the x- and y-values shown in the table. Which expression could have been evaluated to give the values shown in the third column?

x	y	Value of Expression
0	0	0
-1	-1	0
1	1	0
1	-1	4

    Ⓐ $x^2 - y^2$

    Ⓑ $x^2 + 2xy + y^2$

    Ⓒ $x^2 - 2xy + y^2$

    Ⓓ None of the above

48. The area of a square is $4x^2 + 20x + 25$. Which expression can also be used to model the area of the square?

    Ⓕ $(2x - 5)(5 - 2x)$ Ⓗ $(2x - 5)^2$

    Ⓖ $(2x + 5)(2x - 5)$ Ⓙ $(2x + 5)^2$

49. Gridded Response Evaluate the polynomial expression $x^2 - 18x + 81$ for $x = 10$.

CHALLENGE AND EXTEND

50. The binomial $81x^4 - 16$ can be factored using the rule for a difference of two squares.

    a. Fill in the factorization: $81x^4 - 16$

$$\left(9x^2 + \blacksquare\right)\left(\blacksquare - \blacksquare\right)$$

    b. One binomial from part **a** can be further factored. Identify the binomial and factor it.

    c. Write your own binomial that can be factored twice as the difference of two squares.

51. The expression $4 - (v + 2)^2$ is the difference of two squares, because it fits the rule $a^2 - b^2$.

    a. Identify a and b in the expression.

    b. Factor and simplify $4 - (v + 2)^2$.

The *difference of cubes* is an expression of the form $a^3 - b^3$. It can be factored according to the rule $a^3 - b^3 = (a - b)(a^2 + ab + b^2)$. For each binomial, identify a and b, and factor using the rule.

52. $x^3 - 1$ **53.** $27y^3 - 64$ **54.** $n^6 - 8$

FOCUS ON MATHEMATICAL PRACTICES

H.O.T. 55. Error Analysis Jesse attempted to factor the polynomial $9x^2 + 16y^2$:

$$= -\left(-9x^2 - 16y^2\right)$$

$$= -\left(-3x + 4y\right)\left(-3x - 4y\right)$$

$$= -\left(3x - 4y\right)\left(3x + 4y\right)$$

What error did he make in his calculation?

H.O.T. 56. Number Sense What restrictions must be placed on the value of n so that $x^n - y^n$ is a difference of squares? Explain why $x^n - y^{n+1}$ is never the difference of two squares, no matter what restrictions are placed on the value of n.

Mental Math

Recognizing patterns of special products can help you perform multiplication mentally.

Remember these special products.

Patterns of Special Products	
Difference of Two Squares	$(a + b)(a - b) = a^2 - b^2$
Perfect-Square Trinomial	$(a + b)^2 = a^2 + 2ab + b^2$ $(a - b)^2 = a^2 - 2ab + b^2$

Example 1

Simplify $17^2 - 7^2$.

This expression is a difference of two squares with $a = 17$ and $b = 7$.

$a^2 - b^2 = (a + b)(a - b)$ *Write the rule for a difference of two squares.*

$17^2 - 7^2 = (17 + 7)(17 - 7)$ *Substitute 17 for a and 7 for b.*

$= (24)(10)$ *Simplify.*

$= 240$

Example 2

Simplify $14^2 + 2(14)(6) + 6^2$.

This expression is a perfect-square trinomial with $a = 14$ and $b = 6$.

$a^2 + 2ab + b^2 = (a + b)^2$ *Write the rule for a perfect-square trinomial.*

$14^2 + 2(14)(6) + 6^2 = (14 + 6)^2$ *Substitute 14 for a and 6 for b.*

$= (20)^2$ *Simplify.*

$= 400$

Try This

Simplify each expression using the rules for special products.

1. $18^2 - 12^2$

2. $11^2 + 2(11)(14) + 14^2$

3. $22^2 - 18^2$

4. $38^2 - 2(38)(27) + 27^2$

5. $29^2 - 2(29)(17) + 17^2$

6. $55^2 + 2(55)(45) + 45^2$

7. $14^2 - 9^2$

8. $13^2 - 12^2$

9. $14^2 + 2(14)(16) + 16^2$

Ready to Go On?

my.hrw.com
Assessment and Intervention

14-1 Factoring $x^2 + bx + c$

Factor each trinomial. Check your answer.

1. $n^2 + 9n + 20$ **2.** $d^2 - 6d - 7$ **3.** $x^2 - 6x + 8$

4. $y^2 + 7y - 30$ **5.** $k^2 - 6k + 5$ **6.** $c^2 - 10c + 24$

7. $x^2 + 6x + 5$ **8.** $x^2 + 6x + 8$ **9.** $x^2 + 8x + 15$

10. $x^2 - 8x + 12$ **11.** $x^2 + 10x + 25$ **12.** $x^2 - 13x + 22$

13. Simplify and factor the expression $n(n + 3) - 4$. Show that the original expression and the factored form have the same value for $n = 0, 1, 2, 3,$ and 4.

14-2 Factoring $ax^2 + bx + c$

Factor each trinomial. Check your answer.

14. $2x^2 + 11x + 5$ **15.** $3n^2 + 16n + 21$ **16.** $5y^2 - 7y - 6$

17. $4g^2 - 10g + 6$ **18.** $6p^2 - 18p - 24$ **19.** $12d^2 + 7d - 12$

20. $2x^2 + 11x + 5$ **21.** $3x^2 + 10x + 7$ **22.** $2x^2 - 3x + 1$

23. $3x^2 + 8x + 4$ **24.** $5x^2 + 28x + 15$ **25.** $6x^2 - 19x + 15$

26. The area of a rectangle is $(8x^2 + 8x + 2)$ cm^2. The width is $(2x + 1)$ cm. What is the length of the rectangle?

14-3 Factoring Special Products

Determine whether each trinomial is a perfect square. If so, factor. If not, explain.

27. $x^2 + 8x + 16$ **28.** $4x^2 - 20x + 25$ **29.** $x^2 + 3x + 9$

30. $2x^2 - 4x + 4$ **31.** $9x^2 - 12x + 4$ **32.** $x^2 - 12x - 36$

33. An architect is designing square windows with an area of $(x^2 + 20x + 100)$ ft^2. The dimensions of the windows are of the form $ax + b$, where a and b are whole numbers. Find an expression for the perimeter of the windows. Find the perimeter of a window when $x = 4$ ft.

Determine whether each trinomial is a difference of two squares. If so, factor. If not, explain.

34. $x^2 - 121$ **35.** $4t^2 - 20$ **36.** $1 - 9y^4$

37. $25m^2 - 4m^6$ **38.** $16x^2 + 49$ **39.** $r^4 - t^2$

40. The area of a square is $(36d^2 - 36d + 9)$ in^2.

   a. What expression represents the length of a side of the square?

   b. What expression represents the perimeter of the square?

   c. What are the length of a side, the perimeter, and the area of the square when $d = 2$ in.?

PARCC Assessment Readiness

Selected Response

1. Factor $x^2 + 20x + 36$.

- **A** $(x + 20)(x + 36)$
- **B** $(x + 10)(x + 10)$
- **C** $(x + 2)(x + 18)$
- **D** $(x + 4)(x + 9)$

2. Determine whether $81 - 49n^4$ is a difference of two squares. If so, factor it. If not, explain why.

- **F** $(9 - 7n^4)(9 + 7n^4)$
- **G** $(9 + 7n^2)(9 - 7n^2)$
- **H** $(9 - 7n^2)(9 - 7n^2)$
- **J** Not a difference of squares because $-49n^4$ is not a perfect square.

3. Determine whether $16x^2 - 24x + 9$ is a perfect square. If so, factor it. If not, explain why.

- **A** No, $16x^2 - 24x + 9$ is not a perfect square. $16x^2$ and 9 are perfect squares, but $24x$ is not a perfect square. So $16x^2 - 24x + 9$ is not a perfect square.
- **B** Yes, $16x^2 - 24x + 9$ is a perfect square. $(4x + 3)^2$
- **C** Yes, $16x^2 - 24x + 9$ is a perfect square. $(4x - 3)^2$
- **D** Yes, $16x^2 - 24x + 9$ is a perfect square. $(16x - 9)^2$

4. Factor $-3x^2 + 26x - 16$.

- **F** $-(x - 8)(3x - 2)$
- **G** $(3x - 2)(x - 8)$
- **H** $-(x + 8)(3x + 2)$
- **J** $(3x - 2)(x + 8)$

5. Factor $2x^2 + 7x + 6$.

- **A** $(x + 2)(2x - 3)$
- **B** $(x + 2)(x + 3)$
- **C** $(x + 3)(2x + 2)$
- **D** $(x + 2)(2x + 3)$

6. Factor the trinomial $x^4 + 50x^2 + 625$.

- **F** $(x + 25)^4$
- **G** $(x^2 + 50)^2$
- **H** $(x^2 + 25)^2$
- **J** $2(x^2 + 25)^2$

7. Factor $3x^2 + 2x - 8$ by guess and check.

- **A** $(x + 2)(3x - 4)$
- **B** $(x - 2)(3x + 4)$
- **C** $(x - 2)(3x - 4)$
- **D** $(x + 2)(3x + 4)$

8. Factor the trinomial $42n^2 - n - 30$.

- **F** $(6n + 5)(7n - 6)$
- **G** $(6n + 6)(7n - 5)$
- **H** $(6n - 5)(7n + 6)$
- **J** Cannot be factored

9. Which expression is *not* a factor of the binomial $x^4 - 16$?

- **A** $x - 2$
- **B** $x + 2$
- **C** $x - 4$
- **D** $x^2 + 4$

Mini-Tasks

10. Find three possible values of b such that $4x^2 + bx + 3$ can be factored.

11. Write the polynomial that the model shown below displays. Then write an equivalent expression using factoring.

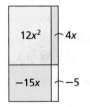

15 Graphing Quadratic Functions

COMMON
CORE GPS

Contents

MATHEMATICAL PRACTICES   The Common Core Georgia Performance Standards for Mathematical Practice describe varieties of expertise that all students should seek to develop. Opportunities to develop these practices are integrated throughout this program.

1 Make sense of problems and persevere in solving them.
2 Reason abstractly and quantitatively.
3 Construct viable arguments and critique the reasoning of others.
4 Model with mathematics.
5 Use appropriate tools strategically.
6 Attend to precision.
7 Look for and make use of structure.
8 Look for and express regularity in repeated reasoning.

Unpacking the Standards

my.hrw.com
Multilingual Glossary

Understanding the standards and the vocabulary terms in the standards will help you know exactly what you are expected to learn in this chapter.

 MCC9-12.F.IF.7a

Graph … quadratic functions and show intercepts, maxima, and minima.

Key Vocabulary

quadratic function (función cuadrática)
A function that can be written in the form $f(x) = ax^2 + bx + c$, where a, b, and c are real numbers and $a \neq 0$, or in the form $f(x) = a(x - h)^2 + k$, where a, h, and k are real numbers and $a \neq 0$.

x-intercept (intersección con el eje x)
The x-coordinate(s) of the point(s) where a graph intersects the x-axis.

y-intercept (intersección con el eje y)
The y-coordinate(s) of the point(s) where a graph intersects the y-axis.

maximum/minimum value of a function (máximo/mínimo de una función) The y-value of the highest/lowest point on the graph of the function.

What It Means For You

The graph of a quadratic function has key features that are helpful when interpreting a real-world quadratic model: the intercepts and the maximum or minimum value.

EXAMPLE   Graph of $y = x^2 + 2x - 3$

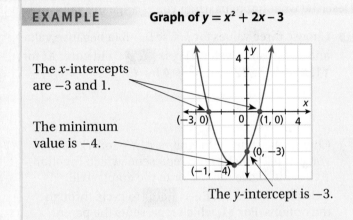

The x-intercepts are -3 and 1.

The minimum value is -4.

The y-intercept is -3.

15-1 Technology TASK

Use with Using Transformations to Graph Quadratic Functions

Explore Parameter Changes

You can use a graphing calculator to explore how changes in the parameters of a function affect its graph.

 MATHEMATICAL PRACTICES **Use appropriate tools strategically.**

MCC9-12.F.BF.3 Identify the effect on the graph of replacing $f(x)$ by $f(x) + k$, $k\,f(x)$, $f(kx)$, and $f(x + k)$ … Experiment with cases and illustrate an explanation of the effects on the graph using technology.

Activity

Describe what happens when you change the value of k in the function $g(x) = x^2 + k$.

1 Choose three values for k. Use 0, −5 (a negative value), and 4 (a positive value). Press **Y=** , and enter **X²** for **Y1**, **X² − 5** for **Y2**, and **X² + 4** for **Y3**.

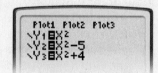

2 Change the style of the graphs of **Y1** and **Y2** so that you can tell which graph represents which function. To do this, move the cursor to the graph style indicator next to **Y1**. Press **ENTER** to cycle through the options. For **Y1**, which represents the parent function, choose the thick line.

3 Next, change the line style for **Y2** to the dotted line.

4 Graph the functions in the square window by pressing **ZOOM** and choosing **5 : ZSquare**.

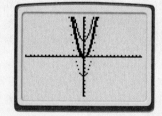

Notice that the graphs are identical except that the graph of **Y2** is shifted 5 units down and the graph of **Y3** has been shifted 4 units up from the graph of **Y1**.

You can conclude that the parameter k in the function $g(x) = x^2 + k$ has the effect of translating the parent function $f(x) = x^2$ a distance of k units up if k is positive and $|k|$ units down if k is negative.

Try This

Use your graphing calculator to compare the graph of each function to the graph of $f(x) = x^2$. Describe how the graphs differ.

1. $g(x) = (x - 4)^2$ **2.** $g(x) = (x + 3)^2$ **3.** $g(x) = -x^2$

4. Make a Conjecture Use your graphing calculator to determine what happens when you change the value of h in the function $g(x) = (x - h)^2$. Check both positive and negative values of h.

5. Make a Conjecture Use your graphing calculator to determine what happens when you change the value of a in the function $g(x) = ax^2$. Check values of a that are greater than 1 and values of a that are between 0 and 1.

15-1 Using Transformations to Graph Quadratic Functions

Essential Question: How do you graph quadratic functions and transform them on the coordinate plane?

Objectives
Transform quadratic functions.

Describe the effects of changes in the parameters of $y = a(x - h)^2 + k$.

Vocabulary
quadratic function
parabola
vertex of a parabola
vertex form

Why learn this?
You can use transformations of quadratic functions to analyze changes in braking distance. (See Example 5.)

You have studied linear functions of the form $f(x) = mx + b$. A **quadratic function** is a function that can be written in the form $f(x) = a(x - h)^2 + k \, (a \neq 0)$. In a quadratic function, the variable is always squared. The table shows the linear and quadratic parent functions.

Linear and Quadratic Parent Functions

ALGEBRA	NUMBERS						GRAPH
Linear Parent Function $f(x) = x$							
	x	-2	-1	0	1	2	
	$f(x) = x$	-2	-1	0	1	2	
Quadratic Parent Function $f(x) = x^2$							
	x	-2	-1	0	1	2	
	$f(x) = x^2$	4	1	0	1	4	

Notice that the graph of the parent function $f(x) = x^2$ is a U-shaped curve called a **parabola**. As with other functions, you can graph a quadratic function by plotting points with coordinates that make the equation true.

COMMON CORE GPS
MCC9-12.A.REI.10

EXAMPLE 1 Graphing Quadratic Functions Using a Table

Graph $f(x) = x^2 - 6x + 8$ by using a table.

my.hrw.com

Online Video Tutor

Make a table. Plot enough ordered pairs to see both sides of the curve.

x	$f(x) = x^2 - 6x + 8$	$(x, f(x))$
1	$f(1) = 1^2 - 6(1) + 8 = 3$	$(1, 3)$
2	$f(2) = 2^2 - 6(2) + 8 = 0$	$(2, 0)$
3	$f(3) = 3^2 - 6(3) + 8 = -1$	$(3, -1)$
4	$f(4) = 4^2 - 6(4) + 8 = 0$	$(4, 0)$
5	$f(5) = 5^2 - 6(5) + 8 = 3$	$(5, 3)$

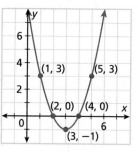

1. Graph $g(x) = -x^2 + 6x - 8$ by using a table.

You can also graph quadratic functions by applying transformations to the parent function $f(x) = x^2$. Transforming quadratic functions is similar to transforming linear functions.

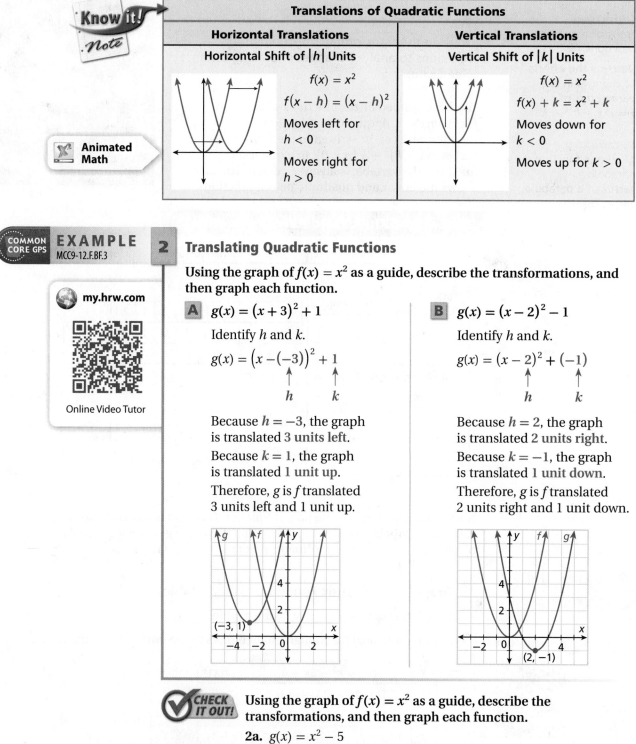

Know it!
Note

Animated Math

Translations of Quadratic Functions	
Horizontal Translations	**Vertical Translations**
Horizontal Shift of $\lvert h \rvert$ Units	**Vertical Shift of $\lvert k \rvert$ Units**

$f(x) = x^2$

$f(x - h) = (x - h)^2$

Moves left for
$h < 0$

Moves right for
$h > 0$

$f(x) = x^2$

$f(x) + k = x^2 + k$

Moves down for
$k < 0$

Moves up for $k > 0$

COMMON CORE GPS
MCC9-12.F.BF.3

EXAMPLE 2 Translating Quadratic Functions

my.hrw.com

Online Video Tutor

Using the graph of $f(x) = x^2$ as a guide, describe the transformations, and then graph each function.

A $g(x) = (x + 3)^2 + 1$

Identify h and k.

$$g(x) = \left(x - (-3)\right)^2 + 1$$

$\uparrow \quad \uparrow$
$h \quad k$

Because $h = -3$, the graph is translated **3 units left**.

Because $k = 1$, the graph is translated **1 unit up**.

Therefore, g is f translated 3 units left and 1 unit up.

B $g(x) = (x - 2)^2 - 1$

Identify h and k.

$$g(x) = (x - 2)^2 + (-1)$$

$\uparrow \quad \uparrow$
$h \quad k$

Because $h = 2$, the graph is translated **2 units right**.

Because $k = -1$, the graph is translated **1 unit down**.

Therefore, g is f translated 2 units right and 1 unit down.

CHECK IT OUT! Using the graph of $f(x) = x^2$ as a guide, describe the transformations, and then graph each function.

2a. $g(x) = x^2 - 5$
2b. $g(x) = (x + 3)^2 - 2$

Recall that functions can also be reflected, stretched, or compressed.

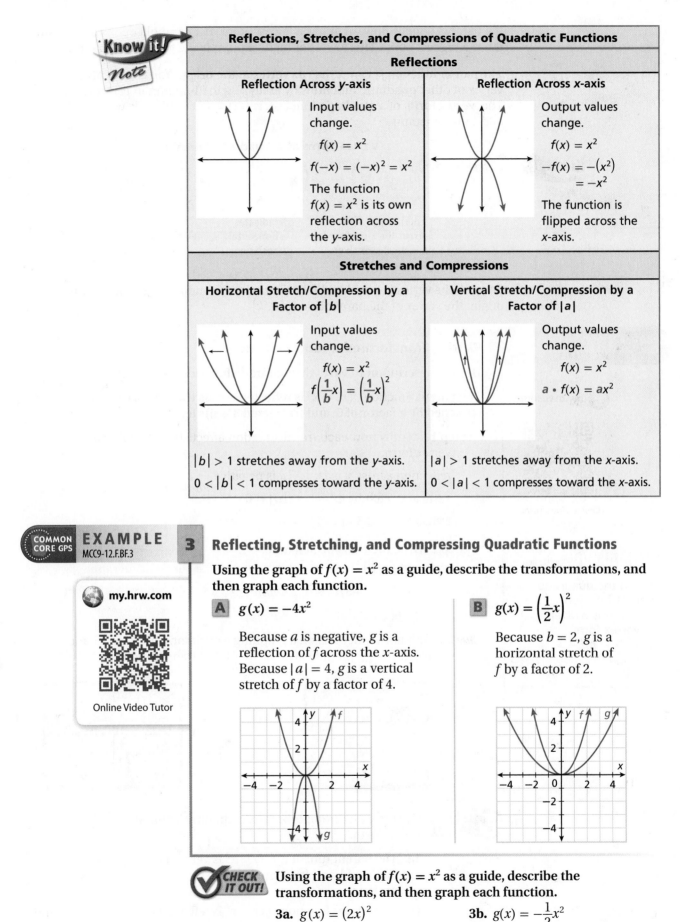

Know it! Note

Reflections, Stretches, and Compressions of Quadratic Functions

Reflections

Reflection Across *y*-axis	Reflection Across *x*-axis
Input values change. $f(x) = x^2$ $f(-x) = (-x)^2 = x^2$ The function $f(x) = x^2$ is its own reflection across the *y*-axis.	Output values change. $f(x) = x^2$ $-f(x) = -(x^2)$ $= -x^2$ The function is flipped across the *x*-axis.

Stretches and Compressions

Horizontal Stretch/Compression by a Factor of $|b|$	Vertical Stretch/Compression by a Factor of $|a|$
Input values change. $f(x) = x^2$ $f\left(\frac{1}{b}x\right) = \left(\frac{1}{b}x\right)^2$	Output values change. $f(x) = x^2$ $a \cdot f(x) = ax^2$
$|b| > 1$ stretches away from the *y*-axis. $0 < |b| < 1$ compresses toward the *y*-axis.	$|a| > 1$ stretches away from the *x*-axis. $0 < |a| < 1$ compresses toward the *x*-axis.

COMMON CORE GPS MCC9-12.F.BF.3

EXAMPLE 3

my.hrw.com

Online Video Tutor

Reflecting, Stretching, and Compressing Quadratic Functions

Using the graph of $f(x) = x^2$ as a guide, describe the transformations, and then graph each function.

A $g(x) = -4x^2$

Because *a* is negative, *g* is a reflection of *f* across the *x*-axis. Because $|a| = 4$, *g* is a vertical stretch of *f* by a factor of 4.

B $g(x) = \left(\frac{1}{2}x\right)^2$

Because $b = 2$, *g* is a horizontal stretch of *f* by a factor of 2.

CHECK IT OUT! Using the graph of $f(x) = x^2$ as a guide, describe the transformations, and then graph each function.

3a. $g(x) = (2x)^2$

3b. $g(x) = -\frac{1}{2}x^2$

If a parabola opens upward, it has a lowest point. If a parabola opens downward, it has a highest point. This lowest or highest point is the **vertex of a parabola**.

The parent function $f(x) = x^2$ has its vertex at the origin. You can identify the vertex of other quadratic functions by analyzing the function in *vertex form*. The **vertex form** of a quadratic function is $f(x) = a(x - h)^2 + k$, where a, h, and k are constants.

Vertex Form of a Quadratic Function

$$f(x) = a(x - h)^2 + k$$

a indicates a reflection across the *x*-axis and/or a vertical stretch or compression.

h indicates a horizontal translation.

k indicates a vertical translation.

Because the vertex is translated h horizontal units and k vertical units from the origin, the vertex of the parabola is at (h, k).

COMMON CORE GPS
MCC9-12.F.BF.3

my.hrw.com

Online Video Tutor

EXAMPLE 4 Writing Transformed Quadratic Functions

Use the description to write the quadratic function in vertex form.

The parent function $f(x) = x^2$ is reflected across the *x*-axis, vertically stretched by a factor of 6, and translated 3 units left to create g.

Step 1 Identify how each transformation affects the constants in vertex form.

reflection across *x*-axis: a is negative $\Bigg\}\ a = -6$

vertical stretch by 6: $|a| = 6$

translation left 3 units: $h = -3$

Step 2 Write the transformed function.

$g(x) = a(x - h)^2 + k$ *Vertex form of a quadratic function*

$= -6\big(x - (-3)\big)^2 + 0$ *Substitute −6 for a, −3 for h, and 0 for k.*

$= -6(x + 3)^2$ *Simplify.*

Check Graph both functions on a graphing calculator. Enter f as **Y1** and g as **Y2**. The graph indicates the identified transformations.

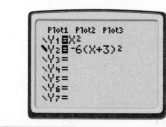

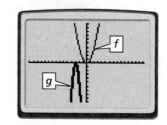

Helpful Hint

When the quadratic parent function $f(x) = x^2$ is written in vertex form, $y = a(x - h)^2 + k$, $a = 1$, $h = 0$, and $k = 0$.

 CHECK IT OUT! **Use the description to write the quadratic function in vertex form.**

4a. The parent function $f(x) = x^2$ is vertically compressed by a factor of $\frac{1}{3}$ and translated 2 units right and 4 units down to create g.

4b. The parent function $f(x) = x^2$ is reflected across the *x*-axis and translated 5 units left and 1 unit up to create g.

EXAMPLE **5** *Automotive Application*

The minimum braking distance d in feet for a vehicle on dry concrete is approximated by the function $d(v) = 0.045v^2$, where v is the vehicle's speed in miles per hour. If the vehicle's tires are in poor condition, the braking-distance function is $d_p(v) = 0.068v^2$. What kind of transformation describes this change, and what does the transformation mean?

Examine both functions in vertex form.

$$d(v) = 0.045(v - 0)^2 + 0 \qquad d_p(v) = 0.068(v - 0)^2 + 0$$

The value of a has increased from 0.045 to 0.068. The increase indicates a vertical stretch.

Find the stretch factor by comparing the new a-value to the old a-value:

$$\frac{a \text{ from } d_p(v)}{a \text{ from } d(v)} = \frac{0.068}{0.045} \approx 1.5$$

The function d_p represents a vertical stretch of d by a factor of approximately 1.5. Because the value of each function approximates braking distance, a vehicle with tires in poor condition takes about 1.5 times as many feet to stop as a vehicle with good tires does.

Check Graph both functions on a graphing calculator. The graph of d_p appears to be vertically stretched compared with the graph of d.

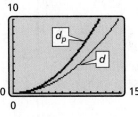

CHECK IT OUT! Use the information above to answer the following.

5. The minimum braking distance d_n in feet for a vehicle with new tires at optimal inflation is $d_n(v) = 0.039v^2$, where v is the vehicle's speed in miles per hour. What kind of transformation describes this change from $d(v) = 0.045v^2$, and what does this transformation mean?

THINK AND DISCUSS

1. Explain how the values of a, h, and k in the vertex form of a quadratic function affect the function's graph.

2. Explain how to determine which of two quadratic functions expressed in vertex form has a narrower graph.

3. GET ORGANIZED Copy and complete the graphic organizer. In each row, write an equation that represents the indicated transformation of the quadratic parent function, and show its graph.

Transformation	Equation	Graph
Vertical translation		
Horizontal translation		
Reflection		
Vertical stretch		
Vertical compression		

GUIDED PRACTICE

1. **Vocabulary** The highest or lowest point on the graph of a quadratic function is the __?__ . (*vertex* or *parabola*)

SEE EXAMPLE 1   Graph each function by using a table.

2. $f(x) = -2x^2 - 4$ 3. $g(x) = -x^2 + 3x - 2$ 4. $h(x) = x^2 + 2x$

SEE EXAMPLE 2   Using the graph of $f(x) = x^2$ as a guide, describe the transformations, and then graph each function.

5. $d(x) = (x - 4)^2$ 6. $g(x) = (x - 3)^2 + 2$ 7. $h(x) = (x + 1)^2 - 3$

SEE EXAMPLE 3   8. $g(x) = 3x^2$ 9. $h(x) = \left(\frac{1}{8}x\right)^2$ 10. $p(x) = 0.25x^2$

11. $h(x) = -(5x)^2$ 12. $g(x) = 4.2x^2$ 13. $d(x) = -\frac{2}{3}x^2$

SEE EXAMPLE 4   Use the description to write each quadratic function in vertex form.

14. The parent function $f(x) = x^2$ is vertically stretched by a factor of 2 and translated 3 units left to create g.

15. The parent function $f(x) = x^2$ is reflected across the x-axis and translated 6 units down to create h.

SEE EXAMPLE 5   16. **Physics** The safe working load L in pounds for a natural rope can be estimated by $L(r) = 5920r^2$, where r is the radius of the rope in inches. For an old rope, the function $L_o(r) = 4150r^2$ is used to estimate its safe working load. What kind of transformation describes this change, and what does this transformation mean?

PRACTICE AND PROBLEM SOLVING

Graph each function by using a table.

17. $f(x) = -x^2 + 4$ 18. $g(x) = x^2 - 2x + 1$ 19. $h(x) = 2x^2 + 4x - 1$

Using the graph of $f(x) = x^2$ as a guide, describe the transformations, and then graph each function.

20. $g(x) = x^2 - 2$ 21. $h(x) = (x + 5)^2$ 22. $j(x) = (x - 1)^2$

23. $g(x) = (x + 4)^2 - 3$ 24. $h(x) = (x + 2)^2 + 2$ 25. $j(x) = (x - 4)^2 - 9$

26. $g(x) = \frac{4}{7}x^2$ 27. $h(x) = -20x^2$ 28. $j(x) = \left(\frac{1}{3}x\right)^2$

my.hrw.com

Online Extra Practice

Use the description to write each quadratic function in vertex form.

29. The parent function $f(x) = x^2$ is reflected across the x-axis, vertically compressed by a factor of $\frac{1}{2}$, and translated 1 unit right to create g.

30. The parent function $f(x) = x^2$ is vertically stretched by a factor of 2.5 and translated 2 units left and 1 unit up to create h.

31. **Consumer Economics** The average gas mileage m in miles per gallon for a compact car is modeled by $m(s) = -0.015(s - 47)^2 + 33$, where s is the car's speed in miles per hour. The average gas mileage for an SUV is modeled by $m_u(s) = -0.015(s - 47)^2 + 15$. What kind of transformation describes this change, and what does this transformation mean?

H.O.T. **32. Pets** Keille is building a rectangular pen for a pet rabbit. She can buy wire fencing in a roll of 40 ft or a roll of 80 ft. The graph shows the area of pens she can build with each type of roll.

    a. Describe the function for an 80 ft roll of fencing as a transformation of the function for a 40 ft roll of fencing.

    b. Is the largest pen Keille can build with an 80 ft roll of fencing twice as large as the largest pen she can build with a 40 ft roll of fencing? Explain.

Using $f(x) = x^2$ as a guide, describe the transformations for each function.

33. $p(x) = -(x - 4)^2$ **34.** $g(x) = 8(x + 2)^2$

35. $h(x) = 4x^2 - 2$ **36.** $p(x) = \frac{1}{4}x^2 + 2$

37. $g(x) = (3x)^2 + 1$ **38.** $h(x) = -\left(\frac{1}{3}x\right)^2$

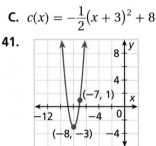

Possible Area of Pen

Area (ft²) vs *Width (ft)*
- ■ 40 ft roll
- ■ 80 ft roll

Match each graph with one of the following functions.

  A. $a(x) = 4(x + 8)^2 - 3$ **B.** $b(x) = -2(x - 8)^2 + 3$ **C.** $c(x) = -\frac{1}{2}(x + 3)^2 + 8$

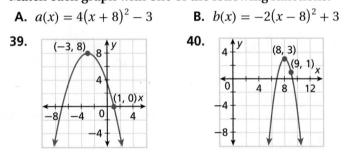

39.   **40.**   **41.**

H.O.T. **42. Geometry** The area A of the circle in the figure can be represented by $A(r) = \pi r^2$, where r is the radius.

    a. Write a function B in terms of r that represents the area of the shaded portion of the figure.

    b. Describe B as a transformation of A.

    c. What are the reasonable domain and range for each function? Explain.

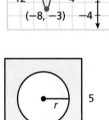

43. Critical Thinking What type of graph would a function of the form $f(x) = a(x - h)^2 + k$ have if $a = 0$? What type of function would it be?

H.O.T. **44. Write About It** Describe the graph of $f(x) = 999{,}999(x + 5)^2 + 5$ without graphing it.

Real-World Connections

45. The height h in feet of a baseball on Earth after t seconds can be modeled by the function $h(t) = -16(t - 1.5)^2 + 36$, where -16 is a constant in ft/s² due to Earth's gravity.

    a. What if…? The gravity on Mars is only 0.38 times that on Earth. If the same baseball were thrown on Mars, it would reach a maximum height 59 feet higher and 2.5 seconds later than on Earth. Describe the transformations that must be applied to make the function model the height of the baseball on Mars.

    b. Write a height function for the baseball thrown on Mars.

TEST PREP

Use the graph for Exercises 46 and 47.

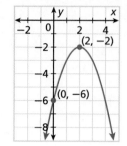

46. Which best describes how the graph of the function $y = -x^2$ was transformed to produce the graph shown?

   (A) Translation 2 units right and 2 units up

   (B) Translation 2 units right and 2 units down

   (C) Translation 2 units left and 2 units up

   (D) Translation 2 units left and 2 units down

47. Which gives the function rule for the parabola shown?

   (F) $f(x) = (x + 2)^2 - 2$ (H) $f(x) = (x - 2)^2 - 2$

   (G) $f(x) = -(x + 2)^2 - 2$ (J) $f(x) = -(x - 2)^2 - 2$

48. Which shows the functions below in order from widest to narrowest of their corresponding graphs?

   $$m(x) = \frac{1}{6}x^2 \qquad n(x) = 4x^2 \qquad p(x) = 6x^2 \qquad q(x) = -\frac{1}{2}x^2$$

   (A) m, n, p, q   (C) m, q, n, p

   (B) q, m, n, p   (D) q, p, n, m

49. Which of the following functions has its vertex below the x-axis?

   (F) $f(x) = (x - 7)^2$ (H) $f(x) = -2x^2$

   (G) $f(x) = x^2 - 8$ (J) $f(x) = -(x + 3)^2$

50. **Gridded Response** What is the y-coordinate of the vertex of the graph of $f(x) = -3(x - 1)^2 + 5$?

CHALLENGE AND EXTEND

51. Identify the transformations of the graph of $f(x) = -3(x + 3)^2 - 3$ that would cause the graph's image to have a vertex at $(3, 3)$. Then write the transformed function.

H.O.T. 52. Consider the functions $f(x) = (2x)^2 - 2$ and $g(x) = 4x^2 - 2$.

   a. Describe each function as a transformation of the quadratic parent function.

   b. Graph both functions on the coordinate plane.

   c. Make a conjecture about the relationship between the two functions.

   d. Write the rule for a horizontal compression of the parent function that would give the same graph as $f(x) = 9x^2$.

FOCUS ON MATHEMATICAL PRACTICES

H.O.T. 53. **Error Analysis** James tried to graph $g(x) = 2(x - 1)^2 + 1$ by transforming the graph of $f(x) = x^2$. What two mistakes did James make? What should he have done?

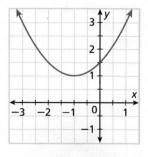

H.O.T. 54. **Modeling** Bev and Scott throw baseballs at the same time, with the same speed and trajectory. Bev releases hers 5 feet off the ground, and Scott, standing on the roof of a building, releases his 100 feet off the ground. If $f(t)$ and $g(t)$ represent the heights of Bev's and Scott's baseballs, respectively, t seconds after they are thrown, how can the graph of $f(t)$ be transformed to coincide with the graph of $g(t)$?

Properties of Quadratic Functions in Standard Form

? **Essential Question:** What do the coefficients of a quadratic function in standard form tell you about the key features of its graph?

Objectives
Define, identify, and graph quadratic functions.

Identify and use maximums and minimums of quadratic functions to solve problems.

Vocabulary
axis of symmetry
standard form
minimum value
maximum value

Why learn this?

Quadratic functions can be used to find the maximum power generated by the engine of a speedboat. (See Example 4.)

When you transformed quadratic functions previously, you saw that reflecting the parent function across the y-axis results in the same function.

$f(x) = x^2$
$g(x) = (-x)^2 = x^2$

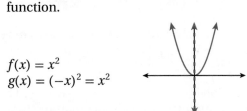

This shows that parabolas are symmetric curves. The **axis of symmetry** is the line through the vertex of a parabola that divides the parabola into two congruent halves.

Know it! Note

Axis of Symmetry	Quadratic Functions	
WORDS	**ALGEBRA**	**GRAPH**
The axis of symmetry is a vertical line through the vertex of the function's graph.	The graph of the quadratic function $f(x) = a(x - h)^2 + k$ has the axis of symmetry $x = h$.	(h, k)

COMMON CORE GPS MCC9-12.F.IF.8

EXAMPLE 1 **Identifying the Axis of Symmetry**

Identify the axis of symmetry for the graph of $f(x) = 2(x + 2)^2 - 3$.

my.hrw.com

Online Video Tutor

Rewrite the function to find the value of h.

$$f(x) = 2[x - (-2)]^2 - 3$$

Because $h = -2$, the axis of symmetry is the vertical line $x = -2$.

Check Analyze the graph on a graphing calculator. The parabola is symmetric about the vertical line $x = -2$.

CHECK IT OUT! **1.** Identify the axis of symmetry for the graph of $f(x) = (x - 3)^2 + 1$.

Another useful form of writing quadratic functions is the *standard form*. The **standard form** of a quadratic function is $f(x) = ax^2 + bx + c$, where $a \neq 0$.

The coefficients a, b, and c can show properties of the graph of the function. You can determine these properties by expanding the vertex form.

$$f(x) = a(x - h)^2 + k$$

$$f(x) = a(x^2 - 2xh + h^2) + k \qquad \textit{Multiply to expand } (x - h)^2.$$

$$f(x) = a(x^2) - a(2hx) + a(h^2) + k \qquad \textit{Distribute a.}$$

$$f(x) = ax^2 + (-2ah)x + (ah^2 + k) \qquad \textit{Simplify and group like terms.}$$

$$\underset{\downarrow}{a = a} \qquad \underset{\downarrow}{-2ah = b} \qquad \underset{\downarrow}{ah^2 + k = c}$$

$$f(x) = ax^2 + bx + c$$

$a = a$ $\begin{cases} a \text{ in standard form is the same as in vertex form. It indicates} \\ \text{whether a reflection and/or vertical stretch or compression} \\ \text{has been applied.} \end{cases}$

$b = -2ah$ $\begin{cases} \text{Solving for } h \text{ gives } h = \frac{b}{-2a} = -\frac{b}{2a}. \text{ Therefore, the axis of} \\ \text{symmetry, } x = h, \text{ for a quadratic function in standard form is} \\ x = -\frac{b}{2a}. \end{cases}$

$c = ah^2 + k$ $\begin{cases} \text{Notice that the value of } c \text{ is the same value given by the vertex} \\ \text{form of } f \text{ when } x = 0 : f(0) = a(0 - h)^2 + k = ah^2 + k. \text{ So } c \text{ is the} \\ y\text{-intercept.} \end{cases}$

These properties can be generalized to help you graph quadratic functions.

Know it! Note

Properties of a Parabola

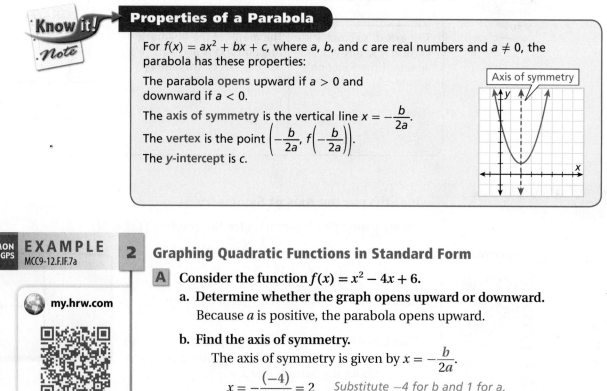

For $f(x) = ax^2 + bx + c$, where a, b, and c are real numbers and $a \neq 0$, the parabola has these properties:

The parabola **opens** upward if $a > 0$ and downward if $a < 0$.

The **axis of symmetry** is the vertical line $x = -\frac{b}{2a}$.

The **vertex** is the point $\left(-\frac{b}{2a}, f\left(-\frac{b}{2a} \right) \right)$.

The **y-intercept** is c.

Axis of symmetry

COMMON CORE GPS MCC9-12.F.IF.7a

my.hrw.com

Online Video Tutor

EXAMPLE 2   Graphing Quadratic Functions in Standard Form

A Consider the function $f(x) = x^2 - 4x + 6$.

  a. Determine whether the graph opens upward or downward.
  Because a is positive, the parabola opens upward.

  b. Find the axis of symmetry.
  The axis of symmetry is given by $x = -\frac{b}{2a}$.

  $$x = -\frac{(-4)}{2(1)} = 2 \qquad \textit{Substitute } -4 \textit{ for b and 1 for a.}$$

  The axis of symmetry is the line $x = 2$.

c. **Find the vertex.**

The vertex lies on the axis of symmetry, so the x-coordinate is 2. The y-coordinate is the value of the function at this x-value, or $f(2)$.

$$f(2) = (2)^2 - 4(2) + 6 = 2$$

The vertex is $(2, 2)$.

d. **Find the y-intercept.**

Because $c = 6$, the y-intercept is 6.

e. **Graph the function.**

Graph by sketching the axis of symmetry and then plotting the vertex and the intercept point, $(0, 6)$. Use the axis of symmetry to find another point on the parabola. Notice that $(0, 6)$ is 2 units left of the axis of symmetry. The point on the parabola symmetrical to $(0, 6)$ is 2 units right of the axis at $(4, 6)$.

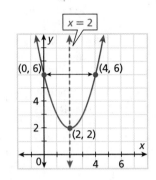

B Consider the function $f(x) = -4x^2 - 12x - 3$.

a. **Determine whether the graph opens upward or downward.**

Because a is negative, the parabola opens downward.

b. **Find the axis of symmetry.**

The axis of symmetry is given by $x = -\dfrac{b}{2a}$.

$$x = -\frac{(-12)}{2(-4)} = -\frac{3}{2} \quad \textit{Substitute } -12 \textit{ for b and } -4 \textit{ for a.}$$

The axis of symmetry is the line $x = -\dfrac{3}{2}$, or $x = -1.5$.

c. **Find the vertex.**

The vertex lies on the axis of symmetry, so the x-coordinate is -1.5. The y-coordinate is the value of the function at this x-value, or $f(-1.5)$.

$$f(-1.5) = -4(-1.5)^2 - 12(-1.5) - 3 = 6$$

The vertex is $(-1.5, 6)$.

d. **Find the y-intercept.**

Because $c = -3$, the y-intercept is -3.

e. **Graph the function.**

Graph by sketching the axis of symmetry and then plotting the vertex and the intercept point, $(0, -3)$. Use the axis of symmetry to find another point on the parabola. Notice that $(0, -3)$ is 1.5 units right of the axis of symmetry. The point on the parabola symmetrical to $(0, -3)$ is 1.5 units left of the axis at $(-3, -3)$.

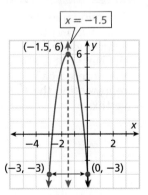

For each function, (a) determine whether the graph opens upward or downward, (b) find the axis of symmetry, (c) find the vertex, (d) find the y-intercept, and (e) graph the function.

2a. $f(x) = -2x^2 - 4x$ **2b.** $g(x) = x^2 + 3x - 1$

Substituting any real value of x into a quadratic equation results in a real number. Therefore, the domain of any quadratic function is all real numbers, $\mathbb{R}$. The range of a quadratic function depends on its vertex and the direction that the parabola opens.

Know it! Note

Minimum and Maximum Values

OPENS UPWARD	OPENS DOWNWARD
When a parabola opens upward, the y-value of the vertex is the **minimum value**.	When a parabola opens downward, the y-value of the vertex is the **maximum value**.
D: $\left\{x \mid x \in \mathbb{R}\right\}$ R: $\left\{y \mid y \geq k\right\}$	D: $\left\{x \mid x \in \mathbb{R}\right\}$ R: $\left\{y \mid y \leq k\right\}$
The domain is all real numbers, $\mathbb{R}$. The range is all values greater than or equal to the minimum.	The domain is all real numbers, $\mathbb{R}$. The range is all values less than or equal to the maximum.

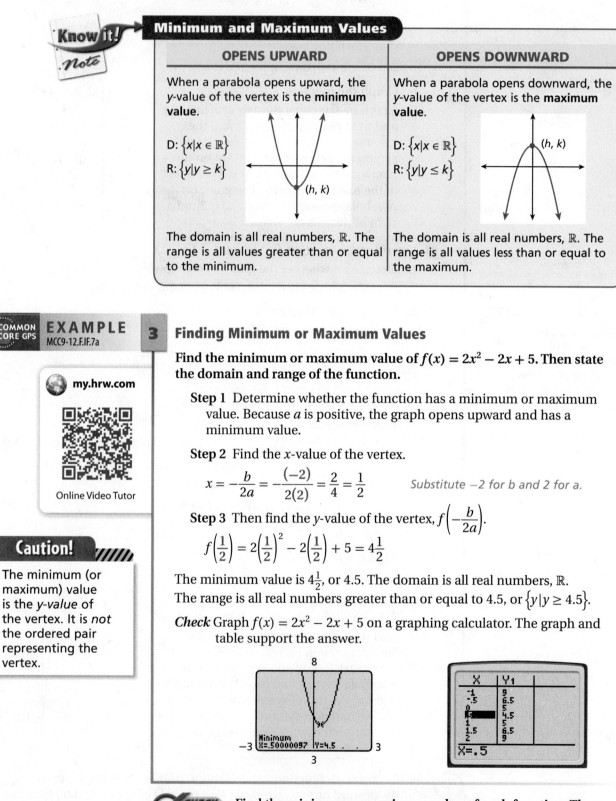

COMMON CORE GPS
MCC9-12.F.IF.7a

my.hrw.com

Online Video Tutor

EXAMPLE 3

Finding Minimum or Maximum Values

Find the minimum or maximum value of $f(x) = 2x^2 - 2x + 5$. Then state the domain and range of the function.

Step 1 Determine whether the function has a minimum or maximum value. Because a is positive, the graph opens upward and has a minimum value.

Step 2 Find the x-value of the vertex.

$$x = -\frac{b}{2a} = -\frac{(-2)}{2(2)} = \frac{2}{4} = \frac{1}{2} \qquad \textit{Substitute } -2 \textit{ for b and 2 for a.}$$

Step 3 Then find the y-value of the vertex, $f\left(-\frac{b}{2a}\right)$.

$$f\left(\frac{1}{2}\right) = 2\left(\frac{1}{2}\right)^2 - 2\left(\frac{1}{2}\right) + 5 = 4\frac{1}{2}$$

The minimum value is $4\frac{1}{2}$, or 4.5. The domain is all real numbers, $\mathbb{R}$. The range is all real numbers greater than or equal to 4.5, or $\left\{y \mid y \geq 4.5\right\}$.

Check Graph $f(x) = 2x^2 - 2x + 5$ on a graphing calculator. The graph and table support the answer.

Caution!

The minimum (or maximum) value is the *y-value* of the vertex. It is *not* the ordered pair representing the vertex.

CHECK IT OUT! Find the minimum or maximum value of each function. Then state the domain and range of the function.

3a. $f(x) = x^2 - 6x + 3$ **3b.** $g(x) = -2x^2 - 4$

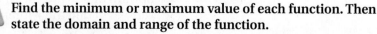

Transportation Application

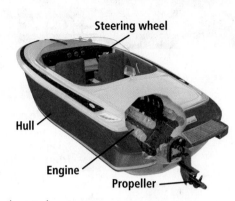

Steering wheel

Hull

Engine

Propeller

The power p in horsepower (hp) generated by a high-performance speedboat engine operating at r revolutions per minute (rpm) can be modeled by the function $p(r) = -0.0000147r^2 + 0.18r - 251$. What is the maximum power of this engine to the nearest horsepower? At how many revolutions per minute must the engine be operating to achieve this power?

The maximum value will be at the vertex $(r, p(r))$.

Step 1 Find the r-value of the vertex using $a = -0.0000147$ and $b = 0.18$.

$$r = -\frac{b}{2a} = -\frac{0.18}{2(-0.0000147)} \approx 6122$$

Step 2 Substitute this r-value into p to find the corresponding maximum, $p(r)$.

$$p(r) = -0.0000147r^2 + 0.18r - 251$$

$$p(6122) = -0.0000147(6122)^2 + 0.18(6122) - 251 \quad \textit{Substitute 6122 for r.}$$

$$p(6122) \approx 300 \qquad\qquad\qquad\qquad\qquad\qquad \textit{Use a calculator.}$$

The maximum power is about 300 hp at 6122 rpm.

Check Graph the function on a graphing calculator. Use the **maximum** feature under the **CALCULATE** menu to approximate the maximum. The graph supports your answer.

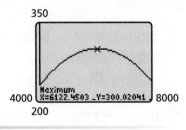

350

4000   Maximum
       X=6122.4503 Y=300.02041   8000

200

CHECK IT OUT!

4. The highway mileage m in miles per gallon for a compact car is approximated by $m(s) = -0.025s^2 + 2.45s - 30$, where s is the speed in miles per hour. What is the maximum mileage for this compact car to the nearest tenth of a mile per gallon? What speed results in this mileage?

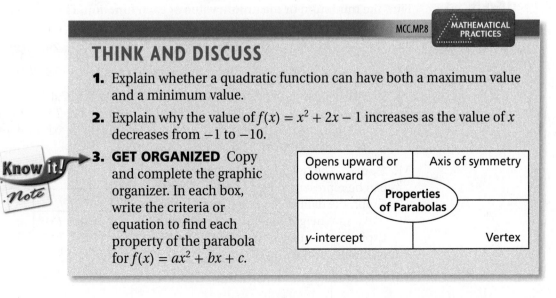

MCC.MP.8

MATHEMATICAL PRACTICES

THINK AND DISCUSS

1. Explain whether a quadratic function can have both a maximum value and a minimum value.

2. Explain why the value of $f(x) = x^2 + 2x - 1$ increases as the value of x decreases from -1 to -10.

3. GET ORGANIZED Copy and complete the graphic organizer. In each box, write the criteria or equation to find each property of the parabola for $f(x) = ax^2 + bx + c$.

Know it! Note

Opens upward or downward	Axis of symmetry
Properties of Parabolas	
y-intercept	Vertex

GUIDED PRACTICE

1. **Vocabulary** If the graph of a quadratic function opens upward, the y-value of the vertex is a ___?___ value. (*maximum* or *minimum*)

SEE EXAMPLE 1 Identify the axis of symmetry for the graph of each function.

2. $f(x) = -2(x-2)^2 - 4$ 3. $g(x) = 3x^2 + 4$ 4. $h(x) = (x+5)^2$

SEE EXAMPLE 2 For each function, (a) determine whether the graph opens upward or downward, (b) find the axis of symmetry, (c) find the vertex, (d) find the y-intercept, and (e) graph the function.

5. $f(x) = -x^2 - 2x - 8$ 6. $g(x) = x^2 - 3x + 2$ 7. $h(x) = 4x - x^2 - 1$

SEE EXAMPLE 3 Find the minimum or maximum value of each function. Then state the domain and range of the function.

8. $f(x) = x^2 - 1$ 9. $g(x) = -x^2 + 3x - 2$ 10. $h(x) = -16x^2 + 32x + 4$

SEE EXAMPLE 4

11. **Sports** The path of a soccer ball is modeled by the function $h(x) = -0.005x^2 + 0.25x$, where h is the height in meters and x is the horizontal distance that the ball travels in meters. What is the maximum height that the ball reaches?

PRACTICE AND PROBLEM SOLVING

my.hrw.com

Online Extra Practice

Identify the axis of symmetry for the graph of each function.

12. $f(x) = -x^2 + 4$ 13. $g(x) = (x-1)^2$ 14. $h(x) = 2(x+1)^2 - 3$

For each function, (a) determine whether the graph opens upward or downward, (b) find the axis of symmetry, (c) find the vertex, (d) find the y-intercept, and (e) graph the function.

15. $f(x) = x^2 + x - 2$ 16. $g(x) = -3x^2 + 6x$ 17. $h(x) = 0.5x^2 - 2x - 4$

18. $f(x) = -2x^2 + 8x + 5$ 19. $g(x) = 3x^2 + 2x - 8$ 20. $h(x) = 2x - 1 + x^2$

21. $f(x) = -(2 + x^2)$ 22. $g(x) = 0.5x^2 + 3x - 5$ 23. $h(x) = \frac{1}{4}x^2 + x + 2$

Find the minimum or maximum value of each function. Then state the domain and range of the function.

24. $f(x) = -2x^2 + 7x - 3$ 25. $g(x) = 6x - x^2$ 26. $h(x) = x^2 - 4x + 3$

27. $f(x) = -\frac{1}{2}x^2 - 4$ 28. $g(x) = -x^2 - 6x + 1$ 29. $h(x) = x^2 + 8x + 16$

30. **Weather** The daily high temperature in Death Valley, California, in 2003 can be modeled by $T(d) = -0.0018d^2 + 0.657d + 50.95$, where T is temperature in degrees Fahrenheit and d is the day of the year. What was the maximum temperature in 2003 to the nearest degree?

31. **Sports** The height of a golf ball over time can be represented by a quadratic function. Graph the data in the table. What is the maximum height that the ball will reach? Explain your answer in terms of the axis of symmetry and vertex of the graph.

Golf Ball Height					
Time (s)	0	0.5	1	2	3
Height (ft)	0	28	48	64	48

H.O.T. 32. Manufacturing A roll of aluminum with a width of 32 cm is to be bent into rain gutters by folding up two sides at 90° angles. A rain gutter's greatest capacity, or volume, is determined by the gutter's greatest cross-sectional area, as shown.

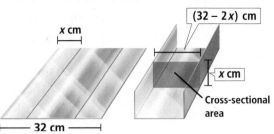

a. Write a function C to describe the cross-sectional area in terms of the width of the bend x.

b. Make a table, and graph the function.

c. Identify the meaningful domain and range of the function.

d. Find the value of x that maximizes the cross-sectional area.

33. Biology The spittlebug is the world's highest jumping animal relative to its body length of about 6 mm. The height h of a spittlebug's jump in millimeters can be modeled by the function $h(t) = -4000t^2 + 3000t$, where t is the time in seconds.

a. What is the maximum height that the spittlebug will reach?

b. What is the ratio of a spittlebug's maximum jumping height to its body length? In the best human jumpers, this ratio is about 1.38. Compare the ratio for spittlebugs with the ratio for the best human jumpers.

c. What if...? Suppose humans had the same ratio of maximum jumping height to body length as spittlebugs. How high would a person with a height of 1.8 m be able to jump?

34. Gardening The function $A(x) = x(10 - x)$ describes the area A of a rectangular flower garden, where x is its width in yards. What is the maximum area of the garden?

Graphing Calculator Once you have graphed a function, the graphing calculator can automatically find the minimum or maximum value. From the **CALC** menu, choose the **minimum** or **maximum** feature.

Use a graphing calculator to find the approximate minimum or maximum value of each function.

35. $f(x) = 5.23x^2 - 4.84x - 1.91$

36. $g(x) = -12.8x^2 + 8.73x + 11.69$

37. $h(x) = \frac{1}{12}x^2 - \frac{4}{5}x + \frac{2}{3}$

38. $j(x) = -\frac{5}{3}x^2 + \frac{9}{10}x + \frac{21}{4}$

H.O.T. 39. Critical Thinking Suppose you are given a parabola with two points that have the same y-value, such as $(-7, 11)$ and $(3, 11)$. Explain how to find the equation for the axis of symmetry of this parabola, and then determine this equation.

H.O.T. 40. Write About It Can a maximum value for a quadratic function be negative? Can a minimum value for a quadratic function be positive? Explain by using examples.

Real-World Connections

41. A baseball is thrown with a vertical velocity of 50 ft/s from an initial height of 6 ft. The height h in feet of the baseball can be modeled by $h(t) = -16t^2 + 50t + 6$, where t is the time in seconds since the ball was thrown.

a. Approximately how many seconds does it take the ball to reach its maximum height?

b. What is the maximum height that the ball reaches?

Use the graph for exercises 42 and 43.

42. What is the range of the function graphed?

    (A) All real numbers

    (B) $y \geq -2$

    (C) $y \leq 2$

    (D) $-2 \leq y \leq 2$

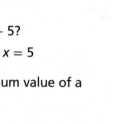

43. The graph shown represents which quadratic function?

    (F) $f(x) = x^2 + 2x - 2$

    (G) $f(x) = -x^2 + 4x - 2$

    (H) $f(x) = x^2 - 4x - 2$

    (J) $f(x) = -x^2 - 2x + 2$

44. Which of the following is NOT true of the graph of the function $f(x) = -x^2 - 6x + 5$?

    (A) Its vertex is at $(-3, 14)$.

    (B) Its axis of symmetry is $x = 14$.

    (C) Its maximum value is 14.

    (D) Its y-intercept is 5.

45. Which equation represents the axis of symmetry for $f(x) = 2x^2 - 4x + 5$?

    (F) $x = -4$ (G) $x = 1$ (H) $x = 2$ (J) $x = 5$

46. **Short Response** Explain how to find the maximum value or minimum value of a quadratic function such as $f(x) = -x^2 - 8x + 4$.

CHALLENGE AND EXTEND

47. Write the equations in standard form for two quadratic functions that have the same vertex but open in different directions.

48. The graph of a quadratic function passes through the point $(-5, 8)$, and its axis of symmetry is $x = 3$.

    a. What are the coordinates of another point on the graph of the function? Explain how you determined your answer.

    b. Can you determine whether the graph of the function opens upward or downward? Explain.

49. **Critical Thinking** What conclusions can you make about the axis of symmetry and the vertex of a quadratic function of the form $f(x) = ax^2 + c$? [H.O.T.]

50. **Critical Thinking** Given the quadratic function f and the fact that $f(-1) = f(2)$, how can you find the axis of symmetry of this function?

FOCUS ON MATHEMATICAL PRACTICES

MATHEMATICAL PRACTICES

51. **Reasoning** How many different parabolas have an axis of symmetry of $x = -2$ and a minimum value of 3? Explain your answer. [H.O.T.]

52. **Properties** The graph shown is for a function of the form $f(x) = ax^2 + bx + c$. Can the signs for a, b, and c be determined from the graph? Explain. If so, find them. [H.O.T.]

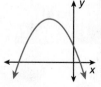

53. **Analysis** If $f(x) = ax^2 + bx + c$, which of the constants a, b, and c could you change to produce a parabola that is not congruent to the original parabola? Explain your answer. [H.O.T.]

15-2
Technology TASK

Comparing Functions

A function may be represented by an equation, a graph, a table, or a verbal description. You can use your graphing calculator to help you compare functions that are represented in different ways.

Use with Properties of Quadratic Functions in Standard Form

MATHEMATICAL PRACTICES — **Use appropriate tools strategically.**

MCC9-12.F.IF.9 Compare properties of two functions each represented in a different way (algebraically, graphically, numerically in tables, or by verbal descriptions).

The populations of three small towns since 2000 are given as follows. The population of Town A is shown in the table. The population of Town B is given by the equation $y = 150 + x^2$, where x is the number of years since 2000. The population of Town C is 100 in 2000, and it increases by 10% every year thereafter.

Year	2000	2001	2002	2003	2004
Population	163	173	183	193	203

Compare the graphs of the towns' populations.

1. Enter the data for Town A in two lists. Press **STAT** and choose **1:edit**. Enter the values 0, 1, 2, 3, and 4 in list **L1**. (These represent the number of years since 2000). Enter the corresponding populations in list **L2**.

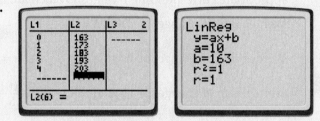

2. Because the population in Town A increases by 10 each year, the function is a linear function. To find an equation for the function, press **STAT**, access the **CALC** menu, and then choose **4:LinReg (ax + b)**. Pressing **ENTER** twice shows that $a = 10$ and $b = 163$. The equation for the population is $y = 10x + 163$.

3. Enter the equation for Town A as **Y1** and the equation for Town B as **Y2**. The population of Town C grows exponentially with a growth factor of 1.1, so its equation is $y = 100 (1.1)^x$. Enter this as **Y3**.

4. Use the window shown here to view and compare the graphs.

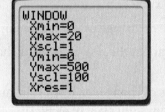 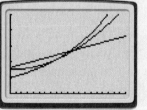

Try This

For Exercises 1–4, assume the towns' populations can be modeled indefinitely using the above functions.

1. Which town will have the greatest population in 2020?

2. What do the graphs tell you about the towns' populations from 2000 to 2020?

3. Suppose the population of Town C increases at 8% per year rather than 10%. Would the population of Town C still eventually overtake the populations of Towns A and B? If so, when? Make a new set of graphs to help you explain your answer.

4. Suppose the population of Town B were given by the equation $y = 200 + 2x^2$. Would the population of Town B still be overtaken at some point by the population of Town C? If so, when? Make a new set of graphs to help you explain your answer.

The *average rate of change* of a function is the change in the dependent variable divided by the corresponding change in the independent variable between two points. For example, the average rate of change of the population of Town A from 2000 to 2002 is

$$\frac{183 - 163}{2002 - 2000} = \frac{20}{2} = 10 \text{ people per year.}$$

Activity 2

Compare the average rate of change of the towns' populations from 2005 to 2010.

① Press **2nd** **WINDOW** and enter the values shown in the Table Setup menu.

② Press **2nd** **GRAPH** to view a table of values for the three functions. (Use the right arrow key to scroll to the right to view values for **Y3**.)

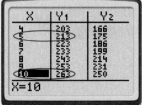

③ Scroll down until the values in the X column include 5 and 10. Then use the appropriate corresponding *y*-values to calculate the rates of change.

$$\text{Average rate of change for Town A} = \frac{263 - 213}{10 - 5} = \frac{50}{5} = 10 \text{ people per year}$$

$$\text{Average rate of change for Town B} = \frac{250 - 175}{10 - 5} = \frac{75}{5} = 15 \text{ people per year}$$

$$\text{Average rate of change for Town C} = \frac{259.37 - 161.05}{10 - 5} = \frac{98.32}{5} \approx 19.66 \text{ people per year}$$

Try This

For Exercises 5–9, use your graphs and tables from the activities.

5. What do the average rates of change for the three towns tell you about their graphs on the interval from $x = 5$ to $x = 10$?

6. Find the average rate of change of the town's populations from 2010 to 2020.

7. What do you notice about the average rate of change for Town A? Why does this make sense?

8. Find the average rate of change for Town C from 2000 to 2010, from 2010 to 2020, from 2020 to 2030, and from 2030 to 2040. How do your findings relate to the graph of the function?

9. Suppose the population of Town B had been given by $y = 350 + x^2$. How would this affect the average rate of change of the population from 2005 to 2010? Explain.

For Exercises 10 and 11, use the graph shown below.

10. The thin curve shows the population of Town D from 1900 to 2000 ($x = 0$ to $x = 100$). Estimate the average rate of change of the population from 1910 to 1930.

11. The heavy line shows the population of Town E during the same period. Estimate the average rate of change of the population from 1900 to 2000.

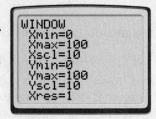
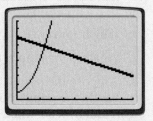

Mastering *the* Standards

for Mathematical Practice

The topics described in the Standards for Mathematical Content will vary from year to year. However, the *way* in which you learn, study, and think about mathematics will not. The Standards for Mathematical Practice describe skills that you will use in all of your math courses.

Mathematical Practices

1. Make sense of problems and persevere in solving them.
2. Reason abstractly and quantitatively.
3. Construct viable arguments and critique the reasoning of others.
4. Model with mathematics.
5. Use appropriate tools strategically.
6. Attend to precision.
7. Look for and make use of structure.
8. Look for and express regularity in repeated reasoning.

⑤ Use appropriate tools strategically.

Mathematically proficient students consider the available tools when solving a... problem... [and] are... able to use technological tools to explore and deepen their understanding...

In your book

Algebra Tasks and **Technology Tasks** use concrete and technological tools to explore mathematical concepts.

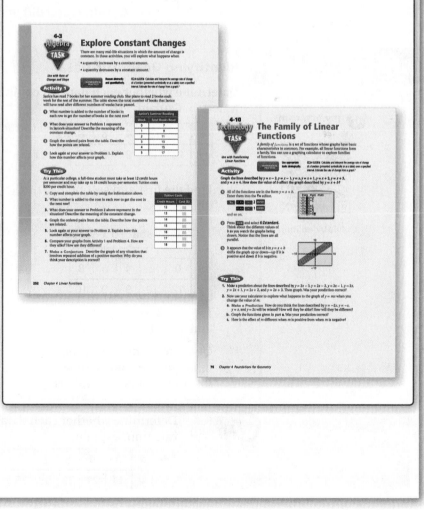

Curve Fitting with Quadratic Models

Essential Question: How can you model data using quadratic functions?

Objectives
Use quadratic functions to model data.

Use quadratic models to analyze and predict.

Vocabulary
quadratic model
quadratic regression

Who uses this?
Film preservationists use quadratic relationships to estimate film run times. (See Example 3.)

Recall that you can use differences to analyze patterns in data. For a set of ordered pairs with equally spaced x-values, a quadratic function has constant nonzero second differences, as shown below.

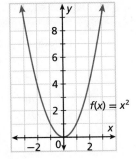
The Granger Collection, New York

Equally spaced x-values

x	−3	−2	−1	0	1	2	3
$f(x) = x^2$	9	4	1	0	1	4	9

1st differences   −5 −3 −1   1   3   5
2nd differences   2   2   2   2   2

Constant 2nd differences

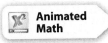 **Animated Math**

EXAMPLE 1 MCC9-12.F.IF.4

Identifying Quadratic Data

my.hrw.com

Online Video Tutor

Determine whether each data set could represent a quadratic function. Explain.

A

x	0	2	4	6	8
y	12	10	9	9	10

Find the first and second differences.

Equally spaced x-values

x	0	2	4	6	8
y	12	10	9	9	10

1st   −2 −1   0   1
2nd   1   1   1

Quadratic function; second differences are constant for equally spaced x-values.

B

x	−2	−1	0	1	2
y	1	2	4	8	16

Find the first and second differences.

Equally spaced x-values

x	−2	−1	0	1	2
y	1	2	4	8	16

1st   1   2   4   8
2nd   1   2   4

Not a quadratic function; second differences are not constant for equally spaced x-values.

 CHECK IT OUT!
Determine whether each data set could represent a quadratic function. Explain.

1a.

x	3	4	5	6	7
y	11	21	35	53	75

1b.

x	10	9	8	7	6
y	6	8	10	12	14

Just as two points define a linear function, three noncollinear points define a quadratic function. You can find the three coefficients, *a*, *b*, and *c*, of $f(x) = ax^2 + bx + c$ by using a system of three equations, one for each point. The points do not need to have equally spaced *x*-values.

EXAMPLE MCC9-12.A.CED.2

2

Writing a Quadratic Function from Data

Write a quadratic function that fits the points $(0, 5)$, $(2, 1)$, and $(3, 2)$.

my.hrw.com

Online Video Tutor

Use each point to write a system of equations to find *a*, *b*, and *c* in $f(x) = ax^2 + bx + c$.

(x, y)	$f(x) = ax^2 + bx + c$	System in a, b, c
(0, 5)	$5 = a(0)^2 + b(0) + c$	$c = 5$ ❶
(2, 1)	$1 = a(2)^2 + b(2) + c$	$4a + 2b + c = 1$ ❷
(3, 2)	$2 = a(3)^2 + b(3) + c$	$9a + 3b + c = 2$ ❸

Substitute $c = 5$ from equation ❶ into both equation ❷ and equation ❸.

❷ $4a + 2b + c = 1$ ❸ $9a + 3b + c = 2$
$4a + 2b + 5 = 1$ $9a + 3b + 5 = 2$
$4a + 2b = -4$ ❹ $9a + 3b = -3$ ❺

Solve equation ❹ and equation ❺ for *a* and *b* using elimination.

❹ $3(4a + 2b) = 3(-4)$ → $12a + 6b = -12$ *Multiply by 3.*
❺ $-2(9a + 3b) = -2(-3)$ → $\underline{-18a - 6b = 6}$ *Multiply by −2.*
$-6a = -6$ *Add the equations.*
$a = 1$

Substitute 1 for *a* into equation ❹ or equation ❺ to find *b*.

❹ $4a + 2b = -4$ → $4(1) + 2b = -4$
$2b = -8$
$b = -4$

Write the function using $a = 1$, $b = -4$, and $c = 5$.

$f(x) = ax^2 + bx + c \rightarrow f(x) = 1x^2 - 4x + 5$, or $f(x) = x^2 - 4x + 5$

Check Substitute or create a table to verify that $(0, 5)$, $(2, 1)$, and $(3, 2)$ satisfy the function rule.

```
0²-4(0)+5
                    5
2²-4(2)+5
                    1
3²-4(3)+5
                    2
```

CHECK IT OUT! **2.** Write a quadratic function that fits the points $(0, -3)$, $(1, 0)$, and $(2, 1)$.

You may use any method that you studied to solve the system of three equations in three variables. For example, you can use a matrix equation as shown.

$$\begin{cases} c = 5 \\ 4a + 2b + c = 1 \\ 9a + 3b + c = 2 \end{cases} \rightarrow \begin{bmatrix} 0 & 0 & 1 \\ 4 & 2 & 1 \\ 9 & 3 & 1 \end{bmatrix} \begin{bmatrix} a \\ b \\ c \end{bmatrix} = \begin{bmatrix} 5 \\ 1 \\ 2 \end{bmatrix} \rightarrow \begin{bmatrix} a \\ b \\ c \end{bmatrix} = \begin{bmatrix} 1 \\ -4 \\ 5 \end{bmatrix}$$

```
[A]⁻¹[B]
            [[1 ]
             [-4]
             [5 ]]
```

A **quadratic model** is a quadratic function that represents a real data set. Models are useful for making estimates.

You have used a graphing calculator to perform a *linear regression* and make predictions. You can apply a similar statistical method to make a quadratic model for a given data set using **quadratic regression.**

EXAMPLE 3

Film Application

The table shows approximate run times for 16 mm films, given the diameter of the film on the reel. Find a quadratic model for the run time given the diameter. Use the model to estimate the run time for a reel of film with a diameter of 15 in.

Film Run Times (16 mm)		
Diameter (in.)	Reel Length (ft)	Run Time (min)
5	200	5.55
7	400	11.12
9.25	600	16.67
10.5	800	22.22
12.25	1200	33.33
13.75	1600	44.45

Step 1 Enter the data into two lists in a graphing calculator.

Step 2 Use the quadratic regression feature.

Step 3 Graph the data and function model to verify that the model fits the data.

Step 4 Use the table feature to find the function value at $x = 15$.

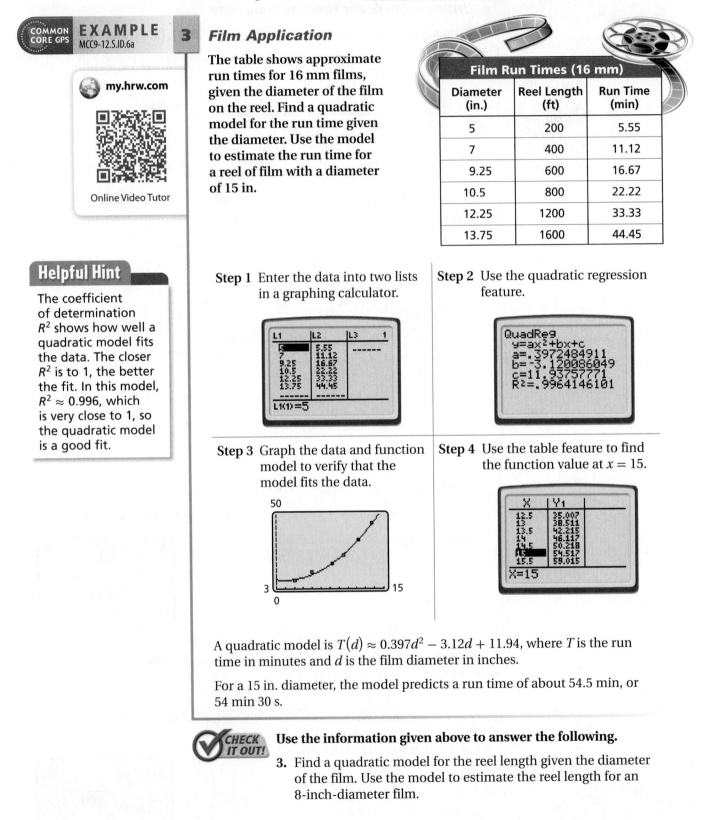

A quadratic model is $T(d) \approx 0.397d^2 - 3.12d + 11.94$, where T is the run time in minutes and d is the film diameter in inches.

For a 15 in. diameter, the model predicts a run time of about 54.5 min, or 54 min 30 s.

CHECK IT OUT! Use the information given above to answer the following.

3. Find a quadratic model for the reel length given the diameter of the film. Use the model to estimate the reel length for an 8-inch-diameter film.

THINK AND DISCUSS

1. Describe how to determine if a data set is quadratic.

2. Explain whether a quadratic function is a good model for the path of an airplane that ascends, descends, and rises again out of view.

3. GET ORGANIZED
Copy and complete the graphic organizer. Compare the different quadratic models presented in the lesson.

Quadratic Model	When Appropriate	Procedure
Exact model		
Approximate model		

15-3 Exercises

my.hrw.com
Homework Help

GUIDED PRACTICE

1. Vocabulary How does a *quadratic model* differ from a linear model?

SEE EXAMPLE 1
Determine whether each data set could represent a quadratic function. Explain.

2.
x	−2	−1	0	1	2
y	16	8	0	−8	−16

3.
x	1	2	3	4	5
y	1	3	9	27	81

4.
x	2	4	6	8	10
y	4	−5	−8	−5	4

SEE EXAMPLE 2
Write a quadratic function that fits each set of points.

5. $(-2, 5)$, $(0, -3)$, and $(3, 0)$

6. $(0, 1)$, $(2, -1)$, and $(3, -8)$

7. $(-1, 8)$, $(0, 4)$, and $(2, 2)$

8. $(-4, 9)$, $(0, -7)$, and $(1, -1)$

9. $(2, 3)$, $(6, 3)$, and $(8, -3)$

10. $(-1, -12)$, $(1, 0)$, and $(2, 9)$

SEE EXAMPLE 3
11. Hobbies The cost of mounting different-sized photos is shown in the table. Find a quadratic model for the cost given the average side length. (For an 8 in. × 10 in. photo, the average side length is $\frac{8 + 10}{2} = 9$ in.) Estimate the cost of mounting a 24 in. × 36 in. photo.

Costs of Mounting Photos	
Size (in.)	Cost ($)
8 × 10	10
14 × 18	16
16 × 20	19
24 × 30	27
32 × 40	39

PRACTICE AND PROBLEM SOLVING

Determine whether each data set could represent a quadratic function. Explain.

12.
x	0	2	4	6	8
f(x)	−1	2	11	26	47

13.
x	0	1	2	3	4
f(x)	10	9	6	1	−6

14.
x	1	2	3	4	5
f(x)	−3	0	3	6	9

Independent Practice

For Exercises	See Example
12–14	1
15–18	2
19	3

my.hrw.com

Online Extra Practice

Write a quadratic function that fits each set of points.

15. $(-2, 5)$, $(-1, 0)$, and $(1, -2)$

16. $(1, 2)$, $(2, -1)$, and $(5, 2)$

17. $(-4, 12)$, $(-2, 0)$, and $(2, -12)$

18. $(-1, 2.6)$, $(1, 4.2)$, and $(2, 14)$

19. Gardening The table shows the amount spent on water gardening in the United States between 1999 and 2003. Find a quadratic model for the annual amount in millions of dollars spent on water gardening based on number of years since 1999. Estimate the amount that people in the United States will spend on water gardening in 2015.

Water Gardening	
Year	Amount Spent (million $)
1999	806
2000	943
2001	1205
2002	1441
2003	1565

Write a function rule for each situation, and identify each relationship as linear, quadratic, or neither.

20. the circumference C of a bicycle wheel, given its radius r

21. the area of a triangle A with a constant height, given its base length b

22. the population of bacteria P in a petri dish doubling every hour t

23. the area of carpet A needed for square rooms of length s

24. Physics In the past, different mathematical descriptions of falling objects were proposed.

    a. Which rule shows the greatest increase in the distance fallen per second and thus the greatest rate of increase in speed?

    b. Identify each rule as linear, quadratic, or neither.

    c. Describe the differences in da Vinci's rule, and compare it with the differences in Galileo's.

    d. The most accurate rule is sometimes described as the odd-number law. Which rule shows an odd-number pattern of first differences and correctly describes the distance for falling objects?

Relative Distance Fallen (units)			
Time Interval (s)	Aristotle's Rule	da Vinci's Rule	Galileo's Rule
0	0	0	0
1	1	1	1
2	2	3	4
3	3	6	9
4	4	10	16

Find the missing value for each quadratic function.

25.

x	−1	0	1	2	3
f(x)	0	1	0	▮	−8

26.

x	−3	−2	−1	0	1
f(x)	12	2	▮	0	8

27.

x	−2	0	2	4	6
f(x)	−2	▮	2	7	14

Real-World Connections

28. A home-improvement store sells several sizes of rectangular tiles, as shown in the table.

    a. Find a quadratic model for the area of a tile based on its length.

    b. The store begins selling a new size of tile with a length of 9 in. Based on your model, estimate the area of a tile of this size.

Length (in.)	Area (in²)
4	28
6	54
8	88
10	130

H.O.T. 29. Food The pizza prices for DeAngelo's pizza parlor are shown at right.

16 in.
$16.⁹⁵

14 in.
$13.⁹⁵

12 in.
$9.⁹⁵

 a. Find a quadratic model for the price of a pizza based upon the size (diameter).

 b. Use the quadratic model to find the price of a pizza with an 18 in. diameter.

 c. Graph the quadratic function. Does the function have a minimum or maximum point? What does this point represent?

 d. What if...? According to the model, how much should a 30 in. pizza cost? How much should an 8 in. pizza cost?

 e. Is the quadratic function a good model for the price of DeAngelo's pizza? Explain your reasoning.

Determine whether each data set could represent a quadratic function. If so, find a quadratic function rule.

30.

x	0	1	2	3	4
y	−1	0	−1	−4	−9

31.

x	1	2	3	4	5
y	10	20	40	60	80

32.

x	2	4	6	8	10
y	−1	0	1	3	5

33.

x	−2	−1	0	1	2
y	16	3	0	7	24

34.

x	0	1	2	3	4
y	9	5	3	1	0

35.

x	−2	−1	0	1	2
y	0	3	9	27	81

36. Winter Sports The diagram shows the motion of a skier following a jump. Find a quadratic model of the skier's height h in meters based on time t in seconds. Estimate the skier's height after 2 s.

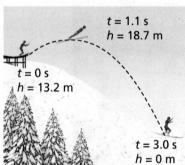

$t = 1.1$ s
$h = 18.7$ m

$t = 0$ s
$h = 13.2$ m

$t = 3.0$ s
$h = 0$ m

H.O.T. 37. Data Collection Use a graphing calculator and a motion detector to measure the height of a basketball over time. Drop the ball from a height of 1 m, and let it bounce several times. Position the motion detector 0.5 m above the release point of the ball.

 a. What is the greatest height the ball reaches during its first bounce?

 b. Find an appropriate model for the height of the ball as a function of time during its first bounce.

38. Safety The light produced by high-pressure sodium vapor streetlamps for different energy usages is shown in the table.

High-Pressure Sodium Vapor Streetlamps					
Energy Use (watts)	35	50	70	100	150
Light Output (lumens)	2250	4000	5800	9500	16,000

 a. Find a quadratic model for the light output with respect to energy use.

 b. Find a linear model for the light output with respect to energy use.

 c. Apply each model to estimate the light output in lumens of a 200-watt bulb.

 d. Which model gives the better estimate? Explain.

39. Sports The table lists the average distance that a normal shot travels for different golf clubs.

Average Distance for Normal Shot								
Club Iron (no.)	2	3	4	5	6	7	8	9
Loft Angle	16°	20°	24°	28°	32°	36°	40°	44°
Distance (yd)	186	176	166	155	143	132	122	112

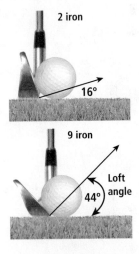

2 iron

16°

9 iron

Loft angle

44°

a. Select three data values (club number, distance), and use a system of equations to find a quadratic model. Check your model by using a quadratic regression.

b. Is there a quadratic relationship between club number and average distance of a normal shot? Explain.

c. Is the relationship between club number and loft angle quadratic or linear? Find a model of this relationship.

H.O.T. 40. Multi-Step Use the table of alloy-steel chain data.

a. Do each of the last two columns appear to be quadratic functions with respect to the nominal chain size? Explain.

b. Verify your response in part **a** by finding each of the quadratic regression equations. Do the models fit the data well? Explain.

c. Predict the values for the last two columns for a chain with a nominal size of $\frac{5}{8}$ in.

Alloy-Steel Chain Specifications		
Nominal Size (in.)	Maximum Length 100 Links (in.)	Maximum Weight 100 Links (lb)
$\frac{1}{4}$	98	84
$\frac{1}{2}$	156	288
$\frac{3}{4}$	208	655
1	277	1170
$1\frac{1}{4}$	371	1765

41. Math History The Greek mathematician Pythagoras developed a formula for triangular numbers, the first four of which are shown. Write a quadratic function that determines a triangular number t in terms of its place in the sequence n. (*Hint:* The fourth triangular number has $n = 4$.)

1   3   6   10

42. Critical Thinking Two points define a unique line. How many points define a unique parabola, and what restriction applies to the points?

43. Critical Thinking Consider the following data set.

x	10	8	13	9	11	14	6	4	12	7	5
y	9.14	8.14	8.74	8.77	9.29	8.1	6.13	3.1	9.13	7.26	4.74

a. Create a scatter plot of the data.

b. Perform a linear regression on the data.

c. Perform a quadratic regression on the data.

d. Which model best describes the data set? Explain your answer.

44. Write About It What does it mean when the coefficient a in a quadratic regression model is zero?

45. Which of the following would best be modeled by a quadratic function?

(A) Relationship between circumference and diameter

(B) Relationship between area of a square and side length

(C) Relationship between diagonal of a square and side length

(D) Relationship between volume of a cube and side length

46. If $(7, 11)$ and $(3, 11)$ are two points on a parabola, what is the x-value of the vertex of this parabola?

(F) 3   (G) 5   (H) 7   (J) 11

47. If y is a quadratic function of x, which value completes the table?

x	−2	0	2	4	6
y	−8	0	12	28	▣

(A) 12   (B) 20   (C) 44   (D) 48

48. The graph of a quadratic function having the form $f(x) = ax^2 + bx + c$ passes through the points $(0, -8)$, $(3, 10)$, and $(6, 34)$. What is the value of the function when $x = -3$?

(F) −32   (G) −26   (H) −20   (J) 10

H.O.T. 49. Extended Response Write a quadratic function in standard form that fits the data points $(0, -5)$, $(1, -3)$, and $(2, 3)$. Use a system of equations, and show all of your work.

CHALLENGE AND EXTEND

50. Three points defining a quadratic function are $(1, 2)$, $(4, 6)$, and $(7, w)$.

a. If $w = 9$, what is the quadratic function? Does it have a maximum value or a minimum value? What is the vertex?

b. If $w = 11$, what is the quadratic function? Does it have a maximum value or a minimum value? What is the vertex?

c. If $w = 10$, what function best fits the points?

H.O.T. 51. Explain how you can determine from three points whether the parabola that fits the points opens upward or downward.

MATHEMATICAL PRACTICES

FOCUS ON MATHEMATICAL PRACTICES

H.O.T. 52. Communication Geri said two points define a linear function. How many points define a unique quadratic equation? Justify your answer.

H.O.T. 53. Graphing Calculator Gold's closing price each year is shown in the table.

Year	2000	2001	2002	2003	2004	2005	2006	2007	2008	2009	2010
Price ($/oz)	273	277	343	417	436	513	636	837	870	1088	1420

a. Orlando looked carefully at the table of data and said it appears to represent a quadratic function. Do you agree? Explain.

b. Find a quadratic model for the gold price over time using $x = 0$ for 2000. Does the model provide a good fit for the data? Explain.

Ready to Go On?

my.hrw.com
Assessment and Intervention

15-1 Using Transformations to Graph Quadratic Functions

Using the graph of $f(x) = x^2$ as a guide, describe the transformations, and then graph each function.

1. $g(x) = (x + 2)^2 - 4$ **2.** $g(x) = -4(x - 1)^2$ **3.** $g(x) = \frac{1}{2}x^2 + 1$

Use the description to write each quadratic function in vertex form.

4. $f(x) = x^2$ is vertically stretched by a factor of 9 and translated 2 units left to create g.

5. $f(x) = x^2$ is reflected across the x-axis and translated 4 units up to create g.

15-2 Properties of Quadratic Functions in Standard Form

For each function, (a) determine whether the graph opens upward or downward, (b) find the axis of symmetry, (c) find the vertex, (d) find the y-intercept, and (e) graph the function.

6. $f(x) = x^2 - 4x + 3$ **7.** $g(x) = -x^2 + 2x - 1$ **8.** $h(x) = x^2 - 6x$

9. A football kick is modeled by the function $h(x) = -0.0075x^2 + 0.5x + 5$, where h is the height of the ball in feet and x is the horizontal distance in feet that the ball travels. Find the maximum height of the ball to the nearest foot.

15-3 Curve Fitting with Quadratic Models

Determine whether each data set could represent a quadratic function. Explain.

10.

x	5	6	7	8	9
y	13	11	7	1	−7

11.

x	−4	−2	0	2	4
y	10	8	4	8	10

Write a quadratic function that fits each set of points.

12. $(0, 4), (2, 0)$, and $(3, 1)$

13. $(1, 3), (2, 5)$, and $(4, 3)$

For Exercises 14–16, use the table of maximum load allowances for various heights of spruce columns.

14. Find a quadratic regression equation to model the maximum load given the height.

15. Use your model to predict the maximum load allowed for a 6.5 ft spruce column.

16. Use your model to predict the maximum load allowed for an 8 ft spruce column.

Maximum Load Allowance No. 1 Common Spruce	
Height of Column (ft)	Maximum Load (lb)
4	7280
5	7100
6	6650
7	5960

PARCC Assessment Readiness

Selected Response

1. What sequence of transformations can you use to map the graph of $f(x) = x^2$ onto the graph of $g(x) = -8x^2$?

- Ⓐ A reflection across the x-axis and a vertical stretch by a factor of 8.
- Ⓑ A reflection across the x-axis and a horizontal compression by a factor of 8.
- Ⓒ A reflection across the x-axis and a horizontal stretch by a factor of 8.
- Ⓓ A reflection across the x-axis and a vertical compression by a factor of 8.

2. Find the minimum or maximum value of $f(x) = x^2 - 2x - 6$. Then state the domain and range of the function.

- Ⓕ The maximum value is 1.
  D: {all real numbers}; R: $\{y \mid y \geq -7\}$
- Ⓖ The minimum value is −7.
  D: $\{x \mid x \geq -7\}$; R: {all real numbers}
- Ⓗ The maximum value is 1.
  D: $\{x \mid x \geq -7\}$; R: {all real numbers}
- Ⓙ The minimum value is −7.
  D: {all real numbers}; R: $\{y \mid y \geq -7\}$

3. The distance d in meters traveled by a skateboard on a ramp is related to the time traveled t in seconds. This is modeled by the function: $d(t) = 4.9t^2 - 2.3t + 5$. What is the maximum distance the skateboard can travel, and at what time would it achieve this distance? Round your answers to the nearest hundredth.

- Ⓐ 5.00 meters in 0 seconds
- Ⓑ 0.23 meters at 4.73 seconds
- Ⓒ 4.73 meters at 0.23 seconds
- Ⓓ 5.00 meters at 0.47 seconds

4. The minimum braking distance d in feet for a properly loaded truck on dry concrete is approximated by the function $d(v) = 0.065v^2$, where v is the vehicle's speed in miles per hour. If the truck is overloaded, the braking-distance function is $d_0(v) = 0.078v^2$. What kind of transformation describes this change, and what does the transformation mean?

- Ⓕ The value of a has increased from 0.065 to 0.078. The increase indicates a *vertical stretch* by a factor of 1.2. Thus, an overloaded truck takes about 1.2 times as many feet to stop as a properly loaded truck.
- Ⓖ The value of a has increased from 0.065 to 0.078. The increase indicates a *vertical stretch* by a factor of 1.2. Thus, a properly loaded truck takes about 1.2 times as many feet to stop as an overloaded truck.
- Ⓗ The value of a has increased from 0.065 to 0.078. The increase indicates a *horizontal stretch* by a factor of 1.2. Thus, an overloaded truck takes about 1.2 times as many feet to stop as a properly loaded truck.
- Ⓙ The value of a has increased from 0.065 to 0.078. The increase indicates a *horizontal stretch* by a factor of 1.2. Thus, a properly loaded truck takes about 1.2 times as many feet to stop as an overloaded truck.

Mini-Task

5. If y is a quadratic function of x, what value completes the table?

x	−4	−2	0	2	4
y	81	49	25	?	1

UNIT 5

Module

16 Solving Quadratic Equations

COMMON
CORE GPS

MCC9-12.A.SSE.1, MCC9-12.A.SSE.2,
MCC9-12.A.SSE.3a,
MCC9-12.A.CED.2, MCC9-12.A.REI.4

MCC9-12.A.SSE.1, MCC9-12.A.SSE.2,
MCC9-12.A.SSE.3b, MCC9-12.A.CED.2,
MCC9-12.A.REI.4a, MCC9-12.A.REI.4b

MCC9-12.A.REI.4a, MCC9-12.A.REI.4b,
MCC9-12.N.CN.7, MCC9-12.A.CED.1

MCC9-12.A.REI.7

Contents

MATHEMATICAL PRACTICES The Common Core Georgia Performance Standards for Mathematical Practice describe varieties of expertise that all students should seek to develop. Opportunities to develop these practices are integrated throughout this program.

1 Make sense of problems and persevere in solving them.

2 Reason abstractly and quantitatively.

3 Construct viable arguments and critique the reasoning of others.

4 Model with mathematics.

5 Use appropriate tools strategically.

6 Attend to precision.

7 Look for and make use of structure.

8 Look for and express regularity in repeated reasoning.

Unpacking the Standards

Understanding the standards and the vocabulary terms in the standards will help you know exactly what you are expected to learn in this chapter.

COMMON CORE GPS **MCC9-12.A.REI.4b**

Solve quadratic equations by inspection (e.g., for $x^2 = 49$), taking square roots, completing the square, the quadratic formula and factoring, as appropriate to the initial form of the equation. Recognize when the quadratic formula gives complex solutions and write them as $a \pm bi$ for real numbers a and b.

Key Vocabulary

quadratic equation (ecuación cuadrática) An equation that can be written in the form $ax^2 + bx + c = 0$, where a, b, and c are real numbers and $a \neq 0$.

completing the square (completar el cuadrado) A process used to form a perfect-square trinomial. To complete the square of $x^2 + bx$, add $\left(\dfrac{b}{2}\right)^2$.

Quadratic Formula (fórmula cuadrática) The formula

$$x = \frac{-b \pm \sqrt{b^2 - 4ac}}{2a}$$

which gives solutions, or roots, of equations in the form $ax^2 + bx + c = 0$, where a, b, and c are real numbers and $a \neq 0$.

What It Means For You

Knowing how to solve quadratic equations gives you tools to understand many situations, including the laws of motion. Recognizing the best solution method for a situation allows you to work efficiently.

EXAMPLE

The height h in feet of a baseball leaving a certain batter's bat is $h(t) = -16t^2 + 63t + 4$, where t is in seconds. When does the ball hit the ground?

$-16t^2 + 63t + 4 = 0$ *The ball hits the ground when $h = 0$.*

$-1(16t + 1)(t - 4) = 0$ *You can factor the equation.*

$t = -\dfrac{1}{16}$ or $t = 4$ *The factors give these solutions.*

The ball hits the ground in 4 seconds. (The negative value is not reasonable in the real-world context.)

16-1 Solving Quadratic Equations by Graphing and Factoring

Essential Question: How can you solve quadratic equations by graphing a related quadratic function or by factoring?

Objectives
Solve quadratic equations by graphing or factoring.

Determine a quadratic function from its roots.

Vocabulary
zero of a function
root of an equation
binomial
trinomial

Why learn this?
You can use quadratic functions to model the height of a football, baseball, or soccer ball. (See Example 3.)

When a soccer ball is kicked into the air, how long will the ball take to hit the ground? The height h in feet of the ball after t seconds can be modeled by the quadratic function $h(t) = -16t^2 + 32t$. In this situation, the value of the function represents the height of the soccer ball. When the ball hits the ground, the value of the function is zero.

A **zero of a function** is a value of the input x that makes the output $f(x)$ equal zero. The zeros of a function are the x-intercepts.

Unlike linear functions, which have no more than one zero, quadratic functions can have two zeros, as shown at right. These zeros are always symmetric about the axis of symmetry.

$f(x) = ax^2 + bx + c$

The x-coordinates are the zeros.

COMMON CORE GPS
MCC9-12.F.IF.7a

EXAMPLE 1 Finding Zeros by Using a Graph or Table

Online Video Tutor

Find the zeros of $f(x) = x^2 + 2x - 3$ by using a graph and table.

Method 1 Graph the function $f(x) = x^2 + 2x - 3$.

The graph opens upward because $a > 0$. The y-intercept is -3 because $c = -3$.

Find the vertex: $x = -\dfrac{b}{2a} = -\dfrac{2}{2(1)} = -1$ *The x-coordinate of the vertex is $-\frac{b}{2a}$.*

Find $f(-1)$: $f(x) = x^2 + 2x - 3$

$$f(-1) = (-1)^2 + 2(-1) - 3$$ *Substitute -1 for x.*

$$f(-1) = -4$$

The vertex is $(-1, -4)$.

Plot the vertex and the y-intercept. Use symmetry and a table of values to find additional points.

x	-3	-2	-1	0	1
$f(x)$	0	-3	-4	-3	0

The table and the graph indicate that the zeros are -3 and 1.

Helpful Hint

Recall that for the graph of a quadratic function, *any* pair of points with the same y-value are symmetric about the axis of symmetry.

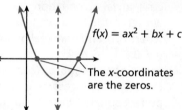

$(-3, 0)$ $(1, 0)$

Find the zeros of $f(x) = x^2 + 2x - 3$ by using a graph and table.

Method 2 Use a calculator.

Enter $y = x^2 + 2x - 3$ into a graphing calculator.

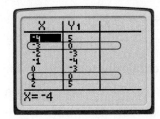 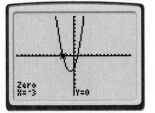

Both the table and the graph show that $y = 0$ at $x = -3$ and $x = 1$. These are the zeros of the function.

 1. Find the zeros of $g(x) = -x^2 - 2x + 3$ by using a graph and a table.

Reading Math

- Functions have *zeros* or *x-intercepts*.
- Equations have *solutions* or *roots*.

You can also find zeros by using algebra. For example, to find the zeros of $f(x) = x^2 + 2x - 3$, you can set the function equal to zero. The solutions to the related equation $x^2 + 2x - 3 = 0$ represent the zeros of the function.

The solutions to a quadratic equation of the form $ax^2 + bx + c = 0$ are *roots*. The **roots of an equation** are the values of the variable that make the equation true.

You can find the roots of some quadratic equations by factoring and applying the Zero Product Property.

Zero Product Property

For all real numbers a and b,

WORDS	NUMBERS	ALGEBRA
If the product of two quantities equals zero, at least one of the quantities equals zero.	$3(0) = 0$ $0(4) = 0$	If $ab = 0$, then $a = 0$ or $b = 0$.

COMMON CORE GPS MCC9-12.A.SSE.3a

EXAMPLE 2 **Finding Zeros by Factoring**

Find the zeros of each function by factoring.

A $f(x) = x^2 - 8x + 12$

$\quad x^2 - 8x + 12 = 0$ *Set the function equal to 0.*

$\quad (x - 2)(x - 6) = 0$ *Factor: Find factors of 12 that add to −8.*

$\quad x - 2 = 0 \text{ or } x - 6 = 0$ *Apply the Zero Product Property.*

$\quad\quad x = 2 \text{ or } x = 6$ *Solve each equation.*

my.hrw.com

Online Video Tutor

Check

$x^2 - 8x + 12 = 0$		$x^2 - 8x + 12 = 0$		*Substitute each*
$(2)^2 - 8(2) + 12$	0	$(6)^2 - 8(6) + 12$	0	*value into*
$4 - 16 + 12$	0	$36 - 48 + 12$	0	*the original*
	$0 \mid 0$ ✔		$0 \mid 0$ ✔	*equation.*

Find the zeros of each function by factoring.

B $g(x) = 3x^2 + 12x$

$$3x^2 + 12x = 0 \qquad \text{Set the function equal to 0.}$$

$$3x(x + 4) = 0 \qquad \text{Factor: The GCF is } 3x.$$

$$3x = 0 \text{ or } x + 4 = 0 \qquad \text{Apply the Zero Product Property.}$$

$$x = 0 \text{ or } x = -4 \qquad \text{Solve each equation.}$$

Check Check algebraically and by graphing.

$3x^2 + 12x = 0$		$3x^2 + 12x = 0$	
$3(0)^2 + 12(0)$	0	$3(-4)^2 + 12(-4)$	0
$0 + 0$	$0 ✔$	$48 - 48$	$0 ✔$

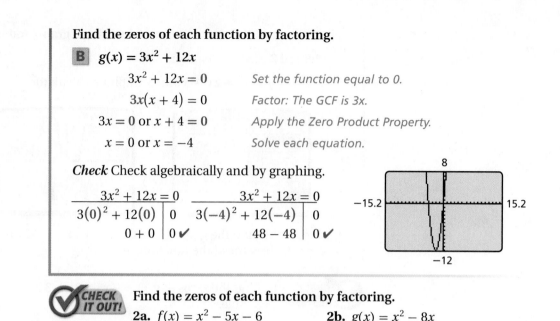

CHECK IT OUT! Find the zeros of each function by factoring.

2a. $f(x) = x^2 - 5x - 6$ **2b.** $g(x) = x^2 - 8x$

Any object that is thrown or launched into the air, such as a baseball, basketball, or soccer ball, is a *projectile*. The general function that approximates the height *h* in feet of a projectile on Earth after *t* seconds is given below.

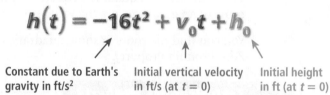

$$h(t) = -16t^2 + v_0t + h_0$$

Constant due to Earth's gravity in ft/s²   Initial vertical velocity in ft/s (at $t = 0$)   Initial height in ft (at $t = 0$)

Note that this model has limitations because it does not account for air resistance, wind, and other real-world factors.

COMMON CORE GPS
MCC9-12.F.IF.8a

EXAMPLE 3

my.hrw.com

Online Video Tutor

Sports Application

A soccer ball is kicked from ground level with an initial vertical velocity of 32 ft/s. After how many seconds will the ball hit the ground?

$$h(t) = -16t^2 + v_0t + h_0 \qquad \text{Write the general projectile function.}$$

$$h(t) = -16t^2 + 32t + 0 \qquad \text{Substitute 32 for } v_0 \text{ and 0 for } h_0.$$

The ball will hit the ground when its height is zero.

$$-16t^2 + 32t = 0 \qquad \text{Set } h(t) \text{ equal to 0.}$$

$$-16t(t - 2) = 0 \qquad \text{Factor: The GCF is } -16t.$$

$$-16t = 0 \text{ or } (t - 2) = 0 \qquad \text{Apply the Zero Product Property.}$$

$$t = 0 \text{ or } t = 2 \qquad \text{Solve each equation.}$$

The ball will hit the ground in 2 seconds. Notice that the height is also zero when $t = 0$, the instant that the ball is kicked.

Check The graph of the function $h(t) = -16t^2 + 32t$ shows its zeros at 0 and 2.

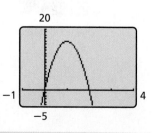

3. A football is kicked from ground level with an initial vertical velocity of 48 ft/s. How long is the ball in the air?

Quadratic expressions can have one, two, or three terms, such as $-16t^2$, $-16t^2 + 25t$, or $-16t^2 + 25t + 6$. Quadratic expressions with two terms are **binomials**. Quadratic expressions with three terms are **trinomials**. Some quadratic expressions with perfect squares have special factoring rules.

Know it!
Note

Special Products and Factors	
Difference of Two Squares	**Perfect-Square Trinomial**
$a^2 - b^2 = (a + b)(a - b)$	$a^2 - 2ab + b^2 = (a - b)^2$ $a^2 + 2ab + b^2 = (a + b)^2$

COMMON CORE GPS
EXAMPLE **4**
MCC9-12.A.SSE.2

my.hrw.com

Online Video Tutor

Finding Roots by Using Special Factors

Find the roots of each equation by factoring.

A $9x^2 = 1$

$$9x^2 - 1 = 0 \qquad \text{\textit{Rewrite in standard form.}}$$
$$(3x)^2 - (1)^2 = 0 \qquad \text{\textit{Write the left side as } } a^2 - b^2.$$
$$(3x + 1)(3x - 1) = 0 \qquad \text{\textit{Factor the difference of squares.}}$$
$$3x + 1 = 0 \text{ or } 3x - 1 = 0 \qquad \text{\textit{Apply the Zero Product Property.}}$$
$$x = -\frac{1}{3} \text{ or } x = \frac{1}{3} \qquad \text{\textit{Solve each equation.}}$$

Check Graph each side of the equation on a graphing calculator. Let **Y1** equal $9x^2$, and let **Y2** equal 1. The graphs appear to intersect at $x = -\frac{1}{3}$ and at $x = \frac{1}{3}$.

3

−4.5 ———————— 4.5

Intersection
X=-.3333333 Y=1

−3

B $40x = 8x^2 + 50$

$$8x^2 - 40x + 50 = 0 \qquad \text{\textit{Rewrite in standard form.}}$$
$$2(4x^2 - 20x + 25) = 0 \qquad \text{\textit{Factor. The GCF is 2.}}$$
$$4x^2 - 20x + 25 = 0 \qquad \text{\textit{Divide both sides by 2.}}$$
$$(2x)^2 - 2(2x)(5) + (5)^2 = 0 \qquad \text{\textit{Write the left side as } } a^2 - 2ab + b^2.$$
$$(2x - 5)^2 = 0 \qquad \text{\textit{Factor the perfect-square trinomial: } } (a - b)^2.$$
$$2x - 5 = 0 \text{ or } 2x - 5 = 0 \qquad \text{\textit{Apply the Zero Product Property.}}$$
$$x = \frac{5}{2} \text{ or } x = \frac{5}{2} \qquad \text{\textit{Solve each equation.}}$$

Helpful Hint

A quadratic equation can have two roots that are equal, such as $x = \frac{5}{2}$ and $x = \frac{5}{2}$. Two equal roots are sometimes called a double root.

Check Substitute the root $\frac{5}{2}$ into the original equation.

$$\frac{40x = 8x^2 + 50}{}$$
$$40\left(\frac{5}{2}\right) \ \bigg| \ 8\left(\frac{5}{2}\right)^2 + 50$$
$$100 \ \bigg| \ 100 \ \checkmark$$

CHECK IT OUT! **Find the roots of each equation by factoring.**

4a. $x^2 - 4x = -4$ **4b.** $25x^2 = 9$

If you know the zeros of a function, you can work backward to write a rule for the function.

COMMON CORE GPS **EXAMPLE** 5
Ext. of MCC9-12.A.SSE.3a

Using Zeros to Write Function Rules

Write a quadratic function in standard form with zeros 2 and −1.

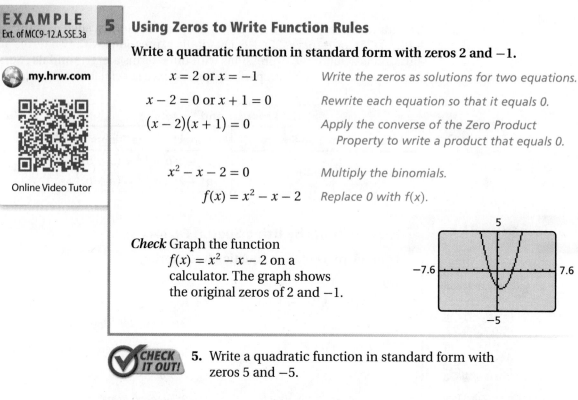

$x = 2$ or $x = -1$	*Write the zeros as solutions for two equations.*
$x - 2 = 0$ or $x + 1 = 0$	*Rewrite each equation so that it equals 0.*
$(x - 2)(x + 1) = 0$	*Apply the converse of the Zero Product Property to write a product that equals 0.*
$x^2 - x - 2 = 0$	*Multiply the binomials.*
$f(x) = x^2 - x - 2$	*Replace 0 with f(x).*

my.hrw.com

Online Video Tutor

Check Graph the function $f(x) = x^2 - x - 2$ on a calculator. The graph shows the original zeros of 2 and −1.

CHECK IT OUT! **5.** Write a quadratic function in standard form with zeros 5 and −5.

Note that there are many quadratic functions with the same zeros. For example, the functions $f(x) = x^2 - x - 2$, $g(x) = -x^2 + x + 2$, and $h(x) = 2x^2 - 2x - 4$ all have zeros at 2 and −1.

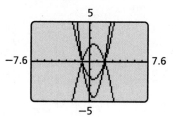

MCC.MP.7 **MATHEMATICAL PRACTICES**

THINK AND DISCUSS

1. Describe the zeros of a function whose terms form a perfect square trinomial.

2. Compare the *x*- and *y*-intercepts of a quadratic function with those of a linear function.

3. A quadratic equation has no real solutions. Describe the graph of the related quadratic function.

Know it! *Note*

4. GET ORGANIZED Copy and complete the graphic organizer. In each box, give information about special products and factors.

Name	Rule	Example	Graph
Difference of Two Squares			
Perfect-Square Trinomial			

GUIDED PRACTICE

1. **Vocabulary** The solutions of the equation $3x^2 + 2x + 5 = 0$ are its __?__ . (*roots* or *zeros*)

SEE EXAMPLE 1   **Find the zeros of each function by using a graph and table.**

2. $f(x) = x^2 + 4x - 5$ 3. $g(x) = -x^2 + 6x - 8$ 4. $f(x) = x^2 - 1$

SEE EXAMPLE 2   **Find the zeros of each function by factoring.**

5. $f(x) = x^2 - 7x + 6$ 6. $g(x) = 2x^2 - 5x + 2$ 7. $h(x) = x^2 + 4x$

8. $f(x) = x^2 + 9x + 20$ 9. $g(x) = x^2 - 6x - 16$ 10. $h(x) = 3x^2 + 13x + 4$

SEE EXAMPLE 3   11. **Archery** The height h of an arrow in feet is modeled by $h(t) = -16t^2 + 63t + 4$, where t is the time in seconds since the arrow was shot. How long is the arrow in the air?

SEE EXAMPLE 4   **Find the roots of each equation by factoring.**

12. $x^2 - 6x = -9$ 13. $5x^2 + 20 = 20x$ 14. $x^2 = 49$

SEE EXAMPLE 5   **Write a quadratic function in standard form for each given set of zeros.**

15. 3 and 4   16. -4 and -4 17. 3 and 0

PRACTICE AND PROBLEM SOLVING

Independent Practice	
For Exercises	See Example
18–20	1
21–26	2
27	3
28–33	4
34–36	5

my.hrw.com

Online Extra Practice

Find the zeros of each function by using a graph and table.

18. $f(x) = -x^2 + 4x - 3$ 19. $g(x) = x^2 + x - 6$ 20. $f(x) = x^2 - 9$

Find the zeros of each function by factoring.

21. $f(x) = x^2 + 11x + 24$ 22. $g(x) = 2x^2 + x - 10$ 23. $h(x) = -x^2 + 9x$

24. $f(x) = x^2 - 15x + 54$ 25. $g(x) = x^2 + 7x - 8$ 26. $h(x) = 2x^2 - 12x + 18$

27. **Biology** A bald eagle snatches a fish from a lake and flies to an altitude of 256 ft. The fish manages to squirm free and falls back down into the lake. Its height h in feet can be modeled by $h(t) = 256 - 16t^2$, where t is the time in seconds. How many seconds will the fish fall before hitting the water?

Find the roots of each equation by factoring.

28. $x^2 + 8x = -16$ 29. $4x^2 = 81$ 30. $9x^2 + 12x + 4 = 0$

31. $36x^2 - 9 = 0$ 32. $x^2 - 10x + 25 = 0$ 33. $49x^2 = 28x - 4$

Write a quadratic function in standard form for each given set of zeros.

34. 5 and -1 35. 6 and 2   36. 3 and 3

Find the zeros of each function.

37. $f(x) = 6x - x^2$ 38. $g(x) = x^2 - 25$ 39. $h(x) = x^2 - 12x + 36$

40. $f(x) = 3x^2 - 12$ 41. $g(x) = x^2 - 22x + 121$ 42. $h(x) = 30 + x - x^2$

43. $f(x) = x^2 - 11x + 30$ 44. $g(x) = x^2 - 8x - 20$ 45. $h(x) = 2x^2 + 18x + 28$

H.O.T. 46. Movies A stuntwoman jumps from a building 73 ft high and lands on an air bag that is 9 ft tall. Her height above ground h in feet can be modeled by $h(t) = 73 - 16t^2$, where t is the time in seconds.

    a. Multi-Step How many seconds will the stuntwoman fall before touching the air bag? (*Hint:* Find the time t when the stuntwoman's height above ground is 9 ft.)

    b. What if...? Suppose the stuntwoman jumps from a building that is half as tall. Will she be in the air for half as long? Explain.

47. Entertainment A juggler throws a ball into the air from a height of 5 ft with an initial vertical velocity of 16 ft/s.

    a. Write a function that can be used to model the height h of the ball in feet t seconds after the ball is thrown.

    b. How long does the juggler have to catch the ball before it hits the ground?

Find the roots of each equation.

48. $x^2 - 2x + 1 = 0$ **49.** $x^2 + 6x = -5$ **50.** $25x^2 + 40x = -16$

51. $9x^2 + 6x = -1$ **52.** $5x^2 = 45$ **53.** $x^2 - 6 = x$

For each function, (a) find its vertex, (b) find its y-intercept, (c) find its zeros, and (d) graph it.

54. $f(x) = x^2 + 2x - 8$ **55.** $g(x) = x^2 - 16$ **56.** $h(x) = x^2 - x - 12$

57. $f(x) = -2x^2 + 4x$ **58.** $g(x) = x^2 - 5x - 6$ **59.** $h(x) = 3x^2 + x - 4$

60. Geometry The hypotenuse of a right triangle is 2 cm longer than one leg and 4 cm longer than the other leg.

    a. Let x represent the length of the hypotenuse. Use the Pythagorean Theorem to write an equation that can be solved for x.

    b. Find the solutions of the equation from part **a.**

    c. Are both solutions reasonable in the context of the problem situation? Explain.

Geometry Find the dimensions of each rectangle.

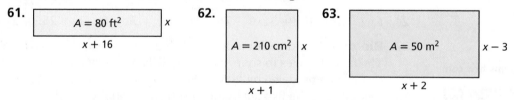

61. $A = 80$ ft^2, x, $x + 16$

62. $A = 210$ cm^2, x, $x + 1$

63. $A = 50$ m^2, $x - 3$, $x + 2$

H.O.T. 64. Critical Thinking Will a function whose rule can be factored as a binomial squared ever have two different zeros? Explain.

H.O.T. 65. Write About It Explain how the Zero Product Property can be used to help determine the zeros of quadratic functions.

66. A baseball player hits a ball toward the outfield. The height h of the ball in feet is modeled by $h(t) = -16t^2 + 22t + 3$, where t is the time in seconds. In addition, the function $d(t) = 85t$ models the horizontal distance d traveled by the ball.

    a. If no one catches the ball, how long will it stay in the air?

    b. What is the horizontal distance that the ball travels before it hits the ground?

67. Use the graph provided to choose the best description of what the graph represents.

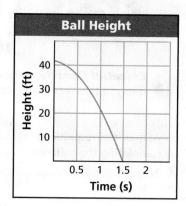

Ball Height

(A) A ball is dropped from a height of 42 feet and lands on the ground after 3 seconds.

(B) A ball is dropped from a height of 42 feet and lands on the mathematic after 1.5 seconds.

(C) A ball is shot up in the air and reaches a height of 42 feet after 1 second.

(D) A ball is shot up in the air, reaches a height of 42 feet, and lands on the ground after 1.5 seconds.

68. Which function has -7 as its only zero?

(F) $f(x) = x(x - 7)$

(G) $h(x) = (x - 7)^2$

(H) $g(x) = (x + 1)(x + 7)$

(J) $j(x) = (x + 7)^2$

69. Which expression is a perfect square trinomial?

(A) $25y^2 - 16$

(B) $25y^2 - 20y + 16$

(C) $25y^2 - 40y + 16$

(D) $25y^2 - 10y + 16$

70. **Gridded Response** Find the positive root of $x^2 + 4x - 21 = 0$.

CHALLENGE AND EXTEND

Find the roots of each equation by factoring.

71. $3(x^2 - x) = x^2$

72. $x^2 = \frac{1}{3}x$

73. $x^2 - \frac{3}{4}x + \frac{1}{8} = 0$

74. $x^2 + x + 0.21 = 0$

H.O.T. 75. Another special factoring case involves perfect cubes. The sum of two cubes can be factored by using the formula $a^3 + b^3 = (a + b)(a^2 - ab + b^2)$.

 a. Verify the formula by multiplying the right side of the equation.

 b. Factor the expression $8x^3 + 27$.

 c. Use multiplication and guess and check to find the factors of $a^3 - b^3$.

 d. Factor the expression $x^3 - 1$.

FOCUS ON MATHEMATICAL PRACTICES

MATHEMATICAL PRACTICES

H.O.T. 76. **Problem Solving** On Mercury, the constant due to gravity for projectile motion is -6, not -16 as on Earth, so $h(t) = -6t^2 + v_0t + h_0$. If a meteorite impact on Mercury causes a rock to be launched from the ground at an initial velocity of 75 feet per second, after how many seconds will the rock hit the ground?

H.O.T. 77. **Estimation** Ephraim throws a baseball from a height of 4 feet at an initial velocity of 63 feet per second. Draw a graph of the height of the baseball t seconds after it is thrown, ignoring air resistance. On the same axes, sketch what the graph might look like if air resistance were taken into account.

H.O.T. 78. **Make a Conjecture** Find the zeros of the functions $f(x) = x^2 - 25$ and $g(x) = x^2 - 36$. From this information, what can you determine about the zeros of $h(x) = x^2 - 30$? Can you find the exact zeros of $h(x)$ by factoring? Explain.

16-2 Completing the Square

Essential Question: How can you solve quadratic equations by using square roots or by completing the square?

Objectives
Solve quadratic equations by completing the square.

Write quadratic equations in vertex form.

Vocabulary
completing the square

Why learn this?
You can solve quadratic equations to find how long water takes to fall from the top to the bottom of a waterfall. (See Exercise 39.)

Many quadratic equations contain expressions that cannot be easily factored. For equations containing these types of expressions, you can use square roots to find roots.

Know it! Note

Square-Root Property		
WORDS	**NUMBERS**	**ALGEBRA**
To solve a quadratic equation, you can take the square root of both sides. Be sure to consider the positive and negative square roots.	$x^2 = 15$ $\lvert x \rvert = \sqrt{15}$ $x = \pm\sqrt{15}$	If $x^2 = a$ and a is a nonnegative real number, then $x = \pm\sqrt{a}$.

COMMON CORE GPS

EXAMPLE 1
MCC9-12.A.REI.4b

Solving Equations by Using the Square Root Property

Solve each equation.

my.hrw.com

Online Video Tutor

A $3x^2 - 4 = 68$

$$3x^2 = 72 \qquad \textit{Add 4 to both sides.}$$
$$x^2 = 24 \qquad \textit{Divide both sides by 3 to isolate the squared term.}$$
$$x = \pm\sqrt{24} \qquad \textit{Take the square root of both sides.}$$
$$x = \pm2\sqrt{6} \qquad \textit{Simplify.}$$

Check Use a graphing calculator.

```
3*(2√(6))²-4
                68
3*(-2√(6))²-4
                68
```

B $x^2 - 10x + 25 = 27$

$$(x - 5)^2 = 27 \qquad \textit{Factor the perfect square trinomial.}$$
$$x - 5 = \pm\sqrt{27} \qquad \textit{Take the square root of both sides.}$$
$$x = 5 \pm \sqrt{27} \qquad \textit{Add 5 to both sides.}$$
$$x = 5 \pm 3\sqrt{3} \qquad \textit{Simplify.}$$

Check Use a graphing calculator.

```
(5+3√(3))²-10(5+
3√(3))+25
                27
(5-3√(3))²-10(5-
3√(3))+25
                27
```

Reading Math

Read $\pm\sqrt{a}$ as "plus or minus square root of a."

CHECK IT OUT! Solve each equation.

1a. $4x^2 - 20 = 5$ **1b.** $x^2 + 8x + 16 = 49$

The methods in the previous examples can be used only for expressions that are perfect squares. However, you can use algebra to rewrite any quadratic expression as a perfect square.

You can use algebra tiles to model a perfect square trinomial as a perfect square. The area of the square at right is $x^2 + 2x + 1$. Because each side of the square measures $x + 1$ units, the area is also $(x + 1)(x + 1)$, or $(x + 1)^2$. This shows that $(x + 1)^2 = x^2 + 2x + 1$.

If a quadratic expression of the form $x^2 + bx$ *cannot* model a square, you can add a term to form a perfect square trinomial. This is called **completing the square**.

Know it! Note

Completing the Square

WORDS	NUMBERS	ALGEBRA
To complete the square of $x^2 + bx$, add $\left(\dfrac{b}{2}\right)^2$.	$x^2 + 6x + \blacksquare$ $x^2 + 6x + \left(\dfrac{6}{2}\right)^2$ $x^2 + 6x + 9$ $(x + 3)^2$	$x^2 + bx + \blacksquare$ $x^2 + bx + \left(\dfrac{b}{2}\right)^2$ $\left(x + \dfrac{b}{2}\right)^2$

The model shows completing the square for $x^2 + 6x$ by adding 9 unit tiles. The resulting perfect square trinomial is $x^2 + 6x + 9$. Note that completing the square does not produce an equivalent expression.

$x^2 + 6x$ $x^2 + 6x + 9$

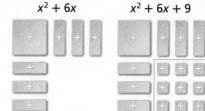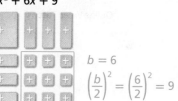

$b = 6$

$\left(\dfrac{b}{2}\right)^2 = \left(\dfrac{6}{2}\right)^2 = 9$

COMMON CORE GPS
MCC9-12.A.SSE.2

EXAMPLE **2** Completing the Square

my.hrw.com

Online Video Tutor

Complete the square for each expression. Write the resulting expression as a binomial squared.

A $x^2 - 2x + \blacksquare$

$\left(\dfrac{-2}{2}\right)^2 = (-1)^2 = 1$ *Find* $\left(\dfrac{b}{2}\right)^2$.

$x^2 - 2x + 1$ *Add.*

$(x - 1)^2$ *Factor.*

Check Find the square of the binomial.

$(x - 1)^2 = (x - 1)(x - 1)$

$= x^2 - 2x + 1$

B $x^2 + 5x + \blacksquare$

$\left(\dfrac{5}{2}\right)^2 = \dfrac{25}{4}$ *Find* $\left(\dfrac{b}{2}\right)^2$.

$x^2 + 5x + \dfrac{25}{4}$ *Add.*

$\left(x + \dfrac{5}{2}\right)^2$ *Factor.*

Check Find the square of the binomial.

$\left(x + \dfrac{5}{2}\right)^2 = \left(x + \dfrac{5}{2}\right)\left(x + \dfrac{5}{2}\right)$

$= x^2 + 5x + \dfrac{25}{4}$

 CHECK IT OUT! Complete the square for each expression. Write the resulting expression as a binomial squared.

2a. $x^2 + 4x + \blacksquare$ **2b.** $x^2 - 4x + \blacksquare$ **2c.** $x^2 + 3x + \blacksquare$

You can complete the square to solve quadratic equations.

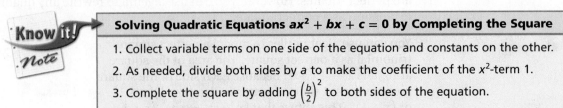

Solving Quadratic Equations $ax^2 + bx + c = 0$ by Completing the Square

1. Collect variable terms on one side of the equation and constants on the other.
2. As needed, divide both sides by a to make the coefficient of the x^2-term 1.
3. Complete the square by adding $\left(\frac{b}{2}\right)^2$ to both sides of the equation.
4. Factor the variable expression as a perfect square.
5. Take the square root of both sides of the equation.
6. Solve for the values of the variable.

COMMON CORE GPS · MCC9-12.A.REI.4a

EXAMPLE 3 Solving a Quadratic Equation by Completing the Square

my.hrw.com

Online Video Tutor

Solve each equation by completing the square.

A $x^2 = 27 - 6x$

$x^2 + 6x = 27$	Collect variable terms on one side.
$x^2 + 6x + \blacksquare = 27 + \blacksquare$	Set up to complete the square.
$x^2 + 6x + \left(\frac{6}{2}\right)^2 = 27 + \left(\frac{6}{2}\right)^2$	Add $\left(\frac{b}{2}\right)^2$ to both sides.
$x^2 + 6x + 9 = 27 + 9$	Simplify.
$(x + 3)^2 = 36$	Factor.
$x + 3 = \pm\sqrt{36}$	Take the square root of both sides.
$x + 3 = \pm 6$	Simplify.
$x + 3 = 6 \text{ or } x + 3 = -6$	Solve for x.
$x = 3 \text{ or } x = -9$	

Caution!

To keep the equation balanced, you must add $\left(\frac{b}{2}\right)^2$ to both sides of the equation.

B $2x^2 + 8x = 12$

$x^2 + 4x = 6$	Divide both sides by 2.
$x^2 + 4x + \blacksquare = 6 + \blacksquare$	Set up to complete the square.
$x^2 + 4x + \left(\frac{4}{2}\right)^2 = 6 + \left(\frac{4}{2}\right)^2$	Add $\left(\frac{b}{2}\right)^2$ to both sides.
$x^2 + 4x + 4 = 6 + 4$	Simplify.
$(x + 2)^2 = 10$	Factor.
$x + 2 = \pm\sqrt{10}$	Take the square root of both sides.
$x = -2 \pm \sqrt{10}$	Solve for x.

 CHECK IT OUT! Solve each equation by completing the square.

3a. $x^2 - 2 = 9x$ **3b.** $3x^2 - 24x = 27$

Recall the vertex form of a quadratic function is $f(x) = a(x - h)^2 + k$, where the vertex is (h, k).

You can complete the square to rewrite any quadratic function in vertex form.

Writing a Quadratic Function in Vertex Form

Write each function in vertex form, and identify its vertex.

A $f(x) = x^2 + 10x - 13$

$f(x) = \left(x^2 + 10x + \blacksquare\right) - 13 - \blacksquare$ *Set up to complete the square.*

$f(x) = \left[x^2 + 10x + \left(\dfrac{10}{2}\right)^2\right] - 13 - \left(\dfrac{10}{2}\right)^2$ *Add and subtract $\left(\dfrac{b}{2}\right)^2$.*

$f(x) = (x + 5)^2 - 38$ *Simplify and factor.*

Because $h = -5$ and $k = -38$, the vertex is $(-5, -38)$.

Check Use the axis of symmetry formula to confirm the vertex.

$x = -\dfrac{b}{2a} = -\dfrac{10}{2(1)} = -5$ $y = f(-5) = (-5)^2 + 10(-5) - 13 = -38$ ✔

B $g(x) = 2x^2 - 8x + 3$

$g(x) = 2\left(x^2 - 4x\right) + 3$ *Factor so the coefficient of x^2 is 1.*

$g(x) = 2\left(x^2 - 4x + \blacksquare\right) + 3 - \blacksquare$ *Set up to complete the square.*

$g(x) = 2\left(x^2 - 4x + \left(\dfrac{-4}{2}\right)^2\right) + 3 - 2\left(\dfrac{-4}{2}\right)^2$ *Add $\left(\dfrac{b}{2}\right)^2$. Because $\left(\dfrac{b}{2}\right)^2$ is multiplied by 2, you must subtract $2\left(\dfrac{b}{2}\right)^2$.*

$g(x) = 2\left(x^2 - 4x + 4\right) - 5$ *Simplify.*

$g(x) = 2(x - 2)^2 - 5$ *Factor.*

Because $h = 2$ and $k = -5$, the vertex is $(2, -5)$.

Check A graph of the function on a graphing calculator supports your answer.

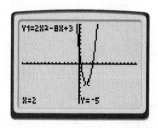

Y1=2X²-8X+3

X=2   Y=-5

Helpful Hint

In Example 3, the equation was balanced by adding $\left(\dfrac{b}{2}\right)^2$ to *both* sides. Here, the equation is balanced by adding and subtracting $\left(\dfrac{b}{2}\right)^2$ on *one* side.

my.hrw.com

Online Video Tutor

CHECK IT OUT!

Write each function in vertex form, and identify its vertex.

4a. $f(x) = x^2 + 24x + 145$ **4b.** $g(x) = 5x^2 - 50x + 128$

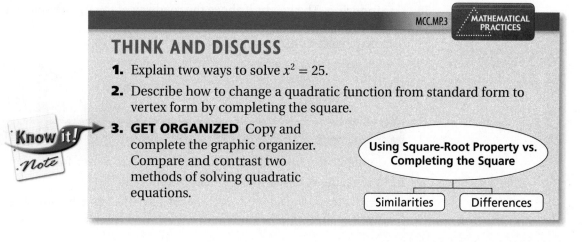

MCC.MP.3   **MATHEMATICAL PRACTICES**

THINK AND DISCUSS

1. Explain two ways to solve $x^2 = 25$.

2. Describe how to change a quadratic function from standard form to vertex form by completing the square.

3. GET ORGANIZED Copy and complete the graphic organizer. Compare and contrast two methods of solving quadratic equations.

Know it! Note

Using Square-Root Property vs. Completing the Square

Similarities   Differences

GUIDED PRACTICE

1. **Vocabulary** What must you add to the expression $x^2 + bx$ to *complete the square*?

SEE EXAMPLE **1** Solve each equation.

2. $(x - 2)^2 = 16$ 3. $x^2 - 10x + 25 = 16$ 4. $x^2 - 2x + 1 = 3$

SEE EXAMPLE **2** Complete the square for each expression. Write the resulting expression as a binomial squared.

5. $x^2 + 14x + $ ▓   6. $x^2 - 12x + $ ▓   7. $x^2 - 9x + $ ▓

SEE EXAMPLE **3** Solve each equation by completing the square.

8. $x^2 - 6x = -4$ 9. $x^2 + 8 = 6x$ 10. $2x^2 - 20x = 8$

11. $x^2 = 24 - 4x$ 12. $10x + x^2 = 42$ 13. $2x^2 + 8x - 15 = 0$

SEE EXAMPLE **4** Write each function in vertex form, and identify its vertex.

14. $f(x) = x^2 + 6x - 3$ 15. $g(x) = x^2 - 10x + 11$ 16. $h(x) = 3x^2 - 24x + 53$

17. $f(x) = x^2 + 8x - 10$ 18. $g(x) = x^2 - 3x + 16$ 19. $h(x) = 3x^2 - 12x - 4$

PRACTICE AND PROBLEM SOLVING

Independent Practice

For Exercises	See Example
20–22	1
23–25	2
26–31	3
32–37	4

my.hrw.com

Online Extra Practice

Solve each equation.

20. $(x + 2)^2 = 36$ 21. $x^2 - 6x + 9 = 100$ 22. $(x - 3)^2 = 5$

Complete the square for each expression. Write the resulting expression as a binomial squared.

23. $x^2 - 18x + $ ▓   24. $x^2 + 10x + $ ▓   25. $x^2 - \frac{1}{2}x + $ ▓

Solve each equation by completing the square.

26. $x^2 + 2x = 7$ 27. $x^2 - 4x = -1$ 28. $2x^2 - 8x = 22$

29. $8x = x^2 + 12$ 30. $x^2 + 3x - 5 = 0$ 31. $3x^2 + 6x = 1$

Write each function in vertex form, and identify its vertex.

32. $f(x) = x^2 - 4x + 13$ 33. $g(x) = x^2 + 14x + 71$ 34. $h(x) = 9x^2 + 18x - 3$

35. $f(x) = x^2 + 4x - 7$ 36. $g(x) = x^2 - 16x + 2$ 37. $h(x) = 2x^2 + 6x + 25$

38. **Engineering** The height h above the roadway of the main cable of the Golden Gate Bridge can be modeled by the function $h(x) = \frac{1}{9000}x^2 - \frac{7}{15}x + 500$, where x is the distance in feet from the left tower.

a. Complete the square, and write the function in vertex form.

b. What is the vertex, and what does it represent?

c. **Multi-Step** The left and right towers have the same height. What is the distance in feet between them?

39. Waterfalls Angel Falls in Venezuela is the tallest waterfall in the world. Water falls uninterrupted for 2421 feet before entering the river below. The height h above the river in feet of water going over the edge of the waterfall is modeled by $h(t) = -16t^2 + 2421$, where t is the time in seconds after the initial fall.

   a. Estimate the time it takes for the water to reach the river.

   b. Multi-Step Ribbon Falls in California has a height of 1612 ft. Approximately how much longer does it take water to reach the bottom when going over Angel Falls than when going over Ribbon Falls?

H.O.T. 40. Sports A basketball is shot with an initial vertical velocity of 24 ft/s from 6 ft above the ground. The ball's height h in feet is modeled by $h(t) = -16t^2 + 24t + 6$, where t is the time in seconds after the ball is shot. What is the maximum height of the ball, and when does the ball reach this height?

Solve each equation using square roots.

41. $x^2 - 1 = 2$ **42.** $25x^2 = 0$ **43.** $8x^2 - 200 = 0$

44. $-3x^2 + 6 = -1$ **45.** $(x + 13)^2 = 7$ **46.** $\left(x + \dfrac{1}{4}\right)^2 - \dfrac{9}{16} = 0$

47. $\left(x + \dfrac{3}{2}\right)^2 = \dfrac{25}{2}$ **48.** $x^2 + 14x + 49 = 64$ **49.** $9x^2 + 18x + 9 = 5$

H.O.T. 50. ///ERROR ANALYSIS/// Two attempts to write $f(x) = 2x^2 - 8x$ in vertex form are shown. Which is incorrect? Explain the error.

A
$f(x) = 2x^2 - 8x$
$f(x) = 2(x^2 - 4x)$
$f(x) = 2(x^2 - 4x + 4) - 4$
$f(x) = 2(x - 2)^2 - 4$

B
$f(x) = 2x^2 - 8x$
$f(x) = 2(x^2 - 4x)$
$f(x) = 2(x^2 - 4x + 4) - 8$
$f(x) = 2(x - 2)^2 - 8$

Solve each equation by completing the square.

51. $x^2 + 8x = -15$ **52.** $x^2 + 22x = -21$ **53.** $3x^2 + 4x = 1$

54. $2x^2 = 5x + 12$ **55.** $x^2 - 7x - 2 = 0$ **56.** $x^2 = 4x + 11$

57. $x^2 + 6x + 4 = 0$ **58.** $5x^2 + 10x - 7 = 0$ **59.** $x^2 - 8x = 24$

60. Sports A diver's height h in meters above the water is approximated by $h(t) = h_0 - 5t^2$, where h_0 is the initial height in meters, -5 is a constant based on the acceleration due to gravity in m/s², and t is the time in seconds that the diver falls through the air.

   a. Find the total time that the diver falls through the air for each type of dive in the table.

   b. How high is a dive that keeps the diver in the air twice as long as a 5-meter dive?

   c. The speed of a diver entering the water can be approximated by $s = 18t$, where s is the speed in kilometers per hour and t is the time in seconds. Using your results from part **a**, find the speed of the diver entering the water for each dive height.

   d. How many times as high is a dive that results in a speed that is twice as fast?

Dive Heights	
Type	**Height (m)**
Platform	5
Platform	10
Cliff	20
Cliff	30

Acapulco, Mexico, is famous for its cliff-diving shows. Divers perform complicated acrobatic dives from heights of up to 80 feet.

61. The height h in feet of a baseball hit from home plate can be modeled by the function $h(t) = -16t^2 + 32t + 5.5$, where t is the time in seconds since the ball was hit. The ball is descending when it passes 7.5 ft over the head of a 6 ft player standing on the ground.

   a. To the nearest tenth of a second, how long after the ball is hit does it pass over the player's head?

   b. The horizontal distance between the player and home plate is 120 ft. Use your answer from part **a** to determine the horizontal speed of the ball to the nearest foot per second.

62. Estimation A bag of grass seed will cover 525 square feet. Twenty bags of seed are used to cover an area shaped like a square. Estimate the side length of the square. Check your answer with a calculator.

63. Critical Thinking The functions f and g are defined by $f(x) = x^2 + 2x - 2$ and $g(x) = (x + 1)^2 - 3$. Use algebra to prove that f and g represent the same function.

H.O.T. 64. Sports A player bumps a volleyball with an initial vertical velocity of 20 ft/s.

   a. Write a function h in standard form for the ball's height in feet in terms of the time t in seconds after the ball is hit.

   b. Complete the square to rewrite h in vertex form.

   c. What is the maximum height of the ball?

   d. What if...? Suppose the volleyball were hit under the same conditions, but with an initial velocity of 32 ft/s. How much higher would the ball go?

Graphing Calculator Use a graphing calculator to approximate the roots of each equation to the nearest thousandth.

65. $x^2 - 15 = 40$ **66.** $x^2 = 2.85$ **67.** $1.4x^2 = 24.6$

68. $(x + 0.6)^2 = 7.4$ **69.** $\dfrac{x^2}{7} = \dfrac{1}{3}$ **70.** $\left(x + \dfrac{1}{4}\right)^2 = \dfrac{5}{6}$

71. Critical Thinking Why do equations of the form $x^2 = k$ have no real solution when $k < 0$?

H.O.T. 72. Write About It Compare the methods of factoring and completing the square for solving quadratic equations.

TEST PREP

73. Which gives the solution to $3x^2 = 33$?

   Ⓐ $\pm\sqrt{3}$ Ⓑ $\pm\sqrt{11}$ Ⓒ 11   Ⓓ 121

74. Which equation represents the graph at right?

   Ⓕ $y = (x - 2)^2 + 1$
   Ⓖ $y = (x - 2)^2 - 1$
   Ⓗ $y = (x + 2)^2 + 1$
   Ⓙ $y = (x + 2)^2 - 1$

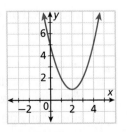

75. Which gives the vertex of the graph of $y = 3(x - 1)^2 - 22$?

  (A) $(1, -22)$ (B) $(-1, -22)$ (C) $(3, -22)$ (D) $(-3, -22)$

76. Which number should be added to $x^2 + 14x$ to make a perfect square trinomial?

  (F) 7   (G) 14   (H) 49   (J) 196

77. Gridded Response What is the positive root of the equation $2x^2 - x = 10$?

78. Extended Response Solve the quadratic equation $x^2 - 6x = 16$ by completing the square. Explain each step of the solution process, and check your answer.

CHALLENGE AND EXTEND

Find the value of b in each perfect square trinomial.

79. $x^2 - bx + 144$ **80.** $4x^2 - bx + 16$

81. $3x^2 + bx + 27$ **82.** $ax^2 + bx + c$

Find the zeros of each function.

83. $f(x) = x^2 - 4x\sqrt{5} + 19$ **84.** $f(x) = x^2 + 6x\sqrt{3} + 23$

H.O.T. 85. Farming To create a temporary grazing area, a farmer is using 1800 feet of electric fencing to enclose a rectangular field and then to subdivide the field into two plots. The fence that divides the field into two plots is parallel to the field's shorter sides.

  a. What is the largest area of the field that the farmer can enclose?

  b. What are the dimensions of the field with the largest area?

  c. What if...? What would be the largest area of a square field that the farmer could enclose and divide into two plots?

Plot 1
Plot 2

MATHEMATICAL PRACTICES

FOCUS ON MATHEMATICAL PRACTICES

H.O.T. 86. Modeling What perfect square trinomial is modeled by the algebra tiles shown?

H.O.T. 87. Error Analysis Theo finds the zero(s) of $h(x) = x^2 + 6x + 7$ as shown:

$$x^2 + 6x + 7 = 0$$
$$x^2 + 6x = -7$$
$$x^2 + 6x + 9 = -7 + 9$$
$$(x + 3)^2 = 2$$
$$x + 3 = \sqrt{2}$$
$$x = -3 + \sqrt{2}$$

What mistake did Theo make? What is the correct answer?

H.O.T. 88. Communication Would you prefer to find the zeros of the function $f(x) = 5x^2 + 2x - 3$ using factoring or by completing the square? Explain why.

H.O.T. 89. Problem Solving The height h, in feet, of a kicked soccer ball can be modeled by the function $h(t) = -16t^2 + 24t + 1$, where t is in seconds. On its way down, the ball bounces off the crossbar of the goal, which is 8 feet off the ground. To the nearest tenth of a second, when did the ball hit the crossbar?

H.O.T. 90. Reasoning When would a function of the form $f(x) = x^2 + 10x + c$ not have any real zeros? Use completing the square to explain your answer.

16-3 The Quadratic Formula

Essential Question: How can you derive the Quadratic Formula and use it to solve any quadratic equation?

Objectives

Solve quadratic equations using the Quadratic Formula.

Classify roots using the discriminant.

Vocabulary

discriminant

Who uses this?

Firefighting pilots can use the Quadratic Formula to estimate when to release water on a fire. (See Example 4.)

You have learned several methods for solving quadratic equations: graphing, making tables, factoring, using square roots, and completing the square. Another method is to use the *Quadratic Formula*, which allows you to solve a quadratic equation in standard form.

By completing the square on the standard form of a quadratic equation, you can determine the Quadratic Formula.

Numbers		**Algebra**
$3x^2 + 5x + 1 = 0$		$ax^2 + bx + c = 0 \ (a \neq 0)$
$x^2 + \dfrac{5}{3}x + \dfrac{1}{3} = 0$	*Divide by a.*	$x^2 + \dfrac{b}{a}x + \dfrac{c}{a} = 0$
$x^2 + \dfrac{5}{3}x = -\dfrac{1}{3}$	*Subtract $\dfrac{c}{a}$.*	$x^2 + \dfrac{b}{a}x = -\dfrac{c}{a}$
$x^2 + \dfrac{5}{3}x + \left(\dfrac{5}{2(3)}\right)^2 = -\dfrac{1}{3} + \left(\dfrac{5}{2(3)}\right)^2$	*Complete the square.*	$x^2 + \dfrac{b}{a}x + \left(\dfrac{b}{2a}\right)^2 = -\dfrac{c}{a} + \left(\dfrac{b}{2a}\right)^2$
$\left(x + \dfrac{5}{6}\right)^2 = \dfrac{25}{36} - \dfrac{1}{3}$	*Factor.*	$\left(x + \dfrac{b}{2a}\right)^2 = \dfrac{b^2}{4a^2} - \dfrac{c}{a}$
$x + \dfrac{5}{6} = \pm\sqrt{\dfrac{13}{36}}$	*Take square roots.*	$x + \dfrac{b}{2a} = \pm\sqrt{\dfrac{b^2 - 4ac}{4a^2}}$
$x = -\dfrac{5}{6} \pm \dfrac{\sqrt{13}}{6}$	*Subtract $\dfrac{b}{2a}$.*	$x = -\dfrac{b}{2a} \pm \dfrac{\sqrt{b^2 - 4ac}}{2a}$
$x = \dfrac{-5 \pm \sqrt{13}}{6}$	*Simplify.*	$x = \dfrac{-b \pm \sqrt{b^2 - 4ac}}{2a}$

Remember!

To subtract fractions, you need a common denominator.

$$\dfrac{b^2}{4a^2} - \dfrac{c}{a}$$

$$\dfrac{b^2}{4a^2} - \dfrac{c}{a}\left(\dfrac{4a}{4a}\right)$$

$$\dfrac{b^2 - 4ac}{4a^2}$$

The symmetry of a quadratic function is evident in the next to last step, $x = -\dfrac{b}{2a} \pm \dfrac{\sqrt{b^2 - 4ac}}{2a}$. These two zeros are the same distance, $\dfrac{\sqrt{b^2 - 4ac}}{2a}$, away from the axis of symmetry, $x = -\dfrac{b}{2a}$, with one zero on either side of the vertex.

Know it!

Note

The Quadratic Formula

If $ax^2 + bx + c = 0 \ (a \neq 0)$, then the solutions, or roots, are

$$x = \dfrac{-b \pm \sqrt{b^2 - 4ac}}{2a}.$$

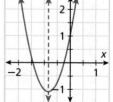

© Reuters/CORBIS

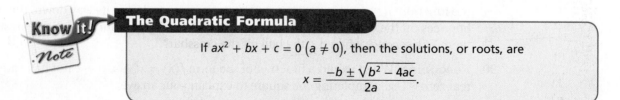

You can use the Quadratic Formula to solve any quadratic equation that is written in standard form, including equations with real solutions or complex solutions.

EXAMPLE 1
MCC9-12.A.REI.4b

my.hrw.com

Online Video Tutor

Quadratic Functions with Real Zeros

Find the zeros of $f(x) = x^2 + 10x + 2$ by using the Quadratic Formula.

$$x^2 + 10x + 2 = 0 \qquad\qquad \text{Set } f(x) = 0.$$

$$x = \frac{-b \pm \sqrt{b^2 - 4ac}}{2a} \qquad\qquad \text{Write the Quadratic Formula.}$$

$$x = \frac{-10 \pm \sqrt{(10)^2 - 4(1)(2)}}{2(1)} \qquad\qquad \text{Substitute 1 for a, 10 for b, and 2 for c.}$$

$$x = \frac{-10 \pm \sqrt{100 - 8}}{2} = \frac{-10 \pm \sqrt{92}}{2} \qquad \text{Simplify.}$$

$$x = \frac{-10 \pm 2\sqrt{23}}{2} = -5 \pm \sqrt{23} \qquad \text{Write in simplest form.}$$

Check Solve by completing the square.

$$x^2 + 10x + 2 = 0$$

$$x^2 + 10x = -2$$

$$x^2 + 10x + 25 = -2 + 25$$

$$(x + 5)^2 = 23$$

$$x = -5 \pm \sqrt{23} \ ✔$$

CHECK IT OUT! Find the zeros of each function by using the Quadratic Formula.

1a. $f(x) = x^2 + 3x - 7$ **1b.** $g(x) = x^2 - 8x + 10$

EXAMPLE 2
MCC9-12.N.CN.7

my.hrw.com

Online Video Tutor

Quadratic Functions with Complex Zeros

Find the zeros of $f(x) = 2x^2 - x + 2$ by using the Quadratic Formula.

$$2x^2 - x + 2 = 0 \qquad\qquad \text{Set } f(x) = 0.$$

$$x = \frac{-b \pm \sqrt{b^2 - 4ac}}{2a} \qquad\qquad \text{Write the Quadratic Formula.}$$

$$x = \frac{-(-1) \pm \sqrt{(-1)^2 - 4(2)(2)}}{2(2)} \qquad\qquad \text{Substitute 2 for a, −1 for b, and 2 for c.}$$

$$x = \frac{1 \pm \sqrt{1 - 16}}{4} = \frac{1 \pm \sqrt{-15}}{4} \qquad \text{Simplify.}$$

$$x = \frac{1 \pm i\sqrt{15}}{4} = \frac{1}{4} \pm \frac{\sqrt{15}}{4}i \qquad \text{Write in terms of i.}$$

CHECK IT OUT! **2.** Find the zeros of $g(x) = 3x^2 - x + 8$ by using the Quadratic Formula.

The **discriminant** is part of the Quadratic Formula that you can use to determine the number of real roots of a quadratic equation.

$$x = \frac{-b \pm \sqrt{b^2 - 4ac}}{2a} \quad \longleftarrow \text{Discriminant}$$

Discriminant

The discriminant of the quadratic equation $ax^2 + bx + c = 0$ $(a \neq 0)$ is $b^2 - 4ac$.

$b^2 - 4ac > 0$	$b^2 - 4ac = 0$	$b^2 - 4ac < 0$
two distinct real solutions	one distinct real solution	two distinct nonreal complex solutions

Caution!

Make sure the equation is in standard form before you evaluate the discriminant, $b^2 - 4ac$.

COMMON CORE GPS
EXAMPLE 3
MCC9-12.A.REI.4b

my.hrw.com

Online Video Tutor

Analyzing Quadratic Equations by Using the Discriminant

Find the type and number of solutions for each equation.

A $x^2 - 6x = -7$

$x^2 - 6x + 7 = 0$

$b^2 - 4ac$

$(-6)^2 - 4(1)(7)$

$36 - 28 = 8$

$b^2 - 4ac > 0$; the equation has two distinct real solutions.

B $x^2 - 6x = -9$

$x^2 - 6x + 9 = 0$

$b^2 - 4ac$

$(-6)^2 - 4(1)(9)$

$36 - 36 = 0$

$b^2 - 4ac = 0$; the equation has one distinct real solution.

C $x^2 - 6x = -11$

$x^2 - 6x + 11 = 0$

$b^2 - 4ac$

$(-6)^2 - 4(1)(11)$

$36 - 44 = -8$

$b^2 - 4ac < 0$; the equation has two distinct nonreal complex solutions.

CHECK IT OUT!

Find the type and number of solutions for each equation.

3a. $x^2 - 4x = -4$ **3b.** $x^2 - 4x = -8$ **3c.** $x^2 - 4x = 2$

The graph shows the related functions for Example 3. Notice that the number of real solutions for the equation can be changed by changing the value of the constant c.

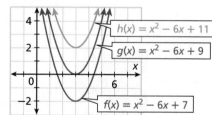

$h(x) = x^2 - 6x + 11$

$g(x) = x^2 - 6x + 9$

$f(x) = x^2 - 6x + 7$

Student to Student

Double-Checking Roots

If I get integer roots when I use the Quadratic Formula, I know that I can quickly factor to check the roots. Look at my work for the equation $x^2 - 7x + 10 = 0$.

Quadratic Formula:

$$x = \frac{-(-7) \pm \sqrt{(-7)^2 - 4(1)(10)}}{2(1)}$$

$$= \frac{7 \pm \sqrt{9}}{2} = \frac{10}{2} \text{ or } \frac{4}{2} = 5 \text{ or } 2$$

Factoring:

$x^2 - 7x + 10 = 0$

$(x - 5)(x - 2) = 0$

$x = 5$ or $x = 2$

Terry Cannon,
Carver High School

EXAMPLE **4**

Aviation Application

The pilot of a helicopter plans to release a bucket of water on a forest fire. The height y in feet of the water t seconds after its release is modeled by $y = -16t^2 - 2t + 500$. The horizontal distance x in feet between the water and its point of release is modeled by $x = 91t$. At what horizontal distance from the fire should the pilot start releasing the water in order to hit the target?

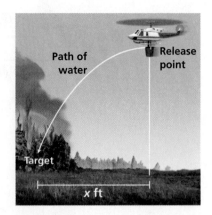

Path of water
Release point
Target
x ft

Step 1 Use the first equation to determine how long it will take the water to hit the ground. Set the height of the water equal to 0 feet, and use the quadratic formula to solve for t.

$$y = -16t^2 - 2t + 500$$

$$0 = -16t^2 - 2t + 500 \qquad \text{Set } y \text{ equal to 0.}$$

$$t = \frac{-b \pm \sqrt{b^2 - 4ac}}{2a} \qquad \text{Use the Quadratic Formula.}$$

$$t = \frac{-(-2) \pm \sqrt{(-2)^2 - 4(-16)(500)}}{2(-16)} \qquad \text{Substitute for a, b, and c.}$$

$$t = \frac{2 \pm \sqrt{32{,}004}}{-32} \qquad \text{Simplify.}$$

$$t \approx -5.65 \text{ or } t \approx 5.53$$

The time cannot be negative, so the water lands on the target about 5.5 seconds after it is released.

Step 2 Find the horizontal distance that the water will have traveled in this time.

$$x = 91t$$

$$x = 91(5.5) \qquad \text{Substitute 5.5 for t.}$$

$$x = 500.5 \qquad \text{Simplify.}$$

The water will have traveled a horizontal distance of about 500 feet. Therefore, the pilot should start releasing the water when the horizontal distance between the helicopter and the fire is 500 feet.

Check Use substitution to check that the water hits the ground after about 5.53 seconds.

$$y = -16t^2 - 2t + 500$$

$$y = -16(5.53)^2 - 2(5.53) + 500$$

$$y \approx -0.3544 \checkmark \qquad \text{The height is approximately equal to 0 when } t = 5.53.$$

> **Caution!** //////
>
> Once you have found the value of t, you have solved only part of the problem. You will use this value to find the answer you are looking for.

 CHECK IT OUT! **Use the information given above to answer the following.**

4. The pilot's altitude decreases, which changes the function describing the water's height to $y = -16t^2 - 2t + 400$. To the nearest foot, at what horizontal distance from the target should the pilot begin releasing the water?

Summary of Solving Quadratic Equations

Method	When to Use	Examples
Graphing	Only approximate solutions or the number of real solutions is needed.	$2x^2 + 5x - 14 = 0$ 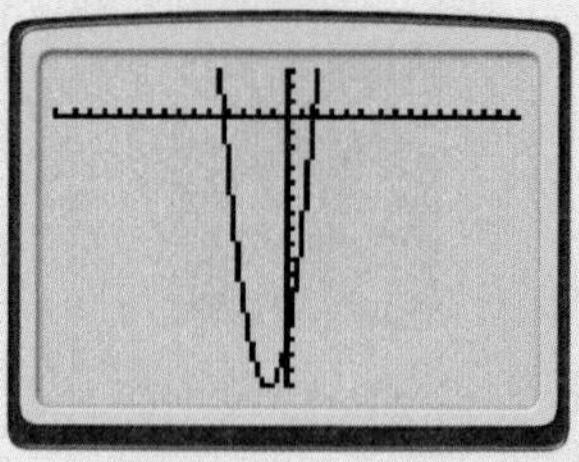 $x \approx -4.2 \text{ or } x \approx 1.7$
Factoring	$c = 0$ or the expression is easily factorable.	$x^2 + 4x + 3 = 0$ $(x + 3)(x + 1) = 0$ $x = -3 \text{ or } x = -1$
Square roots	The variable side of the equation is a perfect square.	$(x - 5)^2 = 24$ $\sqrt{(x-5)^2} = \pm\sqrt{24}$ $x - 5 = \pm 2\sqrt{6}$ $x = 5 \pm 2\sqrt{6}$
Completing the square	$a = 1$ and b is an even number.	$x^2 + 6x = 10$ $x^2 + 6x + \blacksquare = 10 + \blacksquare$ $x^2 + 6x + \left(\dfrac{6}{2}\right)^2 = 10 + \left(\dfrac{6}{2}\right)^2$ $(x + 3)^2 = 19$ $x = -3 \pm \sqrt{19}$
Quadratic Formula	Numbers are large or complicated, and the expression does not factor easily.	$5x^2 - 7x - 8 = 0$ $x = \dfrac{-(-7) \pm \sqrt{(-7)^2 - 4(5)(-8)}}{2(5)}$ $x = \dfrac{7 \pm \sqrt{209}}{10}$

Helpful Hint

No matter which method you use to solve a quadratic equation, you should get the same answer.

MCC.MP.7   MATHEMATICAL PRACTICES

THINK AND DISCUSS

1. Describe how the graphs of quadratic functions illustrate the type and number of zeros.

2. Describe the values of c for which the equation $x^2 + 8x + c = 0$ will have zero, one, or two distinct solutions.

3. **GET ORGANIZED** Copy and complete the graphic organizer. Describe the possible solution methods for each value of the discriminant.

Value of Discriminant	Type of Solutions	Possible Solution Methods
Negative		
Zero		
Positive		

Know it!
Note

my.hrw.com
Homework Help

GUIDED PRACTICE

1. Vocabulary What information does the value of the *discriminant* give about a quadratic equation?

SEE EXAMPLE 1 **Find the zeros of each function by using the Quadratic Formula.**

2. $f(x) = x^2 + 7x + 10$ **3.** $g(x) = 3x^2 - 4x - 1$ **4.** $h(x) = 3x^2 - 5x$

5. $g(x) = -x^2 - 5x + 6$ **6.** $h(x) = 4x^2 - 5x - 6$ **7.** $f(x) = 2x^2 - 19$

SEE EXAMPLE 2 **8.** $f(x) = 2x^2 - 2x + 3$ **9.** $r(x) = x^2 + 6x + 12$ **10.** $h(x) = 3x^2 + 4x + 3$

11. $p(x) = x^2 + 4x + 10$ **12.** $g(x) = -5x^2 + 7x - 3$ **13.** $f(x) = 10x^2 + 7x + 4$

SEE EXAMPLE 3 **Find the type and number of solutions for each equation.**

14. $4x^2 + 1 = 4x$ **15.** $x^2 + 2x = 10$ **16.** $2x - x^2 = 4$

SEE EXAMPLE 4 **17. Geometry** One leg of a right triangle is 6 in. longer than the other leg. The hypotenuse of the triangle is 25 in. What is the length of each leg to the nearest inch?

PRACTICE AND PROBLEM SOLVING

Find the zeros of each function by using the Quadratic Formula.

18. $f(x) = 3x^2 - 10x + 3$ **19.** $g(x) = x^2 + 6x$ **20.** $h(x) = x(x - 3) - 4$

21. $g(x) = -x^2 - 2x + 9$ **22.** $p(x) = 2x^2 - 7x - 8$ **23.** $f(x) = 7x^2 - 3$

24. $r(x) = x^2 + x + 1$ **25.** $h(x) = -x^2 - x - 1$ **26.** $f(x) = 2x^2 + 8$

27. $f(x) = 2x^2 + 7x - 13$ **28.** $g(x) = x^2 - x - 5$ **29.** $h(x) = -3x^2 + 4x - 4$

Independent Practice	
For Exercises	See Example
18–23	1
24–29	2
30–35	3
36	4

my.hrw.com

Online Extra Practice

Find the type and number of solutions for each equation.

30. $2x^2 + 5 = 2x$ **31.** $2x^2 - 3x = 8$ **32.** $2x^2 - 16x = -32$

33. $4x^2 - 28x = -49$ **34.** $3x^2 - 8x + 8 = 0$ **35.** $3.2x^2 - 8.5x + 1.3 = 0$

36. Safety If a tightrope walker falls, he will land on a safety net. His height h in feet after a fall can be modeled by $h(t) = 60 - 16t^2$, where t is the time in seconds. How many seconds will the tightrope walker fall before landing on the safety net?

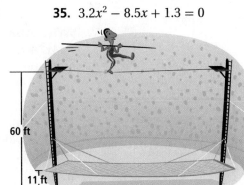

60 ft

11 ft

H.O.T. **37. Physics** A bicyclist is riding at a speed of 20 mi/h when she starts down a long hill. The distance d she travels in feet can be modeled by the function $d(t) = 5t^2 + 20t$, where t is the time in seconds.

   a. The hill is 585 ft long. To the nearest second, how long will it take her to reach the bottom?

   b. What if...? Suppose the hill were only half as long. To the nearest second, how long would it take the bicyclist to reach the bottom?

Find the zeros of each function. Then graph the function.

38. $f(x) = 3x^2 - 4x - 2$ **39.** $g(x) = 2x^2 - 2x - 1$ **40.** $h(x) = 2x^2 + 6x + 5$

41. $p(x) = 2x^2 + 3x - 1$ **42.** $h(x) = 3x^2 - 5x - 4$ **43.** $r(x) = x^2 - x + 22$

44. **Aerospace** In 2004, the highest spaceplane flight was made by Brian Binnie in *SpaceShipOne*. A flight with this altitude can be modeled by the function $h(t) = -0.17t^2 + 187t + 61{,}000$, where h is the altitude in meters and t is flight time in seconds.

    a. Approximately how long did the flight last?

    b. What was the highest altitude to the nearest thousand meters?

    c. The table shows the altitudes of layers of Earth's atmosphere. According to the model, which of these layers did *SpaceShipOne* enter, and at what time(s) did the spaceplane enter them?

Earth's Atmosphere	
Layer	**Altitude (in km)**
Troposphere	0 to 10
Stratosphere	10 to 50
Mesosphere	50 to 85
Thermosphere	85 to 600

Solve each equation by any method.

45. $x^2 - 3x = 10$ **46.** $x^2 - 16 = 0$ **47.** $4x^2 + 4x = 15$

48. $x^2 + 2x - 2 = 0$ **49.** $x^2 - 4x - 21 = 0$ **50.** $4x^2 - 4x - 1 = 0$

51. $6x^2 = 150$ **52.** $x^2 = 7$ **53.** $x^2 - 16x + 64 = 0$

54. **Critical Thinking** If you are solving a real-world problem involving a quadratic equation, and the discriminant is negative, what can you conclude?

55. **Multi-Step** The outer dimensions of a picture frame are 25 inches by 20 inches. If the area inside the picture frame is 266 square inches, what is the width w of the frame?

$w \longleftarrow$

H.O.T. Critical Thinking Find the values of c that make each equation have one real solution.

56. $x^2 + 8x + c = 0$ **57.** $x^2 + 12x = c$ **58.** $x^2 + 2cx + 49 = 0$

H.O.T. 59. **Write About It** What method would you use to solve the equation $-14x^2 + 6x = 2.7$? Why would this method be easier to use than the other methods?

60. An outfielder throws a baseball to the player on third base. The height h of the ball in feet is modeled by the function $h(t) = -16t^2 + 19t + 5$, where t is time in seconds. The third baseman catches the ball when it is 4 ft above the ground.

    a. To the nearest tenth of a second, how long was the ball in the air before it was caught?

    b. A player on the opposing team starts running from second base to third base 1.2 s before the outfielder throws the ball. The distance between the bases is 90 ft, and the runner's average speed is 27 ft/s. Will the runner reach third base before the ball does? Explain.

61. Which best describes the graph of a quadratic function with a discriminant of -3?

    Ⓐ Parabola with two x-intercepts

    Ⓑ Parabola with no x-intercepts

    Ⓒ Parabola that opens upward

    Ⓓ Parabola that opens downward

62. What is the discriminant of the equation $2x^2 - 8x = 14$?

    Ⓕ 48   Ⓗ 176

    Ⓖ -48 Ⓙ -176

63. Which function has zeros of $3 \pm i$?

    Ⓐ $f(x) = x^2 + 6x + 10$ Ⓒ $g(x) = x^2 - 6x + 10$

    Ⓑ $f(x) = x^2 + 6x - 10$ Ⓓ $h(x) = x^2 - 6x - 10$

64. Which best describes the discriminant of the function whose graph is shown?

    Ⓕ Positive   Ⓗ Negative

    Ⓖ Zero   Ⓙ Undefined

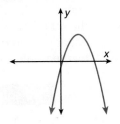

CHALLENGE AND EXTEND

65. Geometry The perimeter of a right triangle is 40 cm, and its hypotenuse measures 17 cm. Find the length of each leg.

66. Geometry The perimeter of a rectangle is 88 cm.

    a. Find the least possible value of the length of the diagonal. Round to the nearest tenth of a centimeter.

    b. What are the dimensions of the rectangle with this diagonal?

Write a quadratic equation whose solutions belong to the indicated sets.

67. integers   **68.** irrational real numbers   **69.** complex numbers

70. A quadratic equation has the form $ax^2 + bx + c = 0$ $(a \neq 0)$.

    a. What is the sum of the roots of the equation? the product of the roots?

    b. Determine the standard form of a quadratic equation whose roots have a sum of 2 and a product of -15.

H.O.T. **71.** Describe the solutions of a quadratic equation for which $a = b = c$.

FOCUS ON MATHEMATICAL PRACTICES

H.O.T. **72. Analysis** A quadratic function $f(x) = ax^2 + bx + c$ has $a < 0$, $b = 0$, and $c > 0$. Describe the location of its zeros. Use the quadratic formula to explain your answer.

H.O.T. **73. Communication** When do you like to complete the square to solve a quadratic equation? When do you prefer to use the quadratic formula?

H.O.T. **74. Reasoning** The zeros of a quadratic function are rational numbers. What must be true about the discriminant of the function? Explain your answer.

16-4 Nonlinear Systems

Essential Question: What methods can you use to solve a system that includes a linear equation and a quadratic equation?

Objective
Solve systems of equations in two variables in which one equation is linear and the other is quadratic.

Vocabulary
nonlinear system of equations

Why learn this?
You can solve a nonlinear system to find how long it takes for two objects to reach the same height. (See Example 4.)

Recall that a system of linear equations is a set of two or more linear equations. A solution of a system is an ordered pair that satisfies each equation in the system. Points where the graphs of the equations intersect represent solutions of the system.

A **nonlinear system of equations** is a system in which at least one of the equations is nonlinear. In this lesson, you will solve nonlinear systems using the set of real numbers as the domain. A system that contains one quadratic equation and one linear equation can have no real solution, one real solution, or two real solutions, as shown below.

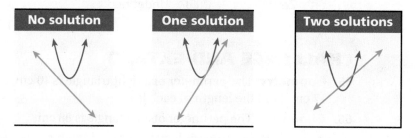

No solution   One solution   Two solutions

COMMON CORE GPS MCC9-12.A.REI.7

EXAMPLE 1

my.hrw.com

Online Video Tutor

Solving a Nonlinear System by Graphing

Solve the system by graphing. Check your answer.

$$\begin{cases} y = x^2 - 2x - 3 \\ y = -x - 1 \end{cases}$$

Step 1 Graph $y = x^2 - 2x - 3$.

The axis of symmetry is $x = 1$.

The vertex is $(1, -4)$.

The y-intercept is -3.

Another point is $(-1, 0)$.

Graph the points and reflect them across the axis of symmetry.

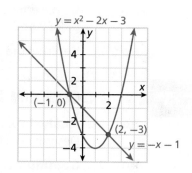

Step 2 Graph $y = -x - 1$.

The slope is -1.

The y-intercept is -1.

Step 3 Find the points where the two graphs intersect.

The solutions appear to be $(-1, 0)$ and $(2, -3)$.

Check

Substitute $(-1, 0)$ into the system.   Substitute $(2, -3)$ into the system.

$y = x^2 - 2x - 3$		$y = -x - 1$		$y = x^2 - 2x - 3$		$y = -x - 1$	
0	$(-1)^2 - 2(-1) - 3$	0	$-(-1) - 1$	-3	$2^2 - 2(2) - 3$	-3	$-2 - 1$
0	$1 + 2 - 3$	0	$1 - 1$	-3	$4 - 4 - 3$	-3	-3 ✓
0	0 ✓	0	0 ✓	-3	-3 ✓		

The solutions are $(-1, 0)$ and $(2, -3)$.

CHECK IT OUT! **1.** Solve the system by graphing. Check your answer.
$$\begin{cases} y = x^2 - 4x + 5 \\ y = x + 1 \end{cases}$$

COMMON CORE GPS
MCC9-12.A.REI.7

my.hrw.com

Online Video Tutor

EXAMPLE 2 Solving a Nonlinear System by Substitution

Solve the system by substitution.
$$\begin{cases} y = 2x^2 - 3x + 4 \\ y = x + 2 \end{cases}$$

$y = 2x^2 - 3x + 4$ *Both equations are solved for y.*
$y = x + 2$

     $y = 2x^2 - 3x + 4$

     $x + 2 = 2x^2 - 3x + 4$ *Substitute x + 2 for y in the first equation.*

     $\underline{-(x + 2) \qquad -(x + 2)}$ *Subtract x + 2 from both sides.*

         $0 = 2x^2 - 4x + 2$

         $0 = 2(x^2 - 2x + 1)$ *Factor out the GCF, 2.*

         $0 = 2(x - 1)(x - 1)$ *Factor the trinomial.*

         $2 \neq 0;$ $x - 1 = 0$ *Use the Zero Product Property; 2 cannot equal 0.*

                 $x = 1$ *Solve the remaining equation.*

$y = x + 2$ *Write one of the original equations.*

$y = 1 + 2$ *Substitute 1 for x.*

$y = 3$

The solution is $(1, 3)$.

Check
Use a graphing calculator.

The graph supports the result found above. This system has exactly one real solution. The graph of the system consists of a line and a parabola that meet in exactly one point.

Remember!

The substitution method is a good choice when either equation is solved for a variable, both equations are solved for the same variable, or a variable in either equation has a coefficient of 1 or −1.

CHECK IT OUT! **2.** Solve the system by substitution. Check your answer.
$$\begin{cases} y = 3x^2 - 3x + 1 \\ y = -3x + 4 \end{cases}$$

Solving a Nonlinear System by Elimination

Solve each system by elimination.

A $\begin{cases} 4x - y = 2 \\ y = x^2 + 1 \end{cases}$

$4x - y = 2$ *Write the system to align the y-terms.*

$+ \quad y = x^2 + 1$ *Add the equations to eliminate y.*

$\overline{\quad 4x = x^2 + 3 \quad}$

$\underline{-4x \qquad -4x}$ *Subtract 4x from both sides.*

$0 = x^2 - 4x + 3$

$0 = (x - 1)(x - 3)$ *Factor the trinomial.*

$x - 1 = 0 \quad \text{or} \quad x - 3 = 0$ *Use the Zero Product Property.*

$x = 1 \quad \text{or} \qquad x = 3$ *Solve the equations.*

$y = x^2 + 1 \qquad y = x^2 + 1$ *Write one of the original equations.*

$y = 1^2 + 1 \qquad y = 3^2 + 1$ *Substitute each x-value and solve for y.*

$y = 2 \qquad\qquad y = 10$

The solutions are $(1, 2)$ and $(3, 10)$.

B $\begin{cases} y = x^2 + x - 1 \\ 2x - 3y = 6 \end{cases}$

$y = x^2 + x - 1$ *Write the system to align the y-terms.*

$2x - 3y = 6$

$3(y) = 3(x^2 + x - 1)$ *Multiply each term in the first equation by 3.*

$2x - 3y = 6$

$3y = 3x^2 + 3x - 3$

$\underline{+ \; 2x - 3y = 6}$ *Add the second equation to the new first equation to eliminate y.*

$2x = 3x^2 + 3x + 3$

$0 = 3x^2 + x + 3$ *Subtract 2x from both sides.*

$x = \dfrac{-1 \pm \sqrt{(1)^2 - 4(3)(3)}}{2(3)}$ *Use the Quadratic Formula, $x = \dfrac{-b \pm \sqrt{b^2 - 4ac}}{2a}$.*

$x = \dfrac{-1 \pm \sqrt{1 - 36}}{6}$

$x = \dfrac{-1 \pm \sqrt{-35}}{6}$ *Note the discriminant: $b^2 - 4ac = -35$. Its value is negative, so there are no real solutions.*

There are no real solutions.

Check Use a graphing calculator.
To graph $2x - 3y = 6$, first solve for y.

$2x - 3y = 6$

$-3y = -2x + 6$

$y = \dfrac{2}{3}x - 2$

The graph supports that there are no real solutions.

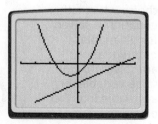

> **Remember!**
>
> The elimination method is a good choice when both equations have the same variable term with the same or opposite coefficients or when a variable term in one equation is a multiple of the corresponding variable term in the other equation.

CHECK IT OUT! Solve each system by elimination. Check your answers.

3a. $\begin{cases} 2x - y = 2 \\ y = x^2 - 5 \end{cases}$ **3b.** $\begin{cases} y = x^2 - 2x - 5 \\ 5x - 2y = 5 \end{cases}$

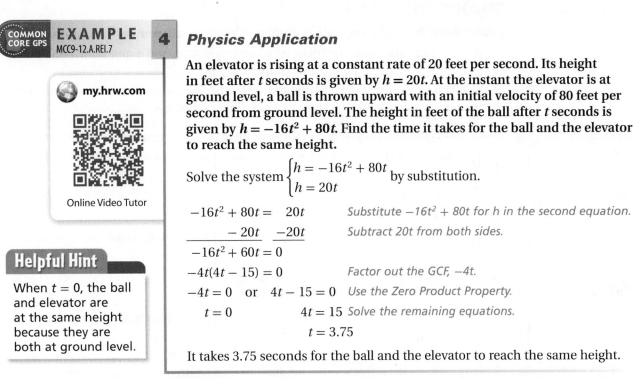

COMMON CORE GPS
EXAMPLE 4
MCC9-12.A.REI.7

my.hrw.com

Online Video Tutor

Physics Application

An elevator is rising at a constant rate of 20 feet per second. Its height in feet after t seconds is given by $h = 20t$. At the instant the elevator is at ground level, a ball is thrown upward with an initial velocity of 80 feet per second from ground level. The height in feet of the ball after t seconds is given by $h = -16t^2 + 80t$. Find the time it takes for the ball and the elevator to reach the same height.

Solve the system $\begin{cases} h = -16t^2 + 80t \\ h = 20t \end{cases}$ by substitution.

$-16t^2 + 80t = 20t$ *Substitute $-16t^2 + 80t$ for h in the second equation.*

$\underline{ - 20t -20t}$ *Subtract 20t from both sides.*

$-16t^2 + 60t = 0$

$-4t(4t - 15) = 0$ *Factor out the GCF, $-4t$.*

$-4t = 0$ or $4t - 15 = 0$ *Use the Zero Product Property.*

$t = 0$ $4t = 15$ *Solve the remaining equations.*

$t = 3.75$

It takes 3.75 seconds for the ball and the elevator to reach the same height.

Helpful Hint

When $t = 0$, the ball and elevator are at the same height because they are both at ground level.

 CHECK IT OUT! **4.** An elevator is rising at a constant rate of 8 feet per second. Its height in feet after t seconds is given by $h = 8t$. At the instant the elevator is at ground level, a ball is dropped from a height of 120 feet. The height in feet of the ball after t seconds is given by $h = -16t^2 + 120$. Find the time it takes for the ball and the elevator to reach the same height.

MCC.MP.3   **MATHEMATICAL PRACTICES**

THINK AND DISCUSS

1. How is solving the systems in this lesson similar to solving systems of linear equations? How is it different?

2. When using elimination to solve a linear/quadratic system, which variable will be eliminated? Why?

3. A system of linear equations can have infinitely many solutions. Why can't a linear/quadratic system have infinitely many solutions?

4. GET ORGANIZED Copy and complete the graphic organizer by sketching diagrams to show examples. Write *not possible* for any cases that are not possible.

System of Equations	Real Solutions			
	0	1	2	infinite
Linear				
Linear/Quadratic				

GUIDED PRACTICE

Vocabulary Apply the vocabulary from this lesson to answer each question.

1. A system of equations that includes a linear equation and a quadratic equation is
   _____?_____. (*linear, nonlinear,* or *quadratic*)

2. Sketch a nonlinear system of equations that has two solutions. The system should include one quadratic equation and one linear equation.

SEE EXAMPLE **1** Solve each system by graphing. Check your answers.

3. $\begin{cases} y = 2x^2 - 7x + 6 \\ y = x \end{cases}$

4. $\begin{cases} y = x^2 - 2x - 5 \\ y = 2x - 8 \end{cases}$

SEE EXAMPLE **2** Solve each system by substitution. Check your answers.

5. $\begin{cases} y = x^2 - 4x + 3 \\ y = x - 3 \end{cases}$

6. $\begin{cases} y = 2x^2 - 5x + 3 \\ y = -3x + 15 \end{cases}$

SEE EXAMPLE **3** Solve each system by elimination. Check your answers.

7. $\begin{cases} y = x^2 - 3 \\ 4x - y = 6 \end{cases}$

8. $\begin{cases} y = x^2 + 7x + 12 \\ 3x - y = 5 \end{cases}$

SEE EXAMPLE **4**
9. **Physics** A bird is flying upwards such that its height in feet after t seconds is given by $h = 4t$. At the instant the bird passes the height of a ball being held out of a window, the ball is thrown upward with an initial velocity of 80 feet per second. The height in feet of the ball after t seconds is given by $h = -16t^2 + 80t$. Find the time it takes for the ball and the bird to reach the same height.

PRACTICE AND PROBLEM SOLVING

Independent Practice	
For Exercises	**See Example**
10–13	1
14–17	2
18–21	3
22–25	4

my.hrw.com

Online Extra Practice

Solve each system by graphing. Check your answers.

10. $\begin{cases} y = x^2 - 4 \\ y = 5x - 10 \end{cases}$

11. $\begin{cases} y = x^2 - 3 \\ x - 6y = 18 \end{cases}$

12. $\begin{cases} y = x^2 + 4x + 7 \\ y = x + 5 \end{cases}$

13. $\begin{cases} y = 2x^2 - 8x + 3 \\ y = 6x - 21 \end{cases}$

Solve each system by substitution. Check your answers.

14. $\begin{cases} y = x^2 + 7x + 2 \\ y = 5x + 5 \end{cases}$

15. $\begin{cases} y = 2x^2 - 3 \\ y = 2x + 9 \end{cases}$

16. $\begin{cases} y = x^2 - 5 \\ y = -2x + 3 \end{cases}$

17. $\begin{cases} y = 5x^2 - 2x \\ y = 10x + 9 \end{cases}$

Solve each system by elimination. Check your answers.

18. $\begin{cases} y = 2x^2 - 3x + 1 \\ 5x - y = -1 \end{cases}$

19. $\begin{cases} y = x^2 - 5 \\ x - 3y = 15 \end{cases}$

20. $\begin{cases} y = 2x^2 - x + 7 \\ 2x + 3y = 6 \end{cases}$

21. $\begin{cases} y = x^2 + 5x \\ 9x - y = 3 \end{cases}$

22. **Demographics** The growing population of town A can be modeled by the equation $P(t) = 8t^2 + 2000$, where t represents number of years after 2010. The growing population of town B can be modeled by the equation $P(t) = 100t + 3000$. In which year will the populations of the towns be approximately equal?

23. **Finance** The value of Danielle's investments is modeled by the equation $V(t) = 3t^2 + 70t + 100$, where t represents the number of months after she made her initial investment. Jeffrey has no money invested in stocks, but he deposits the same amount every month into a savings account that he opened at the same time as Danielle began investing. His savings account balance can be modeled by the equation $V(t) = 50t + 275$. After how many months will the value of Danielle's investments be equal to the balance of Jeffrey's savings account?

24. **Amusement Parks** A ride at an amusement park consists of an observation deck that travels directly up into the air at a constant rate of 40 feet per second. Its height in feet after t seconds is given by $h = 40t$. At the instant the deck is at ground level, a ball is thrown up with initial velocity 60 feet per second from ground level. The height in feet of the ball after t seconds is given by $h = -16t^2 + 60t$. Find the time it takes for the ball and the deck to reach the same height. Round your answer to the nearest hundredth.

25. **Business** A company's weekly revenue can be modeled by the equation $C(p) = 0.75p^2 + 10p + 200$, where p represents the number of products sold. The weekly cost of running the business is modeled by the equation $C(p) = 80p + 700$. How many products must the company sell in a week to break even (when revenue equal the costs of running the business)?

Determine whether the point is a solution of the system of equations.

26. $\begin{cases} y = x^2 - 9x + 2 \\ 2x + y = -16 \end{cases}$; $(-2, -12)$

27. $\begin{cases} y = x^2 + 2x - 9 \\ y = 8x \end{cases}$; $(3, 24)$

28. $\begin{cases} y = x^2 - 6x - 1 \\ 3x - 4y = -3 \end{cases}$; $(7, 6)$

29. $\begin{cases} y = 3x^2 - 7x + 6 \\ y = x + 1 \end{cases}$; $(1, 2)$

30. $\begin{cases} y = 2x^2 - 5x + 5 \\ y = x + 5 \end{cases}$; $(3, 8)$

31. $\begin{cases} y = 3x^2 + 4x - 1 \\ 9x - 2y = -5 \end{cases}$; $(-1, -2)$

32. $\begin{cases} y = 2x^2 - 25 \\ 4x - y = 5 \end{cases}$; $(5, 25)$

33. $\begin{cases} y = x^2 + 3x + 8 \\ 5x - y = 28 \end{cases}$; $(2, -18)$

H.O.T. 34. **Write About It** Explain in your own words when you should use the substitution method to solve a nonlinear system, and when you should use the elimination method.

H.O.T. 35. **Critical Thinking** Describe a scenario in which you might use the graphing method to solve a system of nonlinear equations, even if you didn't expect the solution(s) to consist of integer coordinates.

36. **Estimation** Estimate the solution(s) to the system by graphing.

$\begin{cases} y = x^2 + 6x - 2 \\ y = 0.5x + 7 \end{cases}$

H.O.T. **37.** ///**ERROR ANALYSIS**/// Below are two solutions to the system of equations $\begin{cases} y = x^2 - 4x + 5 \\ 4x + 3y = 11 \end{cases}$. Which is incorrect? Explain the error.

A

$y = x^2 - 4x + 5 \longrightarrow \quad -3y = -3x^2 + 12x - 15$

$4x + 3y = 11 \quad \longrightarrow 4x + 3y = 11$

$\overline{\qquad\qquad\qquad\qquad\qquad}$

$\qquad\qquad\qquad\quad 4x + 0 = -3x^2 + 12x - 4$

$\qquad\qquad\qquad\quad\; 0 = -3x^2 + 8x - 4$

$\qquad\qquad\qquad\quad\; 0 = (-3x + 2)(x - 2)$

$\qquad -3x + 2 = 0 \quad \text{or} \quad x - 2 = 0$

$\qquad\qquad -3x = -2 \qquad\qquad x = 2$

$\qquad\qquad\quad\; x = \dfrac{2}{3}$

$\quad 4x + 3y = 11 \qquad\qquad 4x + 3y = 11$

$\quad 4\left(\dfrac{2}{3}\right) + 3y = 11 \qquad 4(2) + 3y = 11$

$\quad \dfrac{8}{3} + 3y = 11 \qquad\qquad 8 + 3y = 11$

$\qquad\quad 3y = \dfrac{25}{3} \qquad\qquad\quad 3y = 3$

$\qquad\quad\; y = \dfrac{25}{9} \qquad\qquad\qquad y = 1$

The solutions are $\left(\dfrac{2}{3}, \dfrac{25}{9}\right)$ *and* (2, 1).

B

$y = x^2 - 4x + 5 \longrightarrow \quad -3y = x^2 - 4x + 5$

$4x + 3y = 11 \quad \longrightarrow 4x + 3y = 11$

$\overline{\qquad\qquad\qquad\qquad\qquad}$

$\qquad\qquad\qquad\quad 4x + 0 = x^2 - 4x + 5$

$\qquad\qquad\qquad\quad\; 0 = x^2 - 8x + 5$

$\qquad\qquad x = \dfrac{-b \pm \sqrt{b^2 - 4ac}}{2a}$

$\qquad\qquad x = \dfrac{-(-8) \pm \sqrt{(-8)^2 - 4(1)(5)}}{2(1)}$

$\qquad\qquad x = \dfrac{8 \pm \sqrt{44}}{2}$

$\qquad\qquad x = \dfrac{8 \pm 2\sqrt{11}}{2}$

$\qquad\qquad x = 4 \pm \sqrt{11} \approx 7.32 \quad \text{or} \quad 0.68$

$\quad 4x + 3y \approx 11 \qquad\qquad 4x + 3y \approx 11$

$\quad 4(7.32) + 3y \approx 11 \qquad 4(0.68) + 3y \approx 11$

$\quad 29.28 + 3y \approx 11 \qquad\quad 2.72 + 3y \approx 11$

$\qquad\quad 3y \approx -18.28 \qquad\qquad 3y \approx 8.28$

$\qquad\quad\; y \approx -6.09 \qquad\qquad\quad y \approx 2.76$

The solutions are approximately (7.32, −6.09) *and* (0.68, 2.76).

TEST PREP

38. Which are the solutions to the system of equations below?

$\begin{cases} y = x^2 - 5x - 2 \\ y = -7x + 1 \end{cases}$

  A (−3, 22) and (1, −6)   **C** (−1, 8) and (2, −10)

  B (−3, 22) and (−1, 8)   **D** (1, −6) and (2, −10)

39. For which system of equations is (2, 6) a solution?

  F $\begin{cases} y = x^2 + 4x - 2 \\ y = -3x - 2 \end{cases}$ **H** $\begin{cases} y = 3x^2 - x - 4 \\ y = -5x + 16 \end{cases}$

  G $\begin{cases} y = x^2 - 4x + 14 \\ x - y = 4 \end{cases}$ **J** $\begin{cases} y = 2x^2 + 9 \\ y = 5x - 4 \end{cases}$

40. Which system below has no real solutions?

  A $\begin{cases} 3y + x = 9 \\ y = (x - 3)^2 \end{cases}$ **C** $\begin{cases} y = x - 4x^2 \\ x = -2 - y \end{cases}$

  B $\begin{cases} y = 2x^2 - 2 \\ x - y = 5 \end{cases}$ **D** $\begin{cases} y = 2x - 7 \\ y = x^2 - 7 \end{cases}$

41. Which is the graph of $\begin{cases} y = 2x - 1 \\ y = 2x^2 + 4x - 5 \end{cases}$?

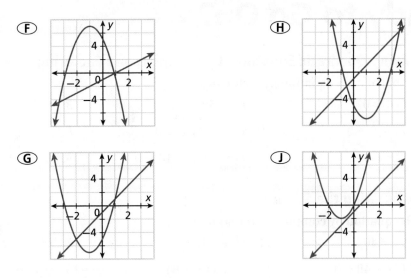

Ⓕ

Ⓗ

Ⓖ

Ⓙ

CHALLENGE AND EXTEND

Find the x-coordinate(s) of the solution(s) of each system.

42. $\begin{cases} y = 3x^2 + 4x - 7 \\ 3x + 5y = 8 \end{cases}$
43. $\begin{cases} y = x^2 - 3x - 5 \\ 3x + 2y = 8 \end{cases}$
44. $\begin{cases} y = x^2 + x - 2 \\ 3x + 2y = 3 \end{cases}$
45. $\begin{cases} y = 4x^2 - 9 \\ y = 7x - 2 \end{cases}$

46. A system of two equations contains one quadratic equation and one linear equation. The quadratic equation in the system is $y = x^2 + 5x - 9$. The solutions of the system are (3, 15) and (−1, −13). What is the linear equation in the system?

H.O.T. **47. Physics** The formula for the height of an object in free fall (neglecting air resistance) is $h(t) = -16t^2 + v_0 t + h_0$, where v_0 is the object's initial velocity in feet per second and h_0 is the object's initial height above the ground in feet. One ball is thrown with an initial velocity of 90 ft/s from a height of 20 ft. A second ball is thrown at the exact same instant with an initial velocity of 80 ft/s and a height of 30 ft. After how many seconds will the balls reach the same height?

FOCUS ON MATHEMATICAL PRACTICES

H.O.T. **48. Analysis** Sometimes a system of linear equations is dependent, which means that the graphs of the two lines are the same and there are an infinite number of solutions. Is it possible for a nonlinear system made up of a linear equation and a quadratic equation to be dependent? Explain why or why not.

H.O.T. **49. Problem Solving** A baseball is thrown straight up in the air. Its height in feet t seconds after being thrown can be modeled by $f(t) = -16t^2 + 56t + 4$. At the same instant, a model helicopter takes off from the ground and travels straight up at a constant speed of 14 feet per second. When is the helicopter at the same height as the baseball? Round your answer to the nearest hundredth of a second. Is the baseball moving up or down when it is at the same height as the helicopter? Explain.

H.O.T. **50. Reasoning** A nonlinear system of equations includes a parabola and a vertical line. How many solutions does the system have? How can you find the solution or solutions?

Ready to Go On?

my.hrw.com
Assessment and Intervention

✓ 16-1 Solving Quadratic Equations by Graphing and Factoring

Find the roots of each equation by factoring.

1. $x^2 - 100 = 0$ **2.** $x^2 + 5x = 24$ **3.** $4x^2 + 8x = 0$

4. $x^2 - 7x - 8 = 0$ **5.** $x^2 - 5x + 6 = 0$ **6.** $x^2 = 144$

7. $x^2 - 21x = 0$ **8.** $4x^2 - 16x + 16 = 0$ **9.** $2x^2 + 8x + 6 = 0$

✓ 16-2 Completing the Square

Solve each equation by completing the square.

10. $x^2 - 6x = 40$ **11.** $x^2 + 18x = 15$ **12.** $x^2 + 14x = 8$

13. $x^2 - 16x + 48 = 0$ **14.** $x^2 + 20x + 84 = 0$ **15.** $x^2 - 6x = 16$

Write each function in vertex form, and identify its vertex.

16. $f(x) = x^2 + 24x + 138$ **17.** $g(x) = x^2 - 12x + 39$ **18.** $h(x) = 5x^2 - 20x + 9$

✓ 16-3 The Quadratic Formula

Find the zeros of each function by using the Quadratic Formula.

19. $f(x) = (x + 6)^2 + 2$ **20.** $g(x) = x^2 + 7x + 15$ **21.** $h(x) = 2x^2 - 5x + 3$

22. $f(x) = x^2 - 3x - 8$ **23.** $h(x) = (x - 5)^2 + 12$ **24.** $f(x) = 2x^2 - 10x + 18$

25. A bicyclist is riding at a speed of 18 mi/h when she starts down a long hill. The distance d she travels in feet can be modeled by $d(t) = 4t^2 + 18t$, where t is the time in seconds. How long will it take her to reach the bottom of a 400-foot-long hill?

✓ 16-4 Nonlinear Systems

Solve the system by graphing or substitution.

26. $y = x^2 - 7$
    $y = x - 7$

27. $y = 2x^2 - x + 7$
    $y = 4x + 5$

28. $y = -x^2 + 2x - 2$
    $y = -1$

Solve each system.

29. $\begin{cases} y = x^2 - 4 \\ y = -2x - 1 \end{cases}$ **30.** $\begin{cases} y = x^2 - 3x - 1 \\ y = 2x - 5 \end{cases}$ **31.** $\begin{cases} y = x^2 + 5x + 4 \\ y = -2x - 6 \end{cases}$

PARCC Assessment Readiness

Selected Response

1. Complete the square for the expression $x^2 - 16x + \underline{\quad}$. Write the resulting expression as a binomial squared.

- **A** $(x - 8)^2$
- **B** $(x + 8)^2$
- **C** $(x + 16)^2$
- **D** $(x - 16)^2$

2. Find the zeros of $f(x) = x^2 + 7x + 9$ by using the Quadratic Formula.

- **F** $x = -7 \pm \sqrt{13}$
- **G** $x = \dfrac{-7 \pm \sqrt{13}}{2}$
- **H** $x = \dfrac{3 \pm \sqrt{7}}{2}$
- **J** $x = 3 \pm \sqrt{7}$

3. Find the zeros of the function $h(x) = x^2 + 23x + 60$ by factoring.

- **A** $x = -20$ or $x = -3$
- **B** $x = 4$ or $x = 15$
- **C** $x = -4$ or $x = -15$
- **D** $x = 20$ or $x = 3$

4. Solve the equation $x^2 = 3 - 2x$ by completing the square.

- **F** $x = 2$ or $x = -2$
- **G** $x = 1$ or $x = -3$
- **H** $x = -1$ or $x = 3$
- **J** $x = 2$ or $x = -6$

5. Find the zeros of $g(x) = 4x^2 - x + 5$ by using the Quadratic Formula.

- **A** $x = \dfrac{1}{2} \pm \dfrac{\sqrt{79}}{2}i$
- **B** $x = -\dfrac{1}{8} \pm \dfrac{\sqrt{79}}{8}i$
- **C** $x = \dfrac{1}{8} \pm \dfrac{\sqrt{81}}{8}i$
- **D** $x = \dfrac{1}{8} \pm \dfrac{\sqrt{79}}{8}i$

6. Find the roots of the equation $30x - 45 = 5x^2$ by factoring.

- **F** $x = 9$
- **G** $x = -9$
- **H** $x = 3$
- **J** $x = -3$

7. During the eruption of Mount St. Helens in 1980, debris was ejected at a speed of over 440 feet per second (300 miles per hour). The height in feet of a rock ejected at an angle of 75° is given by the equation $y(t) = -16t^2 + 425t + 8200$, where t is the time in seconds after the eruption. The rock's horizontal distance in feet from the point of ejection is given by $x(t) = 113t$. Assuming the elevation of the surrounding countryside is 0 feet, what is the horizontal distance from the point of ejection to where the rock would have landed? Round your answer to the nearest foot.

- **A** 2,234 ft
- **B** 8,932 ft
- **C** 4,467 ft
- **D** 1,117 ft

8. Solve the equation $x^2 - 10x + 25 = 54$.

- **F** $x = 5 \pm 3\sqrt{6}$
- **G** $x = 5 + 3\sqrt{6}$
- **H** $x = 5 - 3\sqrt{6}$
- **J** $x = 5 \pm 6\sqrt{3}$

Mini-Tasks

9. What is the x-coordinate of the vertex of the graph of $f(x) = -7(x - 9)^2 + 3$?

10. Write a quadratic function in standard form that has 17 and −5 as zeros.

PARCC Assessment Readiness

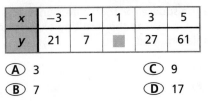

Selected Response

1. Which of the following is true of the graph of the function $f(x) = x^2 + 2x + 3$?

Statement 1: Its y-intercept is 3.
Statement 2: The vertex is at $(-1, 2)$.
Statement 3: Its x-intercept is -1.

  A Statement 1 only.

  B Statement 1 and statement 2.

  C Statement 1 and statement 3.

  D All three statements are true.

2. Which of these functions does NOT have zeros at -1 and 4?

  F $f(x) = x^2 - 3x - 4$

  G $f(x) = 2x^2 + 6x - 8$

  H $f(x) = -x^2 + 3x + 4$

  J $f(x) = 2x^2 - 6x - 8$

3. Which of the following is the graph of $f(x) = -x^2 + 2$?

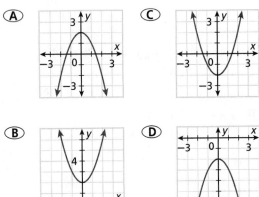

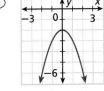

4. Which function's graph is a translation of the graph of $f(x) = 3x^2 + 4$ seven units down?

  F $f(x) = -4x^2 + 4$

  G $f(x) = 10x^2 + 4$

  H $f(x) = 3x^2 - 3$

  J $f(x) = 3x^2 + 11$

5. If the relationship between x and y is quadratic, which value of y completes the table?

x	-3	-1	1	3	5
y	21	7	■	27	61

  A 3   **C** 9

  B 7   **D** 17

6. The graph of which quadratic function has an axis of symmetry of $x = -2$?

  F $y = 2x^2 - x + 3$

  G $y = 4x^2 + 2x + 3$

  H $y = x^2 - 2x + 3$

  J $y = x^2 + 4x + 3$

7. What value of x makes the equation $x^2 + 64 = 16x$ true?

  A -8 **C** 4

  B -4 **D** 8

8. The value of y varies directly with x, and $y = 40$ when $x = -5$. Find y when $x = 8$.

  F 25   **H** -8

  G -1 **J** -64

9. What is the x-value of the vertex of $f(x) = x^2 - 2x - 15$?

  A -3 **C** 3

  B 1   **D** 5

10. A rectangle has an area of $(x^2 + 5x - 24)$ square units. Which of the following are possible expressions for the length and the width of the rectangle?

  F Length: $(x - 24)$ units; width: $(x + 1)$ units

  G Length: $(x - 4)$ units; width: $(x + 6)$ units

  H Length: $(x - 3)$ units; width: $(x + 8)$ units

  J Length: $(x + 12)$ units; width: $(x - 2)$ units

11. Which of the following expressions is equivalent to $x^2 - 8x + 16$?

Ⓐ $(x + 4)^2$

Ⓑ $(x + 4)(x - 4)$

Ⓒ $(x + 8)(x + 2)$

Ⓓ $(x - 4)^2$

12. Which of the following is not a perfect square trinomial?

Ⓕ $x^2 + 6x + 9$

Ⓖ $x^2 - 6x + 9$

Ⓗ $x^2 + 12x + 36$

Ⓙ $x^2 + 36x + 36$

13. Which of the following shows the complete factorization of $2x^3 + 4x^2 - 6x$?

Ⓐ $(2x^2 - 2x)(x + 3)$

Ⓑ $2x(x^2 + 2x - 3)$

Ⓒ $2x(x - 1)(x + 3)$

Ⓓ $2(x^3 + 2x^2 - 3x)$

14. Which point lies on the graph of both functions?

$f(x) = 2x - 10$
$g(x) = 10 - 2x$

Ⓕ $(5, 0)$

Ⓖ $(1, -8)$

Ⓗ $(0, 0)$

Ⓙ $(2, 6)$

15. Hayley plans to solve the system below.

$$\begin{cases} x + 3y = 8 \\ 5x - y = 8 \end{cases}$$

Which of the following does NOT show an equation Hayley can use to solve the system?

Ⓐ $x + 3(5x - 8) = 8$

Ⓑ $5(8 - 3y) - y = 8$

Ⓒ $x = 8 - 3y$

Ⓓ $5x - (-x + 8) = 8$

16. Which value of b would make $x^2 + bx - 2$ factorable?

Ⓕ -2

Ⓖ -1

Ⓗ 0

Ⓙ 3

17. The expression $x^2 + x + b$ is a perfect-square trinomial. Which is the value of b?

Ⓐ $\frac{1}{4}$

Ⓑ $\frac{x}{2}$

Ⓒ $\frac{1}{2}$

Ⓓ 1

18. Consider the function $f(x) = -4x^2 - 8x + 10$. Determine whether the graph opens upward or downward. Find the axis of symmetry, the vertex and the y-intercept.

Ⓕ The parabola opens downward.
The axis of symmetry is the line $x = -1$.
The vertex is the point $(-1, 14)$.
The y-intercept is 10.

Ⓖ The parabola opens upward.
The axis of symmetry is the line $x = -1$.
The vertex is the point $(-1, -6)$.
The y-intercept is -5.

Ⓗ The parabola opens downward.
The axis of symmetry is the line $x = -1$.
The vertex is the point $(-1, 7)$.
The y-intercept is 5.

Ⓙ The parabola opens upward.
The axis of symmetry is the line $x = -1$.
The vertex is the point $(-1, 14)$.
The y-intercept is 10.

19. A square piece of fabric has an area of $16x^2 + 40x + 25$ square inches. The length of each side of the fabric is $cx + d$, where c and d are whole numbers. Find an expression in terms of x for the perimeter of the piece of fabric. Then find the perimeter when $x = 2$.

Ⓐ An expression for the perimeter is $16x + 5$. The perimeter is 37 inches.

Ⓑ An expression for the perimeter is $(4x + 5)(4x + 5)$. The perimeter is 169 inches.

Ⓒ An expression for the perimeter is $16x + 20$. The perimeter is 52 inches.

Ⓓ An expression for the perimeter is $4x + 5$. The perimeter is 13 inches.

20. Tell whether the expression $6y^2(y^2 + 6y + 9)$ is completely factored. If not, factor it.

   (F) Yes.

   (G) No; $6y^2(y + 3)(y - 3)$.

   (H) No; $6y^4 + 36y^3 + 54y^2$.

   (J) No; $6y^2(y + 3)^2$.

21. A golfer hits the golf ball. The quadratic function $y = -16x^2 + 80x$ models the height of the golf ball after x seconds. How long does it take for the golf ball to return to the ground?

   (A) 16 sec

   (B) 5 sec

   (C) 10 sec

   (D) 80 sec

22. Solve $2x^2 + 12x = -10$ by completing the square.

   (F) No real solutions

   (G) The solution is -5.

   (H) The solutions are -1 and 5.

   (J) The solutions are -1 and -5.

23. The parent function $f(x) = x^2$ is reflected across the x-axis, vertically stretched by a factor of 10, and translated right 10 units to create $g(x)$. Use the description to write the quadratic function in vertex form.

   (A) $g(x) = 10(x + 10)^2$

   (B) $g(x) = -10(x - 10)^2$

   (C) $g(x) = 10(x - 10)^2$

   (D) $g(x) = -10(x + 10)^2$

24. Find the roots of the equation $30x - 45 = 5x^2$ by factoring.

   (F) $x = 9$

   (G) $x = -9$

   (H) $x = 3$

   (J) $x = -3$

25. Write a quadratic function that fits the points $(0, 6)$, $(2, 4)$, and $(3, 6)$.

   (A) $f(x) = -3x^2 + x + 6$

   (B) $f(x) = x^2 - 3x + 6$

   (C) $f(x) = x^2 + 3x + 6$

   (D) $f(x) = x^2 + 6x - 3$

26. Describe the graph of $g(x) = (x + 6) - 2$ in terms of transformations of the graph of the parent function $f(x) = x^2$.

   (F) The graph of $g(x)$ is the graph of $f(x)$ translated 2 units right and 6 units up.

   (G) The graph of $g(x)$ is the graph of $f(x)$ translated 6 units left and 2 units down.

   (H) The graph of $g(x)$ is the graph of $f(x)$ translated 2 units left and 6 units down.

   (J) The graph of $g(x)$ is the graph of $f(x)$ translated 6 units right and 2 units up.

Mini-Tasks

27. Determine whether the data set could represent a quadratic function. Explain.

x	-90	-75	-60	-45	-30
y	3	1	2	6	13

28. Answer the following questions using the function $f(x) = 2x^2 + 4x - 1$.

   a. Make a table of values and give five points on the graph.

   b. Find the axis of symmetry and vertex. Show all calculations.

29. Consider the function $f(x) = x^2 - 2x - 48$.

   a. Determine the roots of the function. Show your work.

   b. The function f is translated to produce the function g. The vertex of g is the point $(3, 30)$. Write the function rule for g in vertex form, and explain how you determined your answer.

30. The area of a circle is $\pi(9x^2 + 6x + 1)$ square centimeters. Find an expression for the length of the circle's radius. Explain how you found your answer.

31. A rectangle has an area of $(x^2 - 25)$ square feet.

   a. Use factoring to write possible expressions for the length and width of the rectangle.

   b. Use your expressions from part **a** to write an expression for the perimeter of the rectangle. Simplify the expression.

   c. Use your expressions from parts **a** and **b** to find the perimeter and the area of the rectangle when $x = 10$ feet. Show your work.

32. What are 2 values of b that will make $2x^2 - bx - 20$ factorable? Explain your answer.

33. Show that you can factor the expression $x^2y - 12 + 3y - 4x^2$ by grouping in two different ways.

Performance Tasks

34. Marcus is designing a swimming pool with a walkway around it. The length of the pool will be twice the width and the walkway will be 3 feet wide, as shown below. *x* is measured in feet.

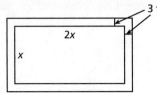

3 ft

2*x*

x

a. Write binomials that represent the length and width of the pool plus walkway.

b. Multiply the binomials you found in part **a** and write the area as a single trinomial.

c. Marcus is considering adding a patio area to the right of the pool, as shown below.

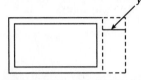

y

The combined area of the pool, walkway, and patio is represented by $2x^2 + 24x + 72$. What is the area of the patio? Write it as an algebraic expression with *x* as the only variable. Explain how you got your answer.

d. What is the length *y* of the patio? Write your answer as a single number. Explain how you got your answer.

35. A music company allows users to download songs for $1 each and has 10,000 downloads per day. The company has found that for every $0.01 decrease in the price of a song, the number of songs downloaded increases by 500 per day. Its marketing department wants to determine the price per song that would maximize the company's earnings.

a. Suppose *x* represents the number of $0.01 decreases in the price of a song. What binomial expression represents the price of a song based on the number of $0.01 decreases? What binomial expression represents the number of songs downloaded per day based on the number of $0.01 decreases?

b. Write a function that represents the amount of money that the company collects per day based on the number of $0.01 decreases by finding the product of the binomials that you wrote in part **a**. Multiply the binomials, simplify, and rearrange terms so that the function is in standard form.

c. Rewrite the function that you found in part **b** in vertex form by completing the square and determine the vertex of the graph of the function. Sketch a graph of the function.

d. What point of the graph shows the maximum earnings the company could make? What is the price per song that would maximize the company's earnings?

Are You Ready?

my.hrw.com
Assessment and Intervention

☑ Vocabulary

Match each term on the left with a definition on the right.

1. acute angle

2. congruent segments

3. obtuse angle

4. postulate

5. triangle

A. a statement that is accepted as true without proof

B. an angle that measures greater than 90° and less than 180°

C. a statement that you can prove

D. segments that have the same length

E. a three-sided polygon

F. an angle that measures greater than 0° and less than 90°

☑ Measure Angles

Use a protractor to measure each angle.

6.

7.

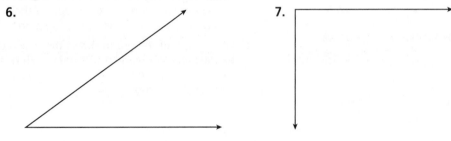

Use a protractor to draw an angle with each of the following measures.

8. 20°

9. 63°

10. 105°

11. 158°

☑ Solve Equations with Fractions

Solve.

12. $\frac{9}{2}x + 7 = 25$

13. $3x - \frac{2}{3} = \frac{4}{3}$

14. $x - \frac{1}{5} = \frac{12}{5}$

15. $2y = 5y - \frac{21}{2}$

Career Readiness Surveyors

Surveyors measure distances, directions, and angles to establish relative positions of points on, above, or beneath Earth's surface, and to establish official boundaries. They use surveying instruments, including the Global Positioning System (GPS). To be licensed, a surveyor usually must take courses, pass written tests, and work under an experienced surveyor. Some states require a college degree. Most surveyors work for engineers, architects, surveying companies, or government agencies.

Modeling Geometry

Online Edition

my.hrw.com

Access the complete online textbook, interactive features, and additional resources.

Online Video Tutor

Watch full explanations of every example in the textbook with these online videos.

Animated Math

Interactively explore key concepts with these online tutorials.

Portable Devices

eTextbook

Access your full textbook on your tablet or e-reader.

HMH Fuse

Make your learning experience completely portable and interactive with this app for iPad®.

Chapter Resources

Scan with your smart phone to jump directly to the online edition.

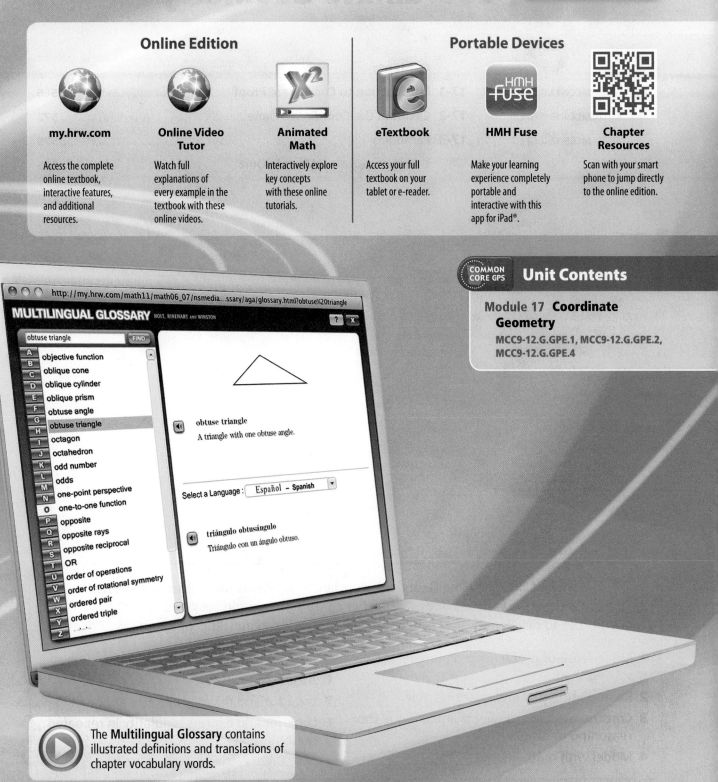

The **Multilingual Glossary** contains illustrated definitions and translations of chapter vocabulary words.

UNIT 6

Module

17

Coordinate Geometry

COMMON CORE GPS

Contents

MATHEMATICAL PRACTICES   The Common Core Georgia Performance Standards for Mathematical Practice describe varieties of expertise that all students should seek to develop. Opportunities to develop these practices are integrated throughout this program.

1 Make sense of problems and persevere in solving them.

2 Reason abstractly and quantitatively.

3 Construct viable arguments and critique the reasoning of others.

4 Model with mathematics.

5 Use appropriate tools strategically.

6 Attend to precision.

7 Look for and make use of structure.

8 Look for and express regularity in repeated reasoning.

Unpacking the Standards

Understanding the standards and the vocabulary terms in the standards will help you know exactly what you are expected to learn in this chapter.

 MCC9-12.G.GPE.4

Use coordinates to prove simple geometric theorems algebraically.

Key Vocabulary

coordinate (coordenada)
A number used to identify the location of a point. On a number line, one coordinate is used. On a coordinate plane, two coordinates are used, called the *x*-coordinate and the *y*-coordinate. In space, three coordinates are used, called the *x*-coordinate, the *y*-coordinate, and the *z*-coordinate.

What It Means For You

Positioning geometric diagrams on a coordinate grid makes algebraic tools such as the Midpoint and Distance Formulas available to you to prove geometric relationships.

EXAMPLE

You can use coordinates and the distance formula to prove that $\overline{AB}$, which joins the midpoints of $\overline{PR}$ and $\overline{QR}$, is half as long as $\overline{PQ}$.

$$AB = \sqrt{(4-0)^2 + (0-3)^2}$$
$$= \sqrt{16 + 9}$$
$$= 5$$
$$PQ = \sqrt{(8-0)^2 + (0-6)^2}$$
$$= \sqrt{64 + 36}$$
$$= 10$$

 MCC9-12.G.GPE.1

Derive the equation of a circle of given center and radius using the Pythagorean Theorem; …

Key Vocabulary

circle (círculo)
The set of points in a plane that are a fixed distance from a given point called the *center of the circle*.

radius of a circle (radio de un círculo)
A segment whose endpoints are the center of a circle and a point on the circle; the distance from the center of a circle to any point on the circle.

Pythagorean Theorem (Teorema de Pitágoras) If a right triangle has legs of lengths *a* and *b* and a hypotenuse of length *c*, then $a^2 + b^2 = c^2$.

What It Means For You

You can use the Pythagorean Theorem to derive the Distance Formula. In turn, you can use the Distance Formula to derive the general form of the equation of a circle.

EXAMPLE

For the circle shown, the distance from the center (h, k) to any point (x, y) on the circle is the radius. The center is at $(-1, 2)$ and the radius is 3. Using the Distance Formula:

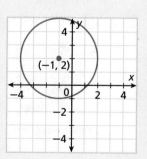

$$\sqrt{(x-h)^2 + (y-k)^2} = r$$
$$\sqrt{(x-(-1))^2 + (y-2)^2} = 3$$
$$\sqrt{(x+1)^2 + (y-2)^2} = 3$$

Squaring both sides of the equation gives the equation of the circle, $(x+1)^2 + (y-2)^2 = 9$.

Introduction to Coordinate Proof

? Essential Question: What is a coordinate proof in geometry?

Objectives
Position figures in the coordinate plane for use in coordinate proofs.

Prove geometric concepts by using coordinate proof.

Vocabulary
coordinate proof

Who uses this?
The Bushmen in South Africa use the Global Positioning System to transmit data about endangered animals to conservationists. (See Exercise 24.)

You have used coordinate geometry to find the midpoint of a line segment and to find the distance between two points. Coordinate geometry can also be used to prove conjectures.

A **coordinate proof** is a style of proof that uses coordinate geometry and algebra. The first step of a coordinate proof is to position the given figure in the plane. You can use any position, but some strategies can make the steps of the proof simpler.

Strategies for Positioning Figures in the Coordinate Plane

- Use the origin as a vertex, keeping the figure in Quadrant I.
- Center the figure at the origin.
- Center a side of the figure at the origin.
- Use one or both axes as sides of the figure.

EXAMPLE 1
MCC9-12.G.GPE.4

Positioning a Figure in the Coordinate Plane

Position a rectangle with a length of 8 units and a width of 3 units in the coordinate plane.

my.hrw.com

Online Video Tutor

Method 1 You can center the longer side of the rectangle at the origin.

Method 2 You can use the origin as a vertex of the rectangle.

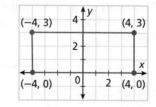

Depending on what you are using the figure to prove, one solution may be better than the other. For example, if you need to find the midpoint of the longer side, use the first solution.

 CHECK IT OUT!

1. Position a right triangle with leg lengths of 2 and 4 units in the coordinate plane. (*Hint:* Use the origin as the vertex of the right angle.)

Once the figure is placed in the coordinate plane, you can use slope, the coordinates of the vertices, the Distance Formula, or the Midpoint Formula to prove statements about the figure.

Writing a Proof Using Coordinate Geometry

Write a coordinate proof.

Given: Right $\triangle ABC$ has vertices $A(0, 6)$, $B(0, 0)$, and $C(4, 0)$. D is the midpoint of $\overline{AC}$.

Prove: The area of $\triangle DBC$ is one half the area of $\triangle ABC$.

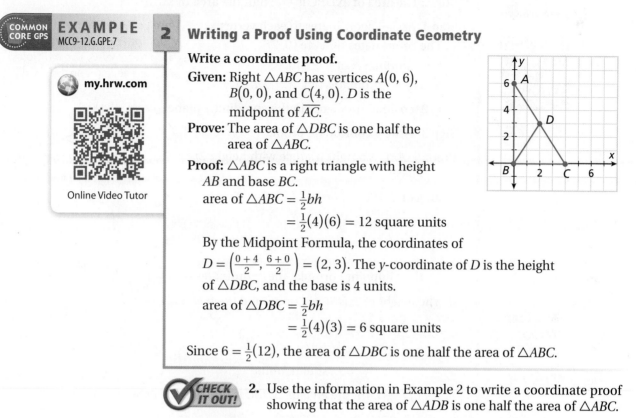

Proof: $\triangle ABC$ is a right triangle with height AB and base BC.

$$\text{area of } \triangle ABC = \tfrac{1}{2}bh$$
$$= \tfrac{1}{2}(4)(6) = 12 \text{ square units}$$

By the Midpoint Formula, the coordinates of $D = \left(\frac{0+4}{2}, \frac{6+0}{2} \right) = (2, 3)$. The y-coordinate of D is the height of $\triangle DBC$, and the base is 4 units.

$$\text{area of } \triangle DBC = \tfrac{1}{2}bh$$
$$= \tfrac{1}{2}(4)(3) = 6 \text{ square units}$$

Since $6 = \tfrac{1}{2}(12)$, the area of $\triangle DBC$ is one half the area of $\triangle ABC$.

CHECK IT OUT!

2. Use the information in Example 2 to write a coordinate proof showing that the area of $\triangle ADB$ is one half the area of $\triangle ABC$.

A coordinate proof can also be used to prove that a certain relationship is always true. You can prove that a statement is true for all right triangles without knowing the side lengths. To do this, assign variables as the coordinates of the vertices.

Assigning Coordinates to Vertices

Position each figure in the coordinate plane and give the coordinates of each vertex.

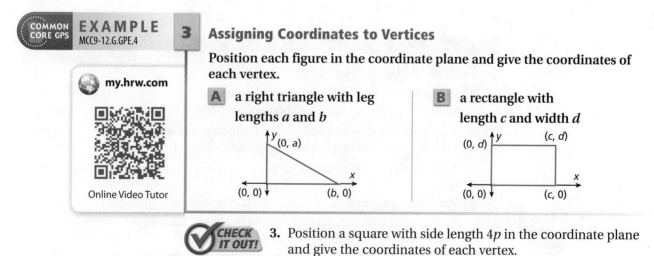

A a right triangle with leg lengths a and b

B a rectangle with length c and width d

CHECK IT OUT!

3. Position a square with side length $4p$ in the coordinate plane and give the coordinates of each vertex.

If a coordinate proof requires calculations with fractions, choose coordinates that make the calculations simpler. For example, use multiples of 2 when you are to find coordinates of a midpoint. Once you have assigned the coordinates of the vertices, the procedure for the proof is the same, except that your calculations will involve variables.

EXAMPLE **4** **Writing a Coordinate Proof**

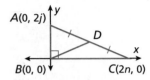

my.hrw.com

Online Video Tutor

Given: $\angle B$ is a right angle in $\triangle ABC$. D is the midpoint of $\overline{AC}$.
Prove: The area of $\triangle DBC$ is one half the area of $\triangle ABC$.

Step 1 Assign coordinates to each vertex.
The coordinates of A are $(0, 2j)$,
the coordinates of B are $(0, 0)$,
and the coordinates of C are $(2n, 0)$.

Since you will use the Midpoint Formula to find the coordinates of D, use multiples of 2 for the leg lengths.

Step 2 Position the figure in the coordinate plane.

Step 3 Write a coordinate proof.

Proof: $\triangle ABC$ is a right triangle with height $2j$ and base $2n$.

$$\text{area of } \triangle ABC = \tfrac{1}{2}bh$$
$$= \tfrac{1}{2}(2n)(2j)$$
$$= 2nj \text{ square units}$$

By the Midpoint Formula, the coordinates of $D = \left(\frac{0 + 2n}{2}, \frac{2j + 0}{2}\right) = (n, j)$.

The height of $\triangle DBC$ is j units, and the base is $2n$ units.

$$\text{area of } \triangle DBC = \tfrac{1}{2}bh$$
$$= \tfrac{1}{2}(2n)(j)$$
$$= nj \text{ square units}$$

Since $nj = \tfrac{1}{2}(2nj)$, the area of $\triangle DBC$ is one half the area of $\triangle ABC$.

4. Use the information in Example 4 to write a coordinate proof showing that the area of $\triangle ADB$ is one half the area of $\triangle ABC$.

THINK AND DISCUSS

1. When writing a coordinate proof why are variables used instead of numbers as coordinates for the vertices of a figure?

2. How does the way you position a figure in the coordinate plane affect your calculations in a coordinate proof?

3. Explain why it might be useful to assign $2p$ as a coordinate instead of just p.

4. GET ORGANIZED Copy and complete the graphic organizer. In each row, draw an example of each strategy that might be used when positioning a figure for a coordinate proof.

Positioning Strategy	Example
Use origin as a vertex.	
Center figure at origin.	
Center side of figure at origin.	
Use axes as sides of figure.	

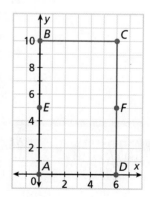
GUIDED PRACTICE

1. **Vocabulary** What is the relationship between *coordinate geometry*, *coordinate plane*, and *coordinate proof*?

SEE EXAMPLE 1 Position each figure in the coordinate plane.

2. a rectangle with a length of 4 units and width of 1 unit

3. a right triangle with leg lengths of 1 unit and 3 units

SEE EXAMPLE 2 Write a proof using coordinate geometry.

4. **Given:** Right $\triangle PQR$ has coordinates $P(0, 6)$, $Q(8, 0)$, and $R(0, 0)$. A is the midpoint of $\overline{PR}$. B is the midpoint of $\overline{QR}$.
   Prove: $AB = \frac{1}{2}PQ$

SEE EXAMPLE 3 Position each figure in the coordinate plane and give the coordinates of each vertex.

5. a right triangle with leg lengths m and n

6. a rectangle with length a and width b

SEE EXAMPLE 4 **Multi-Step** Assign coordinates to each vertex and write a coordinate proof.

7. **Given:** $\angle R$ is a right angle in $\triangle PQR$. A is the midpoint of $\overline{PR}$. B is the midpoint of $\overline{QR}$.
   Prove: $AB = \frac{1}{2}PQ$

PRACTICE AND PROBLEM SOLVING

Independent Practice

For Exercises	See Example
8–9	1
10	2
11–12	3
13	4

my.hrw.com

Online Extra Practice

Position each figure in the coordinate plane.

8. a square with side lengths of 2 units

9. a right triangle with leg lengths of 1 unit and 5 units

Write a proof using coordinate geometry.

10. **Given:** Rectangle $ABCD$ has coordinates $A(0, 0)$, $B(0, 10)$, $C(6, 10)$, and $D(6, 0)$. E is the midpoint of $\overline{AB}$, and F is the midpoint of $\overline{CD}$.
    Prove: $EF = BC$

Position each figure in the coordinate plane and give the coordinates of each vertex.

11. a square with side length $2m$

12. a rectangle with dimensions x and $3x$

Multi-Step Assign coordinates to each vertex and write a coordinate proof.

13. **Given:** E is the midpoint of $\overline{AB}$ in rectangle $ABCD$. F is the midpoint of $\overline{CD}$.
    Prove: $EF = AD$

H.O.T. 14. **Critical Thinking** Use variables to write the general form of the endpoints of a segment whose midpoint is $(0, 0)$.

H.O.T. **15. Recreation** A hiking trail begins at $E(0, 0)$. Bryan hikes from the start of the trail to a waterfall at $W(3, 3)$ and then makes a 90° turn to a campsite at $C(6, 0)$.

   a. Draw Bryan's route in the coordinate plane.

   b. If one grid unit represents 1 mile, what is the total distance Bryan hiked? Round to the nearest tenth.

Find the perimeter and area of each figure.

16. a right triangle with leg lengths of a and $2a$ units

17. a rectangle with dimensions s and t units

Find the missing coordinates for each figure.

18.

19.

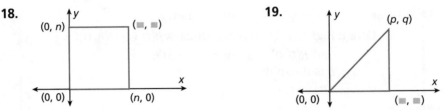

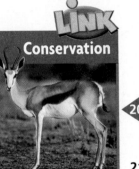
20. Conservation The Bushmen have sighted animals at the following coordinates: $(-25, 31.5)$, $(-23.2, 31.4)$, and $(-24, 31.1)$. Prove that the distance between two of these locations is approximately twice the distance between two other.

21. Navigation Two ships depart from a port at $P(20, 10)$. The first ship travels to a location at $A(-30, 50)$, and the second ship travels to a location at $B(70, -30)$. Each unit represents one nautical mile. Find the distance to the nearest nautical mile between the two ships. Verify that the port is at the midpoint between the two.

Write a coordinate proof.

22. Given: Rectangle $PQRS$ has coordinates $P(0, 2)$, $Q(3, 2)$, $R(3, 0)$, and $S(0, 0)$.
$\overline{PR}$ and $\overline{QS}$ intersect at $T(1.5, 1)$.
Prove: The area of $\triangle RST$ is $\frac{1}{4}$ of the area of the rectangle.

23. Given: $A(x_1, y_1)$, $B(x_2, y_2)$, with midpoint $M\left(\frac{x_1 + x_2}{2}, \frac{y_1 + y_2}{2}\right)$
Prove: $AM = \frac{1}{2}AB$

24. Plot the points on a coordinate plane and connect them to form $\triangle KLM$ and $\triangle MPK$. Write a coordinate proof.
Given: $K(-2, 1)$, $L(-2, 3)$, $M(1, 3)$, $P(1, 1)$
Prove: $\triangle KLM \cong \triangle MPK$

25. Write About It When you place two sides of a figure on the coordinate axes, what are you assuming about the figure?

26. Paul designed a doghouse to fit against the side of his house. His plan consisted of a right triangle on top of a rectangle.

   a. Find BD and CE.

   b. Before building the doghouse, Paul sketched his plan on a coordinate plane. He placed A at the origin and $\overline{AB}$ on the x-axis. Find the coordinates of B, C, D, and E, assuming that each unit of the coordinate plane represents one inch.

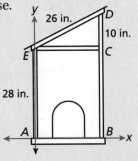

TEST PREP

27. The coordinates of the vertices of a right triangle are $(0, 0)$, $(4, 0)$, and $(0, 2)$. Which is a true statement?

Ⓐ The vertex of the right angle is at $(4, 2)$.

Ⓑ The midpoints of the two legs are at $(2, 0)$ and $(0, 1)$.

Ⓒ The hypotenuse of the triangle is $\sqrt{6}$ units.

Ⓓ The shortest side of the triangle is positioned on the *x*-axis.

28. A rectangle has dimensions of 2*g* and 2*f* units. If one vertex is at the origin, which coordinates could NOT represent another vertex?

Ⓕ $(2f, g)$ Ⓖ $(2f, 0)$ Ⓗ $(2g, 2f)$ Ⓙ $(-2f, 2g)$

29. The coordinates of the vertices of a rectangle are $(0, 0)$, $(a, 0)$, (a, b), and $(0, b)$. What is the perimeter of the rectangle?

Ⓐ $a + b$ Ⓑ ab Ⓒ $\frac{1}{2}ab$ Ⓓ $2a + 2b$

30. A coordinate grid is placed over a map. City A is located at $(-1, 2)$ and city C is located at $(3, 5)$. If city C is at the midpoint between city A and city B, what are the coordinates of city B?

Ⓕ $(1, 3.5)$ Ⓖ $(-5, -1)$ Ⓗ $(7, 8)$ Ⓙ $(2, 7)$

CHALLENGE AND EXTEND

Find the missing coordinates for each figure.

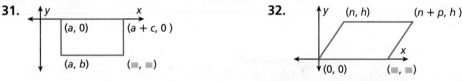

31.   **32.**

33. The vertices of a right triangle are at $(-2s, 2s)$, $(0, 2s)$, and $(0, 0)$. What coordinates could be used so that a coordinate proof would be easier to complete?

 34. Rectangle *ABCD* has dimensions of 2*f* and 2*g* units. The equation of the line containing $\overline{BD}$ is $y = \frac{g}{f}x$, and the equation of the line containing $\overline{AC}$ is $y = -\frac{g}{f}x + 2g$. Use algebra to show that the coordinates of *E* are (f, g).

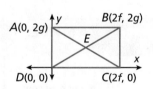

FOCUS ON MATHEMATICAL PRACTICES

MATHEMATICAL PRACTICES

H.O.T. **35. Proof** A triangle with coordinates $A(a, b)$, $B(a, c)$, and $C(d, c)$ is reflected across the *x*-axis. Prove that $\triangle ABC \cong \triangle A'B'C'$.

H.O.T. **36. Make a Conjecture** Two diagonals of a quadrilateral are congruent segments that are perpendicular bisectors of each other. To determine the shape of the quadrilateral, would it be easier to place the diagonals along the *x*- and *y*-axes, or along the lines $y = x$ and $y = -x$? Explain.

H.O.T. **37. Communication** Identify the angles that are challenging to use in a coordinate proof. Then discuss which postulates and theorems are most likely to be used to prove triangle congruence in a coordinate proof.

17-2 Circles in the Coordinate Plane

Essential Question: How can you write an equation for a circle in the coordinate plane with known center and radius?

Objectives
Write equations and graph circles in the coordinate plane.

Use the equation and graph of a circle to solve problems.

Who uses this?

Meteorologists use circles and coordinates to plan the location of weather stations. (See Example 3.)

The equation of a circle is based on the Distance Formula and the fact that all points on a circle are equidistant from the center.

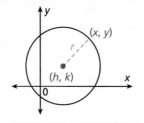

 Animated Math

$$d = \sqrt{(x_2 - x_1)^2 + (y_2 - y_1)^2}$$ *Distance Formula*

$$r = \sqrt{(x - h)^2 + (y - k)^2}$$ *Substitute the given values.*

$$r^2 = (x - h)^2 + (y - k)^2$$ *Square both sides.*

Know it! Note

Theorem 17-2-1   **Equation of a Circle**

The equation of a circle with center (h, k) and radius r is $(x - h)^2 + (y - k)^2 = r^2$.

COMMON CORE GPS
MCC9-12.G.GPE.1

EXAMPLE **1**   **Writing the Equation of a Circle**

Write the equation of each circle.

A ⊙A with center $A(4, -2)$ and radius 3

$$(x - h)^2 + (y - k)^2 = r^2$$ *Equation of a circle*

$$(x - 4)^2 + (y - (-2))^2 = 3^2$$ *Substitute 4 for h, −2 for k, and 3 for r.*

$$(x - 4)^2 + (y + 2)^2 = 9$$ *Simplify.*

B ⊙B that passes through $(-2, 6)$ and has center $B(-6, 3)$

$$r = \sqrt{(-2 - (-6))^2 + (6 - 3)^2}$$ *Distance Formula*

$$= \sqrt{25} = 5$$ *Simplify.*

$$(x - (-6))^2 + (y - 3)^2 = 5^2$$ *Substitute −6 for h, 3 for k, and 5 for r.*

$$(x + 6)^2 + (y - 3)^2 = 25$$ *Simplify.*

my.hrw.com

Online Video Tutor

 CHECK IT OUT!   Write the equation of each circle.

1a. ⊙P with center $P(0, -3)$ and radius 8

1b. ⊙Q that passes through $(2, 3)$ and has center $Q(2, -1)$

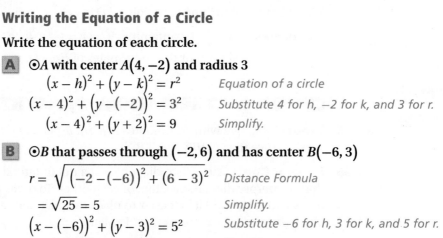

CHANGING WEATHER PATTERNS

off the mark by Mark Parisi, www.ofthemark.com
Atlantic Feature Synd. ©1999 Mark Parisi

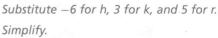

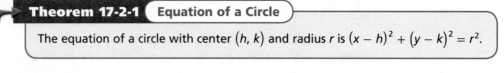

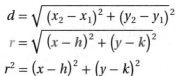

If you are given the equation of a circle, you can graph the circle by making a table or by identifying its center and radius.

COMMON CORE GPS
MCC9-12.G.GPE.1

EXAMPLE **2** **Graphing a Circle**

Graph each equation.

A $x^2 + y^2 = 25$

Step 1 Make a table of values.

Since the radius is $\sqrt{25}$, or 5, use ± 5 and the values between for x-values.

x	−5	−4	−3	0	3	4	5
y	0	± 3	± 4	± 5	± 4	± 3	0

Step 2 Plot the points and connect them to form a circle.

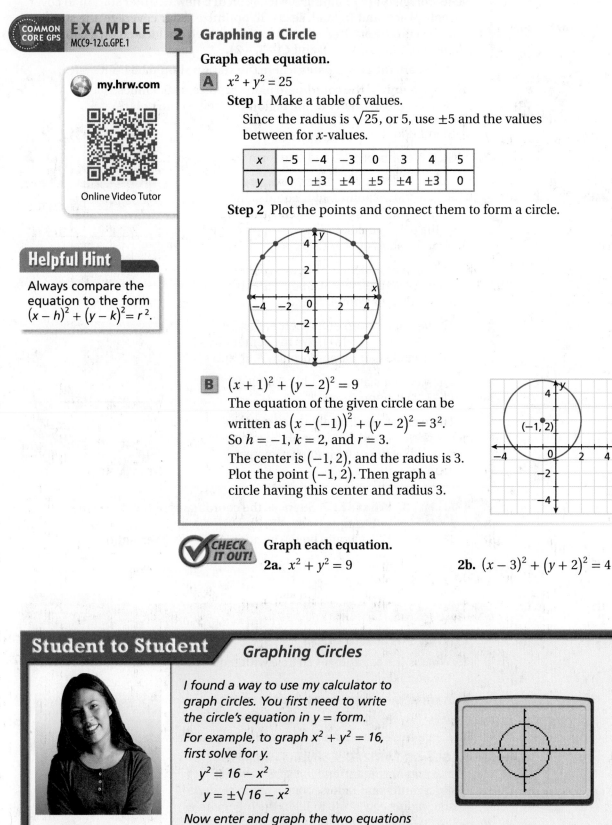

my.hrw.com

Online Video Tutor

Helpful Hint

Always compare the equation to the form $(x - h)^2 + (y - k)^2 = r^2$.

B $(x + 1)^2 + (y - 2)^2 = 9$

The equation of the given circle can be written as $\left(x - (-1)\right)^2 + (y - 2)^2 = 3^2$. So $h = -1$, $k = 2$, and $r = 3$.

The center is $(-1, 2)$, and the radius is 3. Plot the point $(-1, 2)$. Then graph a circle having this center and radius 3.

CHECK IT OUT! Graph each equation.

2a. $x^2 + y^2 = 9$

2b. $(x - 3)^2 + (y + 2)^2 = 4$

Student to Student **Graphing Circles**

I found a way to use my calculator to graph circles. You first need to write the circle's equation in $y =$ form.

For example, to graph $x^2 + y^2 = 16$, first solve for y.

$$y^2 = 16 - x^2$$
$$y = \pm\sqrt{16 - x^2}$$

Now enter and graph the two equations

$$y_1 = \sqrt{16 - x^2} \text{ and } y_2 = -\sqrt{16 - x^2}.$$

Christina Avila
Crockett High School

COMMON CORE GPS **EXAMPLE** **3** *Meteorology Application*
MCC9-12.G.GPE.1

my.hrw.com

Online Video Tutor

Meteorologists are planning the location of a new weather station to cover Osceola, Waco, and Ireland, Texas. To optimize radar coverage, the station must be equidistant from the three cities which are located on a coordinate plane at $A(2, 5)$, $B(3, -2)$, and $C(-5, -2)$.

a. What are the coordinates where the station should be built?

b. If each unit of the coordinate plane represents 8.5 miles, what is the diameter of the region covered by the radar?

Step 1 Plot the three given points.

Step 2 Connect A, B, and C to form a triangle.

Step 3 Find a point that is equidistant from the three points by constructing the perpendicular bisectors of two of the sides of $\triangle ABC$.

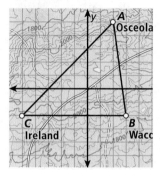

Remember!

The perpendicular bisectors of a triangle are concurrent at a point equidistant from each vertex.

The perpendicular bisectors of the sides of $\triangle ABC$ intersect at a point that is equidistant from A, B, and C.

The intersection of the perpendicular bisectors is $P(-1, 1)$. P is the center of the circle that passes through A, B, and C.

The weather station should be built at $P(-1, 1)$, Clifton, Texas.

There are approximately 10 units across the circle. So the diameter of the region covered by the radar is approximately 85 miles.

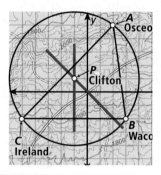

 CHECK IT OUT!

3. What if...? Suppose the coordinates of the three cities in Example 3 are $D(6, 2)$, $E(5, -5)$, and $F(-2, -4)$. What would be the location of the weather station?

MCC.MP.1  **MATHEMATICAL PRACTICES**

THINK AND DISCUSS

1. What is the equation of a circle with radius r whose center is at the origin?

2. A circle has a diameter with endpoints $(1, 4)$ and $(-3, 4)$. Explain how you can find the equation of the circle.

3. Can a circle have a radius of -6? Justify your answer.

4. GET ORGANIZED Copy and complete the graphic organizer. First select values for a center and radius. Then use the center and radius you wrote to fill in the other circles. Write the corresponding equation and draw the corresponding graph.

Center and radius ↔ Equation
↘ ↙
Graph

GUIDED PRACTICE

SEE EXAMPLE 1 Write the equation of each circle.

1. $\odot A$ with center $A(3, -5)$ and radius 12

2. $\odot B$ with center $B(-4, 0)$ and radius 7

3. $\odot M$ that passes through $(2, 0)$ and that has center $M(4, 0)$

4. $\odot N$ that passes through $(2, -2)$ and that has center $N(-1, 2)$

SEE EXAMPLE 2 **Multi-Step** Graph each equation.

5. $(x - 3)^2 + (y - 3)^2 = 4$

6. $(x - 1)^2 + (y + 2)^2 = 9$

7. $(x + 3)^2 + (y + 4)^2 = 1$

8. $(x - 3)^2 + (y + 4)^2 = 16$

SEE EXAMPLE 3

9. **Communications** A radio antenna tower is kept perpendicular to the ground by three wires of equal length. The wires touch the ground at three points on a circle whose center is at the base of the tower. The wires touch the ground at $A(2, 6)$, $B(-2, -2)$, and $C(-5, 7)$.

   a. What are the coordinates of the base of the tower?

   b. Each unit of the coordinate plane represents 1 ft. What is the diameter of the circle?

PRACTICE AND PROBLEM SOLVING

Write the equation of each circle.

10. $\odot R$ with center $R(-12, -10)$ and radius 8

11. $\odot S$ with center $S(1.5, -2.5)$ and radius $\sqrt{3}$

12. $\odot C$ that passes through $(2, 2)$ and that has center $C(1, 1)$

13. $\odot D$ that passes through $(-5, 1)$ and that has center $D(1, -2)$

Multi-Step Graph each equation.

14. $x^2 + (y - 2)^2 = 9$

15. $(x + 1)^2 - y^2 = 16$

16. $x^2 + y^2 = 100$

17. $x^2 + (y + 2)^2 = 4$

18. **Anthropology** Hundreds of stone circles can be found along the Gambia River in western Africa. The stones are believed to be over 1000 years old. In one of the circles at Ker Batch, three stones have approximate coordinates of $A(3, 1)$, $B(4, -2)$, and $C(-6, -2)$.

   a. What are the coordinates of the center of the stone circle?

   b. Each unit of the coordinate plane represents 1 ft. What is the diameter of the stone circle?

Algebra Write the equation of each circle.

19.
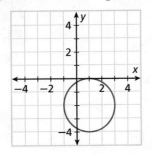

20.
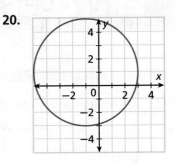

21. Entertainment In 2004, the world's largest carousel was located at the House on the Rock, in Spring Green, Wisconsin. Suppose that the center of the carousel is at the origin and that one of the animals on the circumference of the carousel has coordinates $(24, 32)$.

    a. If one unit of the coordinate plane equals 1 ft, what is the diameter of the carousel?

    b. As the carousel turns, the animals follow a circular path. Write the equation of this circle.

H.O.T. Determine whether each statement is true or false. If false, explain why.

22. The circle $x^2 + y^2 = 7$ has radius 7.

23. The circle $(x - 2)^2 + (y + 3)^2 = 9$ passes through the point $(-1, -3)$.

24. The center of the circle $(x - 6)^2 + (y + 4)^2 = 1$ lies in the second quadrant.

25. The circle $(x + 1)^2 + (y - 4)^2 = 4$ intersects the y-axis.

26. The equation of the circle centered at the origin with diameter 6 is $x^2 + y^2 = 36$.

27. Estimation You can use the graph of a circle to estimate its area.

    a. Estimate the area of the circle by counting the number of squares of the coordinate plane contained in its interior. Be sure to count partial squares.

    b. Find the radius of the circle. Then use the area formula to calculate the circle's area to the nearest tenth.

    c. Was your estimate in part **a** an overestimate or an underestimate?

H.O.T. **28.** Consider the circle whose equation is $(x - 4)^2 + (y + 6)^2 = 25$. Write, in point-slope form, the equation of the line tangent to the circle at $(1, -10)$.

Real-World Connections

29. A *hogan* is a traditional Navajo home. An artist is using a coordinate plane to draw the symbol for a hogan. The symbol is based on eight equally spaced points placed around the circumference of a circle.

    a. She positions the symbol at $A(-3, 5)$ and $C(0, 2)$. What are the coordinates of E and G?

    b. What is the length of a diameter of the symbol?

    c. Use your answer from part **b** to write an equation of the circle.

Find the center and radius of each circle.

30. $(x - 2)^2 + (y + 3)^2 = 81$ **31.** $x^2 + (y + 15)^2 = 25$ **32.** $(x + 1)^2 + y^2 = 7$

Find the area and circumference of each circle. Express your answer in terms of π.

33. circle with equation $(x + 2)^2 + (y - 7)^2 = 9$

34. circle with equation $(x - 8)^2 + (y + 5)^2 = 7$

35. circle with center $(-1, 3)$ that passes through $(2, -1)$

36. Critical Thinking Describe the graph of the equation $x^2 + y^2 = r^2$ when $r = 0$.

Geology

The New Madrid earthquake of 1811 was one of the largest earthquakes known in American history. Large areas sank into the earth, new lakes were formed, forests were destroyed, and the course of the Mississippi River was changed.

The Granger Collection, New York

37. Geology A seismograph measures ground motion during an earthquake. To find the epicenter of an earthquake, scientists take readings in three different locations. Then they draw a circle centered at each location. The radius of each circle is the distance the earthquake is from the seismograph. The intersection of the circles is the epicenter. Use the data below to find the epicenter of the New Madrid earthquake.

Seismograph	Location	Distance to Earthquake
A	$(-200, 200)$	300 mi
B	$(400, -100)$	600 mi
C	$(100, -500)$	500 mi

38. For what value(s) of the constant k is the circle $x^2 + (y - k)^2 = 25$ tangent to the x-axis?

39. $\odot A$ has a diameter with endpoints $(-3, -2)$ and $(5, -2)$. Write the equation of $\odot A$.

40. Recall that a locus is the set of points that satisfy a given condition. Draw and describe the locus of points that are 3 units from $(2, 2)$.

H.O.T. 41. Write About It The equation of $\odot P$ is $(x - 2)^2 + (y - 1)^2 = 9$. Without graphing, explain how you can determine whether the point $(3, -1)$ lies on $\odot P$, in the interior of $\odot P$, or in the exterior of $\odot P$.

TEST PREP

42. Which of these circles intersects the x-axis?

   Ⓐ $(x - 3)^2 + (y + 3)^2 = 4$ Ⓒ $(x + 2)^2 + (y + 1)^2 = 1$

   Ⓑ $(x + 1)^2 + (y - 4)^2 = 9$ Ⓓ $(x + 1)^2 + (y + 4)^2 = 9$

43. What is the equation of a circle with center $(-3, 5)$ that passes through the point $(1, 5)$?

   Ⓕ $(x + 3)^2 + (y - 5)^2 = 4$ Ⓗ $(x + 3)^2 + (y - 5)^2 = 16$

   Ⓖ $(x - 3)^2 + (y + 5)^2 = 4$ Ⓙ $(x - 3)^2 + (y + 5)^2 = 16$

44. On a map of a park, statues are located at $(4, -2)$, $(-1, 3)$, and $(-5, -5)$. A circular path connects the three statues, and the circle has a fountain at its center. Find the coordinates of the fountain.

   Ⓐ $(-1, -2)$ Ⓑ $(2, 1)$ Ⓒ $(-2, 1)$ Ⓓ $(1, -2)$

CHALLENGE AND EXTEND

45. In three dimensions, the equation of a sphere is similar to that of a circle. The equation of a sphere with center (h, j, k) and radius r is $(x - h)^2 + (y - j)^2 + (z - k)^2 = r^2$.

    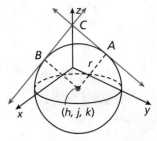

    a. Write the equation of a sphere with center $(2, -4, 3)$ that contains the point $(1, -2, -5)$.

    b. $\overleftrightarrow{AC}$ and $\overleftrightarrow{BC}$ are tangents from the same exterior point. If $AC = 15$ m, what is BC? Explain.

46. **Algebra** Find the point(s) of intersection of the line $x + y = 5$ and the circle $x^2 + y^2 = 25$ by solving the system of equations. Check your result by graphing the line and the circle.

H.O.T. 47. Find the equation of the circle with center $(3, 4)$ that is tangent to the line whose equation is $y = 2x + 3$. (*Hint:* First find the point of tangency.)

FOCUS ON MATHEMATICAL PRACTICES

H.O.T. 48. **Error Analysis** A circle has a center at $(3, -9)$ and a radius of 4. Brock wrote $(x - 3)^2 + (y - 9)^2 = 16$ as the equation for this circle. What error did he make? What should he have written?

H.O.T. 49. **Problem Solving** $\overline{AB}$ and $\overline{CD}$ are chords of the same circle with endpoints $A(5, -9)$, $B(12, -2)$, $C(8, -10)$ and $D(13, -5)$.

    a. Can the perpendicular bisector of each chord be used to locate the center of the circle? Explain.

    b. What method could be used to find the center of this circle?

    c. Write an equation for the circle.

H.O.T. Find the real solution(s), if any, of each system of equations.

50. $\begin{cases} y = x + 16 \\ x^2 + y^2 = 100 \end{cases}$

51. $\begin{cases} y = 12 \\ x^2 + y^2 = 1369 \end{cases}$

52. $\begin{cases} 4x - 3y = 25 \\ x^2 + y^2 = 25 \end{cases}$

Career Path

Bryan Moreno
Furniture Maker

Q: What math classes did you take in high school?

A: I took Algebra 1 and Geometry. I also took Drafting and Woodworking. Those classes aren't considered math classes, but for me they were since math was used in them.

Q: How do you use math?

A: Taking appropriate and precise measurements is very important. If wood is not measured correctly, the end result doesn't turn out as expected. Understanding angle measures is also important. Some of the furniture I build has 30° or 40° angles at the edges.

Q: What are your future plans?

A: Someday I would love to design all the furniture in my own home. It would be incredibly satisfying to know that all my furniture was made with quality and attention to detail.

17-3 Parabolas

 Essential Question: How can you derive an equation for a parabola using a focus and a directrix?

Objectives
Write the standard equation of a parabola and its axis of symmetry.

Graph a parabola, and identify its focus, directrix, and axis of symmetry.

Vocabulary
focus of a parabola
directrix

Why learn this?

Parabolas are used with microphones to pick up sounds from sports events. (See Example 4.)

The graph of a quadratic function is a parabola. A parabola can also be defined geometrically in terms of distances.

A parabola is the set of all points $P(x, y)$ in a plane that are an equal distance from both a fixed point, the **focus**, and a fixed line, the **directrix**. A parabola has an axis of symmetry perpendicular to its directrix and that passes through its vertex. The vertex of a parabola is the midpoint of the segment connecting the focus and the directrix.

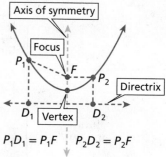

$$P_1D_1 = P_1F \qquad P_2D_2 = P_2F$$

COMMON CORE GPS
MCC9-12.G.GPE.2

EXAMPLE **1**

Using the Distance Formula to Write the Equation of a Parabola

Use the Distance Formula to find the equation of a parabola with focus $F(0, 3)$ and directrix $y = -3$.

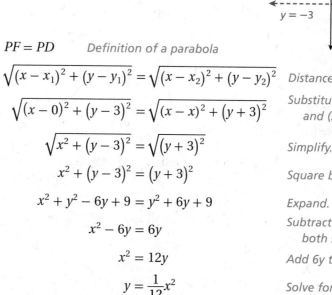

my.hrw.com

Online Video Tutor

$PF = PD$	*Definition of a parabola*
$\sqrt{(x - x_1)^2 + (y - y_1)^2} = \sqrt{(x - x_2)^2 + (y - y_2)^2}$	*Distance Formula*
$\sqrt{(x - 0)^2 + (y - 3)^2} = \sqrt{(x - x)^2 + (y + 3)^2}$	*Substitute (0, 3) for (x_1, y_1) and $(x, -3)$ for (x_2, y_2).*
$\sqrt{x^2 + (y - 3)^2} = \sqrt{(y + 3)^2}$	*Simplify.*
$x^2 + (y - 3)^2 = (y + 3)^2$	*Square both sides.*
$x^2 + y^2 - 6y + 9 = y^2 + 6y + 9$	*Expand.*
$x^2 - 6y = 6y$	*Subtract y^2 and 9 from both sides.*
$x^2 = 12y$	*Add 6y to both sides.*
$y = \frac{1}{12}x^2$	*Solve for y.*

Remember!

The distance from a point to a line is defined as the length of the line segment from the point perpendicular to the line.

 CHECK IT OUT!

1. Use the Distance Formula to find the equation of a parabola with focus $F(0, 4)$ and directrix $y = -4$.

Previously, you have graphed parabolas with vertical axes of symmetry that open upward or downward. Parabolas may also have horizontal axes of symmetry and may open to the left or right.

The equations of parabolas use the parameter p. The $|p|$ gives the distance from the vertex to both the focus and the directrix.

Know it!
Note

Standard Form for the Equation of a Parabola — Vertex at $(0, 0)$

AXIS OF SYMMETRY	HORIZONTAL $y = 0$	VERTICAL $x = 0$
Equation	$x = \dfrac{1}{4p}y^2$	$y = \dfrac{1}{4p}x^2$
Direction	Opens right if $p > 0$ Opens left if $p < 0$	Opens upward if $p > 0$ Opens downward if $p < 0$
Focus	$(p, 0)$	$(0, p)$
Directrix	$x = -p$	$y = -p$
Graph	$D(-p, y)$ $\quad$ $P(x, y)$ $\quad$ $F(p, 0)$ $\quad$ $x = -p$	$F(0, p)$ $\quad$ $P(x, y)$ $\quad$ $y = -p$ $\quad$ $D(x, -p)$

EXAMPLE 2
MCC9-12.G.GPE.2

Writing Equations of Parabolas

Write the equation in standard form for each parabola.

A

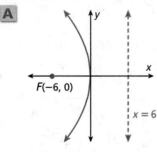

$F(-6, 0)$

$x = 6$

Step 1 Because the axis of symmetry is horizontal and the parabola opens to the left, the equation is in the form $x = \frac{1}{4p}y^2$ with $p < 0$.

Step 2 The distance from the focus $(-6, 0)$ to the vertex $(0, 0)$ is 6, so $p = -6$ and $4p = -24$.

Step 3 The equation of the parabola is $x = -\frac{1}{24}y^2$.

Check Use your graphing calculator. The graph of the equation appears to match.

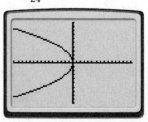

Write the equation in standard form for each parabola.

B the parabola with vertex $(0, 0)$ and directrix $y = -2.5$.

Step 1 Because the directrix is a horizontal line, the equation is in the form $y = \frac{1}{4p}x^2$. The vertex is above the directrix, so the graph will open upward.

Step 2 Because the directrix is $y = -2.5$, $p = 2.5$ and $4p = 10$.

Step 3 The equation of the parabola is $y = \frac{1}{10}x^2$.

Check Use your graphing calculator.

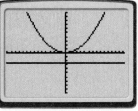

 Write the equation in standard form for each parabola.

2a. vertex $(0, 0)$, directrix $x = 1.25$

2b. vertex $(0, 0)$, focus $(0, -7)$

The vertex of a parabola may not always be the origin. Adding or subtracting a value from x or y translates the graph of a parabola. Also notice that the values of p stretch or compress the graph.

Know It! Note

Standard Form for the Equation of a Parabola — Vertex at (h, k)

AXIS OF SYMMETRY	HORIZONTAL $y = k$	VERTICAL $x = h$
Equation	$x - h = \frac{1}{4p}(y - k)^2$	$y - k = \frac{1}{4p}(x - h)^2$
Direction	Opens right if $p > 0$ Opens left if $p < 0$	Opens upward if $p > 0$ Opens downward if $p < 0$
Focus	$(h + p, k)$	$(h, k + p)$
Directrix	$x = h - p$	$y = k - p$
Graph		

COMMON CORE GPS MCC9-12.A.SSE.1a

EXAMPLE 3 **Graphing Parabolas**

Find the vertex, value of p, axis of symmetry, focus, and directrix of the parabola $x - 2 = -\frac{1}{16}(y + 5)^2$. Then graph.

Step 1 The vertex is $(2, -5)$.

Step 2 $\frac{1}{4p} = -\frac{1}{16}$, so $4p = -16$ and $p = -4$.

Step 3 The graph has a horizontal axis of symmetry, with equation $y = -5$, and opens left.

Step 4 The focus is $(2 + (-4), -5)$, or $(-2, -5)$.

Step 5 The directrix is a vertical line
$x = 2 - (-4)$, or $x = 6$.

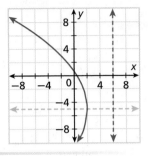

 CHECK IT OUT! Find the vertex, value of p, axis of symmetry, focus, and directrix of each parabola. Then graph.

3a. $x - 1 = \frac{1}{12}(y - 3)^2$

3b. $y - 4 = -\frac{1}{2}(x - 8)^2$

Light or sound waves collected by a parabola will be reflected by the curve through the focus of the parabola, as shown in the figure. Waves emitted from the focus will be reflected out parallel to the axis of symmetry of a parabola. This property is used in communications technology.

EXAMPLE 4
MCC9-12.G.MG.1

Using the Equation of a Parabola

Engineers are constructing a parabolic microphone for use at sporting events. The surface of the parabolic microphone will reflect sounds to the focus of the microphone at the end of a part called a feedhorn. The equation for the cross section of the parabolic microphone dish is $x = \frac{1}{32}y^2$, measured in inches. How long should the engineers make the feedhorn?

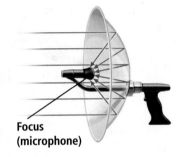

Focus
(microphone)

The equation for the cross section is in the form $x = \frac{1}{4p}y^2$, so $4p = 32$ and $p = 8$. The focus should be 8 inches from the vertex of the cross section. Therefore, the feedhorn should be 8 inches long.

 CHECK IT OUT! **4.** Find the length of the feedhorn for a microphone with a cross section equation $x = \frac{1}{44}y^2$.

MCC.MP.1   **MATHEMATICAL PRACTICES**

THINK AND DISCUSS

1. By using the standard form of a parabola's equation, how can you tell which direction a parabola opens?

2. How does knowing the value of p help you in finding the focus and the directrix of a parabola?

3. GET ORGANIZED Copy and complete the graphic organizer. Sketch an example and give an equation for each type of parabola.

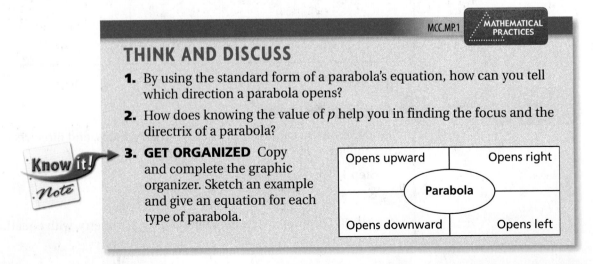

Opens upward	Opens right
Parabola	
Opens downward	Opens left

GUIDED PRACTICE

1. **Vocabulary** Describe the relationship between a parabola and its *directrix*.

SEE EXAMPLE **1** Use the distance formula to find the equation of a parabola with the given focus and directrix.

2. $F(0, -5)$, $y = 5$ 3. $F(7, 0)$, $x = -7$ 4. $F(-3, 0)$, $x = 6$

SEE EXAMPLE **2** Write the equation in standard form for each parabola.

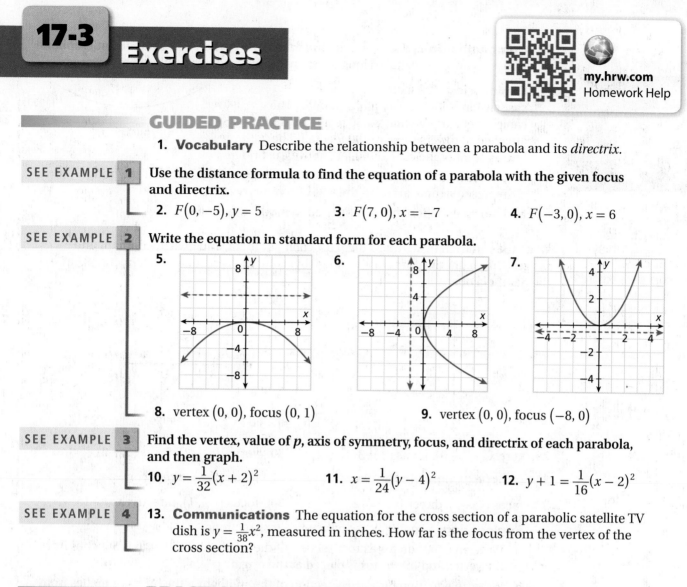

5.   6.   7.

8. vertex $(0, 0)$, focus $(0, 1)$ 9. vertex $(0, 0)$, focus $(-8, 0)$

SEE EXAMPLE **3** Find the vertex, value of *p*, axis of symmetry, focus, and directrix of each parabola, and then graph.

10. $y = \dfrac{1}{32}(x + 2)^2$ 11. $x = \dfrac{1}{24}(y - 4)^2$ 12. $y + 1 = \dfrac{1}{16}(x - 2)^2$

SEE EXAMPLE **4** 13. **Communications** The equation for the cross section of a parabolic satellite TV dish is $y = \dfrac{1}{38}x^2$, measured in inches. How far is the focus from the vertex of the cross section?

PRACTICE AND PROBLEM SOLVING

Independent Practice	
For Exercises	See Example
14–16	1
17–21	2
22–24	3
25	4

Use the distance formula to find the equation of a parabola with the given focus and directrix.

14. $F(0, 3)$, $y = -5$ 15. $F(-2, 0)$, $x = 8$ 16. $F(7, 0)$, $x = -1$

Write the equation in standard form for each parabola.

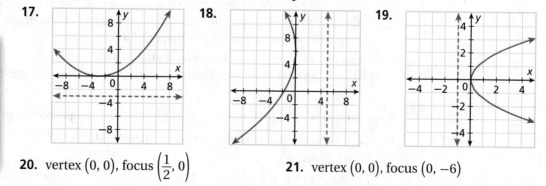

17.   18.   19.

20. vertex $(0, 0)$, focus $\left(\dfrac{1}{2}, 0\right)$ 21. vertex $(0, 0)$, focus $(0, -6)$

Find the vertex, value of *p*, axis of symmetry, focus, and directrix of each parabola, and then graph.

22. $y = \dfrac{1}{8}(x - 1)^2$ 23. $x = 2y^2 + 1$ 24. $x - 2 = \dfrac{1}{2}(y + 1)^2$

25. **Communications** Find an equation for a cross section of a parabolic microphone whose feedhorn is 9 inches long if the end of the feedhorn is placed at the origin.

26. **Engineering** The main cables of a suspension bridge are ideally parabolic. The cables over a bridge that is 400 feet long are attached to towers that are 100 feet tall. The lowest point of the cable is 40 feet above the bridge.

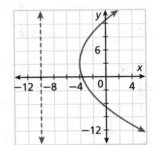

a. Find the coordinates of the vertex and the tops of the towers if the bridge represents the *x*-axis and the axis of symmetry is the *y*-axis.

b. Find an equation that can be used to model the cables.

Write the equation in standard form for each parabola, and give the domain and range. (*Hint:* Find the domain and range by using the vertex and the direction that the parabola opens.)

27.

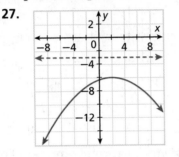

28.

29. vertex $(-7, -3)$, focus $(2, -3)$

30. vertex $(5, -2)$, focus $(5, -8)$

31. focus $(0, 0)$, directrix $y = 10$

32. focus $(2, 6)$, directrix $y = -8$

33. focus $(4, -5)$, directrix $x = 12$

34. focus $(-3, 1)$, directrix $x = -15$

H.O.T. 35. **Engineering** A spotlight has parabolic cross sections.

a. Write an equation for a cross section of the spotlight if the bulb is 5 inches from the vertex and the vertex is placed at the origin.

b. Write an equation for a cross section of the spotlight if the bulb is 4 inches from the vertex and the bulb is placed at the origin.

c. If the spotlight has a diameter of 24 inches at its opening, find the depth of the spotlight if the bulb is 5 inches from the vertex.

H.O.T. 36. **Sports** When a football is kicked, the path that the ball travels can be modeled by a parabola.

a. A placekicker kicks a football, which reaches a maximum height of 8 yards and lands 50 yards away. Assuming that the football was at the origin when it was kicked, write an equation for the height of the football.

b. **What if...?** If the placekicker was trying to kick the ball over a 10-foot-high goalpost 40 yards away, was the football high enough to go over the goalpost? Explain.

H.O.T. 37. **Astrophysics** The path of a comet is modeled by the parabola with equation $y = -\frac{1}{532}(x + 96)^2 + 174$, where each unit of the coordinate plane represents 1 million kilometers.

a. The Sun is at the focus of the parabolic path. Find the coordinates of the Sun.

b. How close does the comet come to the Sun?

c. What are the coordinates of the comet when it is at its closest point to the Sun?

© AFP/Getty Images

Graph each equation. Identify the vertex, value of p, axis of symmetry, focus, and directrix for each equation.

38. $20(y - 2) = (x + 6)^2$

39. $y = -2(x + 4)^2 + 5$

40. $(y + 7)^2 = \dfrac{x}{16}$

41. $x + 3 = \dfrac{1}{8}(y - 2)^2$

H.O.T. 42. Critical Thinking Find the distance d from the focus to the points on the parabola that are on the line perpendicular to the axis of symmetry and through the focus. Explain your answer.

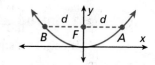

H.O.T. 43. Write About It Explain how changing the value of p will affect the vertex, focus, and directrix of the parabola $y - k = \dfrac{1}{4p}(x - h)^2$.

TEST PREP

44. The graph of which of the following parabolas opens to the left?

   (A) $16y - 4x^2 = 12$ (B) $16y + 4x^2 = 12$ (C) $16x - 4y^2 = 12$ (D) $16x + 4y^2 = 12$

45. Which of the following is the axis of symmetry for the graph of $x - 4 = \dfrac{1}{8}(y + 2)^2$?

   (F) $x = 0$ (G) $y = -2$ (H) $x = 4$ (J) $y = 8$

46. Which of the following graphs has the directrix $y = 4$?

   (A) $y + 3 = \dfrac{1}{4}(x - 1)^2$ (C) $x - 5 = \dfrac{1}{4}(y + 4)^2$

   (B) $y - 5 = \dfrac{1}{4}(x + 2)^2$ (D) $x + 3 = \dfrac{1}{4}(y - 2)^2$

47. Short Response What are the coordinates of the focus for the graph of $x - 3 = \dfrac{1}{16}y^2$?

CHALLENGE AND EXTEND

Write the equation in standard form for each parabola.

48. vertex $(6, 8)$, contains the point $(4, -2)$, axis of symmetry $x = 6$

49. focus $(6, 5)$, axis of symmetry $x = 6$, contains the point $(10, 5)$

Multi-Step The latus rectum of a parabola is the line segment perpendicular to the axis of symmetry through the focus, with endpoints on the parabola. Find the length of the latus rectum of each parabola.

50. $y = \dfrac{1}{8}x^2$

51. $y - k = \dfrac{1}{4p}(x - h)^2$

FOCUS ON MATHEMATICAL PRACTICES

H.O.T. 52. Patterns As the focus of a parabola moves closer to its directrix, what happens to the shape of the parabola? Extend this pattern to speculate about what happens when the distance between the focus and the directrix is zero.

H.O.T. 53. Modeling A parabolic satellite dish has a opening diameter of 8 feet and its depth is 1 foot. Where is the focus of the dish located?

H.O.T. 54. Make a Conjecture If, instead of having a horizontal or vertical directrix, a parabola had a diagonal directrix with a slope of -1, how might the graph of the parabola be different? Make a sketch of what the graph might look like.

Ready to Go On?

my.hrw.com
Assessment and Intervention

17-1 Introduction to Coordinate Proof

1. Position a square with side lengths of 9 units in the coordinate plane

2. Assign coordinates to each vertex and write a coordinate proof.
   Given: $ABCD$ is a rectangle with M as the midpoint of $\overline{AB}$. N is the midpoint of $\overline{AD}$.
   Prove: The area of $\triangle AMN$ is $\frac{1}{8}$ the area of rectangle $ABCD$.

Position each figure in the coordinate plane and give the coordinates of each vertex.

3. a right triangle with leg lengths r and s

4. a rectangle with length $2p$ and width p

5. a square with side length $8m$

17-2 Circles in the Coordinate Plane

Write the equation of each circle.

6. $\odot A$ with center $A(-2, -3)$ and radius 3

7. $\odot B$ that passes through $(1, 1)$ and that has center $B(4, 5)$

8. $\odot C$ with center $C(-4, -3)$ and diameter 6

9. $\odot D$ that passes through $(-2, -2)$ and that has center $D(-2, 0)$

10. A television station serves residents of three cities located at $J(5, 2)$, $K(-7, 2)$, and $L(-5, -8)$. The station wants to build a new broadcast facility that is equidistant from the three cities. What are the coordinates of the location where the facility should be built?

17-3 Parabolas

Find the vertex, value of p, axis of symmetry, focus, and directrix for each parabola.

11. $x = -\dfrac{1}{12}y^2$

12. $y = 2(x + 3)^2 + 4$

13. $y = -\dfrac{1}{12}x^2$

14. $x = 2y^2$

15. $y - 5 = (x + 4)^2$

16. $x - 4 = -\dfrac{1}{6}(y + 2)^2$

Write the equation in standard form for each parabola.

17. vertex $(4, 6)$, axis of symmetry $y = 6$, $p = -2.5$

18. focus $(12, -4)$ and directrix $x = 6$

19. A cross section of a parabolic microphone has the equation $35x = y^2$, where x and y are measured in inches. How far from the vertex of the microphone should the feedhorn be placed?

PARCC Assessment Readiness

Selected Response

1. Given: $\triangle PQR$ has vertices $P(0, 8)$, $Q(0, 0)$, and $R(-3, 0)$. S is the midpoint of $\overline{PQ}$ and T is the midpoint of $\overline{RP}$.
Prove: The area of $\triangle PST$ is one fourth the area of $\triangle PQR$.

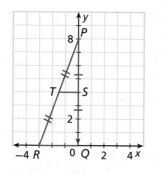

Complete the paragraph proof by replacing each number in square brackets with the appropriate missing information.

Proof: $\triangle PQR$ is [1] triangle with height PQ and base QR. The area of $\triangle PQR$ = [2] square units. By the [3] Formula, the coordinates of $S = (0, 4)$ and the coordinates of $T = \left(-\frac{3}{2}, 4\right)$. Thus $\triangle PST$ is [4] triangle with height PS and base ST. So the area of $\triangle PST$ = [5] square units. So, the area of $\triangle PST$ is one fourth the area of $\triangle PQR$.

Ⓐ [1] a right
[2] 24
[3] Distance
[4] a right
[5] 6

Ⓒ [1] an isosceles
[2] 24
[3] Distance
[4] an isosceles
[5] 6

Ⓑ [1] a right
[2] 12
[3] Midpoint
[4] a right
[5] 3

Ⓓ [1] an isosceles
[2] 12
[3] Midpoint
[4] an isosceles
[5] 3

2. Find the center and radius of the circle with equation $(x - 3)^2 + (y + 2)^2 = 25$.

Ⓕ center: $(3, -2)$; radius: 25

Ⓖ center: $(-2, 3)$; radius: 5

Ⓗ center: $(3, -2)$; radius: 5

Ⓙ center: $(-3, 2)$; radius: 5

3. Write the equation of the circle shown.

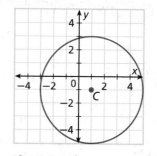

Ⓐ $(x + 1)^2 + (y - 1)^2 = 4$

Ⓑ $(x + 1)^2 + (y - 1)^2 = 5$

Ⓒ $(x - 1)^2 + (y + 1)^2 = 16$

Ⓓ $(x - 1)^2 + (y + 1)^2 = 25$

4. Write the equation in standard form of the parabola with vertex $(3, 0)$ and directrix $y = 5$.

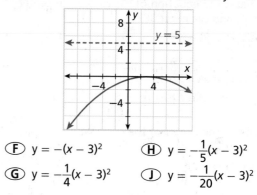

Ⓕ $y = -(x - 3)^2$

Ⓗ $y = -\frac{1}{5}(x - 3)^2$

Ⓖ $y = -\frac{1}{4}(x - 3)^2$

Ⓙ $y = -\frac{1}{20}(x - 3)^2$

Mini-Task

5. Given: $\angle B$ is a right angle in isosceles right $\triangle ABC$. E is the midpoint of $\overline{AB}$. D is the midpoint of $\overline{CB}$. $\overline{AB} \cong \overline{CB}$
Prove: $\overline{CE} \cong \overline{AD}$

Hint: Use $A(0, 2a)$, $B(0, 0)$, and $C(2a, 0)$.

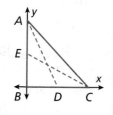

Selected Response

1. What is the equation of the circle with center $(0, 0)$ and radius 10?

   (A) $x^2 + y^2 = 10$

   (B) $x^2 + y^2 = 100$

   (C) $x^2 - y^2 = 100$

   (D) $(x + 10)^2 + (y + 10)^2 = 100$

2. What is the radius of the circle with the equation $(x + 16)^2 + (y - 9)^2 = 25$?

   (F) 3

   (G) 4

   (H) 5

   (J) 25

3. What is the equation of the circle with center $(0, 0)$ and diameter 36?

   (A) $x^2 + y^2 = 18$

   (B) $x^2 + y^2 = 36$

   (C) $x^2 + y^2 = 324$

   (D) $x^2 + y^2 = 1296$

4. What is the center of the circle with the equation $(x + 8)^2 + (y - 3)^2 = 1$?

   (F) $(8, 3)$

   (G) $(8, -3)$

   (H) $(-8, 3)$

   (J) $(-8, -3)$

5. What is the equation of the circle with center $(-5, 2)$ and radius 9?

   (A) $(x^2 - 5) + (y^2 + 2) = 81$

   (B) $(x + 5)^2 - (y - 2)^2 = 81$

   (C) $(x - 5)^2 + (y + 2)^2 = 81$

   (D) $(x + 5)^2 + (y - 2)^2 = 81$

6. The points $(-1, 1)$ and $(3, -5)$ are endpoints of a diameter of a circle. What is the equation of the circle?

   (F) $(x + 1)^2 + (y - 2)^2 = 13$

   (G) $(x - 1)^2 + (y + 2)^2 = 13$

   (H) $(x + 1)^2 + (y - 2)^2 = 26$

   (J) $(x - 1)^2 + (y + 2)^2 = 52$

7. What is the radius of the circle with the equation $x^2 + 6x + y^2 = 16$?

   (A) 4

   (B) 5

   (C) 16

   (D) 25

8. What is the center of the circle with the equation $x^2 + y^2 - 10y = 75$?

   (F) $(0, 5)$

   (G) $(0, -5)$

   (H) $(0, 10)$

   (J) $(0, -10)$

9. The focus of a parabola is $(3, -5)$ and the vertex is $(3, 1)$. What is an equation for the directrix of the parabola?

   (A) $x = 3$

   (B) $y = -11$

   (C) $y = -2$

   (D) $y = 7$

10. What is the focus of the parabola graphed below?

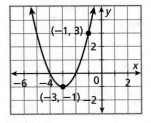

   (F) $(-3, 0.25)$

   (G) $(-3, -0.75)$

   (H) $(-3, -1)$

   (J) $(-3, -1.25)$

11. What is an equation that represents the parabola with directrix $x = -5$ and focus $(5, 0)$?

   (A) $x = -\dfrac{1}{20} y^2$

   (B) $x = \dfrac{1}{20} y^2$

   (C) $y = \dfrac{1}{20} x^2$

   (D) $y = -\dfrac{1}{20} x^2$

12. What is an equation that represents the parabola with directrix $y = 0$ and focus $(0, 12)$?

- Ⓕ $x - 6 = \frac{1}{24}y^2$
- Ⓖ $y - 12 = \frac{1}{48}x^2$
- Ⓗ $y + 6 = \frac{1}{24}x^2$
- Ⓙ $y - 6 = \frac{1}{24}x^2$

13. What are the focus and directrix of the parabola with the equation $y - 15 = \frac{1}{40}(x - 20)^2$?

- Ⓐ focus $(20, 25)$; directrix $y = 5$
- Ⓑ focus $(0, 10)$; directrix $y = -10$
- Ⓒ focus $(-20, -5)$; directrix $y = -25$
- Ⓓ focus $(25, 20)$; directrix $x = 5$

14. $\triangle ABC$ has vertices $A(0, 8)$, $B(8, 9)$, and $C(6, 1)$. Which coordinate proof correctly shows that $\triangle ABC$ is a scalene triangle?

- Ⓕ $AC = \sqrt{(6 - 0)^2 + (1 - 8)^2} = \sqrt{85}$
  $BC = \sqrt{(6 - 8)^2 + (1 - 9)^2} = \sqrt{68}$
  $AB = \sqrt{(8 - 0)^2 + (9 - 8)^2} = \sqrt{65}$

  The sides of the triangle are all of different lengths which means that $\triangle ABC$ is a scalene triangle.

- Ⓖ $AC = \sqrt{(6 - 0)^2 + (1 - 8)^2} = \sqrt{85}$
  $BC = \sqrt{(6 - 8)^2 + (1 - 9)^2} = \sqrt{68}$
  $AB = \sqrt{(8 - 0)^2 + (9 - 8)^2} = \sqrt{65}$

  The sides of the triangle are all of different lengths which means that $\triangle ABC$ is an isosceles triangle.

- Ⓗ $AC = \sqrt{(6 - 0)^2 + (1 - 8)^2} = \sqrt{85}$
  $BC = \sqrt{(6 - 8)^2 + (1 - 9)^2} = \sqrt{68}$

  AC and BC are not equal, which means that $\triangle ABC$ is a scalene triangle.

- Ⓙ $AC = \sqrt{(6 - 0)^2 + (1 - 8)^2} = \sqrt{85}$
  $AB = \sqrt{(8 - 0)^2 + (9 - 8)^2} = \sqrt{65}$

  AC and AB are not equal, which means that $\triangle ABC$ is a scalene triangle.

Mini-Tasks

15. Three friends are planning to visit each other. To optimize travel time, they want the meeting place to be equidistant from the three different cities they live in. The cities are located at $A(-16, -1)$, $B(1, 6)$, and $C(1, -18)$. What are the coordinates where the meeting should take place?

16. Find the missing coordinates for the rhombus.

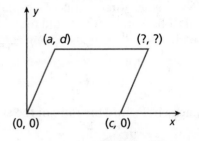

17. A spotlight uses a parabolic reflector, a surface with a parabolic cross section, and a light bulb at the focus of the parabola. If the bulb is 4.5 inches from the vertex reflector, what is the equation of the parabola? Show your work and explain your reasoning.

18. The equation of $\odot C$ is $x^2 + (y + 1)^2 = 25$.

  a. Graph $\odot C$.

  b. Write the equation of the line that is tangent to $\odot C$ at $(3, 3)$. Show your work or explain in words how you determined your answer.

Performance Task

19. Given: $\angle Q$ is a right angle in $\triangle PQR$. S is the midpoint of $\overline{PQ}$ and T is the midpoint of $\overline{RP}$.

  Prove: The area of $\triangle PST$ is one-fourth the area of $\triangle PQR$.

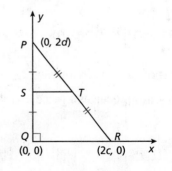

my.hrw.com
Online Assessment
Go online for updated, PARCC-aligned assessment readiness.

Are You Ready?

my.hrw.com
Assessment and Intervention

✓ Tree Diagrams

1. Natalie has three colors of wrapping paper (purple, blue, and yellow) and three colors of ribbon (gold, white, and red). Make a tree diagram showing all possible ways that she can wrap a present using one color of paper and one color of ribbon.

✓ Ratios

For each circle, find the ratio of the shaded area to the entire area.

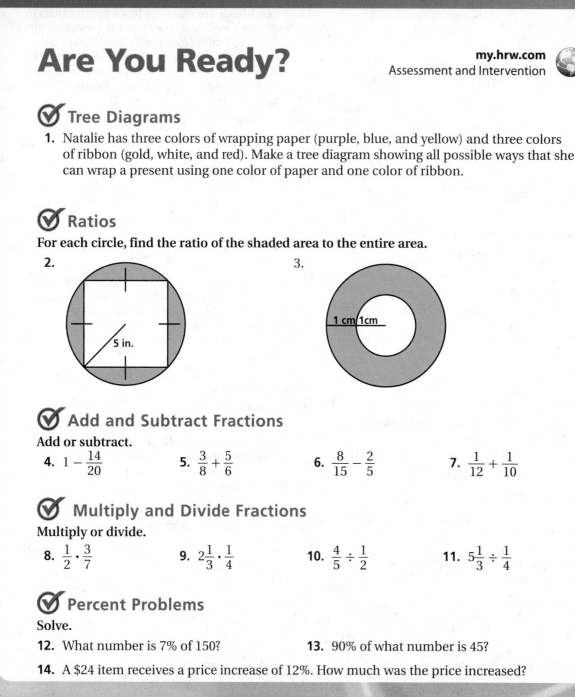

2.

5 in.

3.

1 cm 1cm

✓ Add and Subtract Fractions

Add or subtract.

4. $1 - \dfrac{14}{20}$

5. $\dfrac{3}{8} + \dfrac{5}{6}$

6. $\dfrac{8}{15} - \dfrac{2}{5}$

7. $\dfrac{1}{12} + \dfrac{1}{10}$

✓ Multiply and Divide Fractions

Multiply or divide.

8. $\dfrac{1}{2} \cdot \dfrac{3}{7}$

9. $2\dfrac{1}{3} \cdot \dfrac{1}{4}$

10. $\dfrac{4}{5} \div \dfrac{1}{2}$

11. $5\dfrac{1}{3} \div \dfrac{1}{4}$

✓ Percent Problems

Solve.

12. What number is 7% of 150?

13. 90% of what number is 45?

14. A $24 item receives a price increase of 12%. How much was the price increased?

Career Readiness Political Analyst

Political analysts research political issues and analyze policies. They gather statistical data to investigate how individuals and groups, including governments, make decisions, and they help solve social and governmental problems. They analyze and interpret voting results, and use probability to predict election outcomes. Political analysts must have a college degree. They work for the government, in labor or political organizations, or in media such as newspapers or television.

Conditional Probability

Online Edition

my.hrw.com

Access the complete online textbook, interactive features, and additional resources.

Homework Help

Get instant help with tutorial videos, practice problems, and step-by-step solutions.

TI-Nspire™ Activities

Enhance your learning with cutting edge technology from Texas Instruments.

Portable Devices

On the Spot

Watch video tutorials anywhere, anytime with this app for iPhone® and iPad®.

eTextbook

Access your full textbook on your tablet or e-reader.

Chapter Resources

Scan with your smart phone to jump directly to the online edition.

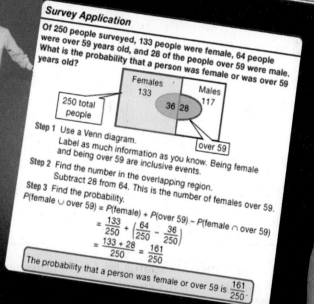

Survey Application

Of 250 people surveyed, 133 people were female, 64 people were over 59 years old, and 28 of the people over 59 were male. What is the probability that a person was female or was over 59 years old?

Females 133   Males 117

250 total people

36   28

over 59

Step 1 Use a Venn diagram.
Label as much information as you know. Being female and being over 59 are inclusive events.

Step 2 Find the number in the overlapping region.
Subtract 28 from 64. This is the number of females over 59.

Step 3 Find the probability.

$$P(\text{female} \cup \text{over } 59) = P(\text{female}) + P(\text{over } 59) - P(\text{female} \cap \text{over } 59)$$

$$= \frac{133}{250} + \left(\frac{64}{250} - \frac{36}{250} \right)$$

$$= \frac{133 + 28}{250} = \frac{161}{250}$$

The probability that a person was female or over 59 is $\frac{161}{250}$.

Use **On the Spot** videos to learn about conditional probability.

Probability

COMMON
CORE GPS

Contents

MATHEMATICAL PRACTICES   The Common Core Georgia Performance Standards for Mathematical Practice describe varieties of expertise that all students should seek to develop. Opportunities to develop these practices are integrated throughout this program.

1 Make sense of problems and persevere in solving them.

2 Reason abstractly and quantitatively.

3 Construct viable arguments and critique the reasoning of others.

4 Model with mathematics.

5 Use appropriate tools strategically.

6 Attend to precision.

7 Look for and make use of structure.

8 Look for and express regularity in repeated reasoning.

Unpacking the Standards

Understanding the standards and the vocabulary terms in the standards will help you know exactly what you are expected to learn in this chapter.

 COMMON CORE GPS **MCC9-12.S.CP.9(+)**

Use permutations and combinations to compute probabilities of compound events and solve problems.

Key Vocabulary

permutation (permutación)
An arrangement of a group of objects in which order is important. The number of permutations of r objects from a group of n objects is denoted $_nP_r$.

combination (combinación)
A selection of a group of objects in which order is *not* important. The number of combinations of r objects chosen from a group of n objects is denoted $_nC_r$.

probability (probabilidad) A number from 0 to 1 (or 0% to 100%) that is the measure of how likely an event is to occur.

event (suceso) An outcome or set of outcomes in a probability experiment.

compound event (suceso compuesto)
An event made up of two or more simple events.

What It Means For You

A permutation is an arrangement of objects in which order is important. A combination is an arrangement of objects in which order is not important. Both permutations and combinations can be used to find probabilities.

EXAMPLE   **Permutations**

Lindsey will choose two of these pictures to hang next to each other on her bedroom wall.

This is an example of a permutation because the order is important. Hanging the mountain picture to the right of the sunset picture is different from hanging the mountain picture to the left of the sunset picture.

EXAMPLE   **Combinations**

You can choose three toppings for your hamburger.

This is an example of a combination because the order is not important. Tomato, onions, and pickles is the same as pickles, tomato, and onions.

18-1 Geometric Probability

Essential Question: How can some probability problems be modeled by using geometry?

Objectives
Calculate geometric probabilities.

Use geometric probability to predict results in real-world situations.

Vocabulary
geometric probability

Why learn this?

You can use geometric probability to estimate how long you may have to wait to cross a street. (See Example 2.)

Remember that in probability, the set of all possible outcomes of an experiment is called the *sample space*. Any set of outcomes is called an *event*.

If every outcome in the sample space is equally likely, the *theoretical probability* of an event is

$$P = \frac{\text{number of outcomes in the event}}{\text{number of outcomes in the sample space}}.$$

Geometric probability is used when an experiment has an infinite number of outcomes. In **geometric probability**, the probability of an event is based on a ratio of geometric measures such as length or area. The outcomes of an experiment may be points on a segment or in a plane figure. Three models for geometric probability are shown below.

Know it!
Note

Geometric Probability			
Model	**Length**	**Angle Measure**	**Area**
Example	A B C D		
Sample space	All points on $\overline{AD}$	All points in the circle	All points in the rectangle
Event	All points on $\overline{BC}$	All points in the shaded region	All points in the triangle
Probability	$P = \dfrac{BC}{AD}$	$P = \dfrac{\text{measure of angle}}{360°}$	$P = \dfrac{\text{area of triangle}}{\text{area of rectangle}}$

COMMON CORE GPS
MCC9-12.S.CP.1

EXAMPLE 1

Using Length to Find Geometric Probability

A point is chosen randomly on $\overline{AD}$. Find the probability of each event.

A The point is on $\overline{AC}$.

$P = \dfrac{AC}{AD} = \dfrac{7}{12}$

A   4   B   3 C   5   D

my.hrw.com

Online Video Tutor

B The point is not on $\overline{AB}$.

First find the probability that the point is on $\overline{AB}$.

$P(\overline{AB}) = \dfrac{AB}{AD} = \dfrac{4}{12} = \dfrac{1}{3}$

Subtract from 1 to find the probability that the point is not on $\overline{AB}$.

$P(\text{not on } \overline{AB}) = 1 - \dfrac{1}{3} = \dfrac{2}{3}$

A point is chosen randomly on $\overline{AD}$.
Find the probability of each event.

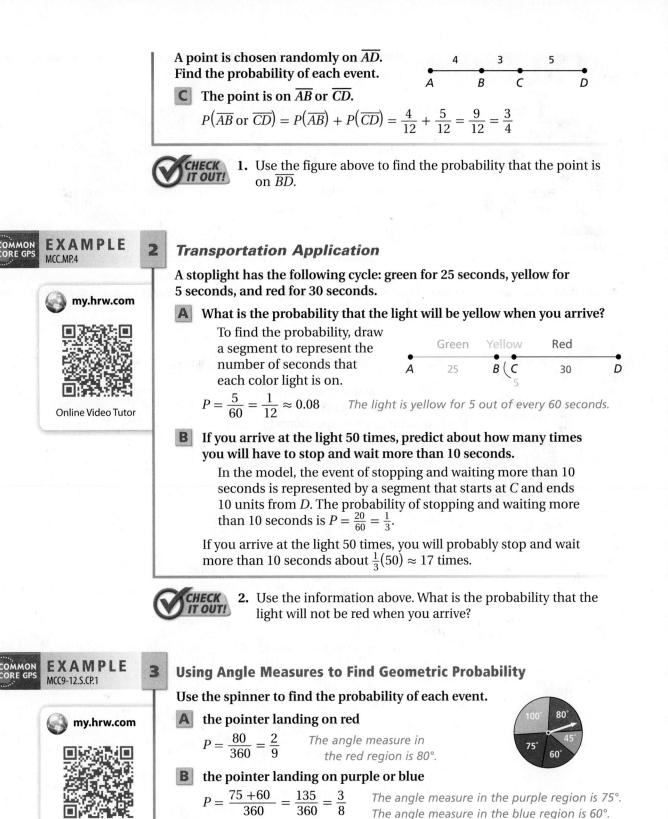

C The point is on $\overline{AB}$ or $\overline{CD}$.

$$P(\overline{AB} \text{ or } \overline{CD}) = P(\overline{AB}) + P(\overline{CD}) = \frac{4}{12} + \frac{5}{12} = \frac{9}{12} = \frac{3}{4}$$

CHECK IT OUT! **1.** Use the figure above to find the probability that the point is on $\overline{BD}$.

COMMON CORE GPS
MCC.MP.4

EXAMPLE **2**

Transportation Application

A stoplight has the following cycle: green for 25 seconds, yellow for 5 seconds, and red for 30 seconds.

my.hrw.com

Online Video Tutor

A What is the probability that the light will be yellow when you arrive?

To find the probability, draw a segment to represent the number of seconds that each color light is on.

$$P = \frac{5}{60} = \frac{1}{12} \approx 0.08$$ *The light is yellow for 5 out of every 60 seconds.*

B If you arrive at the light 50 times, predict about how many times you will have to stop and wait more than 10 seconds.

In the model, the event of stopping and waiting more than 10 seconds is represented by a segment that starts at C and ends 10 units from D. The probability of stopping and waiting more than 10 seconds is $P = \frac{20}{60} = \frac{1}{3}$.

If you arrive at the light 50 times, you will probably stop and wait more than 10 seconds about $\frac{1}{3}(50) \approx 17$ times.

CHECK IT OUT! **2.** Use the information above. What is the probability that the light will not be red when you arrive?

COMMON CORE GPS
MCC9-12.S.CP.1

EXAMPLE **3**

Using Angle Measures to Find Geometric Probability

Use the spinner to find the probability of each event.

my.hrw.com

Online Video Tutor

A the pointer landing on red

$$P = \frac{80}{360} = \frac{2}{9}$$ *The angle measure in the red region is 80°.*

B the pointer landing on purple or blue

$$P = \frac{75 + 60}{360} = \frac{135}{360} = \frac{3}{8}$$ *The angle measure in the purple region is 75°. The angle measure in the blue region is 60°.*

C the pointer not landing on yellow

$$P = \frac{360 - 100}{360}$$ *The angle measure in the yellow region is 100°. Substract this angle measure from 360°.*

$$= \frac{260}{360} = \frac{13}{18}$$

Helpful Hint

In Example 3C, you can also find the probability of the pointer landing on yellow, and subtract from 1.

CHECK IT OUT! **3.** Use the spinner above to find the probability of the pointer landing on red or yellow.

Geometric Probability

I like to write a probability as a percent to see if my answer is reasonable.

The probability of the pointer landing on red is $\frac{80°}{360°} = \frac{2}{9} \approx 22\%$.

The angle measure is close to $90°$, which is 25% of the circle, so the answer is reasonable.

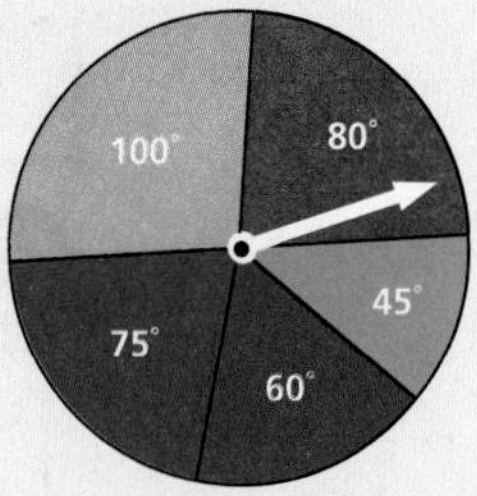

Jeremy Denton
Memorial High
School

COMMON
CORE GPS

EXAMPLE **4**
MCC9-12.G.MG.1

my.hrw.com

Online Video Tutor

Using Area to Find Geometric Probability

Find the probability that a point chosen randomly inside the rectangle is in each given shape. Round to the nearest hundredth.

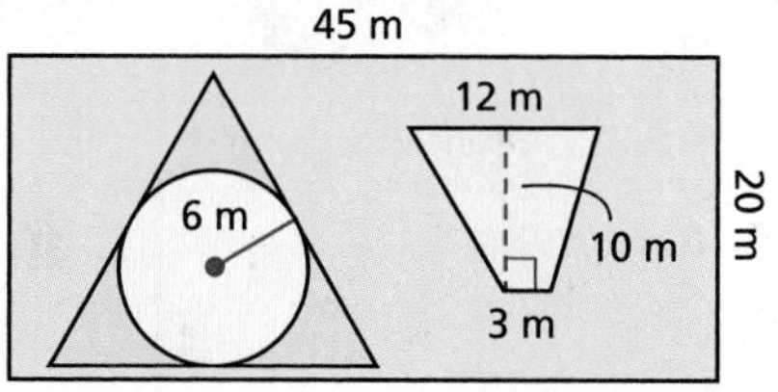

A **the equilateral triangle**

The area of the triangle is $A = \frac{1}{2}aP$

$$= \frac{1}{2}(6)\left(36\sqrt{3}\right) \approx 187 \text{ m}^2.$$

The area of the rectangle is $A = bh$

$$= 45(20) = 900 \text{ m}^2.$$

The probability is $P = \dfrac{187}{900} \approx 0.21$.

B **the trapezoid**

The area of the trapezoid is $A = \frac{1}{2}\left(b_1 + b_2\right)h$

$$= \frac{1}{2}(3 + 12)(10) = 75 \text{ m}^2.$$

The area of the rectangle is $A = bh$

$$= 45(20) = 900 \text{ m}^2.$$

The probability is $P = \dfrac{75}{900} \approx 0.08$.

C **the circle**

The area of the circle is $A = \pi r^2$

$$= \pi\left(6^2\right) = 36\pi \approx 113.1 \text{ m}^2.$$

The area of the rectangle is $A = bh$

$$= 45(20) = 900 \text{ m}^2.$$

The probability is $P = \dfrac{113.1}{900} \approx 0.13$.

CHECK
IT OUT!

4. Use the diagram above. Find the probability that a point chosen randomly inside the rectangle is not inside the triangle, circle, or trapezoid. Round to the nearest hundredth.

Warren Morgan/CORBIS

THINK AND DISCUSS

1. Explain why the ratio used in theoretical probability cannot be used to find geometric probability.

2. A spinner is one-half red and one-third blue, and the rest is yellow. How would you find the probability of the pointer landing on yellow?

3. **GET ORGANIZED** Copy and complete the graphic organizer. In each box, give an example of the geometric probability model.

Know it! Note

Geometric Probability
- Length model
- Angle measure model
- Area model

18-1 Exercises

GUIDED PRACTICE

1. **Vocabulary** Give an example of a model used to find *geometric probability*.

SEE EXAMPLE **1** A point is chosen randomly on $\overline{WZ}$. Find the probability of each event.

```
   2      5      3
W    X         Y    Z
```

   2. The point is on $\overline{XZ}$.

   3. The point is not on $\overline{XY}$.

   4. The point is on $\overline{WX}$ or $\overline{YZ}$.

   5. The point is on $\overline{WY}$.

SEE EXAMPLE **2** **Transportation** A bus comes to a station once every 10 minutes and waits at the station for 1.5 minutes.

   6. Find the probability that the bus will be at the station when you arrive.

   7. If you go to the station 20 times, predict about how many times you will have to wait less than 3 minutes.

SEE EXAMPLE **3** Use the spinner to find the probability of each event.

   8. the pointer landing on green

   9. the pointer landing on orange or blue

  10. the pointer not landing on red

  11. the pointer landing on yellow or blue

SEE EXAMPLE **4** **Multi-Step** Find the probability that a point chosen randomly inside the rectangle is in each shape. Round to the nearest hundredth.

  12. the triangle

  13. the trapezoid

  14. the square

  15. the part of the rectangle that does not include the square, triangle, or trapezoid

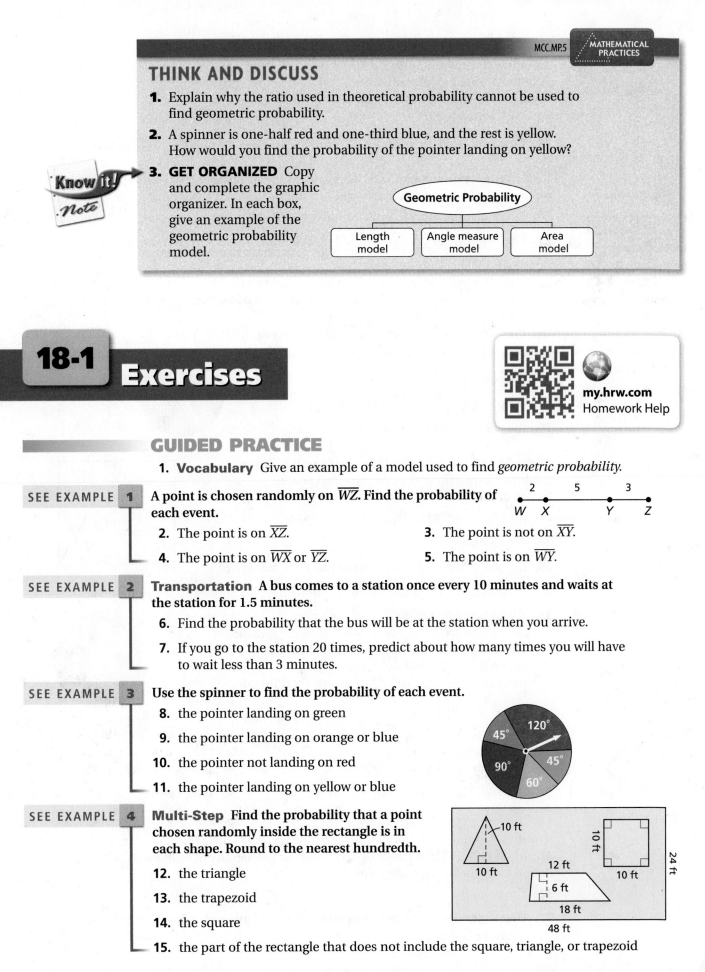

PRACTICE AND PROBLEM SOLVING

Independent Practice

For Exercises	See Example
16–19	1
20–22	2
23–26	3
27–30	4

A point is chosen randomly on $\overline{HM}$. Find the probability of each event. Round to the nearest hundredth.

16. The point is on $\overline{JK}$.

17. The point is not on $\overline{LM}$.

18. The point is on $\overline{HJ}$ or $\overline{KL}$.

19. The point is not on $\overline{JK}$ or $\overline{LM}$.

Communications A radio station gives a weather report every 15 minutes. Each report lasts 45 seconds. Suppose you turn on the radio at a random time.

20. Find the probability that the weather report will be on when you turn on the radio.

21. Find the probability that you will have to wait more than 5 minutes to hear the weather report.

22. If you turn on the radio at 50 random times, predict about how many times you will have to wait less than 1 minute before the start of the next weather report.

Use the spinner to find the probability of each event.

23. the pointer landing on red

24. the pointer landing on yellow or blue

25. the pointer not landing on green

26. the pointer landing on red or green

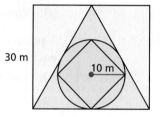

Multi-Step Find the probability that a point chosen randomly inside the rectangle is in each shape. Round to the nearest hundredth, if necessary.

27. the equilateral triangle

28. the square

29. the part of the circle that does not include the square

30. the part of the rectangle that does not include the square, circle, or triangle

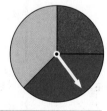

31. **/// ERROR ANALYSIS ///** In the spinner at right, the angle measure of the red region is 90°. The angle measure of the yellow region is 135°, and the angle measure of the blue region is 135°. Which value of the probability of the spinner landing on yellow is incorrect? Explain.

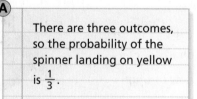

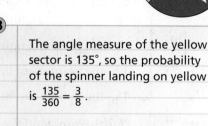

A There are three outcomes, so the probability of the spinner landing on yellow is $\frac{1}{3}$.

B The angle measure of the yellow sector is 135°, so the probability of the spinner landing on yellow is $\frac{135}{360} = \frac{3}{8}$.

Algebra A point is chosen randomly inside rectangle $ABCD$ with vertices $A(2, 8)$, $B(15, 8)$, $C(15, 1)$, and $D(2, 1)$. Find the probability of each event. Round to the nearest hundredth.

32. The point lies in $\triangle KLM$ with vertices $K(4, 3)$, $L(5, 7)$, and $M(9, 5)$.

33. The point does not lie in $\odot P$ with center $P(2, 5)$ and radius 3. (*Hint:* draw the rectangle and circle.)

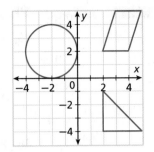

Algebra A point is chosen at random in the coordinate plane such that $-5 \le x \le 5$ and $-5 \le y \le 5$. Find the probability of each event. Round to the nearest hundredth.

34. The point is inside the parallelogram.

35. The point is inside the circle.

36. The point is inside the triangle or the circle.

37. The point is not inside the triangle, the parallelogram, or the circle.

38. **Sports** The point value of each region of an Olympic archery target is shown in the diagram. The outer diameter of each ring is 12.2 cm greater than the inner diameter.

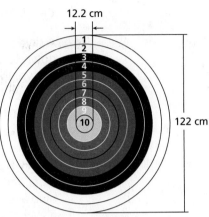

12.2 cm

122 cm

a. What is the probability of hitting the center?

b. What is the probability of hitting a blue or black ring?

c. What is the probability of scoring higher than five points?

d. **Write About It** In an actual event, why might the probabilities be different from those you calculated in parts **a**, **b**, and **c**?

A point is chosen randomly in each figure. Describe an event with a probability of $\frac{1}{2}$.

39.

A   B   C   D   E

40.

41.

42. If a fly lands randomly on the tangram, what is the probability that it will land on each of the following pieces?

a. the blue parallelogram

b. the medium purple triangle

c. the large yellow triangle

d. **Write About It** Do the probabilities change if you arrange the tangram pieces differently? Explain.

H.O.T. **43.** **Critical Thinking** If a rectangle is divided into 8 congruent regions and 4 of them are shaded, what is the probability that you will randomly pick a point in the shaded area? Does it matter which four regions are shaded? Explain.

44. A carnival game board consists of balloons that are 3 inches in diameter and are attached to a rectangular board. A player who throws a dart at the board wins a prize if the dart pops a balloon.

50 in.

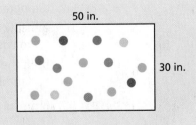

30 in.

a. Find the probability of winning if there are 40 balloons on the board.

b. How many balloons must be on the board for the probability of winning to be at least 0.25?

TEST PREP

45. What is the probability that a ball thrown randomly at the backboard of the basketball goal will hit the inside rectangle?

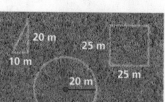

Ⓐ 0.14   Ⓒ 0.26

Ⓑ 0.21   Ⓓ 0.27

46. Point *B* is between *A* and *C*. If *AB* = 18 inches and *BC* = 24 inches, what is the probability that a point chosen at random is on $\overline{AB}$?

Ⓕ 0.18   Ⓖ 0.43   Ⓗ 0.57   Ⓙ 0.75

47. A skydiver jumps from an airplane and parachutes down to the 70-by-100-meter rectangular field shown. What is the probability that he will miss all three targets?

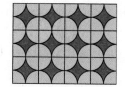

Ⓐ 0.014   Ⓒ 0.089

Ⓑ 0.180   Ⓓ 0.717

48. Short Response A spinner is divided into 12 congruent regions, colored red, blue, and green. Landing on red is twice as likely as landing on blue. Landing on blue and landing on green are equally likely.

   a. What is the probability of landing on green? Show your work or explain in words how you got your answer.

   b. How many regions of the spinner are colored green? Explain your reasoning.

CHALLENGE AND EXTEND

H.O.T. 49. If you randomly choose a point on the grid, what is the probability that it will be in a red region?

H.O.T. 50. You are designing a target that is a square inside an 18 ft by 24 ft rectangle. What size should the square be in order for the target to have a probability of $\frac{1}{3}$? to have a probability of $\frac{3}{4}$?

H.O.T. 51. Recreation How would you design a spinner so that 1 point is earned for landing on yellow, 3 points for landing on blue and 6 points for landing on red? Explain.

FOCUS ON MATHEMATICAL PRACTICES

H.O.T. 52. Problem Solving A person playing a target game must toss a circular chip, with diameter 3 inches, so that it lands entirely within the inner circle of a larger circular target. The circular target has a diameter of 36 inches. The inner circle has a diameter of 12 inches.

   a. How far from the center of the target must the center of the chip land in order to win the game?

   b. If the center of the chip lands on the target, find the probability of it landing entirely within the inner circle.

H.O.T. 53. Number Sense Points *B* and *C* lie on a measuring stick with endpoints *A* and *D*. If a fly lands at random on the stick, the probability of landing on $\overline{AC}$ is 0.8, and the probability of landing on $\overline{BC}$ is 0.5.

   a. What is the probability of landing on $\overline{AB}$? Explain.

   b. What is the probability of landing on $\overline{CD}$? Explain.

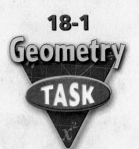

18-1
Geometry TASK

Use Geometric Probability to Estimate π

In this task, you will use geometric probability to estimate π. The squares in the grid below are the same width as the diameter of a penny: 0.75 in., or 19.05 mm.

Use with Geometric Probability

 **Model with mathematics.**

Activity

1 Toss a penny onto the grid 20 times. Let x represent the number of times the penny lands touching or covering an intersection of two grid lines.

2 Estimate π using the formula $\pi \approx 4 \cdot \dfrac{x}{20}$.

Try This

1. How close is your result to π? Average the results of the entire class to get a more accurate estimate.

2. In order for a penny to touch or cover an intersection, the center of the penny can land anywhere in the shaded area.

   a. Find the area of the shaded region. (*Hint:* Each corner part is one fourth of the circle. Put the four corner parts together to form a circle with radius r.)

   b. Find the area of the square.

   c. Write the expressions as a ratio and simplify to determine the probability of the center of the penny landing in the shaded area.

3. Explain why the formula in the activity can be used to estimate π.

18-2 Permutations and Combinations

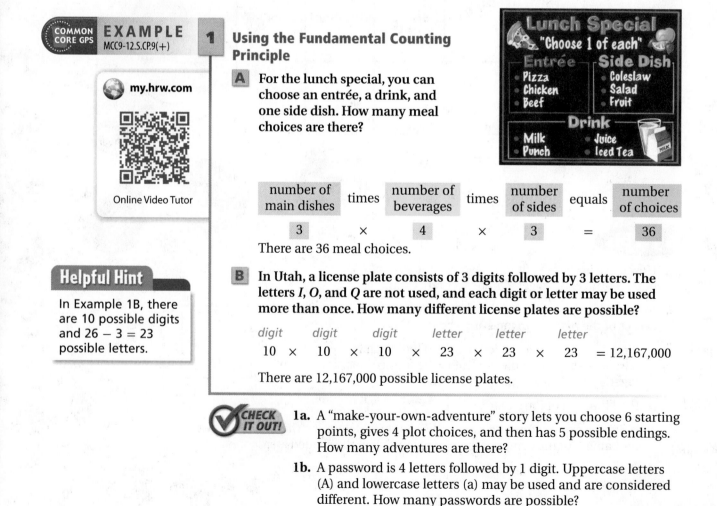

Essential Question: How many ways can you select items from a group of objects if order is important or order is not important?

Objectives
Solve problems involving the Fundamental Counting Principle.

Solve problems involving permutations and combinations.

Vocabulary
Fundamental Counting Principle
permutation
factorial
combination

Why learn this?

Permutations can be used to determine the number of ways to select and arrange artwork so as to give a new look each day. (See Example 2B.)

You have previously used tree diagrams to find the number of possible combinations of a group of objects. In this lesson, you will learn to use the **Fundamental Counting Principle**.

Fundamental Counting Principle

Know it! Note

If there are n items and m_1 ways to choose a first item, m_2 ways to choose a second item after the first item has been chosen, and so on, then there are $m_1 \cdot m_2 \cdot \ldots \cdot m_n$ ways to choose n items.

COMMON CORE GPS
MCC9-12.S.CP.9(+)

EXAMPLE 1 Using the Fundamental Counting Principle

my.hrw.com

Online Video Tutor

A For the lunch special, you can choose an entrée, a drink, and one side dish. How many meal choices are there?

number of main dishes	times	number of beverages	times	number of sides	equals	number of choices
3	×	4	×	3	=	36

There are 36 meal choices.

Helpful Hint

In Example 1B, there are 10 possible digits and 26 − 3 = 23 possible letters.

B In Utah, a license plate consists of 3 digits followed by 3 letters. The letters I, O, and Q are not used, and each digit or letter may be used more than once. How many different license plates are possible?

digit		digit		digit		letter		letter		letter		
10	×	10	×	10	×	23	×	23	×	23	=	12,167,000

There are 12,167,000 possible license plates.

CHECK IT OUT!

1a. A "make-your-own-adventure" story lets you choose 6 starting points, gives 4 plot choices, and then has 5 possible endings. How many adventures are there?

1b. A password is 4 letters followed by 1 digit. Uppercase letters (A) and lowercase letters (a) may be used and are considered different. How many passwords are possible?

Sam Dudgeon/HMH/Artwork by Teri Jonas, Courtesy Wally Workman Gallery, Austin, TX

A **permutation** is a selection of a group of objects in which order is important.

There is one way to arrange one item A.

A second item B can be placed first or second.

A third item C can be first, second, or third for each order above.

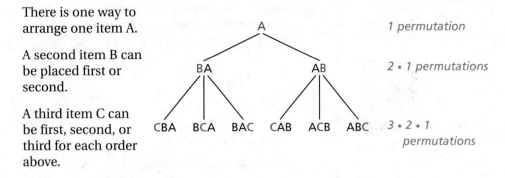

1 permutation

2 · 1 permutations

3 · 2 · 1 permutations

You can see that the number of permutations of 3 items is 3 · 2 · 1. You can extend this to permutations of n items, which is $n \cdot (n-1) \cdot (n-2) \cdot (n-3) \cdot \ldots \cdot 1$. This expression is called n *factorial*, and is written as $n!$.

n Factorial

For any whole number *n*,

WORDS	NUMBERS	ALGEBRA
The **factorial** of a number is the product of the natural numbers less than or equal to the number. 0! is defined as 1.	$6! =$ $6 \cdot 5 \cdot 4 \cdot 3 \cdot 2 \cdot 1 = 720$	$n! =$ $n \cdot (n-1) \cdot (n-2) \cdot (n-3) \cdot \ldots \cdot 1$

Sometimes you may not want to order an entire set of items. Suppose that you want to select and order 3 people from a group of 7. One way to find possible permutations is to use the Fundamental Counting Principle.

First Person   Second Person   Third Person   *There are 7 people. You are choosing 3 of them in order.*

7 choices · 6 choices · 5 choices = 210 permutations

Another way to find the possible permutations is to use factorials. You can divide the total number of arrangements by the number of arrangements that are not used. In the example above, there are 7 total people and 4 whose arrangements do not matter.

$$\frac{\text{arrangements of 7 people}}{\text{arrangements of 4 people}} = \frac{7!}{4!} = \frac{7 \cdot 6 \cdot 5 \cdot \cancel{4} \cdot \cancel{3} \cdot \cancel{2} \cdot \cancel{1}}{\cancel{4} \cdot \cancel{3} \cdot \cancel{2} \cdot \cancel{1}} = 210$$

This can be generalized as a formula, which is useful for large numbers of items.

Permutations

NUMBERS	ALGEBRA
The number of permutations of 7 items taken 3 at a time is $$_7P_3 = \frac{7!}{(7-3)!} = \frac{7!}{4!}.$$	The number of permutations of n items taken r at a time is $$_nP_r = \frac{n!}{(n-r)!}.$$

EXAMPLE 2 Finding Permutations

A How many ways can a club select a president, a vice president, and a secretary from a group of 5 people?

This is the equivalent of selecting and arranging 3 items from 5.

$$_5P_3 = \frac{5!}{(5-3)!} = \frac{5!}{2!}$$ *Substitute 5 for n and 3 for r in $\frac{n!}{(n-r)!}$.*

$$= \frac{5 \cdot 4 \cdot 3 \cdot 2 \cdot 1}{2 \cdot 1}$$ *Divide out common factors.*

$$= 5 \cdot 4 \cdot 3 = 60$$

There are 60 ways to select the 3 people.

Helpful Hint

The number of factors left after dividing is the number of items selected. In Example 2B, there are 4 photographs and 4 factors in $9 \cdot 8 \cdot 7 \cdot 6$.

B An art gallery has 9 fine-art photographs from an artist and will display 4 from left to right along a wall. In how many ways can the gallery select and display the 4 photographs?

$$_9P_4 = \frac{9!}{(9-4)!} = \frac{9!}{5!} = \frac{9 \cdot 8 \cdot 7 \cdot 6 \cdot 5 \cdot 4 \cdot 3 \cdot 2 \cdot 1}{5 \cdot 4 \cdot 3 \cdot 2 \cdot 1}$$ *Divide out common factors.*

$$= 9 \cdot 8 \cdot 7 \cdot 6$$
$$= 3024$$

There are 3024 ways that the gallery can select and display the photographs.

 CHECK IT OUT!

2a. Awards are given out at a costume party. How many ways can "most creative," "silliest," and "best" costume be awarded to 8 contestants if no one gets more than one award?

2b. How many ways can a 2-digit number be formed by using only the digits 5–9 and by each digit being used only once?

A **combination** is a grouping of items in which order does not matter. There are generally fewer ways to select items when order does not matter. For example, there are 6 ways to order 3 items, but they are all the same combination:

6 permutations → {ABC, ACB, BAC, BCA, CAB, CBA}

1 combination   → {ABC}

To find the number of combinations, the formula for permutations can be modified.

$$\frac{\text{number of}}{\text{permutations}} = \frac{\text{ways to arrange all items}}{\text{ways to arrange items not selected}}$$

Because order does not matter, divide the number of permutations by the number of ways to arrange the selected items.

$$\frac{\text{number of}}{\text{combinations}} = \frac{\text{ways to arrange all items}}{(\text{ways to arrange selected items})(\text{ways to arrange items not selected})}$$

Combinations

NUMBERS	ALGEBRA
The number of combinations of 7 items taken 3 at a time is $$_7C_3 = \frac{7!}{3!(7-3)!}.$$	The number of combinations of n items taken r at a time is $$_nC_r = \frac{n!}{r!(n-r)!}.$$

When deciding whether to use permutations or combinations, first decide whether order is important. Use a permutation if order matters and a combination if order does not matter.

COMMON CORE GPS
MCC9-12.S.CP.9(+)

EXAMPLE 3

Pet Adoption Application

my.hrw.com

Online Video Tutor

Katie is going to adopt kittens from a litter of 11. How many ways can she choose a group of 3 kittens?

Step 1 Determine whether the problem represents a permutation or combination.

The order does not matter. The group Kitty, Smoky, and Tigger is the same as Tigger, Kitty, and Smoky. It is a combination.

Step 2 Use the formula for combinations.

$$_{11}C_3 = \frac{11!}{3!(11-3)!} = \frac{11!}{3!(8!)} \quad n = 11 \text{ and } r = 3$$

$$= \frac{11 \cdot 10 \cdot 9 \cdot 8 \cdot 7 \cdot 6 \cdot 5 \cdot 4 \cdot 3 \cdot 2 \cdot 1}{3 \cdot 2 \cdot 1(8 \cdot 7 \cdot 6 \cdot 5 \cdot 4 \cdot 3 \cdot 2 \cdot 1)} \quad \textit{Divide out common factors.}$$

$$= \frac{11 \cdot 10 \cdot 9}{3 \cdot 2 \cdot 1} = \frac{11 \cdot \cancel{10}^5 \cdot \cancel{9}^3}{\cancel{3} \cdot \cancel{2} \cdot 1} = 165$$

There are 165 ways to select a group of 3 kittens from 11.

Helpful Hint

You can find permutations and combinations by using **nPr** and **nCr**, respectively, on scientific and graphing calculators.

CHECK IT OUT!

3. The swim team has 8 swimmers. Two swimmers will be selected to swim in the first heat. How many ways can the swimmers be selected?

MCC.MP.2 | **MATHEMATICAL PRACTICES**

THINK AND DISCUSS

1. Give a situation in which order matters and one in which order does not matter.

2. Give the value of $_nC_n$, where n is any integer. Explain your answer.

3. Tell what $_3C_4$ would mean in the real world and why it is not possible.

4. GET ORGANIZED Copy and complete the graphic organizer.

	Fundamental Counting Principle	Permutation	Combination
Formula			
Examples			

GUIDED PRACTICE

1. **Vocabulary** When you open a rotating combination lock, order is __?__ (*important* or *not important*), so this is a __?__ (*permutation* or *combination*).

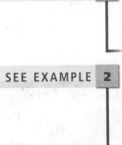

SEE EXAMPLE 1

2. Jamie purchased 3 blouses, 3 jackets, and 2 skirts. How many different outfits using a blouse, a jacket, and a skirt are possible?

3. An Internet code consists of one digit followed by one letter. The number zero and the letter *O* are excluded. How many codes are possible?

SEE EXAMPLE 2

4. Nate is on a 7-day vacation. He plans to spend one day jet skiing and one day golfing. How many ways can Nate schedule the 2 activities?

5. How many ways can you listen to 3 songs from a CD that has 12 selections?

6. Members from 6 different school organizations decorated floats for the homecoming parade. How many different ways can first, second, and third prize be awarded?

SEE EXAMPLE 3

7. A teacher wants to send 4 students to the library each day. There are 21 students in the class. How many ways can he choose 4 students to go to the library on the first day?

8. Gregory has a coupon for $1 off the purchase of 3 boxes of Munchie brand cereal. The store has 5 different varieties of Munchie brand cereal. How many ways can Gregory choose 3 boxes of cereal so that each box is a different variety?

PRACTICE AND PROBLEM SOLVING

Independent Practice

For Exercises	See Example
9–10	1
11–13	2
14	3

my.hrw.com

Online Extra Practice

9. **Hiking** A hiker can take 4 trails to the lake and then 3 trails from the lake to the cabins. How many routes are there from the lake to the cabins?

10. The cheerleading squad is making posters. They have 3 different colors of poster board and 4 different colors of markers. How many different posters can be made by using one poster board and one marker?

11. How many ways can you choose a manager and assistant from a 9-person task force?

12. How many identification codes are possible by using 3 letters if no letter may be repeated?

13. There are 5 airplanes ready to depart. Runway A and runway D are available. How many ways can 2 planes be assigned to runways without using the same runway?

14. **Food** How many choices of 3 hamburger toppings are possible?

15. **What if...?** In the United Kingdom's National Lottery, you must correctly select a group of 6 numbers from 49. Suppose that the contest were changed to selecting 7 numbers. How many more ways would there be to select the numbers?

Evaluate.

16. $_6P_6$

17. $_5C_5$

18. $_9P_1$

19. $_6C_1$

20. $\dfrac{2!}{6!}$

21. $\dfrac{4!3!}{2!}$

22. $\dfrac{9!}{7!}$

23. $\dfrac{8! - 5!}{(8 - 5)!}$

H.O.T. **Geometry** Find the number of ways that each selection can be made.

24. two marked points to determine slope

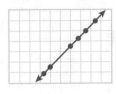

25. four points to form a quadrilateral

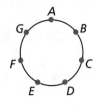

Compare. Write > , < , or = .

26. $_7P_3$ ▨ $_7C_4$ **27.** $_7P_4$ ▨ $_7P_3$ **28.** $_7C_3$ ▨ $_7C_4$ **29.** $_{10}C_{10}$ ▨ $_{10}P_{10}$

30. Copy and complete the table. Use the table to explain why 0! is defined as 1.

$n!$	4!	3!	2!	1!
$n(n-1)!$	$4(3!) = 24$	▨	▨	▨

31. **Critical Thinking** Why are there more unique permutations of the letters in YOUNG than in GEESE?

32. **Music** In change ringing, a *peal* is the ringing of all possible sequences of a number of bells. Suppose that 8 bells are used and it takes 0.25 second to ring each bell. How long would it take to ring a complete peal?

33. **Multi-Step** Amy, Bob, Charles, Dena, and Esther are club officers.

  a. Copy and complete the table to show the ways that a president, a vice president, and a secretary can be chosen if Amy is chosen president. (Use first initials for names.)

President	A	A	A	A	A	A	A	A	A	A	A	A
Vice President	B	B	B	C	C	C	▨	▨	▨	▨	▨	▨
Secretary	C	D	E	▨	▨	▨	▨	▨	▨	▨	▨	▨

  b. Extend the table to show the number of ways that the three officers can be chosen if Bob is chosen president. Make a conjecture as to the number of ways that a president, a vice president, and a secretary can be chosen.

  c. Use a formula to find the number of different ways that a president, a vice president, and a secretary can be chosen. Compare your result with part **b**.

  d. How many different ways can 3 club officers be chosen to form a committee? Compare this with the answer to part **c**. Which answer is a number of permutations? Which answer is a number of combinations?

H.O.T. **34.** **Critical Thinking** Use the formulas to divide $_nP_r$ by $_nC_r$. Predict the result of dividing $_6P_3$ by $_6C_3$. Check your prediction. What meaning does the result have?

H.O.T. **35.** **Write About It** Find $_9C_2$ and $_9C_7$. Find $_{10}C_6$ and $_{10}C_4$. Explain the results.

Real-World Connections

36. While playing the game of Yahtzee, Jen rolls 5 dice and gets the result shown at right.

  a. How many different ways can she arrange the dice from left to right?

  b. How many different ways can she choose 3 of the dice to reroll?

Music

There are many change-ringing societies and groups, especially in the United Kingdom. Bell ringers work together to follow patterns and called changes to avoid repeating sequences.

37. **///ERROR ANALYSIS///** Below are two solutions for "How many Internet codes can be made by using 3 digits if 0 is excluded and digits may not be repeated?" Which is incorrect? Explain the error.

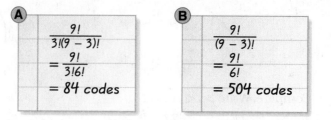

A
$$\frac{9!}{3!(9-3)!}$$
$$= \frac{9!}{3!6!}$$
$$= 84 \text{ codes}$$

B
$$\frac{9!}{(9-3)!}$$
$$= \frac{9!}{6!}$$
$$= 504 \text{ codes}$$

38. **Critical Thinking** Explain how to use the Fundamental Counting Principle to answer the question in Exercise 37.

TEST PREP

39. There are 14 players on the team. Which of the following expressions models the number of ways that the coach can choose 5 players to start the game?

  Ⓐ $5!$ Ⓑ $\dfrac{14!}{5!}$ Ⓒ $\dfrac{14!}{9!}$ Ⓓ $\dfrac{14!}{5!9!}$

40. Which of the following has the same value as $_9C_4$?

  Ⓕ $_9P_4$ Ⓖ $_4C_9$ Ⓗ $_9P_5$ Ⓙ $_9C_5$

41. **Short Response** Rene can choose 1 elective each of the 4 years that she is in high school. There are 15 electives. How many ways can Rene choose her electives?

CHALLENGE AND EXTEND

H.O.T. 42. **Geometry** Consider a circle with two points, A and B. You can form exactly 1 segment, $\overline{AB}$. If there are 3 points, you can form 3 segments as shown in the diagram.

  a. How many segments can be formed from 4 points, 5 points, 6 points, and n points? Write your answer for n points as a permutation or combination.

  b. How many segments can be formed from 20 points?

H.O.T. 43. **Government** How many ways can a jury of 12 and 2 alternate jurors be selected from a pool of 30 potential jurors? (*Hint:* Consider how order is both important and unimportant in selection.) Leave your answer in unexpanded notation.

FOCUS ON MATHEMATICAL PRACTICES

H.O.T. 44. **Comparison** Find the number of 4-letter permutations and 4-letter combinations that can be made from the letters in the word PASTRY. What percent of the number of permutations is the number of combinations?

H.O.T. 45. **Counterexamples** Elliot believes that the number of permutations of a group of items is always greater than the number of combinations of the same group: $_xP_y > _xC_y$ for any whole numbers x and y where $x \geq y$. Find a counterexample to Elliot's conjecture.

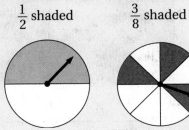

Relative Area

Connecting Geometry to Probability

In *geometric probability*, the probability of an event corresponds to ratios of the areas (or lengths or volumes) or parts of one or more figures.

In the spinners shown, the probability of landing on a color is based on relative area.

$\frac{1}{2}$ shaded $\frac{3}{8}$ shaded $\frac{1}{4}$ shaded

Area Formulas	
Figure	**Formula**
Rectangle	$A = bh$
Square	$A = s^2$
Triangle	$A = \frac{1}{2}bh$
Trapezoid	$A = \frac{1}{2}h(b_1 + b_2)$
Circle	$A = \pi r^2$

Use the area formulas at right to help you determine relative area.

Example

What portion of the rectangle is shaded? Write the relative area as a fraction, a decimal, and a percent.

3 in.
5 in.
10 in.

Find the ratio of the area of the shaded region to the area of the rectangle.

$A = 10(5) = 50$ in^2 *Area of the rectangle: A = bh*

$A = \frac{1}{2}(3)(10) = 15$ in^2 *Area of the unshaded triangle: A = $\frac{1}{2}$bh*

$$\frac{\text{area of shaded region}}{\text{area of the rectangle}} = \frac{50 - 15}{50} = \frac{35}{50} = \frac{7}{10} = 0.7, \text{ or } 70\%$$

Try This

What portion of each figure is shaded? Write the relative area as a fraction, a decimal, and a percent.

1.
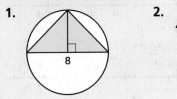
8

2.

4
8

3.

3   3   6

4.
5
3
9

5. Write the relative area of each sector of the spinner as a fraction, decimal, and percent.

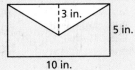

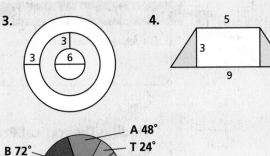

A 48°
T 24°
B 72°
D 96°
G 120°

18-3 Theoretical and Experimental Probability

? **Essential Question:** How can you express and solve problems about probability using ratios?

Objectives
Find the theoretical probability of an event.

Find the experimental probability of an event.

Vocabulary
probability
outcome
sample space
event
equally likely outcomes
favorable outcomes
theoretical probability
complement
geometric probability
experiment
trial
experimental probability

Why learn this?

You can use probability to find the chances of hitting or missing a target in the game Battleship. (See Example 2.)

Probability is the measure of how likely an event is to occur. Each possible result of a probability experiment or situation is an **outcome**. The **sample space** is the set of all possible outcomes. An **event** is an outcome or set of outcomes.

Experiment or Situation	Rolling a number cube	Spinning a spinner
Sample Space	{1, 2, 3, 4, 5, 6}	{red, blue, green, yellow}

Probabilities are written as fractions or decimals from 0 to 1, or as percents from 0% to 100%.

Impossible	As likely as not	Certain
0		1
0%	0.5, $\frac{1}{2}$, 50%	100%

Equally likely outcomes have the same chance of occurring. When you toss a fair coin, heads and tails are equally likely outcomes. **Favorable outcomes** are outcomes in a specified event. For equally likely outcomes, the **theoretical probability** of an event is the ratio of the number of favorable outcomes to the total number of outcomes.

Know it! **Note**

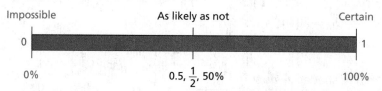

Theoretical Probability

For equally likely outcomes,
$$P(\text{event}) = \frac{\text{number of favorable outcomes}}{\text{number of outcomes in the sample space}}.$$

COMMON CORE GPS MCC9-12.S.CP.1

EXAMPLE 1 **Finding Theoretical Probability**

A A CD has 5 upbeat dance songs and 7 slow ballads. What is the probability that a randomly selected song is an upbeat dance song?

There are 12 possible outcomes and 5 favorable outcomes.

$$P(\text{upbeat dance song}) = \frac{5}{12} \approx 41.7\%$$

B A red number cube and a blue number cube are rolled. If all numbers are equally likely, what is the probability that the sum is 10?

There are 36 possible outcomes.

11	12	13	14	15	16
21	22	23	24	25	26
31	32	33	34	35	36
41	42	43	44	45	4 6
51	52	53	54	5 5	56
61	62	63	6 4	65	66

$$P(\text{sum is } 10) = \frac{\text{number of outcomes with sum of } 10}{36}$$

$$P(\text{sum is } 10) = \frac{3}{36} = \frac{1}{12}$$

3 outcomes with a sum of 10: (4, 6) (5, 5), and (6, 4)

CHECK IT OUT! A red number cube and a blue number cube are rolled. If all numbers are equally likely, what is the probability of each event?

1a. The sum is 6.

1b. The difference is 6.

1c. The red cube is greater.

The sum of all probabilities in the sample space is 1. The **complement** of an event E is the set of all outcomes in the sample space that are not in E.

Know it! Note

Complement

The probability of the complement of event E is

$$P(\text{not } E) = 1 - P(E).$$

EXAMPLE 2

Entertainment Application

The game Battleship is played with 5 ships on a 100-hole grid. Players try to guess the locations of their opponent's ships and sink them. At the start of the game, what is the probability that the first shot misses all targets?

$P(\text{miss}) = 1 - P(\text{hit})$ *Use the complement.*

$P(\text{miss}) = 1 - \dfrac{17}{100}$ *There are 17 total holes covered by game pieces.*

$= \dfrac{83}{100}$, or 83%

There is an 83% chance of the first shot missing all targets.

Battleship Pieces	
Game Piece	**Number of Holes Covered**
Destroyer	2
Cruiser	3
Submarine	3
Battleship	4
Carrier	5

CHECK IT OUT!

2. Two integers from 1 to 10 are randomly selected. The same number may be chosen twice. What is the probability that both numbers are less than 9?

EXAMPLE 3
MCC9-12.S.CP.9(+)

Finding Probability with Permutations or Combinations

Each student received a 4-digit code to use the library computers, with no digit repeated. Manu received the code 7654. What was the probability that he would receive a code of consecutive numbers?

Step 1 Determine whether the code is a permutation or a combination.
Order is important, so it is a permutation.

Step 2 Find the number of outcomes in the sample space.
The sample space is the number of permutations of 4 of 10 digits.

$$_{10}P_4 = \frac{10!}{6!} = \frac{10 \cdot 9 \cdot 8 \cdot 7 \cdot \cancel{6 \cdot 5 \cdot 4 \cdot 3 \cdot 2 \cdot 1}}{\cancel{6 \cdot 5 \cdot 4 \cdot 3 \cdot 2 \cdot 1}} = 5040$$

Step 3 Find the favorable outcomes.
The favorable outcomes are the codes 0123, 1234, 2345, 3456, 4567, 5678, 6789, and the reverse of each of these numbers. There are 14 favorable outcomes.

Step 4 Find the probability.

$$P(\text{consecutive numbers}) = \frac{14}{5040} = \frac{1}{360}$$

The probability that Manu would receive a code of consecutive numbers was $\frac{1}{360}$.

CHECK IT OUT!

3. A DJ randomly selects 2 of 8 ads to play before her show. Two of the ads are by a local retailer. What is the probability that she will play both of the retailer's ads before her show?

Geometric probability is a form of theoretical probability determined by a ratio of lengths, areas, or volumes.

EXAMPLE 4
MCC9-12.G.MG.1

Finding Geometric Probability

Three semicircles with diameters 2, 4, and 6 cm are arranged as shown in the figure. If a point inside the figure is chosen at random, what is the probability that the point is inside the shaded region?

Find the ratio of the area of the shaded region to the area of the entire semicircle. The area of a semicircle is $\frac{1}{2}\pi r^2$.

First, find the area of the entire semicircle.

$$A_t = \frac{1}{2}\pi(3^2) = 4.5\pi \qquad \textit{Total area of largest semicircle}$$

Next, find the unshaded area.

$$A_u = \left[\frac{1}{2}\pi(2^2)\right] + \left[\frac{1}{2}\pi(1^2)\right] = 2\pi + 0.5\pi = 2.5\pi \qquad \textit{Sum of areas of the unshaded semicircles}$$

Subtract to find the shaded area.

$$A_s = 4.5\pi - 2.5\pi = 2\pi \qquad \textit{Area of shaded region}$$

$$\frac{A_s}{A_t} = \frac{2\pi}{4.5\pi} = \frac{2}{4.5} = \frac{4}{9} \qquad \textit{Ratio of shaded region to total area}$$

The probability that the point is in the shaded region is $\frac{4}{9}$.

4. Find the probability that a point chosen at random inside the large triangle is in the small triangle.

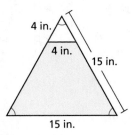

4 in.

4 in.

15 in.

15 in.

You can estimate the probability of an event by using data, or by **experiment** . For example, if a doctor states that an operation "has an 80% probability of success," 80% is an estimate of probability based on similar case histories.

Each repetition of an experiment is a **trial** . The sample space of an experiment is the set of all possible outcomes. The **experimental probability** of an event is the ratio of the number of times that the event occurs, the *frequency*, to the number of trials.

Know it!
Note

Experimental Probability

$$\text{experimental probability} = \frac{\text{number of times the event occurs}}{\text{number of trials}}$$

Experimental probability is often used to estimate theoretical probability and to make predictions.

COMMON CORE GPS

EXAMPLE 5
MCC9-12.S.CP.1

Finding Experimental Probability

The bar graph shows the results of 100 tosses of an oddly shaped number cube. Find each experimental probability.

my.hrw.com

Online Video Tutor

A rolling a 3

The outcome 3 occurred 16 times out of 100 trials.

$$P(3) = \frac{16}{100} = \frac{4}{25} = 0.16$$

B rolling a perfect square

$$P(\text{perfect square}) = \frac{17 + 11}{100}$$

$$= \frac{28}{100} = \frac{7}{25} = 0.28$$

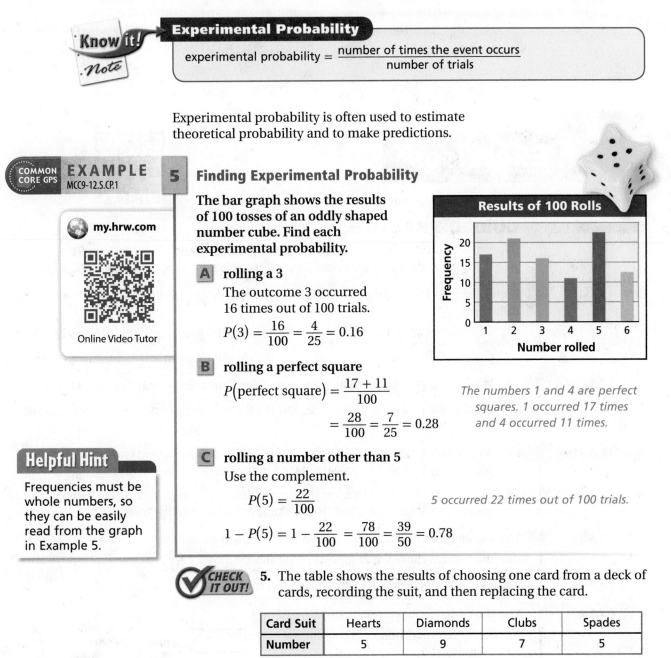

Results of 100 Rolls

The numbers 1 and 4 are perfect squares. 1 occurred 17 times and 4 occurred 11 times.

Helpful Hint

Frequencies must be whole numbers, so they can be easily read from the graph in Example 5.

C rolling a number other than 5

Use the complement.

$$P(5) = \frac{22}{100}$$

5 occurred 22 times out of 100 trials.

$$1 - P(5) = 1 - \frac{22}{100} = \frac{78}{100} = \frac{39}{50} = 0.78$$

CHECK IT OUT!

5. The table shows the results of choosing one card from a deck of cards, recording the suit, and then replacing the card.

Card Suit	Hearts	Diamonds	Clubs	Spades
Number	5	9	7	5

5a. Find the experimental probability of choosing a diamond.

5b. Find the experimental probability of choosing a card that is not a club.

Sam Dudgeon/HMH

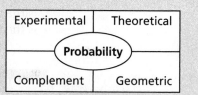

THINK AND DISCUSS

1. Explain whether the probability of an event can be 1.5.

2. Tell which events have the same probability when two number cubes are tossed: sum of 7, sum of 5, sum of 9, and sum of 11.

3. Compare the theoretical and experimental probabilities of getting heads when tossing a coin if Joe got heads 8 times in 20 tosses of the coin.

4. **GET ORGANIZED** Copy and complete the graphic organizer. Give an example of each probability concept.

Experimental	Theoretical
Probability	
Complement	Geometric

18-3 Exercises

my.hrw.com
Homework Help

GUIDED PRACTICE

1. **Vocabulary** A fair coin is tossed 8 times and lands heads up 3 times. The __?__ of landing heads is $\frac{1}{2}$. (*theoretical probability* or *experimental probability*)

SEE EXAMPLE 1 **A quarter, a nickel, and a penny are flipped. Find the probability of each of the following.**

2. The quarter shows heads.

3. The penny and nickel show heads.

4. One coin shows heads.

5. All three coins land the same way.

SEE EXAMPLE 2

6. What is the probability that a random 2-digit number (00-99) does not end in 5?

7. What is the probability that a randomly selected date in one year is not in the month of December or January?

SEE EXAMPLE 3

8. A clerk has 4 different letters that need to go in 4 different envelopes. What is the probability that all 4 letters are placed in the correct envelopes?

9. There are 12 balloons in a bag: 3 each of blue, green, red, and yellow. Three balloons are chosen at random. Find the probability that all 3 of the balloons are green.

SEE EXAMPLE 4 **Use the diagram for Exercises 10 and 11. Find each probability.**

10. that a point chosen at random is in the shaded area

11. that a point chosen at random is in the smallest circle

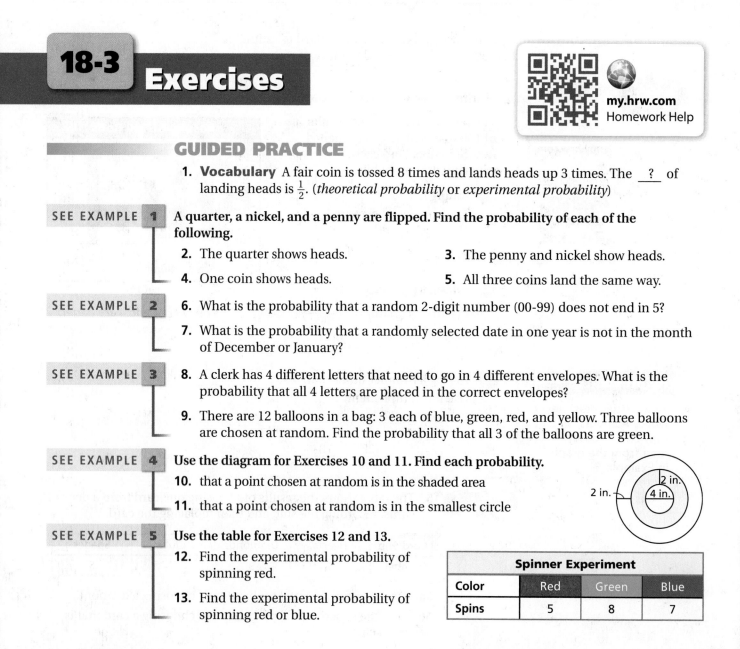

2 in.

2 in.

4 in.

SEE EXAMPLE 5 **Use the table for Exercises 12 and 13.**

12. Find the experimental probability of spinning red.

13. Find the experimental probability of spinning red or blue.

Spinner Experiment			
Color	Red	Green	Blue
Spins	5	8	7

PRACTICE AND PROBLEM SOLVING

my.hrw.com

Online Extra Practice

There are 3 green marbles, 7 red marbles, and 5 white marbles in a bag. Find the probability of each of the following.

14. The chosen marble is white.

15. The chosen marble is red or white.

16. Two integers from 1 to 8 are randomly selected. The same number can be chosen both times. What is the probability that both numbers are greater than 2?

17. Swimming The coach randomly selects 3 swimmers from a team of 8 to swim in a heat. What is the probability that she will choose the three strongest swimmers?

18. Books There are 7 books numbered 1–7 on the summer reading list. Peter randomly chooses 2 books. What is the probability that Peter chooses books numbered 1 and 2?

19. Games In the game of corntoss, players throw corn-filled bags at a hole in a wooden platform. If a bag that hits the platform can hit any location with an equal likelihood, find the probability that a tossed bag lands in the hole.

20. Cards An experiment consists of choosing one card from a standard deck and then replacing it. The experiment was done several times, and the results are: 8 hearts, 8 diamonds, 6 spades, and 6 clubs. Find the experimental probability that a card is red.

21. Critical Thinking Explain whether the experimental probability of tossing tails when a fair coin is tossed 25 times is always, sometimes, or never equal to the theoretical probability.

22. Games A radio station in Mississippi is giving away a trip to the Mississippi coast from any other state in the United States. Assuming an equally likely chance for a winner from any other state, what is the probability that the winner will be from a state that does not border Mississippi?

H.O.T. 23. Geometry Use the figure.

   a. A circle with radius r is inscribed in a square with side length $2r$. What is the ratio of the area of the circle to the area of the square?

   b. A square board has an inscribed circle with a 15 in. radius. A small button is dropped 10,000 times on the board, landing inside the circle 7852 times. How can you use this experiment to estimate a value for π?

H.O.T. 24. Games The sides of a backgammon die are marked with the numbers 2, 4, 8, 16, 32, and 64. Describe an outcome that has a probability of $\frac{2}{3}$.

25. Computer A player in a computer basketball program has a constant probability of making each free throw. Jack notes the success rate over a period of time.

   a. Find the experimental probability for each set of 25 attempts as a decimal.

   b. Find the experimental probability for the entire experiment.

   c. What is the best estimate of the theoretical probability? Justify your answer.

Free Throw Shooting	
Attempts	Free Throws Made
1–25	17
26–50	21
51–75	19
76–100	16

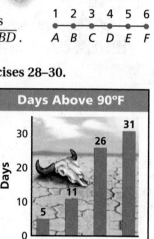

26. While playing Yahtzee and rolling 5 dice, Mei gets the result shown at right. Mei decides to keep the three 4's and reroll the other 2 dice.

   a. What is the probability that Mei will have 5 of a kind?

   b. What is the probability that she will have 4 of a kind (four 4's plus something else)?

   c. What is the probability that she will have exactly three 4's?

   d. How are the answers to parts **a, b,** and **c** related?

27. **Geometry** The points along $\overline{AF}$ are evenly spaced. A point is randomly chosen. Find the probability that the point lies on $\overline{BD}$.

$$\begin{array}{cccccc} 1 & 2 & 3 & 4 & 5 & 6 \\ \bullet & \bullet & \bullet & \bullet & \bullet & \bullet \\ A & B & C & D & E & F \end{array}$$

H.O.T. **Weather** Use the graph and the following information for Exercises 28–30.

The table shows the number of days that the maximum temperature was above 90°F in Death Valley National Park in 2002.

28. What is the experimental probability that the maximum temperature will be greater than 90°F on a given day in April?

29. For what month would you estimate the theoretical probability of a maximum temperature no greater than 90°F to be about 0.13? Explain.

30. May has 31 days. How would the experimental probability be affected if someone mistakenly used 30 days to calculate the experimental probability that the maximum temperature will not be greater than 90°F on a given day in May?

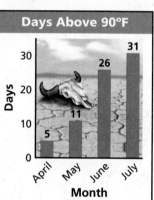

Days Above 90°F

H.O.T. 31. **Critical Thinking** Is it possible for the experimental probability of an event to be 0 if the theoretical probability is 1? Is it possible for the experimental probability of an event to be 0 if the theoretical probability is 0.99? Explain.

32 **Geometry** The two circles circumscribe and inscribe the square. Find the probability that a random point in the large circle is within the inner circle. (*Hint:* Use the Pythagorean Theorem.)

33. **Critical Thinking** Lexi tossed a fair coin 20 times, resulting in 12 heads and 8 tails. What is the theoretical probability that Lexi will get heads on the next toss? Explain.

34. **Athletics** Do male or female high school basketball players have a better chance of playing on college teams? on professional teams? Explain.

35. **Write About It** Describe the difference between theoretical probability and experimental probability. Give an example in which they may differ.

U.S. Basketball Players		
	Men	**Women**
High School Players	549,500	456,900
College Players	4,500	4,100
College Players Drafted by Pro Leagues	44	32

Source: www.ncaa.org

Sam Dudgeon/HMH

36. A fair coin is tossed 25 times, landing tails up 14 times. What is the experimental probability of heads?

Ⓐ 0.44   Ⓑ 0.50   Ⓒ 0.56   Ⓓ 0.79

37. Geometry Find the probability that a point chosen at random in the large rectangle at right will lie in the shaded area, to the nearest percent.

Ⓕ 18%   Ⓖ 45%   Ⓗ 55%   Ⓙ 71%

38. How many outcomes are in the sample space when a quarter, a dime, and a nickel are tossed?

Ⓐ 3   Ⓑ 6   Ⓒ 8   Ⓓ 12

39. Two number cubes are rolled. What is the theoretical probability that the sum is 5?

Ⓕ $\frac{1}{3}$ Ⓖ $\frac{1}{6}$ Ⓗ $\frac{1}{9}$ Ⓙ $\frac{1}{12}$

40. Short Response Find the probability that a point chosen at random on the part of the number line shown will lie between points *B* and *C*.

CHALLENGE AND EXTEND

41. The graph illustrates a statistical property known as the *law of large numbers*. Make a conjecture about the effect on probability as the number of trials gets very large. Give an example of how the probability might be affected for a real-world situation.

42. Four trumpet players' instruments are mixed up, and the trumpets are given to the players just before a concert. What is the probability that *no one* gets his or her trumpet back?

H.O.T. **43.** The table shows the data from a spinner experiment. Draw a reasonable spinner with 6 regions that may have been used for this experiment.

Spinner Experiment			
Color	Red	Blue	Green	Yellow
Occurrences	23	44	7	26

FOCUS ON MATHEMATICAL PRACTICES

H.O.T. **44. Problem Solving** Yves throws a dart at the target shown. The small circles all have the same radius, and the large circle's radius is three times as large. Yves has a 25% chance of missing the target, and he is as likely to hit one spot on the target as any other. What is the probability that Yves hits one of the small circles?

H.O.T. **45. Number Sense** Farouk rolls a number cube 200 times. He rolls a one 25 times, a two 27 times, a three 26 times, a four 22 times, a five 48 times, and a six 52 times. What do you notice about the results? Do you think the number cube is fair?

Ready to Go On?

18-1 Geometric Probability

Use the spinner to find the probability of each event.

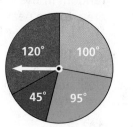

1. the pointer landing on red

2. the pointer landing on red or yellow

3. the pointer not landing on green

4. the pointer landing on yellow or blue

5. A radio station plays 12 commercials per hour. Each commercial is 1 minute long. If you turn on the radio at a random time, find the probability that a commercial will be playing.

Find the probability that a point chosen randomly inside the 40 m by 24 m rectangle is in each shape. Round to the nearest hundredth.

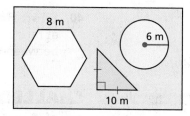

6. the regular hexagon

7. the triangle

8. the circle or the triangle

9. inside the rectangle but not inside the hexagon, triangle, or circle

18-2 Permutations and Combinations

10. A security code consists of 5 digits (0–9), and a digit may not be used more than once. How many possible security codes are there?

11. Adric owns 8 pairs of shoes. How many ways can he choose 4 pairs of shoes to pack into his luggage?

12. A plumber received calls from 5 customers. There are 6 open slots on today's schedule. How many ways can the plumber schedule the customers?

13. How many different 7-digit telephone numbers can be made if the first digit cannot be 7, 8, or 9?

14. From a group of 12 volunteers, a surveyor must choose 5 to complete an advanced survey. How many groups of 5 people can be chosen?

15. In one day, a salesman plans to visit 6 out of 14 companies that are in the neighborhood. How many ways can he plan the visits?

16. How many ways can 7 people arrange themselves inside a van that has 10 seats?

17. The caterer told Kathy that she can choose 3 entrées from the 6 listed on the menu. How many groups of 3 entrées can she choose?

18-3 Theoretical and Experimental Probability

18. A cooler contains 18 cans: 9 of lemonade, 3 of iced tea, and 6 of cola. Dee selects a can without looking. What is the probability that Dee selects iced tea?

19. Jordan has 9 pens in his desk; 2 are out of ink. If his mom selects 2 pens from his desk, what is the probability that both are out of ink?

20. Find the probability that a point chosen at random inside the figure shown is in the shaded area.

21. A number cube is tossed 50 times, and a 2 is rolled 12 times. Find the experimental probability of not rolling a 2.

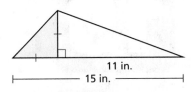

The bar graph shows the results of tossing two pennies 50 times. Find the experimental probability of each of the following.

22. tossing 2 heads

23. tossing at least 1 tail

24. not tossing a head

25. tossing exactly 1 tail

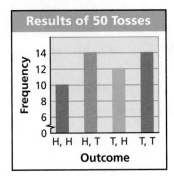

PARCC Assessment Readiness

Selected Response

1. An experiment consists of rolling a number cube. What is the probability of rolling a number greater than 4? Express your answer as a fraction in simplest form.

(A) $\frac{1}{3}$

(C) $\frac{2}{3}$

(B) $\frac{1}{6}$

(D) $\frac{1}{2}$

2. An experiment consists of spinning a spinner. The table shows the results. Find the experimental probability that the spinner does not land on red. Express your answer as a fraction in simplest form.

Outcome	Frequency
red	10
purple	11
yellow	13

(F) $\frac{21}{34}$

(H) $\frac{5}{17}$

(G) $\frac{12}{17}$

(J) $\frac{13}{34}$

3. Joel owns 12 shirts and is selecting the ones he will wear to school next week. How many different ways can Joel choose a group of 5 shirts? (Note that he will not wear the same shirt more than once during the week.)

(A) 792 ways

(C) 95,040 ways

(B) 17 ways

(D) 60 ways

Mini-Task

4. Find the probability of the pointer landing on a new house.

19 Conditional Probability

MCC9-12.S.CP.2, MCC9-12.S.CP.3,
MCC9-12.S.CP.5, MCC9-12.S.CP.6

MCC9-12.S.CP.4

MCC9-12.S.CP.5, MCC9-12.S.CP.7

Contents

MATHEMATICAL PRACTICES The Common Core Georgia Performance Standards for Mathematical Practice describe varieties of expertise that all students should seek to develop. Opportunities to develop these practices are integrated throughout this program.

1 Make sense of problems and persevere in solving them.

2 Reason abstractly and quantitatively.

3 Construct viable arguments and critique the reasoning of others.

4 Model with mathematics.

5 Use appropriate tools strategically.

6 Attend to precision.

7 Look for and make use of structure.

8 Look for and express regularity in repeated reasoning.

Unpacking the Standards

Understanding the standards and the vocabulary terms in the standards will help you know exactly what you are expected to learn in this chapter.

COMMON CORE GPS **MCC9-12.S.CP.4**

Construct and interpret two-way frequency tables of data when two categories are associated with each object being classified. Use the two-way table as a sample space to decide if events are independent and to approximate conditional probabilities.

Key Vocabulary

frequency table (tabla de frecuencia) A table that lists the number of times, or frequency, that each data value occurs.

independent events (sucesos independientes) Events for which the occurrence or non-occurrence of one event does not affect the probability of the other event.

conditional probability (probabilidad condicional) The probability of event B, given that event A has already occurred or is certain to occur, denoted $P(B|A)$.

What It Means For You

A two-way table organizes data about two variables. A two-way frequency table can be very helpful when finding probabilities.

EXAMPLE **Finding Conditional Probability**

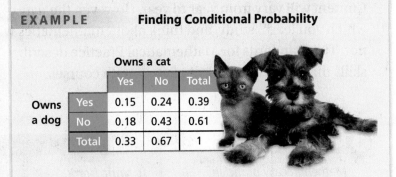

		Owns a cat		
		Yes	No	Total
Owns a dog	Yes	0.15	0.24	0.39
	No	0.18	0.43	0.61
	Total	0.33	0.67	1

This two-way frequency table describes data collected by a sociologist who surveyed 100 randomly selected people about their pets. You can use this table to answer the question, "If a person in this survey has a dog, what is the probability that he or she also has a cat?"

Mastering the Standards

for Mathematical Practice

The topics described in the Standards for Mathematical Content will vary from year to year. However, the *way* in which you learn, study, and think about mathematics will not. The Standards for Mathematical Practice describe skills that you will use in all of your math courses.

Mathematical Practices

1. *Make sense of problems and persevere in solving them.*
2. *Reason abstractly and quantitatively.*
3. *Construct viable arguments and critique the reasoning of others.*
4. *Model with mathematics.*
5. *Use appropriate tools strategically.*
6. *Attend to precision.*
7. *Look for and make use of structure.*
8. *Look for and express regularity in repeated reasoning.*

④ Model with mathematics.

Mathematically proficient students can apply... mathematics... to... problems... in everyday life, society, and the workplace...

In your book

Real-World Connections and **Focus on Mathematical Practices** exercises apply mathematics to other disciplines and in real-world scenarios.

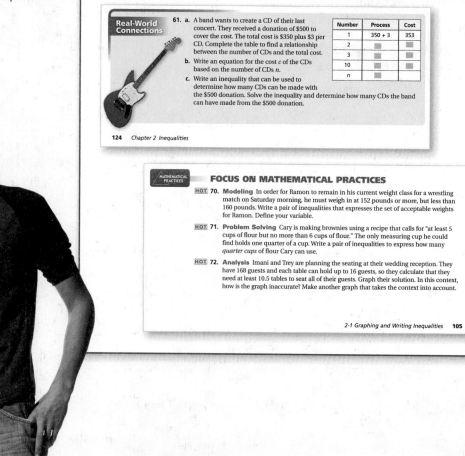

Real-World Connections

61. a. A band wants to create a CD of their last concert. They received a donation of $500 to cover the cost. The total cost is $350 plus $3 per CD. Complete the table to find a relationship between the number of CDs and the total cost.

Number	Process	Cost
1	350 + 3	353
2		
3		
10		
n		

b. Write an equation for the cost c of the CDs based on the number of CDs n.

c. Write an inequality that can be used to determine how many CDs can be made with the $500 donation. Solve the inequality and determine how many CDs the band can have made from the $500 donation.

124 Chapter 2 Inequalities

FOCUS ON MATHEMATICAL PRACTICES

HOT **70. Modeling** In order for Ramon to remain in his current weight class for a wrestling match on Saturday morning, he must weigh in at 152 pounds or more, but less than 160 pounds. Write a pair of inequalities that expresses the set of acceptable weights for Ramon. Define your variable.

HOT **71. Problem Solving** Cary is making brownies using a recipe that calls for "at least 5 cups of flour but no more than 6 cups of flour." The only measuring cup he could find holds one quarter of a cup. Write a pair of inequalities to express how many *quarter cups* of flour Cary can use.

HOT **72. Analysis** Imani and Trey are planning the seating at their wedding reception. They have 168 guests and each table can hold up to 16 guests, so they calculate that they need at least 10.5 tables to seat all of their guests. Graph their solution. In this context, how is the graph inaccurate? Make another graph that takes the context into account.

2-1 Graphing and Writing Inequalities **105**

PhotoDisc/Getty Images

19-1

Independent and Dependent Events

? Essential Question: How do you use conditional probability to find the probability of dependent events?

Objectives
Determine whether events are independent or dependent.

Find the probability of independent and dependent events.

Vocabulary
independent events
dependent events
conditional probability

Who uses this?
Political analysts can use demographic information and probabilities to predict the results of elections. (See Example 3.)

Events are **independent events** if the occurrence of one event does not affect the probability of the other.

If a coin is tossed twice, its landing heads up on the first toss and landing heads up on the second toss are independent events. The outcome of one toss does not affect the probability of heads on the other toss. To find the probability of tossing heads twice, multiply the individual probabilities, $\frac{1}{2} \cdot \frac{1}{2}$, or $\frac{1}{4}$.

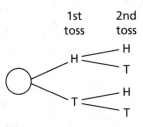

Know it! .note

Probability of Independent Events

If A and B are independent events, then $P(A \text{ and } B) = P(A) \cdot P(B)$.

COMMON CORE GPS **EXAMPLE** **1**
MCC9-12.S.CP.2

my.hrw.com

Online Video Tutor

Finding the Probability of Independent Events

Find each probability.

A spinning 4 and then 4 again on the spinner

Spinning a 4 once does not affect the probability of spinning a 4 again, so the events are independent.

$P(4 \text{ and then } 4) = P(4) \cdot P(4)$

$\frac{3}{8} \cdot \frac{3}{8} = \frac{9}{64}$ *3 of the 8 equal sectors are labeled 4.*

B spinning red, then green, and then red on the spinner

The result of any spin does not affect the probability of any other outcome.

$P(\text{red, then green, and then red}) = P(\text{red}) \cdot P(\text{green}) \cdot P(\text{red})$

$= \frac{1}{4} \cdot \frac{3}{8} \cdot \frac{1}{4} = \frac{3}{128}$ *2 of the 8 equal sectors are red; 3 are green.*

CHECK IT OUT! Find each probability.

1a. rolling a 6 on one number cube and a 6 on another number cube

1b. tossing heads, then heads, and then tails when tossing a coin 3 times

Adey Bryant/www.CartoonStock.com

Events are **dependent events** if the occurrence of one event affects the probability of the other. For example, suppose that there are 2 lemons and 1 lime in a bag. If you pull out two pieces of fruit, the probabilities change depending on the outcome of the first.

The tree diagram shows the probabilities for choosing two pieces of fruit from a bag containing 2 lemons and 1 lime.

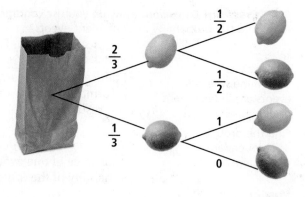

The probability of a specific event can be found by multiplying the probabilities on the branches that make up the event. For example, the probability of drawing two lemons is $\frac{2}{3} \cdot \frac{1}{2} = \frac{1}{3}$.

To find the probability of dependent events, you can use **conditional probability** $P(B \mid A)$, the probability of event B, given that event A has occurred.

Know it! Note

Probability of Dependent Events

If A and B are dependent events, then $P(A \text{ and } B) = P(A) \cdot P(B \mid A)$, where $P(B \mid A)$ is the probability of B, given that A has occurred.

COMMON CORE GPS MCC9-12.S.CP.3

EXAMPLE 2

Finding the Probability of Dependent Events

Two number cubes are rolled—one red and one blue. Explain why the events are dependent. Then find the indicated probability.

my.hrw.com

Online Video Tutor

A The red cube shows a 1, and the sum is less than 4.

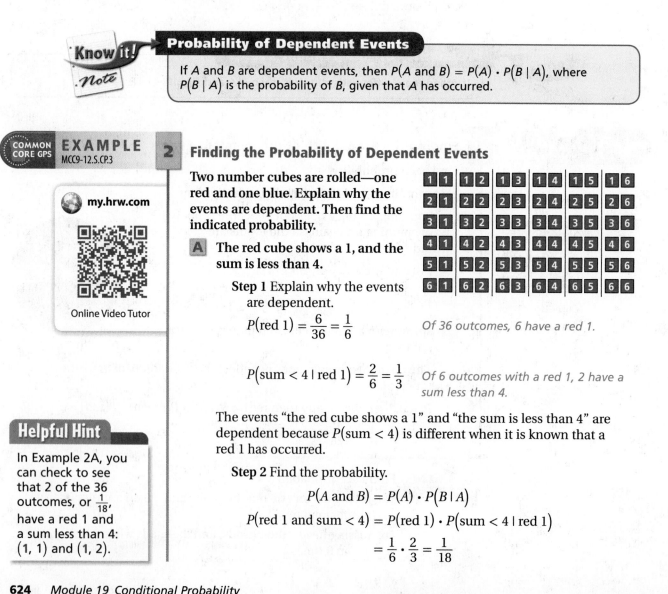

Step 1 Explain why the events are dependent.

$P(\text{red } 1) = \frac{6}{36} = \frac{1}{6}$ *Of 36 outcomes, 6 have a red 1.*

$P(\text{sum} < 4 \mid \text{red } 1) = \frac{2}{6} = \frac{1}{3}$ *Of 6 outcomes with a red 1, 2 have a sum less than 4.*

The events "the red cube shows a 1" and "the sum is less than 4" are dependent because $P(\text{sum} < 4)$ is different when it is known that a red 1 has occurred.

Step 2 Find the probability.

$$P(A \text{ and } B) = P(A) \cdot P(B \mid A)$$
$$P(\text{red } 1 \text{ and sum} < 4) = P(\text{red } 1) \cdot P(\text{sum} < 4 \mid \text{red } 1)$$
$$= \frac{1}{6} \cdot \frac{2}{3} = \frac{1}{18}$$

Helpful Hint

In Example 2A, you can check to see that 2 of the 36 outcomes, or $\frac{1}{18}$, have a red 1 and a sum less than 4: $(1, 1)$ and $(1, 2)$.

Explain why the events are dependent. Then find the indicated probability.

B **The blue cube shows a multiple of 3, and the sum is 8.**

The events are dependent because $P(\text{sum is 8})$ is different when the blue cube shows a multiple of 3.

$P(\text{blue multiple of 3}) = \dfrac{2}{6} = \dfrac{1}{3}$

Of 6 outcomes for blue, 2 have a multiple of 3.

$P(\text{sum is 8} \mid \text{blue multiple of 3}) = \dfrac{2}{12} = \dfrac{1}{6}$

Of 12 outcomes that have a blue multiple of 3, 2 have a sum 8.

$P(\text{blue multiple of 3 and sum is 8}) =$

$P(\text{blue multiple of 3}) \cdot P(\text{sum is 8} \mid \text{blue multiple of 3}) = \left(\dfrac{1}{3}\right)\left(\dfrac{1}{6}\right) = \dfrac{1}{18}$

CHECK IT OUT! **Two number cubes are rolled—one red and one black. Explain why the events are dependent, and then find the indicated probability.**

2. The red cube shows a number greater than 4, and the sum is greater than 9.

Conditional probability often applies when data fall into categories.

COMMON CORE GPS
EXAMPLE 3
MCC9-12.S.CP.6

Using a Table to Find Conditional Probability

my.hrw.com

Online Video Tutor

Largest Texas Counties' Votes for President 2004 (thousands)			
County	Bush	Kerry	Other
Harris	581	472	5
Dallas	345	336	4
Tarrant	349	207	3
Bexar	260	210	3
Travis	148	197	5

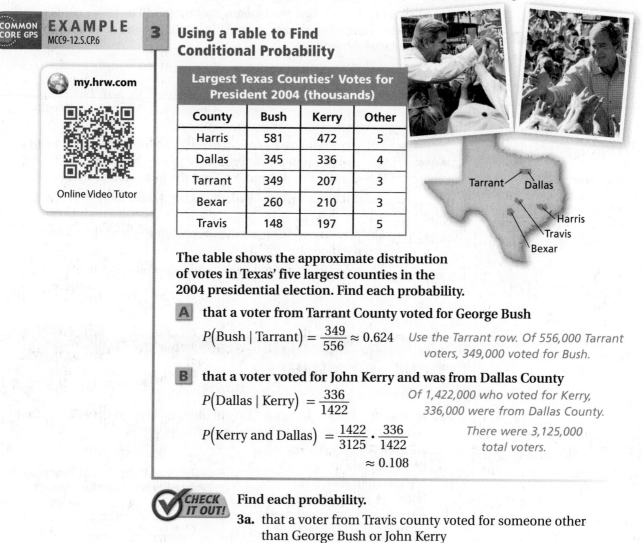

The table shows the approximate distribution of votes in Texas' five largest counties in the 2004 presidential election. Find each probability.

A **that a voter from Tarrant County voted for George Bush**

$P(\text{Bush} \mid \text{Tarrant}) = \dfrac{349}{556} \approx 0.624$ *Use the Tarrant row. Of 556,000 Tarrant voters, 349,000 voted for Bush.*

B **that a voter voted for John Kerry and was from Dallas County**

$P(\text{Dallas} \mid \text{Kerry}) = \dfrac{336}{1422}$ *Of 1,422,000 who voted for Kerry, 336,000 were from Dallas County.*

$P(\text{Kerry and Dallas}) = \dfrac{1422}{3125} \cdot \dfrac{336}{1422}$ *There were 3,125,000 total voters.*

≈ 0.108

CHECK IT OUT! **Find each probability.**

3a. that a voter from Travis county voted for someone other than George Bush or John Kerry

3b. that a voter was from Harris county and voted for George Bush

In many cases involving random selection, events are independent when there is replacement and dependent when there is not replacement.

COMMON CORE GPS

EXAMPLE **4**
MCC9-12.S.CP.8(+)

my.hrw.com

Online Video Tutor

Determining Whether Events Are Independent or Dependent

Two cards are drawn from a deck of 52. Determine whether the events are independent or dependent. Find the probability.

A selecting two aces when the first card is replaced

Replacing the first card means that the occurrence of the first selection will not affect the probability of the second selection, so the events are independent.

$P(\text{ace} \mid \text{ace on first draw}) = P(\text{ace}) \cdot P(\text{ace})$

$= \dfrac{4}{52} \cdot \dfrac{4}{52} = \dfrac{1}{169}$ *4 of the 52 cards are aces.*

B selecting a face card and then a 7 when the first card is not replaced

Not replacing the first card means that there will be fewer cards to choose from, affecting the probability of the second selection, so the events are dependent.

$P(\text{face card}) \cdot P(7 \mid \text{first card was a face card})$

$= \dfrac{12}{52} \cdot \dfrac{4}{51} = \dfrac{4}{221}$ *There are 12 face cards, four 7's and 51 cards available for the second selection.*

Remember!

A standard card deck contains 4 suits of 13 cards each. The face cards are the jacks, queens, and kings.

CHECK IT OUT! A bag contains 10 beads—2 black, 3 white, and 5 red. A bead is selected at random. Determine whether the events are independent or dependent. Find the indicated probability.

4a. selecting a white bead, replacing it, and then selecting a red bead

4b. selecting a white bead, not replacing it, and then selecting a red bead

4c. selecting 3 nonred beads without replacement

MCC.MP.8   **MATHEMATICAL PRACTICES**

THINK AND DISCUSS

1. Describe some independent events.

2. Extend the rule for the probability of independent events to more than two independent events. When might this be used?

Know it! Note

3. GET ORGANIZED Copy and complete the graphic organizer. In each box, compare independent and dependent events and their related probabilities.

Probability of Independent Events vs. Probability of Dependent Events

Similarities   Differences

Sam Dudgeon/HMH

GUIDED PRACTICE

1. **Vocabulary** Two events are ___?___ if the occurrence of one event does not affect the probability of the other event. (*independent* or *dependent*)

SEE EXAMPLE 1 Find each probability.

2. rolling a 1 and then another 1 when a number cube is rolled twice

3. a coin landing heads up on every toss when it is tossed 3 times

SEE EXAMPLE 2 Two number cubes are rolled—one blue and one yellow. Explain why the events are dependent. Then find the indicated probability.

4. The blue cube shows a 4 and the product is less than 20.

5. The yellow cube shows a multiple of 3, given that the product is 6.

SEE EXAMPLE 3 The table shows the results of a quality-control study of a lightbulb factory. A lightbulb from the factory is selected at random. Find each probability.

6. that a shipped bulb is not defective

7. that a bulb is defective and shipped

Lightbulb Quality		
	Shipped	**Not Shipped**
Defective	10	45
Not Defective	942	3

SEE EXAMPLE 4 A bag contains 20 checkers—10 red and 10 black. Determine whether the events are independent or dependent. Find the indicated probability.

8. selecting 2 black checkers when they are chosen at random with replacement

9. selecting 2 black checkers when they are chosen at random without replacement

PRACTICE AND PROBLEM SOLVING

Independent Practice

For Exercises	See Example
10–11	1
12–14	2
15–16	3
17–18	4

my.hrw.com

Online Extra Practice

Find each probability.

10. choosing the same activity when two friends each randomly choose 1 of 4 extracurricular activities to participate in

11. rolling an even number and then rolling a 6 when a number cube is rolled twice

Two number cubes are rolled—one blue and one yellow. Explain why the events are dependent. Then find the indicated probability.

12. The yellow cube is greater than 5 and the product is greater than 24.

13. The blue cube is less than 3 and the product is 8.

14. The table shows immigration to the United States from three countries in three different years. A person is randomly selected. Find each probability.

   a. that a selected person is from Cuba, given that the person immigrated in 1990

   b. that a person came from Spain and immigrated in 2000

   c. that a selected person immigrated in 1995, given that the person was from Ghana.

Immigration to the United States			
Country	**1990**	**1995**	**2000**
Cuba	10,645	17,937	20,831
Ghana	4,466	3,152	4,344
Spain	1,886	1,321	1,264

Employment Find each probability.

15. that a person with an advanced degree is employed

16. that a person is not a high school graduate and is not employed

Employment by Education Level, Ages 21–24		
Education Level	Employed (millions)	Not employed (millions)
Not a high school graduate	1.060	0.834
High school graduate	2.793	1.157
Some college	4.172	1.634
Bachelor's degree	1.53	0.372
Advanced degree	0.104	0.041

A bag contains number slips numbered 1 to 9. Determine whether the events are independent or dependent, and find the indicated probability.

17. selecting 2 even numbers when 2 slips are chosen without replacement

18. selecting 2 even numbers when 2 slips are chosen with replacement

Determine whether the events are independent or dependent.

19. A coin comes up heads, and a number cube rolled at the same time comes up 6.

20. A 4 is drawn from a deck of cards, set aside, and then an ace is drawn.

21. A 1 is rolled on a number cube, and then a 4 is rolled on the same number cube.

22. A dart hits the bull's-eye, and a second dart also hits the bull's eye.

Tennis

Wimbledon has been played annually since 1877 at the All England Lawn Tennis and Croquet Club.

23. **Tennis** In the 2004 Wimbledon Men's Tennis Championship final, Roger Federer defeated Andy Roddick in three sets.

   a. What was the probability that Federer won the point when his second serve was in?

   b. When Federer lost a point, what was the probability that he *double faulted*?

Roger Federer's Service Points		
	Won	Lost
First Serve In	64	31
Second Serve In	34	22
Second Serve Out (Double Fault)	0	3

24. **Multi-Step** At one high school, the probability that a student is absent today, given that the student was absent yesterday, is 0.12. The probability that a student is absent today, given that the student was present yesterday, is 0.05. The probability that a student was absent yesterday is 0.1. Draw a tree diagram to represent the situation. What is the probability that a randomly selected student was present yesterday and today?

Real-World Connections

25. While playing Yahtzee, Jake rolls 5 dice and gets the result shown at right. The rules allow him to reroll these dice 2 times. Jake decides to try for all 5's, so he rerolls the 2 and the 3.

   a. What is the probability that Jake gets no additional 5's in either of the 2 rolls?

   b. What is the probability that he gets all 5's on his first reroll of the 2 and the 3?

   c. What is the probability that he gets all 5's on his first reroll, given that at least one of the dice is a 5?

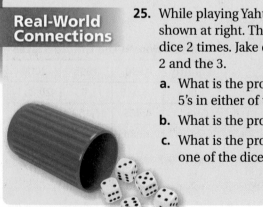

Estimation Use the graph to estimate each probability.

26. that a Spanish club member is a girl

27. that a senior Spanish club member is a girl

28. that a male Spanish club member is a senior

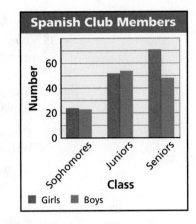

Spanish Club Members

Girls ▪ Boys ▪

H.O.T. **29. Critical Thinking** A box contains 100 balloons. Eighty are yellow, and 20 are green. Fifty are marked "Happy Birthday!" and 50 are not. A balloon is randomly chosen from the box. How many yellow "Happy Birthday!" balloons must be in the box if the event "a balloon is yellow" and the event "a balloon is marked 'Happy Birthday!'" are independent?

H.O.T. **30. Travel** Airline information for three years is given in the table.

   a. Complete the table.

   b. What was the probability that a scheduled flight in 2004 was canceled?

   c. An on-time flight is selected randomly for study. What is the probability that it was a flight from 2005?

Scheduled Flights (thousands) January to July				
	2003	**2004**	**2005**	**Total**
On Time	▪	3197	3237	▪
Delayed	598	▪	877	2321
Canceled	61	68	▪	▪
Total	3761	▪	4196	▪

Source: Bureau of Transportation Statistics

H.O.T. **31. Write About It** The "law of averages" is a nonmathematical term that means that events eventually "average out." So, if a coin comes up heads 10 tosses in a row, there is a greater probability that it will come up tails on the eleventh toss. Explain the error in this thinking.

TEST PREP

32. What is the probability that a person's birthday falls on a Saturday next year, given that it falls on a Saturday this year?

   ⓐ 0   ⓑ $\frac{1}{7}$ ⓒ $\frac{1}{2}$ ⓓ 1

33. Which of the following has the same probability as rolling doubles on 2 number cubes 3 times in a row?

   ⓕ A single number cube is rolled 3 times. The cube shows 5 each time.

   ⓖ Two number cubes are rolled 3 times. Each time the sum is 6.

   ⓗ Two number cubes are rolled 3 times. Each time the sum is greater than 2.

   ⓙ Three number cubes are rolled twice. Each time all cubes show the same number (triples).

H.O.T. **34. Extended Response** Use the tree diagram.

   a. Find $P(D \mid A)$, $P(D \mid B)$, and $P(D \mid C)$.

   b. Does the tree diagram represent independent or dependent events? Explain your answer.

   c. Describe a scenario for which the tree diagram could be used to find probabilities.

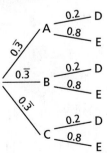

35. Two number cubes are rolled in succession and the numbers that they show are added together. What is the only sum for which the probability of the sum is independent of the number shown on the first roll? Explain.

36. Birthdays People born on February 29 have a birthday once every 4 years.

a. What is the smallest group of people in which there is a greater than 50% chance that 2 people share a birthday? (Do not include February 29.)

b. What is the probability that in a group of 150 people, none are born on February 29?

c. What is the least number of people such that there is a greater than 50% chance that one of the people in the group has a birthday on February 29?

37. There are 150 people at a play. Ninety are women, and 60 are men. Half are sitting in the lower level, and half are sitting in the upper level. There are 35 women sitting in the upper level. A person is selected at random for a prize. What is the probability that the person is sitting in the lower level, given that the person is a woman? Is the event "person is sitting in the lower level" independent of the event "person is a woman"? Explain.

H.O.T. 38. Medicine Suppose that strep throat affects 2% of the population and a test to detect it produces an accurate result 99% of the time.

a. Complete the table.

b. What is the probability that someone who tests positive actually has strep throat?

Per 10,000 People Tested			
	Have strep	Do not have strep	Total
Test Positive	▦	▦	▦
Test Negative	▦	▦	▦
Total	▦	▦	10,000

FOCUS ON MATHEMATICAL PRACTICES

H.O.T. 39. Error Analysis A bag contains 28 tiles, 12 vowels and 16 consonants. Topher wants to find the probability of getting all vowels when drawing 3 tiles without replacement. His work is shown. Describe and correct his error.

$$\frac{12}{28} \cdot \frac{12}{28} \cdot \frac{12}{28} = \frac{3}{7} \cdot \frac{3}{7} \cdot \frac{3}{7} = \frac{27}{343} \approx 0.0787$$

H.O.T. 40. Problem Solving If it is cloudy in the morning, the probability it will rain is 0.34. If it is not cloudy in the morning, the probability it will not rain is 0.92. The probability that it is cloudy in the morning is 0.4. What is the probability that it is not cloudy in the morning and it rains?

H.O.T. 41. Counterexamples Francine rolls a number cube and then picks a number from a bag containing tiles numbered 1 through 9. She asserts that any probability based on these two events must treat them as independent events, since the number cube and the tiles do not affect each other. Is she correct? If not, find a counterexample to Francine's assertion.

19-2 Two-Way Tables

Essential Question: How can you organize categorical data using two-way tables to find conditional probabilities?

Objectives
Construct and interpret two-way frequency tables of data when two categories are associated with each object being classified.

Vocabulary
joint relative frequency
marginal relative frequency
conditional relative frequency

Who uses this?
Commuters can use two-way tables to determine the best route to work. (See Example 3.)

A *two-way table* is a useful way to organize data that can be categorized by two variables. Suppose you asked 20 children and adults whether they liked broccoli. The table shows one way to arrange the data.

The **joint relative frequencies** are the values in each category divided by the total number of values, shown by the shaded cells in the table. Each value is divided by 20, the total number of individuals.

The **marginal relative frequencies** are found by adding the joint relative frequencies in each row and column.

	Yes	No
Children	3	8
Adults	7	2

	Yes	No	Total
Children	0.15	0.4	0.55
Adults	0.35	0.1	0.45
Total	0.5	0.5	1

EXAMPLE MCC9-12.S.ID.5 **1**

Finding Joint and Marginal Relative Frequencies

my.hrw.com

Online Video Tutor

The table shows the results of a poll of 80 randomly selected high school students who were asked if they prefer math or English. Make a table of the joint and marginal relative frequencies.

	9th grade	10th grade	11th grade	12th grade
Math	10	12	11	8
English	12	11	8	8

Divide each value by the total of 80 to find the joint relative frequencies, and add each row and column to find the marginal relative frequencies.

	9th grade	10th grade	11th grade	12th grade	Total
Math	0.125	0.15	0.1375	0.1	0.5125
English	0.15	0.1375	0.1	0.1	0.4875
Total	0.275	0.2875	0.2375	0.2	1

1. The table shows the number of books sold at a library sale. Make a table of the joint and marginal relative frequencies.

	Fiction	Nonfiction
Hardcover	28	52
Paperback	94	36

To find a **conditional relative frequency**, divide the joint relative frequency by the marginal relative frequency. Conditional relative frequencies can be used to find conditional probabilities.

Using Conditional Relative Frequency to Find Probability

A sociologist collected data on the types of pets in 100 randomly selected households, and summarized the results in a table.

		Owns a cat	
		Yes	No
Owns a dog	Yes	15	24
	No	18	43

A Make a table of the joint and marginal relative frequencies.

		Owns a cat		
		Yes	No	Total
Owns a dog	Yes	0.15	0.24	0.39
	No	0.18	0.43	0.61
	Total	0.33	0.67	1

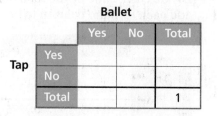

B If you are given that a household has a dog, what is the probability that the household also has a cat?

Use the conditional relative frequency for the row with the condition "Owns a dog." The total for households with dogs is 0.39, or 39%. Out of these, 0.15, or 15%, also have cats. The conditional relative frequency is $\frac{0.15}{0.39} \approx 0.38$.

Given that a household has a dog, there is a probability of about 0.38 that the household also has a cat.

The classes at a dance academy include ballet and tap dancing. Enrollment in these classes is shown in the table.

		Ballet	
		Yes	No
Tap	Yes	38	52
	No	86	24

2a. Copy and complete the table of the joint relative frequencies and marginal relative frequencies.

		Ballet		
		Yes	No	Total
Tap	Yes			
	No			
	Total			1

2b. If you are given that a student is taking ballet, what is the probability that the student is not taking tap?

Notice that in Example 2, the conditional relative frequency could have been found from the original data:

$$\frac{0.15}{0.39} = \frac{15}{39} \approx 0.38$$

Idamini/Alamy

EXAMPLE **3** MCC9-12.S.MD.7(+)

Comparing Conditional Probabilities

Tomas is trying to decide on the best possible route to drive to work. He has a choice of three possible routes. On each day, he randomly selects a route and keeps track of whether he is late. After a 40-day trial, his notes look like this.

	Late	Not Late
Route A	IIII	HHT HHT
Route B	III	HHT II
Route C	IIII	HHT HHT II

Use conditional probabilities to determine the best route for Tomas to take to work.

Create a table of joint and marginal relative frequencies. There are 40 data values, so divide each frequency by 40.

To find the conditional probabilities, divide the joint relative frequency of being late by the marginal relative frequency in each row.

	Late	Not late	Total
Route A	0.1	0.25	0.35
Route B	0.075	0.175	0.25
Route C	0.1	0.3	0.4
Total	0.275	0.725	1

$P(\text{being late if driving Route A}) = \dfrac{0.1}{0.35} \approx 0.29$

$P(\text{being late if driving Route B}) = \dfrac{0.075}{0.25} = 0.3$

$P(\text{being late if driving Route C}) = \dfrac{0.1}{0.4} = 0.25$

The probability of being late is least for Route C. Based on the sample, Tomas is least likely to be late if he takes Route C.

CHECK IT OUT!

3. Francine is evaluating three driving schools. She asked 50 people who attended the schools whether they passed their driving tests on the first try.

Use conditional probabilities to determine which is the best school.

	Pass	Fail
Al's Driving	HHT HHT IIII	HHT III
Drive Time	HHT HHT I	HHT II
Crash Course	HHT	HHT

MCC.MP.5 **MATHEMATICAL PRACTICES**

THINK AND DISCUSS

1. Describe the relationship between joint relative frequencies and marginal relative frequencies.

2. Explain how to find the conditional relative frequencies from a two-way table showing joint and marginal relative frequencies.

3. **GET ORGANIZED** Copy and complete the graphic organizer at right. In each column, explain how to find the relative frequency from a two-way table.

Relative Frequencies		
Joint	Marginal	Conditional

GUIDED PRACTICE

Vocabulary Apply the vocabulary from this lesson to answer each question.

1. The ___?___ relative frequencies are the sums of each row and column in a two-way table. (*joint, marginal,* or *conditional*)

2. You can compare ___?___ probabilities to evaluate the best one out of a number of options. (*joint, marginal,* or *conditional*)

SEE EXAMPLE 1

3. The table shows the results of a poll of randomly selected high school students who were asked if they prefer to hear all-school announcements in the morning or afternoon.

	Underclassmen	Upperclassmen
Morning	8	14
Afternoon	18	10

Make a table of the joint and marginal relative frequencies.

4. **Customer Service** The table shows the results of a customer satisfaction survey for a cellular service provider, by location of the customer. In the survey, customers were asked whether they would recommend a plan with the provider to a friend.

	Arlington	Towson	Parkville
Yes	40	35	41
No	18	10	6

Make a table of the joint and marginal relative frequencies. Round to the nearest hundredth where appropriate.

SEE EXAMPLE 2

5. **School** Pamela has collected data on the number of students in the sophomore class who play a sport or play a musical instrument.

		Plays a sport	
		Yes	No
Plays an instrument	Yes	47	38
	No	51	67

a. Copy and complete the table of the joint and marginal relative frequencies. Round to the nearest hundredth where appropriate.

		Play Sport		
		Yes	No	Total
Play instrument	Yes			
	No			
	Total			

b. If you are given that a student plays an instrument, what is the probability that the student also plays a sport? Round your answer to the nearest hundredth.

c. If you are given that a student plays a sport, what is the probability that the student also plays an instrument? Round your answer to the nearest hundredth.

Anville/Getty Images

6. **Business** Roberto is the owner of a car dealership. He is assessing the success rates of his top three salespeople in order to offer one of them a promotion. Over two months, for each attempted sale, he records whether the salesperson made a successful sale or not. The results are shown in the chart below.

	Successful	Unsuccessful
Becky	6	6
Raul	4	5
Darrell	6	9

a. Make a table of the joint relative frequencies and marginal relative frequencies. Round to the nearest hundredth where appropriate.

b. Find the probability that each salesperson will make a successful sale. Round to the nearest hundredth where appropriate.

c. Determine which salesperson has the highest success rate.

PRACTICE AND PROBLEM SOLVING

Independent Practice

For Exercises	See Example
7–8	1
9–12	2
13	3

my.hrw.com

Online Extra Practice

7. **Fundraising** The table shows the number of T-shirts and sweatshirts sold at a fundraiser during parent visitation night at Preston High School.

	Students	Adults
T-Shirts	16	23
Sweatshirts	7	14

Make a table of the joint relative frequencies and marginal relative frequencies.

8. **Write About It** Describe in your own words the process you use to write marginal relative frequencies for data given in a two-way table.

9. **Customer Service** The claims handlers at a car insurance company help customers with insurance issues when there has been an accident, so their customer service skills are very important.

The claims handlers at the Trust Auto Insurance Company are divided into three teams. For one month, a customer satisfaction survey was given for each team. The results of the surveys are shown below.

	Satisfied	Dissatisfied
Team 1	20	8
Team 2	34	12
Team 3	34	10

a. Make a table of the joint relative frequencies and marginal relative frequencies. Round to the nearest hundredth where appropriate.

b. Find the probability that a customer will be satisfied after working with each team. Round to the nearest hundredth where appropriate.

c. Determine which team has the highest rate of customer satisfaction.

H.O.T. 10. **Critical Thinking** What do you notice about the value that always falls in the cell to the lower right of a two-way table when marginal relative frequencies have been written in? What does this value represent?

11. **///ERROR ANALYSIS///** One hundred adults and children were randomly selected and asked whether they spoke more than one language fluently. The data were recorded in a two-way table. Maria and Brennan each used the data to make the tables of joint relative frequencies shown below, but their results are slightly different. The difference is shaded. Can you tell by looking at the tables which of them made an error? Explain.

Maria's table

	Yes	No
Children	0.15	0.25
Adults	0.1	0.6

Brennan's table

	Yes	No
Children	0.15	0.25
Adults	0.1	0.5

12. **Estimation** A total of 107 brownies and muffins was sold at a school bake sale. The joint relative frequency representing muffins sold to seniors was 0.48. Use mental math to find approximately how many muffins were sold to seniors.

H.O.T. 13. **Public Transit** A town planning committee is considering a new system for public transit. Residents of the town were randomly selected to answer two questions: "Do you work less than 5 miles from home?" and "Would you use the new system to get to work, if it were available?"
The results are shown below.

		Work less than 5 miles from home?	
		Yes	No
Use new system?	Yes	24	32
	No	44	20

a. Make a table of the joint relative frequencies and marginal relative frequencies. Round to the nearest hundredth where appropriate.

b. If residents work less than 5 miles from home, what is the probability that they would use the new system? Round to the nearest hundredth.

c. If residents are willing to use the new system, what is the probability that they don't work less than 5 miles from home? Round to the nearest hundredth.

TEST PREP

14. Students and teachers at a school were polled to see if they were in favor of extending the parking lot into part of the athletic fields. The results of the poll are shown in the two-way table.

	In Favor	Not in Favor
Students	16	23
Teachers	9	14

Which of the following statements is false?

Ⓐ Thirty-nine students were polled in all.

Ⓑ Fourteen teachers were polled in all.

Ⓒ Twenty-three students are not in favor of extending the parking lot.

Ⓓ Nine teachers are in favor of extending the parking lot.

15. A group of students were polled to find out how many were planning to major in a scientific field of study in college. The results of the poll are shown in the two-way table.

		Majoring in a science field	
		Yes	No
Class	Junior	150	210
	Senior	112	200

Which of the following statements is true?

Ⓐ Three hundred sixty students were polled in all.

Ⓑ A student in the senior class is more likely to be planning on a scientific major than a nonscientific major.

Ⓒ A student planning on a scientific major is more likely to be a junior than a senior.

Ⓓ More seniors than juniors plan to enter a scientific field of study.

16. Gridded Response A group of children and adults were polled about whether they watch a particular TV show. The survey results, showing the joint relative frequencies and marginal relative frequencies, are shown in the two-way table.

	Yes	No	Total
Children	0.3	0.4	0.7
Adults	0.25	x	0.3
Total	0.55	0.45	1

What is the value of x?

CHALLENGE AND EXTEND

The table shows the joint relative frequencies for data on how many children and teenagers attended a fair in one evening, and whether each bought a booklet of tickets for rides at the entrance gate.

	Yes	No
Children	0.125	0.1
Teenagers	0.725	0.05

H.O.T. Use the table to answer questions 17–20. Round answers to the nearest hundredth where appropriate.

17. Find the marginal relative frequencies for the data.

18. Based on this data, use a percentage to express how likely it is that tomorrow evening a teenager at the fair will buy a ticket booklet at the entrance. Round your answer to the nearest whole percent, if necessary.

19. If the data represent 80 teenagers and children altogether, how many children will have bought a ticket booklet at the entrance?

20. If 12 children did not buy ticket booklets at the entrance, then how many children and teenagers altogether does the data represent?

21. A poll with the options of 'yes' and 'no' was given. If the marginal relative frequency of 'yes' is 1.0, what was the marginal relative frequency of 'no'?

	Yes	No	Total
Group 1	0.24	?	?
Group 2	0.76	?	?
Total	1.0	?	?

22. Short Response What is the maximum a marginal relative frequency can be, and why?

FOCUS ON MATHEMATICAL PRACTICES

H.O.T. 23. Error Analysis The frequencies of the marbles in a bag are shown in the table. Antoine wants to find $P(\text{green} \mid \text{large})$. He finds the probability to be $\frac{2}{2+8} = \frac{2}{10} = \frac{1}{5}$. What error did he make? What is the correct probability?

	Green	Blue
Large	2	4
Small	8	12

H.O.T. 24. Analysis A survey asked a large sample of people whether they enjoyed classical music. 44% of the people surveyed were women. 25% of the women and 21% of the overall people surveyed said they enjoyed classical music. Is it possible to make a complete two-way relative frequency table from this information? If so, do so. If not, explain what further information is needed.

Career Path

Shawn Innes
Actuarial Science major

Q: What math classes did you take in high school?

A: In high school, I took algebra, geometry, and precalculus.

Q: What do actuaries do?

A: Basically, actuaries evaluate the likelihood of certain events and try to find creative ways to reduce the chances of undesirable outcomes. Actuaries are involved in many different industries such as business and finance, health, retirement planning, and insurance.

Q: How do you become an actuary?

A: To become a full actuary, a series of exams must be completed. These exams cover topics like calculus, economics, and finance.

Q: What are your future plans?

A: I'd like to work at the consulting firm where I interned. They specialize in retirement planning and benefits. There, I tested formulas used to calculate pensions for client companies.

Compound Events

Essential Question: How can you find the probabilities of mutually exclusive or inclusive compound events?

Objectives
Find the probability of mutually exclusive events.

Find the probability of inclusive events.

Vocabulary
simple event
compound event
mutually exclusive events
inclusive events

Why learn this?
You can use the probability of compound events to determine the likelihood that a person of a specific gender is color-blind. (See Example 3.)

A **simple event** is an event that describes a single outcome. A **compound event** is an event made up of two or more simple events. **Mutually exclusive events** are events that cannot both occur in the same trial of an experiment. Rolling a 1 and rolling a 2 on the same roll of a number cube are mutually exclusive events.

Mutually Exclusive Events

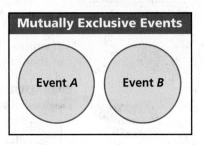

Event A   Event B

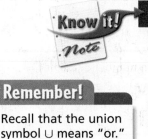

Mutually Exclusive Events

WORDS	ALGEBRA	EXAMPLE
The probability of two mutually exclusive events *A* or *B* occurring is the sum of their individual probabilities.	For two mutually exclusive events *A* and *B*, $P(A \cup B) = P(A) + P(B)$.	When a number cube is rolled, $P(\text{less than } 3) =$ $P(1 \text{ or } 2) =$ $P(1) + P(2) = \frac{1}{6} + \frac{1}{6} = \frac{1}{3}$.

Remember!
Recall that the union symbol ∪ means "or."

COMMON CORE GPS
MCC9-12.S.CP.1

EXAMPLE 1

my.hrw.com

Online Video Tutor

Finding Probabilities of Mutually Exclusive Events

A drink company applies one label to each bottle cap: "free drink," "free meal," or "try again." A bottle cap has a $\frac{1}{10}$ probability of being labeled "free drink" and a $\frac{1}{25}$ probability of being labeled "free meal."

a. Explain why the events "free drink" and "free meal" are mutually exclusive.

Each bottle cap has only one label applied to it.

b. What is the probability that a bottle cap is labeled "free drink" or "free meal"?

$P(\text{free drink} \cup \text{free meal}) = P(\text{free drink}) + P(\text{free meal})$
$= \frac{1}{10} + \frac{1}{25} = \frac{5}{50} + \frac{2}{50} = \frac{7}{50}$

1. Each student cast one vote for senior class president. Of the students, 25% voted for Hunt, 20% for Kline, and 55% for Vila. A student from the senior class is selected at random.

a. Explain why the events "voted for Hunt," "voted for Kline," and "voted for Vila" are mutually exclusive.

b. What is the probability that a student voted for Kline or Vila?

Inclusive events are events that have one or more outcomes in common. When you roll a number cube, the outcomes "rolling an even number" and "rolling a prime number" are not mutually exclusive. The number 2 is both prime and even, so the events are inclusive.

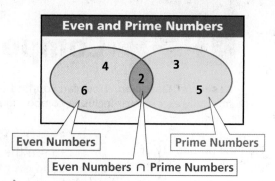

Even and Prime Numbers

4   3
6 2 5

Even Numbers   Prime Numbers

Even Numbers ∩ Prime Numbers

Remember!

Recall that the intersection symbol ∩ means "and."

There are 3 ways to roll an even number, $\{2, 4, 6\}$.

There are 3 ways to roll a prime number, $\{2, 3, 5\}$.

The outcome "2" is counted twice when outcomes are added $(3 + 3)$. The actual number of ways to roll an even number or a prime is $3 + 3 - 1 = 5$. The concept of subtracting the outcomes that are counted twice leads to the following probability formula.

Know it! Note

Inclusive Events

WORDS	The probability of two inclusive events *A* or *B* occurring is the sum of their individual probabilities minus the probability of *both* occurring.
ALGEBRA	For two inclusive events *A* and *B*, $$P(A \cup B) = P(A) + P(B) - P(A \cap B).$$
EXAMPLE	When you roll a number cube, $P(\text{even number or prime}) =$ $P(\text{even or prime}) = P(\text{even}) + P(\text{prime}) - P(\text{even and prime})$ $$= \frac{3}{6} + \frac{3}{6} - \frac{1}{6} = \frac{5}{6}.$$

COMMON CORE GPS
EXAMPLE 2
MCC9-12.S.CP.7

my.hrw.com

Online Video Tutor

Finding Probabilities of Inclusive Events

Find each probability on a die.

A rolling a 5 or an odd number
$$P(5 \text{ or odd}) = P(5) + P(\text{odd}) - P(5 \text{ and odd})$$
$$= \frac{1}{6} + \frac{3}{6} - \frac{1}{6} \qquad \textit{5 is also an odd number.}$$
$$= \frac{1}{2}$$

B rolling at least one 4 when rolling 2 dice
$$P(4 \text{ or } 4) = P(4) + P(4) - P(4 \text{ and } 4)$$
$$= \frac{1}{6} + \frac{1}{6} - \frac{1}{36} \qquad \textit{There is 1 outcome in 36 where both dice show 4.}$$
$$= \frac{11}{36}$$

CHECK IT OUT! **A card is drawn from a deck of 52. Find the probability of each.**

2a. drawing a king or a heart

2b. drawing a red card (hearts or diamonds) or a face card (jack, queen, or king)

Sam Dudgeon/HMH

EXAMPLE **3**
MCC9-12.S.CP.7

Health Application

Of 3510 drivers surveyed, 1950 were male and 103 were color-blind. Only 6 of the color-blind drivers were female. What is the probability that a driver was male or was color-blind?

Step 1 Use a Venn diagram.

Label as much information as you know. Being male and being color-blind are inclusive events.

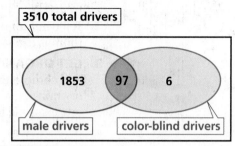

Step 2 Find the number in the overlapping region.

Subtract 6 from 103. This is the number of color-blind males, 97.

Step 3 Find the probability.

$$= P(\text{male} \cup \text{color-blind}) =$$
$$= P(\text{male}) + P(\text{color-blind}) - P(\text{male} \cap \text{color-blind})$$
$$= \frac{1950}{3510} + \frac{103}{3510} - \frac{97}{3510} = \frac{1956}{3510} \approx 0.557$$

The probability that a driver was male or was color-blind is about 55.7%.

CHECK IT OUT!

3. Of 160 beauty spa customers, 96 had a hair styling and 61 had a manicure. There were 28 customers who had only a manicure. What is the probability that a customer had a hair styling or a manicure?

Recall that the complement of an event with probability p, all outcomes that are not in the event, has a probability of $1 - p$. You can use the complement to find the probability of a compound event.

EXAMPLE **4**
MCC9-12.S.CP.9(+)

Book Club Application

There are 5 students in a book club. Each student randomly chooses a book from a list of 10 titles. What is the probability that at least 2 students in the group choose the same book?

$P(\text{at least 2 students choose same}) = 1 - P(\text{all choose different})$ *Use the complement.*

$$P(\text{all choose different}) = \frac{\text{number of ways 5 students can choose different books}}{\text{total number of ways 5 students can choose books}}$$
$$= \frac{{}_{10}P_5}{10^5}$$
$$= \frac{10 \cdot 9 \cdot 8 \cdot 7 \cdot 6}{10 \cdot 10 \cdot 10 \cdot 10 \cdot 10} = \frac{30{,}240}{100{,}000} = 0.3024$$

$P(\text{at least 2 students choose same}) = 1 - 0.3024 = 0.6976$

The probability that at least 2 students choose the same book is 0.6976, or 69.76%.

CHECK IT OUT!

4. In one day, 5 different customers bought earrings from the same jewelry store. The store offers 62 different styles. Find the probability that at least 2 customers bought the same style.

THINK AND DISCUSS

1. Explain why the formula for inclusive events, $P(A \cup B) = P(A) + P(B) - P(A \cap B)$, also applies to mutually exclusive events.

2. Tell whether the probability of sharing a birthday with someone else in the room is the same whether your birthday is March 13 or February 29. Explain.

3. **GET ORGANIZED** Copy and complete the graphic organizer. Give at least one example for each.

Adding probabilities → Probabilities → Mutually exclusive events
Multiplying probabilities → Probabilities → Inclusive events
Probabilities → Compound events

19-3 Exercises

my.hrw.com
Homework Help

GUIDED PRACTICE

1. **Vocabulary** A compound event where one outcome overlaps with another is made up of two __?__ . (*inclusive event* or *mutually exclusive events*)

A bag contains 25 marbles: 10 black, 13 red, and 2 blue. A marble is drawn from the bag at random.

SEE EXAMPLE 1

2. Explain why the events "getting a black marble" and "getting a red marble" are mutually exclusive.

3. What is the probability of getting a red or a blue marble?

4. A car approaching an intersection has a 0.1 probability of turning left and a 0.2 probability of turning right. Explain why the events are mutually exclusive. What is the probability that the car will turn?

SEE EXAMPLE 2 **Numbers 1–10 are written on cards and placed in a bag. Find each probability.**

5. choosing a number greater than 5 or choosing an odd number

6. choosing an 8 or choosing a number less than 5

7. choosing at least one even number when selecting 2 cards from the bag

SEE EXAMPLE 3 **Five years after 650 high school seniors graduated, 400 had a college degree and 310 were married. Half of the students with a college degree were married.**

8. What is the probability that a student has a college degree or is married?

9. What is the probability that a student has a college degree or is not married?

10. What is the probability that a student does not have a college degree or is married?

SEE EXAMPLE 4 11. A vending machine offers 8 different drinks. One day, 6 employees each purchased a drink from the vending machine. Find the probability that at least 2 employees purchased the same drink.

PRACTICE AND PROBLEM SOLVING

Independent Practice

For Exercises	See Example
12–13	1
14–15	2
16–18	3
19	4

my.hrw.com

Online Extra Practice

Jump ropes are given out during gym class. A student has a $\frac{1}{6}$ chance of getting a red jump rope and a $\frac{1}{3}$ chance of getting a green jump rope. Meg is given a jump rope.

12. Explain why the events "getting a red jump rope" and "getting a green jump rope" are mutually exclusive.

13. What is the probability that Meg gets a red or green jump rope?

The letters *A–P* are written on cards and placed in a bag. Find the probability of each outcome.

14. choosing an *E* or choosing a *G*

15. choosing an *E* or choosing a vowel

Lincoln High School has 98 teachers. Of the 42 female teachers, 8 teach math. One-seventh of all of the teachers teach math.

16. What is the probability that a teacher is a woman or teaches math?

17. What is the probability that a teacher is a man or teaches math?

18. What is the probability that a teacher is a man or does not teach math?

19. A card is drawn from a deck of 52 and recorded. Then the card is replaced, and the deck is shuffled. This process is repeated 13 times. What is the probability that at least one of the cards drawn is a heart?

20. Critical Thinking Events *A* and *B* are mutually exclusive. Must the complements of events *A* and *B* be mutually exclusive? Explain by example.

Television

21. Television According to Nielsen Media Research, on June 21, 2005, from 9 to 10 P.M., the NBA Finals Game 7 between San Antonio and Detroit had a 22 *share* (was watched by 22% of television viewers), while *CSI* had a 15 share. What is the probability that someone who was watching television during this time watched the NBA Finals or *CSI*? Do you think that this is theoretical or experimental probability? Explain.

In 2004, about 109.6 million U.S. households had televisions. Nielsen's *rating points*, such as those for *CSI*, represent the percent of these households tuned to a show.

School Arts Use the table for Exercises 22 and 23.

22. What would you need to know to find the probability that a U.S. public school offers music or dance classes?

23. What is the minimum probability that a U.S. public school offers visual arts or drama? What is the maximum probability?

Arts Offered by U.S. Public Schools				
Class Type	Music	Visual arts	Dance	Drama and theater
Percent of Schools	94%	87%	20%	19%

24. Geometry A square dartboard contains a red square and a blue square that overlap. A dart hits a random point on the board.

   a. Find $P(\text{red} \cap \text{blue})$.   **b.** Find $P(\text{red})$.

   c. Find $P(\text{red} \cup \text{blue})$.   **d.** Find $P(\text{yellow})$.

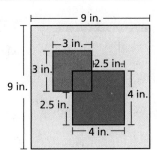

H.O.T. **25. Genetics** One study found that 8% of men and 0.5% of women are born color-blind. Of the study participants, 52% were men.

   a. Which probability would you expect to be greater: that a study participant is male *and* born color-blind or that a participant is male *or* born color-blind? Explain.

   b. What is the probability that a study participant is male and born color-blind? What is the probability that a study participant is male or born color-blind?

CBS/Landov

Real-World Connections

26. While playing Yahtzee, Amanda rolls five dice and gets the result shown. She decides to keep the 1, 2, and 4, and reroll the 5 and 6.

   a. After rerolling the 5 and 6, what is the probability that Amanda will have a "large straight" (1-2-3-4-5) or three 4's?

   b. After rerolling the 5 and 6, what is the probability that Amanda will have a "small straight" (1-2-3-4 plus anything else) or a pair of 3's?

27. **Public Safety** In a study of canine attacks, the probability that the victim was under 18 years of age was 0.8. The probability that the attack occurred on the dog owner's property was 0.64. The probability that the victim was under 18 years of age or the attack occurred on the owner's property was 0.95. What was the probability that the victim was under 18 years of age and the attack occurred on the owner's property?

H.O.T. 28. **Politics** A 4-person leadership committee is randomly chosen from a group of 24 candidates. Ten of the candidates are men, and 14 are women.

   a. What is the probability that the committee is all male or all female?

   b. What is the probability that the committee has at least 1 man or at least 1 woman?

H.O.T. 29. **Multi-Step** The game Scrabble contains letter tiles that occur in different numbers. Suppose that one tile is selected.

   a. What is the probability of choosing a vowel if Y is not included?

   b. What is the probability of choosing a Y?

   c. What is the probability of choosing a vowel if Y is included? How does this relate to the answer to parts **a** and **b**?

H.O.T. 30. **Write About It** Demonstrate two ways to find the probability of a coin's landing heads up at least once in 2 tosses of a coin.

Distribution of Scrabble Tiles	
Tiles	Frequency
J, K, Q, X, Z	1
B, C, F, H, M, P, V, W, Y, blank	2
G	3
D, L, S, U	4
N, R, T	6
O	8
A, I	9
E	12

TEST PREP

31. For a quilt raffle, 2500 tickets numbered 0001–2500 are sold. Jamie has number 1527. The winning raffle number is read one digit at a time. The first winning number begins "One...". After the first digit is called, Jamie's chances of winning do which of the following?

   (A) Go to 0

   (B) Stay the same

   (C) Increase from $\frac{1}{2500}$ to $\frac{1}{1527}$

   (D) Increase from $\frac{1}{2500}$ to $\frac{1}{1000}$

32. A fair coin is tossed 4 times. Given that each of the first 3 tosses land tails up, what is the probability that all 4 tosses land tails up?

   (F) 0.5

   (G) Greater than 0.5

   (H) 0.5^4

   (J) Between 0.5^4 and 0.5

33. If Travis rolls a 5 on a number cube, he lands on "roll again." If Travis rolls a number greater than 3, he'll pass "start" and collect $100. What is the probability that Travis rolls again or collects $100?

     Ⓐ $\frac{1}{6}$ Ⓑ $\frac{1}{5}$ Ⓒ $\frac{1}{4}$ Ⓓ $\frac{1}{2}$

34. Short Response What is the probability of an event or its complement? Explain.

CHALLENGE AND EXTEND

H.O.T. **35.** What is the probability that at least 2 people in a group of 10 people have the same birthday? (Assume no one in the group was born on February 29th.)

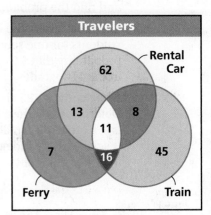

Travel For Exercises 36–38, use the Venn diagram, which shows the transportation methods used by 162 travelers. Find each probability if a traveler is selected at random.

36. $P(\text{ferry or train})$

37. $P(\text{ferry or rental car})$

38. $P(\text{train and ferry, or train and rental car})$

Use the table of probabilities and the following information for Exercises 39–41. Hint: Draw a Venn diagram.

For any three events A, B, and C, $P(A \text{ or } B \text{ or } C) =$
$$P(A) + P(B) + P(C) - P(A \cap B) - P(A \cap C) - P(B \cap C) + P(A \cap B \cap C)$$

Event	$P(A)$	$P(B)$	$P(C)$	$P(A \cap B)$	$P(A \cap C)$	$P(B \cap C)$	$P(A \cap B \cap C)$
Probability	0.5	0.3	0.7	0.2	0.3	0.1	0.1

39. Find $P(B \cup C)$.   **40.** Find $P(A \cup B \cup C)$.   **41.** Find $P(B \cap (A \cup C))$.

FOCUS ON MATHEMATICAL PRACTICES

H.O.T. **42. Problem Solving** In a high school, the probability that a student studies art is 0.1, and the probability that a student studies theater is 0.15. The probability that a student studies art or theater is 0.19. What is the probability that a student studies art and theater?

H.O.T. **43. Communication** Describe two ways of finding the probability of rolling a number cube twice and getting at least one 5.

H.O.T. **44. Reasoning** Two events, A and B, are inclusive. $P(A) = 0.3$ and $P(B) = 0.4$. What is the smallest possible value for $P(A \cup B)$? Explain your reasoning.

H.O.T. **45. Analysis** In a survey, 30 students were asked to pick one or two of their favorite colors from a list of three. The results of the survey are shown.

    a. What combination of colors was not chosen by any student?

    b. Find $P(\text{orange} \cup \text{blue})$.

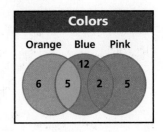

Ready to Go On?

my.hrw.com
Assessment and Intervention

19-1 Independent and Dependent Events

1. Explain why the events "getting tails, then tails, then tails, then tails, then heads when tossing a coin 5 times" are independent, and find the probability.

2. Two number cubes are rolled—one red and one black. Explain why the events "the red cube shows a 6" and "the sum is greater than or equal to 10" are dependent, and find the probability.

3. The table shows the breakdown of math students for one school year. Find the probability that a Geometry student is in the 11th grade.

4. A bag contains 25 checkers—15 red and 10 black. Determine whether the events "a red checker is selected, not replaced, and then a black checker is selected" are independent or dependent, and find the probability.

Math Students by Grade

	Geometry	Algebra 2
9th Grade	26	0
10th Grade	68	24
11th Grade	33	94

19-2 Two-Way Tables

A bookshop surveys its customers about their magazine-buying habits, summarized in the table.

5. Make a table of the joint relative frequencies and the marginal relative frequencies.

6. Given that a customer reads *Super News*, what is the probability that he or she also reads *Look Around*?

7. Given that a customer reads *Look Around,* what is the probability that he or she also reads *Super News?*

		Reads *Look Around*	
		Yes	No
Reads *Super News*	Yes	62	15
	No	21	136

19-3 Compound Events

Numbers 1–30 are written on cards and placed in a bag. One card is drawn. Find each probability.

8. drawing an even number or a 1

9. drawing an even number or a multiple of 7

10. Of a company's 85 employees, 60 work full time and 40 are married. Half of the full-time workers are married. What is the probability that an employee works part time or is not married?

PARCC Assessment Readiness

Selected Response

1. Joyce asked 50 randomly-selected students at her school whether they have one or more brothers or sisters. The table shows the results of Joyce's poll. Make a table of the joint and marginal relative frequencies. Express percentages in decimal form.

	Brother(s)	No Brothers
Sister(s)	9	14
No Sisters	13	14

(A)

	Brother(s)	No Brothers	Total
Sister(s)	0.18	0.28	0.39
No Sisters	0.26	0.28	0.48
Total	0.41	0.5	1

(B)

	Brother(s)	No Brothers	Total
Sister(s)	0.18	0.26	0.44
No Sisters	0.28	0.28	0.56
Total	0.46	0.54	1

(C)

	Brother(s)	No Brothers	Total
Sister(s)	0.18	0.28	0.46
No Sisters	0.26	0.28	0.54
Total	0.44	0.56	1

(D)

	Brother(s)	No Brothers	Total
Sister(s)	0.18	0.26	0.41
No Sisters	0.28	0.28	0.5
Total	0.39	0.48	1

2. In a survey about a change in public policy, 100 people were asked if they favor the change, oppose the change, or have no opinion about the change. Of the 100 people surveyed, 50 are male and 37 oppose the change in policy. Of the 37 who oppose the change, 25 are female. What is the probability that a randomly selected respondent to the survey is a man or opposes the change in policy? Express your answer as a percent.

(F) 25% **(H)** 75%

(G) 100% **(J)** 50%

3. A poll of 100 senior citizens in a retirement community asked about the types of electronic communication they used. The table shows the joint and marginal frequencies from the poll results. If you are given that one of the people polled uses text messaging, what is the probability that the person is also using e-mail? Express your answer as a decimal. If necessary, round your answer to the nearest hundredth.

Uses text messaging

		Yes	No	Total
Uses e-mail	**Yes**	0.17	0.66	0.83
	No	0.11	0.06	0.17
	Total	0.28	0.72	1

(A) 0.65 **(C)** 0.8

(B) 0.61 **(D)** 0.13

Mini-Task

4. Randa is playing a board game. The players take turns rolling a pair of number cubes and finding their sum. On her next turn, Randa must roll a 5 to win the game, but if she rolls doubles, she gets an extra turn. Explain why the events "roll a 5" and "roll doubles" are mutually exclusive. If the probability of rolling a 5 is $\frac{1}{9}$ and the probability of rolling doubles is $\frac{1}{6}$, what is the probability that Randa rolls either a 5 or doubles on her next turn? Express your answer as a fraction in simplest form.

PARCC Assessment Readiness

Selected Response

1. There were 8 dogs in a litter. How many ways can Mike choose 2 dogs?

(A) 20,160

(B) 56

(C) 28

(D) $\frac{1}{28}$

2. In a two-way table, the _____ are the values in each category divided by the total number of values.

(F) conditional relative frequencies

(G) marginal relative frequencies

(H) joint relative frequencies

(J) conditional probabilities

3. The table shows the number of teachers, coaches, and students of each gender at a high school. What is the probability, to the nearest hundredth, that a coach is male?

School Population and Gender		
	Male	Female
Teachers	12	24
Coaches	17	9
Students	429	453

(A) 0.65

(B) 0.35

(C) 0.04

(D) 0.02

4. A movie has 14 dialogue scenes and 10 action scenes. If these are the only two types of scenes, what is the probability that a randomly selected scene will be an action scene?

(F) $\frac{5}{12}$

(G) $\frac{7}{12}$

(H) $\frac{5}{7}$

(J) $\frac{7}{5}$

Use the spinner for Items 5 and 6.

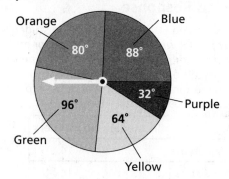

5. What is the probability of the spinner landing on the orange or purple sector, to the nearest hundredth?

(A) 0.09   (C) 0.31

(B) 0.22   (D) 1.12

6. What is the probability that the spinner will land on green in at least 2 of the next 3 spins? Write the answer to the nearest thousandth.

(F) 0.156   (H) 0.213

(G) 0.175   (J) 0.232

7. A point is chosen randomly on $\overline{AC}$. Find the probability that the point is not on $\overline{AB}$.

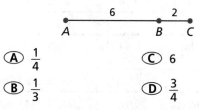

(A) $\frac{1}{4}$ (C) 6

(B) $\frac{1}{3}$ (D) $\frac{3}{4}$

8. Find the probability of the pointer landing on the region labeled "Celia".

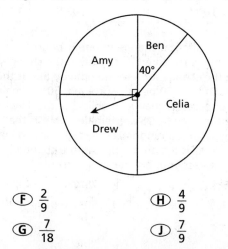

(F) $\frac{2}{9}$ (H) $\frac{4}{9}$

(G) $\frac{7}{18}$ (J) $\frac{7}{9}$

9. Find the probability that a point chosen randomly inside the circle is in the trapezoid. Round to the nearest hundredth.

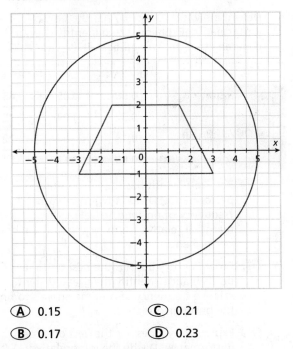

(A) 0.15

(C) 0.21

(B) 0.17

(D) 0.23

10. Louise wears an outfit everyday that consists of one top (shirt, T-shirt, or blouse), one bottom (pants or skirt) and one scarf. Her wardrobe consists of a tan skirt, a pair of black pants, 2 T-shirts, one silk blouse, 1 button-down shirt, and a set of 3 scarves. How many different outfits can Louise put together?

(F) 3 outfits

(H) 6 outfits

(G) 9 outfits

(J) 24 outfits

11. A person is selected at random. What is the probability that the person was not born on a Monday? Express your answer as a percent. If necessary, round your answer to the nearest tenth of a percent.

(A) 85.7%

(C) 80.0%

(B) 14.3%

(D) 20.0%

12. A circle is inscribed in a square with a side length of 4. If a point in the square is chosen at random, what is the probability that the point is in the square but not in the circle? Express your answer as a percent, and round to the nearest tenth.

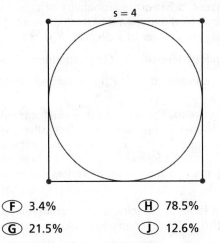

(F) 3.4%

(H) 78.5%

(G) 21.5%

(J) 12.6%

13. A bag contains hair ribbons for a spirit rally. The bag contains 3 black ribbons and 17 green ribbons. Lila and Jessica are drawing from the bag at random without replacement. Explain why the events are dependent. Then find the indicated probability.

Lila selects a black ribbon and then Jessica selects a green ribbon.

Express your answer as a fraction in simplest form.

(A) The events are dependent because *P*(Jessica green) is different when Lila has already removed one ribbon from the bag.

$\frac{51}{380}$

(B) The events are dependent because *P*(Jessica green) is the same when Lila has already removed one ribbon from the bag.

$\frac{12}{95}$

(C) The events are dependent because *P*(Jessica green) is different when Lila has already removed one ribbon from the bag.

$\frac{17}{190}$

(D) The events are dependent because *P*(Jessica green) is the same when Lila has already removed one ribbon from the bag.

$\frac{51}{400}$

14. A grab bag contains 8 football cards and 2 basketball cards. An experiment consists of taking one card out of the bag, replacing it, and then selecting another card. Determine whether the events are independent or dependent. What is the probability of selecting a football card and then a basketball card? Express your answer as a decimal.

(F) independent; 0.18   (H) dependent; 0.64

(G) dependent; 0.04   (J) independent; 0.16

15. In recent years, the three most popular car colors in the United States have been black, silver, and white. Suppose a poll of 40 randomly-selected car buyers gave the following results. The table shows how men's and women's preferences differed in the poll.

Make a table of the joint and marginal relative frequencies. Express percentages in decimal form.

	Black	Silver	White	Other
Men	4	4	4	8
Women	3	3	3	11

(A)

	Black	Silver	White	Other	Total
Men	0.1	0.1	0.1	0.2	0.5
Women	0.065	0.085	0.065	0.285	0.5
Total	0.165	0.185	0.165	0.485	1

(B)

	Black	Silver	White	Other	Total
Men	0.075	0.075	0.075	0.275	0.5
Women	0.1	0.1	0.1	0.2	0.5
Total	0.175	0.175	0.175	0.475	1

(C)

	Black	Silver	White	Other	Total
Men	0.2	0.2	0.2	0.4	0.5
Women	0.15	0.15	0.15	0.55	0.5
Total	0.35	0.35	0.35	0.95	1

(D)

	Black	Silver	White	Other	Total
Men	0.1	0.1	0.1	0.2	0.5
Women	0.075	0.075	0.075	0.275	0.5
Total	0.175	0.175	0.175	0.475	1

16. A study compared the on-time performance for three bus companies. A table with the joint and marginal frequencies of the results is shown.

Determine which company has the best on-time performance. Explain how to identify the company that performed best.

	On-time	Late	Total
Cross-Country Bus	0.38	0.05	0.43
Express Way Lines	0.32	0.03	0.35
Red Dog Transit	0.18	0.04	0.22
Total	0.88	0.12	1

(F) Red Dog Transit has the best on-time performance. Divide the joint relative frequency of on-time arrival by the marginal relative frequency to find the best performance.

(G) Cross-Country Bus has the best on-time performance. Identify the greatest joint relative frequency of on-time arrivals to find the best performance.

(H) Express Way Lines has the best on-time performance. Divide the joint relative frequency of on-time arrival by the marginal relative frequency to find the best performance.

(J) Cross-Country Bus has the best on-time performance. Divide the joint relative frequency of on-time arrival by the marginal relative frequency to find the best performance.

Mini-Tasks

17. The chart below shows the names of the students on the academic bowl team.

Robin	Drew	Jim
Greg	Sarah	Mindy
Ashley	Tina	Justin
David	Amy	Kevin

a. Only 2 students can be chosen for the final academic bowl. How many different ways can the students be selected?

b. Explain why you solved the problem the way that you did.

18. An experiment consists of tossing 3 coins at the same time.

a. Identify the sample space.

b. What is the probability of tossing 2 tails and 1 head?

c. Which is more likely to occur: tossing exactly 1 tail or tossing at least 2 heads? Explain.

19. A test to be on a trivia show has two parts. 60% of contestants pass the first part, and 20% pass the second part.

   a. If a contestant must pass both parts of the test to be on the show, how many contestants out of a group of 50 would likely make the show? Show your work.

   b. Is it more likely that a contestant would pass both parts or fail both parts of the test? Explain.

20. The Badgers won 70% of their games this season. They won 5 of the 12 games they played during their last road trip. Before the road trip, the Badgers had won 75% of their games.

   a. How many wins and losses did the Badgers have during the season?

   b. How many wins and losses did the Badgers have before their last road trip?

21. On a field trip, 4 students bring bag lunches. On the way there, the bag lunches get mixed up. What is the probability that exactly 1 student gets his or her own bag lunch back?

Performance Task

22. Jessica is a member of the basketball team at her high school and has a free throw shooting percentage of 85%. She is competing in a national free throw competition and needs to make at least 23 of 25 free throws to win. She will shoot all 25 free throws even if she makes 23 of 23 or 23 of 24 free throws. To compute the probability of her making r free throws in n attempts, the expression $_nC_r \cdot p^r \cdot (1 - p)^{n-r}$ can be used, where n is the number of trials, r is the number of successful free throws, and p is the probability of making a successful free throw in one attempt.

   a. What are the values of n, r, and p when using the expression to compute the probability of Jessica making exactly 23 of 25 free throws?

   b. Find the probability of Jessica making exactly 23 of 25 free throws, exactly 24 of 25 free throws, and 25 of 25 free throws. Round each probability to the nearest thousandth.

   c. Are the three probabilities you found in part **b** inclusive or exclusive? Explain how you know.

   d. What is the probability Jessica makes *at least* 23 of 25 free throws?

23. You are a contestant on a game show and have the chance to win a car by simply rolling five dice. Each die has three sides that say CAR and three sides that are blank. In order for you to win the car you must roll CAR on all five dice. Luckily, you have three chances to roll the dice. On each roll, you "keep" any dice that come up CAR and re-roll only the dice that come up blank.

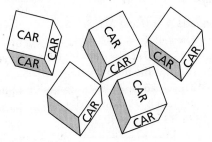

Imagine that you roll one die three times.

   Part A: If you roll a die once and get CAR, you would keep it. What is the probability of this happening?

   Part B: With two rolls, what is the probability that you first roll a blank, and then roll CAR on the second roll?

   Part C: With three rolls, what is the probability that you roll a blank twice, and then roll CAR on the third roll?

   Part D: Using your answers from *Parts A-C*, what is the probability that you get CAR and keep it, in one, two, or three rolls?

   Part E: Compare the probability in *Part D* to the probability of the complement of never rolling CAR.

my.hrw.com
Online Assessment

Go online for updated, PARCC-aligned assessment readiness.

1-1

Check It Out! **1a.** $3\frac{1}{2}$ **1b.** $4\frac{1}{2}$
3a. $1\frac{2}{3}$ **3b.** 24 **4.** 591.25 m
5. $RS = 4$; $ST = 4$; $RT = 8$

Exercises **1.** $\overline{XM}$ and $\overline{MY}$ **3.** 3.5
7. 29 **9.** $x = 4$; $KL = 7$; $JL = 14$
11. $5\frac{11}{12}$ **15.** 5 **17.** $DE = EF = 14$; DF
$= 28$ **19a.** C is the mdpt. of $\overline{AE}$.
b. 16 **21.** 7.1 **23.** 4 **25.** S
27. Statement A **29.** 6.5; -1.5
31. 3.375 **33.** 9 **37.** J **39.** H

41.

43. 14.02 m

1-2

Check It Out! **1.** $\angle RTQ$, $\angle T$,
$\angle STR$, $\angle 1$, $\angle 2$ **2a.** 40°; acute
2b. 125°; obtuse **2c.** 105°; obtuse
3. 62° **4a.** 34° **4b.** 46°

Exercises **1.** $\angle A$, $\angle R$, $\angle O$
3. $\angle AOB$, $\angle BOA$, or $\angle 1$; $\angle BOC$,
$\angle COB$, or $\angle 2$; $\angle AOC$ or $\angle COA$
5. 105°; obtuse **7.** 70° **9.** 28°
11. $\angle 1$ or $\angle JMK$; $\angle 2$ or $\angle LMK$;
$\angle M$ or $\angle JML$ **13.** 93°; obtuse
15. 66.6° **17.** 20° **19.** acute
21. acute **27.** 67.5°; 22.5° **29.** $16\frac{1}{3}$
31. 9 **33a.** 9 **b.** 12 **c.** $0 < x < 15.6$
35. $m\angle COD = 72°$; $m\angle BOC = 90°$
37. No; an obtuse $\angle$ measures
greater than 90°, so it cannot be $\cong$
to an acute $\angle$ (less than 90°).
41. D **43.** C **45.** The $\angle$ are acute.
An obtuse $\angle$ measures between 90°
and 180°. Since $\frac{1}{2}$ of 180 is 90, the
resulting $\angle$ must measure less than
90°. **47.** 36° or 4° **49.** 8100

1-3

Check It Out! **1.** 0.0004 **2.** odd
3. Female whales are longer than
male whales. **4a.** Possible answer: x
$= \frac{1}{2}$ **4b.** Possible answer:

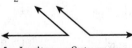

4c. Jupiter or Saturn

Exercises **3.** $\frac{4}{6}$ **5.** even
7. The number of bacteria doubles
every 20 minutes. **9.** The 3 pts. are
collinear. **11.** 5 P.M.

13.

15. $n - 1$ **17.** Possible answer:
$y = -1$ **19.** $m\angle 1 = m\angle 2 = 90°$
21. Possible answer: each term is
the previous term multiplied
by $\frac{1}{2}$; $\frac{1}{16}$; $\frac{1}{32}$. **23.** $2n + 1$ **25.** F
27. T **29.** $\frac{1}{11} = 0.\overline{09}$, $\frac{2}{11} = 0.\overline{18}$, $\frac{3}{11}$
$= 0.\overline{27}$,...; the fraction pattern is
multiples of $\frac{1}{11}$, and the decimal
pattern is repeating multiples of
0.09. **31.** 34, 55, 89; each term is
the sum of the 2 previous terms.
33. odd **37.** C **39.** D **41.** 12 years
43. $m\angle CAB = m\angle CBA$; $AC = CB$

1-4

Check It Out! **1.** Hypothesis:
A number is divisible by 6.
Conclusion: A number is divisible
by 3. **2.** If 2 $\angle$ are comp., then they
are acute. **3.** F; possible answer: 7
4. Converse: If an animal has
4 paws, then it is a cat; F. Inverse: If
an animal is not a cat, then it does
not have 4 paws; F. Contrapositive:
If an animal does not have 4 paws,
then it is not a cat; T.

Exercises **1.** converse
3. Hypothesis: A person is at least
16 years old. Conclusion: A person
can drive a car. **5.** Hypothesis:
$a - b < a$. Conclusion: b is a
positive number. **7.** If $0 < a < b$,
then $\left(\frac{a}{b}\right)^2 < \frac{a}{b}$. **9.** T **11.** F
13. Hypothesis: An animal is a
tabby. Conclusion: An animal is a
cat. **15.** Hypothesis: 8 ounces of
cereal cost $2.99. Conclusion:
16 ounces of cereal cost $5.98.
17. If the batter makes 3 strikes,
then the batter is out. **19.** T **21.** T
25. T **27.** F **29.** F **35.** If a person
is a Texan, then the person is an
American. **37a.** H: Only you can
find it. C: Everything's got a moral.
b. If only you can find it, then
everything's got a moral. **43.** If a
mineral has a hardness less than 5,
then it is not apatite; T. **45.** If a
mineral is not apatite, then it is
calcite; F. **47.** If a mineral is calcite,
then it has a hardness less than 5; T.

51. H **53.** J **55.** Some students are
adults. Some adults are students.
57. 3

1-5

Check It Out! **1.** deductive
reasoning **2.** valid **3.** valid
4. Polygon P is not a quad.

Exercises **3.** deductive
reasoning **5.** valid **7.** invalid
9. deductive reasoning
11. invalid **13.** Dakota gets better
grades in Social Studies.
15. valid **17.** valid **19.** yes; no;
because the first conditional is false
23. D **25.** 196 **27a.** If you live in
San Diego, then you live in the
United States. **b.** If you do not live
in California, then you do not live
in San Diego. If you do not live in
the United States, then you do not
live in California. **c.** If you do not
live in the United States, then you
do not live in San Diego. **d.** They
are contrapositives of each other.

2-1

Check It Out! **1a.** Conditional: If
an $\angle$ is acute, then its measure is
greater than 0° and less than 90°.
Converse: If an $\angle$'s measure is
greater than 0° and less than 90°,
then the $\angle$ is acute.
1b. Conditional: If Cho is a
member, then he has paid the
$5 dues. Converse: If Cho has paid
the $5 dues, then he is a member.
2a. Converse: If it is Independence
Day, then the date is July 4th.
Biconditional: It is July 4th if and
only if it is Independence Day.
2b. Converse: If pts. are collinear,
then they lie on the same line.
Biconditional: Pts. lie on the
same line if and only if they are
collinear. **3a.** T **3b.** F; $y = 5$
4a. A figure is a quad. if and only
if it is a 4-sided polygon. **4b.** An
$\angle$ is a straight $\angle$ if and only if its
measure is 180°.

Exercises **3.** Conditional: If
your medicine will be ready by

5 P.M. , then you dropped your prescription off by 8 A.M. Converse: If you drop your prescription off by 8 A.M. , then your medicine will be ready by 5 P.M. **5.** Converse: If 2 segs. are ≅, then they have the same length. Biconditional: 2 segs. have the same length if and only if they are ≅. **7.** F **9.** An animal is a hummingbird if and only if it is a tiny, brightly colored bird with narrow wings, a slender bill, and a long tongue. **11.** Conditional: If a ▱ is a rect., then it has 4 rt. ∡. Converse: If a ▱ has 4 rt. ∡, then it is a rect. **13.** Converse: If it is the weekend, then today is Saturday or Sunday. Biconditional: Today is Saturday or Sunday if and only if it is the weekend. **15.** Converse: If a △ is a rt. △, then it contains a rt. ∠. Biconditional: A △ contains a rt. ∠ if and only if it is a rt. △. **17.** T **19.** A player is a catcher if and only if the player is positioned behind home plate and catches throws from the pitcher. **21.** yes **23.** no **25.** A square is a quad. with 4 ≅ sides and 4 rt. ∡. **31.** no **33.** 5 **37a.** If I say it, then I mean it. If I mean it, then I say it. **39.** G **43a.** If an ∠ does not measure 105°, then the ∠ is not obtuse. **b.** If an ∠ is not obtuse, then it does not measure 105°. **c.** It is the contrapositive of the original. **d.** F; the inverse is false, and its converse is true.

2-2

Check It Out! **1.** $\frac{1}{2}t = -7$ (Given); $2\left(\frac{1}{2}t\right) = 2(-7)$ (Mult. Prop. of =); $t = -14$ (Simplify.) **2.** $C = \frac{5}{9}(F - 32)$ (Given); $C = \frac{5}{9}(86 - 32)$ (Subst.); $C = \frac{5}{9}(54)$ (Simplify.); $C = 30$ (Simplify.) **3.** ∠ Add. Post.; Subst.; Subtr. Prop. of =; Mult. Prop. of = **4a.** Sym. Prop. of = **4b.** Reflex. Prop. of = **4c.** Trans. Prop. of = **4d.** Sym. Prop. of ≅

Exercises **3.** $t - 3.2 = -8.3$ (Given); $t = -5.1$ (Add. Prop. of =) **5.** $\frac{x+3}{-2} = 8$ (Given); $x + 3 = -16$ (Mult. Prop.

of =); $x = -19$ (Subtr. Prop. of =) **7.** $0 = 2(r - 3) + 4$ (Given); $0 = 2r - 6 + 4$ (Distrib. Prop.); $0 = 2r - 2$ (Simplify.); $2 = 2r$ (Add. Prop. of =); $1 = r$ (Div. Prop. of =) **9.** $C = \$5.75 + \$0.89m$ (Given); $\$11.98 = \$5.75 + \$0.89m$ (Subst.); $\$6.23 = \$0.89m$ (Subtr. Prop. of =); $m = 7$ (Div. Prop. of =) **11.** Seg. Add. Post.; Subst.; Subtr. Prop. of =; Add. Prop. of =; Div. Prop. of = **13.** Trans. Prop. of = **15.** Trans. Prop. of ≅ **17.** $1.6 = 3.2n$ (Given); $0.5 = n$ (Div. Prop. of =) **19.** $-(h + 3) = 72$ (Given); $-h - 3 = 72$ (Distrib. Prop.); $-h = 75$ (Add. Prop. of =); $h = -75$ (Mult. Prop. of =) **21.** $\frac{1}{2}(p - 16) = 13$ (Given); $\frac{1}{2}p - 8 = 13$ (Distrib. Prop.); $\frac{1}{2}p = 21$ (Add. Prop. of =); $p = 42$ (Mult. Prop. of =) **23.** ∠ Add. Post.; Subst.; Simplify.; Subtr. Prop. of =; Add. Prop. of =; Div. Prop. of = **25.** Sym. Prop. of ≅ **27.** Trans. Prop. of = **29.** $x = 16$; $2(3.1x - 0.87) = 94.36$ (Given); $6.2x - 1.74 = 94.36$ (Distrib. Prop.); $6.2x = 96.1$ (Add. Prop. of =); $x = 15.5$ (Div. Prop. of =); possible answer: the exact solution rounds to the estimate. **31.** $\angle A \cong \angle T$ **33.** $\frac{x+1}{2} = 3$ (Mdpt. Formula;) $x + 1 = 6$ (Mult. Prop. of =); $x = 5$ (Subtr. Prop. of =); $\frac{1+y}{2} = 5$ (Mdpt. Formula); $1 + y = 10$ (Mult. Prop. of =); $y = 9$ (Subtr. Prop. of =) **35a.** $1733.65 = 92.50 + 79.96 + 983 + 10,820x$ (Given); $1733.65 = 1155.46 + 10,820x$ (Simplify.); $578.19 = 10,820x$ (Subtr. Prop. of =); $0.05 \approx x$ (Div. Prop. of =) **b.** $\$1.71$ **37a.** $x + 15 \le 63$ (Given); $x \le 48$ (Subtr. Prop. of Inequal.) **b.** $-2x > 36$ (Given); $x < -18$ (Div. Prop. of Inequal.) **39.** B **41.** D **43.** $PR = PA + RA$ (Seg. Add. Post.); $PA = QB, QB = RA$ (Given); $PA = RA$ (Trans. Prop. of =); $PR = PA + PA$ (Subst.); $PA = 18$(Given); $PR = 18 + 18$ (Subst.); $PR = 36$ in. (Simplify.) **45.** $7 - 3x > 19$ (Given); $-3x > 12$ (Subtr. Prop. of Inequal.); $x < -4$ (Div. Prop. of Inequal.)

2-3

Check It Out!
1. 1. Given
  2. Def. of mdpt.
  3. Given
  4. Trans. Prop. of ≅

2a. ∠1 and ∠2 are supp., and ∠2 and ∠3 are supp. **2b.** m∠1 + m∠2 = m∠2 + m∠3 **2c.** Subtr. Prop. of = **2d.** ∠1 ≅ ∠3

3. 1. ∠1 and ∠2 are comp. ∠2 and ∠3 are comp. (Given)
  2. m∠1 + m∠2 = 90°, m∠2 + m∠3 = 90° (Def. of comp. ∡)
  3. m∠1 + m∠2 = m∠2 + m∠3 (Subst.)
  4. m∠2 = m∠2 (Reflex. Prop. of =)
  5. m∠1 = m∠3 (Subtr. Prop. of =)
  6. ∠1 ≅ ∠3 (Def. of ≅ ∡)

Exercises **1.** statements; reasons

3. 1. Given
  2. Subst.
  3. Simplify.
  4. Add. Prop. of =
  5. Simplify.
  6. Def. of supp. ∡

5. 1. X is the mdpt. of $\overline{AY}$. Y is the mdpt. of $\overline{XB}$. (Given)
  2. $\overline{AX} \cong \overline{XY}, \overline{XY} \cong \overline{YB}$ (Def. of mdpt.)
  3. $\overline{AX} \cong \overline{YB}$ (Trans. Prop. of ≅)

7a. m∠1 + m∠2 = 180°, m∠3 + m∠4 = 180° **b.** Subst. **c.** m∠1 = m∠4 **d.** Def. of ≅ ∡

9. 1. $\overline{BE} \cong \overline{CE}, \overline{DE} \cong \overline{AE}$ (Given)
  2. BE = CE, DE = AE (Def. of ≅ segs.)
  3. AE + BE = AB, CE + DE = CD (Seg. Add. Post.)
  4. DE + CE = AB (Subst.)
  5. AB = CD (Subst.)
  6. $\overline{AB} \cong \overline{CD}$ (Def. of ≅ segs.)
11. 132° **13.** 59° **17.** S **19.** N
21. $x = 16$ **25.** C **27.** D **29.** $a = 17$; 37.5°, 52.5°, and 37.5°

2-4

Check It Out!
1. 1. $RS = UV$, $ST = TU$ (Given)
2. $RS + ST = TU + UV$ (Add. Prop. of =)
3. $RS + ST = RT$, $TU + UV = TV$ (Seg. Add. Post.)
4. $RT = TV$ (Subst.)
5. $\overline{RT} \cong \overline{TV}$ (Def. of $\cong$ segs.)

2.

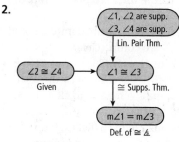

3. 1. $\angle WXY$ is a rt. $\angle$. (Given)
2. $m\angle WXY = 90°$ (Def. of rt. $\angle$)
3. $m\angle 2 + m\angle 3 = m\angle WXY$ ($\angle$ Add. Post.)
4. $m\angle 2 + m\angle 3 = 90°$ (Subst.)
5. $\angle 1 \cong \angle 3$ (Given)
6. $m\angle 1 = m\angle 3$ (Def. of $\cong$ $\angle$)
7. $m\angle 2 + m\angle 1 = 90°$ (Subst.)
8. $\angle 1$ and $\angle 2$ are comp. (Def. of comp. $\angle$)

4. It is given that $\angle 1 \cong \angle 4$. By the Vert. $\angle$ Thm., $\angle 1 \cong \angle 2$ and $\angle 3 \cong \angle 4$. By the Trans. Prop. of $\cong$, $\angle 2 \cong \angle 4$. Similarly, $\angle 2 \cong \angle 3$.

Exercises 1. flowchart
3. 1. $\angle 1 \cong \angle 2$ (Given)
2. $\angle 1$ and $\angle 2$ are supp. (Lin. Pair Thm.)
3. $\angle 1$ and $\angle 2$ are rt. $\angle$. ($\cong$ $\angle$ supp. → rt. $\angle$)
5. 1. $\angle 2 \cong \angle 4$ (Given)
2. $\angle 1 \cong \angle 2$, $\angle 3 \cong \angle 4$ (Vert. $\angle$ Thm.)
3. $\angle 1 \cong \angle 4$ (Trans. Prop. of $\cong$)
4. $\angle 1 \cong \angle 3$ (Trans. Prop. of $\cong$)
7. 1. B is the mdpt. of $\overline{AC}$. (Given)
2. $\overline{AB} \cong \overline{BC}$ (Def. of mdpt.)
3. $AB = BC$ (Def. of $\cong$ segs.)
4. $AD + DB = AB$, $BE + EC = BC$ (Seg. Add. Post.)
5. $AD + DB = BE + EC$ (Subst.)
6. $AD = EC$ (Given)
7. $DB = BE$ (Subtr. Prop. of =)

9. 1. $\angle 1 \cong \angle 4$ (Given)
2. $\angle 1 \cong \angle 2$ (Vert. $\angle$ Thm.)
3. $\angle 4 \cong \angle 2$ (Trans. Prop. of $\cong$)
4. $m\angle 4 = m\angle 2$ (Def. of $\cong$ $\angle$)
5. $\angle 3$ and $\angle 4$ are supp. (Lin. Pair Thm.)
6. $m\angle 3 + m\angle 4 = 180°$ (Def. of supp. $\angle$)
7. $m\angle 3 + m\angle 2 = 180°$ (Subst.)
8. $\angle 2$ and $\angle 3$ are supp. (Def. of supp. $\angle$)
11. 13 cm; conv. of the Common Segs. Thm. **13.** 37°, Vert. $\angle$ Thm.
15. $y = 11$ **17.** A **21.** C **23.** D
25. 1. $\angle AOC \cong \angle BOD$ (Given)
2. $m\angle AOC = m\angle BOD$ (Def. of $\cong$ $\angle$)
3. $m\angle AOB + m\angle BOC = m\angle AOC$, $m\angle BOC + m\angle COD = m\angle BOD$ ($\angle$ Add. Post.)
4. $m\angle AOB + m\angle BOC = m\angle BOC + m\angle COD$ (Subst.)
5. $m\angle BOC = m\angle BOC$ (Reflex. Prop. of =)
6. $m\angle AOB = m\angle COD$ (Subtr. Prop. of =)
7. $\angle AOB \cong \angle COD$ (Def. of $\cong$ $\angle$)
27. $x = 31$ and $y = 11.5$; 86°, 94°, 86°, and 94°

3-1

Check It Out! 1. $m\angle QRS = 62°$
2. $m\angle ABD = 60°$ **3.** 55° and 60°

Exercises 1. $m\angle JKL = 127°$ **3.** $m\angle 1 = 90°$ **5.** $x = 8$; $y = 9$ **7.** $m\angle VYX = 100°$ **9.** $m\angle EFG = 102°$ **11.** $m\angle STU = 90°$ **13.** 120°; Corr. $\angle$ Post.
15. 60°; Same-Side Int. $\angle$ Thm.
17. 60°; Lin. Pair Thm. **19.** 120°; Vert. $\angle$ Thm. **21.** $x = 4$; Same-Side Int. $\angle$ Thm.; $m\angle 3 = 103°$; $m\angle 4 = 77°$
23. $x = 3$; Corr. $\angle$ Post.; $m\angle 1 = m\angle 4 = 42°$ **25a.** $\angle 1 \cong \angle 3$ **b.** Corr. $\angle$ Post. **c.** $\angle 1 \cong \angle 2$ **d.** Trans. Prop. of $\cong$ **29a.** same-side int. $\angle$ **b.** By the Same-Side Int. $\angle$ Thm., $m\angle QRT + m\angle STR = 180°$. $m\angle QRT = 25° + 90° = 115°$, so $m\angle STR = 65°$.
31. A **35.** J **37.** $m\angle 1 = 75°$
39. $x = 4$; $y = 12$

3-2

Check It Out! 1a. $\angle 1 \cong \angle 3$, so $\ell \parallel m$ by the Conv. of Corr. $\angle$ Post.
1b. $m\angle 7 = 77°$ and $m\angle 5 = 77°$, so $\angle 7 \cong \angle 5$. $\ell \parallel m$ by the Conv. of Corr. $\angle$ Post. **2a.** $\angle 4 \cong \angle 8$, so $r \parallel s$ by the Conv. of Alt. Int. $\angle$ Thm.
2b. $m\angle 3 = 100°$ and $m\angle 7 = 100°$, so $\angle 3 \cong \angle 7$. $r \parallel s$ by the Conv. of Alt. Int. $\angle$ Thm.

3. 1. $\angle 1 \cong \angle 4$ (Given)
2. $m\angle 1 = m\angle 4$ (Def. $\cong$ $\angle$)
3. $\angle 3$ and $\angle 4$ are supp. (Given)
4. $m\angle 3 + m\angle 4 = 180°$ (Def. supp. $\angle$)
5. $m\angle 3 + m\angle 1 = 180°$ (Subst.)
6. $m\angle 2 = m\angle 3$ (Vert. $\angle$ Thm.)
7. $m\angle 2 + m\angle 1 = 180°$ (Subst.)
8. $\ell \parallel m$ (Conv. of Same-Side Int. $\angle$ Thm.)

4. $4y - 2 = 4(8) - 2 = 30°$; $3y + 6 = 3(8) + 6 = 30°$; The $\angle$ are $\cong$, so the oars are $\parallel$ by the Conv. of Corr. $\angle$ Post.

Exercises 1. $\angle 4 \cong \angle 5$, so $p \parallel q$ by the Conv. of Corr. $\angle$ Post. **3.** $m\angle 4 = 47°$, and $m\angle 5 = 47°$, so $\angle 4 \cong \angle 5$. $p \parallel q$ by the Conv. of Corr. $\angle$ Post. **5.** $\angle 3$ and $\angle 4$ are supp., so $r \parallel s$ by the Conv. of Same-Side Int. $\angle$ Thm. **7.** $m\angle 4 = 61°$, and $m\angle 8 = 61°$, so $\angle 4 \cong \angle 8$. $r \parallel s$ by the Conv. of Alt. Int. $\angle$ Thm. **9.** $m\angle 2 = 132°$, and $m\angle 6 = 132°$, so $\angle 2 \cong \angle 6$. $r \parallel s$ by the Conv. of Alt. Ext. $\angle$ Thm. **11.** $m\angle 1 = 60°$, and $m\angle 2 = 60°$, so $\angle 1 \cong \angle 2$. By the Conv. of Alt. Int. $\angle$ Thm., the landings are $\parallel$. **13.** $m\angle 4 = 54°$, and $m\angle 8 = 54°$, so $\angle 4 \cong \angle 8$. $\ell \parallel m$ by the Conv. of Corr. $\angle$ Post. **15.** $m\angle 1 = 55°$, and $m\angle 5 = 55°$, so $\angle 1 \cong \angle 5$. $\ell \parallel m$ by the Conv. of Corr. $\angle$ Post. **17.** $\angle 2 \cong \angle 7$, so $n \parallel p$ by the Conv. of Alt. Ext. $\angle$ Thm. **19.** $m\angle 1 = 105°$, and $m\angle 8 = 105°$, so $\angle 1 \cong \angle 8$. $n \parallel p$ by the Conv. of Alt. Ext. $\angle$ Thm. **21.** $m\angle 3 = 75°$, and $m\angle 5 = 105°$. $75° + 105° = 180°$, so $\angle 3$ and $\angle 5$ are supp. $n \parallel p$ by the Conv. of Same-Side Int. $\angle$ Thm. **23.** If $x = 6$, then $m\angle 1 = 20°$ and $m\angle 2 = 20°$. So $\overline{DJ} \parallel \overline{EK}$ by the

Conv. of Corr. ∡ Post. **25.** Conv. of Alt. Ext. ∡ Thm. **27.** Conv. of Corr. ∡ Post. **29.** Conv. of Same-Side Int. ∡ Thm. **31.** $m \parallel n$; Conv. of Same-Side Int. ∡ Thm. **33.** $m \parallel n$; Conv. of Alt. Ext. ∡ Thm. **35.** $\ell \parallel n$; Conv. of Same-Side Int. ∡ Thm. **37a.** $\angle URT$; m$\angle URT$ = m$\angle URS$ + m$\angle SRT$ by the ∠ Add. Post. It is given that m$\angle SRT$ = 25° and m$\angle URS$ = 90°, so m$\angle URT$ = 25° + 90° = 115°. **b.** It is given that m$\angle SUR$ = 65°. From part **a,** m$\angle URT$ = 115°. 65° + 115° = 180°, so $\overleftrightarrow{SU} \parallel \overleftrightarrow{RT}$ by the Conv. of Same-Side Int. ∡ Thm. **39.** It is given that $\angle 1$ and $\angle 2$ are supp., so m$\angle 1$ + m$\angle 2$ = 180°. By the Lin. Pair Thm., m$\angle 2$ + m$\angle 3$ = 180°. By the Trans. Prop. of =, m$\angle 1$ + m$\angle 2$ = m$\angle 2$ + m$\angle 3$. By the Subtr. Prop. of =, m$\angle 1$ = m$\angle 3$. By the Conv. of Corr. ∡ Post., $\ell \parallel m$. **41.** The Reflex. Prop. is not true for $\parallel$ lines, because a line is not $\parallel$ to itself. The Sym. Prop. is true, because if $\ell \parallel m$, then ℓ and m are coplanar and do not intersect. So $m \parallel \ell$. The Trans. Prop. is not true for $\parallel$ lines, because if $\ell \parallel m$ and $m \parallel n$, then ℓ and n could be the same line. So they would not be $\parallel$. **43.** C **45.** 15 **47.** No lines can be proven $\parallel$. **49.** $q \parallel r$ by the Conv. of Alt. Int. ∡ Thm. **51.** $s \parallel t$ by the Conv. of Alt. Ext. ∡ Thm. **53.** No lines can be proven $\parallel$. **55.** By the Vert. ∡ Thm., $\angle 6 \cong \angle 3$, so m$\angle 6$ = m$\angle 3$. It is given that m$\angle 2$ + m$\angle 3$ = 180°. By subst., m$\angle 2$ + m$\angle 6$ = 180°. By the Conv. of Same-Side Int. ∡ Thm., $\ell \parallel m$.

3-3

Check It Out! 1a. $\overline{AB}$ **1b.** $x < 17$
2. 1. $\angle EHF \cong \angle HFG$ (Given)
  2. $\overleftrightarrow{EH} \parallel \overleftrightarrow{FG}$ (Conv. of Alt. Int. ∡ Thm.)
  3. $\overleftrightarrow{FG} \perp \overleftrightarrow{GH}$ (Given)
  4. $\overleftrightarrow{EH} \perp \overleftrightarrow{GH}$ (⊥ Transv. Thm.)

3. The shoreline and the path of the swimmer should both be ⊥ to the current, so they should be $\parallel$ to each other.

Exercises 1. $\overleftrightarrow{AB}$ and $\overleftrightarrow{CD}$ are ⊥. $\overline{AC}$ and $\overline{BC}$ are $\cong$. **3.** $x > -5$ **5.** The service lines are coplanar lines that are ⊥ to the same line (the center line), so they must be $\parallel$ to each other. **7.** $x < 11$ **9.** Both the frets are lines that are ⊥ to the same line (the string), so the frets must be $\parallel$ to each other. **11.** $x > \frac{8}{3}$ **13.** $x = 6$, $y = 15$ **15.** $x = 60$, $y = 60$ **17.** no **19.** no **21.** yes **23a.** It is given that $\overline{QR} \perp \overline{PQ}$ and $\overline{PQ} \parallel \overline{RS}$, so $\overline{QR} \perp \overline{RS}$ by the ⊥ Transv. Thm. It is given that $\overline{PS} \parallel \overline{QR}$. Since $\overline{QR} \perp \overline{RS}$, $\overline{PS} \perp \overline{RS}$ by the ⊥ Transv. Thm. **b.** It is given that $\overline{PS} \parallel \overline{QR}$ and $\overline{QR} \perp \overline{PQ}$. So $\overline{PQ} \perp \overline{PS}$ by the ⊥Transv. Thm.
25. Possible answer: 1.6 cm
31. C **33.** D **35a.** $n \perp p$ **b.** AB; AB; the shortest distance from a point to a line is measured along a perpendicular segment. **c.** The distance between two parallel lines is the length of a segment that is perpendicular to both lines and has one endpoint on each line.

4-1

Check It Out! 1. $D'(3, 9)$, $E'(3, -6)$, $F'(9, 0)$; dilation with scale factor 3 **2.** The triangles are congruent because $\triangle ABC$ can be mapped to $\triangle PQR$ by a rotation: $(x, y) \longrightarrow (-y, x)$. **3.** The polygons are congruent because $\triangle ABC$ can be mapped to $\triangle A'B'C'$ by a translation: $(x, y) \longrightarrow (x + 5, y + 2)$; and then $\triangle A'B'C'$ can be mapped to $\triangle PQR$ by a reflection $(x, y) \longrightarrow (x, -y)$.

Exercises 1. are not **3.** $A'(2, -1)$, $B'(5, -4)$, $C'(5, -1)$; This is a reflection across the x-axis. **5.** $L'(2, -1)$, $M'(5, -4)$, $N'(5, -1)$, $O'(5, -1)$; This is a 90° rotation clockwise with a center of rotation $(0, 0)$. **7.** The rectangles are not congruent because rectangle $ABCD$ can be mapped to rectangle $WXYZ$ by a dilation with scale factor $k \neq 1$. $(x, y) \longrightarrow (0.5x, 0.5y)$. **9.** The triangles are congruent because $\triangle MNO$ can be mapped to $\triangle M'N'O'$

by a reflection: $(x, y) \longrightarrow (-x, y)$. And then $\triangle M'N'O'$ can be mapped to $\triangle JKL$ by a translation: $(x, y) \longrightarrow (x, y + 2)$. **11.** Repeated horizontal reflections and horizontal translations create the wallpaper pattern. The large flower at the top is translated right and left while the stem, leaves, smaller flowers, and background design are reflected to the left and right to create an image that is congruent to the pre-image. **13.** $G'(9, -5)$, $H'(12, -1)$, $I'(12, -5)$; This is a translation 5 units right and 4 units down. **15.** $L'(-1.5, 6)$, $M'(-6, 6)$, $N'(-6, 4.5)$; This is a dilation with scale factor 1.5 and center $(0, 0)$. **17.** $N'(0, -1)$, $O'(-1, 5)$, $P'(1, 5)$; This is a translation 1 unit left and 1 unit up. **19.** Yes, the rectangles are congruent because rectangle $JKLM$ can be mapped to rectangle $ABCD$ by a rotation: $(x, y) \longrightarrow (y, -x)$. **21.** Yes, the triangles are congruent because $\triangle EFG$ can be mapped to $\triangle UVW$ by a translation: $(x, y) \longrightarrow (x, y + 3)$. **23.** The triangles are congruent because $\triangle ABC$ can be mapped to $\triangle A'B'C'$ by a rotation: $(x, y) \longrightarrow (y, -x)$, and then $\triangle A'B'C'$ can be mapped to $\triangle DEF$ by a translation: $(x, y) \longrightarrow (x - 2, y)$. **25a.** The pattern was created with a 90° counterclockwise rotation and translation to the right and down. Then another 90° rotation clockwise and a translation right and down. This then repeats to fill the rectangular quilt area. **b.** The thin rectangles are congruent, as are the quilt block squares. c. The quilt would look more like a checkerboard pattern. **27.** $X'(4, 6)$, $Y'(4, -4)$, $Z'(-2, 0)$; This is a rotation 90° clockwise about $(0, 0)$ 29. $A'(2, -5)$, $B'(4, -4)$, $C'(-1, 2)$; This is a reflection across the x-axis and a translation 3 units to the right. **31.** Starting in the upper left, Frank reflected his shape horizontally. Then he rotated it 90° counterclockwise and translated it to the right and up. The he reflected it vertically. This whole row he then rotated 180° and translated down. **33.** Dave is correct because the triangle was reflected, not rotated. **35.** The dilation of the figure with a scale factor of 2 will be 4 times as large as the figure with a scale factor of 0.5. A scale factor of 2 increases the figure to twice its original size. A scale factor of 0.5 decreases the figure to half its original size. **37.** D

Check It Out! 1. 32° **2a.** 26.3° **2b.** $(90 - x)°$ **2c.** $41\frac{3}{5}°$ **3.** 141° **4.** 32°; 32°

Exercises 3. auxiliary lines **5.** 36°; 80°; 64° **7.** $(90 - y)°$ **9.** 28° **11.** 52°; 63° **13.** 89°; 89° **15.** 84° **17.** $(90 - 2x)°$ **19.** 162° **21.** 48°; 48° **23.** 15°; 60°; 105° **29.** 36° **31.** 48° **33.** 120°; 360° **35.** 18° **37.** The ext. ∡ at the same vertex of a △ are vert. ∡. Since vert. ∡ are ≅, the 2 ext. ∡ have the same measure. **41.** C **43.** D **45.** $y = 7$ or $y = -7$ **47.** Since an ext. ∠ is = to a sum of 2 remote int. ∡, it must be greater than either ∠. Therefore it cannot be ≅ to a remote int. ∠. **49.** 38°

Check It Out! 1. $\angle L \cong \angle E$, $\angle M \cong \angle F$, $\angle N \cong \angle G$, $\angle P \cong \angle H$, $\overline{LM} \cong \overline{EF}$, $\overline{MN} \cong \overline{FG}$, $\overline{NP} \cong \overline{GH}$, $\overline{LP} \cong \overline{EH}$
2a. 4 **2b.** 37°

3. 1. $\angle A \cong \angle D$ (Given)
2. $\angle BCA \cong \angle ECD$ (Vert. ∡ are ≅.)
3. $\angle ABC \cong \angle DEC$ (Third ∡ Thm.)
4. $\overline{AB} \cong \overline{DE}$ (Given)
5. $\overline{AD}$ bisects $\overline{BE}$, and $\overline{BE}$ bisects $\overline{AD}$. (Given)
6. $\overline{BC} \cong \overline{EC}$, $\overline{AC} \cong \overline{DC}$ (Def. of bisector)
7. $\triangle ABC \cong \triangle DEC$ (Def. of ≅ △)
4. 1. $\overline{JK} \parallel \overline{ML}$ (Given)
2. $\angle KJN \cong \angle MLN$, $\angle JKN \cong \angle LMN$ (Alt. Int. ∡ Thm.)
3. $\angle JNK \cong \angle LNM$ (Vert. ∡ Thm.)
4. $\overline{JK} \cong \overline{ML}$ (Given)
5. $\overline{MK}$ bisects $\overline{JL}$, and $\overline{JL}$

bisects $\overline{MK}$. (Given)
6. $\overline{JN} \cong \overline{LN}$, $\overline{MN} \cong \overline{KN}$ (Def. of bisector)
7. $\triangle JKN \cong \triangle MLN$ (Def. of ≅ △)

Exercises 1. You find the ∡ and sides that are in the same, or matching, places in the 2 △. **3.** $\overline{LM}$ **5.** $\angle M$ **7.** $\angle R$ **9.** $KL = 9$ **11a.** Given **b.** Alt. Int. ∡ Thm. **c.** Given **d.** Given **e.** $\overline{AE} \cong \overline{CE}$, $\overline{DE} \cong \overline{BE}$; **f.** Vert. ∡ Thm. **g.** Def. of ≅ △ **13.** $\overline{LM}$ **15.** $\angle N$ **17.** $m\angle C = 31°$ **19a.** Given **b.** Given **c.** $\angle NMP \cong \angle RMP$ **d.** $\angle NPM \cong \angle RPM$ **e.** Given **f.** $\overline{PN} \cong \overline{PR}$ **g.** Given **h.** Reflex. Prop. of ≅ **21.** $\triangle GSR \cong \triangle KPH$; $\triangle SRG \cong \triangle PHK$; $\triangle RGS \cong \triangle HKP$ **23.** $x = 30$; $AB = 50$ **25.** $x = 2$; $BC = 17$ **29.** solution A **31.** B **33.** D **35.** $x = 5.5$; yes; $UV = WV = 41.5$, and $UT = WT = 33$. $TV = TV$ by the Reflex. Prop. of =. It is given that $\angle VWT \cong \angle VUT$ and $\angle WTV \cong \angle UTV$. $\angle WVT \cong \angle UVT$ by the Third ∡ Thm. Thus $\triangle TUV \cong \triangle TWV$ by the def. of ≅ △.

5-1

Check It Out! 1. It is given that $\overline{AB} \cong \overline{CD}$ and $\overline{BC} \cong \overline{DA}$. By the Reflex. Prop. of ≅, $\overline{AC} \cong \overline{CA}$. So $\triangle ABC \cong \triangle CDA$ by SSS. **2.** It is given that $\overline{BA} \cong \overline{BD}$ and $\angle ABC \cong \angle DBC$. By the Reflex. Prop. of ≅, $\overline{BC} \cong \overline{BC}$. So $\triangle ABC \cong \triangle DBC$ by SAS. **3.** $DA = DC = 13$, so $\overline{DA} \cong \overline{DC}$ by def. of ≅. $m\angle ADB = m\angle CDB = 32°$, so $\angle ADB \cong \angle CDB$ by def. of ≅. $\overline{DB} \cong \overline{DB}$ by the Reflex. Prop. of ≅. Therefore $\triangle ADB \cong \triangle CDB$ by SAS.
4. 1. $\overline{QR} \cong \overline{QS}$ (Given)
2. $\overrightarrow{QP}$ bisects $\angle RQS$. (Given)
3. $\angle RQP \cong \angle SQP$ (Def. of bisector)
4. $\overline{QP} \cong \overline{QP}$ (Reflex. Prop. of ≅)
5. $\triangle RQP \cong \triangle SQP$ (SAS Steps 1, 3, 4)

Exercises 1. $\angle T$ **3.** It is given that $\overline{MN} \cong \overline{MQ}$ and $\overline{NP} \cong \overline{QP}$. $\overline{MP} \cong \overline{MP}$ by the Reflex. Prop. of ≅. Thus $\triangle MNP \cong \triangle MQP$ by SSS.

5. When $x = 4$, $HI = GH = 3$, and $IJ = GJ = 5$. $\overline{HJ} \cong \overline{HJ}$ by the Reflex. Prop. of ≅. Therefore $\triangle GHJ \cong \triangle IHJ$ by SSS. **7a.** Given **b.** $\angle JKL \cong \angle MLK$ **c.** Reflex. Prop. of ≅ **d.** SAS Steps 1, 2, 3 **9.** It is given that $\overline{KJ} \cong \overline{LJ}$ and $\overline{GK} \cong \overline{GL}$. $\overline{GJ} \cong \overline{GJ}$ by the Reflex. Prop. of ≅. So $\triangle GJK \cong \triangle GJL$ by SSS. **11.** When $y = 3$, $NQ = NM = 3$, and $QP = MP = 4$. So by the def. of ≅, $\overline{NQ} \cong \overline{NM}$ and $\overline{QP} \cong \overline{MP}$. $m\angle M = m\angle Q = 90°$, so $\angle M \cong \angle Q$ by the def. of ≅. Thus $\triangle MNP \cong \triangle QNP$ by SAS. **13a.** Given **b.** $\overline{DB} \cong \overline{CB}$ **c.** $\overline{AB} \perp \overline{DC}$ **d.** Def. of ⊥ **e.** Rt. ∠ ≅ Thm. **f.** $\overline{AB} \cong \overline{AB}$ **g.** SAS Steps 2, 5, 6 **15.** SAS **17.** neither **19.** $QS = TV = \sqrt{5}$. $SR = VU = 4$. $QR = TU = \sqrt{13}$. The △ are ≅ by SSS. **21a.** Given **b.** Def. of ≅ **c.** $m\angle WVY = m\angle ZYV$ **d.** Def. of ≅ **e.** Given **f.** $\overline{VY} \cong \overline{YV}$ **g.** SAS Steps 6, 5, 7 **25.** Measure the lengths of the logs. If the lengths of the logs in 1 wing deflector match the lengths of the logs in the other wing deflector, the △ will be ≅ by SAS or SSS. **27.** Yes; if each side is ≅ to the corr. side of the second △, they can be in any order. **29.** G **31.** J **35.** $x = 27$; $FK = FH = 171$, so $\overline{FK} \cong \overline{FH}$ by the def of ≅. $\angle KFJ \cong \angle HFJ$ by the def. of ∠ bisector. $\overline{FJ} \cong \overline{FJ}$ by the Reflex. Prop. of ≅. So $\triangle FJK \cong \triangle FJH$ by SAS.

5-2

Check It Out! 1. Yes; the △ is uniquely determined by AAS.
2. By the Alt. Int. ∡ Thm., $\angle KLN \cong \angle MNL$. $\overline{LN} \cong \overline{LN}$ by the Reflex. Prop. of ≅. No other congruence relationships can be determined, so ASA cannot be applied.
3. Given: $\overline{JL}$ bisects $\angle KLM$, and $\angle K \cong \angle M$.
Prove: $\triangle JKL \cong \triangle JML$

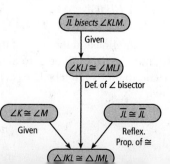

4. Yes; it is given that $\overline{AC} \cong \overline{DB}$. $\overline{CB} \cong \overline{CB}$ by the Reflex. Prop. of $\cong$. Since $\angle ABC$ and $\angle DCB$ are rt. $\angle$s, $\triangle ABC$ and $\triangle DCB$ are rt. $\triangle$s, $\triangle ABC \cong \triangle DCB$ by HL.

Exercises 1. The included side $\overline{BC}$ is enclosed between $\angle ABC$ and $\angle ACB$. **3.** Yes, the $\triangle$ is determined by AAS. **5.** No; you need to know that a pair of corr. sides are $\cong$. **7.** Yes; it is given that $\angle D$ and $\angle B$ are rt. $\angle$ and $\overline{AD} \cong \overline{BC}$. $\triangle ABC$ and $\triangle CDA$ are rt. $\triangle$ by def. $\overline{AC} \cong \overline{CA}$ by the Reflex. Prop. of $\cong$. So $\triangle ABC \cong \triangle CDA$ by HL.

9.

11. No; you need to know that $\angle MKJ \cong \angle MKL$. **13a.** $\angle A \cong \angle D$ **b.** Given **c.** $\angle C \cong \angle F$ **d.** AAS
15. Yes; E is a mdpt. So by def., $\overline{BE} \cong \overline{CE}$, and $\overline{AE} \cong \overline{DE}$. $\angle A$ and $\angle D$ are $\cong$ by the Rt. $\angle$ Thm. By def. $\triangle ABE$ and $\triangle DCE$ are rt. $\triangle$s. So $\triangle ABE \cong \triangle DCE$ by HL. **17.** $\triangle FEG \cong \triangle QSR$; rotation **19a.** No; there is not enough information given to use any of the congruence theorems. **b.** HL **21.** It is given that $\triangle ABC$ and $\triangle DEF$ are rt.$\triangle$. $\overline{AC} \cong \overline{DF}$, $\overline{BC} \cong \overline{EF}$, and $\angle C$ and $\angle F$ are rt. $\angle$. $\angle C \cong \angle F$ by the Rt. $\angle$ Thm. Thus $\triangle ABC \cong \triangle DEF$ by SAS.
27. J **29.** G **31.** Yes; the sum of the $\angle$ measures in each $\triangle$ must be 180°, which makes it possible to solve for x and y. The value of x is 15, and the value of y is 12. Each $\triangle$ has $\angle$ measuring 82°, 68°, and 30°. $\overline{VU} \cong \overline{VU}$ by the Reflex. Prop. of $\cong$. So $\triangle VSU \cong \triangle VTU$ by ASA or AAS.

5-3

Check It Out! 1. 41 ft
2.

```
┌─────────────────┐  ┌───────────────┐  ┌──────────────┐
│ PR̄ bisects ∠QPS │  │  PR̄ ≅ PR̄     │  │ ∠QPR ≅ ∠SPR  │
│ and ∠QRS.       │  │               │  │ ∠QRP ≅ ∠SRP  │
└─────────────────┘  └───────────────┘  └──────────────┘
    Given          Reflex. Prop. of ≅    Def. of ∠
                                          bisector
              └──────────┬──────────────────┘
                  ┌──────────────┐
                  │ △PQR ≅ △PSR  │
                  └──────────────┘
                        ASA
                  ┌──────────────┐
                  │  PQ̄ ≅ PS̄    │
                  └──────────────┘
                       CPCTC
```

3. 1. J is the mdpt. of $\overline{KM}$ and $\overline{NL}$. (Given)
  2. $\overline{KJ} \cong \overline{MJ}, \overline{NJ} \cong \overline{LJ}$ (Def. of mdpt.)
  3. $\angle KJL \cong \angle MJN$ (Vert. $\angle$ Thm.)
  4. $\triangle KJL \cong \triangle MJN$ (SAS *Steps 2, 3*)
  5. $\angle LKJ \cong \angle NMJ$ (CPCTC)
  6. $\overline{KL} \parallel \overline{MN}$ (Conv. of Alt. Int. $\angle$ Thm.)
4. $RJ = JL = \sqrt{5}$, $RS = JK = \sqrt{10}$, and $ST = KL = \sqrt{17}$. So $\triangle JKL \cong \triangle RST$ by SSS. $\angle JKL \cong \angle RST$ by CPCTC.

Exercises 1. corr. $\angle$ and corr. sides. **3a.** Def. of $\perp$ **b.** Rt. $\angle \cong$ Thm. **c.** Reflex. Prop. of $\cong$ **d.** Def. of mdpt. **e.** $\triangle RXS \cong \triangle RXT$ **f.** CPCTC
5. $EF = JK = 2$ and $EG = FG = JL = KL = \sqrt{10}$. So $\triangle EFG \cong \triangle JKL$ by SSS. $\angle EFG \cong \angle JKL$ by CPCTC.
7. 420 ft
9. 1. $\overline{WX} \cong \overline{XY} \cong \overline{YZ} \cong \overline{ZW}$ (Given)
  2. $\overline{ZX} \cong \overline{ZX}$ (Reflex. Prop. of $\cong$)
  3. $\triangle WXZ \cong \triangle YZX$ (SSS)
  4. $\angle W \cong \angle Y$ (CPCTC)
11. 1. $\overline{LM}$ bisects $\angle JLK$. (Given)
  2. $\angle JLM \cong \angle KLM$ (Def. of $\angle$ bisector)
  3. $\overline{JL} \cong \overline{KL}$ (Given)
  4. $\overline{LM} \cong \overline{LM}$ (Reflex. Prop. of $\cong$)
  5. $\triangle JLM \cong \triangle KLM$ (SAS *Steps 3, 2, 4*)
  6. $\overline{JM} \cong \overline{KM}$ (CPCTC)
  7. M is the mdpt. of $\overline{JK}$. (Def. of mdpt.)
13. $AB = DE = \sqrt{13}$, $BC = EF = 5$, and $AC = DF = \sqrt{18} = 3\sqrt{2}$. So $\triangle ABC \cong \triangle DEF$ by SSS. $\angle BAC \cong \angle EDF$ by CPCTC.
15. 1. E is the mdpt. of $\overline{AC}$ and $\overline{BD}$. (Given)
  2. $\overline{AE} \cong \overline{CE}; \overline{BE} \cong \overline{DE}$ (Def. of mdpt.)

3. $\angle AEB \cong \angle CED$ (Vert. $\angle$ Thm.)
4. $\triangle AEB \cong \triangle CED$ (SAS *Steps 2, 3*)
5. $\angle A \cong \angle C$ (CPCTC)
6. $\overline{AB} \parallel \overline{CD}$ (Conv. of Alt. Int. $\angle$ Thm.)
17. 14 **25.** G **27.** G **29.** Any diag. on any face of the cube is the hyp. of a rt. $\triangle$ whose legs are edges of the cube. Any 2 of these $\triangle$ are $\cong$ by SAS. Therefore any 2 diags. are $\cong$ by CPCTC.

5-4

Check It Out! 1. 4.2×10^{13}; since it is 6 months between September and March, the $\angle$ measures will be the same between Earth and the star. By the Conv. of the Isosc. $\triangle$ Thm., the $\triangle$ created are isosc. and the dist. is the same. **2a.** 66°
2b. 48° **3.** 10 **4.** By the Mdpt. Formula, the coords. of X are $(-a, b)$, the coords. of Y are (a, b), and the coords. of Z are $(0, 0)$. By the Dist. Formula, $XZ = YZ = \sqrt{a^2 + b^2}$. So $\overline{XZ} \cong \overline{YZ}$ and $\triangle XYZ$ is isosc.

Exercises 1. legs: $\overline{KJ}$ and $\overline{KL}$; base: $\overline{JL}$; base $\angle$: $\angle J$ and $\angle L$ **3.** 118°
5. 27° **7.** $y = 5$ **9.** 20 **11.** It is given that $\triangle ABC$ is rt. isosc., $\overline{AB} \cong \overline{BC}$, and X is the mdpt. of $\overline{AC}$. By the Mdpt. Formula, the coords. of X are (a, a). By the Dist. Formula, $AX = BX = a\sqrt{2}$. So $\triangle AXB$ is isosc. by def. of an isosc. $\triangle$. **13.** 69° **15.** 130° or 172° **17.** $z = 92$ **19.** 26 **21.** It is given that $\triangle ABC$ is isosc., $\overline{AB} \cong \overline{AC}$, P is the mdpt. of $\overline{AB}$, and Q is the mdpt. of $\overline{AC}$. By the Mdpt. Formula, the coords. of P are (a, b) and the coords. of Q are $(3a, b)$. By the Dist. Formula, $PC = QB = \sqrt{9a^2 + b^2}$, so $\overline{PC} \cong \overline{QB}$ by the def of $\cong$ segs. **23.** S **25.** N **27a.** 38° **b.** $m\angle PQR = m\angle PRQ = 53°$ **29.** $m\angle 1 = 127°$; $m\angle 2 = 26.5°$; $m\angle 3 = 53°$ **33.** 20
39. 1. $\triangle ABC \cong \triangle CBA$ (Given)
  2. $\overline{AB} \cong \overline{CB}$ (CPCTC)
  3. $\triangle ABC$ is isosceles (Def. of Isosc)

43. H **47.** $(2a, 0)$, $(0, 2b)$, or any pt. on the ⊥ bisector of $\overline{AB}$

6-1

Check It Out! 1a. 14.6 **1b.** 10.4
2a. 3.05 **2b.** 126° **3.** $\overrightarrow{QS}$ bisects $\angle PQR$. **4.** $y + 1 = -\frac{2}{3}(x - 3)$

Exercises 1. perpendicular bisector
3. 25.9 **5.** 21.9 **7.** 38° **9.** $y - 1 = x + 2$ **11.** $y - 2 = \frac{4}{3}(x + 3)$
13. 26.5 **15.** 1.3 **17.** 54° **19.** $y + 3 = -\frac{1}{2}(x + 2)$ **21.** $y + 3 = \frac{5}{2}(x - 2)$
23. 38 **25.** 38 **27.** 24 **29.** Possible answer: $C(3, 2)$
31. 1. $\overrightarrow{PS}$ bisects $\angle QPR$. $\overline{SQ} \perp \overrightarrow{PQ}$, $\overline{SR} \perp \overrightarrow{PR}$ (Given)
  2. $\angle QPS \cong \angle RPS$ (Def. of $\angle$ bisector)
  3. $\angle SQP$ and $\angle SRP$ are rt. $\angle$s. (Def. of ⊥)
  4. $\angle SQP \cong \angle SRP$ (Rt. $\angle \cong$ Thm.)
  5. $\overline{PS} \cong \overline{PS}$ (Reflex. Prop. of $\cong$)
  6. $\triangle PQS \cong \triangle PRS$ (AAS)
  7. $\overline{SQ} \cong \overline{SR}$ (CPCTC)
  8. $SQ = SR$ (Def. of $\cong$ segs.)
33a. $y = -\frac{3}{4}x + 2$ **b.** 2 **c.** 6.4 mi
35. D **39.** the lines $y = x$ and $y = -x$

6-2

Check It Out! 1a. 14.5 **1b.** 18.6
1c. 19.9 **2.** $(4, -4.5)$ **3a.** 19.2
3b. 52°

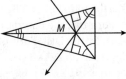

4. By the Incenter Thm., the incenter of a △ is equidistant from the sides of the △. Draw the △ formed by the streets and draw the ∠ bisectors to find the incenter, point M. The city should place the monument at point M.

Exercises 1. They do not intersect at a single point. **3.** 5.64 **5.** 3.95
7. $(2, 6)$ **9.** 42.1 **11.** The largest possible ⊙ in the int. of the △ is its inscribed ⊙, and the center of the inscribed ⊙ is the incenter. Draw the △ and its ∠ bisectors. Center the ⊙ at E, the pt. of concurrency of the ∠ bisectors. **13.** 63.9

15. 63.9 **17.** $(-1.5, 9.5)$ **19.** 55°
23. perpendicular bisector **25.** angle bisector **27.** neither **29.** S **31.** N
33. $(4, 3)$ **35a.** ∠ Bisector Thm.
b. the bisector of $\angle B$ **c.** $PX = PZ$
37a. $\left(4, -\frac{7}{6}\right)$ **b.** outside **c.** 4.2 mi
41. F

6-3

Check It Out! 1a. 21 **1b.** 5.4
2. 3; 4; possible answer: the x-coordinate of the centroid is the average of the x-coordinates of the vertices of the △, and the y-coordinate of the centroid is the average of the y-coordinates of the vertices of the △. **3.** Possible answer: An equation of the altitude to $\overline{JK}$ is $y = -\frac{1}{2}x + 3$. It is true that $4 = -\frac{1}{2}(-2) + 3$, so $(-2, 4)$ is a solution of this equation. Therefore this altitude passes through the orthocenter.

Exercises 1. centroid **3.** 136 **5.** 156
7. $(4, 2)$ **9.** $(2, -3)$ **11.** $(-1, 2)$
13. 7.2 **15.** 5.8 **17.** $(0, -2)$
19. $(-2, 9)$ **21.** 12 **23.** 5 **25.** 36 units
27. $(10, -2)$ **29.** 54 **31.** 48
33. Possible answer: ⊥ bisector of the base; bisector of the vertex ∠; median to the base; altitude to the base **35.** A **37.** A **41.** D **43.** D
45a. slope of $\overline{RS} = \frac{c}{b}$; slope of $\overline{ST} = \frac{c}{b-a}$; slope of $\overline{RT} = 0$
b. Since $\ell \perp \overline{RS}$, slope of $\ell = -\frac{b}{c}$. Since $m \perp \overline{ST}$, slope of $m = -\frac{b-a}{c} = \frac{a-b}{c}$. Since $n \perp \overline{RT}$, n is a vertical line, and its slope is undefined.
c. An equation of ℓ is $y - 0 = -\frac{b}{c}(x - a)$, or $y = -\frac{b}{c}x + \frac{ab}{c}$.
An equation of m is $y - 0 = \frac{a-b}{c}(x - 0)$, or $y = \frac{a-b}{c}x$.
An equation of n is $x = b$.
d. $\left(b, \frac{ab - b^2}{c}\right)$ **e.** Since the equation of line n is $x = b$ and the x-coordinate of P is b, P lies on n.
f. Lines ℓ, m, and n are concurrent at P.

6-4

Check It Out! 1. $M(1, 1)$; $N(3, 4)$; slope of $\overline{MN} = \frac{3}{2}$; slope of $\overline{RS} = \frac{3}{2}$; since the slopes are the same,

$\overline{MN} \parallel \overline{RS}$. $MN = \sqrt{13}$; $RS = \sqrt{52} = 2\sqrt{13}$; the length of $\overline{MN}$ is half the length of $\overline{RS}$. **2a.** 72 **2b.** 48.5
2c. 102° **3.** 775 m

Exercises 1. midpoints **3.** 5.1
5. 5.6 **7.** 29° **9.** less than 5 yd
11. 38 **13.** 19 **15.** 55° **17.** yes
19. 17 **21.** $n = 36$ **23.** $n = 8$
25. $n = 4$ **27.** B **29.** Possible answer: about 18 parking spaces
31. 11 **33.** 57° **35.** 123°
37a. 2.25 mi **b.** 28.5 mi **39.** D
41. D **43.** equilateral and equiangular **45.** 7 **47a.** 32; 16; 8; 4
b. $\frac{1}{4}$ **c.** $64\left(\frac{1}{2}\right)^n = 2^{6-n}$

7-1

Check It Out! 1a. 28 in. **1b.** 74°
1c. 13 in. **2a.** 12 **2b.** 18 **3.** $(7, 6)$
4. 1. $GHJN$ and $JKLM$ are ▱. (Given)
  2. $\angle N$ and $\angle HJN$ are supp. $\angle K$ and $\angle MJK$ are supp. (▱ →cons. $\angle$s supp.)
  3. $\angle HJN \cong \angle MJK$ (Vert. $\angle$s Thm.)
  4. $\angle N \cong \angle K$ ($\cong$ Supps. Thm.)

Exercises 3. 36 **5.** 18 **7.** 70°
9. 24.5 **11.** 51° **13.** $(-6, -1)$
15. 82.9 **17.** 82.9 **19.** 130° **21.** 10
23. 28 **25.** $(-1, 3)$ **27.** $PQ = QR = RS = SP = 21$ **29.** $PQ = RS = 17.5$; $QR = SP = 24.5$ **31a.** $\angle 3 \cong \angle 1$ (Corr. $\angle$s Post.); $\angle 6 \cong \angle 1$ (▱ → opp. $\angle$s $\cong$); $\angle 8 \cong \angle 1$ (▱ → opp. $\angle$s $\cong$) **b.** $\angle 2$ is supp. to $\angle 1$ (▱ → cons. $\angle$s supp.); $\angle 4$ is supp. to $\angle 1$ (▱ → cons. $\angle$s supp.); $\angle 5$ is supp. to $\angle 1$ (▱ → cons. $\angle$s supp.); $\angle 7$ is supp. to $\angle 1$ (Subst.) **33.** $\angle KMP$ (▱ → opp. $\angle$s $\cong$) **35.** $\overline{KM}$ (▱ → opp. sides $\cong$) **37.** $\overline{RP}$ (Def. of ▱) **39.** $\angle RTP$ (Vert. $\angle$s Thm.) **41.** $x = 119$; $y = 61$; $z = 119$ **43.** $x = 24$; $y = 50$; $z = 50$
47. $x = 5$; $y = 8$ **49a.** no **b.** no
51. A **53.** 26.4 **55.** $(2, 4)$, $(4, -6)$, $(-6, -2)$

7-2

Check It Out! 1. $PQ = RS = 16.8$, so $\overline{PQ} \cong \overline{RS}$. m$\angle Q = 74°$, and m$\angle R = 106°$, so $\angle Q$ and $\angle R$ are supp., which means that $\overline{PQ} \parallel \overline{RS}$. So 1 pair of opp. sides of $PQRS$ are ∥ and $\cong$. By Thm. 7-2-1, $PQRS$ is a ▱.

2a. Yes; possible answer: the diag. of the quad. forms 2 △. 2 ∠ of 1 △ are ≅ to 2 ∠ of the other, so the third pair of ∠ are ≅ by the Third ∠ Thm. So both pairs of opp. ∠ of the quad. are ≅. By Thm. 7-2-3, the quad. is a ▱. **2b.** No; 2 pairs of cons. sides are ≅. None of the sets of conditions for a ▱ are met. **3.** Possible answer: slope of $\overline{KL}$ = slope of $\overline{MN}$ = $-\frac{7}{2}$; slope of $\overline{LM}$ = slope of $\overline{NK}$ = $-\frac{1}{4}$; both pairs of opp. sides have the same slope, so $\overline{KL} \parallel \overline{MN}$ and $\overline{LM} \parallel \overline{NK}$; by def., *KLMN* is a ▱. **4.** Possible answer: Since *ABRS* is a ▱, it is always true that $\overline{AB} \parallel \overline{RS}$. Since $\overline{AB}$ stays vert., $\overline{RS}$ also remains vert. no matter how the frame is adjusted. Therefore the viewing ∠ never changes.

Exercises 1. $FJ = HJ = 10$, so $\overline{FJ} \cong \overline{HJ}$. Thus $\overline{EG}$ bisects $\overline{FH}$. $EJ = GJ = 18$, so $\overline{EJ} \cong \overline{GJ}$. Thus $\overline{FH}$ bisects $\overline{EG}$. So the diags. of *EFGH* bisect each other. By Thm. 7-2-5, *EFGH* is a ▱. **3.** yes **5.** yes **7.** Possible answer: slope of $\overline{ST}$ = slope of $\overline{UR}$ = 0; $\overline{ST}$ and $\overline{UR}$ have the same slope, so $\overline{ST} \parallel \overline{UR}$; $ST = UR = 6$; 1 pair of opp. sides are $\parallel$ and ≅; by Thm. 6-3-1, *RSTU* is a ▱. **9.** $BC = GH = 16.6$, so $\overline{BC} \cong \overline{GH}$. $CG = HB = 28$, so $\overline{CG} \cong \overline{HB}$. Since both pairs of opp. sides of *BCGH* are ≅, *BCGH* is a ▱ by Thm. 7-2-2. **11.** yes **13.** no **15.** Possible answer: slope of $\overline{PQ}$ = slope of $\overline{RS}$ = $\frac{5}{3}$; $\overline{PQ}$ and $\overline{RS}$ have the same slope, so $\overline{PQ} \parallel \overline{RS}$; $PQ = RS = \sqrt{34}$; 1 pair of opp. sides are $\parallel$ and ≅; by Thm. 7-2-1, *PQRS* is a ▱. **17.** no **19.** yes **21.** $a = 16.5$; $b = 23.2$ **23.** $a = 8.4$; $b = 20$ **27a.** $\angle Q$ **b.** $\angle S$. **c.** $\overline{SP}$ **d.** $\overline{RS}$ **e.** ▱ **35.** B **37.** no **39.** $(3, 1)$; $(-6, -3.5)$

7-3

Check It Out! 1a. 48 in. **1b.** 61.6 in. **2a.** 42.5 **2b.** 17° **3.** $SV = TW = \sqrt{122}$, so $\overline{SV} \cong \overline{TW}$. Slope of $\overline{SV} = \frac{1}{11}$, and slope of $\overline{TW} = -11$, so $\overline{SV} \perp \overline{TW}$. The coordinates of the

mdpt. of $\overline{SV}$ and $\overline{TW}$ are $\left(\frac{1}{2}, -\frac{7}{2}\right)$, so $\overline{SV}$ and $\overline{TW}$ bisect each other. So the diags. of *STVW* are ≅ ⊥ bisectors of each other.
4. Possible answer:
  1. *PQTS* is a rhombus. (Given)
  2. $\overline{PT}$ bisects$\angle QPS$. (Rhombus → each diag. bisects opp. ∠.)
  3. $\angle QPR \cong \angle SPR$ (Def. of ∠ bisector)
  4. $\overline{PQ} \cong \overline{PS}$ (Def. of rhombus)
  5. $\overline{PR} \cong \overline{PR}$ (Reflex. Prop. of ≅)
  6. $\triangle QPR \cong \triangle SPR$ (SAS)
  7. $\overline{RQ} \cong \overline{RS}$ (CPCTC)

Exercises 1. rhombus; rectangle; square **3.** 160 ft **5.** 380 ft **7.** 122°
9. Possible answer:
  1. *RECT* is a rect. $\overline{RX} \cong \overline{TY}$ (Given)
  2. $\overline{XY} \cong \overline{XY}$ (Reflex. Prop. of ≅)
  3. $RX = TY$, $XY = XY$ (Def. of ≅ segs.)
  4. $RX + XY = TY + XY$ (Add. Prop. of =)
  5. $RX + XY = RY$, $TY + XY = TX$ (Seg. Add. Post.)
  6. $RY = TX$ (Subst.)
  7. $\overline{RY} \cong \overline{TX}$ (Def. of ≅ segs.)
  8. $\angle R$ and $\angle T$ are rt. ∠. (Def. of rect.)
  9. $\angle R \cong \angle T$ (Rt. ∠ ≅ Thm.)
  10. *RECT* is a ▱. (Rect. → ▱)
  11. $\overline{RE} \cong \overline{TC}$ (▱ → opp. sides ≅)
  12. $\triangle REY \cong \triangle TCX$ (SAS)
11. 25 **13.** $14\frac{1}{2}$ **15.** m$\angle VWX = 132$°; m$\angle WYX = 66$°
17. Possible answer:
  1. *RHMB* is a rhombus. $\overline{HB}$ is a diag. of *RHMB*. (Given)
  2. $\overline{MH} \cong \overline{RH}$ (Def. of rhombus)
  3. $\overline{HB}$ bisects $\angle RHM$. (Rhombus → each diag. bisects opp. ∠)
  4. $\angle MHX \cong \angle RHX$ (Def. of ∠ bisector)
  5. $\overline{HX} \cong \overline{HX}$ (Reflex. Prop. of ≅)
  6. $\triangle MHX \cong \triangle RHX$ (SAS)
  7. $\angle HMX \cong \angle HRX$ (CPCTC)
19. m$\angle 1 = 54$°; m$\angle 2 = 36$°; m$\angle 3 = 54$°; m$\angle 4 = 108$°; m$\angle 5 = 72$°
21. m$\angle 1 = 126$°; m$\angle 2 = 27$°; m$\angle 3 = 27$°; m$\angle 4 = 126$°; m$\angle 5 = 27$°
23. m$\angle 1 = 64$°; m$\angle 2 = 64$°; m$\angle 3 =$

26°; m$\angle 4 = 90$°; m$\angle 5 = 64$° **25.** S **27.** S **29.** A **31.** S **35a.** Rect. → ▱ **b.** $\overline{HG}$ **c.** Reflex. Prop. of ≅ **d.** Def. of rect. **e.** $\angle GHE$ **f.** SAS **g.** CPCTC **41.** $28\sqrt{2}$ in. ≈ 39.60 in.; 98 in² **45.** D **47.** H **51.** 45

7-4

Check It Out! 1. Both pairs of opp. sides of *WXYZ* are ≅, so *WXYZ* is a ▱. The contractor can use the carpenter's square to see if 1 ∠ of *WXYZ* is a rt. ∠. If 1 ∠ is a rt. ∠, then by Thm. 7-4-1 the frame is a rect. **2.** Not valid; by Thm. 7-4-1, if 1 ∠ of a ▱ is a rt. ∠, then the ▱ is a rect. To apply this thm., you need to know that *ABCD* is a ▱. **3a.** rect., rhombus, square **3b.** rhombus

Exercises 3. valid **5.** rhombus **7.** valid **9.** square, rect., rhombus **11.** ▱, rect. **13.** ▱, rect., rhombus, square **15.** ▱, rect., rhombus, square **17.** B **19.** $\overline{PR} \cong \overline{QS}$ **21.** $(2, 6)$ **23.** $(-2, -2)$ **25.** $x = 3$ **27.** rhombus **29a.** slope of $\overline{AB}$ = slope of $\overline{CD} = -\frac{1}{3}$; slope of $\overline{AD}$ = slope of $\overline{CB} = -3$ **b.** Slope of $\overline{AC}$ = -1; slope of $\overline{BD} = 1$; the slopes are negative reciprocals of each other, so $\overline{AC} \perp \overline{BD}$. **c.** *ABCD* is a rhombus, since it is a ▱ and its diags. are ⊥ (Thm. 7-4-4.) **33b.** ▱ **c.** square **39.** A **41a.** $15x = 13x + 12$; $x = 6$ **b.** yes **c.** no **d.** yes **43b.** no **c.** no

8-1

Check It Out! 1. $\angle A \cong \angle J$; $\angle B \cong \angle G$; $\angle C \cong \angle H$; $\frac{AB}{JG} = \frac{BC}{GH} = \frac{AC}{JH} = 2$ **2.** yes; $\frac{5}{2}$; $\triangle LMJ \sim \triangle PNS$ **3.** 5 in.

Exercises 3. $\angle A \cong \angle H$; $\angle B \cong \angle J$; $\angle C \cong \angle K$; $\angle D \cong \angle L$; $\frac{AB}{HJ} = \frac{BC}{JK} = \frac{CD}{KL} = \frac{DA}{LH} = \frac{2}{3}$ **5.** yes; $\frac{2}{3}$; $\triangle RMP \sim \triangle XWU$ **7.** $\angle J \cong \angle S$; $\angle K \cong \angle T$; $\angle L \cong \angle U$; $\angle M \cong \angle V$; $\frac{JK}{ST} = \frac{KL}{TU} = \frac{LM}{UV} = \frac{MJ}{VS} = \frac{5}{6}$ **9.** yes; $\frac{7}{8}$; $\triangle RSQ \sim \triangle UZX$ **11.** 14 ft **13.** S **15.** N **17.** S **19.** 5 **23.** $\angle O$; $\angle Q$ **27.** C **29.** The ratios of the sides are not the same; $\frac{12}{3.5} = \frac{24}{7}$; $\frac{10}{2.5} = 4$; $\frac{6}{1.5} = 4$. **33a.** rect. *ABCD* ~ rect. *BCFE*. **b.** $\frac{\ell}{1} = \frac{1}{\ell - 1}$ **c.** $\ell = \frac{1 + \sqrt{5}}{2}$ **d.** $\ell \approx 1.6$

8-2

Check It Out! **1.** $D'(-2, 0)$, $E'(-2, -1)$, $F'(-1, -2)$; dilation with center $(0, 0)$ and scale factor $\frac{1}{4}$ **2.** The triangles are similar because $\triangle ABC$ can be mapped to $\triangle A'B'C'$ by a rotation: $(x, y) \longrightarrow (-y, x)$, and then $\triangle A'B'C'$ can be mapped to $\triangle PQR$ by a dilation: $(x, y) \longrightarrow (3x, 3y)$. **3.** Circle A can be mapped to circle A' by a translation: $(x, y) \longrightarrow (x-3, y-2)$. Then circle A' can be mapped to circle B by a dilation with center $(-1, -1)$ and scale factor $\frac{1}{2}$. So, circles A and B are similar. **4.** Apply the dilation with center $(0, 0)$ and scale factor 4: $(x, y) \longrightarrow (4x, 4y)$.

Exercises **1.** similarity **3.** dilation about $(0, 0)$ with a scale factor of 4; $A'(-4, -4)$, $B'(8, 4)$, $C'(-8, 4)$ **5.** dilation about $(0, 0)$ with a scale factor of 2.5; $A'(5, 7.5)$, $B'(12.5, -5)$, $C'(-10, -5)$ **7.** Similar; to map $LMNO$ to $PQRS$, first dilate by a scale factor of 2: $(x, y) \longrightarrow (2x, 2y)$. Then translate 13 units up: $(x, y) \longrightarrow (x, y + 13)$. **9.** Similar; to map ABC to XYZ, first reflect: $(x, y) \longrightarrow (x, -y)$. Then dilate by a scale factor of $\frac{4}{3}$: $(x, y) \longrightarrow (\frac{4}{3}x, \frac{4}{3}y)$. The transformations could also be done in the other order. **11.** To map A to B, first translate 10 units to the left and 3 units down: $(x, y) \longrightarrow (x - 10, y - 3)$. Then dilate by a scale factor of $\frac{3}{5}$: $(x, y) \longrightarrow (\frac{3}{5}x, \frac{3}{5}y)$. **13.** Apply a dilation with center $(0, 0)$ and scale factor 4 to the small triangle on the grid: $(x, y) \longrightarrow (4x, 4y)$. The image represents the shape of the large triangle. **15.** dilation about $(0, 0)$ with a scale factor of 0.5; $A'(6, 3)$, $B'(0, -3)$, $C'(3, 9)$ **17.** Similar; to map ABC to XYZ, first translate 4 units to the left and 6 units up: $(x, y) \longrightarrow (x - 4, y + 6)$. Then dilate by a scale factor of $\frac{2}{3}$: $(x, y) \longrightarrow (\frac{2}{3}x, \frac{2}{3}y)$. **19.** Similar; to map $GHJK$ to $LMNO$, dilate by a scale factor of 0.5: $(x, y) \longrightarrow (0.5x, 0.5y)$; to map $LMNO$ to $GHJK$, dilate by a scale factor of 2: $(x, y) \longrightarrow (2x, 2y)$. **21.** Reggie made an error. The scale factor from ABC

to $A'B'C'$ is $\frac{2}{3}$, not $\frac{3}{2}$. **23.** Place the drawing of the smaller building on a coordinate plane in a convenient position in the first quadrant. Apply the dilation with center $(0, 0)$ and scale factor 5: $(x, y) \longrightarrow (5x, 5y)$. The image represents the larger building. **25.** A

8-3

Check It Out! **1.** By the $\triangle$ Sum Thm., $m\angle C = 47°$, so $\angle C \cong \angle F$. $\angle B \cong \angle E$ by the Rt. $\angle \cong$ Thm. Therefore $\triangle ABC \sim \triangle DEF$ by AA $\sim$. **2.** $\angle TXU \cong \angle VXW$ by the Vert. $\angle$ Thm. $\frac{TX}{VX} = \frac{12}{16} = \frac{3}{4}$, and $\frac{XU}{XW} = \frac{15}{20} = \frac{3}{4}$. Therefore $\triangle TXU \sim \triangle VXW$ by SAS $\sim$. **3.** It is given that $\angle RSV \cong \angle T$. By the Reflex. Prop. of $\cong$, $\angle R \cong \angle R$. Therefore $\triangle RSV \sim \triangle RTU$ by AA $\sim$. $RT = 15$. **4.1.** M is the mdpt. of $\overline{JK}$, N is the mdpt. of $\overline{KL}$, and P is the mdpt. of $\overline{JL}$. (Given) **2.** $MP = \frac{1}{2}KL$, $MN = \frac{1}{2}JL$, $NP = \frac{1}{2}KJ$ ($\triangle$Midsegs. Thm.) **3.** $\frac{MP}{KL} = \frac{MN}{JL} = \frac{NP}{KJ} = \frac{1}{2}$ (Div. Prop. of =) **4.** $\triangle JKL \sim \triangle NPM$ (SSS $\sim$ *Step 3*) **5.** 5

Exercises **1.** By the $\triangle$ Sum Thm., $m\angle A = 47°$. So by the def. of $\cong$, $\angle A \cong \angle F$, and $\angle C \cong \angle H$. Therefore $\triangle ABC \sim \triangle FGH$ by AA $\sim$. **3.** $\frac{DF}{JL} = \frac{DE}{JK} = \frac{EF}{KL} = \frac{1}{2}$, so $\triangle DEF \sim \triangle JKL$ by SSS $\sim$. **5.** It is given that $\angle AED \cong \angle ACB$. $\angle A \cong \angle A$ by the Reflex. Prop. of $\cong$. Therefore $\triangle AED \sim \triangle ACB$ by AA $\sim$. $AB = 10$ **7.1.** $\overline{MN} \parallel \overline{KL}$ (Given) **2.** $\angle JMN \cong \angle JKL$, $\angle JNM \cong \angle JLK$ (Corr. $\angle$ Post.) **3.** $\triangle JMN \sim \triangle JKL$ (AA $\sim$ *Step 2*) **9.** SAS or SSS $\sim$ Thm. **11.** It is given that $\angle GLH \cong \angle K$. $\angle G \cong \angle G$ by the Reflex. Prop. of $\cong$. Therefore $\triangle HLG \sim \triangle JKG$ by AA $\sim$. **13.** $\angle K \cong \angle K$ by the Reflex. Prop. of $\cong$. $\frac{KL}{KN} = \frac{KM}{KL} = \frac{3}{2}$. Therefore $\triangle KLM \sim \triangle KNL$ by SAS $\sim$. **15.** It is given that $\angle ABD \cong \angle C$. $\angle A \cong \angle A$ by the Reflex. Prop. of $\cong$. Therefore $\triangle ABD \sim \triangle ACB$ by AA $\sim$.

$AB = 8$

17.1. $CD = 3AC$, $CE = 3BC$ (Given) **2.** $\frac{CD}{AC} = 3$, $\frac{CE}{BC} = 3$ (Div. Prop. of =) **3.** $\angle ACB \cong \angle DCE$ (Vert. $\angle$ Thm.) **4.** $\triangle ABC \sim \triangle DEC$ (SAS $\sim$ *Steps 2, 3*)

19. 1.5 ft **21.** yes; SSS $\sim$ **23.** $x = 3$ **25a.** Pyramids A and C are $\sim$ because the ratios of their corr. side lengths are =. **b.** $\frac{5}{4}$ **27.** 2 ft; 4 ft **31a.** The $\triangle$ are $\sim$ by AA $\sim$ if you assume that the camera is $\parallel$ to the hurricane (that is, $\overline{YX} \parallel \overline{AB}$). **b.** $\triangle YWZ \sim \triangle BCZ$, and $\triangle XWZ \sim \triangle ACZ$, also by AA $\sim$. **c.** 105 mi **35.** J **37.** 30

8-4

Check It Out! **1.** 7.5 **2.** $AD = 16$, and $BE = 12$, so $\frac{DC}{AD} = \frac{20}{16} = \frac{5}{4}$, and $\frac{EC}{BE} = \frac{15}{12} = \frac{5}{4}$. Since $\frac{DC}{AD} = \frac{EC}{BE}$, $\overline{DE} \parallel \overline{AB}$ by the Conv. of the $\triangle$ Proportionality Thm. **3.** $LM \approx 1.5$ cm; $MN \approx 2.4$ cm **4.** $AC = 16$; $DC = 9$

Exercises **1.** 30 **3.** $\frac{EC}{AC} = 1$, and $\frac{ED}{DB} = 1$. Since $\frac{EC}{AC} = \frac{ED}{DB}$, $\overline{AB} \parallel \overline{CD}$ by the Conv. of the $\triangle$ Proportionality Thm. **5.** 286 ft **7.** $CD = 4$; $AD = 6$ **9.** 20 **11.** $\frac{PM}{MQ} = \frac{6.3}{2.7} = 2\frac{1}{3}$, and $\frac{PN}{NR} = \frac{7}{3} = 2\frac{1}{3}$. Since $\frac{PM}{MQ} = \frac{PN}{NR}$, $\overline{MN} \parallel \overline{QR}$ by the Conv. of the $\triangle$ Proportionality Thm. **13.** $BC = 6$; $CD = 5$ **15.** CE **17.** BD **19.** DF **21.** 15 in. or $26\frac{2}{3}$ in. **23.1.** $\frac{AE}{EB} = \frac{AF}{FC}$ (Given) **2.** $\angle A \cong \angle A$ (Reflex. Prop. of $\square$) **3.** $\triangle AEF \sim \triangle ABC$ (SAS $\sim$ *Steps 1, 2*) **4.** $\angle AEF \cong \angle ABC$ (Def. of $\sim \triangle$) **5.** $\overleftrightarrow{EF} \parallel \overleftrightarrow{BC}$ (Conv. of Corr. $\angle$ Post.)

25a. $PR = 6$; $RT = 8$; $QS = 3$; $SU = 4$ **b.** $\frac{PR}{RT} = \frac{QS}{SU}$, or $\frac{6}{8} = \frac{3}{4}$ **27.** 15 **33.** J

8-5

Check It Out! **1.** The photo should have vertices $A'(0, 0)$, $B'(0, 2)$, $C'(1.5, 2)$, and $D'(1.5, 0)$. **2.** $N(0, -20)$; $\frac{2}{3}$ **3.** $RS = \sqrt{2}$, $RU = 3\sqrt{2}$, $RT = \sqrt{5}$, and $RV = 3\sqrt{5}$, so $\frac{RS}{RU} = \frac{RT}{RV} = \frac{1}{3}$. $\angle R \cong \angle R$ by the Reflex. Prop. of $\cong$. So $\triangle RST \sim \triangle RUV$ by SAS $\sim$. **4.** Check students' work. The image of $\triangle MNP$ has vertices $M'(-6, 3)$, $N'(6, 6)$, and $P'(-3, -3)$. $MP = \sqrt{5}$, $MN = \sqrt{17}$, and $PN = 3\sqrt{2}$. $M'P' = 3\sqrt{5}$, $M'N' = 3\sqrt{17}$, and $P'N' = 9\sqrt{2}$. $\frac{M'P'}{MP} = \frac{M'N'}{MN} = \frac{P'N'}{PN} = 3$. So $\triangle M'N'P' \sim \triangle MNP$ by SSS $\sim$.

Exercises 1. dilation

5. $S(0, -8)$; $\frac{5}{2}$ **7.** $JK = 2\sqrt{5}$, $JM = 3\sqrt{5}$, $JL = 2\sqrt{5}$, and $JN = 3\sqrt{5}$, so $\frac{JK}{JM} = \frac{JL}{JN} = \frac{2}{3}$. $\angle J \cong \angle J$ by the

Reflex. Prop. of $\cong$. So $\triangle JKL \sim \triangle JMN$ by SAS $\sim$. **9.** The image of $\triangle RST$ has vertices $R'(-3, 3)$, $S'(3, 6)$, and $T'(0, -3)$. $RS = 2\sqrt{5}$, $RT = 2\sqrt{5}$, and $ST = 2\sqrt{10}$. $R'S' = 3\sqrt{5}$, $R'T' = 3\sqrt{5}$, and $S'T' = 3\sqrt{10}$. $\frac{R'S'}{RS} = \frac{R'T'}{RT} = \frac{S'T'}{ST} = \frac{3}{2}$. So $\triangle RST \sim \triangle R'S'T'$ by SSS $\sim$. **11.** $X(-24, 0)$; $\frac{8}{3}$ **13.** $DE = 2\sqrt{5}$, $DG = 3\sqrt{5}$, $DF = 4\sqrt{2}$, and $DH = 6\sqrt{2}$, so $\frac{DE}{DG} = \frac{DF}{DH} = \frac{2}{3}$. $\angle D \cong \angle D$ by the Reflex. Prop. of $\cong$. So $\triangle DEF \sim \triangle DGH$ by SAS $\sim$. **15.** The image of $\triangle JKL$ has vertices

$J'(-6, 0)$, $K'(-3, -3)$, and $L'(-9, -6)$. $JK = \sqrt{2}$, $JL = \sqrt{5}$, and $LK = \sqrt{5}$. $J'K' = 3\sqrt{2}$, $J'L' = 3\sqrt{5}$, and $L'K' = 3\sqrt{5}$. $\frac{J'K'}{JK} = \frac{J'L'}{JL} = \frac{L'K'}{LK} = 3$. So $\triangle JKL \sim \triangle J'K'L'$ by SSS $\sim$. **17.** It is not a dilation; because it changes the shape of the figure. **21.** A **23.** A **25.** 12

9-1

Check It Out! 1a. $x = 4\sqrt{5}$
1b. $x = 16$ **2.** 29 ft 1 in. **3a.** $2\sqrt{41}$;
no; $2\sqrt{41}$ is not a whole number.
3b. 10; yes; the 3 side lengths are
nonzero whole numbers that
satisfy the equation $a^2 + b^2 = c^2$.
3c. 2.6; no; 2.4 and 2.6 are not
whole numbers. **3d.** 34; yes; the
3 side lengths are nonzero whole
numbers that satisfy the equation
$a^2 + b^2 = c^2$. **4a.** yes; obtuse **4b.** no
4c. yes, acute

Exercises 1. no **3.** $x = 6\sqrt{2}$
5. width: 14.8 in.; height: 11.9 in.
7. 16; yes **9.** triangle; acute
11. triangle; right **13.** triangle;
acute **15.** $x = 10$ **17.** $x = 24$ **19.** 6;
no **21.** $3\sqrt{5}$; no **23.** not a triangle
25. triangle; right **27.** triangle;
acute **29.** B **31.** $x = 8 + \sqrt{13}$
33. $x = 4\sqrt{6}$ **35.** $x = 6\sqrt{13}$
39. perimeter: $16 + 4\sqrt{7}$ units; area:
$12\sqrt{7}$ square units
41. perimeter: $14 + 2\sqrt{13}$ units;
area: 18 square units
43. perimeter: 22 units; area:
26 square units **47a.** King City
b. m$\angle SRM > 90°$ **49.** B
51a. $PA = \sqrt{2}$; $PB = \sqrt{3}$; $PC = 2$;
$PD = \sqrt{5}$; $PE = \sqrt{6}$; $PF = \sqrt{7}$
55a. no **b.** yes. **c.** no **d.** no

9-2

Check It Out! 1a. $x = 20$ **1b.** $x = 8\sqrt{2}$ **2.** 43 cm **3a.** $x = 9\sqrt{3}$; $y = 27$
3b. $x = 5\sqrt{3}$; $y = 10$ **3c.** $x = 12$;
$y = 12\sqrt{3}$ **3d.** $x = 6\sqrt{3}$; $y = 3\sqrt{3}$
4. 34.6 cm

Exercises 1. $x = 14\sqrt{2}$ **3.** $x = 9$
5. $x = 3$; $y = 3\sqrt{3}$ **7.** $x = 21$;
$y = 14\sqrt{3}$ **9.** $x = \frac{15\sqrt{2}}{2}$ **11.** $x = 18$

13. $x = 48$; $y = 24\sqrt{3}$ **15.** $x = \frac{2\sqrt{3}}{3}$;
$y = \frac{4\sqrt{3}}{3}$ **17.** perimeter:
$\left(12 + 12\sqrt{2}\right)$ in.; area: 36 in^2
19. perimeter: $36\sqrt{2}$ m; area:
162 m^2 **21.** perimeter: $60\sqrt{3}$ yd;
area: $300\sqrt{3}$ yd^2 **23.** no **25.** $(10, 3)$
27. $\left(5, 10 - 12\sqrt{3}\right)$ **29a.** 640 mi
b. 453 mi **c.** 234 mi **31.** F
33. 443.4 **35.** $x = \frac{32}{9}$

10-1

Check It Out! 1a. $\frac{24}{25} = 0.96$ **1b.** $\frac{24}{7}$
≈ 3.43 **1c.** $\frac{24}{25} = 0.96$ **2.** $\frac{s}{s} = 1$
3a. 0.19 **3b.** 0.88 **3c.** 0.87
4a. 21.87 m **4b.** 7.06 in. **4c.** 36.93 ft
4d. 6.17 cm **5.** 14.34 ft

Exercises 1. $\frac{LK}{JL}$ **3.** $\frac{4}{5} = 0.80$ **5.** $\frac{4}{5} = 0.80$ **7.** $\frac{4}{3} \approx 1.33$ **9.** $\frac{1}{2}$ **11.** $\frac{\sqrt{2}}{2}$ **13.** 0.39
15. 0.03 **17.** 0.16 **19.** 9.65 m
21. 7 ft 6 in. **23.** $\frac{15}{8} \approx 1.88$ **25.** $\frac{15}{17} \approx$
0.88 **27.** $\frac{15}{17} \approx 0.88$ **29.** $\frac{1}{2}$ **31.** 1.23
33. 0.22 **35.** 0.82 **37.** 3.58 cm
39. 19.67 ft **41.** 5.27 ft **43.** 6.10 m
45. sine; cosine **47.** 60° **49.** 1.2 ft
53. 0.6 **55.** 753 ft **59.** $\left(\frac{1}{2}\right)^2 + \left(\frac{\sqrt{3}}{2}\right)^2 =$
$\frac{1}{4} + \frac{3}{4} = 1$ **61a.** $\sin A = \frac{a}{c}$; $\cos A = \frac{b}{c}$
b. $(\sin A)^2 + (\cos A)^2 = \left(\frac{a}{c}\right)^2 + \left(\frac{b}{c}\right)^2$
$= \frac{a^2}{c^2} + \frac{b^2}{c^2} = \frac{a^2 + b^2}{c^2} = \frac{c^2}{c^2} = 1$
63. 18.64 cm; 16.00 cm^2
65. 22.60 in.; 14.69 in^2 **69.** H
71. $x \approx 5$; $AB \approx 20$; $BC \approx 18$;
$AC \approx 27$ **75.** 1.25 **77.** 0.75

10-2

Check It Out! 1a. $\angle 2$ **1b.** $\angle 1$
2a. 37° **2b.** 87° **2c.** 42° **3.** $DF \approx$
16.51; $EF \approx 8.75$; m$\angle D = 32°$
4. $RS = ST = 7$; $RT \approx 9.90$; m$\angle S = 90°$; m$\angle R = $ m$\angle T = 45°$ **5.** 21°

Exercises 1. $\angle 1$ **3.** $\angle 1$ **5.** $\angle 2$ **7.** 65°
9. 34° **11.** 38° **13.** $RP \approx 9.42$; m$\angle P$

$\approx 19°$; m$\angle R \approx 71°$ **15.** $YZ \approx 13.96$;
m$\angle Y \approx 38°$; m$\angle Z \approx 52°$ **17.** $RS = 5$;
$ST = 6$; $RT \approx 7.81$; m$\angle S = 90°$; m$\angle R$
$\approx 50°$; m$\angle T \approx 40°$ **19.** $AB = 2$; BC
$= 4$; $AC \approx 4.47$; m$\angle B = 90°$; m$\angle A \approx$
63°; m$\angle C \approx 27°$ **21.** $\angle 2$ **23.** $\angle 1$
25. $\angle 2$ **27.** 18° **29.** 37° **31.** 57°
33. $JK \approx 2.88$; $LK \approx 1.40$; m$\angle L = 64°$
35. $QR \approx 4.90$; m$\angle P \approx 36°$; m$\angle R \approx$
54° **37.** $MN = NP = 4$; $MP \approx 5.66$;
m$\angle N = 90°$; m$\angle M = $ m$\angle P = 45°$
39. 74° **41.** cos **43.** 0.93 **47a.** 5°
b. 85° **c.** 31 ft 1 in. **49.** 23°; 67°
51. The acute $\angle$ measure changes
from about 58° to about 73°, an
increase by a factor of 1.26.
53a. $AB = 5\sqrt{2}$; $BC = 2\sqrt{10}$; AC
$= \sqrt{10}$ **b.** $AC^2 + BC^2 = AB^2$, so
$\triangle ABC$ is a rt. $\triangle$, and $\angle C$ is the rt. $\angle$.
c. m$\angle A = 63°$; m$\angle B = 27°$ **55.** 35°
57. 62° **59.** 72° **61.** 39° **65.** D **67.** A
69. 58° **71.** 34° **73.** x

10-3

Check It Out! 1a. angle of
depression **1b.** angle of elevation
2. 6314 ft **3.** 1717 ft **4.** 32,300 ft

Exercises 1. elevation **3.** angle of
elevation **5.** angle of elevation
7. 18 ft **9.** 64.6 m **11.** angle of
elevation **13.** angle of depression
15. 1962 ft **17.** T **19.** F **21.** $\angle 1$ and
$\angle 3$ **25a.** 424 ft **b.** 276 ft
27a. 2080 ft **b.** 14 s **29.** J **31.** 98 m
33. 1318 ft

11-1

Check It Out! **1.** $A = \left(4x^2 - 12x + 9\right)\pi$ m^2
2. $C \approx 31.4$ in.; $C \approx 37.7$ in.; $C \approx 44.0$ in. **3.** $A \approx 77.3$ cm^2

Exercises **1.** Draw a segment perpendicular to a side with one endpoint at the center. The apothem is $\frac{1}{2}s$. **3.** $A = 9x^2\pi$ in^2 **5.** $A \approx 50.3$ in^2; $A \approx 78.5$ in^2; $A \approx 113.1$ in^2 **7.** $A \approx 32.7$ cm^2 **9.** $A \approx 279.9$ m^2 **11.** $C = 5\pi$ m **13.** $A \approx 962.1$ ft^2; $A \approx 1963.5$ ft^2; $A \approx 3421.2$ ft^2 **15.** $A \approx 13.3$ ft^2 **17.** $A \approx 14.5$ ft^2 **19.** 90° **21.** 60° **23.** 45° **25.** 36° **27.** $A \approx 84.3$ cm^2 **29.** $A \approx 46.8$ m^2 **31.** $A \approx 90.8$ ft^2 **35.** $20\frac{\sqrt{\pi}}{\pi}$; $10\frac{\sqrt{\pi}}{\pi}$; $20\sqrt{\pi}$ **37.** 36; 18; 324π **39a.** $A \approx 745.6$ in^2 **b.** $A \approx 1073.6$ in^2 **c.** 44% **43.** B **45.** B **47.** $A = \frac{C^2}{4\pi}$

11-2

Check It Out! **1.** $V = 157.5$ yd^3 **2.** 859,702 gal; 7,161,318 lb **3.** $V = 1088\pi$ in$^3 \approx 3418.1$ in^3 **4.** The volume is multiplied by 8. **5.** $V \approx 51.4$ cm^3

Exercises **1.** the same length as **3.** $V \approx 748.2$ m^3 **5.** 2552 gal; 12,071 lb **7.** $V = 45\pi$ m$^3 \approx 141.4$ m^3 **9.** The volume is multiplied by $\frac{1}{64}$. **11.** $V \approx 1209.1$ ft^3 **13.** $V = 810$ yd^3 **15.** $V = 245$ ft^3 **17.** $V = 1764\pi$ cm$^3 \approx 5541.8$ cm^3 **19.** $V = 384\pi$ cm$^3 \approx 1206.4$ cm^3 **21.** The volume is multiplied by $\frac{27}{125}$. **23.** $V \approx 242.3$ ft^3 **25a.** 235.6 in^2 **25b.** 0.04 **27.** $h = 11$ ft **29.** $V = 392\pi$ m^3 **31.** 576 in^3, or $\frac{1}{3}$ ft^3 **33.** 2,468,729 gal **37.** A **39.** B **41.** $V = x^3 + x^2 - 2x$ **43.** $V = \frac{x^3\sqrt{3} + x^2\sqrt{3}}{4}$

11-3

Check It Out! **1.** $V = 36$ cm^3 **2.** 107,800 yd^3 or 2,910,600 ft^3 **3.** $V = 216\pi$ m$^3 \approx 678.6$ m^3 **4.** The volume is multiplied by 8. **5.** $V = 3000$ ft^3

Exercises **1.** perpendicular **3.** $V = 96$ cm^3 **5.** $V \approx 65$ mm^3 **7.** $V =$

1440π in$^3 \approx 4523.9$ in^3 **9.** The volume is multiplied by 27. **11.** $V = 2592$ cm^3 **13.** $V = 160$ ft^3 **15.** $V = 384$ ft^3 **17.** $V = 1107\pi$ m$^3 \approx 3477.7$ m^3 **19.** $V = 144\pi$ ft$^3 \approx 452.4$ ft^3 **21.** The volume is multiplied by 216. **23.** $V = 150$ ft^3 **25.** $V = \frac{25\pi}{6}$ m^3 **27.** $V = 240\pi$ cm^3 **29.** 1350 m^3 **31.** 166.3 cm^3 **33.** $C = 10\pi\sqrt{3}$ cm **35.** $V = 1280$ in^3 **37.** $V = 17.5$ units^3 **39.** 3:2 **41a.** 33.5 in^3 **b.** 134.0 in^3 **c.** $5; the large size holds 4 times as much. **43.** H **45.** 9 **47.** $V = \frac{2\pi}{3}$ ft^3 **49.** $V = \frac{1000\sqrt{2}}{3}$ cm^3

11-4

Check It Out! **1.** $r = 12$ ft **2.** about 72.3 times as great **3.** $S = 2500\pi$ cm^2 **4.** The surface area is divided by 9. **5.** $S = 57\pi$ ft^2; $V = 27\pi$ ft^3

Exercises **1.** One endpoint is the center of the sphere, and the other is a point on the sphere. **3.** $V = \frac{4\pi}{3}$ m^3 **5.** about 8 times as great **7.** $S = 196\pi$ cm^2 **9.** The surface area is multiplied by 4. **11.** $S = 36\pi$ ft^2; $V = \frac{92\pi}{3}$ ft^3 **13.** $V = 972\pi$ cm^3 **15.** $d = 36$ in. **17.** $S = 1764\pi$ in^2 **19.** $V = \frac{15,625\pi}{6}$ m^3 **21.** The volume is multiplied by 216. **23.** $S \approx 1332.0$ mm^2; $V \approx 1440.9$ mm^3 **25.** $C = 2\pi\sqrt{15}$ in. **27.** $S = 196\pi$ units^2; $V = \frac{1372\pi}{3}$ units^3 **29.** 5.28 in.; 8.87 in^2; 2.48 in^3 **31.** 7.85 in.; 19.63 in^2; 8.18 in^3 **33.** Possible answer: 14,293 in^3 **35.** about 1408 times as great **37.** The surface area of Saturn is greater. **39.** The cross section of the hemisphere is a circle with radius $\sqrt{r^2 - x^2}$, so its area is $A = \pi\left(r^2 - x^2\right)$. The cross section of the cylinder with the cone removed has an outer radius of r and an inner radius of x, so the area is $A = \pi r^2 - \pi x^2 = \pi\left(r^2 - x^2\right)$. **41a.** 33.5 in^3 **b.** 44.6 in^3 **43.** H **45.** 1 in. **47.** The volume of the cylinder is 1.5 times the volume of the sphere.

12-1

Check It Out! **1.** chords: $\overline{QR}$, $\overline{ST}$; secant: $\overleftrightarrow{ST}$; tangent: $\overleftrightarrow{UV}$; diam.: $\overline{ST}$; radii: $\overline{PQ}$, $\overline{PT}$, $\overline{PS}$ **2.** radius of $\odot C$: 1; radius of $\odot D$: 3; pt. of tangency: $(2, -1)$; eqn. of tangent line: $y = -1$ **3.** 171 mi **4a.** 2.1 **4b.** 7

Exercises **1.** secant **3.** congruent **5.** chord: $\overline{QS}$; secant: $\overleftrightarrow{QS}$; tangent: $\overleftrightarrow{ST}$; diam.: $\overline{QS}$; radii: $\overline{PR}$, $\overline{PQ}$, $\overline{PS}$ **7.** radius of $\odot R$: 2; radius of $\odot S$: 2; pt. of tangency: $(1, 2)$; eqn. of tangent line: $x = 1$ **9.** 19 **11.** chords: $\overline{RS}$, $\overline{VW}$; secant: $\overleftrightarrow{VW}$; tangent: ℓ; diam.: $\overline{VW}$; radii: $\overline{PV}$, $\overline{PW}$ **13.** radius of $\odot C$: 2; radius of $\odot D$: 4; pt. of tangency: $(-4, 0)$; eqn. of tangent line: $x = -4$ **15.** 413 km **17.** 7 **19.** N **21.** A **23.** $\overline{AC}$ **25.** $\overline{AC}$ **27.** 45° **31.** 8 **33.** 22 **35a.** rect.; $\angle BCD$ and $\angle EDC$ are rt. $\angle$s because a line tangent to a $\odot$ is $\perp$ to a radius. It is given that $\angle DEB$ is a rt. $\angle$. $\angle CBE$ must also be a rt. $\angle$ because the sum of the $\angle$s of a quad. is 360°. Thus $BCDE$ has 4 rt. $\angle$s and is a rect. **b.** 17 in.; 2 in. **c.** 17.1 in. **39.** G **43.** 18.6 in.

12-2

Check It Out! **1a.** 108° **1b.** 270° **1c.** 36° **2a.** 140° **2b.** 295° **3a.** 12 **3b.** 100° **4.** 34.6

Exercises **1.** semicircle **3.** major arc **5.** 162° **7.** 61.2° **9.** 39.6° **11.** 129° **13.** 108° **15.** 24 **17.** 24.0 **19.** 122.3° **21.** 122.3° **23.** 237.7° **25.** 152° **27.** 155° **29.** 147° **31.** 6.6 **33.** F **35.** T **37.** 45°; 60°; 75° **39.** 108° **41.** **1.** $\overset{\frown}{BC} \cong \overset{\frown}{DE}$ (Given) **2.** m$\overset{\frown}{BC}$ = m$\overset{\frown}{DE}$ (Def. of $\cong$ arcs) **3.** m$\angle BAC$ = m$\angle DAE$ (Def. of arc measures) **4.** $\angle BAC \cong \angle DAE$ (Def. of $\cong$ $\angle$s) **43.** **1.** $\overline{JK}$ is the $\perp$ bisector of $\overline{GH}$. (Given) **2.** A is equidistant from G and H. (Def. of center of $\odot$)

3. *A* lies on the ⊥ bisector of $\overline{GH}$. (⊥ Bisector Thm.)
4. $\overline{JK}$ is a diam. of ⊙*A*. (Def. of diam.)
45. Solution A **47a.** 13.5 in.; 6.5 in. **b.** 11.8 in. **c.** 23.7 in. **49.** F
51. 48.2° **53a.** 90°; 60°; 45° **b.** $\frac{3}{4}\pi$; $\frac{3}{2}\pi$

12-3

Check It Out! 1a. $\frac{\pi}{4}$ m²; 0.79 m²
1b. 25.6π in²; 80.42 in² **2.** 203,575 ft²
3. 4.57 m² **4a.** $\frac{4}{3}\pi$ m; 4.19 m
4b. 3π cm; 9.42 cm

Exercises 1. seg. **3.** 24π cm²;
75.40 cm² **5.** 12 mi² **7.** 36.23 m²

9. 4π ft; 12.57 ft **11.** $\frac{2}{3}\pi$ in; 2.09 in.
13. $\frac{45}{2}\pi$ in²; 70.69 in² **15.** 628 in²
17. 15.35 in² **19.** $\frac{25}{18}\pi$ mm; 4.36 mm
21. $\frac{1}{10}\pi$ ft; 0.31 ft **23.** N **25.** A **27.** 12
29a. 3.9 ft **b.** 103° **33.** G **35.** $\frac{7}{3}\pi$
37a. $\frac{1}{8}$ **b.** $\frac{3}{8}$ **c.** $\frac{1}{2}$

12-4

Check It Out! 1a. 270° **1b.** 38°
2. 43°; 120° **3a.** 12 **3b.** 39° **4.** 51°;
129°; 72°; 108°

Exercises 1. inscribed **3.** 58°
5. 26° **7.** 112.5 **9.** 46° **11.** 70°; 110°;
115°; 65° **13.** 47.5° **15.** 47.6° **17.** ±6
19. 100° **21.** 100°; 39°, 80°; 141°
23. A **25.** S **27.** 115° **29a.** 30°

b. 120° **c.** Rt.; ∠*FBC* is inscribed in a semicircle, so it must be a rt. ∠; therefore △*FBC* is a rt. △.
33. 72°; 99°; 108°; 81° **35a.** $AB^2 + AC^2 = BC^2$, so by the Conv. of the Pyth. Thm., △*ABC* is a rt. △ with rt. ∠*A*. Since ∠*A* is an inscribed rt. ∠, it intercepts a semicircle. This means that $\overline{BC}$ is a diam. **b.** 102° **39.** D
41. C **45.** 134°

13-1

Check It Out! 1a. $2i\sqrt{3}$ b. $12i$
c. $-i\sqrt{7}$ 2a. $x = \pm 6i$ b. $x = \pm 4i\sqrt{3}$
c. $x = \pm\frac{5}{3}i$ 3a. $x = -4; y = -\frac{3}{10}$
b. $x = -\frac{8}{5}; y = -\frac{\sqrt{6}}{6}$ 4a. $-2 + 3i$
b. $4 \pm i\sqrt{2}$ 5a. $9 + i$ b. $\sqrt{3} - i$ c. $8i$

Exercises 1. imaginary **3.** $2i$
5. $12i$ **7.** $x = \pm 6i$ **9.** $x = \pm 11i$
11. $x = 1; y = -1$ **13.** $-3 \pm 5i$
15. $\sqrt{5} - 5i$ **17.** $6 - i\sqrt{2}$ **19.** $-i\sqrt{10}$
21. $5i\sqrt{2}$ **23.** $x = \pm 4i$ **25.** $x = \pm 8i$
27. $x = -3; y = -5$ **29.** $\frac{3 \pm i\sqrt{7}}{8}$
31. $\frac{3 \pm i\sqrt{21}}{3}$ **33.** $-\frac{\sqrt{3}}{2} + 2i$
35. $-1 - \frac{i}{10}$ **37.** $1 - 14i$
39. $-2\sqrt{5} - 4i$ **41.** $9 + i\sqrt{2}$
43. $c = 0, d = 5$ **45.** $c = \pm 2, d = 4$
47. $x = \pm 9i$ **49.** $x = \pm 12i$
51. $x = \pm 2i\sqrt{2}$ **53.** $x = -5 \pm 2i$
55. $x = -1 \pm 2i$ **57.** $x = 12 \pm i\sqrt{5}$
59. always true **61.** sometimes
true **63.** sometimes true
65. sometimes true **67.** $-1 \pm 4i$
69. $-8 \pm 3i$ **71.** $8 \pm 2i$
73. The complex conjugate of a real
number a is the number a.
75a. $t = \frac{7}{2} \pm \frac{\sqrt{3}}{2}i$ b. no c. 196 ft
77. F **79.** G **81.** When $a < 0$, the
2 solutions are imaginary and
complex. When $a > 0$, the 2
solutions are real and complex.

13-2

Check It Out!
1.
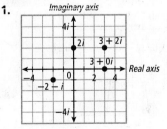

2a. $\sqrt{5}$ b. $\frac{1}{2}$ c. 23 **3a.** $-3 - i$
b. $-3 - 3i$ c. 8
4a.
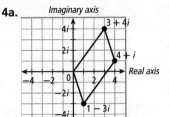

$4 + i$

b.
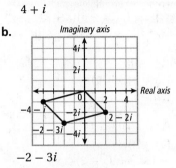

$-2 - 3i$

5a. $10 + 6i$ b. $20 - 28i$
c. 13 **6a.** $-\frac{1}{2}i$ b. -1
7a. $-8 + 3i$ b. $\frac{7}{5} + \frac{1}{5}i$
Exercises 1. real; imaginary
3, 5.
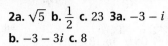

7. 33.3 **9.** 13 **11.** 15 **13.** $3 - 5i$
15. $-9 + 15i$ **17.** $-28 - 19i$
19. $-3 - i$ **21.** 5 **23.** $37 - 5i$
25. $8 + 6i$ **27.** $-i$ **29.** -1 **31.** $\frac{21}{10} + \frac{17}{10}i$
33. $4 - i$ **35.** $-2 + \frac{1}{2}i$

37, 39.
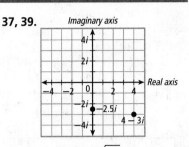

41. 18 **43.** 10 **45.** $2\sqrt{29}$ **47.** $-11 + 7i$
49. $28 + 41i$ **51.** $-4 + 9i$ **53.** $4 + 6i$
55. $48 + 12i$ **57.** 53 **59.** $24 + 78i$
61. $-i$ **63.** -5 **65.** $\frac{13}{10} - \frac{11}{10}i$
67. $4 + i$ **69.** $\frac{3}{4} + \frac{9}{4}i$ **71.** $3i$
73. $-2 - i$ **75.** $\sqrt{10}$ **77.** $2\sqrt{10}$
79. 0 **81.** $\frac{\sqrt{10}}{2}$ **83.** $\sqrt{11}$ **85.** $9.5 + 2.9i$
87. $-9.7 + 1.3i$ **89.** $-1 + 4i$
91. $-5 + 12i$ **93.** $10 - 5i$ **95.** 0
97. $1 - 12i$ **99.** $\frac{26}{37} + \frac{8}{37}i$
101. $\frac{8}{13} + \frac{12}{13}i$ **103.** $Z_{eq} = \frac{7}{4} - i$
105. always true **107.** always true
109. A is incorrect. **113.** D **115.** C
119. $\frac{ac + bd}{c^2 + d^2} + \frac{(bc - ad)}{c^2 + d^2}i$

14-1

Check It Out! **1a.** $(x+4)(x+6)$
1b. $(x+4)(x+3)$ **2a.** $(x+6)(x+2)$
2b. $(x-6)(x+1)$ **2c.** $(x+6)(x+7)$
2d. $(x-8)(x-5)$ **3a.** $(x+5)(x-3)$
3b. $(x-4)(x-2)$ **3c.** $(x-10)$
$(x+2)$

4.

n	$n^2 - 7n + 10$
0	$0^2 - 7(0) + 10 = 10$
1	$1^2 - 7(1) + 10 = 4$
2	$2^2 - 7(2) + 10 = 0$
3	$3^2 - 7(3) + 10 = -2$
4	$4^2 - 7(4) + 10 = -2$

n	$(n-5)(n-2)$
0	$(0-5)(0-2) = 10$
1	$(1-5)(1-2) = 4$
2	$(2-5)(2-2) = 0$
3	$(3-5)(3-2) = -2$
4	$(4-5)(4-2) = -2$

Exercises **1.** $(x+4)(x+9)$
3. $(x+4)(x+10)$ **5.** $(x+2)(x+8)$
7. $(x-1)(x-6)$ **9.** $(x-3)(x-8)$
11. $(x+9)(x-3)$ **13.** $(x-2)(x+1)$
15. $(x-9)(x+5)$ **17.** $(x+3)(x+10)$
19. $(x+4)(x+12)$ **21.** $(x+2)$
$(x+14)$ **23.** $(x-1)(x-5)$
25. $(x-4)(x-8)$ **27.** $(x+7)(x-3)$
29. $(x-13)(x+1)$ **31.** $(x-7)(x+5)$
33. C **35.** D **37.** They are inverse
operations. **39.** $(x-2)(x-9)$
41. $(x+1)(x+9)$ **43.** $(x+6)(x+7)$
45. $(x+2)(x+9)$ **47.** $(x-3)(x+8)$
49. $(x-5)(x+9)$ **51.** approximately
1.5 **55.** $x^2 + 6x + 8; (x+4)(x+2)$
57. Positive; $-$, $-$; Both negative
59. Negative; $+$, $-$; Positive;
Negative **61a.** $d = t^2$ **b.** $d = 4t$
c. $t(t-4)$ **63.** true **65.** false **67.** 4
69. 4 **71a.** $(x+10)$ ft **b.** $\ell = (x+14)$ ft;
$w = (x+6)$ ft **c.** $A = (x^2 + 20x + 84)$
ft^2
73. D **75.** C **77.** $(x^2+9)(x^2+9)$
79. $(d^2+21)(d^2+1)$
81. $(de-5)(de+4)$ **83.** 16; 11; 29
85a. $(x+7)$ ft **b.** $(4x+26)$ ft
c. \$92.00 **d.** \$36.96 **e.** \$128.96

14-2

Check It Out! **1a.** $(3x+1)(2x+3)$
1b. $(3x+4)(x-2)$
2a. $(2x+5)(3x+1)$
2b. $(3x-4)(3x-1)$
2c. $(3x+4)(x+3)$
3a. $(3x-1)(2x+3)$
3b. $(4n+3)(n-1)$
4a. $-1(2x+3)(3x+4)$
4b. $-1(3x+2)(x+5)$

Exercises **1.** $(2x+5)(x+2)$
3. $(5x-3)(x+2)$ **5.** $(3x+4)(x-6)$
7. $(x+2)(5x+1)$
9. $(4x-5)(x-1)$
11. $(5x+4)(x+1)$
13. $(2a-1)(2a+5)$
15. $(2x-3)(x+2)$
17. $(10x+1)(x-1)$
19. $(2x+3)(4-x)$
21. $-1(5x+3)(x-2)$
23. $-1(2x-1)(2x+5)$
25. $(3x+2)(3x+1)$
27. $(n+2)(3n+2)$
29. $(4c-5)(c-3)$
31. $(2x+5)(4x+1)$
33. $(5x-6)(x+3)$
35. $(10n-7)(n-1)$
37. $(7x+1)(x+2)$
39. $(3x-4)(x-5)$
41. $(x-7)(4x-3)$
43. $(4y-1)(3y+5)$
45. $(2x-1)(2x+3)$
47. $(3x+5)(x-3)$
49. $-1(2x-3)(2x+5)$
51. $-1(3x-2)(x+1)$
53. $2x^2 - 5x + 2; (x-2)(2x-1)$
55. $(9n+8)(n+1)$
57. $(2x-1)(2x-5)$
59. $(3x+8)(x+2)$
61. $(3x+4)(2x-3)$
63. $(2x-3)(2x-3)$
65. $(2x+3)(3x+2)$
69a. $-16t^2 + 20t + 6$
b. $-2(4t+1)(2t-3)$ **c.** 10 ft **71.** D
73. B **77.** B **79.** A
81. $(2x+1)(2x+1)$
83. $(9x+1)(9x+1)$
85. $(5x+2)(5x+2)$ **87.** $-7; -5; 5; 7$
89. $-6; 6$

14-3

Check It Out! **1a.** yes; $(x+2)^2$
1b. yes; $(x-7)^2$ **1c.** no; $-6x \neq$
$2(3x)(2)$ **2.** $4(3x+1)$ m; 40 m
3a. yes; $(1-2x)(1+2x)$
3b. yes; $(p^4 + 7q^3)(p^4 - 7q^3)$
3c. No; $4y^5$ is not a perfect square.

Exercises **1.** yes; $(x-2)^2$ **3.** yes;
$(3x-2)^2$ **5.** yes; $(x-3)^2$
7. $4(x+12)$; 88 yd **9.** yes; $(s+4)$
$(s-4)$ **11.** yes; $(2x^2 + 3y)(2x^2 - 3y)$
13. yes; $x^3 + 3x^3 - 3$ **15.** No; the
last term must be positive. **17.** no;
$10x \neq 2(5x)(2)$ **19.** yes; $(4x-5)^2$
21. yes; $(1+2x)(1-2x)$ **23.** No;
$4x$ and $9y$ are not perfect squares.
25. yes; $(9-10x^2)(9+10x^2)$
27. 49 **29.** $4y^2$
31. $(10x+9y)(10x-9y)$; difference
of 2 squares
33. $(2r^3 + 5s^3)(2r^3 - 5s^3)$;
difference of 2 squares
35. $(x^7 + 12)(x^7 - 12)$; difference of
2 squares **39.** $c = 32$ **41a.** $5z - 4$
b. $20z - 16$ **c.** 11; 44; 121
43a. 0; 0; 100; 100; 0 **b.** 16; 16; 36;
36; -24 **c.** 25; 25; 25; 25; -25
d. 36; 36; 16; 16; -24 **e.** 100; 100; 0;
0; 0 **45.** $a - b; a + b$ **47.** C **49.** 1
51a. $a = 2; b = v + 2$
b. $[2 + (v+2)][2 - (v+2)] =$
$(v+4)(-v) = -v^2 - 4v$ **53.** $a = 3y;$
$b = y; (3y-4)(9y^2 + 12y + 16)$

15-1

Check It Out!

1.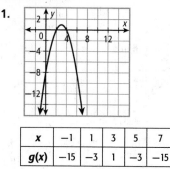

x	-1	1	3	5	7
$g(x)$	-15	-3	1	-3	-15

2a.

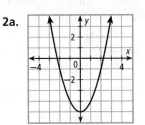

g is f translated 5 units down.

b.

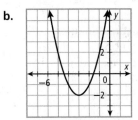

h is f translated 3 units left and 2 units down.

3a.

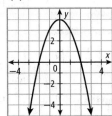

g is a horizontal compression of f by a factor of $\frac{1}{2}$.

b.

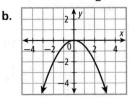

h is f reflected across the x-axis and vertically compressed by a factor of $\frac{1}{2}$. **4a.** $g(x) = \frac{1}{3}(x - 2)^2 - 4$
b. $g(x) = -(x + 5)^2 + 1$ **5.** Vertical compression by a factor of $\frac{13}{15}$; the braking distance will be less with optimally inflated new tires than with tires having more wear.

Exercises 1. vertex

3.

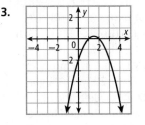

5. d is f translated 4 units right.
7. h is f translated 1 unit left and 3 units down. **9.** h is a horizontal stretch of f by a factor of 8.
11. h is f reflected across the x-axis and horizontally compressed by a factor of $\frac{1}{5}$. **13.** d is f reflected across the x-axis and vertically compressed by a factor of $\frac{2}{3}$.
15. $h(x) = -x^2 - 6$

17.

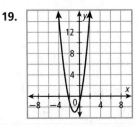

19.

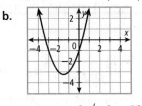

21. h is f translated 5 units left.
23. g is f translated 4 units left and 3 units down. **25.** j is f translated 4 units right and 9 units down.
27. h is f reflected across the x-axis and vertically stretched by a factor of 20. **29.** $g(x) = -\frac{1}{2}(x - 1)^2$
31. Vertical translation; at any given speed, the gas mileage for an SUV is 18 mi/gal less than for a compact car. **33.** p is f reflected across the x-axis and translated 4 units right.
35. h is f vertically stretched by a factor of 4 and translated 2 units down. **37.** g is f horizontally compressed by a factor of $\frac{1}{3}$ and translated 1 unit up.
39. C **41.** A **43.** horizontal line; linear or constant function

45a. vertical compression by a factor of 0.38 and translation 3.5 units right and 59 units up
b. $y = -6.08(t - 4)^2 + 95$ **47.** J
49. G **51.** translation 6 units right and 6 units up: $y = -3(x - 3)^2 + 3$

15-2

Check It Out! 1. $x = 3$

2a.

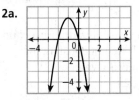

downward; $x = -1$; $(-1, 2)$; 0

b.

upward; $x = -\frac{3}{2}$; $\left(-\frac{3}{2}, -\frac{13}{4}\right)$; -1

3a. minimum: -6; D: $\mathbb{R}$;
R: $\{y|y \geq -6\}$ **b.** maximum: -4;
D: $\mathbb{R}$; R: $\{y|y \leq -4\}$ **4.** 30.0 mi/gal at 49 mi/h

Exercises 1. minimum **3.** $x = 0$
5. downward; $x = -1$; $(-1, -7)$;
-8 **7.** downward; $x = 2$; $(2, 3)$; -1
9. maximum: $\frac{1}{4}$; D: $\mathbb{R}$; R: $\left\{y|y \leq \frac{1}{4}\right\}$
11. 3.125 m **13.** $x = 1$ **15.** upward; $x = -\frac{1}{2}$; $\left(-\frac{1}{2}, -\frac{9}{4}\right)$; -2 **17.** upward; $x = 2$; $(2, -6)$; -4 **19.** upward; $x = -\frac{1}{3}$; $\left(-\frac{1}{3}, -\frac{25}{3}\right)$; -8
21. downward; $x = 0$; $(0, -2)$; -2
23. upward; $x = -2$; $(-2, 1)$; 2
25. maximum: 9; D: $\mathbb{R}$; R: $\{y|y \leq 9\}$
27. maximum: -4; D: $\mathbb{R}$;
R: $\{y|y \leq -4\}$
29. minimum: 0; D: $\mathbb{R}$; R: $\{y|y \geq 0\}$
31. 64 ft **33a.** 562.5 mm
b. 93.75 to 1 **c.** 168.75 m
35. minimum: ≈ -3.029771
37. minimum: ≈ -1.253333
41a. about 1.6 s **b.** about 45 ft
43. G **45.** G

15-3

Check It Out! 1a. Quadratic; second differences are constant for equally spaced x-values.
b. Not quadratic; first differences

are constant so the function is linear. **2.** $f(x) = -x^2 + 4x - 3$

3. $L(d) \approx 14.3d^2 - 112.4d + 430.1$; about 446 ft

Exercises 3. Not quadratic; second differences are not constant for equally spaced x-values.

5. $y = x^2 - 2x - 3$ **7.** $y = x^2 - 3x + 4$

9. $y = -\frac{1}{2}x^2 + 4x - 3$ **11.** $C(x) \approx$

$0.0098x^2 + 0.62x + 3.8$; about $31.20

13. Quadratic; second differences are constant for equally spaced x-values. **15.** $y = \frac{4}{3}x^2 - x - \frac{7}{3}$

17. $y = 0.5x^2 - 3x - 8$

19. $y \approx -3.7x^2 + 216x + 781$; about $3290 million, or $3.29 billion

21. The function is $A(b) = \left(\frac{1}{2}h\right)b$, which is linear. **23.** The function is $A(s) = s^2$, which is quadratic.

25. -3 **27.** -1

29a. $p(s) = -0.125s^2 + 5.25s - 35.05$ **b.** $18.95 **c.** a maximum point; the price and size of the most expensive pizza

d. $9.95; $-1.05 **31.** not quadratic

33. quadratic; $y = 5x^2 + 2x$

35. not quadratic **39a.** $y \approx -10.7x + 208.1$ **b.** no **c.** linear; $y = 4x + 8$

41. $t(n) = \frac{1}{2}n^2 + \frac{1}{2}n$

43b. $y \approx 0.5x + 3$

c. $y \approx -0.13x^2 + 2.8x - 6$

45. B **47.** D

49. $y = 2x^2 - 5$

16-1

Check It Out! 1. $-3, 1$ **2a.** $-1, 6$

b. $0, 8$ **3.** 3 s **4a.** $x = 2$ **b.** $x = -\frac{3}{5}$, $x = \frac{3}{5}$ **5.** Possible answer: $f(x) = x^2 - 25$

Exercises 1. roots **3.** 2, 4 **5.** 1, 6

7. $-4, 0$ **9.** $-2, 8$ **11.** 4 s **13.** $x = 2$

19. $-3, 2$ **21.** $-8, -3$ **23.** 0, 9

25. $-8, 1$ **27.** 4 s **29.** $x = -\frac{9}{2}$, $x = \frac{9}{2}$ **31.** $x = -\frac{1}{2}$, $x = \frac{1}{2}$

33. $x = \frac{2}{7}$ **37.** 0, 6 **39.** 6 **41.** 11

43. 5, 6 **45.** $-7, -2$ **47a.** $h(t) = -16t^2 + 16t + 5$ **b.** 1.25 s

49. $x = -5, x = -1$ **51.** $x = -\frac{1}{3}$

53. $x = -2, x = 3$ **55a.** $(0, -16)$

b. -16 **c.** $-4, 4$ **57a.** $(1, 2)$ **b.** 0

c. 0, 2 **59a.** $\left(-\frac{1}{6}, -4\frac{1}{12}\right)$ **b.** -4

c. $-1\frac{1}{3}$, 1 **61.** 20 ft by 4 ft

63. 10 m by 5 m **67.** B **69.** C

71. $x = 0, x = \frac{3}{2}$ **73.** $x = \frac{1}{4}, x = \frac{1}{2}$

75a. $(a + b)(a^2 - ab + b^2) = a^3 - a^2b + ab^2 + a^2b - ab^2 + b^3 = a^3 + b^3$ **b.** $(2x + 3)(4x^2 - 6x + 9)$

c. $a^3 - b^3 = (a - b)(a^2 + ab + b^2)$

d. $(x - 1)(x^2 + x + 1)$

16-2

Check It Out! 1a. $x = \pm\frac{5}{2}$

b. $x = -11, x = 3$ **2a.** $x^2 + 4x + 4 = (x + 2)^2$ **b.** $x^2 - 4x + 4 = (x - 2)^2$

c. $x^2 + 3x + \frac{9}{4} = \left(x + \frac{3}{2}\right)^2$

3a. $x = \frac{9 \pm \sqrt{89}}{2}$ **b.** $x = -1, x = 9$

4a. $f(x) = (x + 12)^2 + 1$; $(-12, 1)$

b. $g(x) = 5(x - 5)^2 + 3$; $(5, 3)$

Exercises 1. $\left(\frac{b}{2}\right)^2$ **3.** $x = 1, x = 9$

5. $x^2 + 14x + 49 = (x + 7)^2$

7. $x^2 - 9x + \frac{81}{4} = \left(x - \frac{9}{2}\right)^2$

9. $x = 2, x = 4$ **11.** $x = -2 \pm 2\sqrt{7}$

13. $x = -2 \pm \frac{\sqrt{46}}{2}$ **15.** $g(x) = (x - 5)^2 - 14$; $(5, -14)$ **17.** $f(x) = (x + 4)^2 - 26$; $(-4, -26)$ **19.** $h(x) = 3(x - 2)^2 - 16$; $(2, -16)$ **21.** $x = -7, x = 13$ **23.** $x^2 - 18x + 81 = (x - 9)^2$ **25.** $x^2 - \frac{1}{2}x + \frac{1}{16} = \left(x - \frac{1}{4}\right)^2$ **27.** $x = 2 \pm \sqrt{3}$ **29.** $x = 2$, $x = 6$ **31.** $x = -1 \pm \frac{2\sqrt{3}}{3}$ **33.** $g(x) = (x + 7)^2 + 22$; $(-7, 22)$ **35.** $f(x) = (x + 2)^2 - 11$; $(-2, -11)$ **37.** $h(x) = 2(x + 1.5)^2 + 20.5$; $(-1.5, 20.5)$ **39a.** about 12.3 s **b.** about 2.3 s **41.** $x = \pm\sqrt{3}$ **43.** $x = \pm 5$ **45.** $x = -13 \pm \sqrt{7}$ **47.** $x = \frac{-3 \pm 5\sqrt{2}}{2}$ **49.** $x = \frac{-3 \pm \sqrt{5}}{3}$ **51.** $x = -5, x = -3$ **53.** $x = \frac{-2 \pm \sqrt{7}}{3}$ **55.** $x = \frac{7 \pm \sqrt{57}}{2}$ **57.** $x = -3 \pm \sqrt{5}$ **59.** $x = 4 \pm 2\sqrt{10}$ **61a.** 1.7 s **b.** 71 ft/s **65.** $x = \pm 7.416$

67. $x = \pm 4.192$ **69.** $x = \pm 1.528$

73. B **75.** A **77.** 2.5 **79.** $b = \pm 24$

81. $b = \pm 18$ **83.** $2\sqrt{5} \pm 1$

85a. 135,000 ft^2 **b.** 450 ft by 300 ft

c. 129,600 ft^2

16-3

Check It Out! 1a. $\frac{-3 \pm \sqrt{37}}{2}$

b. $4 \pm \sqrt{6}$ **2.** $\frac{1}{6} \pm \frac{\sqrt{95}}{6}i$

3a. 1 distinct real solution

b. 2 distinct nonreal complex solutions **c.** 2 distinct real solutions **4.** 449 ft

Exercises 3. $\frac{2 \pm \sqrt{7}}{3}$ **5.** $-6, 1$

7. $\pm\frac{\sqrt{38}}{2}$ **9.** $-3 \pm i\sqrt{3}$ **11.** $-2 \pm i\sqrt{6}$

13. $\frac{-7 \pm i\sqrt{111}}{20}$ **15.** 2 distinct real solutions **17.** 14 in. and 20 in.

19. $-6, 0$ **21.** $-1 \pm \sqrt{10}$ **23.** $\pm\frac{\sqrt{21}}{7}$

25. $\frac{-1 \pm i\sqrt{3}}{2}$ **27.** $\frac{-7 \pm 3\sqrt{17}}{4}$

29. $\frac{2 \pm 2i\sqrt{2}}{3}$ **31.** 2 distinct real solutions **33.** 1 distinct real solution **35.** 2 distinct real solutions

37a. 9 s **b.** 6 s **39.** $\frac{1 \pm \sqrt{3}}{2}$

41. $\frac{-3 \pm \sqrt{17}}{4}$ **43.** $\frac{1 \pm i\sqrt{87}}{2}$

45. $x = -2, x = 5$ **47.** $x = -2.5$, $x = 1.5$ **49.** $x = -3, x = 7$

51. $x = \pm 5$ **53.** $x = 8$ **55.** 3 in.

57. $c = -36$ **61.** B **63.** C

65. 15 cm and 8 cm

16-4

Check It Out! 1. $(1, 2), (4, 5)$

2. $(-1, 7), (1, 1)$ **3a.** $(3, 4), (-1, -4)$

3b. $(5, 10), (-0.5, -3.75)$ **4.** 2.5 s

Exercises 1. nonlinear **3.** $(1, 1)$, $(3, 3)$ **5.** $(3, 0), (2, -1)$ **7.** $(1, -2), (3, 6)$ **9.** 4.75 s **11.** $(0, -3)$ **13.** $(3, -3)$, $(4, 3)$ **15.** $(3, 15), (-2, 5)$ **17.** $(3, 39)$, $\left(-\frac{3}{5}, 3\right)$ **19.** $(0, -5), \left(\frac{1}{3}, -\frac{44}{9}\right)$ **21.** $(1, 6), (3, 24)$ **23.** 5 mo **25.** 100 **27.** no **29.** yes **31.** yes **33.** no **37.** B; the left side of the equation was multiplied by -3, but the right side was not.

39. H **41.** G **43.** $\frac{-3 \pm \sqrt{153}}{-4}$

45. $\frac{7 \pm \sqrt{161}}{8}$ **47.** 1 s

17-1

Check It Out!

1. Possible answer:

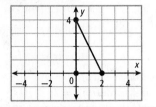

2. $\triangle ABC$ is a rt. $\triangle$ with height AB and base BC. The area of $\triangle ABC$ is $\frac{1}{2}(4)(6) = 12$ square units. By the Mdpt. Formula, the coords. of D are $\left(\frac{0+4}{2}, \frac{6+0}{2}\right) = (2, 3)$. With $\overline{AB}$ as the base of $\triangle ADB$, the x-coord. of D gives the height of $\triangle ADB$. The area of $\triangle ADB = \frac{1}{2}bh = \frac{1}{2}(6)(2) = 6$ square units. Since $6 = \frac{1}{2}(12)$, the area of $\triangle ADB$ is the area of $\triangle ABC$.

3. Possible answer:

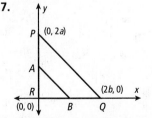

4. $\triangle ABC$ is a rt. $\triangle$ with height $2j$ and base $2n$. The area of $\triangle ABC = \frac{1}{2}bh = \frac{1}{2}(2n)(2j) = 2nj$ square units. By the Mdpt. Formula, the coords. of D are (n, j). The base of $\triangle ABD$ is $2j$ units and the height is n units. So the area of $\triangle ADB = \frac{1}{2}bh = \frac{1}{2}(2j)(n) = nj$ square units. Since $nj = \frac{1}{2}(2nj)$, the area of $\triangle ADB$ is $\frac{1}{2}$ the area of $\triangle ABC$.

Exercises

7.

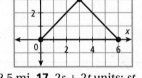

By the Mdpt. Formula, the coords. of A are $(0, a)$ and the coords. of B are $(b, 0)$. By the Dist. Formula,
$PQ = \sqrt{(0 - 2b)^2 + (2a)^2} = \sqrt{(-2b)^2 + (2a)^2} = \sqrt{4b^2 + 4a^2} = 2\sqrt{b^2 + a^2}$ units.

$AB = \sqrt{(0 - b)^2 + (a - 0)^2}$
$= \sqrt{(-b)^2 + a^2} = \sqrt{b^2 + a^2}$ units.
So $AB = \frac{1}{2}PQ$.

13.

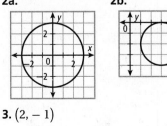

By the Mdpt. Formula, the coords. of E are $(0, a)$ and the coords. of F are $(2c, a)$. By the Dist. Formula,
$AD = \sqrt{(2c - 0)^2 + (2a - 2a)^2} = \sqrt{(2c)^2} = 2c$ units. Similarly,
$EF = \sqrt{(2c - 0)^2 + (a - a)^2} = \sqrt{(2c)^2} = 2c$ units. So $EF = AD$.

15a.

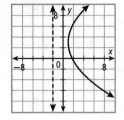

b. 8.5 mi **17.** $2s + 2t$ units; st square units **19.** $(p, 0)$ **21.** $AB \approx$ 128 nautical miles; $AP = BP \approx 64$ nautical miles; so P is the mdpt. of $\overline{AB}$. **23.** By the Dist. Formula, $AB = \sqrt{(x_2 - x_1)^2 + (y_2 - y_1)^2}$ and $AM = \sqrt{\left(\frac{x_1 + x_2}{2} - x_1\right)^2 + \left(\frac{y_1 + y_2}{2} - y_1\right)^2} = \sqrt{\left(\frac{x_1 + x_2}{2} - \frac{2x_1}{2}\right)^2 + \left(\frac{y_1 + y_2}{2} - \frac{2y_1}{2}\right)^2} = \sqrt{\frac{1}{4}(x_2 - x_1)^2 + \frac{1}{4}(y_2 - y_1)^2} = \frac{1}{2}\sqrt{(x_2 - x_1)^2 + (y_2 - y_1)^2}$. So $AM = \frac{1}{2}AB$. **27.** B **29.** D **31.** $(a + c, b)$

17-2

Check It Out!

1a. $x^2 + (y + 3)^2 = 64$ **1b.** $(x - 2)^2 + (y + 1)^2 = 16$

2a. **2b.**

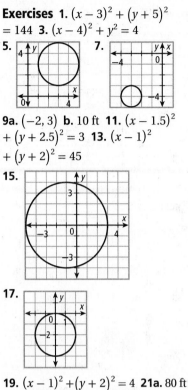

3. $(2, -1)$

Exercises

1. $(x - 3)^2 + (y + 5)^2 = 144$ **3.** $(x - 4)^2 + y^2 = 4$

5. **7.**

9a. $(-2, 3)$ **b.** 10 ft **11.** $(x - 1.5)^2 + (y + 2.5)^2 = 3$ **13.** $(x - 1)^2 + (y + 2)^2 = 45$

15.

17.

19. $(x - 1)^2 + (y + 2)^2 = 4$ **21a.** 80 ft **b.** $x^2 + y^2 = 1600$ **23.** T **25.** T **29a.** $E(-3, -1)$; $G(-6, 2)$ **b.** 6 **c.** $(x + 3)^2 + (y - 2)^2 = 9$ **31.** $(0, -15)$; 5 **33.** $A = 9\pi$; $C = 6\pi$ **35.** $A = 25\pi$; $C = 10\pi$ **37.** $(-200, -100)$ **39.** $(x - 1)^2 + (y + 2)^2 = 16$ **43.** H **45a.** $(x - 2)^2 + (y + 4)^2 + (z - 3)^2 = 69$ **b.** 15; if 2 segs. are tangent to a $\odot$ or sphere from the same ext. pt., then the segs. are $\cong$. **47.** $(x - 3)^2 + (y - 4)^2 = 5$

17-3

Check It Out!

1. $y = \frac{1}{16}x^2$

2. a. $x = -\frac{1}{5}y^2$ **b.** $y = -\frac{1}{28}x^2$

3a. vertex: $(1, 3)$; $p = 3$; axis of symmetry: $y = 3$; focus: $(4, 3)$; directrix: $x = -2$

b. vertex: (8, 4); $p = -\dfrac{1}{2}$; axis of symmetry: $x = 8$; focus: (8, 3.5); directrix: $y = 4.5$

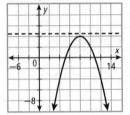

4. 11 in.

Exercises 3. $x = \dfrac{1}{28}y^2$

5. $y = -\dfrac{1}{16}x^2$ **7.** $y = \dfrac{1}{2}x^2$

9. $x = -\dfrac{1}{32}y^2$ **11.** vertex: (0, 4);

$p = 6$; axis of symmetry: $y = 4$; focus: (6, 4); directrix: $x = -6$

13. 9.5 in **15.** $x - 3 = -\dfrac{1}{20}y^2$

17. $y = \dfrac{1}{12}(x + 3)^2$ **19.** $x = \dfrac{1}{4}y^2$

21. $y = -\dfrac{1}{24}x^2$ **23.** vertex: (1, 0);

$p = \dfrac{1}{8}$; axis of symmetry: $y = 0$;

focus: $\left(\dfrac{9}{8}, 0\right)$; directrix: $x = \dfrac{7}{8}$

27. $y + 6 = -\dfrac{1}{12}(x - 2)^2$;

D: $\{x \mid x \in \mathbb{R}\}$; R: $\{y \mid y \le -6\}$

29. $x + 7 = \dfrac{1}{36}(y + 3)^2$;

D: $\{x \mid x \ge -7\}$; R: $\{y \mid y \in \mathbb{R}\}$

31. $y - 5 = -\dfrac{1}{20}x^2$; D: $\{x \mid x \in \mathbb{R}\}$;

R: $\{y \mid y \le 5\}$ **33.** $x - 8 =$

$-\dfrac{1}{16}(y + 5)^2$; D: $\{x \mid x \le 8\}$;

R: $\{y \mid y \in \mathbb{R}\}$ **35a.** $y = \dfrac{1}{20}x^2$

b. $y + 4 = \dfrac{1}{16}x^2$ **c.** 7.2 in

37a. (−96, 41) **b.** 133 million km

c. (−96, 174) **39.** vertex: (−4, 5);

$p = -\dfrac{1}{8}$; axis of symmetry: $x = -4$;

focus: $\left(-4, 4\dfrac{7}{8}\right)$; directrix: $y = 5\dfrac{1}{8}$

41. vertex: (−3, 2); $p = 2$;

axis of symmetry: $y = 2$;

focus: (−1, 2); directrix: $x = -5$

45. G **47.** (7, 0) **49.** $y - 7 =$

$-\dfrac{1}{8}(x-6)^2$ or $y - 3 = \dfrac{1}{8}(x - 6)^2$

51. $4p$

Selected Answers ▪ Unit 7

18-1

Check It Out! 1. $\frac{2}{3}$ 2. $\frac{1}{2}$ 3. $\frac{1}{2}$ 4. 0.71

Exercises 3. $\frac{1}{2}$ 5. $\frac{7}{10}$ 7. 9 times
9. $\frac{3}{8}$ 11. $\frac{5}{12}$ 13. 0.08 15. 0.79
17. 0.78 19. 0.46 21. 0.62 23. $\frac{1}{2}$
25. $\frac{3}{4}$ 27. 0.5 29. 0.11 31. A 33. 0.84
35. 0.13 37. 0.77 39–41. Possible
answers given. 39. The point
lies on AC. 41. The point lies in
the blue triangle or the green
triangle. 43. $\frac{1}{2}$; it does not matter
which regions are shaded because
they all have the same area.
45. A 47. D

18-2

Check It Out! 1a. 120
b. 73,116,160 2a. 336 b. 20 3. 28

Exercises 1. important;
permutation 3. 225 5. 1320
7. 5985 9. 12 11. 72 13. 20
15. 71,916,768 17. 1 19. 6 21. 72
23. 6700 25. 35 27. > 29. <
33a.

President	A	A	A	A	A	A	A	A	A	A	A	A
Vice President	B	B	B	C	C	C	D	D	D	E	E	E
Secretary	C	D	E	B	D	E	B	C	E	B	C	D

b.

President	B	B	B	B	B	B	B	B	B	B	B	B
Vice President	A	A	A	C	C	C	D	D	D	E	E	E
Secretary	C	D	E	A	D	E	A	C	E	A	C	D

60 ways

c. 60 d. 10; 60; 10 37. A 39. D
41. 1365 43. $(_{30}C_{12})(_{18}C_2)$

18-3

Check It Out! 1a. $\frac{5}{36}$ b. 0
c. $\frac{5}{12}$ 2. $\frac{16}{25}$ 3. $\frac{1}{28}$ 4. $\frac{16}{225}$
5a. $\frac{9}{26}$ b. $\frac{19}{26}$

Exercises 1. theoretical
probability 3. $\frac{1}{4}$ 5. $\frac{1}{4}$ 7. $\frac{303}{365}$
9. $\frac{1}{220}$ 11. $\frac{1}{9}$ 13. $\frac{3}{5}$ 15. $\frac{4}{5}$ 17. $\frac{1}{56}$
19. $\approx \frac{1}{42}$ 21. never 23a. $\frac{\pi}{4}$
25a. 0.68; 0.84; 0.76; 0.64
b. 0.73 27. $\frac{2}{5}$ 29. June; ≈ 0.13
31. no; yes 33. $\frac{1}{2}$ 37. G 39. H

19-1

Check It Out! 1a. $\frac{1}{36}$ b. $\frac{1}{8}$
2. $\frac{5}{36}$ 3a. ≈ 0.014 b. ≈ 0.186
4a. independent; $\frac{3}{20}$
b. dependent; $\frac{1}{6}$ c. dependent; $\frac{1}{12}$

Exercises 1. independent
3. $\frac{1}{8}$ 5. The probability that the
yellow cube shows a multiple of 3
increases from $\frac{1}{3}$ if the product is 6;
$\frac{1}{2}$ 7. $\frac{1}{100}$ 9. dependent; $\frac{9}{38}$
11. $\frac{1}{12}$ 13. The probability that the
product is 8 increases from $\frac{1}{18}$
if the blue cube is less than 3; $\frac{1}{36}$
15. ≈ 0.72 17. dependent; $\frac{1}{6}$
19. independent
21. independent 23a. ≈ 0.61
b. ≈ 0.05 25a. $\frac{625}{1296}$ b. $\frac{1}{36}$
c. $\frac{1}{6}$ 27. ≈ 0.6 29. 40 33. F
35. 7

19-2

Check It Out!

1.

	Fiction	Nonfiction	Total
Hardcover	0.133	0.248	0.381
Paperback	0.448	0.171	0.619
Total	0.581	0.419	1

2a.

| | Ballet | | |
Tap	Yes	No	Total
Yes	0.19	0.26	0.45
No	0.43	0.12	0.55
Total	0.62	0.38	1

b. 0.69 or 69%

3. Al's Driving has the best pass
rate, about 64%, versus 61% for
Drive Time and 50% for Crash
Course.

Exercises 1. marginal

3.

	Under-classmates	Upper-classmates	Total
Morning	0.16	0.28	0.44
Afternoon	0.36	0.2	0.56
Total	0.52	0.48	1

5a.

| | Play Sport | | |
Play instrument	Yes	No	Total
Yes	0.23	0.19	0.42
No	0.25	0.33	0.58
Total	0.48	0.52	1

b. 0.55

c. 0.48

7.

	Students	Adults	Total
T-Shirts	0.267	0.383	0.65
Sweatshirts	0.117	0.233	0.35
Total	0.384	0.616	1

9a.

	Satisfied	Dissatisfied	Total
Team 1	0.17	0.07	0.24
Team 2	0.29	0.1	0.39
Team 3	0.29	0.08	0.37
Total	0.75	0.25	1

b. Team 1: 0.71; Team 2: 0.74; Team 3: 0.78

c. Team 3 has the highest rate of customer satisfaction.

11. Maria made an error; Possible answer: You can tell because the four relative frequencies have a sum of 1.1, rather than 1.

13a.

| | Work less than 5 miles from home? | | |
Use new system?	Yes	No	Total
Yes	0.2	0.27	0.47
No	0.37	0.17	0.54
Total	0.57	0.44	1

b. 0.35

c. 0.57

15. C

17.

	Yes	No	Total
Children	0.125	0.1	0.225
Teenagers	0.725	0.05	0.775
Total	0.85	0.15	1

19. 10 children

21. 0

19-3

Check It Out! **1a.** Each student can vote only once. **b.** 75%

2a. $\frac{4}{13}$ **b.** $\frac{8}{13}$ **3.** $\frac{31}{40}$ **4.** ≈ 0.1524

Exercises **1.** inclusive events

3. $\frac{3}{5}$ **5.** $\frac{4}{5}$ **7.** $\frac{7}{9}$ **9.** $\frac{54}{65}$ **11.** ≈ 0.92 **13.** $\frac{1}{2}$ **15.** $\frac{1}{4}$ **17.** $\frac{32}{49}$ **19.** $1 - 0.75^{13} \approx 0.976$ **21.** 0.37; experimental **23.** 87%; 100% **25b.** 4.16%; 52.24% **27.** 0.49

29a. 0.42 **b.** 0.02 **c.** 0.44; it is the sum of the probabilities. **31.** D **33.** D **35.** ≈ 0.12 **37.** $\frac{13}{18}$ **39.** 0.9 **41.** 0.2

Glossary/Glosario

A

ENGLISH	SPANISH	EXAMPLES
absolute value of a complex number The absolute value of $a + bi$ is the distance from the origin to the point (a, b) in the complex plane and is denoted $\|a + bi\| = \sqrt{a^2 + b^2}$.	**valor absoluto de un número complejo** El valor absoluto de $a + bi$ es la distancia desde el origen hasta el punto (a, b) en el plano complejo y se expresa $\|a + bi\| = \sqrt{a^2 + b^2}$.	$\|2 + 3i\| = \sqrt{2^2 + 3^2} = \sqrt{13}$
acute angle An angle that measures greater than 0° and less than 90°.	**ángulo agudo** Ángulo que mide más de 0° y menos de 90°.	
acute triangle A triangle with three acute angles.	**triángulo acutángulo** Triángulo con tres ángulos agudos.	
adjacent angles Two angles in the same plane with a common vertex and a common side, but no common interior points.	**ángulos adyacentes** Dos ángulos en el mismo plano que tienen un vértice y un lado común pero no comparten puntos internos.	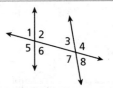 ∠1 and ∠2 are adjacent angles.
adjacent arcs Two arcs of the same circle that intersect at exactly one point.	**arcos adyacentes** Dos arcos del mismo círculo que se cruzan en un punto exacto.	$\overset{\frown}{RS}$ and $\overset{\frown}{ST}$ are adjacent arcs.
alternate exterior angles For two lines intersected by a transversal, a pair of angles that lie on opposite sides of the transversal and outside the other two lines.	**ángulos alternos externos** Dadas dos líneas cortadas por una transversal, par de ángulos no adyacentes ubicados en los lados opuestos de la transversal y fuera de las otras dos líneas.	∠4 and ∠5 are alternate exterior angles.
alternate interior angles For two lines intersected by a transversal, a pair of nonadjacent angles that lie on opposite sides of the transversal and between the other two lines.	**ángulos alternos internos** Dadas dos líneas cortadas por una transversal, par de ángulos no adyacentes ubicados en los lados opuestos de la transversal y entre las otras dos líneas.	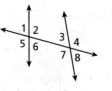 ∠3 and ∠6 are alternate interior angles.
altitude of a cone A segment from the vertex to the plane of the base that is perpendicular to the plane of the base.	**altura de un cono** Segmento que se extiende desde el vértice hasta el plano de la base y es perpendicular al plano de la base.	

Glossary/Glosario

ENGLISH	SPANISH	EXAMPLES
altitude of a cylinder A segment with its endpoints on the planes of the bases that is perpendicular to the planes of the bases.	**altura de un cilindro** Segmento con sus extremos en los planos de las bases que es perpendicular a los planos de las bases.	
altitude of a prism A segment with its endpoints on the planes of the bases that is perpendicular to the planes of the bases.	**altura de un prisma** Segmento con sus extremos en los planos de las bases que es perpendicular a los planos de las bases.	
altitude of a pyramid A segment from the vertex to the plane of the base that is perpendicular to the plane of the base.	**altura de una pirámide** Segmento que se extiende desde el vértice hasta el plano de la base y es perpendicular al plano de la base.	
altitude of a triangle A perpendicular segment from a vertex to the line containing the opposite side.	**altura de un triángulo** Segmento perpendicular que se extiende desde un vértice hasta la línea que forma el lado opuesto.	
ambiguous case of the Law of Sines If two sides and a nonincluded angle of a triangle are given in order to solve the triangle using the Law of Sines, it is possible to have two different answers.	**caso ambiguo de la ley de los senos** Si se conocen dos lados y un ángulo no incluido de un triángulo y se quiere resolver el triángulo aplicando la ley de los senos, es posible obtener dos respuestas diferentes.	
angle A figure formed by two rays with a common endpoint.	**ángulo** Figura formada por dos rayos con un extremo común.	
angle bisector A ray that divides an angle into two congruent angles.	**bisectriz de un ángulo** Rayo que divide un ángulo en dos ángulos congruentes.	$\overrightarrow{JK}$ is an angle bisector of $\angle LJM$.
angle of depression The angle formed by a horizontal line and a line of sight to a point below.	**ángulo de depresión** Ángulo formado por una línea horizontal y una línea visual a un punto inferior.	
angle of elevation The angle formed by a horizontal line and a line of sight to a point above.	**ángulo de elevación** Ángulo formado por una línea horizontal y una línea visual a un punto superior.	
angle of rotation An angle formed by a rotating ray, called the terminal side, and a stationary reference ray, called the initial side.	**ángulo de rotación** Ángulo formado por un rayo rotativo, denominado lado terminal, y un rayo de referencia estático, denominado lado inicial.	The angle of rotation is 135°.

ENGLISH	SPANISH	EXAMPLES

angle of rotational symmetry
The smallest angle through which a figure with rotational symmetry can be rotated to coincide with itself.

ángulo de simetría de rotación El ángulo más pequeño alrededor del cual se puede rotar una figura con simetría de rotación para que coincida consigo misma.

---

annulus The region between two concentric circles.

corona circular Región comprendida entre dos círculos concéntricos.

---

apothem The perpendicular distance from the center of a regular polygon to a side of the polygon.

apotema Distancia perpendicular desde el centro de un polígono regular hasta un lado del polígono.

---

arc An unbroken part of a circle consisting of two points on the circle, called the endpoints, and all the points on the circle between them.

arco Parte continua de una circunferencia formada por dos puntos de la circunferencia denominados extremos y todos los puntos de la circunferencia comprendidos entre éstos.

---

arc length The distance along an arc measured in linear units.

longitud de arco Distancia a lo largo de un arco medida en unidades lineales.

$m\overset{\frown}{CD} = 5\pi$ ft

---

arc marks Marks used on a figure to indicate congruent angles.

marcas de arco Marcas utilizadas en una figura para indicar ángulos congruentes.

---

area The number of nonoverlapping unit squares of a given size that will exactly cover the interior of a plane figure.

área Cantidad de cuadrados unitarios de un determinado tamaño no superpuestos que cubren exactamente el interior de una figura plana.

The area is 10 square units.

---

arrow notation A symbol used to describe a transformation.

notación de flecha Símbolo utilizado para describir una transformación.

$\triangle ABC \longrightarrow \triangle A'B'C'$

---

auxiliary line A line drawn in a figure to aid in a proof.

línea auxiliar Línea dibujada en una figura como ayuda en una demostración.

---

axiom *See* postulate.

axioma *Ver* postulado.

Glossary/Glosario

ENGLISH	SPANISH	EXAMPLES
axis of a cone The segment with endpoints at the vertex and the center of the base.	**eje de un cono** Segmento cuyos extremos se encuentran en el vértice y en el centro de la base.	 Axis
axis of a cylinder The segment with endpoints at the centers of the two bases.	**eje de un cilindro** Segmentos cuyos extremos se encuentran en los centros de las dos bases.	 Axis
axis of symmetry A line that divides a plane figure or a graph into two congruent reflected halves.	**eje de simetría** Línea que divide una figura plana o una gráfica en dos mitades reflejadas congruentes.	 Axis of symmetry

B

ENGLISH	SPANISH	EXAMPLES
base angle of a trapezoid One of a pair of consecutive angles whose common side is a base of the trapezoid.	**ángulo base de un trapecio** Uno de los dos ángulos consecutivos cuyo lado en común es la base del trapecio.	 Base angles
base angle of an isosceles triangle One of the two angles that have the base of the triangle as a side.	**ángulo base de un triángulo isósceles** Uno de los dos ángulos que tienen como lado la base del triángulo.	 Base angle Base angle
base of a cone The circular face of the cone.	**base de un cono** Cara circular del cono.	 Base
base of a cylinder One of the two circular faces of the cylinder.	**base de un cilindro** Una de las dos caras circulares del cilindro.	 Bases
base of a geometric figure A side of a polygon; a face of a three-dimensional figure by which the figure is measured or classified.	**base de una figura geométrica** Lado de un polígono; cara de una figura tridimensional por la cual se mide o clasifica la figura.	 Bases
base of a prism One of the two congruent parallel faces of the prism.	**base de un prisma** Una de las dos caras paralelas y congruentes del prisma.	 Bases
base of a pyramid The face of the pyramid that is opposite the vertex.	**base de una pirámide** Cara de la pirámide opuesta al vértice.	 Base
base of a trapezoid One of the two parallel sides of the trapezoid.	**base de un trapecio** Uno de los dos lados paralelos del trapecio.	 b_1 b_2

ENGLISH	SPANISH	EXAMPLES

base of a triangle Any side of a triangle. | **base de un triángulo** Cualquier lado de un triángulo. |

base of an isosceles triangle The side opposite the vertex angle. | **base de un triángulo isósceles** Lado opuesto al ángulo del vértice. |

bearing Indicates direction. The number of degrees in the angle whose initial side is a line due north and whose terminal side is determined by a clockwise rotation. | **rumbo** Indica dirección. La cantidad de grados en el ángulo cuyo lado inicial es una línea recta en dirección norte y cuyo lado terminal se determina por una rotación en el sentido de las agujas del reloj. |

between Given three points A, B, and C, B is between A and C if and only if all three of the points lie on the same line, and $AB + BC = AC$. | **entre** Dados tres puntos A, B y C, B está entre A y C si y sólo si los tres puntos se encuentran en la misma línea y $AB + BC = AC$. |

biconditional statement A statement that can be written in the form "p if and only if q." | **enunciado bicondicional** Enunciado que puede expresarse en la forma "p si y sólo si q". | A figure is a triangle if and only if it is a three-sided polygon.

binomial A polynomial with two terms. | **binomio** Polinomio con dos términos. | $x + y$
 $2a^2 + 3$
 $4m^3n^2 + 6mn^4$

bisect To divide into two congruent parts. | **trazar una bisectriz** Dividir en dos partes congruentes. |
 $\overrightarrow{JK}$ bisects $\angle LJM$.

C

Cartesian coordinate system *See* coordinate plane. | **sistema de coordenadas cartesianas** *Ver* plano cartesiano. |

center of a circle The point inside a circle that is the same distance from every point on the circle. | **centro de un círculo** Punto dentro de un círculo que se encuentra a la misma distancia de todos los puntos del círculo. |

center of a regular polygon The point that is equidistant from all vertices of the regular polygon. | **centro de un polígono regular** Punto equidistante de todos los vértices del polígono regular. |

center of a sphere The point inside a sphere that is the same distance from every point on the sphere. | **centro de una esfera** Punto dentro de una esfera que está a la misma distancia de cualquier punto de la esfera. |

ENGLISH	SPANISH	EXAMPLES
center of dilation The intersection of the lines that connect each point of the image with the corresponding point of the preimage.	**centro de dilatación** Intersección de las líneas que conectan cada punto de la imagen con el punto correspondiente de la imagen original.	center
center of rotation The point around which a figure is rotated.	**centro de rotación** Punto alrededor del cual rota una figura.	90° 90° Center 90° 90°
central angle of a circle An angle whose vertex is the center of a circle.	**ángulo central de un círculo** Ángulo cuyo vértice es el centro de un círculo.	
central angle of a regular polygon An angle whose vertex is the center of the regular polygon and whose sides pass through consecutive vertices.	**ángulo central de un polígono regular** Ángulo cuyo vértice es el centro del polígono regular y cuyos lados pasan por vértices consecutivos.	Central angle
centroid of a triangle The point of concurrency of the three medians of a triangle. Also known as the *center of gravity*.	**centroide de un triángulo** Punto donde se encuentran las tres medianas de un triángulo. También conocido como *centro de gravedad*.	B X P Y A Z C The centroid is *P*.
chord A segment whose endpoints lie on a circle.	**cuerda** Segmento cuyos extremos se encuentran en un círculo.	A Chord B
circle The set of points in a plane that are a fixed distance from a given point called the center of the circle.	**círculo** Conjunto de puntos en un plano que se encuentran a una distancia fija de un punto determinado denominado centro del círculo.	
circle graph A way to display data by using a circle divided into non-overlapping sectors.	**gráfica circular** Forma de mostrar datos mediante un círculo dividido en sectores no superpuestos.	**Residents of Mesa, AZ** 65+ Under 45–64 13% 18 19% 27% 11% 30% 18–24 25–44
circumcenter of a triangle The point of concurrency of the three perpendicular bisectors of a triangle.	**circuncentro de un triángulo** Punto donde se cortan las tres mediatrices de un triángulo.	B P A C The circumcenter is *P*.

ENGLISH	SPANISH	EXAMPLES
circumference The distance around the circle.	**circunferencia** Distancia alrededor del círculo.	Circumference
circumscribed circle Every vertex of the polygon lies on the circle.	**círculo circunscrito** Todos los vértices del polígono se encuentran sobre el círculo.	
circumscribed polygon Each side of the polygon is tangent to the circle.	**polígono circunscrito** Todos los lados del polígono son tangentes al círculo.	
cofunction The trigonometric function of the complement of an angle.	**cofuncion** La funciona trigonométrica del complemento de un ángulo.	
coincide To correspond exactly; to be identical.	**coincidir** Corresponder exactamente, ser idéntico.	
collinear Points that lie on the same line.	**colineal** Puntos que se encuentran sobre la misma línea.	K L M K, L, and M are collinear points.
combination A selection of a group of objects in which order is *not* important. The number of combinations of r objects chosen from a group of n objects is denoted $_nC_r$.	**combinación** Selección de un grupo de objetos en la cual el orden *no* es importante. El número de combinaciones de r objetos elegidos de un grupo de n objetos se expresa así: $_nC_r$.	For 4 objects A, B, C, and D, there are $_4C_2 = 6$ different combinations of 2 objects: AB, AC, AD, BC, BD, CD.
common tangent A line that is tangent to two circles.	**tangente común** Línea que es tangente a dos círculos.	
complement of an angle The sum of the measures of an angle and its complement is 90°.	**complemento de un ángulo** La suma de las medidas de un ángulo y su complemento es 90°.	The complement of a 53° angle is a 37° angle.
complement of an event All outcomes in the sample space that are not in an event E, denoted $\overline{E}$.	**complemento de un suceso** Todos los resultados en el espacio muestral que no están en el suceso E y se expresan $\overline{E}$.	In the experiment of rolling a number cube, the complement of rolling a 3 is rolling a 1, 2, 4, 5, or 6.
complementary angles Two angles whose measures have a sum of 90°.	**ángulos complementarios** Dos ángulos cuyas medidas suman 90°.	

ENGLISH	SPANISH	EXAMPLES
completing the square A process used to form a perfect-square trinomial. To complete the square of $x^2 + bx$, add $\left(\dfrac{b}{2}\right)^2$.	**completar el cuadrado** Proceso utilizado para formar un trinomio cuadrado perfecto. Para completar el cuadrado de $x^2 + bx$, hay que sumar $\left(\dfrac{b}{2}\right)^2$.	$x^2 + 6x +$ ■ Add $\left(\dfrac{6}{2}\right)^2 = 9$. $x^2 + 6x + 9$ $(x + 3)^2$ *is a perfect square.*
complex conjugate The complex conjugate of any complex number $a + bi$, denoted $\overline{a + bi}$, is $a - bi$.	**conjugado complejo** El conjugado complejo de cualquier número complejo $a + bi$, expresado como $\overline{a + bi}$, es $a - bi$.	$\overline{4 + 3i} = 4 - 3i$ $\overline{4 - 3i} = 4 + 3i$
complex number Any number that can be written as $a + bi$, where a and b are real numbers and $i = \sqrt{-1}$.	**número complejo** Todo número que se puede expresar como $a + bi$, donde a y b son números reales e $i = \sqrt{-1}$.	$4 + 2i$ $5 + 0i = 5$ $0 - 7i = -7i$
complex plane A set of coordinate axes in which the horizontal axis is the real axis and the vertical axis is the imaginary axis; used to graph complex numbers.	**plano complejo** Conjunto de ejes cartesianos en el cual el eje horizontal es el eje real y el eje vertical es el eje imaginario; se utiliza para representar gráficamente números complejos.	
component form The form of a vector that lists the vertical and horizontal change from the initial point to the terminal point.	**forma de componente** Forma de un vector que muestra el cambio horizontal y vertical desde el punto inicial hasta el punto terminal.	 The component form of $\overrightarrow{CD}$ is $\langle 2, 3 \rangle$.
composite figure A plane figure made up of triangles, rectangles, trapezoids, circles, and other simple shapes, or a three-dimensional figure made up of prisms, cones, pyramids, cylinders, and other simple three-dimensional figures.	**figura compuesta** Figura plana compuesta por triángulos, rectángulos, trapecios, círculos y otras figuras simples, o figura tridimensional compuesta por prismas, conos, pirámides, cilindros y otras figuras tridimensionales simples.	
composition of transformations One transformation followed by another transformation.	**composición de transformaciones** Una transformación seguida de otra transformación.	
compound event An event made up of two or more simple events.	**suceso compuesto** Suceso formado por dos o más sucesos simples.	In the experiment of tossing a coin and rolling a number cube, the event of the coin landing heads and the number cube landing on 3.
compound statement Two statements that are connected by the word *and* or *or*.	**enunciado compuesto** Dos enunciados unidos por la palabra *y* u *o*.	The sky is blue and the grass is green. I will drive to school or I will take the bus.
concave polygon A polygon in which a diagonal can be drawn such that part of the diagonal contains points in the exterior of the polygon.	**polígono cóncavo** Polígono en el cual se puede trazar una diagonal tal que parte de la diagonal contiene puntos ubicados fuera del polígono.	 Concave quadrilateral

ENGLISH	SPANISH	EXAMPLES
concentric circles Coplanar circles with the same center.	**círculos concéntricos** Círculos coplanares que comparten el mismo centro.	
conclusion The part of a conditional statement following the word *then*.	**conclusión** Parte de un enunciado condicional que sigue a la palabra *entonces*.	If $x + 1 = 5$, then $x = 4$. Conclusion
concurrent Three or more lines that intersect at one point.	**concurrente** Tres o más líneas que se cortan en un punto.	
conditional probability The probability of event B, given that event A has already occurred or is certain to occur, denoted $P(B \mid A)$; used to find probability of dependent events.	**probabilidad condicional** Probabilidad del suceso B, dado que el suceso A ya ha ocurrido o es seguro que ocurrirá, expresada como $P(B \mid A)$; se utiliza para calcular la probabilidad de sucesos dependientes.	
conditional relative frequency The ratio of a joint relative frequency to a related marginal relative frequency in a two-way table.	**frecuencia relativa condicional** Razón de una frecuencia relativa conjunta a una frecuencia relativa marginal en una tabla de doble entrada.	
conditional statement A statement that can be written in the form "if p, then q," where p is the hypothesis and q is the conclusion.	**enunciado condicional** Enunciado que se puede expresar como "si p, entonces q", donde p es la hipótesis y q es la conclusión.	If $x + 1 = 5$, then $x = 4$. Hypothesis Conclusion
cone A three-dimensional figure with a circular base and a curved lateral surface that connects the base to a point called the vertex.	**cono** Figura tridimensional con una base circular y una superficie lateral curva que conecta la base con un punto denominado vértice.	
congruence statement A statement that indicates that two polygons are congruent by listing the vertices in the order of correspondence.	**enunciado de congruencia** Enunciado que indica que dos polígonos son congruentes enumerando los vértices en orden de correspondencia.	$\triangle HKL \cong \triangle YWX$
congruence transformation *See* isometry.	**transformación de congruencia** *Ver* isometría.	
congruent Having the same size and shape, denoted by $\cong$.	**congruente** Que tiene el mismo tamaño y la misma forma, expresado por $\cong$.	$\overline{PQ} \cong \overline{SR}$
congruent angles Angles that have the same measure.	**ángulos congruentes** Ángulos que tienen la misma medida.	$\angle ABC \cong \angle DEF$

ENGLISH	SPANISH	EXAMPLES
congruent arcs Two arcs that are in the same or congruent circles and have the same measure.	**arcos congruentes** Dos arcos que se encuentran en el mismo círculo o en círculos congruentes y que tienen la misma medida.	
congruent circles Two circles that have congruent radii.	**círculos congruentes** Dos círculos que tienen radios congruentes.	
congruent polygons Two polygons whose corresponding sides and angles are congruent.	**polígonos congruentes** Dos polígonos cuyos lados y ángulos correspondientes son congruentes.	
congruent segments Two segments that have the same length.	**segmentos congruentes** Dos segmentos que tienen la misma longitud.	$\overline{PQ} \cong \overline{SR}$
conjecture A statement that is believed to be true.	**conjetura** Enunciado que se supone verdadero.	A sequence begins with the terms 2, 4, 6, 8, 10. A reasonable conjecture is that the next term in the sequence is 12.
conjunction A compound statement that uses the word *and*.	**conjunción** Enunciado compuesto que contiene la palabra *y*.	3 is less than 5 AND greater than 0.
consecutive interior angles *See* same-side interior angles.	**ángulos internos consecutivos** *Ver* ángulos internos del mismo lado.	
construction A method of creating a figure that is considered to be mathematically precise. Figures may be constructed by using a compass and straightedge, geometry software, or paper folding.	**construcción** Método para crear una figura que es considerado matemáticamente preciso. Se pueden construir figuras utilizando un compás y una regla, un programa de computación de geometría o plegando papeles.	
contraction *See* reduction.	**contracción** *Ver* reducción.	
contrapositive The statement formed by both exchanging and negating the hypothesis and conclusion of a conditional statement.	**contrarrecíproco** Enunciado que se forma al intercambiar y negar la hipótesis y la conclusión de un enunciado condicional.	Statement: If $n + 1 = 3$, then $n = 2$ Contrapositive: If $n \neq 2$, then $n + 1 \neq 3$
converse The statement formed by exchanging the hypothesis and conclusion of a conditional statement.	**recíproco** Enunciado que se forma intercambiando la hipótesis y la conclusión de un enunciado condicional.	Statement: If $n + 1 = 3$, then $n = 2$ Converse: If $n = 2$, then $n + 1 = 3$
convex polygon A polygon in which no diagonal contains points in the exterior of the polygon.	**polígono convexo** Polígono en el cual ninguna diagonal contiene puntos fuera del polígono.	Convex quadrilateral

ENGLISH	SPANISH	EXAMPLES
coordinate A number used to identify the location of a point. On a number line, one coordinate is used. On a coordinate plane, two coordinates are used, called the x-coordinate and the y-coordinate. In space, three coordinates are used, called the x-coordinate, the y-coordinate, and the z-coordinate.	**coordenada** Número utilizado para identificar la ubicación de un punto. En una recta numérica se utiliza una coordenada. En un plano cartesiano se utilizan dos coordenadas, denominadas coordenada x y coordenada y. En el espacio se utilizan tres coordenadas, denominadas coordenada x, coordenada y y coordenada z.	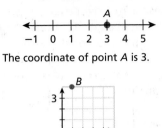 The coordinate of point A is 3. 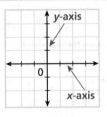 The coordinates of point B are (1, 4).
coordinate plane A plane that is divided into four regions by a horizontal line called the x-axis and a vertical line called the y-axis.	**plano cartesiano** Plano dividido en cuatro regiones por una línea horizontal denominada eje x y una línea vertical denominada eje y.	*y*-axis 0 *x*-axis
coordinate proof A style of proof that uses coordinate geometry and algebra.	**prueba de coordenadas** Tipo de demostración que utiliza geometría de coordenadas y álgebra.	
coplanar Points that lie in the same plane.	**coplanar** Puntos que se encuentran en el mismo plano.	
corollary A theorem whose proof follows directly from another theorem.	**corolario** Teorema cuya demostración proviene directamente de otro teorema.	
corresponding angles of lines intersected by a transversal For two lines intersected by a transversal, a pair of angles that lie on the same side of the transversal and on the same sides of the other two lines.	**ángulos correspondientes de líneas cortadas por una transversal** Dadas dos líneas cortadas por una transversal, el par de ángulos ubicados en el mismo lado de la transversal y en los mismos lados de las otras dos líneas.	1 2 5 6 3 4 7 8 ∠1 and ∠3 are corresponding.
corresponding angles of polygons Angles in the same position in two different polygons that have the same number of angles.	**ángulos correspondientes de los polígonos** Ángulos que tienen la misma posición en dos polígonos diferentes que tienen el mismo número de ángulos.	A B D E C F ∠A and ∠D are corresponding angles.
corresponding sides of polygons Sides in the same position in two different polygons that have the same number of sides.	**lados correspondientes de los polígonos** Lados que tienen la misma posición en dos polígonos diferentes que tienen el mismo número de lados.	A B D E C F $\overline{AB}$ and $\overline{DE}$ are corresponding sides.
cosecant In a right triangle, the cosecant of angle A is the ratio of the length of the hypotenuse to the length of the side opposite A. It is the reciprocal of the sine function.	**cosecante** En un triángulo rectángulo, la cosecante del ángulo A es la razón entre la longitud de la hipotenusa y la longitud del cateto opuesto a A. Es la inversa de la función seno.	opposite hypotenuse A $\csc A = \dfrac{\text{hypotenuse}}{\text{opposite}} = \dfrac{1}{\sin A}$

ENGLISH	SPANISH	EXAMPLES
cosine In a right triangle, the cosine of angle A is the ratio of the length of the leg adjacent to angle A to the length of the hypotenuse. It is the reciprocal of the secant function.	**coseno** En un triángulo rectángulo, el coseno del ángulo A es la razón entre la longitud del cateto adyacente al ángulo A y la longitud de la hipotenusa. Es la inversa de la función secante.	$$\cos A = \frac{\text{adjacent}}{\text{hypotenuse}} = \frac{1}{\sec A}$$
cotangent In a right triangle, the cotangent of angle A is the ratio of the length of the side adjacent to A to the length of the side opposite A. It is the reciprocal of the tangent function.	**cotangente** En un triángulo rectángulo, la cotangente del ángulo A es la razón entre la longitud del cateto adyacente a A y la longitud del cateto opuesto a A. Es la inversa de la función tangente.	$$\cot A = \frac{\text{adjacent}}{\text{opposite}} = \frac{1}{\tan A}$$
counterexample An example that proves that a conjecture or statement is false.	**contraejemplo** Ejemplo que demuestra que una conjetura o enunciado es falso.	
CPCTC An abbreviation for "Corresponding Parts of Congruent Triangles are Congruent," which can be used as a justification in a proof after two triangles are proven congruent.	**PCTCC** Abreviatura que significa "Las partes correspondientes de los triángulos congruentes son congruentes", que se puede utilizar para justificar una demostración después de demostrar que dos triángulos son congruentes (CPCTC, por sus siglas en inglés).	
cross products In the statement $\frac{a}{b} = \frac{c}{d}$, bc and ad are the cross products.	**productos cruzados** En el enunciado $\frac{a}{b} = \frac{c}{d}$, bc y ad son los productos cruzados.	$\frac{1}{2} = \frac{3}{6}$ Product of means: $2 \cdot 3 = 6$ Product of extremes: $1 \cdot 6 = 6$
cross section The intersection of a three-dimensional figure and a plane.	**sección transversal** Intersección de una figura tridimensional y un plano.	
cube A prism with six square faces.	**cubo** Prisma con seis caras cuadradas.	
cylinder A three-dimensional figure with two parallel congruent circular bases and a curved lateral surface that connects the bases.	**cilindro** Figura tridimensional con dos bases circulares congruentes y paralelas y una superficie lateral curva que conecta las bases.	

D

decagon A ten-sided polygon.	**decágono** Polígono de diez lados.	
deductive reasoning The process of using logic to draw conclusions.	**razonamiento deductivo** Proceso en el que se utiliza la lógica para sacar conclusiones.	

ENGLISH	SPANISH	EXAMPLES
definition A statement that describes a mathematical object and can be written as a true biconditional statement.	**definición** Enunciado que describe un objeto matemático y se puede expresar como un enunciado bicondicional verdadero.	
degree A unit of angle measure; one degree is $\frac{1}{360}$ of a circle.	**grado** Unidad de medida de los ángulos; un grado es $\frac{1}{360}$ de un círculo.	
dependent events Events for which the occurrence or nonoccurrence of one event affects the probability of the other event.	**sucesos dependientes** Dos sucesos son dependientes si el hecho de que uno de ellos se cumpla o no afecta la probabilidad del otro.	From a bag containing 3 red marbles and 2 blue marbles, drawing a red marble, and then drawing a blue marble without replacing the first marble.
diagonal of a polygon A segment connecting two nonconsecutive vertices of a polygon.	**diagonal de un polígono** Segmento que conecta dos vértices no consecutivos de un polígono.	
diameter A segment that has endpoints on the circle and that passes through the center of the circle; also the length of that segment.	**diámetro** Segmento que atraviesa el centro de un círculo y cuyos extremos están sobre la circunferencia; longitud de dicho segmento.	
dilation A transformation in which the lines connecting every point P with its preimage P' all intersect at a point C known as the center of dilation, and $\frac{CP'}{CP}$ is the same for every point P; a transformation that changes the size of a figure but not its shape.	**dilatación** Transformación en la cual las líneas que conectan cada punto P con su imagen original P' se cruzan en un punto C conocido como centro de dilatación, y $\frac{CP'}{CP}$ es igual para cada punto P; transformación que cambia el tamaño de una figura pero no su forma.	
directed line segment A segment between two points A and B with a specified direction, from A to B or from B to A.	**segmento de una línea con dirección** Un segmento entro dos puntos con una dirección especificada.	
direct reasoning The process of reasoning that begins with a true hypothesis and builds a logical argument to show that a conclusion is true.	**razonamiento directo** Proceso de razonamiento que comienza con una hipótesis verdadera y elabora un argumento lógico para demostrar que una conclusión es verdadera.	
direct variation A linear relationship between two variables, x and y, that can be written in the form $y = kx$, where k is a nonzero constant.	**variación directa** Relación lineal entre dos variables, x e y, que puede expresarse en la forma $y = kx$, donde k es una constante distinta de cero.	
direction of a vector The orientation of a vector, which is determined by the angle the vector makes with a horizontal line.	**dirección de un vector** Orientación de un vector, determinada por el ángulo que forma el vector con una línea horizontal.	

Glossary/Glosario

ENGLISH	SPANISH	EXAMPLES
directrix A fixed line used to define a *parabola*. Every point on the parabola is equidistant from the directrix and a fixed point called the *focus*.	**directriz** Línea fija utilizada para definir una *parábola*. Cada punto de la parábola es equidistante de la directriz y de un punto fijo denominado *foco*.	$P_1D_1 = P_1F \quad P_2D_2 = P_2F$
discriminant The discriminant of the quadratic equation $ax^2 + bx + c = 0$ is $b^2 - 4ac$.	**discriminante** El discriminante de la ecuación cuadrática $ax^2 + bx + c = 0$ es $b^2 - 4ac$.	The discriminant of $2x^2 - 5x - 3$ is $(-5)^2 - 4(2)(-3) = 25 + 24 = 49$.
disjunction A compound statement that uses the word *or*.	**disyunción** Enunciado compuesto que contiene la palabra *o*.	John will walk to work or he will stay home.
distance between two points The absolute value of the difference of the coordinates of the points.	**distancia entre dos puntos** Valor absoluto de la diferencia entre las coordenadas de los puntos.	$AB = |a - b| = |b - a|$
distance from a point to a line The length of the perpendicular segment from the point to the line.	**distancia desde un punto hasta una línea** Longitud del segmento perpendicular desde el punto hasta la línea.	The distance from P to $\overleftrightarrow{AC}$ is 5 units.
dodecagon A 12-sided polygon.	**dodecágono** Polígono de 12 lados.	
dodecahedron A polyhedron with 12 faces. The faces of a regular dodecahedron are regular pentagons, with three faces meeting at each vertex.	**dodecaedro** Poliedro con 12 caras. Las caras de un dodecaedro regular son pentágonos regulares, con tres caras que concurren en cada vértice.	

E

edge of a graph A curve or segment that joins two vertices of the graph.	**arista de una gráfica** Curva o segmento que une dos vértices de la gráfica.	
edge of a three-dimensional figure A segment that is the intersection of two faces of the figure.	**arista de una figura tridimensional** Segmento que constituye la intersección de dos caras de la figura.	
endpoint A point at an end of a segment or the starting point of a ray.	**extremo** Punto en el final de un segmento o punto de inicio de un rayo.	
enlargement A dilation with a scale factor greater than 1. In an enlargement, the image is larger than the preimage.	**agrandamiento** Dilatación con un factor de escala mayor que 1. En un agrandamiento, la imagen es más grande que la imagen original.	

ENGLISH	SPANISH	EXAMPLES

equal vectors Two vectors that have the same magnitude and the same direction.

vectores iguales Dos vectores de la misma magnitud y con la misma dirección.

$$|\vec{u}| = |\vec{v}| = 2\sqrt{5}$$

---

equally likely outcomes Outcomes are equally likely if they have the same probability of occurring. If an experiment has n equally likely outcomes, then the probability of each outcome is $\frac{1}{n}$.

resultados igualmente probables Los resultados son igualmente probables si tienen la misma probabilidad de ocurrir. Si un experimento tiene n resultados igualmente probables, entonces la probabilidad de cada resultado es $\frac{1}{n}$.

If a coin is tossed, and heads and tails are equally likely, then $P(\text{heads}) = P(\text{tails}) = \frac{1}{2}$.

---

equiangular polygon A polygon in which all angles are congruent.

polígono equiangular Polígono cuyos ángulos son todos congruentes.

---

equiangular triangle A triangle with three congruent angles.

triángulo equiangular Triángulo con tres ángulos congruentes.

---

equidistant The same distance from two or more objects.

equidistante Igual distancia de dos o más objetos.

X is equidistant from A and B.

---

equilateral polygon A polygon in which all sides are congruent.

polígono equilátero Polígono cuyos lados son todos congruentes.

---

equilateral triangle A triangle with three congruent sides.

triángulo equilátero Triángulo con tres lados congruentes.

Euclidean geometry The system of geometry described by Euclid. In particular, the system of Euclidean geometry satisfies the Parallel Postulate, which states that there is exactly one line through a given point parallel to a given line.

geometría euclidiana Sistema geométrico desarrollado por Euclides. Específicamente, el sistema de la geometría euclidiana cumple con el postulado de las paralelas, que establece que por un punto dado se puede trazar una única línea paralela a una línea dada.

Euler line The line containing the circumcenter (U), centroid (C), and orthocenter (O) of a triangle.

recta de Euler Recta que contiene el circuncentro (U), el centroide (C) y el ortocentro (O) de un triángulo.

---

event An outcome or set of outcomes in a probability experiment.

suceso Resultado o conjunto de resultados en un experimento de probabilidad.

In the experiement of rolling a number cube, the event "an odd number" consists of the outcomes 1, 3, 5.

ENGLISH	SPANISH	EXAMPLES
expansion *See* enlargement.	**expansión** *Ver* agrandamiento.	

ENGLISH	SPANISH	EXAMPLES
experiment An operation, process, or activity in which outcomes can be used to estimate probability.	**experimento** Una operación, proceso o actividad en la que se usan los resultados para estimar una probabilidad.	Tossing a coin 10 times and noting the number of heads.
experimental probability The ratio of the number of times an event occurs to the number of trials, or times, that an activity is performed.	**probabilidad experimental** Razón entre la cantidad de veces que ocurre un suceso y la cantidad de pruebas, o veces, que se realiza una actividad.	Kendra made 6 of 10 free throws. The experimental probability that she will make her next free throw is $P(\text{free throw}) = \dfrac{\text{number made}}{\text{number attempted}} = \dfrac{6}{10}$.
exterior of a circle The set of all points outside a circle.	**exterior de un círculo** Conjunto de todos los puntos que se encuentran fuera de un círculo.	Exterior
exterior of an angle The set of all points outside an angle.	**exterior de un ángulo** Conjunto de todos los puntos que se encuentran fuera de un ángulo.	Exterior
exterior of a polygon The set of all points outside a polygon.	**exterior de un polígono** Conjunto de todos los puntos que se encuentran fuera de un polígono.	Exterior
exterior angle of a polygon An angle formed by one side of a polygon and the extension of an adjacent side.	**ángulo externo de un polígono** Ángulo formado por un lado de un polígono y la prolongación del lado adyacente.	$\angle 4$ is an exterior angle.
external secant segment A segment of a secant that lies in the exterior of the circle with one endpoint on the circle.	**segmento secante externo** Segmento de una secante que se encuentra en el exterior del círculo y tiene un extremo sobre el círculo.	$\overline{NM}$ is an external secant segment.
extremes of a proportion In the proportion $\frac{a}{b} = \frac{c}{d}$, a and d are the extremes. If the proportion is written as $a{:}b = c{:}d$, the extremes are in the first and last positions.	**valores extremos de una proporción** En la proporción $\frac{a}{b} = \frac{c}{d}$, a y d son los valores extremos. Si la proporción se expresa como $a{:}b = c{:}d$, los extremos están en la primera y última posición.	

F

face of a polyhedron A flat surface of the polyhedron.

cara de un poliedro Superficie plana de un poliedro.

Face

---

factorial If n is a positive integer, then n factorial, written $n!$, is $n \cdot (n-1) \cdot (n-2) \cdot \ldots \cdot 2 \cdot 1$. The factorial of 0 is defined to be 1.

factorial Si n es un entero positivo, entonces el factorial de n, expresado como $n!$, es $n \cdot (n-1) \cdot (n-2) \cdot \ldots \cdot 2 \cdot 1$. Por definición, el factorial de 0 será 1.

$7! = 7 \cdot 6 \cdot 5 \cdot 4 \cdot 3 \cdot 2 \cdot 1 = 5040$
$0! = 1$

---

fair When all outcomes of an experiment are equally likely.

justo Cuando todos los resultados de un experimento son igualmente probables.

When tossing a fair coin, heads and tails are equally likely. Each has a probability of $\frac{1}{2}$.

---

favorable outcome The occurrence of one of several possible outcomes of a specified event or probability experiment.

resultado favorable Cuando se produce uno de varios resultados posibles de un suceso específico o experimento de probabilidad.

In the experiment of rolling an odd number on a number cube, the favorable outcomes are 1, 3, and 5.

Fibonacci sequence The infinite sequence of numbers beginning with 1, 1, ... such that each term is the sum of the two previous terms.

sucesión de Fibonacci Sucesión infinita de números que comienza con 1, 1, ... de forma tal que cada término es la suma de los dos términos anteriores.

1, 1, 2, 3, 5, 8, 13, 21, ...

---

flip *See* reflection.

inversión *Ver* reflexión.

---

flowchart proof A style of proof that uses boxes and arrows to show the structure of the proof.

demostración con diagrama de flujo Tipo de demostración que se vale de cuadros y flechas para mostrar la estructura de la prueba.

$\angle 1 \cong \angle 2$
Given
$\angle 1$ and $\angle 2$ are supplementary.
$\angle 1$ and $\angle 2$ are right angles.
Lin. Pair Thm.
$\cong \angle$ supp. → rt. $\angle$

---

focus of a parabola A fixed point F used with a *directrix* to define a *parabola*.

foco de una parábola Punto fijo F utilizado con una *directriz* para definir una *parábola*.

Focus
F

---

fractal A figure that is generated by iteration.

fractal Figura generada por iteración.

---

frieze pattern A pattern that has translation symmetry along a line.

patrón de friso Patrón con simetría de traslación a lo largo de una línea.

---

frustum of a cone A part of a cone with two parallel bases.

tronco de cono Parte de un cono con dos bases paralelas.

---

frustum of a pyramid A part of a pyramid with two parallel bases.

tronco de pirámide Parte de una pirámide con dos bases paralelas.

b_1
b_2

Glossary/Glosario

ENGLISH	SPANISH	EXAMPLES

function A relation in which every input is paired with exactly one output.

función Una relación en la que cada entrada corresponde exactamente a una salida.

Function: $\{(0, 5), (1, 3), (2, 1), (3, 3)\}$

Not a Function: $\{(0, 1), (0, 3), (2, 1), (2, 3)\}$

Fundamental Counting Principle For n items, if there are m_1 ways to choose a first item, m_2 ways to choose a second item after the first item has been chosen, and so on, then there are $m_1 \cdot m_2 \cdot \ldots \cdot m_n$ ways to choose n items.

Principio fundamental de conteo Dados n elementos, si existen m_1 formas de elegir un primer elemento, m_2 formas de elegir un segundo elemento después de haber elegido el primero, y así sucesivamente, entonces existen $m_1 \cdot m_2 \cdot \ldots \cdot m_n$ formas de elegir n elementos.

If there are 4 colors of shirts, 3 colors of pants, and 2 colors of shoes, then there are $4 \cdot 3 \cdot 2 = 24$ possible outfits.

---

geometric mean For positive numbers a and b, the positive number x such that $\frac{a}{x} = \frac{x}{b}$. In a geometric sequence, a term that comes between two given nonconsecutive terms of the sequence.

media geométrica Dados los números positivos a y b, el número positivo x tal que $\frac{a}{x} = \frac{x}{b}$. En una sucesión geométrica, un término que está entre dos términos no consecutivos dados de la sucesión.

$$\frac{a}{x} = \frac{x}{b}$$
$$x^2 = ab$$
$$x = \sqrt{ab}$$

---

geometric probability A form of theoretical probability determined by a ratio of geometric measures such as lengths, areas, or volumes.

probabilidad geométrica Una forma de la probabilidad teórica determinada por una razón de medidas geométricas, como longitud, área o volumen.

The probability of the pointer landing on red is $\frac{2}{9}$.

---

glide reflection A composition of a translation and a reflection across a line parallel to the translation vector.

deslizamiento con inversión Composición de una traslación y una reflexión sobre una línea paralela al vector de traslación.

First translate the preimage along $\vec{v}$.

Then reflect the image across line ℓ.

---

glide reflection symmetry A pattern has glide reflection symmetry if it coincides with its image after a glide reflection.

simetría de deslizamiento con inversión Un patrón tiene simetría de deslizamiento con inversión si coincide con su imagen después de un deslizamiento con inversión.

---

golden ratio If a segment is divided into two parts so that the ratio of the lengths of the whole segment to the longer part equals the ratio of the lengths of the longer part to the shorter part, then that ratio is called the golden ratio. The golden ratio is equal to $\frac{1 + \sqrt{5}}{2} \approx 1.618$.

razón áurea Si se divide un segmento en dos partes de forma tal que la razón entre la longitud de todo el segmento y la de la parte más larga sea igual a la razón entre la longitud de la parte más larga y la de la parte más corta, entonces dicha razón se denomina razón áurea. La razón áurea es igual a $\frac{1 + \sqrt{5}}{2} \approx 1.618$.

Golden ratio $= \frac{AC}{AB} = \frac{AB}{BC}$

Create segment such that $\frac{AC}{AB} \approx 1.62$ and $\frac{AB}{BC} \approx 1.62$

Glossary/Glosario

ENGLISH	SPANISH	EXAMPLES

golden rectangle
A rectangle in which the ratio of the lengths of the longer side to the shorter side is the golden ratio.

rectángulo áureo Rectángulo en el cual la razón entre la longitud del lado más largo y la longitud del lado más corto es la razón áurea.

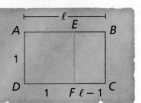

---

great circle A circle on a sphere that divides the sphere into two hemispheres.

círculo máximo En una esfera, círculo que divide la esfera en dos hemisferios.

Great circle

H

head-to-tail method
A method of adding two vectors by placing the tail of the second vector on the head of the first vector; the sum is the vector drawn from the tail of the first vector to the head of the second vector.

método de cola a punta Método para sumar dos vectores colocando la cola del segundo vector en la punta del primer vector. La suma es el vector trazado desde la cola del primer vector hasta la punta del segundo vector.

$\vec{u} + \vec{v}$ $\vec{v}$ $\vec{u}$

---

height of a figure
The length of an altitude of the figure.

altura de una figura Longitud de la altura de la figura.

h

---

height of a triangle
A segment from a vertex that forms a right angle with a line containing the base.

altura de un triángulo Segmento que se extiende desde el vértice y forma un ángulo recto con la línea de la base.

h
b

---

hemisphere Half of a sphere.

hemisferio Mitad de una esfera.

---

heptagon A seven-sided polygon.

heptágono Polígono de siete lados.

---

hexagon A six-sided polygon.

hexágono Polígono de seis lados.

---

horizon The horizontal line in a perspective drawing that contains the vanishing point(s).

horizonte Línea horizontal en un dibujo en perspectiva que contiene el punto de fuga o los puntos de fuga.

Vanishing point
Horizon

ENGLISH	SPANISH	EXAMPLES
hypotenuse The side opposite the right angle in a right triangle.	**hipotenusa** Lado opuesto al ángulo recto de un triángulo rectángulo.	hypotenuse
hypothesis The part of a conditional statement following the word *if*.	**hipótesis** La parte de un enunciado condicional que sigue a la palabra *si*.	If $\underline{x + 1 = 5}$, then $x = 4$. Hypothesis

I

ENGLISH	SPANISH	EXAMPLES
icosahedron A polyhedron with 20 faces. A regular icosahedron has equilateral triangles as faces, with 5 faces meeting at each vertex.	**icosaedro** Poliedro con 20 caras. Las caras de un icosaedro regular son triángulos equiláteros y cada vértice es compartido por 5 caras.	
identity An equation that is true for all values of the variables.	**identidad** Ecuación verdadera para todos los valores de las variables.	$3 = 3$ $2(x - 1) = 2x - 2$
image A shape that results from a transformation of a figure known as the preimage.	**imagen** Forma resultante de la transformación de una figura conocida como imagen original.	
imaginary number The square root of a negative number, written in the form bi, where b is a real number and i is the imaginary unit, $\sqrt{-1}$. Also called a *pure imaginary number*.	**número imaginario** Raíz cuadrada de un número negativo, expresado como bi, donde b es un número real e i es la unidad imaginaria, $\sqrt{-1}$. También se denomina *número imaginario puro*.	$\sqrt{-16} = \sqrt{16} \cdot \sqrt{-1} = 4i$
imaginary part of a complex number For a complex number of the form $a + bi$, the real number b is called the imaginary part, represented graphically as b units on the imaginary axis of a complex plane.	**parte imaginaria de un número complejo** Dado un número complejo del tipo $a + bi$, el número real b se denomina parte imaginaria y se representa gráficamente como b unidades en el eje imaginario de un plano complejo.	$5 + 6i$ real part imaginary part
imaginary unit The unit in the imaginary number system, $\sqrt{-1}$.	**unidad imaginaria** Unidad del sistema de números imaginarios, $\sqrt{-1}$.	$\sqrt{-1} = i$
incenter of a triangle The point of concurrency of the three angle bisectors of a triangle.	**incentro de un triángulo** Punto donde se encuentran las tres bisectrices de los ángulos de un triángulo.	P is the incenter.

ENGLISH	SPANISH	EXAMPLES
included angle The angle formed by two adjacent sides of a polygon.	**ángulo incluido** Ángulo formado por dos lados adyacentes de un polígono.	$\angle B$ is the included angle between $\overline{AB}$ and $\overline{BC}$.
included side The common side of two consecutive angles of a polygon.	**lado incluido** Lado común de dos ángulos consecutivos de un polígono.	$\overline{PQ}$ is the included side between $\angle P$ and $\angle Q$.
inclusive events Events that have one or more outcomes in common.	**sucesos inclusivos** Sucesos que tienen uno o más resultados en común.	In the experiment of rolling a number cube, rolling an even number and rolling a number less than 3 are inclusive events because the outcome 2 is both even and less than 3.
independent events Events for which the occurrence or non-occurrence of one event does not affect the probability of the other event.	**sucesos independientes** Dos sucesos son independientes si el hecho de que se produzca o no uno de ellos no afecta la probabilidad del otro suceso.	From a bag containing 3 red marbles and 2 blue marbles, drawing a red marble, replacing it, and then drawing a blue marble.
indirect measurement A method of measurement that uses formulas, similar figures, and/or proportions.	**medición indirecta** Método para medir objetos mediante fórmulas, figuras semejantes y/o proporciones.	
indirect proof A proof in which the statement to be proved is assumed to be false and a contradiction is shown.	**demostración indirecta** Prueba en la que se supone que el enunciado a demostrar es falso y se muestra una contradicción.	
indirect reasoning *See* indirect proof.	**razonamiento indirecto** *Ver* demostración indirecta.	
inductive reasoning The process of reasoning that a rule or statement is true because specific cases are true.	**razonamiento inductivo** Proceso de razonamiento por el que se determina que una regla o enunciado son verdaderos porque ciertos casos específicos son verdaderos.	
inequality A statement that compares two expressions by using one of the following signs: $<$, $>$, $\leq$, $\geq$, or $\neq$.	**desigualdad** Enunciado que compara dos expresiones utilizando uno de los siguientes signos: $<$, $>$, $\leq$, $\geq$ o $\neq$.	$x \geq 2$ $-1\ 0\ 1\ 2\ 3\ 4\ 5\ 6$
initial point of a vector The starting point of a vector.	**punto inicial de un vector** Punto donde comienza un vector.	$\vec{v}$ A B Initial point

ENGLISH	SPANISH	EXAMPLES
initial side The ray that lies on the positive *x*-axis when an angle is drawn in standard position.	**lado inicial** Rayo que se encuentra sobre el eje *x* positivo cuando se traza un ángulo en posición estándar.	
inscribed angle An angle whose vertex is on a circle and whose sides contain chords of the circle.	**ángulo inscrito** Ángulo cuyo vértice se encuentra sobre un círculo y cuyos lados contienen cuerdas del círculo.	
inscribed circle A circle in which each side of the polygon is tangent to the circle.	**círculo inscrito** Círculo en el que cada lado del polígono es tangente al círculo.	
inscribed polygon A polygon in which every vertex of the polygon lies on the circle.	**polígono inscrito** Polígono cuyos vértices se encuentran sobre el círculo.	
integer A member of the set of whole numbers and their opposites.	**entero** Miembro del conjunto de números cabales y sus opuestos.	$\{\dots -3, -2, -1, 0, 1, 2, 3, \dots\}$
intercepted arc An arc that consists of endpoints that lie on the sides of an inscribed angle and all the points of the circle between the endpoints.	**arco abarcado** Arco cuyos extremos se encuentran en los lados de un ángulo inscrito y consta de todos los puntos del círculo ubicados entre dichos extremos.	$\overset{\frown}{DF}$ is the intercepted arc.
interior angle An angle formed by two sides of a polygon with a common vertex.	**ángulo interno** Ángulo formado por dos lados de un polígono con un vértice común.	∠1 is an interior angle.
interior of a circle The set of all points inside a circle.	**interior de un círculo** Conjunto de todos los puntos que se encuentran dentro de un círculo.	Interior
interior of an angle The set of all points between the sides of an angle.	**interior de un ángulo** Conjunto de todos los puntos entre los lados de un ángulo.	Interior
interior of a polygon The set of all points inside a polygon.	**interior de un polígono** Conjunto de todos los puntos que se encuentran dentro de un polígono.	Interior

ENGLISH	SPANISH	EXAMPLES
inverse The statement formed by negating the hypothesis and conclusion of a conditional statement.	**inverso** Enunciado formado al negar la hipótesis y la conclusión de un enunciado condicional.	Statement: If $n + 1 = 3$, then $n = 2$ Inverse: If $n + 1 \neq 3$, then $n \neq 2$
inverse cosine The measure of an angle whose cosine ratio is known.	**coseno inverso** Medida de un ángulo cuya razón coseno es conocida.	If $\cos A = x$, then $\cos^{-1}x = m\angle A$.
inverse function The function that results from exchanging the input and output values of a one-to-one function. The inverse of $f(x)$ is denoted $f^{-1}(x)$.	**función inversa** Función que resulta de intercambiar los valores de entrada y salida de una función uno a uno. La función inversa de $f(x)$ se indica $f^{-1}(x)$.	 The function $y = \frac{1}{2}x - 2$ is the inverse of the function $y = 2x + 4$.
inverse sine The measure of an angle whose sine ratio is known.	**seno inverso** Medida de un ángulo cuya razón seno es conocida.	If $\sin A = x$, then $\sin^{-1}x = m\angle A$.
inverse tangent The measure of an angle whose tangent ratio is known.	**tangente inversa** Medida de un ángulo cuya razón tangente es conocida.	If $\tan A = x$, then $\tan^{-1}x = m\angle A$.
irrational number A real number that cannot be expressed as the ratio of two integers.	**número irracional** Número real que no se puede expresar como una razón de dos enteros.	$\sqrt{2}$, π, e
irregular polygon A polygon that is not regular.	**polígono irregular** Polígono que no es regular.	
isometric drawing A way of drawing three-dimensional figures using *isometric dot paper*, which has equally spaced dots in a repeating triangular pattern.	**dibujo isométrico** Forma de dibujar figuras tridimensionales utilizando *papel punteado isométrico*, que tiene puntos espaciados uniformemente en un patrón triangular que se repite.	
isometry A transformation that does not change the size or shape of a figure.	**isometría** Transformación que no cambia el tamaño ni la forma de una figura.	Reflections, translations, and rotations are all examples of isometries.
isosceles trapezoid A trapezoid in which the legs are congruent.	**trapecio isósceles** Trapecio cuyos lados no paralelos son congruentes.	
isosceles triangle A triangle with at least two congruent sides.	**triángulo isósceles** Triángulo que tiene al menos dos lados congruentes.	
iteration The repetitive application of the same rule.	**iteración** Aplicación repetitiva de la misma regla.	

J

joint relative frequency The ratio of the frequency in a particular category divided by the total number of data values.

frecuencia relativa conjunta La razón de la frecuencia en una determinada categoría dividida entre el número total de valores.

K

kite A quadrilateral with exactly two pairs of congruent consecutive sides.

cometa o papalote Cuadrilátero con exactamente dos pares de lados congruentes consecutivos.

Kite *ABCD*

Koch snowflake A fractal formed from a triangle by replacing the middle third of each segment with two segments that form a 60° angle.

copo de nieve de Koch Fractal formado a partir de un triángulo sustituyendo el tercio central de cada segmento por dos segmentos que forman un ángulo de 60°.

L

lateral area The sum of the areas of the lateral faces of a prism or pyramid, or the area of the lateral surface of a cylinder or cone.

área lateral Suma de las áreas de las caras laterales de un prisma o pirámide, o área de la superficie lateral de un cilindro o cono.

Lateral area = $4(6)(12) = 288$ cm^2

lateral edge An edge of a prism or pyramid that is not an edge of a base.

arista lateral Arista de un prisma o pirámide que no es la arista de una base.

lateral face A face of a prism or a pyramid that is not a base.

cara lateral Cara de un prisma o pirámide que no es la base.

lateral surface The curved surface of a cylinder or cone.

superficie lateral Superficie curva de un cilindro o cono.

ENGLISH	SPANISH	EXAMPLES
leg of a right triangle One of the two sides of the right triangle that form the right angle.	**cateto de un triángulo rectángulo** Uno de los dos lados de un triángulo rectángulo que forman el ángulo recto.	
leg of a trapezoid One of the two nonparallel sides of the trapezoid.	**cateto de un trapecio** Uno de los dos lados no paralelos del trapecio.	
leg of an isosceles triangle One of the two congruent sides of the isosceles triangle.	**cateto de un triángulo isósceles** Uno de los dos lados congruentes del triángulo isósceles.	
length The distance between the two endpoints of a segment.	**longitud** Distancia entre los dos extremos de un segmento.	$AB = \lvert a - b \rvert = \lvert b - a \rvert$
line An undefined term in geometry, a line is a straight path that has no thickness and extends forever.	**línea** Término indefinido en geometría; una línea es un trazo recto que no tiene grosor y se extiende infinitamente.	ℓ
line of best fit The line that comes closest to all of the points in a data set.	**línea de mejor ajuste** Línea que más se acerca a todos los puntos de un conjunto de datos.	
line of symmetry A line that divides a plane figure into two congruent reflected halves.	**eje de simetría** Línea que divide una figura plana en dos mitades reflejas congruentes.	
line symmetry A figure that can be reflected across a line so that the image coincides with the preimage.	**simetría axial** Figura que puede reflejarse sobre una línea de forma tal que la imagen coincida con la imagen original.	
linear pair A pair of adjacent angles whose noncommon sides are opposite rays.	**par lineal** Par de ángulos adyacentes cuyos lados no comunes son rayos opuestos.	$\angle 3$ and $\angle 4$ form a linear pair.
literal equation An equation that contains two or more variables.	**ecuación literal** Ecuación que contiene dos o más variables.	$d = rt \qquad A = \frac{1}{2}h(b_1 + b_2)$
locus A set of points that satisfies a given condition.	**lugar geométrico** Conjunto de puntos que cumple con una condición determinada.	

ENGLISH	SPANISH	EXAMPLES

logically equivalent statements
Statements that have the same truth value.

enunciados lógicamente equivalentes
Enunciados que tienen el mismo valor de verdad.

M

magnitude The length of a vector, written $\left|\overrightarrow{AB}\right|$ or $\left|\vec{v}\right|$.

magnitud Longitud de un vector, que se expresa $\left|\overrightarrow{AB}\right|$ o $\left|\vec{v}\right|$.

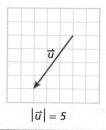

$|\vec{u}| = 5$

---

major arc An arc of a circle whose points are on or in the exterior of a central angle.

arco mayor Arco de un círculo cuyos puntos están sobre un ángulo central o en su exterior.

$\widehat{ADC}$ is a major arc of the circle.

---

mapping An operation that matches each element of a set with another element, its image, in the same set.

correspondencia Operación que establece una correlación entre cada elemento de un conjunto con otro elemento, su imagen, en el mismo conjunto.

---

marginal relative frequency The sum of the joint relative frequencies in a row or column of a two-way table.

frecuencia relativa marginal La suma de las frecuencias relativas conjuntas en una fila o columna de una tabla de doble entrada.

---

matrix A rectangular array of numbers.

matriz Arreglo rectangular de números.

$$\begin{bmatrix} 1 & 0 & 3 \\ -2 & 2 & -5 \\ 7 & -6 & 3 \end{bmatrix}$$

---

maximum value of a function The y-value of the highest point on the graph of the function.

máximo de una función Valor de y del punto más alto en la gráfica de la función.

Maximum value

---

means of a proportion In the proportion $\frac{a}{b} = \frac{c}{d}$, b and c are the means. If the proportion is written as $a{:}b = c{:}d$, the means are in the two middle positions.

valores medios de una proporción En la proporción $\frac{a}{b} = \frac{c}{d}$, b y c son los valores medios. Si la proporción se expresa como $a{:}b = c{:}d$, los valores medios están en las dos posiciones del medio.

---

measure of an angle Angles are measured in degrees. A degree is $\frac{1}{360}$ of a complete circle.

medida de un ángulo Los ángulos se miden en grados. Un grado es $\frac{1}{360}$ de un círculo completo.

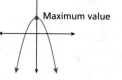

$m\angle M = 26.8°$

ENGLISH	SPANISH	EXAMPLES
measure of a major arc The difference of 360° and the measure of the associated minor arc.	**medida de un arco mayor** Diferencia entre 360° y la medida del arco menor asociado.	$m\overset{\frown}{ADC} = 360° - x°$
measure of a minor arc The measure of its central angle.	**medida de un arco menor** Medida de su ángulo central.	$m\overset{\frown}{AC} = x°$
median of a triangle A segment whose endpoints are a vertex of the triangle and the midpoint of the opposite side.	**mediana de un triángulo** Segmento cuyos extremos son un vértice del triángulo y el punto medio del lado opuesto.	Median
midpoint The point that divides a segment into two congruent segments.	**punto medio** Punto que divide un segmento en dos segmentos congruentes.	B is the midpoint of $\overline{AC}$.
midsegment of a trapezoid The segment whose endpoints are the midpoints of the legs of the trapezoid.	**segmento medio de un trapecio** Segmento cuyos extremos son los puntos medios de los catetos del trapecio.	Midsegment
midsegment of a triangle A segment that joins the midpoints of two sides of the triangle.	**segmento medio de un triángulo** Segmento que une los puntos medios de dos lados del triángulo.	
midsegment triangle The triangle formed by the three midsegments of a triangle.	**triángulo de segmentos medios** Triángulo formado por los tres segmentos medios de un triángulo.	Midsegment triangle: $\triangle XYZ$
minimum value of a function The y-value of the lowest point on the graph of the function.	**mínimo de una función** Valor de y del punto más bajo en la gráfica de la función.	Minimum value
minor arc An arc of a circle whose points are on or in the interior of a central angle.	**arco menor** Arco de un círculo cuyos puntos están sobre un ángulo central o en su interior.	$\overset{\frown}{AC}$ is a minor arc of the circle.
monomial A number or a product of numbers and variables with whole-number exponents, or a polynomial with one term.	**monomio** Número o producto de números y variables con exponentes de números cabales, o polinomio con un término.	$8x$, 9, $3x^2y^4$

ENGLISH	SPANISH	EXAMPLES
mutually exclusive events Two events are mutually exclusive if they cannot both occur in the same trial of an experiment.	**sucesos mutuamente excluyentes** Dos sucesos son mutuamente excluyentes si ambos no pueden ocurrir en la misma prueba de un experimento.	In the experiment of rolling a number cube, rolling a 3 and rolling an even number are mutually exclusive events.

N

natural number A counting number.	**número natural** Número que sirve para contar.	1, 2, 3, 4, 5, 6, …
negation The negation of statement p is "not p," written as $\sim p$.	**negación** La negación de un enunciado p es "no p", que se escribe p.	
negation of a vector The vector obtained by negating each component of a given vector.	**negación de un vector** Vector que se obtiene por la negación de cada componente de un vector dado.	The negation of $\langle 3, -2 \rangle$ is $\langle -3, 2 \rangle$.
net A diagram of the faces of a three-dimensional figure arranged in such a way that the diagram can be folded to form the three-dimensional figure.	**plantilla** Diagrama de las caras de una figura tridimensional que se puede plegar para formar la figura tridimensional.	10 m 6 m 10 m 6 m
network A diagram of vertices and edges.	**red** Diagrama de vértices y aristas.	(0, 0) (1, 0) $\left(0, \frac{3}{4}\right)$
***n*-gon** An n-sided polygon.	***n*-ágono** Polígono de n lados.	
nonagon A nine-sided polygon.	**nonágono** Polígono de nueve lados.	
noncollinear Points that do not lie on the same line.	**no colineal** Puntos que no se encuentran sobre la misma línea.	A B D Points A, B, and D are noncollinear.
non-Euclidean geometry A system of geometry in which the Parallel Postulate, which states that there is exactly one line through a given point parallel to a given line, does not hold.	**geometría no euclidiana** Sistema de geometría en el cual no se cumple el postulado de las paralelas, que establece que por un punto dado se puede trazar una única línea paralela a una línea dada.	In spherical geometry, there are no parallel lines. The sum of the angles in a triangle is always greater than 180°.
noncoplanar Points that do not lie on the same plane.	**no coplanar** Puntos que no se encuentran en el mismo plano.	S T U V $\mathcal{R}$ T, U, V, and S are noncoplanar.

O

oblique cone A cone whose axis is not perpendicular to the base.

cono oblicuo Cono cuyo eje no es perpendicular a la base.

oblique cylinder A cylinder whose axis is not perpendicular to the bases.

cilindro oblicuo Cilindro cuyo eje no es perpendicular a las bases.

oblique prism A prism that has at least one nonrectangular lateral face.

prisma oblicuo Prisma que tiene por lo menos una cara lateral no rectangular.

obtuse angle An angle that measures greater than 90° and less than 180°.

ángulo obtuso Ángulo que mide más de 90° y menos de 180°.

obtuse triangle A triangle with one obtuse angle.

triángulo obtusángulo Triángulo con un ángulo obtuso.

octagon An eight-sided polygon.

octágono Polígono de ocho lados.

octahedron A polyhedron with eight faces.

octaedro Poliedro con ocho caras.

one-point perspective A perspective drawing with one vanishing point.

perspectiva de un punto Dibujo en perspectiva con un punto de fuga.

Vanishing point

opposite rays Two rays that have a common endpoint and form a line.

rayos opuestos Dos rayos que tienen un extremo común y forman una línea.

F   E   G

$\overrightarrow{EF}$ and $\overrightarrow{EG}$ are opposite rays.

opposite reciprocal The opposite of the reciprocal of a number. The opposite reciprocal of a is $-\frac{1}{a}$.

recíproco opuesto Opuesto del recíproco de un número. El recíproco opuesto de a es $-\frac{1}{a}$.

The opposite reciprocal of $\frac{2}{3}$ is $\frac{-3}{2}$

order of rotational symmetry The number of times a figure with rotational symmetry coincides with itself as it rotates 360°.

orden de simetría de rotación Cantidad de veces que una figura con simetría de rotación coincide consigo misma cuando rota 360°.

90°
90°   90°
90°

Order of rotational symmetry: 4

Glossary/Glosario

ENGLISH	SPANISH	EXAMPLES
ordered pair A pair of numbers (x, y) that can be used to locate a point on a coordinate plane. The first number x indicates the distance to the left or right of the origin, and the second number y indicates the distance above or below the origin.	**par ordenado** Par de números (x, y) que se pueden utilizar para ubicar un punto en un plano cartesiano. El primer número indica la distancia a la izquierda o derecha del origen y el segundo número indica la distancia hacia arriba o hacia abajo del origen.	
ordered triple A set of three numbers that can be used to locate a point (x, y, z) in a three-dimensional coordinate system.	**tripleta ordenada** Conjunto de tres números que se pueden utilizar para ubicar un punto (x, y, z) en un sistema de coordenadas tridimensional.	
origin The intersection of the x- and y-axes in a coordinate plane. The coordinates of the origin are $(0, 0)$.	**origen** Intersección de los ejes x e y en un plano cartesiano. Las coordenadas de origen son $(0, 0)$.	
orthocenter of a triangle The point of concurrency of the three altitudes of a triangle.	**ortocentro de un triángulo** Punto de intersección de las tres alturas de un triángulo.	P is the orthocenter.
orthographic drawing A drawing that shows a three-dimensional object in which the line of sight for each view is perpendicular to the plane of the picture.	**dibujo ortográfico** Dibujo que muestra un objeto tridimensional en el que la línea visual para cada vista es perpendicular al plano de la imagen.	
outcome A possible result of a probability experiment.	**resultado** Resultado posible de un experimento de probabilidad.	In the experiment of rolling a number cube, the possible outcomes are 1, 2, 3, 4, 5, and 6.

P

parabola The shape of the graph of a quadratic function. Also, the set of points equidistant from a point F, called the *focus*, and a line d, called the *directrix*.	**parábola** Forma de la gráfica de una función cuadrática. También, conjunto de puntos equidistantes de un punto F, denominado *foco*, y una línea d, denominada *directriz*.	

ENGLISH	SPANISH	EXAMPLES
paragraph proof A style of proof in which the statements and reasons are presented in paragraph form.	**demostración con párrafos** Tipo de demostración en la cual los enunciados y las razones se presentan en forma de párrafo.	
parallel lines Lines in the same plane that do not intersect.	**líneas paralelas** Líneas rectas en el mismo plano que no se cruzan.	$r \parallel s$
parallel planes Planes that do not intersect.	**planos paralelos** Planos que no se cruzan.	Plane *AEF* and plane *CGH* are parallel planes.
parallel vectors Vectors with the same or opposite direction.	**vectores paralelos** Vectores con dirección igual u opuesta.	$\lvert \vec{w} \rvert = 2\sqrt{5}$ $\lvert \vec{x} \rvert = \sqrt{5}$
parallelogram A quadrilateral with two pairs of parallel sides.	**paralelogramo** Cuadrilátero con dos pares de lados paralelos.	
parallelogram method A method of adding two vectors by drawing a parallelogram using the vectors as two of the consecutive sides; the sum is a vector along the diagonal of the parallelogram.	**método del paralelogramo** Método mediante el cual se suman dos vectores dibujando un paralelogramo, utilizando los vectores como dos de los lados consecutivos; el resultado de la suma es un vector a lo largo de la diagonal del paralelogramo.	$\vec{u} + \vec{v}$
parent function The simplest function with the defining characteristics of the family. Functions in the same family are transformations of their parent function.	**función madre** La función más básica que tiene las características distintivas de una familia. Las funciones de la misma familia son transformaciones de su función madre.	$f(x) = x^2$ is the parent function for $g(x) = x^2 + 4$ and $h(x) = 5(x + 2)^2 - 3$.
Pascal's triangle A triangular arrangement of numbers in which every row starts and ends with 1 and each other number is the sum of the two numbers above it.	**triángulo de Pascal** Arreglo triangular de números en el cual cada fila comienza y termina con 1 y cada uno de los otros números es la suma de los dos números que están encima de él.	1 1 1 1 2 1 1 3 3 1 1 4 6 4 1
pentagon A five-sided polygon.	**pentágono** Polígono de cinco lados.	

perimeter The sum of the side lengths of a closed plane figure.

perímetro Suma de las longitudes de los lados de una figura plana cerrada.

18 ft

6ft

Perimeter = 18 + 6 + 18 + 6 = 48 ft

---

permutation An arrangement of a group of objects in which order is important. The number of permutations of *r* objects from a group of *n* objects is denoted $_nP_r$.

permutación Arreglo de un grupo de objetos en el cual el orden es importante. El número de permutaciones de *r* objetos de un grupo de *n* objetos se expresa $_nP_r$.

For 4 objects *A*, *B*, *C*, and *D*, there are $_4P_2 = 12$ different permutations of 2 objects: *AB*, *AC*, *AD*, *BC*, *BD*, *CD*, *BA*, *CA*, *DA*, *CB*, *DB*, and *DC*.

---

perpendicular Intersecting to form 90° angles, denoted by ⊥.

perpendicular Que se cruza para formar ángulos de 90°, expresado por ⊥.

$m \perp n$

---

perpendicular bisector of a segment A line perpendicular to a segment at the segment's midpoint.

mediatriz de un segmento Línea perpendicular a un segmento en el punto medio del segmento.

ℓ is the perpendicular bisector of $\overline{AB}$.

---

perpendicular lines Lines that intersect at 90° angles.

líneas perpendiculares Líneas que se cruzan en ángulos de 90°.

$m \perp n$

---

perspective drawing A drawing in which nonvertical parallel lines meet at a point called a *vanishing point*. Perspective drawings can have one or two vanishing points.

dibujo en perspectiva Dibujo en el cual las líneas paralelas no verticales se encuentran en un punto denominado *punto de fuga*. Los dibujos en perspectiva pueden tener uno o dos puntos de fuga.

Vanishing point

---

pi The ratio of the circumference of a circle to its diameter, denoted by the Greek letter π (pi). The value of π is irrational, often approximated by 3.14 or $\frac{22}{7}$.

pi Razón entre la circunferencia de un círculo y su diámetro, expresado por la letra griega π (pi). El valor de π es irracional y por lo general se aproxima a 3.14 ó $\frac{22}{7}$.

If a circle has a diameter of 5 inches and a circumference of *C* inches, then $\frac{C}{5} = \pi$, or $C = 5\pi$ inches, or about 15.7 inches.

---

plane An undefined term in geometry, it is a flat surface that has no thickness and extends forever.

plano Término indefinido en geometría; un plano es una superficie plana que no tiene grosor y se extiende infinitamente.

plane *R* or plane *ABC*

---

plane symmetry A three-dimensional figure that can be divided into two congruent reflected halves by a plane has plane symmetry.

simetría de plano Una figura tridimensional que se puede dividir en dos mitades congruentes reflejadas por un plano tiene simetría de plano.

Plane symmetry

Platonic solid One of the five regular polyhedra: a tetrahedron, a cube, an octahedron, a dodecahedron, or an icosahedron.

sólido platónico Uno de los cinco poliedros regulares: tetraedro, cubo, octaedro, dodecaedro o icosaedro.

Glossary/Glosario

ENGLISH	SPANISH	EXAMPLES
point An undefined term in geometry, it names a location and has no size.	**punto** Término indefinido de la geometría que denomina una ubicación y no tiene tamaño.	$P \bullet$ point P
point matrix A matrix that represents the coordinates of the vertices of a polygon. The first row of the matrix consists of the x-coordinates of the points, and the second row consists of the y-coordinates.	**matriz de puntos** Matriz que representa las coordenadas de los vértices de un polígono. La primera fila de la matriz contiene las coordenadas x de los puntos y la segunda fila contiene las coordenadas y.	$\begin{bmatrix} 1 & -2 & 3 \\ 2 & 0 & -4 \end{bmatrix}$
point of concurrency A point where three or more lines coincide.	**punto de concurrencia** Punto donde se cruzan tres o más líneas.	
point of tangency The point of intersection of a circle or sphere with a tangent line or plane.	**punto de tangencia** Punto de intersección de un círculo o esfera con una línea o plano tangente.	
point-slope form $y - y_1 = m(x - x_1)$, where m is the slope and (x_1, y_1) is a point on the line.	**forma de punto y pendiente** $(y - y_1) = m(x - x_1)$, donde m es la pendiente y (x_1, y_1) es un punto en la línea.	
polar axis In a polar coordinate system, the horizontal ray with the pole as its endpoint that lies along the positive x-axis.	**eje polar** En un sistema de coordenadas polares, el rayo horizontal, cuyo extremo es el polo, que se encuentra a lo largo del eje x positivo.	
polar coordinate system A system in which a point in a plane is located by its distance r from a point called the pole, and by the measure of a central angle θ.	**sistema de coordenadas polares** Sistema en el cual un punto en un plano se ubica por su distancia r de un punto denominado polo y por la medida de un ángulo central θ.	

ENGLISH	SPANISH	EXAMPLES
polygon A closed plane figure formed by three or more segments such that each segment intersects exactly two other segments only at their endpoints and no two segments with a common endpoint are collinear.	**polígono** Figura plana cerrada formada por tres o más segmentos tal que cada segmento se cruza únicamente con otros dos segmentos sólo en sus extremos y ningún segmento con un extremo común a otro es colineal con éste.	
polyhedron A closed three-dimensional figure formed by four or more polygons that intersect only at their edges.	**poliedro** Figura tridimensional cerrada formada por cuatro o más polígonos que se cruzan sólo en sus aristas.	
polynomial A monomial or a sum or difference of monomials.	**polinomio** Monomio o suma o diferencia de monomios.	$2x^2 + 3x - 7$
postulate A statement that is accepted as true without proof. Also called an *axiom*.	**postulado** Enunciado que se acepta como verdadero sin demostración. También denominado *axioma*.	
preimage The original figure in a transformation.	**imagen original** Figura original en una transformación.	
primes Symbols used to label the image in a transformation.	**apóstrofos** Símbolos utilizados para identificar la imagen en una transformación.	$A'B'C'$
prism A polyhedron formed by two parallel congruent polygonal bases connected by lateral faces that are parallelograms.	**prisma** Poliedro formado por dos bases poligonales congruentes y paralelas conectadas por caras laterales que son paralelogramos.	
probability A number from 0 to 1 (or 0% to 100%) that is the measure of how likely an event is to occur.	**probabilidad** Número entre 0 y 1 (o entre 0% y 100%) que describe cuán probable es que ocurra un suceso.	A bag contains 3 red marbles and 4 blue marbles. The probability of randomly choosing a red marble is $\frac{3}{7}$.
proof An argument that uses logic to show that a conclusion is true.	**demostración** Argumento que se vale de la lógica para probar que una conclusión es verdadera.	
proof by contradiction *See* indirect proof.	**demostración por contradicción** *Ver* demostración indirecta.	

Glossary/Glosario

ENGLISH	SPANISH	EXAMPLES

pyramid A polyhedron formed by a polygonal base and triangular lateral faces that meet at a common vertex.

pirámide Poliedro formado por una base poligonal y caras laterales triangulares que se encuentran en un vértice común.

Pythagorean triple A set of three nonzero whole numbers a, b, and c such that $a^2 + b^2 = c^2$.

Tripleta de Pitágoras Conjunto de tres números cabales distintos de cero a, b y c tal que $a^2 + b^2 = c^2$.

$\{3, 4, 5\}$ $\qquad$ $3^2 + 4^2 = 5^2$

Q

quadrant One of the four regions into which the x- and y-axes divide the coordinate plane.

cuadrante Una de las cuatro regiones en las que los ejes x e y dividen el plano cartesiano.

---

quadratic function A function that can be written in the form $f(x) = ax^2 + bx + c$, where a, b, and c are real numbers and $a \neq 0$, or in the form $f(x) = a(x - h)^2 + k$, where a, h, and k are real numbers and $a \neq 0$.

función cuadrática Función que se puede expresar como $f(x) = ax^2 + bx + c$, donde a, b y c son números reales y $a \neq 0$, o como $f(x) = a(x - h)^2 + k$, donde a, h y k son números reales y $a \neq 0$.

$f(x) = x^2 - 6x + 8$

---

quadratic model A quadratic function used to represent a set of data.

modelo cuadrático Función cuadrática que se utiliza para representar un conjunto de datos.

x	4	6	8	10
$f(x)$	27	52	89	130

A quadratic model for the data is $f(x) = x^2 + 3.3x - 2.6$.

---

quadratic regression A statistical method used to fit a quadratic model to a given data set.

regresión cuadrática Método estadístico utilizado para ajustar un modelo cuadrático a un conjunto de datos determinado.

QuadReg
y=ax²+bx+c
a=.3972484911
b=-3.120086049
c=11.93757771
R²=.9964146181

---

quadrilateral A four-sided polygon.

cuadrilátero Polígono de cuatro lados.

R

radial symmetry *See* rotational symmetry.

simetría radial *Ver* simetría de rotación.

ENGLISH	SPANISH	EXAMPLES
radian A unit of angle measure based on arc length. In a circle of radius r, if a central angle has a measure of 1 radian, then the length of the intercepted arc is r units. 2π radians $= 360°$ 1 radian $\approx 57°$	**radián** Unidad de medida de un ángulo basada en la longitud del arco. En un círculo de radio r, si un ángulo central mide 1 radián, entonces la longitud del arco abarcado es r unidades. 2π radians $= 360°$ 1 radian $\approx 57°$	
radical symbol The symbol $\sqrt{\ }$ used to denote a root. The symbol is used alone to indicate a square root or with an index, $\sqrt[n]{\ }$, to indicate the nth root.	**símbolo de radical** Símbolo $\sqrt{\ }$ que se utiliza para expresar una raíz. Puede utilizarse solo para indicar una raíz cuadrada, o con un índice, $\sqrt[n]{\ }$, para indicar la enésima raíz.	$\sqrt{36} = 6$ $\sqrt[3]{27} = 3$
radicand The expression under a radical sign.	**radicando** Número o expresión debajo del signo de radical.	Expression: $\sqrt{x+3}$ Radicand: $x + 3$
radius of a circle A segment whose endpoints are the center of a circle and a point on the circle; the distance from the center of a circle to any point on the circle.	**radio de un círculo** Segmento cuyos extremos son el centro y un punto de la circunferencia; distancia desde el centro de un círculo hasta cualquier punto de la circunferencia.	Radius
radius of a sphere A segment whose endpoints are the center of a sphere and any point on the sphere; the distance from the center of a sphere to any point on the sphere.	**radio de una esfera** Segmento cuyos extremos son el centro de una esfera y cualquier punto sobre la esfera; distancia desde el centro de una esfera hasta cualquier punto sobre la esfera.	
rate of change A ratio that compares the amount of change in a dependent variable to the amount of change in an independent variable.	**tasa de cambio** Razón que compara la cantidad de cambio de la variable dependiente con la cantidad de cambio de la variable independiente.	Rate of change $= \dfrac{\text{change in } y}{\text{change in } x} = \dfrac{6}{4} = \dfrac{3}{2}$
rational number A number that can be written in the form $\frac{a}{b}$, where a and b are integers and $b \neq 0$.	**número racional** Número que se puede expresar como $\frac{a}{b}$, donde a y b son números enteros y $b \neq 0$.	$3,\ 1.75,\ 0.\overline{3},\ -\frac{2}{3},\ 0$
ray A part of a line that starts at an endpoint and extends forever in one direction.	**rayo** Parte de una línea que comienza en un extremo y se extiende infinitamente en una dirección.	D
real part of a complex number For a complex number of the form $a + bi$, a is the real part.	**parte real de un número complejo** Dado un número complejo del tipo $a + bi$, a es la parte real.	$5 + 6i$ Real part · Imaginary part

ENGLISH	SPANISH	EXAMPLES
rectangle A quadrilateral with four right angles.	**rectángulo** Cuadrilátero con cuatro ángulos rectos.	
reduction A dilation with a scale factor greater than 0 but less than 1. In a reduction, the image is smaller than the preimage.	**reducción** Dilatación con un factor de escala mayor que 0 pero menor que 1. En una reducción, la imagen es más pequeña que la imagen original.	
reflection A transformation across a line, called the line of reflection, such that the line of reflection is the perpendicular bisector of each segment joining each point and its image.	**reflexión** Transformación sobre una línea, denominada la línea de reflexión. La línea de reflexión es la mediatriz de cada segmento que une un punto con su imagen.	
reflection symmetry *See* line symmetry.	**simetría de reflexión** *Ver* simetría axial.	
regular polygon A polygon that is both equilateral and equiangular.	**polígono regular** Polígono equilátero de ángulos iguales.	
regular polyhedron A polyhedron in which all faces are congruent regular polygons and the same number of faces meet at each vertex. *See also* Platonic solid.	**poliedro regular** Poliedro cuyas caras son todas polígonos regulares congruentes y en el que el mismo número de caras se encuentran en cada vértice. *Ver también* sólido platónico.	
regular pyramid A pyramid whose base is a regular polygon and whose lateral faces are congruent isosceles triangles.	**pirámide regular** Pirámide cuya base es un polígono regular y cuyas caras laterales son triángulos isósceles congruentes.	
regular tessellation A repeating pattern of congruent regular polygons that completely covers a plane with no gaps or overlaps.	**teselado regular** Patrón que se repite formado por polígonos regulares congruentes que cubren completamente un plano sin dejar espacios y sin superponerse.	
relation A set of ordered pairs.	**relación** Conjunto de pares ordenados.	$\{(0, 5), (0, 4), (2, 3), (4, 0)\}$
remote interior angle An interior angle of a polygon that is not adjacent to the exterior angle.	**ángulo interno remoto** Ángulo interno de un polígono que no es adyacente al ángulo externo.	The remote interior angles of ∠4 are ∠1 and ∠2

ENGLISH	SPANISH	EXAMPLES
resultant vector The vector that represents the sum of two given vectors.	**vector resultante** Vector que representa la suma de dos vectores dados.	
rhombus A quadrilateral with four congruent sides.	**rombo** Cuadrilátero con cuatro lados congruentes.	
right angle An angle that measures 90°.	**ángulo recto** Ángulo que mide 90°.	
right cylinder A cylinder whose axis is perpendicular to its bases.	**cilindro recto** Cilindro cuyo eje es perpendicular a sus bases.	Axis
right prism A prism whose lateral faces are all rectangles.	**prisma recto** Prisma cuyas caras laterales son todas rectángulos.	
right triangle A triangle with one right angle.	**triángulo rectángulo** Triángulo con un ángulo recto.	
rigid motion *See* isometry.	**movimiento rígido** *Ver* isometría.	
rigid transformation A transformation that does not change the size or shape of a figure.	**transformación rígida** Transformación que no cambia el tamaño o la forma de una figura.	
rise The difference in the y-values of two points on a line.	**distancia vertical** Diferencia entre los valores de y de dos puntos de una línea.	For the points $(3, -1)$ and $(6, 5)$, the rise is $5 - (-1) = 6$.
root of an equation Any value of the variable that makes the equation true.	**raíz de una ecuación** Cualquier valor de la variable que transforme la ecuación en verdadera.	The roots of $(x - 2)(x + 1) = 0$ are 2 and -1.
rotation A transformation about a point P, also known as the center of rotation, such that each point and its image are the same distance from P. All of the angles with vertex P formed by a point and its image are congruent.	**rotación** Transformación sobre un punto P, también conocido como el centro de rotación, tal que cada punto y su imagen estén a la misma distancia de P. Todos los ángulos con vértice P formados por un punto y su imagen son congruentes.	

ENGLISH	SPANISH	EXAMPLES
rotational symmetry A figure that can be rotated about a point by an angle less than 360° so that the image coincides with the preimage has rotational symmetry.	**simetría de rotación** Una figura que puede rotarse alrededor de un punto en un ángulo menor de 360° de forma tal que la imagen coincide con la imagen original tiene simetría de rotación.	Order of rotational symmetry: 4
run The difference in the *x*-values of two points on a line.	**distancia horizontal** Diferencia entre los valores de *x* de dos puntos de una línea.	For the points $(3, -1)$ and $(6, 5)$, the run is $6 - 3 = 3$.

S

same-side interior angles For two lines intersected by a transversal, a pair of angles that lie on the same side of the transversal and between the two lines.	**ángulos internos del mismo lado** Dadas dos líneas cortadas por una transversal, el par de ángulos ubicados en el mismo lado de la transversal y entre las dos líneas.	$\angle 2$ and $\angle 3$ are same-side interior angles.
sample space The set of all possible outcomes of a probability experiment.	**espacio muestral** Conjunto de todos los resultados posibles de un experimento de probabilidad.	in the experiment of rolling a number cube, the sample space is {1, 2, 3, 4, 5, 6}.
scalar multiplication of a vector The process of multiplying a vector by a constant.	**multiplicación escalar de un vector** Proceso por el cual se multiplica un vector por una constante.	$3\langle -8, 1 \rangle = \langle -24, 3 \rangle$
scale The ratio between two corresponding measurements.	**escala** Razón entre dos medidas correspondientes.	1 cm : 5 mi
scale drawing A drawing that uses a scale to represent an object as smaller or larger than the actual object.	**dibujo a escala** Dibujo que utiliza una escala para representar un objeto como más pequeño o más grande que el objeto original.	A blueprint is an example of a scale drawing.
scale factor The multiplier used on each dimension to change one figure into a similar figure.	**factor de escala** El multiplicador utilizado en cada dimensión para transformar una figura en una figura semejante.	Scale factor: 2
scale model A three-dimensional model that uses a scale to represent an object as smaller or larger than the actual object.	**modelo a escala** Modelo tridimensional que utiliza una escala para representar un objeto como más pequeño o más grande que el objeto real.	

ENGLISH	SPANISH	EXAMPLES
scalene triangle A triangle with no congruent sides.	**triángulo escaleno** Triángulo sin lados congruentes.	
scatter plot A graph with points plotted to show a possible relationship between two sets of data.	**diagrama de dispersión** Gráfica con puntos que se usa para demostrar una relación posible entre dos conjuntos de datos.	
secant of a circle A line that intersects a circle at two points.	**secante de un círculo** Línea que corta un círculo en dos puntos.	
secant of an angle In a right triangle, the ratio of the length of the hypotenuse to the length of the side adjacent to angle A. It is the reciprocal of the cosine function.	**secante de un ángulo** En un triángulo rectángulo, la razón entre la longitud de la hipotenusa y la longitud del cateto adyacente al ángulo A. Es la inversa de la función coseno.	$\sec A = \dfrac{\text{hypotenuse}}{\text{adjacent}} = \dfrac{1}{\cos A}$
secant segment A segment of a secant with at least one endpoint on the circle.	**segmento secante** Segmento de una secante que tiene al menos un extremo sobre el círculo.	$\overline{NM}$ is an external secant segment. $\overline{JK}$ is an internal secant segment.
sector of a circle A region inside a circle bounded by two radii of the circle and their intercepted arc.	**sector de un círculo** Región dentro de un círculo delimitado por dos radios del círculo y por su arco abarcado.	
segment bisector A line, ray, or segment that divides a segment into two congruent segments.	**bisectriz de un segmento** Línea, rayo o segmento que divide un segmento en dos segmentos congruentes.	
segment of a circle A region inside a circle bounded by a chord and an arc.	**segmento de un círculo** Región dentro de un círculo delimitada por una cuerda y un arco.	
segment of a line A part of a line consisting of two endpoints and all points between them.	**segmento de una línea** Parte de una línea que consiste en dos extremos y todos los puntos entre éstos.	

ENGLISH	SPANISH	EXAMPLES
self-similar A figure that can be divided into parts, each of which is similar to the entire figure.	**autosemejante** Figura que se puede dividir en partes, cada una de las cuales es semejante a la figura entera.	
semicircle An arc of a circle whose endpoints lie on a diameter.	**semicírculo** Arco de un círculo cuyos extremos se encuentran sobre un diámetro.	
semiregular tessellation A repeating pattern formed by two or more regular polygons in which the same number of each polygon occur in the same order at every vertex and completely cover a plane with no gaps or overlaps.	**teselado semirregular** Patrón formado por dos o más polígonos regulares en el que el mismo número de cada polígono se presenta en el mismo orden en cada vértice y cubren un plano completamente sin dejar espacios vacíos ni superponerse.	
side of a polygon One of the segments that form a polygon.	**lado de un polígono** Uno de los segmentos que forman un polígono.	
side of an angle One of the two rays that form an angle.	**lado de un ángulo** Uno de los dos rayos que forman un ángulo.	$\overrightarrow{AC}$ and $\overrightarrow{AB}$ are sides of $\angle CAB$.
Sierpinski triangle A fractal formed from a triangle by removing triangles with vertices at the midpoints of the sides of each remaining triangle.	**triángulo de Sierpinski** Fractal formado a partir de un triángulo al cual se le recortan triángulos cuyos vértices se encuentran en los puntos medios de los lados de cada triángulo restante.	
similar Two figures are similar if they have the same shape but not necessarily the same size.	**semejantes** Dos figuras con la misma forma pero no necesariamente del mismo tamaño.	
similar polygons Two polygons whose corresponding angles are congruent and whose corresponding side lengths are proportional.	**polígonos semejantes** Dos polígonos cuyos ángulos correspondientes son congruentes y cuyos lados correspondientes tienen longitudes proporcionales.	
similarity ratio The ratio of two corresponding linear measurements in a pair of similar figures.	**razón de semejanza** Razón de dos medidas lineales correspondientes en un par de figuras semejantes.	Similarity ratio: $\frac{3.5}{2.1} = \frac{5}{3}$

ENGLISH	SPANISH	EXAMPLES

similarity statement
A statement that indicates that two polygons are similar by listing the vertices in the order of correspondence.

enunciado de semejanza Enunciado que indica que dos polígonos son semejantes enumerando los vértices en orden de correspondencia.

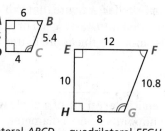

quadrilateral *ABCD* ~ quadrilateral *EFGH*

---

similarity transformation A transformation that produces similar figures.

transformación de semejanza Una transformación que resulta en figuras semejantes.

Dilations are similarity transformations.

---

simple event An event consisting of only one outcome.

suceso simple Suceso que contiene sólo un resultado.

In the experiment of rolling a number cube, the event consisting of the outcome 3 is a simple event.

---

sine In a right triangle, the ratio of the length of the leg opposite $\angle A$ to the length of the hypotenuse.

seno En un triángulo rectángulo, razón entre la longitud del cateto opuesto a $\angle A$ y la longitud de la hipotenusa.

$$\sin A = \frac{\text{opposite}}{\text{hypotenuse}}$$

---

skew lines Lines that are not coplanar.

líneas oblicuas Líneas que no son coplanares.

$\overleftrightarrow{AE}$ and $\overleftrightarrow{CD}$ are skew lines.

---

slide *See* translation.

deslizamiento *Ver* traslación.

---

slope A measure of the steepness of a line. If (x_1, y_1) and (x_2, y_2) are any two points on the line, the slope of the line, known as *m*, is represented by the equation $m = \frac{y_2 - y_1}{x_2 - x_1}$.

pendiente Medida de la inclinación de una línea. Dados dos puntos (x_1, y_1) y (x_2, y_2) en una línea, la pendiente de la línea, denominada *m*, se representa con la ecuación $m = \frac{y_2 - y_1}{x_2 - x_1}$.

---

slope-intercept form The slope-intercept form of a linear equation is $y = mx + b$, where *m* is the slope and *b* is the *y*-intercept.

forma de pendiente-intersección La forma de pendiente-intersección de una ecuación lineal es $y = mx + b$, donde *m* es la pendiente y *b* es la intersección con el eje *y*.

---

solid A three-dimensional figure.

cuerpo geométrico Figura tridimensional.

$y = -2x + 4$
The slope is −2.
The *y*-intercept is 4.

---

solving a triangle Using given measures to find unknown angle measures or side lengths of a triangle.

resolución de un triángulo Utilizar medidas dadas para hallar las medidas desconocidas de los ángulos o las longitudes de los lados de un triángulo.

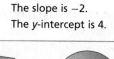

ENGLISH	SPANISH	EXAMPLES
space The set of all points in three dimensions.	**espacio** Conjunto de todos los puntos en tres dimensiones.	
special parallelogram A rectangle, rhombus, or square.	**paralelogramo especial** Un rectángulo, rombo o cuadrado.	
special quadrilateral A parallelogram, rectangle, rhombus, square, kite, or trapezoid.	**cuadrilátero especial** Un paralelogramo, rectángulo, rombo, cuadrado, cometa o trapecio.	
special right triangle A 45°-45°-90° triangle or a 30°-60°-90° triangle.	**triángulo rectángulo especial** Triángulo de 45°-45°-90° o triángulo de 30°-60°-90°.	

ENGLISH	SPANISH	EXAMPLES
sphere The set of points in space that are a fixed distance from a given point called the center of the sphere.	**esfera** Conjunto de puntos en el espacio que se encuentran a una distancia fija de un punto determinado denominado centro de la esfera.	

ENGLISH	SPANISH	EXAMPLES
spherical geometry A system of geometry defined on a sphere. A line is defined as a great circle of the sphere, and there are no parallel lines.	**geometría esférica** Sistema de geometría definido sobre una esfera. Una línea se define como un gran círculo de la esfera y no existen líneas paralelas.	
square A quadrilateral with four congruent sides and four right angles.	**cuadrado** Cuadrilátero con cuatro lados congruentes y cuatro ángulos rectos.	

ENGLISH	SPANISH	EXAMPLES
standard form of a quadratic function $y = ax^2 + bx + c$, where $b \neq 0$.	**forma estándar de una ecuación función** $y = ax^2 + bx + c$, donde $b \neq 0$.	$2x^2 + 3x - 1 = 0$
standard position An angle in standard position has its vertex at the origin and its initial side on the positive x-axis.	**posición estándar** Ángulo cuyo vértice se encuentra en el origen y cuyo lado inicial se encuentra sobre el eje x positivo.	

ENGLISH	SPANISH	EXAMPLES
straight angle A 180° angle.	**ángulo llano** Ángulo que mide 180°.	
subtend A segment or arc subtends an angle if the endpoints of the segment or arc lie on the sides of the angle.	**subtender** Un segmento o arco subtiende un ángulo si los extremos del segmento o arco se encuentran sobre los lados del ángulo.	

If D and F are the endpoints of an arc or chord, and E is a point not on $\overline{DF}$, then $\overset{\frown}{DF}$ or $\overline{DF}$ is said to subtend $\angle DEF$.

ENGLISH	SPANISH	EXAMPLES

supplementary angles Two angles whose measures have a sum of 180°.

ángulos suplementarios Dos ángulos cuyas medidas suman 180°.

∠3 and ∠4 are supplementary angles.

---

surface area The total area of all faces and curved surfaces of a three-dimensional figure.

área total Área total de todas las caras y superficies curvas de una figura tridimensional.

12 cm

6 cm

8 cm

Surface area $= 2(8)(12) + 2(8)(6) + 2(12)(6) = 432 \text{ cm}^2$

---

symmetry In the transformation of a figure such that the image coincides with the preimage, the image and preimage have symmetry.

simetría En la transformación de una figura tal que la imagen coincide con la imagen original, la imagen y la imagen original tienen simetría.

---

symmetry about an axis In the transformation of a figure such that there is a line about which a three-dimensional figure can be rotated by an angle greater than 0° and less than 360° so that the image coincides with the preimage, the image and preimage have symmetry about an axis.

simetría axial En la transformación de una figura tal que existe una línea sobre la cual se puede rotar una figura tridimensional a un ángulo mayor que 0° y menor que 360° de forma que la imagen coincida con la imagen original, la imagen y la imagen original tienen simetría axial.

---

system of equations A set of two or more equations that have two or more variables.

sistema de ecuaciones Conjunto de dos o más ecuaciones que contienen dos o más variables.

$2x + 3y = -1$
$3x - 3y = 4$

T

tangent circles Two coplanar circles that intersect at exactly one point. If one circle is contained inside the other, they are *internally tangent.* If not, they are *externally tangent.*

círculos tangentes Dos círculos coplanares que se cruzan únicamente en un punto. Si un círculo contiene a otro, son *tangentes internamente.* De lo contrario, son *tangentes externamente.*

---

tangent of an angle In a right triangle, the ratio of the length of the leg opposite ∠A to the length of the leg adjacent to ∠A.

tangente de un ángulo En un triángulo rectángulo, razón entre la longitud del cateto opuesto a ∠A y la longitud del cateto adyacente a ∠A.

opposite

adjacent

A

$\tan A = \dfrac{\text{opposite}}{\text{adjacent}}$

---

tangent segment A segment of a tangent with one endpoint on the circle.

segmento tangente Segmento de una tangente con un extremo en el círculo.

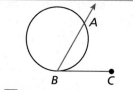

A

B   C

$\overline{BC}$ is a tangent segment.

ENGLISH	SPANISH	EXAMPLES
tangent of a circle A line that is in the same plane as a circle and intersects the circle at exactly one point.	**tangente de un círculo** Línea que se encuentra en el mismo plano que un círculo y lo cruza únicamente en un punto.	
tangent of a sphere A line that intersects the sphere at exactly one point.	**tangente de una esfera** Línea que toca la esfera únicamente en un punto.	
terminal point of a vector The endpoint of a vector.	**punto terminal de un vector** Extremo de un vector.	
terminal side For an angle in standard position, the ray that is rotated relative to the positive *x*-axis.	**lado terminal** Para un ángulo en posición estándar, el rayo que se rota en relación con el eje *x* positivo.	
tessellation A repeating pattern of plane figures that completely covers a plane with no gaps or overlaps.	**teselado** Patrón que se repite formado por figuras planas que cubren completamente un plano sin dejar espacios libres y sin superponerse.	
tetrahedron A polyhedron with four faces. A regular tetrahedron has equilateral triangles as faces, with three faces meeting at each vertex.	**tetraedro** Poliedro con cuatro caras. Las caras de un tetraedro regular son triángulos equiláteros y cada vértice es compartido por tres caras.	
theorem A statement that has been proven.	**teorema** Enunciado que ha sido demostrado.	
theoretical probability The ratio of the number of equally likely outcomes in an event to the total number of possible outcomes.	**probabilidad teórica** Razón entre el número de resultados igualmente probables de un suceso y el número total de resultados posibles.	In the experiment of rolling a number cube, the theoretical probability of rolling an odd number is $\frac{3}{6} = \frac{1}{2}$.
three-dimensional coordinate system A space that is divided into eight regions by an *x*-axis, a *y*-axis, and a *z*-axis. The locations, or coordinates, of points are given by ordered triples.	**sistema de coordenadas tridimensional** Espacio dividido en ocho regiones por un eje *x*, un eje *y* un eje *z*. Las ubicaciones, o coordenadas, de los puntos son dadas por tripletas ordenadas.	

Glossary/Glosario

ENGLISH	SPANISH	EXAMPLES
tick marks Marks used on a figure to indicate congruent segments.	**marcas "|"** Marcas utilizadas en una figura para indicar segmentos congruentes.	Tick marks
tiling *See* tessellation.	**teselación** *Ver* teselado	
transformation A change in the position, size, or shape of a figure or graph.	**transformación** Cambio en la posición, tamaño o forma de una figura o gráfica.	$\triangle ABC \longrightarrow \triangle A'B'C'$
translation A transformation that shifts or slides every point of a figure or graph the same distance in the same direction.	**traslación** Transformación en la que todos los puntos de una figura o gráfica se mueven la misma distancia en la misma dirección.	
translation symmetry A figure has translation symmetry if it can be translated along a vector so that the image coincides with the preimage.	**simetría de traslación** Una figura tiene simetría de traslación si se puede trasladar a lo largo de un vector de forma tal que la imagen coincida con la imagen original.	
transversal A line that intersects two coplanar lines at two different points.	**transversal** Línea que corta dos líneas coplanares en dos puntos diferentes.	Transversal
trapezoid A quadrilateral with exactly one pair of parallel sides.	**trapecio** Cuadrilátero con sólo un par de lados paralelos.	
trial In probability, a single repetition or observation of an experiment.	**prueba** En probabilidad, una sola repetición u observación de un experimento.	In the experiment of rolling a number cube, each roll is one trial.
triangle A three-sided polygon.	**triángulo** Polígono de tres lados.	
triangle rigidity A property of triangles that states that if the side lengths of a triangle are fixed, the triangle can have only one shape.	**rigidez del triángulo** Propiedad de los triángulos que establece que, si las longitudes de los lados de un triángulo son fijas, el triángulo puede tener sólo una forma.	
triangulation The method for finding the distance between two points by using them as vertices of a triangle in which one side has a known, or measurable, length.	**triangulación** Método para calcular la distancia entre dos puntos utilizándolos como vértices de un triángulo en el cual un lado tiene una longitud conocida o medible.	

ENGLISH	SPANISH	EXAMPLES

trigonometric ratio A ratio of two sides of a right triangle.

razón trigonométrica Razón entre dos lados de un triángulo rectángulo.

$\sin A = \frac{a}{c}; \cos A = \frac{b}{c}; \tan A = \frac{a}{b}$

---

trigonometry The study of the measurement of triangles and of trigonometric functions and their applications.

trigonometría Estudio de la medición de los triángulos y de las funciones trigonométricas y sus aplicaciones.

---

trinomial A polynomial with three terms.

trinomio Polinomio con tres términos.

$4x^2 + 3xy - 5y^2$

---

trisect To divide into three equal parts.

trisecar Dividir en tres partes iguales.

$\overline{AD}$ is trisected.

---

truth table A table that lists all possible combinations of truth values for a statement and its components.

tabla de verdad Tabla en la que se enumeran todas las combinaciones posibles de valores de verdad para un enunciado y sus componentes.

---

truth value A statement can have a truth value of true (T) or false (F).

valor de verdad Un enunciado puede tener un valor de verdad verdadero (V) o falso (F).

---

turn *See* rotation.

giro *Ver* rotación.

---

two-column proof A style of proof in which the statements are written in the left-hand column and the reasons are written in the right-hand column.

demostración a dos columnas Estilo de demostración en la que los enunciados se escriben en la columna de la izquierda y las razones en la columna de la derecha.

---

two-point perspective A perspective drawing with two vanishing points.

perspectiva de dos puntos Dibujo en perspectiva con dos puntos de fuga.

Vanishing points

U

undefined term A basic figure that is not defined in terms of other figures. The undefined terms in geometry are point, line, and plane.

término indefinido Figura básica que no está definida en función de otras figuras. Los términos indefinidos en geometría son el punto, la línea y el plano.

---

unit circle A circle with a radius of 1, centered at the origin.

círculo unitario Círculo con un radio de 1, centrado en el origen.

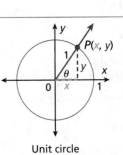

Unit circle

V

vanishing point In a perspective drawing, a point on the horizon where parallel lines appear to meet.

punto de fuga En un dibujo en perspectiva, punto en el horizonte donde todas las líneas paralelas parecen encontrarse.

Vanishing point
Horizon

---

vector A quantity that has both magnitude and direction.

vector Cantidad que tiene magnitud y dirección.

$\vec{u}$

Venn diagram A diagram used to show relationships between sets.

diagrama de Venn Diagrama utilizado para mostrar la relación entre conjuntos.

Transformations
Rotations

---

vertex angle of an isosceles triangle The angle formed by the legs of an isosceles triangle.

ángulo del vértice de un triángulo isósceles Ángulo formado por los catetos de un triángulo isósceles.

vertex angle
E   F

---

vertex form of a quadratic function A quadratic function written in the form $f(x) = a(x - h)^2 + k$, where a, h, and k are constants and (h, k) is the vertex.

forma en vértice de una función cuadrática Una función cuadrática expresada en la forma $f(x) = a(x - h)^2 + k$, donde a, h y k son constantes y (h, k) es el vértice.

$x = 2$
$(0, 6)$ $(4, 6)$
$(2, 2)$
$f(x) = (x - 2)^2 + 2$

---

vertex of a cone The point opposite the base of the cone.

vértice de un cono Punto opuesto a la base del cono.

Vertex

---

vertex of a graph A point on a graph.

vértice de una gráfica Punto en una gráfica.

$(0, 0)$
Vertex
$(1, 0)$ $\left(0, \frac{3}{4}\right)$

---

vertex of a parabola The highest or lowest point on the parabola.

vértice de una parábola Punto más alto o más bajo de una parábola.

Vertex

---

vertex of a polygon The intersection of two sides of the polygon.

vértice de un polígono La intersección de dos lados del polígono.

A B
C
Vertex
E
D

A, B, C, D, and E are vertices of the polygon.

Glossary/Glosario

ENGLISH	SPANISH	EXAMPLES
vertex of a pyramid The point opposite the base of the pyramid.	**vértice de una pirámide** Punto opuesto a la base de la pirámide.	Vertex
vertex of a three-dimensional figure The point that is the intersection of three or more faces of the figure.	**vértice de una figura tridimensional** Punto que representa la intersección de tres o más caras de la figura.	Vertex
vertex of a triangle The intersection of two sides of the triangle.	**vértice de un triángulo** Intersección de dos lados del triángulo.	C A B *A*, *B*, and *C* are vertices of △*ABC*.
vertex of an angle The common endpoint of the sides of the angle.	**vértice de un ángulo** Extremo común de los lados del ángulo.	C A B *A* is the vertex of ∠*CAB*.
vertical angles The nonadjacent angles formed by two intersecting lines.	**ángulos opuestos por el vértice** Ángulos no adyacentes formados por dos rectas que se cruzan.	2 1 3 4 ∠1 and ∠3 are vertical angles. ∠2 and ∠4 are vertical angles.
volume The number of nonoverlapping unit cubes of a given size that will exactly fill the interior of a three-dimensional figure.	**volumen** Cantidad de cubos unitarios no superpuestos de un determinado tamaño que llenan exactamente el interior de una figura tridimensional.	4 ft 3 ft 12 ft Volume = (3)(4)(12) = 144 ft³

W

| **whole number** The set of natural numbers and zero. | **número cabal** Conjunto de los números naturales y cero. | {0, 1, 2, 3, 4, 5, ...} |

X

| **x-axis** The horizontal axis in a coordinate plane. | **eje *x*** Eje horizontal en un plano cartesiano. | *x*-axis 0 |

Glossary/Glosario

ENGLISH	SPANISH	EXAMPLES

Y

y-axis The vertical axis in a coordinate plane.

eje y Eje vertical en un plano cartesiano.

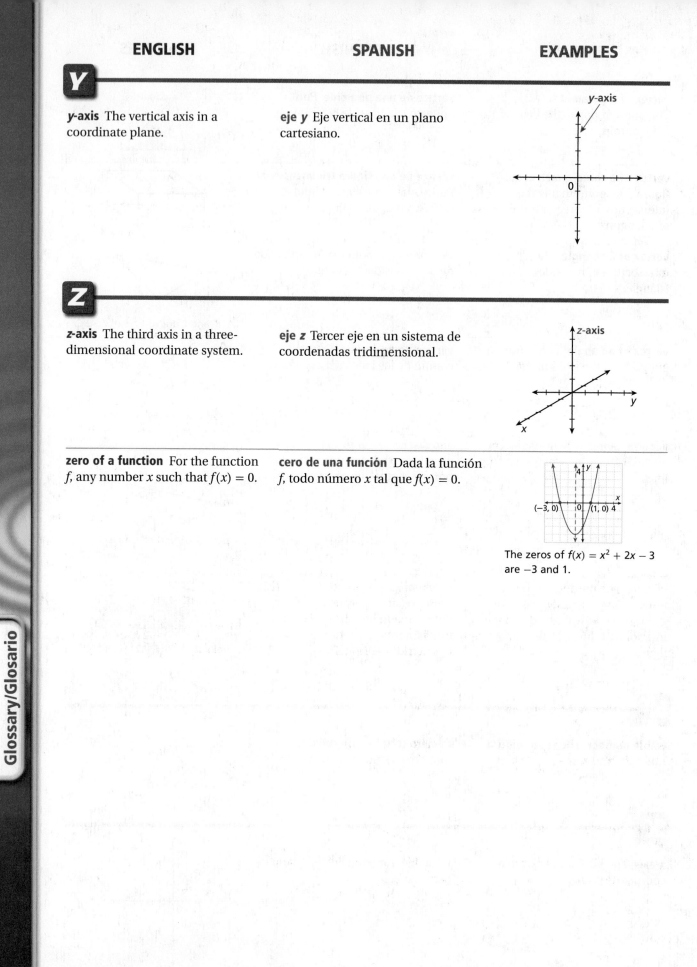

Z

z-axis The third axis in a three-dimensional coordinate system.

eje z Tercer eje en un sistema de coordenadas tridimensional.

zero of a function For the function *f*, any number *x* such that $f(x) = 0$.

cero de una función Dada la función *f*, todo número *x* tal que $f(x) = 0$.

The zeros of $f(x) = x^2 + 2x - 3$ are -3 and 1.

Index

A

Index

Index

Index

Index

Index

Index

Index

Q

R

Index

Index

Index

theorems. *See also* **specific theo-rems,** 392, 393, 401, 402, 418, 419
  proofs of, 397, 402, 406, 423
theoretical probability, 610, 611, 612, 613, 614
Third Angles Theorem, 120
30°-60°-90° triangle, 306
tick marks, 7
tools of geometry, 4
Transformations
  of graphs of quadratic functions, 493, 494, 495, 496, 497
transit tool, 14
Transitive Property, 92, 100
Transitive Property of Similarity, 265
translations, 203
  of quadratic functions, 494
Transportation, 505, 308
transversals
  parallel lines and angles formed by, 79, 80, 81
Travel, 11, 32, 276, 629, 645
tree diagram, 629
trefoil shape, 189
trial, 613
Triangle Angle Bisector Theorem, 275
triangle classification
triangle congruence, 117, 118, 119, 120, 121, 122, 123, 124, 125, 126, 127, 128, 129, 130, 131, 138, 139, 140, 141, 142, 143, 144, 145, 146, 147, 148, 149, 150, 151, 152, 153, 154, 155, 156, 157, 158, 159, 163, 164, 165, 166, 167, 168, 169
  applying ASA, AAS and HL, 146, 147, 148, 149
  applying SSS and SAS, 138, 139, 140, 141
  CPCTC, 154, 155, 156
Triangle Midsegment Theorem, 198, 199, 200
  proof of the, 202
Triangle Proportionality Theorem, 273
  Converse of the, 274
triangle rigidity, 138
Triangle(s)
  altitudes of, 190, 191, 192, 193
    defined, 192
  angle relationships in, 117, 118, 119, 120
  bisectors of, 183, 184, 185, 186

centroid of, 190
  constructing, 190
circumcenter of, 183
  constructing, 183
circumscribe a circle about, 422
classifying, 124
incenter of a, 185
medians of, 190, 191, 192, 193, 194, 195, 196, 198, 199, 200, 201, 202, 203
midsegment, 198
  constructing, 203
orthocenter of a, 192
  constructing, 196
Triangle Sum Theorem, 117
  proof of the, 117
triangular numbers, 518
triangulation, 117
trigonometry, 314
trinomials, 527. *See also* **factoring polynomials; polynomial(s)**
  difference of two squares, 482, 483, 487
  perfect-square, 480, 527
trisecting angles, 19
truth value, 30
Two-Transversal Proportionality Theorem, 274

U

Unpacking the Standards, 5, 45, 77, 107, 135, 175, 207, 245, 295, 315, 351, 389, 433, 461, 491, 523, 565, 593, 621

V

Venn diagram, 641
vertex, 14
  of a parabola, 496
  of a quadratic function, 496
vertex angles, 163
vertex form of a quadratic function, 496
Vertical Angles Theorem, 68, 69, 70
  proof of the, 68
Vocabulary, 2, 11, 18, 32, 70, 121, 128, 141, 150, 156, 166, 187, 193, 200, 213, 228, 292, 300, 348, 395, 404, 420, 430, 437, 444, 458, 498, 506, 515, 529, 536, 544, 548, 562, 583, 590, 606, 614, 627, 631, 642

W

Washington, George, 12
Waterfalls, 537
Weather, 506, 616
What if...?, 20, 89, 124, 147, 165, 199, 240, 265, 297, 305, 307, 437, 482, 499, 507, 517, 530, 538, 539, 544, 584, 606
Wimbledon, 628
Winter Sports, 517
Write About It
  Write About It questions appear in every exercise set. Some examples are, 12, 20, 499
Writing Math, 29, 400

X

x-axis, 440
x-intercepts, 523, 524, 525

Y

y-axis, 440
y-intercepts, 502

Z

Zero Product Property, 525
zeros
  of functions, 524